RELUCTANT CAVALIER

RELUCTANT CAVALIER

A Novel by

DONALD BARR CHIDSEY

CROWN PUBLISHERS, INC.

Printed in the United States of America

TO
JOHN CLARK CHIDSEY

RELUCTANT CAVALIER

1
Come with Clean Hands

George Fitzwilliam kicked off his slippers, leaned back in his chair, put his feet on a window sill, and wriggled his toes.

As one just released from three years in their most noisome cells, he was unlikely to love Spaniards. But—give the Devil his due. They did know how to dress! And his Aunt Jane had done him well at one of the best tailors in Madrid. George was a prince in appearance.

The slippers, cork-soled, were bright blue with black bows.

The hose, twilled sarsenet, crimson in color, yellow-clocked, fitted with never a wrinkle, reaching to his buttocks.

The sword, silver-hilted, like its companion-piece, the dagger, was Toledo; and the hangers and cross-straps were Cordovan.

The doublet, black silk slashed with silver, was picadilled at its base, ruffled at the cuffs, and had a waist that was girlish, its tightness emphasized by the bombast above and by huge shoulder welts. The ruff was short, stiff with starch, bright yellow.

George's beard, until lately Visigothic, had been trimmed almost to the point of invisibility. There was a pearl in the lobe of his left ear; perfume at his armpits; and on his head a high-crowned, narrow-brimmed velvet bonnet.

"So you have actually met King Philip," snorted Master Hawkins.

"Aye."

George still was smiling, a fond bemused smile. He did not like Plymouth, a noisy town; but it was good to be back in England.

"And—did you spread your tail when you bowed?"

George frowned. In this year of Our Lord 1571 each unpropertied person, no matter what his blood, must have a protector. This was in the nature of things, and George did not chafe against it. His own older brother had inherited so little that even for him life would be a struggle: indeed, William Fitzwilliam had been obliged to go to Ireland as deputy lord lieutenant. George knew that he himself would

[9]

have to be somebody's "man," and John Hawkins, though a commoner, was not unkindly. George might have hoped for some post more exalted, since he was connected on his mother's side with the Dormers and the Sidneys, on his father's with John Russell; but there were many cousins and nephews to be cared for, and Hawkins at least was prosperous, a pusher. The trouble was, John Hawkins could not seem to forget George Fitzwilliam's family. It was *he* who, defensively, obliquely, yet unmistakably, sometimes made sarcastic reference, as now, to the difference in their respective stations. *He,* not George, resented it.

"Did I do anything amiss?" George asked mildly.

"Oh, you did well. But—your aunt couldn't get the other prisoners out?"

"Couldn't or wouldn't. Me, I think it was a trick to win some concession from you. Which," George added grimly, "it certainly did."

"And the king believed it?"

"Aye, once I'd told him that you fretted and you'd turn over to him every ship you commanded when the Spanish invasion came, provided the captives from New Spain were freed *and* provided all your mariners' back pay was furnished."

"I had prepared him. I'd already approached his ambassador in London, who's utterly gullible."

"So is Philip. He might be perplexed by your persistence in trying to free those men, but that you should seek to recoup your money losses—that seemed natural to him."

Hawkins liked this young man and valued him, but he suspected he would never understand him.

"*My* persistence?" he said softly. "It was *you* who was ready to move Heaven and Hell if it would get those nineteen men out of jail. It was *you* who returned to Spain with my false offer of a fleet sell-out, though surely you don't fancy that sort of work?"

George said nothing, staring out the window.

"This is praiseworthy, Fitzwilliam, but it's puzzling too. *You*'re out. Why should you spend so much time and trouble—yes, and run such risks—for *them?* Every one is a man of low degree. Oh, I grant that in the eyes of God we are all equal! But you can't pretend that those mariners are men to your own taste?"

George regarded his silken toes for a moment. When he spoke it was low.

"After you've lain in the same lousy straw with men for months on end, and shared the same pail with them, and swatted the same damned cockroaches, rank doesn't seem to make much difference."

[10]

"You're not about to say that you *love* these men?"

"Yes," George said carefully. "Yes, I think I love them."

John Hawkins opened his mouth to laugh, but his servant hadn't stirred; and after a while John Hawkins closed his mouth, having given forth no sound. Embarrassed, he harrumphed.

"Of course King Philip had heard of me?"

"Of course. But he pointed out that he was being asked to take the word of a pirate—"

"A pirate!"

"—as, in his view, sir, you are. I of course drew myself like a man that had been buffeted, and I cried that my master was honorable."

Hawkins grunted with indignation.

"There at least you did not need to lie to him. You, uh, you mislike the rest of it, Fitzwilliam?"

"Aye. Falsehood always has stunk in my nostrils. And it's no joy to call yourself a traitor's go-between. Even though you know better."

"As you do. All I'm working for is the release of those prisoners. Nor do I sally forth on my own. I consulted Burghley first."

"Who?"

"Master secretary Cecil. Sir William. The queen's first minister. He was elevated while you were away. Lord Burghley now."

"I see."

Again George wriggled his toes, glorying in his apparel, watching Plymouth, smelling the air of England. It was almost too good to be true. But the others who had been captured with him at San Juan de Ulua: they must be rescued. There had been forty-one of them, including George, in Mexico. There had been thirty-three when they were shipped across the sea to Seville. There had been nineteen when at last George was able to get a message to his aunt, the former Jane Dormer, presently duchess of Feria. He wondered how many there were now. Whatever the number, they would be lying in clothes that crawled, praying for death, cursing the sturdiness that had caused them to survive.

"And—then?" Hawkins persisted.

"King Philip said he would consider your offer if I got from his 'sister of Scotland,' as he called her, a letter vouching for your *bona fides*. He would write me an introduction to her. Such honor!"

"What would Mary Stuart know about me?"

"Nothing. You're here, and she is a prisoner at Sheffield."

"A guest, you mean."

"I doubt that Philip's English could encompass that distinction. He did ask me if you had ever met, and I was obliged to say no. But the letter he gave me is harmless."

"How do you know?"

"Why, I opened it and read it."

"You— The seal looks solid."

"I used steam. It wasn't hard. And my hands were clean."

"But then—"

"True, there's something written in the margin."

"Ah?"

"You don't see it at first. You must heat the paper. Then it comes out a watery brown, for a little while. I can guess what was used for ink. Any prisoner could. Yet it might have been lemon juice, the effect is similar. They have many lemons in Spain."

"Did you memorize the message in the margin?"

"Of course."

George brought his legs down. Gangling, lazy, he rose. He crossed to John Hawkins' writing desk.

"Here—"

EXTCUVCVKOXVUEKCOUK30GV40RCTCVKCFCIGPF-XOUKPV.

Hawkins' eyes popped like tennis balls.

"It's some sort of cipher!"

"An easy one. I cracked it on the way back."

John Hawkins was a solid, stolid man, a merchant not easy to sway. He was in his middle thirties, well past the hot emotions of youth, and had but lately served a term as lord mayor of Plymouth. Though a great gambler, his daring proverbial, his seamanship celebrated, in person he was staid, a man whose eyes never flashed, who seldom raised his voice, a man as firmly foundationed as this his square stone house in Kinterbury Street. Now, however, he was trembling, and his face gleamed with perspiration.

"Do you know what this means, man? We must make for Burghley!"

George stared at him in amazement.

"I had hoped to ride to Sir John Crofts's place."

"To see Anne? She's still alive. And she knows that you are, too."

"But, sir, I haven't seen her in three years."

"She's not married, if that's what you mean. She can't afford it." George sighed.

"Neither can I—yet."

"Hurry! We're going to London!"

John Hawkins rang for a servant to bring his boots, to saddle horses.

George never had seen him in such a state. A mite awed, despite himself, George retrieved his pantouffles, strapped on his sword-and-dagger.

"And when I meet this new baron, what should I tell him?"

"Why, the truth!"

George sighed again.

"That at least will be a change," he said.

2

Read Me This Riddle

George hated the sea; and understandably he hated seaports even more, since if their stink was much the same as that of any ship—bilge and tar, sour beer and stale vomit—it was multiplied and intensified, and the water bobbed garbage; while the air, what with horses and carts, tuns, levers, and hucksters, was loud with sounds to split the ear.

Once Plymouth was behind them, George expanded, looking right and left, laughing, sometimes singing:

> "In Sherwood lived stout Robin Hood,
> An archer great—none greater.
> His bow and shafts were sure and good,
> Yet Cupid's are much better."

That part of England, the south, is lovely in any season, but it is especially lovely in May. Three weeks earlier, when he first returned from Spain, George had been given no chance to get away from the cacophony that was Plymouth. He had been shoved off on the next ship with instructions to take an offer to his majesty Philip, by grace of God king of Castile, king of Leon, king of Aragon, of the Two Sicilies, Jerusalem, Granada, Toledo, Valencia, Galicia, Sardinia, Cordova, Navarre, Corsica, Murcia, Jaen, Algarve, Algeciras, Gibraltar, the Canary Islands, the East and West Indies, and all the islands and continents of the Ocean, a small, rickety, squinting man with a mean mind and the soul of a clerk, who was also, incidentally, archduke of Austria, duke of Burgundy, duke of Brabant, duke of Milan, count of Hapsburg, count of Flanders, count of Tyrol, count of Barcelona, lord of Biscay, lord of Molina. . . . This, the greatest emperor in the world—one with a mouse's squeal for a voice, and small suspicious eyes—had listened to the glib young ambassador and seemingly had swallowed the fabrication. Now George was back, inhaling England.

> *"Robin could shoot at many a hart and miss;*
> *Cupid at first could hit a heart of his."*

He had no wish to think, only to glory in being alive—much as when he was released from prison and lay on his back, eyes closed, drinking the sunshine through every pore.

Not that there was much sunshine on the east road out of Plymouth. It rained or threatened rain most of the time. George didn't care. This was *clean* rain forsooth, good rain!

He reproached himself for his happiness. Those poor lads still lay, far below the street level, in Seville. He wondered how they were, and whether they still clung to a belief that somehow he would save them. He hoped so, for he meant to. He wondered in particular about Ellis Waters, that seamed, acidulous little prisoner with whom George had shared a leg-iron chain three feet long for more than a year. You got to know a man mighty well in those circumstances. Ellis was a feltmonger's son, illiterate, runty, short of temper too, a boy in age but with mean eyes and the face of an evil monkey. In fact, except in the matter of clothes he much resembled his gracious majesty Philip II, by grace of God king of Castile, king of Leon, etc., etc. Even his fellow mariners looked down upon Ellis Waters. Yet George Fitzwilliam had come to love him and he prayed for him a moment, there on the road. Silently, without moving his lips, he prayed for them all, that they might be delivered out of Hell.

They quit the sea, turning north, and then all the world was not gray but green. Drift-lanes led to the village fields, cowslip and larkspur thick at their edges. Among the fern in the glades hares leapt and flies buzzed, and now and then, abruptly, would come the screech of a woodpecker. The houses smelled of fresh thatch, the woods of mint and acorn. White-painted stiles were jostled by gillyflower and love-lies-a-bleeding. All the while the cuckoo called. And everywhere, making a mingle-mangle of fields and lanes alike, were the hedgerows. The dear hedgerows! George believed that it was them that he'd missed the most.

It was hard to keep his somber thoughts, and hard not to sing, and soon, impulsively, like any lark, he was at it again.

"Hey, jolly Robin!
Ho, jolly Robin!
Hey, jolly, jolly Robin,
Love finds out me
As well as thee
To follow me to the green wood."

His companion was not so gay. Essentially a man of the sea, John Hawkins was not an imposing sight as he sat the stolid shaggy Hungarian. He was very old, nearly forty. Yet he was dogged. He resented every pause, no matter what its purpose; and on the late afternoon of the second day they reached London Bridge.

George sagged with weariness—his muscles, made soft by those years in prison, pleaded for a rest—and he would have sought an inn. To his amazement, John Hawkins commanded that they continue, not drawing rein until they reached Cecil House in the Strand, where the bodyservants were dismissed, while George and Master Hawkins entered, George being struck by the deference shown his paunchy, glum companion.

The place was vast, a palace; yet in a matter of minutes they were ushered into the presence of the queen's first councilor, the most hated man, as he was the most feared, in all the realm.

Burghley harrumphed, nodding; then thoughtfully spat.

"Aye, Hawkins, your courier arrived about noon. So this is the one who will meet Scotland? Sit down, both of you."

George's first thought, an irreverent one, was that his lordship need fear no pun upon his title. He was not burly. Rather, though large, he showed flabbiness, and appeared to have sunk into his bones. He was very old, even older than Hawkins. His ruff was stubby, his doublet and gown and flat cap rich but severe. He wore a massive gold chain around his neck, but no gems. The chain might have been a symbol of office—perhaps a yoke.

This man's eyes, a wishywashy blue, were exceedingly intelligent; and on occasion they could harden. Mostly he kept them cast down. But when he raised them, to look directly at the person he was addressing, it caused a shiver to pass up the back of that person's neck and head.

Burghley never smiled, and he looked as though he had been born grave.

He sat with his back to a window through which, over his shoulder, they could see in the failing afternoon light London's main thoroughfare, the Thames. They could hear the cries of wherrymen and

[15]

bargemen, the bumping of tilt boats, the squeal of tholepins, creak of oars, a tintinnabulant sound that was blurred and seemed far away.

Burghley spat again. Without looking up, he said quietly to the servant who had admitted the callers:

"Close that door, and don't let anybody come near."

By following Burghley's own example and not looking up as he spoke, George found that it was possible to avoid the disconcerting directness of that stare. But he didn't enjoy keeping his head down. It did not become him.

"Why did you open this message?"

"Because I was bored and had nothing else to do. Also because the thing looked strange. Why should a crowned monarch send to an imprisoned exile a request for information about an admiral who has proposed to sell his country's principal war fleet? And do this, mind you, by means of a messenger he professed to esteem a pirate?"

"Did I not understand Master Hawkins here to say that you are kin to the duchess of Feria?"

"Yes, my lord. My aunt, Jane Dormer, was a maid-in-waiting on the late queen, Mary."

"Bloody Mary!"

Elizabeth's minister said this with a vehemence as unexpected in so mild-seeming a man as the roar of a lion would have been from the throat of a rabbit.

"The same, lord. And when Philip of Spain came to this land to wed her—Queen Mary, I mean—he had with him the count de Feria— a count then, not a duke. They met, and they became affianced, and after Feria had returned to Spain he sent for her to come and marry him. That was in '59, before the present queen had ascended to the throne."

"Whom God bless," muttered John Hawkins.

"My aunt traveled in state, as became her fiancé's position," George went on, "and I was a page in her suite. My relatives thought it would be a way for me to become acquainted with the Continent, with no cost to them. For my aunt, being afraid of the sea, went through France—very slowly. I picked up some French then, my lord. And later I was a part of her household in Madrid for more than two years. So I have Spanish as well."

"But who was it taught you that steam will loosen wax? I never would have known that this"—and Burghley tapped the letter—"had been tampered with."

"I think nobody, sir. Certainly I can't *remember* anybody ever telling me that. But I'd noticed that steam undid things, usually. It was worth trying. And it worked."

"Why, so it did. And the message? You memorized that?"

"Not word for word, no. It didn't seem worth the trouble. It was in French, and went something like this—"

Burghley, having heard, belched.

"Now the marginal note? What made you seek for that with heat?"

George shrugged.

"Prisoners are forever hiding things. It's natural. You get very cunning when you haven't anything else to do. And you look for secreted things, for you have plenty of time."

"That message I trust you've remembered exactly?"

"Oh, in truth. Here—"

George wrote. In the dusk, bent over, Lord Burghley peered at what he had made.

"You believe you have broken the cipher?"

"My lord, I'm sure I have. It falls right into place. First, it was a question of what language it would be in. French? But Latin was conceivable. You'll notice there are several *X*'s and *V*'s, and once they come together, *XV*. Those could be Roman numerals. They could also be letters in any European language. And there are at least two Arabic figures—a *3* and, three spaces away, a *4*. Each of those is followed by an *O,* which could be either the letter or the zero. Assuming that each is the figure—which seems a good way to start—that means that there are two letters, *G* and *V,* between two figures, *30* and *40*. In that case the word between them would probably be 'and.' Now that happens to be a two-letter word in both Latin and French, and exactly the same, 'et,' as you probably know, sir."

"Yes, I do know."

"So if we say that *G* represents *E* while *V* represents *T,* then it's easy to see that we have a simple substitutional cipher, the kind they call a Julius Caesar's, because each of those letters is two spaces in the alphabet behind the one it's supposed to represent. The Latin and the French alphabets are the same, you know, sir. They only have twenty-four letters instead of twenty-six, like ours. They're missing the *W* and the *Y*."

"I know that too," said Lord Burghley.

"So it turns out to be Latin after all. It makes sense in Latin."

Poor though the light was, Lord Burghley performed an astonishing feat of concentration. He read off the entire message without a miss.

"Exactly," said George. "Breaking it into letters, in a logical way, you get *CURA STATIM UT SCIAM SI 30 ET 40 PARATI AD AGENDUM SINT.*"

"That is correct," said Lord Burghley.

George, fearing embarrassment, was hoping that his lordship would translate for a puzzled John Hawkins; but when Burghley showed no inclination to do so (perhaps being unable to conceive of a person who was unacquainted with Latin), George diffidently explained.

"It means 'Take care at once that I know whether thirty and forty are ready to act.'"

"It does," bumbled Burghley. "It means exactly that."

The room was quite dark now. The eyes of William Cecil, baron of Burghley, glowed like live coals. Nobody stirred.

"And who," Hawkins asked at last, "are thirty and forty?"

"Cipher names for conspirators, probably, although I don't know," answered Burghley. "The ones I suspect are in high places, and I must step with care. First we shall see what our linguistic young friend here learns for us at Sheffield."

"I had hoped to visit in Northampton—"

"You will go to Sheffield Castle. You will meet Mary, Queen of the Scots. You cannot refuse this, Master Fitzwilliam, for unless I am mistaken—and I'm no alarmist—the safety of the throne, the very future of England, may hang upon what you learn."

"Yes, sir."

"You should be warned that you are about to encounter an extraordinary person. Mary Stuart has been called the most beautiful woman in the world. And she's no fool. I can vouch for that! I met her myself a few months ago, and—well, I am more than twice your age, Fitzwilliam, but I have never been the same since. You understand?"

"I don't believe so, sir."

"You'll learn," promised Burghley.

3

A Wash and a Wet

The inns of England—so visitors from the Continent said— were the finest in the world. Some were sumptuous, and could put up two hundred travelers, more or less. They were expertly staffed—kitchen, court, stables, taproom. They were handsomely furnished. Their food and wines were fabulous, their rooms ducal. They changed sheets with every guest.

The Continentals must have confined their wanderings to the larger highways: the Dover road, up from the Channel; the Chester road, which went by way of Barnet, St. Albans, Dunstable, Lichfield, Stony Stratford, Coventry; the Bristol road, Reading, Marlborough, Chippenham; the Carlisle road south from that town by way of Lancaster, Wigan, Warrington, and Newcastle-under-Lyme, to join the Chester road at Lichfield (a busy intersection); and of course the Great North Road. It is unlikely that they strayed along lesser routes. They would hardly have kept their enthusiasm if they had.

It was the Great North Road that George Fitzwilliam followed for as far as he conveniently could, quitting it at Biggleswade, where he turned west toward Bedford. It was then that he met the mudholes.

Had he planned to go directly to Sheffield, as he'd been ordered to do, he would have stayed on the Great North Road at least as far as Retford. But the queen of Scots could wait. George would not ride half the length of the kingdom without stopping at Okeland Manor to see Anne Crofts. She was not married, Hawkins had said. Good!

It was right in the middle of Northamptonshire, where the road forked—one part going due north toward Market Harborough, Ashby-de-la-Zouch, and Sheffield, and the other, a mere track branching westward to the left, in the direction of Rugby—that there was situated a Crossed Keys.

The grander hostelries were proud of their signs, important accessories since so few of the wayfarers could read. Some of these, men whispered, had cost as much as thirty-five or even forty pounds. However, the sign at the Crossed Keys in Northampton was not such a one. The fee for its painting might have been a jug of wine, paid in advance. That sign swung despondently, at a crazy angle, before a structure badly in need of paint and at first glance deserted. The Crossed Eyes was the neighborhood name for this inn.

Nevertheless, since he was so near to Okeland Manor, George decided to pause for a wash and a wet.

He dismounted, noting that no one offered to hold his horse. There were two living things in sight: a fleabitten dog all but asleep, which lacked even the energy to bark, and a saturnine green-aproned scarecrow who stood in the doorway and must have been the boniface, though his countenance belied this title.

The Chinese have a saying that he whom it hurts to smile never should open a shop. Mine host at the Crossed Keys might have heeded this. Acid-eyed, dour in the droop of his mouth, he was a stranger to George, himself not a stranger to the Crossed Keys. This was not a posting stage and never had paid well: it might have changed hands several times since George Fitzwilliam sailed for America.

"You seek lodgment?"

"At this hour? No, only a yard of ale and a chunk of cheese. Banbury. And water."

"There's the trough over there."

It was a change from the over-exuberance of the usual tub-of-butter host; but it irked George, who watered and walked his own horse, then washed face and hands, the proprietor having disappeared into the shadows of the ordinary.

A lone horseman was coming up the road, coming from the south, approaching the point of the fork where George stood. George wondered at this, for even in broad daylight men usually coursed the back roads in bands. However, George did not stand gawping, for it was his belief that a man who travels alone should mind his own business —or at least should appear to do so.

He loosened the saddle girth, and patted and thanked the horse. Here was no racer! John Hawkins, to the city born and bred, might risk thousands of pounds in maritime gambles on the far side of the world, but he could be uncommonly close, a pinchpenny, in matters near at hand. To him a horse was primarily a pack animal; and he could see no sense in paying the demanded extra fourpence a day for one that could be spurred to ten miles an hour. Yet this mare was what couriers called a good continuer: she had heart and was strong. So George congratulated her.

The cheese was excellent, though the bread, made of rye, was coarse, cretaceous, and the ale was flat.

The boniface, his eyes squinched half-shut in disapproval, his lips twisted as though he held a mouthful of citron juice, watched from the far side of the room, saying never a word. There did not appear to be another person in the inn; and when the court doorway suddenly was darkened it gave both of them a start.

"Your worship?" said the innkeeper uninvitingly.

The newcomer was very large and filled the doorway. Though they could not distinguish his features, the light being behind him, each instantly took him for a foreigner.

"A jack of wine, and some of that cheese our friend here is eating. It looks good."

The speech was accented. An Italian? When they could see him better his beard, trimmed high, would seem to confirm this. His clothes, dark, all but funereal, were neither rich nor drab. The two most remarkable things about him, aside from his great size, were his manner and his rapier.

Your large and powerfully muscled man is seldom truculent, since he knows no need to be. It is the small one, the runt, who shows too ready to fight. Yet about this giant in the Crossed Keys—and this despite the fact that he kept his voice low, his movements lazy—George Fitzwilliam read an inbuilt belligerency, a tenseness always near the snapping-point. It was not simply a superabundance of vitality, though he did have that. It was training. It was the result of deliberate habit, professionalism. The man was a bravo. He was a hired bully.

The sword went with him. It was a Spanish rapier, the longest George ever had seen, with a steel bellguard and long steel outcurved quillons. The hilt like the scabbard was plain, but sturdy. George of course could not see the blade itself, but he had no doubt that it was Toledo of a temper to compare with his own.

There weren't many such blades in England, where indeed there were not many men who knew how to use the rapier, a new weapon imported from Spain, double-edged, dangerous with both cut and thrust, which made it possible to attack and defend at the same time. The broadsword, together with a tiny dishpan-lid buckler held at arm's length, still was the favorite weapon among men of all ranks excepting those fine-feathered ones who spent much time at court; the rapier was esteemed new-fangled, over-fashionable, even effeminate, and no blade for a trueborn Englishman. George, most of his life, had taken the rapier for granted—in Madrid, when he served as a page for his Aunt Jane, he had been a pupil of the illustrious Luis Pacheco de Narvaez himself, and his lessons in fence had been as stringently supervised as those in dancing—but he knew that this was not the case with the majority of his fellow countrymen.

Now, what was a bird of ill omen like this doing in the middle of sleepy Northamptonshire, so far from any court or port?

"The wine, aye," said the innkeeper, who appeared to take a delight in being the bearer of bad news, "but not the cheese. That wedge the gentle over there eats happens to be the last bit of Banbury in the house."

George's dagger, which he had been using, was on the trencher before him. Without hesitation he cut the Banbury in half.

"Please take this," he said. "There's more than I need anyway."

The stranger hooked a foot behind a stool and jerked it to the other side of the table from George—since the boniface showed no readiness to do this for him—and when he sat down he was regarding George intently.

"*Muchas gracias, vuestra merced,*" he said.

George nodded.

"*De nada.*"

"I knew you were Spanish," went on the other, "from your clothes."

"You are very perceptive."

"Whereabouts in Spain did your mercy live?"

George waved vaguely.

"About half the time in the Duke de Feria's palace, the other half of the time in one of the archbishop of Seville's deepest dungeons. They were equally objectionable. Too confining."

He gave his companion no chance to comment on this, but rose, nodding an apology, and paid the shot. He went outside.

Before George had so much as retightened his saddle girth, the big man was by his side.

"I wasn't very hungry," he explained, "and with only a few hours of light left to get to an acceptable stop we'd better push it, eh?"

"We?"

"Why, your worship is riding north. I saw you ahead of me, down the road there. You're making for Leicester, I take it?"

George said nothing.

"Or further. Sheffield, perhaps?"

George mounted.

"Your suggestion has many merits," he said, "but I am taking this turnoff to the west, see? Good afternoon."

A little along the track that led to Okeland, on the pretext of seeking something in his saddlebag, he sneaked a look behind him. The bravo still was standing there, fists on hips, feet spread wide, as he stared after George Fitzwilliam.

George rubbered out his lips, and shook his head.

"Something tells me that I'll see that man again."

4

Beware Jezebel!

As one who had been bitten by a thousand bugs, George Fitzwilliam knew many minor sensitivities. Since his release he could never seem to wash enough, and he bathed his whole body, not simply hands and face. He might do this every week, even two or three times a week. It was an obsession. But he did it gingerly, as though he feared that his flesh would still smart.

Also, he seldom rode forth without a loo, or half-mask. He wore this not, like so many, to advertise his gentility—his sword could do that—but to protect the upper part of his face. His beard, trig though it now was, could guard chin and lips and lower cheek; but the fashion was for extremely short head hair, and George's new velvet bonnet in the latest mode had a curled brim that was no more than a decoration, so that unless he wore this vizard, the upper part of his face— paled and softened in the years of darkness, dampness, and fetid air— would be exposed to sunlight, and dust, fog, rain. This, then, was a part of his usual traveling costume, and he was not miffed when he rode through a village where the yokels guffawed, jeering at him as a lady. George would only grin, and wave to them.

He had, however, forgotten about this mask, so natural a part of him had it come to seem, when he crested a rise and came into sight of Okeland.

Sunlight goldplated the landscape—one of hills, aimless lanes, meadows slightly askew, and a sleepiness that seemed deep-seated. The manor house was new, a simple, two-story, bar-shaped building built of oak and local limestone, a cream color shading into tawny, yet it appeared to have been settled there snugly for a long while. It was not as well windowed as Sir John Crofts would have wished, for glass was expensive, yet such panes as there were glittered brightly. But there was no sign of movement behind them. No one walked the garden. The outbuildings—dairy, dovecote, chickenhouse, stable, cowshed, cider mill—were utterly still. Hazed by the sun, murmurous of bees, sprinkled with birdsong, here was a scene that might have entoiled any poetically minded person from the city. It struck horror to George Fitzwilliam.

Was this the peace of an English countryside—or was it the silence of danger? Had the place been visited? The thousands of masterless rascals who infested the roads of England—the rogues and foists, the Abrahams, the jarkmen, hookers, fraters, whipjacks, dummerers— were desperate persons. The average wayfarer had lost an ear or the end of his nose, or had been branded on the face, to testify that he was an "habitual." Governmental patience would go no further. The next time he was caught he would infallibly be hanged. Knowing this, he was not prone to tame treatment of such as might fall into his hands in out-of-the-way places. Moreover, these rovers always were hungry, even ravenous. Had such a pack . . . ?

Sir John Crofts, as his record in Ireland could attest, was a stout fighting man. But he was only one, and his staff was small.

The thought was an icy hand that squeezed George Fitzwilliam's heart so that he came to a halt. The mare, that good continuer, was willing enough.

George closed his eyes, shook his head, muttered a prayer, then looked again.

Now here indeed was an act of enchantment, for the spell was lifted. Okeland—still for perhaps no more than three beats of a butterfly's wing—suddenly came to life.

There was a rustling flutter at the dovecote; a scullery boy, whistling, crossed the court; somebody opened a window and shook out a duster; a cock, neck outstretched, wattles flopping, started to chase a hen around the chicken run; sensing George for the first time, and ashamed of having been caught asleep, an unseen hound began to bark furiously.

And George saw coming toward him, not twenty feet away, Anne Crofts.

She had not seen him, for she was walking with her head low in thought, making, George supposed, for the strawberry patch behind him. A small woman, compact, round-armed, towheaded, this afternoon she was also bare-headed, a shocking circumstance. Not only did she wear no sort of cap, but her honey-colored hair was innocent of flowers, lace, jewelry. This, together with her plain puce-colored homespun kirtle, her unwired hips, and a petticoat so short that it showed her feet and even at times her ankles, elsewhere would have suggested a peasant.

She was slightly below George, walking an upgrade, and despite the averted head her body moved at a brisk pace, arms swinging, hips aroll, while her breasts, not braced by buskery, jogged.

With a small glad cry, George dismounted directly before her. She looked up, startled.

"Pray what is it you seek?"

"Why, recognition first, my chuck," he cried, snatching off the mask, "and then mayhap a cousinly buss, eh?"

"*George!*"

The kiss was much more than familiar, and a dozen persons in the manor might have seen them on the hillside, and probably did. George reflected, as he held her, patting her, petting her, upon the difference between women of the English countryside and women of Spain or the Spanish colonies he had known. Yet it was good to have Anne again; she must have been twenty, but she was still lovely, especially since the sight of George had taken the cockiness out of her. She clung to him, sobbing with relief.

"They said thou wert dead, but I never did believe it. Then Master Hawkins rode here, and told us that thou wert coming back."

"John Hawkins himself?"

"Oh, aye."

Who would have thought it of that grumpy old man, so squeamish in saddle? He had not told George this, simply mentioning that he had notified Sir John and Mistress Anne. Even if he'd come only from London, where he had an office now, it was full seventy miles; and from Plymouth town it must be more than twice that. George was touched. He resolved to be a better servant in future.

"That was more than a month ago. I'd never believed, before, that thou wert dead, but *then*—I began to believe it."

"I live," George said simply, "though there were times I wished I didn't. But that's past. I would have come instanter upon landing in England, but they sent me back to Spain. Didn't grant me a chance to catch my breath."

"It must have been a most important mission."

"It was," he said cautiously, as he disentangled himself. "Now, how fares thy father?"

The master of Okeland himself answered this question by his arrival, a bit out of breath, from the direction of the house. Sir John was smallish and weather-bitten. An old warrior, he made no show of courtliness. His chest was thin, his face too. He was a notably handsome man, with a graying beard, the nose of an intelligent hawk, and eyes large, dark blue, very expressive—Anne's own eyes.

George felt sorry for Sir John Crofts. As they rushed into each other's arms, whooping their delight, he had caught a glint of gladness in the knight's eyes, a glint he knew had been caused by the sight of his, George's, brave new clothes.

Sir John was anything but greedy, mean of spirit. But he was human; and his road had been a rocky one. A widower, almost landless, he had lost both of his sons, one in Ireland, the other in the Low Countries, and was left with a daughter, so much younger than the dead lads, something indeed of an afterthought, and two aged cantankerous maiden sisters who were dependent upon him.

He adored his daughter. Nothing could have made him so happy as to see her wed where her heart was. And when a young man returns from America in such costly garb, any father might be permitted his instant of wild hope.

"Nay, sir," George laughed as they finished their embrace. "I'm as poor as ever. Aunt Jane Dormer bought me these rags."

"We'd heard that Hawkins heaped it high—till the Spaniards broke their pledge at Ulua. And then he limped home with nothing. But *thou* art back, there's the main thing! Come along. A mug of ale, and then I'll show thee around."

Bored with country life, delighted to have a man to talk with, Sir John prattled on as he led the way to the house. The path was narrow and they passed in single file, Anne in the middle, George last, frankly studying the figure of the woman before him.

For she *was* a woman, and this jolted George. He could not remember a time when he had not meant to marry Anne Crofts. Three years had done a great deal so that she was no longer the wiry wench he'd once climbed trees with, and anticipation tingled him now. Perhaps he should have been ashamed of this feeling; but he wasn't.

A peasant? Oh, no. She was rather a fine healthy animal, despite her smallness. And if those hips and buttocks he looked at, being without whalebone, were somewhat wider and more protuberant than a fine lady of the court would have deemed proper, at least there was no waddle about them. They didn't flap. Here was a woman who, without being smudged by it, belonged to the land. Here, when they could marry, they'd live. George was somewhat shocked by the lack of a bonnet or even a cap, which seemed to him carrying country liberty too far, but the free-swinging body pleased him. You wouldn't see anything like that at court. But Anne was too honest, too straightforward for the court anyway, no woman's paradise at best, since a jealous female, seated on the throne, ruled it. It was bad enough, George reflected, to see men making their knees callous from groveling, slapping smiles upon their mouths as readily as they might slap masks upon their eyes—

> *"Cog, lie, flatter, and face:*
> *Four ways at Court to win your grace."*

—but for a woman, it would be Hell. No matter what happened, George thought, Anne must stay here. She belonged at Okeland.

"Here we are, lad."

George was disappointed by what he saw at the house. Sir John pattered of breeding a rag of colts, of marling and skuttling and the difficulty of hiring sarclers these days; but as George was led through the screens, the spicery, the maltery, the dry and the wet larders, the pewter room, the "warm room" where hams and bacon were being smoked, he shook his head. That garden wall, he had noted, not mentioning it, still was not built. And precious little else, as far as he could see, had been done. Sir John might boast of his boldness in trying an innovation from Holland, the planting-out of turnips in open fields; he might splutter about the poor return from flax and saffron, as he might gloat over the high price of wool; but the fact remained, undeniable, that in the three years since George had been here, not a single painted cloth had been added to the walls of Okeland and hardly another piece of furniture, while the staff, as gathered for food, looked definitely smaller. "But I clack on! *Thou* careth nothing about the saffron crop!"

George did care about it. But he was embarrassed; and just at that moment, at table, he would have preferred to look at Anne Crofts. She was ravishing in a yellow kirtle, white cutwork forepart, a dark blue gown open down the front, and below her bodice the scarlet taffeta stomacher he had brought her from London town. But to see her he would have been obliged to lean far over the table and peer past her two elderly aunts like any gawping fool, while to talk to her he would have had to shout.

The Croftses did not have feudal pretensions. The one real meal of the day, dinner, which started in the middle of the afternoon, they ate in the great-hall with all their servants, to the number of about thirty, excepting those in the kitchen and scullery and those who fetched the food. But all tables, connected, were on the same level, while the food and wine at one end was the same as that at the other. The family and George were the only ones seated above the "salt," a silver cellar that had belonged to Sir John's mother; but it was mere convention because everybody was seated on the same side, since this made it so much easier for the serving men. This was the reason George was not vouchsafed a stare at Anne in her surprisingly wide farthingale, her waist a wasp's, her face now pale as that of any court lady. Perhaps it was just as well.

The food was sound—pigeons, spitchcocked eels, a pasty of fallow deer, carrots, radishes, cabbage, sugar meats, rock samphires, and gallons of perry and of wine—but the noise was such that a man couldn't have heard himself think.

Later, the cloths and crumbs were cleared away, the boards and trestles too, and only Aunt Helen and Aunt Sylvia and Sir John and Anne were left to share the hall with George. There was no fire, and it was too early to light a candle, but the shadows were long across the ceiling, and the rushes, which must have been recently changed, smelled clean and green on the floor. Then George could and did feast his eyes upon Anne.

There were many questions to be answered. He was not eager to talk about his imprisonment, which had been unspeakably dull, and it was needful for him to avoid mention of why he had so soon been sent back to Spain—they would hardly have credited it of Hawkins anyway, and George himself was none too proud of his own part— but he saw no reason to conceal his present mission. He told them, then, that he was carrying a message from King Philip to the Strange Guest.

"*Jezebel!*"

Sir John, ordinarily so mild a man, sat now on the edge of his X-chair, his fists clenched, eyes aflame.

George spread apologetic palms.

"Well, there are all sorts of stories—"

"George, thou'lt meet her? Thou'lt go into her very presence?"

"Why, I suppose so."

The aunts, blurred shadows now, were still. Nor did Anne stir in the failing light as she spoke. She was looking away from George, which was not like this forthright girl. Her lips did not tremble, but her voice did.

"They— They say she's beautiful."

George shrugged.

"I hadn't heard that."

Now she did look at him, not reproachfully but with a hurt astonishment, while he cursed himself for having lied yet again—and so thoughtlessly, so senselessly. He tried to toss it out of his own mind, telling himself that he'd only spoken figuratively, that he had meant that he hadn't hitherto *thought about* Mary Stuart's beauty, of which, like everybody else, he had *heard*. But there was no escape from that harpoon, Anne's stare.

"The Devil can take any form," Sir John cried, "but he remains the Devil all the same."

George glanced at him. George was no stranger to the severer forms of puritanism; but he never could go with the passion it inspired. God knew, George had no love for the Inquisition! But back here in England, where men were more moderate, he knew no need for such choler. He had learned, however, not to argue.

"Steel thyself, lad. They do say that Shrewsbury's got guts of stone, and no heart at all. But steel thyself, dost hear?"

"Aye," said George.

"Aye," murmured Anne in the dusk. "Aye, do that."

[28]

He could not see her face for the shadows, but he sensed her perturbation. Was this because she feared for her father's spleen, or was it because of the nature of George's errand? It was amazing what a difference the naming of Mary Stuart's name had made in that darkening hall. Damn that queen! Why hadn't she stayed in Scotland? Even the aunts, customarily garrulous, refrained from stir, sidewise eyeing their brother in fear. Anne sat breathless. It was as though Satan himself had entered this hall, where the air grew cold, musty, close.

Only with an effort did Sir John recover his composure, reminding himself that it was no time for the vehement expression of religious thought. He asked George if he was weary.

George had been in saddle since sunup, and he welcomed an excuse to retire. Yet he was troubled as he rose. And a little later, in a borrowed nightrail, he drifted into Sir John Crofts's chamber.

The knight was in bed but not asleep. He had whuffed out his candle, and there was only a drizzle of moonlight at the window.

"I'll be calling on thy daughter for a sweet-dreams kiss," George explained.

"Well, don't take all night to do it."

There was no corridor upstairs at Okeland, where there were doorways but not doors, the various bedrooms opening into one another like the links of a chain, the master's being in the middle.

Anne, also in a nightrail, was seated on her bed, a narrow one, untestered, scarcely more than a pallet. Her arms were around her legs, her knees pushed her chin, and she had been looking out her arrowslit of a window at the moon.

Though she must have expected him, and surely as a cousin it was his right and almost his obligation to claim a buss, when George entered she held close over her breast the folds of the nightrail. It was as though she had been startled by the entrance of a stranger. She had never done this before, but always had taken George for granted. She was tense, too, when he kissed her.

He sat by her side.

"Art fearful, chuck?"

"They say many things of that woman."

He held her tight. She was so small and soft! He had come such a long way for this!

And suddenly, again, he was afraid—for her, for them. It was absurd; but he had not shaken off that earlier wing-brushing fear he had felt when he saw Okeland for the first time in three years, a fear, baseless of course, that the place was under a spell, caught up in mysterious unseen toils. Here in the very middle of England he was more frightened than ever he had been in the Indies. Here in his own cousin's house, with his arms around his beloved on a calm and quiet moonlit night, he had to battle panic.

So he held her, hard. Even in this dim room she might read his face, and he wouldn't release her until he had won control of himself. Then he tried a laugh, a sound that sagged.

"I'm off with the dawn, dearest," he whispered. "I may not be able to stop on my way back to London—'tis a matter of what message I carry, if any. It may be a week, weeks."

"They say she's a sorceress."

Now he really did laugh.

"Nay, chuck, I've not outlasted prison and schemed my way back here only to be dizzied by a French witch's brew!"

"George, if she tries to—"

"Besides, here's a headier draft. Give me that mouth again."

She was submissive, but no more than that. The muscles of her arms and shoulders, his hands felt, were taut, tight. George had a conviction that she was struggling against tears as a moment before he himself had struggled with his panic; and he believed that she would break down and weep the moment he left.

He rose, uneasy, sorry that he had come.

"Good night, chuck," he whispered. "God— God be with you."

And he went out.

When he passed through the master's chambers there was no sound from the bed. Was Sir John asleep? George thought not. But if asleep, as if awake, no doubt the knight was plagued by a dream of the queen of Scots. George sighed. He went to bed.

5

Fifty Men a Whistle Away

Rain fell sullenly out of a sky that was the color of a rat's back. The freshets of spring long since had been abated, and the Don ran clear and low, refusing to fill yet at the same time failing to drain the moat of Sheffield Castle, where the scum, which stank, was darkly iridescent.

George had been made to give up his horse at the barbican, a rather perfunctory outwork made of fine-grained bluish-gray stone, so he crossed the bridge on foot, his boots aclack. Two men with mauls were banging the massive lift-chains to knock off the rust. They were methodical like machines, like figures on a clock, and the clangor they set up rang throughout that web of walls and buildings, while the rust flew in red-brown flakes from each impact, littering the bridge.

The gate tower itself was high, thick, square, rimmed by a crenelated parapet. It was gloomy under there, giving George a feeling of immense weight that strove to press down upon him. The gates were open, but hurdles had been set up so that every entrant had to pass through a small space in the middle, where two halberdiers stood. Overhead, slitted into the second story of this tower, the portcullis was suspended on unseen cables. Though it must have weighed several tons, it was so delicately hung that it swayed in the breeze. George, looking up as he passed beneath its sharp spikes, fairly scurried like a rabbit. One of the halberdiers snickered.

A captain, cuirassed, laconic, examined the letter from Lord Burghley. He hmmmed portentously.

"It looks genuine."

"Damn it, man, it *is* genuine! D'ye think I'd ride this far with a forgery?"

"Many of the papers presented here are not what they pretend to be," was the captain's comment. "And many of the men who present 'em too."

The halberdier snickered again, and the officer gave him a spine-straightening glance.

"Come, enough of this," cried George, exasperated. "Take me to her majesty of Scotland."

"Things aren't done that directly at Sheffield," the captain warned him. "You," to the other halberdier, the one who had not laughed, "escort this man to the offices of master secretary Bateman."

"The queen's secretary?" George asked.

"The earl's. You're yet a long way from the queen."

The drawbridge led to the southern face of the castle, so that George had ridden right for it, not seeing a need to circle the place first. In consequence he had little conception of its size. There were towers, a grim dirty gray, wet now with rain but no doubt damp even through sunny hours. There was the barbican and the great gatehouse. This much he had glimpsed.

When he started across the outer court, following the halberdier,

George saw with wonder that he was in a place of immensity, a city in itself. The pavement was flagstone, and it stretched far. There were hawkers, some with tents pitched against the wall, others strolling. There were off-duty guardsmen, gentles, children, villagers. There was a farrier's forge, an armory, a shambles. There was even a tavern, an ale shop of sorts, ramshackle, rickety, but crowded; and somebody was singing in there.

> *"The abbot of Burton he brewed good ale*
> *On Fridays, when they fasted.*
> *But the abbot never tasted his own*
> *As long as his neighbor's lasted."*

At the gate of the inner bailey they were halted, and during the time when the guardsman dickered with somebody inside, George, against the wall out of the rain, idly contemplated that guardsman's weapon. Most persons, he supposed, thought of the halberd as decorative only, a symbol of power. It was much more than that. Despite its old-fashioned and even medieval aspect, it was ideal for the keeping back of crowds, he'd been told; and he could readily believe that. The axe-like edge of this one, so near to George's face, was fully two feet long, and as bright as a beacon, as sharp as a razor. Nobody in his right mind would get close to that edge. The shaft was heavy, necessarily, the thickness of a midget's wrist; yet George had heard that some halberdiers, burly men for the most part and unlikely to be swift in pursuit, could throw their weapon as accurately as a Spaniard his knife: they could cut a cat in half at fifty yards whilst running, or shear off the lower part of a fugitive's leg.

"Very well, sir. This way."

The inner bailey was smaller as it was quieter, and to judge from the facings of some of the buildings even had about it a certain air of elegance. But it was austere elegance. There was no joy here, nor ever had been.

The donjon keep dominated this yard, which indeed had been built around it, a great square shaggy tower made of brownish stone different from the other buildings, much older. Today it was a relic, and not a remarkably picturesque one, used perhaps as a storehouse if it was used at all, kept for sentiment's sake, or, more likely, because it would be too much trouble to tear down. This was the original stronghold, the first fort, and it might have been reared in the days of the Conquest.

The other buildings, set in a square, formed the inner wall, which was also the outer wall on the north and east, the sides of the Don and the Sheaf. They were less martial, but they were hardly more attractive. They all looked the same to George; yet the halberdier without pause went to a certain door, which he opened.

"A visitor to the guest from Scotland."

"Come in, come in. She hasn't had many these days."

John Bateman was the perfect secretary. He could always keep track of things; his beard was scrawny; his chin was long and thin, a pump handle. His gown was long, trailing the floor. His mouth twitched absently. He squinted. The table at which he labored was piled with papers, all of them neatly arranged. The pen he put down was immaculate, and his inkhorn gleamed with oil. Carved into the legs of the table, into the back of the chair in which he sat, and into the keystone of the fireplace, untinctured but clear, were the Talbot arms—argent, a hound courant proper.

He did not look up from the sheet he had just signed and was sanding, nor did he ask George to sit. He put the paper away with one hand, with the other reaching for Lord Burghley's letter. He perused this letter swiftly but with care, rubbering out his lips.

"It really is Cecil's handwriting," he murmured.

"Did you expect it to be the Sultan of Turkey's?"

Bored, yet conscientious, Bateman reached for the message to Mary; and George, without thinking, passed him this, which Bateman immediately began to open, tearing the seal.

"See here, that's for the queen!"

"She'll see it, in time."

"My orders were—"

"Here you take orders from the earl of Shrewsbury."

"God rot it, man! I'll not stand and—"

George stepped forward, instinctively reaching for his sword. But he had forgotten the guardsman, who lowered his halberd. There were no snorts, there was no bluster. The blade itself stopped George, speaking loud words. It shone a few scant inches from George's eyes; and it was bright, seemingly alert, like a live thing.

Bateman looked up, for the first time.

"Guard, this man's armed. How dare you bring him that way! Take his sword and dagger to your officer, and then bring that officer to me."

Resistance would have been fatal. There were fifty men a whistle away. George shrugged, submitting.

"But I want a receipt for it," he grumbled.

The truth is, he was uneasy without that sword. Never a ruffler, not one to cry "Lug it out!" at any slight provocation, he nevertheless valued his Toledo as a true companion, and without it he stood naked, vulnerable.

Bateman was reading King Philip's letter. He appeared to find it in no way extraordinary, and clearly he didn't seek any cipher or secret writing. At last he nodded, and proceeded to leave the room.

"Wait here," he directed George over a shoulder.

Soon the captain of the guard came, an unhappy man; and for some time he and George Fitzwilliam stood before the paper-strewn table, trying to refrain from looking at one another.

"Very well, Fitzwilliam. His lordship will receive you. This way. You," to the captain, "wait for me."

George Talbot, sixth earl of Shrewsbury, knight of the Garter, lord-lieutenant of York, Derby, and Nottingham, master of Sheffield Castle and Sheffield Lodge, of Worksop, Wellneck, Bolsover, Tutbury, Wingfield, Handsworth, and Rufford, and through his wife also of Chatsworth and Hardwick, was a short man with a long silky beard and harassed eyes. His doublet was rich, if somber. Like his secretary he made no move to invite George to sit. Yet there was nothing of arrogance about the man. His voice was low, and somewhat fretful.

"You have asked for an audience. Ordinarily this would not be permitted. Scotland's majesty is not in the best of health, and we are obliged to keep her from overstraining herself."

"I'm sure of that."

"My Lord Burghley's letter makes it otherwise. Why is it you wish this personal interview, may I ask?"

George told him:

"Those men suffer. This I can swear to from the bottom of my heart. For three years they have been starving. Any morning they might be dragged before the Inquisition and sentenced to be burned alive—what's left of 'em. And yet, what have they done? Even pirates should not be treated like that. But they're not pirates."

Shrewsbury, head low, was studying him through frizzy eyebrows.

"You believe that if you explain this to Mary Stuart she will grant you a letter commending Hawkins to her cousin of Spain?"

"I believe so, sir, yes."

"What cares Philip for Master Hawkins anyway?"

George did not answer.

"I see. Well, my Lord Burghley hath his own affairs to arrange. The least we can do here is accommodate him whenever we can. So I have asked Scotland for this interview. It will take some time to prepare. She wishes to receive in state, of course."

"Me?"

"Even you."

The secretary meanwhile had resealed King Philip's message, and this he placed before his master. George noted that the remolding of the seal was not an expert job, as his own had been. He hoped that Queen Mary wouldn't notice.

Conceivably she was used to broken seals. Of one thing he was sure: Nobody had applied heat to this letter.

"Do you speak French, Fitzwilliam?"

"Not well."

"Italian?"

"None at all. Does the queen speak Spanish?"

"I think a little. But she'd be rusty in it. It would be best to stick to English. Only—remember to say the words slowly."

"I see."

"And now you may wash and have some wine. Bateman will send for you. I'll require a little preparing myself. For of course I'll have to present you. Can't do that without a tail, eh?"

"Could I— Could I have my sword and dagger back, sir?"

"Certainly not. Not until you are ready to leave the castle."

Two hours later George was summoned.

Brushed, kempt, he thought he looked well; but he would hardly shine in this company. Lord Shrewsbury now wore an oyster-white silk doublet slashed with silver lace and set with three rows of crystal buttons. His sky-blue hose, too, were silken, as indeed was his manner. There was a velvet bonnet on his head, set with a blue plume caught up with an aigrette of sapphires and diamonds. There was a gold chain around his neck, a huge pearl at his right ear, while his fingers glistened with rings.

He was attended by six gentlemen, one of them master secretary Bateman, each almost as flamboyant as his lordship himself. George noted that they all had swords.

These attendants, neatly in line—while George trailed like a shackled prisoner—followed Shrewsbury by a few steps as the little procession moved out of that building, across the inner court, and to one of the tallest of the towers, the door of which was flanked by guardsmen. This, George was told, was called the Scroll Tower, nobody knew why. It overlooked both the Don and the Sheaf, as well as Shrewsbury Park beyond, and the Lodge; and it might have been the least barnlike part of the castle. The queen of Scots had her throne room on the ground floor, George learned, opening directly off the court. She and her close attendants lived upstairs.

The master of the household, an ascetic Scot in a long cinnamon-colored robe, appeared briefly at the door. He shook his head, and backed away.

"My lady has decided upon another shade of garter ribbon," Bateman ventured under his breath.

"That will do," Lord Shrewsbury said.

Fortunately—for there was no antechamber save this the yard, and it still rained—the wait was not a long one. The master of the household reappeared, to throw open the doors. Shrewsbury and his attendants marched in. George, by instruction, remained outside. The doors were closed again.

George had seen nothing, but he could hear well enough.

"Your majesty!"

"My lord, it is always heartlifting to see you."

The voice was low, limpid, perfectly clear, a somewhat throaty voice with a hint of laughter in it. Even separated from its possessor, that voice was thrilling. George leaned forward, forgetting the rain. It was as though he held a bowl in which he sought to catch every clear sweet syllable.

"Are you amazed to find me alive? The food I'm served has had a curious tang of late. Are you poisoning me, my lord?"

"God forbid!"

"Yes. It would be awkward for my dear cousin Elizabeth of England if I was found dead, wouldn't it?"

"Your grace jests."

"Being still able to, praise the saints. Now—what brings you here this afternoon, my lord of Shrewsbury?"

"A visitor from Plymouth, who bears a message to you from his most catholic majesty Philip of Spain."

"Ah?"

"This young man is a servant of Master John Hawkins, and he would help to free some of Hawkins' men who are within Spain's danger."

"'Awkins? Who is that?"

"A mariner, ma'am. And merchant. He hath been lord mayor of Plymouth. He is admiral of the royal West Channel fleet."

"I see. And the messenger?"

"Nay, I never viewed him before, nor heard of him. But he comes with an authentic letter from my Lord Burghley."

The voice said, warmly, "Why, have him up then, Shrewsbury. Have him up."

The master of the castle called: *"George Fitzwilliam."*

[36]

The doors were flung open.
George took a deep breath, and walked in.

6

More Beautiful than Heaven

He knew only her. The hall, the persons in it, were a smear on
either side, but Mary Stuart directly before him was real, more beautiful than Heaven. He had uncovered before crossing the threshold,
and this was as well, for thereafter he was in a daze, and as he walked
toward the throne, toward the queen, he was unacquainted with anything else: had there been a gaping hole in the floor he would have
fallen in; had there been a stool he would have tripped over it.

Somehow he got there, to the very foot of the dais. He went to one
knee.

"Your majesty."

Even as his eyes turned to the floor they were still full of Mary of
Scotland.

He would always see her. He knew this; he would never be the
same again. God's providence had done this. Or the Devil. It didn't
make much difference just then. Helpless, on one knee, head bowed,
he collected his impressions of Mary.

She was tall, lithe. She wore black, turned over with scarlet, and a
goffered white ruff. An ivory fan hung from her waist at one side, a
gold filigreed pomander on the other. Her hands, startlingly white,
were folded in her lap. The cap she wore, like the rest of her clothes,
was extremely simple, a flat thing of black silk with a white rutching
that served to broaden an already broad forehead as well as to
accentuate the heart-shape of the face.

The features of that face were delicate and small, even the longish
nose being fragile. The chin was tiny, the base of the heart. The mouth
too was small, and it had been grave when George glimpsed it, though
surely a smile would come swiftly to it and perhaps as swiftly go, like
cat's-paws caused by wind upon the surface of a pond. This was no
conventional beauty! The hair was dark but not black—chestnut, he
thought. It was wavy, but unfrilled, and obviously her own. The eyes,
small, though oddly penetrating, were set wide apart. George could

not have told their color: yellow-brown perhaps, or burnt sienna, or even hazel, or somewhat reddish. The upper lids were heavy, and shone a faint blue. The brows were thin and set far apart.

"It was kind of you to come, Master Fitzwilliam." Her voice was clear water purling over clean round shining stones. "Please rise."

He rose, appearing, he hoped, outwardly unrubbed. He sucked his breath when he saw her again in the flesh, so near at hand, gazing at him. His bonnet was in his right hand, properly held over his heart. His left hand felt for the hilt of his sword, which it couldn't find.

Then the queen smiled. It was not a swift passing flashing surface smile, such as George had envisioned whilst kneeling. Rather it was slow to come, slower still to go away. It made her mouth look larger, and George noted that there was no dimple on the chin. That smile could hardly have been called regal. It came close to being a grin.

"You feel lost without your tuck?"

"Ma'am, what is a man without a sword?"

"They are not supposed to be men when they're admitted into my presence. Decorticated conies, I think. But—you are different."

He bowed, not knowing what else to do.

"My Lord Shrewsbury says that you have a tale of English mariners unjustly held by my cousin of Spain?"

He bowed again.

She spoke English slowly, picking her words, having trouble with her aspirants. It was a slightly nasal accent, and she tended to stress the last syllable of any given word, which made for a somewhat sing-song effect. It didn't matter. With that liquid voice she could as well have been talking Chinese. The words themselves were unimportant.

"I know nothing about this, Master Fitzwilliam. But I can be enlightened. I am interested in the welfare of all prisoners anywhere, since I am a prisoner myself."

If this was intended to produce a stir it failed. Nobody so much as shifted his feet. George was becoming aware of the chamber in which he stood, and which he now knew to be small for a throne room, with a ceiling comparatively low, from which was hung a many-prismed chandelier, one of the few pretentious pieces there. The carpet was, appropriately, red; and the somewhat skimpy windows were decorated with red velvet. In addition to the queen herself and George, the two halberdiers at the door, the master of the household, and Shrewsbury and his six attendants, there were only about twenty persons in the room, male and female, all of them obviously part of Mary's suite. The master of the household necessarily carried a sword; but none of the other men behind Mary did.

The throne itself was a handsome high-backed chair of some dark wood, upholstered with crimson damask and raised by three short steps from the level of the floor. Above it was a state canopy of cramoisy woven with gold thread in the arms of France and those of Scotland, the arms of England being prudently omitted, though Mary Stuart, in the eyes of thousands, had a better claim to the English throne than did the woman who sat there, Elizabeth Tudor. There was also a motto of some sort on that cloth of state, something French. George could not keep his eyes away from the queen long enough to read it.

Seemingly unmindful of the bungled seal, she broke open Philip's letter, which she read carefully, nodding a bit. Her lips did not move as she read.

"I had not been told," she said slowly, when she had finished, "that you are a nephew of the duchess of Feria."

"Save for the good offices of my aunt, ma'am, I should be lying in a lousy dungeon right now, along with those others."

"Ah, yes. Tell me about them."

More than once it had been suggested to George Fitzwilliam that he should have been a courtier. He was told that his eloquence was unstrained, persuasive. "You *look* honest, George," a friend once said, "and that's a diplomat's chief need." Yet George disliked the life and would have none of it, excepting when, on occasions like this, he felt a moral obligation to help someone.

They assured him afterward that though he did talk too fast, on the whole he gave Mary Stuart an excellent account of the third Hawkins trading voyage to the New World and the bloody end it came to at San Juan de Ulua. He could recall to memory very little of that talk. They were to tell him that he went into particulars, giving the Hawkins argument, as it was his duty to do; but he was to remember none of this. All he knew at the time was Mary Stuart.

When he had finished she leaned forward to ask him questions, and she listened carefully to the answers.

To his mind, she did this for two reasons. In the first place, she had not been too sure of what he said, though reluctant to admit as much. She had watched him carefully; it was the expression that interested her, the light in the eyes, rather than the words. She would interpret the man himself, and only incidentally the tale he had to tell. She was used to being lied to, anyway.

In the second place, she was lonesome. It brought a lump to George's throat to realize that he was providing pleasure for her with what would ordinarily have been a routine request, a matter to be disposed of, one way or the other, in a few minutes; and she was purposely prolonging the interview. She *enjoyed* the talk with him, every second of it! She hated to have it end!

For three years, since she fled over the border from the rebel Scots led by her own brother yammering at her heels, Mary Stuart had been the captive of her cousin, Queen Elizabeth, the woman upon whose mercy, pledged in advance, she had thrown herself. That confinement, galling to a person of her active mind and ambition, of late had become severe. George had seen this for himself. He'd been told, bluntly, that if it had not been for a letter from Lord Burghley, a most urgent letter, he would not have been admitted into the presence of Mary Stuart, that "guest" about whom the net was being pulled tighter and tighter every day.

George answered each question with care. He told her a great deal about New Spain, a great deal too about the Spanish court and especially about his aunt, matters that, truly, had no bearing upon the case of the imprisoned sailors.

Two or three times Shrewsbury, behind him, coughed. Several men back there stirred restlessly. They should be reprimanded! Didn't they know that they stood before royalty? How dared they to—

For his own part, George Fitzwilliam could have gone on talking all afternoon. But even Mary Stuart, though grateful for the break in the boredom, knew that she must keep bright the fiction of her power. She thanked George, giving him another smile.

"Come to my chambers in an hour's time, and my secretary will give you a letter of reply. Also, I think, a gift for your aunt. It has been kind of you to come."

She glanced at the master of the household, who thudded the floor with his staff.

Queen Mary rose. The others fell to their knees. And then she was gone.

George said little at dinner. He would have preferred to take that meal in the great-hall, where the noise and confusion might serve to hide his feelings, but he could scarcely refuse when the earl of Shrewsbury asked him to dine with him *en famille*. It was an honor, true, but it was also an ordeal. Even the presence of the hatchet-faced countess, the celebrated Bess of Hardwick, surely the most married woman of the time—Shrewsbury was her fourth husband—did not lift George from his thoughts of what had just passed. He tried to be polite, but undeniably he was vague, and he excused himself as early as he could.

The Scroll Tower consisted of four stories, of which the throne room was on the ground level, the next above was largely offices, while the third, George had been told, housed the nearer servants and attendants, and the queen herself lived on the top story. It was upon the third landing that George met a slim dark-haired lad who appeared to have been waiting for him.

"Are you the secretary?"

The other blushed.

"Oh, no. I'm a page. Anthony Babington, sir, at your service."

"At yours, sir."

"The secretary will be out in a moment."

They stood awhile, George studying his companion sidewise.

"You have been in her majesty's service long?" he asked at last.

"Two months, sir."

"You like it?"

Young Babington seemed astonished, and shook his head as though not sure whether he'd heard right.

"Why— Why, it's paradise!"

George looked around.

"A rather grubby paradise, I'd say."

"Oh, no, sir! Not when *she's* here!"

"I see."

"I wonder if you really do, sir. You met her highness for an hour, but can you imagine what it would be like to see her every day?"

George said nothing.

"A kinder, sweeter person never walked the face of this earth. No matter the castle! It's a privilege to serve her. It would be a privilege in a pigsty."

"I see. An angel. The others feel that way too?"

"Why, of course. Everybody who knows her loves her."

"And yet—there are those who say she's an adulterer, a murderer, a traitor, the personification of evil."

"Damn you, if you—"

"Tut, boy! I didn't say *I* thought that. But others do."

"Then they don't know her. Why, for that lady, sir, I swear, I'd let myself be torn to pieces, limb from limb!"

"Let's hope you never have to."

The door was opened, and the secretary, Rollett, called them in. He handed George a letter not dissimilar in appearance to the one George had brought, though sealed with the Stuart arms rather than those of Hapsburg. He had probably been doing a bit of last-minute tampering. The place smelled of snuffed candles.

[41]

"Her highness has been pleased to vouch for the dependability of John Hawkins of Plymouth."

Whom she'd never even heard of a few hours ago, was George's thought.

"She, uh, she said something about a package?" he ventured.

"She will bring it personally. Ah, here she is—"

Mary Stuart came down a circular staircase, as the three men sank to their knees. She was wearing dark blue, an informal garb, somewhat fleecy; and there was a flimsy silk scarf, bright yellow in color, about her neck. In her hands she carried a small prayer book, leather with gold stampings, which she opened.

"You must give this to your aunt when you go back to Madrid. Tell her that I often think of her. See, I have written in it."

Absit nobis gloriari nisi in cruce Domini nostri
Jesu Christi. Maria R.

George took the book, closed it, put it into his purse. He had not raised his head and could not see her face, only the ends of the yellow scarf.

And now there appeared before his eyes her hands holding two large ruby earrings. They were perfectly matched, each the shape of a tear drop, the clasp being gold.

"'Tis the fashion among you men to wear but one of these at a time. When you pass through London again, then, I charge you to leave one with the Spanish ambassador, Don Gerau de Spies, as a token of my esteem."

"And—the other, ma'am?"

"Why, the other, Master Fitzwilliam, I had hoped that you yourself would accept as an unworthy memento of our talk today."

"Majesty!"

"Wear it sometimes and think of this poor caged bird. But not often! You are too long and strong to have many sad thoughts. And now—farewell. God speed you."

She held out her hand, palm down. For an instant George could not believe what he saw; he had never hoped for this. The ruby was riches enough, but—her own hand! Tears scalded his eyes and he sobbed, all unashamed, as he seized the hand in both of his own and reverently kissed it.

Then the queen was going, up and around, around and up, until the staircase itself disappeared into the gloomy shadow of the Scroll Tower.

Half an hour later George Fitzwilliam left Sheffield. He had been offered hospitality, but he was too nervous to remain. Besides, he wished to be alone, without conversation. He reckoned that he could make the inn at Grantham, reputedly a good one, before full darkness.

He walked over the drawbridge, and the heavy wet planks plunked stodgily under his feet. At the barbican he was obliged to pay a tester for the care of his horse, which annoyed him, for the animal hadn't even been fed. He cursed fervently, yet the guardsman beamed.

The rain was relentless—small vindictive drops, slanting angrily.

"You're the last one, sir," the guardsman called. "She'll go up now."

"I could tell you *what* she might go up," George retorted.

Fifty yards away he reined, and turned. His heart felt like a cold crabapple. There was a banging behind his eyes. And he wondered whether he would ever be able to swallow again.

Signals were shouted. The guardsman scampered across the draw to the gatehouse. A windlass in the second floor of the house began to squeal; then another. The big-linked iron chains trembled, growing taut. Very slowly, lurching like a great bear, the bridge rose. The links clanked as they were drawn in, one after another. The bridge shuddered, rainwater dripping from its bottom. Inexorably, noisily, the chains pulled it up, until with a thud that seemed to shake the very earth it fell into its destined position as a part of the castle wall. Thereafter it was motionless, the rain lashing it in vain.

George heard a huge oaken balk being shoved into place. Sheffield Castle was closed.

Higher up, much higher, and further back, at one of the top windows of the Scroll Tower there fluttered a long, bright yellow scarf.

7

In the Dark of the Night

He had miscalculated. Sheffield to Grantham proved a good forty-odd miles, and it was several hours after sunset when he clattered into the innyard. Even so, there was an ostler to take his mount —and take it in such a fashion that George knew the beast would be well cared for. This was no Crossed Keys.

Though George sagged with weariness, his mind was awake. And now he felt like talking. He nodded to the sign.

"That's no bag of nails."

" 'Twasn't once, your worship. I can remember the old one. Master Blake bought it cheap. But he never did like it. Thought it wasn't decent, you might say."

"Decent?"

"Well, it showed a fat man without hardly a stitch of clothing on, except where there had to be, if your worship knows what I mean?"

"I think I do."

"He had some vegetables over his head, and he was holding a mug. That's the part Master Blake *did* like about it. Thought that might egg on guests to buy more beer. But then, there was all that skin . . ."

"I'm beginning to understand."

"The Bacchanals was what it was called then, sir. But these country people around here, they couldn't say that right. They kept calling it Bag o' Nails, and pretty soon that's what everybody called it, even Master Blake himself. And then the paint partly peeled off, and two-three years ago Master Blake got a man to touch it up a bit."

"Yes."

"And Master Blake, he said to that man: 'See if you can make it come out less naked.' So the painter—oh, he was yare, that one!—he made it into a sort of bag. To go with what everybody had been calling the place anyway. The vegetables that had been on the man's head, they got to look like drawstrings, see? And the belly, that was the bulge of the bag itself. He didn't do the whole job. Master Blake wouldn't pay him enough. Still, it shows better'n it did afore. And when you look at it sort of sideways, squinting, it *does* seem sort of like a bag of nails, don't you think, sir?"

"Very interesting," said George. "And now, d'ye suppose I could have a bird and a bottle? Not to mention a bed?"

"Sure to, your worship. Here comes Master Blake right now."

This boniface might have been stingy when he dickered with an itinerant artist, nor was his appearance impressive, for in looks he reminded George of poor squinched little Ellis Waters deep in the archbishop of Seville's dungeons; but he did know how to treat a guest. Within minutes George found himself installed in a large clean room overlooking the yard on one side, the Great North Road on the other. Without undue fuss he was provided with everything he asked for. The night was chill, so a fire was lighted. A chicken for picking and a tankard of ale were produced as though by magic. So too was a tub of water, miraculously warm. Master Blake did not even complain when George asked for two extra candles, though doubtless he made a mental note to put these down on the bill.

Tired as he was, and late though the hour, George yearned for that bath. Even more fervently he yearned to work open Mary Stuart's message to her "cousin of Spain." This latter it was not his business to do; and Burghley might resent it. George did not care. He must know whether the queen of Scots was plotting against the peace of the realm of England, the very life of Queen Elizabeth. George did not believe that Mary was a conspirator—not a woman so sweet and lovely, so beguilingly frank! If the margined cipher had been read, and if it was being answered in kind, it must be the work of the secretary, Rollett.

This was the way George fretted; and despite the excellence of the service he was wishing that Master Blake and his so-efficient lackeys would get it over with and be gone. George did not fail to thank them, yet he shooed them out like geese.

He had already in part undressed, and had sipped the ale and nibbled the bird; but not until he was alone did he drain the stein, which was light, made of latten, and after filling some of this with warm water from the tub placed it on a rack made of his dagger and the rung of a stool, bunching just beneath it three lighted candles. This was the reason he had asked for the extra candles. The fireplace would have been uncertain.

The saying is that a watched pot never boils. George tried *not* to watch. He went out to the jakes. In his room again, he stripped. He washed, thoroughly, determinedly; but this act brought little relief. Garbed only in canions and codpiece, he strode the floor, striving to keep his gaze from the heated container, in which water scarcely had begun to simmer.

He fetched forth his wallet, and from it took the little book of devotions. It was a rich thing, expensively bound, showy; and he noticed for the first time that it was in Latin. He did not try to read it. All he was concerned with was the inscription, "*Absit nobis gloriari* —" The hand was exquisite, the letters cobweb-thin, delicately formed, but regular, and without flourishes. "*Maria R.*" He could see her still.

George and Hawkins had not been entirely uncommunicative in the course of that ride from Plymouth to London, nor had Burghley been mum at the meeting in his room overlooking the River Thames. George knew the situation in general. He knew—his common sense might have told him anyway—that it was to England's advantage to play Spain and France off against one another, at the same time keeping an eye on that small boisterous country just beyond the postern gate to the north, the back door, Scotland. The weaker the government in Scotland, the better for England. As for France and Spain, England could not face either alone, since each was so much larger, richer, more populous. Those two must be kept, if possible, at each other's throats. In no other way could England survive.

So it was Elizabeth's policy to blow hot and cold, now this way, now that; and at the moment, as George knew, she was smiling toward France, the country where the queen of Scots had lived for so many years—she was indeed its dowager queen—and from which aid for the royal Scottish cause normally might be expected. But Elizabeth was countering this danger with a flirtation of her own with the duc D'Anjou, younger brother of the French king, whom she intimated she might marry. D'Anjou was a misshapen, pock-marked midget, twenty years Elizabeth's junior; but this didn't stop her. Elizabeth's antics, not perhaps as silly as they looked, were serving to keep assistance from the imprisoned queen of Scots, at the same time scaring Spain.

Did Mary Stuart know this, or sense it, and was she planning to strike back by means of an alliance with Spain? Burghley believed that. So did Hawkins, as well he might; though Hawkins' chief interest, as it was that of his servant, George Fitzwilliam, was the release of those mariners in the archbishop of Seville's dungeons. Philip had snapped with telling avidity at the bait Hawkins held before him, agreeing almost without hesitation to pay the price the seeming traitor sought. But—who was *30* and who *40*? Were these English noblemen of incalculable power who might co-operate with Spanish landing forces? Why, otherwise, would Philip be asking Mary Stuart, in secret, for affirmation of their treason? Or was he asking *her*? Could it have been Rollett, or somebody else in that pathetic household, that phantom "court"?

The water sang a small song, but there was only the veriest wisp of steam, not nearly enough. Yet more was forming.

"Sssh-blup!"

George put away the devotional. He fished out the ruby earrings. These were striking, perfectly matched, large. It would be a pity to separate them. He hung one in the lobe of his left ear, which had been pierced. He strode back and forth, wishing that he had a mirror. He went to one of the windows, and tried to catch sight of himself in a pane of glass.

He saw that the rain had ceased, the Great North Road being bathed in the thinnest of moonlight. Nobody stirred out there. The inn was utterly silent.

This must have been near midnight, but George knew that he would not sleep until he had learned about that letter.

More steam was forming in the stein. It swirled languorously.

"Blup! Bl-u-u-up!"

His sword had been hung over the back of a chair. He unsheathed it. In guard position, he made sundry passes at air. He must have looked ridiculous; but there was nobody to watch.

George got out of breath easily these days. He was soft, after that long confinement. He should renew his fencing lessons, he told himself. There were places in or near London—Ruffian Hall in West Smithfield, La Belle Sauvage on Ludgate, the Curtain, the Grey Friars, the Bull.

He sheathed, panting.

There was a clank of hooves on the stones of the yard, and a horse exhaled. Without thinking and without caring, George went to the window on that side.

A man was dismounting. He was very large, with bulky shoulders. He was calling in a low caressive voice for the ostler. Somehow that voice, like the form, was familiar.

But George's interest was elsewhere; for at that moment he knew that the water in the tankard was boiling.

He turned away from the window.

He worked slowly on the seal, restraining an impulse to tear it. This must have taken him a quarter of an hour.

The message was conventional enough, written in French, the same spiderweb hand as that in the book of devotions.

Trembling, George took it to the fireplace, where he held it up, moving it back and forth.

Gradually, in the left margin, brownish letters appeared. When he held the paper back to cool, these letters went away. But he had memorized them.

He restored the letter to its envelope, which with great care he resealed. He found he was sobbing.

The message was simple: *ZTCKOGPV*. By use of the same cipher, this became "vraiment," French for "truly." It could only be an answer to the other margined message, which likewise had been written in invisible ink, an answer to the question about the dependability of *30* and *40*.

And the hand was the hand of Mary Stuart.

Nature was kind that night. George soon fell asleep. Not until he was about to take the road again, well after dawn, did he think to ask about the late arrival, who, he learned, already had departed. For

George remembered who it was—that light-moving hulk, that low taunting voice.

It was the bravo of the Crossed Keys.

8

Who Would Rise High

It was two days later.

William Cecil, Lord Burghley, rolled the ruby back and forth on his palm, grunting approval.

"It might bring twenty marks."

"I wouldn't sell it for a hundred!"

Burghley looked up, his rheumy eyes atremble. He was a shaky man anyway, continually quaking, and one who suffered from many ailments—gout, headaches, indigestion. The wonder was, what with all his fussiness, that he could be so incisive in affairs of state.

Now he shoved the gaud back across the table.

"There is no ill in accepting gifts. 'Tis a courier's prerogative. I'll fadge with that. But mind, lad, that you wear this only on your ear, not on your heart."

They were in Cannon Row, an obscure Burghley residence, more a house of work than anything else, filled with clerks, secretaries, copyists, couriers, rather than with place seekers. There was no distracting view of the Thames from Cannon Row, where all was business.

My lord sorted his papers, already serried in rigid neatness.

"Now let's start it all over again, at the beginning, eh?"

George sighed. He saw why they called this man "her majesty's housewife." Elizabeth's first minister liked everything to be on paper, preferably put there by himself. Specifically, he appeared to make two sheets, or lists, of each interview, situation, argument. On one would be the cons; on the other the pros. The report at an end, Lord Burghley would balance these, one in each hand, much as if he were estimating their actual weights. Everything on both sheets, to be sure, was duly numbered, lettered, indexed.

He had already done this once in the case of George Fitzwilliam's account of his mission to Sheffield; and now, as a check, he proposed to do it again.

Burghley heard George's sigh.

"Many lives may be at stake," he said. "The very safety of the realm may be involved. We mustn't skip it lightly."

Resigned, George went over the whole thing again, omitting nothing of what he had seen, heard, felt, or even smelled at Sheffield Castle, though he gave no detail of his journey, coming or going, this not being properly a part of his report. As before, he was amazed at the keenness of Burghley's questions, which were few but astute. My lord, for his part, appeared well satisfied with the account; nor did he exhibit any astonishment at the proof of Mary's duplicity. He only shrugged.

"I have the greatest admiration for that queen and lady," he told George. "But—she plays the game as she found it."

"She wouldn't be human if she didn't hate to be cooped."

"Perhaps a queen is not expected to be human."

"Elizabeth isn't, then?"

Burghley made no reply.

"She called herself a caged bird," George pursued, working himself into a small frenzy of defense. "Can you scold a caged bird for beating the bars with its wings?"

Burghley harrumphed.

"It's not my intent to enter a judgment of Mary Stuart. Let's be back to the queen's business. When you went to Don Gerau's did he receive you personally?"

"Oh, yes. Kept me waiting about an hour, that's all."

"Not long for a Spaniard. They think it enhances their importance, somehow. Now—did he make any mention of Master Hawkins' offer to sell out the fleet to Spain?"

"No."

"Did you?"

"No."

"Do you think he *would* have brought that up, if you'd baited him?"

"Mayhap. I'd say he's a fool."

"He is. And the earring would have impressed him. He's probably at his writing desk this very minute, praising you to his king. That letter will go to Spain on the same vessel that takes you, the hoy at Deptford."

"Speaking of that hoy, sir—"

"It will wait," he said dryly. "Simply make you sure that the project doesn't quail, at sea."

"If I ever get to sea. Those men rotting in prison—"

[49]

"They too can wait a little. Now, when you went to the Spanish embassy, and later when you came away, were you followed?"

George shook a puzzled head.

"Was I attended, you mean? Why, no. I have no servant, sir."

"No, no! I mean did a spy watch you."

"Why should a spy do that?"

"Why not? You're a spy yourself."

George knew this, but he did not like to hear it said; and he winced.

"You set spies on spies, then?"

"Of course. Everybody does. And other spies to spy on *them*. And so on."

"And when they report I assume that they all contradict one another."

"Oh, they do, aye."

"Then which one do you believe?"

Burghley spread pudgy hands.

"That's diplomacy, the selection. It isn't pricing like a merchant, or counting like a clerk. It's— Well, it's an art."

"I think it's one I don't like. Lies, always lies!"

"Sometimes there can be a great good come out of lies, if they're properly valued."

"I'd prefer to leave that to God."

"Don't be saucy, young man."

"I'm sorry, sir."

"Round-aboutness too can have its uses, though it *look* mean enough. Have you never heard that he who would get to a high place must use a winding stair?"

Again George winced. The memory of his last view of Mary Stuart as she climbed that spiral staircase in the Scroll Tower was fresh, even raw; and it stung.

"As for diplomacy, you'll need every bit of that at your command when you go on the errand I'm about to send you on."

"An errand? But see here, my lord, that boat at Deptford—"

"It will not sail without you. Meanwhile, my coach awaits to take you to a certain person who'd question you about the guest at Sheffield. And let me warn you—"

"What person would be of such stature to keep those mariners waiting even one more hour in a Spanish prison, sirrah?"

"Would you esteem the queen of England to be of such stature?"

"*The queen!*"

"Go to, lad. You have looked upon the lady of Scotland, and that lady's cousin, who happens to be at Greenwich right now, is eternally curious about her. She will ask you many questions."

"About Mary Stuart's politics?"

"About Mary Stuart's looks. Confine yourself to that subject, pray. *She* surely will. There's no need to bring up the real reason for your journey, or its result. The queen's highness will know as much of that as she wishes, in good time. Just now it might fluster her."

"My lord, I meant to ask it before: have you learned yet who *30* is and *40?*"

"No. We thought at first that they were Mary Stuart herself and the Spanish ambassador, Don Gerau. But your own marginal messages have made it clear that they're English noblemen. This will go high, lad. We must be sure of ourselves before we strike."

"But you *will* strike?"

"Of course. By the time you return from Madrid I hope to have *30* and *40,* whoever they are, safe in the Tower. I make for that pile myself, this very morning. There is a young man named Bailey, arrested at Dover when he came back from the Low Countries. His papers tell us something, but methinks the boy himself can tell more—such as who those numbers represent. La Gehenna should persuade him."

George shuddered. There were many stories of the horrible things that happened in that little low-ceilinged room in London Tower where La Gehenna, the rack, was maintained. Torture was not a customary practice of the English government, but when it was used it was used with a vengeance. And this same William Cecil, baron of Burghley, who was waggling a schoolmasterish forefinger at George right now, supervised those questionings. He was a man who did thoroughly whatever he took to be his duty. He was known as the most learned rose fancier in the kingdom; and just as he would lean with appreciation and solicitous care over a rosebush, so would he lean over some poor pale screaming sweating prisoner caught up with leather straps. In the one case he would prune tenderly, and clip; in the other he would whisper edged questions, or else instruct a remorseless rackmaster to put on more pressure. He would do each task as well as the other, for he was a conscientious and highly capable old man.

Burghley came around from behind his table, put a hand on George Fitzwilliam's shoulder, and in a burst of graciousness conducted George all the way out into Cannon Row and the coach.

"Don't think of Charles Bailey," he advised. "He'll be unhappy, aye. But—so will you."

There rose from out of my lord something that was almost a chuckle —a grisly sound, in the circumstances.

"You may be wishing in a little while that you could change places with him, Master Fitzwilliam. But—courage! And good luck! You'll need both."

9

Straw-Colored

George had never before been in a coach, and it frightened him. The device had been brought from the Continent, like so many so-called luxuries, and perhaps this accounted for its popularity: there must have been twenty of them in London alone, and almost as many more throughout the rest of the country. In God's name, *why?* Well, the expense might have been one attraction. The man who would maintain a carriage was the kind of man who wished always to be shouting, "See how rich I am!" Burghley of course kept one because in his governmental capacity he could do no less: foreign ambassadors expected this.

Save that it would keep out rain—and as luck would have it this was a sunny morning, the first in more than a week—George could see no advantage to the vehicle. Any horse, even some nag begnawn with the botts, sped with spavins, would be quicker, cleaner, and incalculably more comfortable. The coach creaked; it was slow, drafty, dirty, dark; it proceeded on its lumbrous way in a series of spine-jolting bumps. From time to time it stopped altogether; and when it started forward again it jerked.

Worst of all were the onlookers. My Lord Burghley's professionally inspired extravagance did not extend so far as the hiring of a whiffler, or clearer-away, that long-armed one who strode ahead of a coach making a path for it by the use, when needed, of a bum-walloper or paddle. Some such *fonctionnaire,* George was sure, would have been provided anywhere on the Continent, where, indeed, there would be less need for him, since Continental crowds never had the naughtiness to peer into carriages, an English affectation.

London streets were narrow, so that even a whiffler might have been unable to keep the inquisitive crowds from eddying back. The windows of the coach were wide, and protected only by linen curtains, which were pushed back again and again by persons who stared jeeringly, or laughingly, or fiercely, at the poor bruised occupant. George could do nothing to stop them; and in truth he was afraid of many, for he could not know when one would appear, or on which side, and because the light was behind them he could not see them clearly, getting only a flash of eyes, sometimes of teeth. Shouting at them did no good. They'd reply with smut. And George could not possibly have drawn his sword in that space.

It must be misery, he thought, to be a great man.

Fortunately the ride was not a long one, for they went not to Greenwich but only to Pudding Stairs, where George transferred to a boat.

Here was a sensible way to travel! The craft was royal, but not one of the state barges, which would have drawn attention. It was a small wherry, canopied, steady, and smooth. Excepting the royal badges on the sleeves of the boatmen—a point few watermen noted—there was nothing to connect this craft with any palace. But it went fast. The men who drove it were experts, and *they* at least were aware of the badges they sported, so that they had no hesitancy about bumping other boats, shearing oars, or threatening to; nor did they as much as turn their heads when some of their tactics brought profanity.

Profanity in fact was everywhere, as was blasphemy and garbage. The Thames, George reflected, as he leaned back against the cushions provided for him, was no dream stream, as once it had seemed from a window of Cecil House, Westminster. It was noisy and malodorous. When they passed the Fleet George wished that he had a pomander, and he did hold a sleeve beneath his nose, for the stink was such as to bring tears to the eyes of a cutthroat. Something, George told himself, should be done about the Fleet.

For the rest, he enjoyed every minute of the trip. St. Paul's loomed enormous, a rambling gigantic pile, one of the wonders of the western world. Behind it, higher, the bishop of Ely's palace, lately made over to Christopher Hatton, whose dancing the queen so admired, showed aloof, remote, lovely, the center of a celebrated rose garden.

Then the Bridge. Only four of the twenty arches were open to traffic, and through these, in the middle, the current was wicked, a cataract. Timorous passengers might bypass the Bridge, getting out, climbing over, and hiring another boat. George however had confidence in the royal wherry; and it took him through with a rush, spray flying.

On the south bank the fields were green, and the tower of St. Mary Overy made a mark against the horizon. Then too there was the bishop of Winchester's sprawling palace. Why did bishops need such large buildings in which to live?

On the city side he watched Queenhithe and Billingsgate slide past with their massed quays and wharves, churches, warehouses.

Far back were many steeples—St. Botolph's, the Minories, others.

The Tower. There was a city in itself, a glum one, with the cannons and cranes that lined its wharf, with the louring water-gate, Traitor's Gate, and the pepperpot turrets, the scaffold on the hill . . .

Then St. Katherine's Hospital.

And at last, glorious multi-windowed Greenwich.

At the palace water steps the chief boatman passed some word to a porter, who in turn sent somebody for the gentleman porter, while George, watched like a felon, stretched his legs. The gentleman porter was long in coming, though loud with apologies when he did arrive. He guided George into the palace proper, up one corridor, down another, and at last into a room on which he shut the door.

It was not much of a room. There was but one window, which looked out on a wall. There were no mats or even rushes. The ceiling was low, the room itself small. There was little light, and no furniture.

In this place George, to the best of his calculations—he never heard a clock strike—spent about an hour.

He got fidgety. He walked back and forth. He listened, and could hear little but footsteps, the closing of doors, the creak of stairs, mumbly voices.

One thing he did need; and that was what in a fancy household like this would be called mincingly, the *domicilium necessarium*.

It might be breaking a royal engagement, but nature must be considered, as well as kings and queens.

Angry, his mind made up, he started for the door.

It was flung open from the outside, and a tiny straw-colored old woman burst in. Gawping at George, she came to a halt.

He made a leg. Likely he did this well, for he'd been trained in such bendings at Madrid, and he was a supple man.

He was quick, too, and lithe, in conversation.

"Mistress, it tells me you're seeking the same spot that I was about to seek. Let be! Wherever it is, 'tis not here."

This lady did not glitter, yet there was a certain brightness about her. Her hair, for instance. Her eyebrows and eyelashes alike were thin and washy, neutral, against the faded yellow-brown wash of her freckled face; but the hair of her head was a flaming red: clearly it was a wig, and just now askew. Her yellow gown, though rich enough, was hardly eye-grabbing; but at her waist hung a small mirror that George

[54]

noticed was backed with diamonds, while from her wrist dangled an ivory fan, its handle made up of a gold ring that flared with sapphires. Brighter, and even harder, were her eyes. They were very small suspicious eyes, dark blue, with a purplish gleam.

"Ballocks! I seek no such chamber. What I seek is one Fitzwilliam, a lout who's never learned to kneel before his monarch."

"*Majesty!*"

She might have gloried over his abasement, but she had no time for this. She rapped the side of his jaw with her fan. It was no accolade, and certainly no love-tap. It hurt.

"Hulk, look up at me."

He looked up.

"You find me beautiful?"

George paused. He had heard many times that no flattery was too fulsome for Elizabeth Tudor, who reveled in it, though she pretended to disbelieve it. But—this would be difficult. He swallowed.

She relieved him.

"You're too near," she said crisply.

"It is like being too near the sun, that burns us all," he whispered.

"Stand up, and back away a bit."

Glad to get off his knees, George was equally glad to retreat. The queen of England was flat-chested, though there was little else to be guessed about her figure. From behind, George supposed, if she didn't move, she might have been mistaken for a girl of fourteen. Or twelve. But those eyes, that creased mouth, bloodless, folded like a priest's, and the wrinkles and freckles, were not easily outstared.

"Well, lad?"

George spread his palms.

"Ma'am, nobody in my family, so far as I know, ever was blind."

"That's not answering my question."

It was best not to look at her, and the convention that her beauty dazzled excused George from doing so. You lie best when you don't look directly at the person you are lying to.

"I had been told about England, and I've read many a sonnet in praise of her. But now I know that I should say like Sheba to King Solomon that I hadn't heard half of it."

Elizabeth slipped the fan into the palm of her other hand. George thought that she might strike his face with it as he deserved, after such a clumsy compliment. But she allowed the fan to swing.

"You've looked upon another royal lady this week, Master Fitzwilliam."

It wasn't a question, rather a charge.

George inclined his head.

"You found her, too, to be fair?"

"She is—not ugly, ma'am."

"How does she compare with me, in appearance?"

George did not squirm, for he had expected the question. He shrugged, eyes still downcast.

"She is—taller."

"Clod, I know that! But is she too tall for real beauty?"

"Who am I, ma'am, to know what real beauty is in woman?"

"You're male!"

This accusation being incontestable, George surveyed the queen surreptitiously, estimating her height and weight.

She jiggled, harsh, not prepared for prevarication.

"Well, sir?"

She bit off her syllables the way a seamstress snaps off thread. Her unmammary front rose and fell. And her eyes flared.

"As your highness has so perspicaciously pointed out, I am a man. Aye. And no man wishes his love to be taller than himself, or even as tall, which tends to make her *look* taller. I am graced in this respect, ma'am, for as you see I have height, as the late Lord Darnley did—"

He paused, but got no response.

"Yet an ideal of beauty should not be framed for selfish reasons. And I should say, and indeed I always have said, ma'am, that the truly beautiful woman is a *small* woman."

"And *how* small, prithee?"

"Ah, well, I should say a whit under five feet. Possibly four feet nine inches, ma'am."

She did not show overjoyed, seemed thoughtful rather; and George wondered whether he had misgauged. Flustered, he resumed.

"Such a woman, such a paragon, must be able of course to carry herself with preciseness. She must be slim. She must be slender."

"Has Mary Stuart been putting on weight?"

She leaned forward from the waist, fairly shooting the words with saliva, so that George started. But he spread his hands again.

"Highness, the light was not good, and my mind was on many other things, and—"

"Ballocks! I'll get nothing from thee. For months I've been striving to learn how my cousin of Scotland fares. But can I? Nay! You're all courtiers, every one! All liars!"

There was a rap on the door, and voices called anxiously.

"Your grace?"

She turned her head, scowling, her profile a hawk's.

[56]

"Nay, another moment. I'm safe. Nobody's assassinating me."

She jabbed her fan at George.

"Come, come, clod. At least bob me out."

She lifted her mirror, examined her face, patted her hair, while George Fitzwilliam went half around her, and dropped to both knees, and opened the door.

There was a welling murmur of relief, and pantouffles scuffed as many men went low.

Elizabeth of England leaned over George a little as she swept past, and she tapped him with her fan, whispering.

"You turn to the left, clod. It's the last door down."

Twenty minutes later, having thanked and slipped a fee to the gentleman porter, George strode down to where the wherry waited.

He had been only mildly out of ease, and never would have changed places with poor Charles Bailey, as Burghley had suggested.

Bailey? Was he having his joints torn slowly apart because of him, George Fitzwilliam? Would many others so suffer? Would Mary Stuart?

"The woman's right," he muttered as he stepped into the boat. "She's right. We're all liars."

"Your worship?"

George threw himself upon the cushions.

"Deptford."

10

Parade of the Scarecrows

Some came stumbling, three had to be carried, all of them sobbed, blinking when they emerged into the glare of the sun, which bit them and caused them to whimper. How they had lived this long nobody knew. The *muertos de hambre* they were called, the walking corpses.

A few did not even seem to be certain of George as he faced them, embraced them. They swayed, mumbling. He slapped a smile on his mouth.

"Horace! . . . John! . . . Little Perry, thou'rt looking pert today!"

"Ah, ah, Master Fitzwilliam!"

"It's all right now. You're all going back to England."

It would have been impolite to peer, yet he did seek Ellis Waters. But there were only eighteen scarecrows here, not nineteen.

"God praise you, Master Fitzwilliam. Another month and we'd all have been stiff. Aye, another week! One went only last night."

George kept grinning, but his heart thudded.

"He was the little nasty one you was chained to, sir."

"Ellis? He wasn't nasty," George cried. "He was—unsure of himself."

"He all but fell apart when they lifted him. We watched. We thought a leg would come off, or an arm. Gawd-a-mercy, how he stank!"

"Now, now, don't we all?"

"Ellis was brittle," George conceded.

Then as though at a signal they wept. They sat down and rocked against one another.

Coughing, his eyes bitten with tears, George rose and he spread his arms.

"But—*you* lived! Thank God!"

Only the Spaniards failed to weep. Spaniards, George had noted, do not weep easily—or laugh easily either. Your don was exact, stolid, punctilious, but not emotional. On this occasion the governor of the prison, together with a clerk and two assistants, also three ecclesiastical personages, waited, stone-faced, the clerk methodically checking off each name as it was called and causing the wretches to sign their releases or else to make marks opposite their names, while the governor himself, ceremoniously but without a touch of graciousness, handed to each a coin.

For they were rewarded. The pressure brought upon the court by George's aunt's husband, a duke, and George's own appearance and convincing mendacity, had had their effect. A benign Spanish government would not push these men back into the world without a penny. To each, then, was given an eight-piece, or piece-of-eight, a gold coin sometimes called a dollar, worth about four shillings eight pence in English money. It was not bad pay for three years. Clutching this coin, each miscreant no doubt could go a long way toward forgetting the past.

The mariners made much of these pieces-of-eight, becoming hysterical, as though sudden liberation had gone to their heads like a hot sun.

George had provided asses for the short trip to the river; for though there was only negligible luggage—their pitifully few sleazy belongings they could hold in their hands—he had sensed that some would be unable to walk. Asses were cheaper than horses, and he had used the difference from his expense purse to buy unguents, ointments, balm, and wine. Asses were easier to mount, gentler to ride. The archbishop's office had provided a squad of foot soldiers, lest citizens be tempted to set upon and maul the departing heretics; but these were not needed, for the Spaniards encountered on the way had nothing but scorn for the *muertos de hambre,* these dead men who somehow moved, yet who giggled and whooped while they held up eight-pieces, crowing about the farms they would buy with them, and the beer, and the doublets, when they got back to God's country.

This magpie cackling continued even on the hoy, on the trip down the Guadalquivir, when the men washed most of the time. George, who had taken care to provide extra water, noted that they washed as he himself had done when first out of prison—eagerly yet with frightened hands, afraid of hurting their flesh. But they loved it; and they sang and gloated, and they asked George questions, praising him, thanking him.

It disconcerted George to be hailed a hero. Again and again he explained that the release was the doing of John Hawkins, whose agent he was; but they had known already, learning when George first got out of prison more than a month ago, that it was his relationship to the duchess de Feria that made the difference and they had all known his thoughtfulness, his kindness.

George did not tell them of the weeks of planning, the days of waiting in anterooms, the hours of tortuous, ingenious falsehood. He made no mention of the colossal trick by means of which he had talked King Philip into releasing these wretches at last. Nor did he name the queen of Scots; nor the final touch—his thought, not that of Hawkins (and George was appalled at his own cunning)—the last-minute demand that Philip not only set the mariners free but also grant to John Hawkins a written pardon for all his "piracies" in Caribbean waters and along the Main. This demand had made the whole thing seem real to King Philip, a man not noted for his imagination, and he had gone further, giving George not only the pardon but also a writ of ennoblement, a writ that, as far as George could make out, created John Hawkins if not a grandee at least a minor hidalgo. Don John, forsooth! This paper too reposed in George Fitzwilliam's wallet.

But George did not tell them of this. For one thing, he was not proud of his own part in it. For another, they wouldn't have believed it anyway.

They stopped briefly at Sanlúcar de Barrameda, at the mouth of the river, for more water and for fresh fruits, and then they stood out in the open sea, with a fair breeze and a blue sky, for the roll home. This was when the gambling broke out.

The hoy was a large one, as such unexciting vessels went, not fit for a run to the New World but a dependable coaster. The men were huddled in the waist, where they would be least in the way. Dropping down the Guadalquivir there had been a great deal of handling to be done—resetting of canvas, running out and taking in of preventers, walking of the whipstaff—and the castles fore and aft were scenes of much activity. Though every one of the passengers was himself a seaman, they took no part in the management of the hoy: they were too busy enjoying themselves, swapping gossip and questioning George.

The hoy was a Hawkins property, out of Plymouth town, and George's orders, as was but proper, came direct from the owner. He had been told to arrange for the release of these nineteen men on any reasonable terms he could get, to provide them with food, beer, clothing, and whatever medical attention they might need, and to get them out of Spain as quickly as possible. This immediate departure, indeed, had proved to be something the Spaniards themselves insisted upon, for they feared to have heretics loose in their streets, lest they pollute some of the faithful. The prisoners for their part were more than willing to get right out. As for the men who handled the hoy, none of them was granted so much as a minute of shore leave. Nor would they have taken it if it had been granted, for the Holy Office was known for its habit of picking up stray English sailors, who never were seen again.

George took it to be his obligation to stay with the nineteen men until they had got used to life outside. This was also his preference. Though every one was his inferior, they were his friends, his companions in suffering. Moreover, their faith in him was touching. When he rose to a place where he could afford a body servant, as he hoped soon to do, he would pick one from such a group as this—loyal men, easy laughers, independent, rough, bawdy, and exceedingly hard to kill.

When one of them drew forth a pair of dice he had doubtless fashioned from bones throughout interminable days of rasping against a rough cell wall, and the eight-pieces clacked on the deck while the men eagerly called their bets, it never even occurred to George Fitzwilliam to object.

Not so the captain.

The captain was a young man, known to George slightly—he had been at San Juan de Ulua, commanding one of Hawkins' smaller vessels, *Judith,* in which he'd escaped—and not favorably. This fellow was a relative of John Hawkins', a second or third cousin, George believed.

He was one of the "new men," assiduously on the make, edgy, irascible, efficient, undeviating. Likely enough he was annoyed to be commanding a mere coaster, however well found, as an interim appointment; for that very reason he would be the more touchy on the subject of his dignity.

The captain had been on the poop all the way down the river, a busy man. Now, having supped, he came to the waist.

"Stop this ungodliness!"

His small, intense, light blue eyes flashed. His curly tight red beard glistened. He was stocky, and had all the arrogance of the short; he scarcely came to George's shoulder, though they were of about the same age, twenty-two.

"This is not the Sabbath," George pointed out mildly, for he knew the man to be a hot gospeler, the son of a preaching Puritan, and it was in his experience that such men put a disproportionate importance on the Second and the Fourth commandments. You might raid, rob, even rape, you might covet whatever you felt like coveting, and bear false witness, and even kill, even commit adultery, yet still have some chance of forgiveness, but if at any time you so much as glanced at a graven image, or if on the Day of the Lord you spat on the floor or kissed your wife or picked a flower, then surely were you doomed to everlasting torment.

"Sabbath or any other day, I'll have no such devilish practices aboard my ship!"

They glared at one another. Never friends, they were also rivals, in a sense. The captain was a godson of Francis Russell, the earl of Bedford's heir, and George was Francis Russell's cousin.

"Captain Drake, my orders were to tend these men's material wants, which I take it includes their recreation after long confinement. And I see nothing dangerous in dice."

"Master Fitzwilliam, I have orders from a Higher Source to tend their souls. And I do."

"They are under my command."

"They are on my ship."

Here was your "new man": one who insisted, with vehemence, that the skipper of any vessel should be more, much more, than a glorified sailing master, a skilled laborer hired only to handle that ship, not to fight it or to direct its course. He believed that off soundings a captain should be supreme, a small king, regardless of the rank, position, or ability of anybody else aboard. He believed that the time was past when a ship's commanding officer could be treated with no more respect than a coachman or a mule driver, and he was damned well going to prove it.

George thought fast. In the privacy of a cabin he would have argued, resisted. But the thing was out in the open, and prestige was involved. From what George knew of this particular skipper he was quite capable of clapping all nineteen men into irons for the rest of the voyage to Plymouth. Hawkins might reprimand him for such an act—though he might just conceivably uphold him, for Hawkins himself was essentially a man of the sea—but that would not do the nineteen passengers any good.

And those passengers were in George's thoughts. He could climb down from his dignity, he decided, for their sake.

"I'm glad that you have come, captain," he said affably, taking a new tack, ignoring the other's bristle. "The men and I were just saying that we should have a proper service to thank the Lord for delivering us from the forces of the antichrist, even as long ago he delivered Israel from the Amalekites. And we wondered if you would have the goodness to read to us."

"I'll get my Book," muttered Francis Drake, obviously pleased.

He read well. He rolled the periods, like any shaven priest, with scarcely a hint of Devonshire drawl.

". . . for Achan, the son of Carmi, the son of Zabdi, the son of Zerah, of the tribe of Judah, took the excommunicate thing: wherefore the wrath of the Lord was kindled . . ."

George did note, however, that the captain seldom glanced at the open book before him. When he turned a page he would do so with a portentous flip that seemed to have nothing to do with the message. It could not be the light which though failing still was sound. George decided that the captain wasn't really reading at all: he was reciting from memory.

"And Joshua sent men from Jericho to Ai, which is beside Bethaven, on the east side of Beth-el, and spake unto them, saying, 'Go up and view the country.'"

When he was finished—and it was a passionate finish, appropriately dramatic—they all knelt in prayer. Afterward the men thanked the captain, who, having already supped and now seeing that all was well aloft and alow, went to his cabin to sleep.

The dice were immediately re-produced, and the game continued until the middle of the night, when one man had won all nineteen eight-pieces.

"A diplomat, eh?" George muttered to himself as he stretched out on a sack of straw. "A damned hypocrite!"

Yet the men had been happy on their first day of freedom, as he knew from the snores all around him; and if his methods were devious, at least he *had* done his duty.

11

One White Hand

Not from smacks and crumsters spoken on the way, nor from bumboats in the Catwater, nor yet from waterfront busybodies, did George Fitzwilliam learn what had happened in high political circles during his absence. Not until two nights after the landing, while the released prisoners were being given a banquet in the Guildhall, did this come to his ears. Nor even then was it publicly announced. George heard it at the raised table he shared with sundry prominent county men, substantial men, Grenvilles, Raleighs, Gilberts, and of course a few Hawkinses. John Hawkins himself, who had been on his way to London when he heard of the return of his hoy and who had immediately come back, told George; and what he said was confirmed by others.

The rest of the banqueters were having too good a time to worry about international intrigue or the succession to the throne. The men from the dungeons, the guests of honor, already had been so stuffed by wellwishers that they could scarcely see; but their thirst was unimpaired. Under cover of the clamor, the more serious feasters could cluck their tongues and shake their heads.

"The duke's been arrested."

Only Norfolk could be meant, for there was no other duke in England. The earl marshal, head of the house of Howard, Elizabeth's richest and most powerful subject, who was also, alas, one of the most pusillanimous, had tasted the Tower some months before, when there was reason to believe he was in secret correspondence with the prisoner of Sheffield, and that these two thought of marriage, of an uprising in the north, war, the deposition of Elizabeth. At that time he had stoutly denied—as had Mary Queen of Scots—any such plan. The duke had been released. But he was back again.

"He was *30?*" George whispered.

"He was *40.* Lord Lumley, his brother-in-law, was *30.*"

"It couldn't have been *all* my doing?"

"No. Bailey confessed. Not readily, I believe. They had to work on him several days."

"And—Mary Stuart?"

Hawkins shrugged.

"She's still alive. That much I do know. But if you ask me, she's lost her last chance."

"She is not likely to stop struggling."

"Without a head she could hardly fuss. Chickens do—but not for long."

Dully, making bread crumbs, his wine untasted, George idly heard the lower-level boisterousness. Some of the men down there were singing:

> *"There was a wily lad met with a bonnie lass.*
> *Such pretty sport they had, but I wot not what it was."*

Mary of Scotland and the duke, acting together, had sent an emissary to Alva, the Spanish regent in the Low Countries; to the pope; to Philip II himself. The proposal this man carried involved invasion, assassination. And he had recently reported by letter to Mary Stuart, a letter that had been watched for, intercepted, and, because of previous experience, readily deciphered.

"The duke will go first," Hawkins predicted in that suave undertone so out of place here. "They say the queen's majesty balks at the thought of signing her cousin's death warrant. A queen shouldn't kill a queen, lest that prove her mortal. And Mary Stuart after all is an anointed monarch. But she'll be cooped up much tighter."

> *"He wooed her for a kiss, she plainly said him no.*
> *'I pray,' quoth he. 'Nay, nay,' quoth she,*
> *'I pray you let me go.'"*

George sighed.

"Well, I did see Mary, anyway. The first time and the last."

"I wouldn't be too sure of that."

"Eh?"

"It's my thought that Burghley will send for thee. What better informer than an attractive young man who would thank Mary for her letter to Philip and report that the men are free? She might say things to such an one she would never say to Shrewsbury, and at a time when it's urgent to study how she feels—and how much she knows."

"I hope you're wrong," George muttered.

Yet Hawkins was right, as so often. The very next day there came from London a command that when Master Fitzwilliam returned—for my Lord Burghley could not have heard of the return when he wrote this letter—he should be kept on call at Plymouth, "like a foyer page" in George's own bitter description.

No explanation was given, none being needed. It was George's duty to obey Hawkins, Hawkins' duty to obey Burghley, who in turn obeyed the queen. This was government, this was life.

George had many friends in Plymouth, yet he did not like the town with its bustle and bang, its prevailing smell of brine, bilge, and tar, its ceaseless talk of trade. Was there nothing else to life but money? Plymouth faced the sea, as did the people of Plymouth, and the sea was something George felt it impossible to view in a romantic light. Oh, it was natural enough for some landlubber to thrill at the sight of a ship coming in past Rame Head, all sails snowy in the sun, the wake a dance of delight. George knew that, up close, the canvas was anything but snowy, the wake, blotched with garbage, no needlepoint. George had sailed; and he knew the putrid food, the sour-tasting ale. He knew the ulcers and vomiting, the dysentery, the boils, the intolerable itch of scurvy. He preferred to turn his back upon the sea. The countryside of England was his love. Cut rye was *clean;* a perry mill was *clean;* but no quay ever was.

Feeling that way, perforce he remained in the port for more than a month—a precious late-summer month too, when the countryside would have been at its best—with no more arduous labor than acknowledging again and again, whilst deprecating them, the thanks and praises of the mariners he had helped to raise up out of a dungeon, not to mention those of their relatives and friends. And even when at last he was summoned to London, it was only to loiter in that capital for another month before being ushered into the presence of an overworked Lord Burghley.

George's orders were simple, suspiciously so. After all this delay, to no apparent purpose, he was to ride to Sheffield posthaste, stopping nowhere, sleeping as briefly as possible. He was supplied with money generously, as well as a let-pass issued by the lords in council, which would assure him of the best horses. He was given also a letter to Lord Shrewsbury from Lord Burghley, requesting that George be admitted into the presence of Mary of Scotland for the purpose of thanking her for her assistance in freeing the sailors at Seville. He was to do this, noting her answer, noting everything. If she asked him to carry a message he was to accept it: as a representative of Lord Burghley he would not be searched.

All this was irksome to one who might have spent the summer and early autumn with the Croftses in rustic Northampton, so that George was scowling when at last he set forth on the Great North Road. But at least nothing had been said about hurrying *back,* and he was determined that Okeland would not go unvisited.

Sheffield Castle was grim and glum as before, my Lord Shrewsbury querulous. Shrewsbury was a conscientious man of no notable imagination, a man harassed by worrisome details of wealth, harassed too by an unamiable wife, and now in addition saddled with the care of an expensive royal guest who might yet prove to be the death of him. For if the unmarried Elizabeth were killed, almost certainly this "guest" at Sheffield would be elevated to the throne, in which case Lord Shrewsbury's head would be one of the first to fall. George sensed that Shrewsbury now was annoyed not at George himself, a mere tool, but at Burghley. Shrewsbury must have known that his charge corresponded with persons in England, Scotland, France, Spain, Italy, the Low Countries. He must have worked hard to stop this traffic. And what else could Master Fitzwilliam's visit mean? My lord was not so naïve as to suppose that a personable and wellborn courier would be sent half the length of England to render formal thanks that could have been expressed as well in a letter. What, then, was Burghley up to? Shrewsbury was hurt, and he was also sore.

Nevertheless he made arrangements for an audience. These arrangements took longer than the previous time.

The atmosphere of Sheffield Castle, though it was not changed in any radical way, had tightened. The soldiers were like soldiers on the eve of battle, hushed, full of thought. The servants were stony, scared, excruciatingly exact. The very doors of the massy pile closed with a more ominous thud; the very walls gleamed with an icier wetness.

Mary Stuart herself, just at first, seemed the only unchanged thing. Erect, radiant, she greeted George with a smile. It was not the smile of a politician, but that of a friend. She was glad to see him. She gave him her hand, which he thankfully kissed.

When his heart had slowed to a more normal quap, however, George Fitzwilliam was quick to see that even Mary Stuart had changed—and for the worse. It was but a few months since George's first visit, yet she looked years older. She wore rust-colored sarsenet trimmed with a great deal of gold lace, and wore it well; but her mouth was tighter, her eyes harder. She greeted George from a standing position, but soon afterward she sat, and it seemed to him that she sat with difficulty, as though her side hurt.

The royal cloth where her arms were emblazoned hung above her head as rich as before, but it was badly out of press, and George divined that it had not been used since his other visit. For the first time he could make out the motto: *En ma fin est mon commencement.* Now what did that mean? George translated it as "In my end is my beginning," but he could have been wrong, for his French wobbled.

There were twelve or fourteen persons behind the throne, not half the number he had seen before.

The Queen of Scots asked George about his health and about that of the duke and duchess of Feria and of "our dear cousin of Spain," Philip II. She remembered to ask about Master 'Awkins, to whom she sent gracious regards. George bowed.

She seemed distraught, keeping her mind upon her duties only by an effort of will. Shrewsbury had told George that she had not been notified officially of the arrest of Norfolk, the man she meant to marry and her last hope; but he doubted not, Shrewsbury said, that she knew. George was inclined to agree. She was lost, this lovely lady. She had no chance. Yet he believed that it would be hard to overestimate her courage.

She asked about the fashions in Seville, in Madrid. George had no enthusiasm here.

"Drab, ma'am. Not like London or Paris."

"Alas, I have never seen London."

"They're mostly black in Spain, and they haven't any—any *swirl.* The men, yes. But not the women."

There was a pause, which Mary Stuart broke by asking George if he would like to see her pets, always assuming that my Lord Shrewsbury gave his agreement—or did my lord fear that she might smuggle something out in a grain of birdseed?

Shrewsbury gave permission, though it was clear that he was not pleased. Mary Stuart rose. They all knelt.

She lifted George.

"You come with me, eh? The way is narrow, and I'd have you right behind me lest I slip."

He remembered Burghley's remark that one who aspires to a high place must use a winding stair. It was so again. Four flights they climbed, to the roof of the Scroll Tower. Mary Stuart went first, George, by request, immediately behind her. She did not talk. The dogged Lord Shrewsbury was close after George, being the third in this upspiraling procession, and if the queen of Scots had said anything he would have heard it and noted it. Besides, no doubt she needed her breath. She was panting when they reached the top.

"I spend many hours here, when there's no rain. It rests my eyes after so much needlework. For I age, Master Fitzwilliam, I age."

"No," George objected. "You never will."

She acknowledged this with her small smile-grin, crinkling the corners of her eyes. Her Tudor relation at Greenwich, George reflected, would have simpered.

Most of the pets were birds. They were in gilded cages with silken covers to protect them from sunlight or showers. "Like me," said her majesty of Scotland and the Isles. The cages were presently on the parapet, but at night as in times of bad weather, she told him, they were placed under the overhang of the parapet, protecting them from the elements.

There were turtle-doves and Barbary fowls, canary-birds and parakeets, and many a small, brightly plumaged bird that George had never before seen. The lady had names for them all.

There were also several small dogs of uncertain breed. And there was a pair of rabbits. She told George she kept five cats in her bedchamber. They wouldn't consent to mix with the other pets.

"So you see, I am not unbearably lonesome. Yet it is good to have you come here, Master Fitzwilliam."

The chat and the animals appeared to brighten her, and she was humming as she led the way down to the throne room.

She commented upon George's earring, which he vowed he would always wear.

An attendant had brought a casket, and for a moment George feared he might be gifted again. It would have unsettled him. But Mary had other plans.

"Master Fitzwilliam, I know little of the geography of this realm. When you return to London do you go through any part of Northampton?"

"This time, aye. I'll visit friends there."

"Ah? Do you know, perhaps, a young gentleman named Weddell —Terence Weddell?"

"Slightly, ma'am. He lives near the people I shall visit. Only a few miles away."

"What good chance! He attended me once, when I was in happier circumstances, in Scotland. That was so long ago . . . and I could not be sure that he was still alive."

"So far as I know he is."

"Tomorrow would be his birthday. D'ye suppose you could take this to him, Master Fitzwilliam, as a small token of my admiration? And tell him that I have not forgotten?"

She lifted from the casket an enameled miniature.

"My Lord of Shrewsbury will have to poke and pound it, of course, to make sure that there is no billet-doux. But you could arrange for that."

She held it out, and George came nearer, kneeling.

"Think you it looks like me, Master Fitzwilliam?"

"Nay," he muttered.

"The artist never saw me."

"Anyone who had would know that."

"And yet, in certain lights . . . Look at it this way."

She turned the gaud, holding it low, so that George leaned even further forward. He could feel her breath upon his neck. He saw her left hand move.

Some who stood behind the throne might have seen that hand. None before the throne, save only George, could have done so.

There was a piece of paper, folded many times, scarcely more than a pill held together by sealing-wax.

"And if you would give this to Don Gerau in London? Simply a matter of convenience. By the time Shrewsbury got it translated and made fourteen copies—"

"Of course, ma'am."

She tucked the thing into a pleat of his canions, a sleight that might have been done by a magician.

"Yet if you think this might cause trouble—"

"Ma'am, I'm honored to serve you."

"I thought so too," she said in a louder voice, leaning back. "I am glad that we agree."

George rose, stepping back, holding the miniature, which he would turn over to his host for examination. But almost immediately, with the rest, he was on his knees again; for the queen had risen.

She gave him her hand.

"And now we have to thank you again—"

The audience was over.

12

Visitors

Autumn was coming easily. The leaves had not changed, and would not change with dramatic suddenness but hesitantly, quietly. The rain when George rode south was warm, the air soporific.

Though commanding no such mounts as he could had he returned by way of the Great North Road with its posting stations, George made good time, pushing it. And he had got off to an early start.

In part his thoughts were of Anne Crofts and her father, for George, an orphan, already looked upon Okeland as half a home, and he was sick of wandering the world. But in part too those thoughts were of Terence Weddell.

George scarcely knew him, a quiet young man, something of a student. There were two startling things about him, in George's present interest, however. One was that Mary of Scotland should remember Weddell's birthday after all those years and should ask George whether he planned to ride back through Northampton—not the usual route from Sheffield to London. The other was that Weddell was said to be a papist.

The request might have been coincidence. Mary Stuart could have been ignorant of the English terrain; and though she was esteemed a learned woman, trained to reign, for obvious reasons she would not have had much chance to study maps while under the jailorship of George Talbot, sixth earl of Shrewsbury. Also, she was allowed few guests. She had little choice in the matter of messengers, but must try what she could.

Was Weddell's religion, assuming that he *was* a papist, somehow connected with Mary Stuart's request?

Until recently Catholics in England had not been persecuted. The *official* assertion in this regard was that nobody ever was proceeded against because of his religion, but only if his political standing or political potentialities might imperil the throne; and if his churchly connections forced seditious thoughts upon him, and seditious duties, that was his ill luck. George admitted to himself that from what he had seen and heard of the rest of the world England was, in sober truth, wonderfully tolerant.

Several things had happened lately, however, and all more or less at once, to throttle this rule of moderation.

The papal bull excommunicating Queen Elizabeth and calling upon Catholics to refuse to recognize her authority had been published. The first of a flood of zealous young English priests, Jesuits coached at Douai, dedicated men, eager for martyrdom, had been smuggled back into the land of their birth, where, though outlaws, they were making themselves felt. And finally—though in point of time this was first— Mary Queen of Scots had appeared in England, where she was retained as an embarrassing "guest." Mary was a Roman Catholic, and a convinced one, devout. Even if it could be supposed that she would accept Elizabeth's treatment without demur, she still, inevitably, would be made a rallying-point for the discontented, especially among Catholics, who could not be expected to accept Henry VIII's divorce, Elizabeth's legitimacy, and who, hence, thought Mary the rightful queen of England.

Until lately the only strong anti-Catholic feeling was among the more rabid puritans, who were clustered in the cities, the seaports. For whatever reason, Protestantism and commerce—or as some put it, Protestantism and piracy—seemed entwined. As George saw it, the average Englishman, until stirred from the outside, did not give a hoot. He only asked to be left alone. But the average Englishman *had* been stirred. Now was intolerance making its way inland? Was even sleepy Northampton to be fouled?

Burghley's servant, like Caesar's wife, should be above suspicion. As Mary had known, George was not searched after the audience. Yet Shrewsbury asked him many probing questions; and it was only by a display of his new-found talent for prevarication that George Fitz-william emerged scatheless from that interview.

In the trinket my lord had shown only a perfunctory interest. Mary Stuart's devotion to her attendants, like her prodigality, were well known, making her a contrast to the distrustful, scolding, penny-pinching Elizabeth. Though shabbily provided for just now, Mary of Scotland still owned the duchy of Tuscany, on paper at least. Reports had it that her income, some £12,000 a year, was being systematically looted by her French friends; but there was a great deal left; and what there was, and more, Mary spent.

Weddell Lodge was small, curiously trim, not a working farm-house but a gentleman's residence: the farmer or farmers, George surmised, lived elsewhere. It was about three miles from Okeland.

There was a handsome pair of gates, an avenue of lime trees, very formal, after which the house, though it was modern and well kept and gleamed with windows, came as an anticlimax.

There appeared to be nobody about, and George was reminded of his visit to Okeland early in the summer, when the trance-like stillness that overhung the place had frightened him. As on the previous occasion the lull was broken when a dog awoke to its responsibilities and began to bark.

By then George was no more than a hundred feet from the house, the door of which stood open. He did not see the dog, which might have been chained in the rear, but he did see a white face—a man's face, he thought—appear briefly at one of the downstairs windows, then vanish; and he heard a low scuffle of feet.

George was unruffled, and at the moment uninterested, it being his hope to fulfill this assignment swiftly and be on his way to Anne. He dismounted. For a moment he feared that he'd have to tether his own horse, but soon a groom scuttled around a corner of the house, making for him with bumbled apologies. This fellow, like the dog back there, had been asleep.

"Master Weddell?"

"Uh, yes, your honor. He's here."

"Well, *where* is he?"

"Why, he— Maybe if your worship was to come around back—"

George frowned.

"I am not concerned with the kitchens," he said coldly. "Show me to your master."

"Uh, why, if— Well, there he be now, sir."

Terence Weddell stood in the open doorway. He smiled. He extended a hand.

"Master Fitzwilliam! This is an unexpected pleasure. Come in, sir, come in."

They had met but once, and then briefly, and not here. Before setting out for the West Indies, and hopeful that he might return rich, George had examined a piece of property Weddell had for sale, property that adjoined Okeland, to which farm it would have been a convenient and probably lucrative addition. The land proved rich and well watered, and the price was low. Weddell did not seem immersed in his farming. Had George come back from America with his fortune made he would have bought it, an acquisition that would justify his marriage to Anne and partnership with Sir John Crofts, even though Sir John could not put up a cash dowry. Since he had returned without so much as a tester, George thought no more of Terence Weddell, whose very name he had forgotten until Mary Stuart mentioned it.

Now he met a different man, not a man of business. Weddell was somewhat short, and he was slim, though wiry, with a merry eye. His face and hands were pale, not suggestive of a squire. His shoulders were stooped. He was older than George, yet still less than thirty.

He clattered politeness as he conducted George through the screens, past a dark wooden staircase unexpectedly baronial, and into a library that took the guest's breath away.

In the screens, fleetingly, from a corner of his eye, George thought he glimpsed what might have been an expunged light. This was low against the dark side of the stair, the bottom of a piece of oak paneling. At the same time George fancied that he sniffed a whuffed-out candle, which was odd in a bright hall at that hour of the afternoon.

The library caused him to forget these impressions for a moment. It was not large, but it contained many books, possibly a hundred of them, more than George ever before had seen in one place. He strolled about, glancing at the backs of some of these books, which seemed to be about geography, travel, navigation.

But there was more than books in that library. Besides a table, two chairs, and two goblets half filled with wine, there was distinctly, unmistakably, an aura of recent occupation.

"You've had a visitor?" George asked casually, nodding at the wine goblets. "I hope I'm not interrupting anything?"

"No, no! That was earlier. Most unusual. *Two* visitors in one day. I don't ordinarily get that many in a month."

"It is quiet out here," George conceded. "That's one reason why I hope to move into the neighborhood sometime."

"You'd be a welcome addition, I can tell you. Here—let me get you some wine."

Weddell left for another part of the house.

George went out into the screens and knelt by the side of the stair at the panel where he might have seen light. There was no light now, but he believed that he could smell candlewick.

He put an ear against the paneling. There was a faint mumble; also a sound, very thin, that could have been rosary beads.

He returned to the library.

He was examining some of the books when his host returned: Digges' *Tectonicon, A treatyse of the newe India* by Sebastian Munster, Dee's *Astronomicall and Logisticall Rules,* Cunningham's *Cosmographical Glasse,* Cortes' *The Arte of Navigation,* as translated by Richard Eden, and of course the *Decades of the newe worlde* by Peter Martyr of Angleria, another Eden translation.

They raised their goblets, and Weddell, always courteous, asked George if he cared to propose a toast.

"To Mary Stuart, queen of Scotland," said George.

Weddell all but spilled his wine. He looked flustered, then frightened, and at last puzzled.

"A most estimable lady," he said. "I once attended her as a page, in Scotland. But—why did you name her?"

George produced the miniature.

"Because I have just come from her presence, and she sends this as a gift for your birthday."

The effect upon Weddell was astonishing. Tears leapt to his eyes. He seized the miniature, and passionately, again and again, kissed it. He shook George's hand, in a trembling voice thanking him.

[73]

"She never did forget a birthday or a friend. Forgive the outburst, Master Fitzwilliam, but you've brought up the memory of an angel. Every one who ever attended her feels that way."

George nodded, for he understood. He mentioned young Babington. Did Weddell know Anthony Babington of Dethick? Weddell didn't.

"He feels the same way," George said simply.

Weddell, greatly moved, stalked the room, windmilling his arms.

"Here she is, but a few shires away. I've written her, offering my services, for such as they might be worth. But I doubt that the letter reached her."

"Not likely."

"Certainly it did no good."

"It might have revealed your tendencies to the person who did read it."

"I don't care! Is it a sin to adore a mortal woman as though she were a saint? I'll keep the peace, I'll obey the law, but no one need legislate against my love of Mary Stuart! And if that be treason, by God, then rack me!"

George liked this man and would have talked longer, but he was keen to be off. He nodded to the half-finished wine.

"You referred to another visitor? Do you get many strangers here?"

Weddell's eyes flickered ever so briefly toward the screens. George did not acknowledge this.

"No. And that's a curious thing. This man came only about an hour ago, and he didn't belong to these parts. Truth is, he looked Italian."

George's heart grew small and tight.

"Dark clothes?" he asked. "Very big? Black beard, cut high? And a monstrous long rapier?"

"That's the one. You know him?"

"I've met him. Why was he here?"

"He asked the way to Okeland. There are no real roads around this country, as you know, only lanes, and—"

"I must go. Excuse me, my friend. And many thanks for the drink."

"D'ye think he's dangerous? Perhaps I'd best sword up and go along with you?"

"No. You stay and keep company for that priest under the stair. He must be uncomfortable in such a small space."

13

Die Well, You Fool!

Soon after, slightly asweat, George strode into the great-hall at Okeland, to face three persons.

Anne stood on one side, Sir John on the other, while between them, very much at home, smirking, seated upon a stool, his legs this way and that, was the bravo of the Crossed Keys.

There was no subservience about this bravo now. He showed pleased, sure of himself. He did not rise, but with a sleepy smile extended a hand toward George, the palm up.

"Master Courier, you have a message, eh? Give it to me."

George flared. It was only by a shuddering effort of will that he kept himself quiet.

"We'll talk about that later," he said coldly, and went to Sir John, whom he embraced.

"How long has this lout been here?" he whispered.

"Half an hour. He said he knew thee, so we offered him wine."

"Which he drank?"

"No."

"Probably feared that there was poison in it. That's the kind he is. Tell me, have you seen anything French about him—in his effects maybe?"

"French? Why, no. He looks Italian to me."

"He is. But I think he might be in French pay."

"I see. A spy. So that they can disclaim him, if needs be?"

"Aye."

"*Is* he a spy, then? Should I kill him, George?"

"He might be somewhat hard to kill, sir. I think he's a professional sword-fighter."

"There will be trouble?"

"Probably. But not here."

Mostly this was done in small tight swift whispers as they embraced. Yet the Italian was alert, watching them. In another moment he might have broken in; but George stepped back, smiling, at the same time signaling with his eyes that Sir John should engage the man in talk.

George then went to Anne.

She was frightened. He knew this instantly, even before he had kissed her. Her shoulders trembled, and her hands were tight on George's forearms. Still, she managed a smile. And her kiss was warm.

Since they were cousins it was expected that George would kiss her, and the visitor must have known this—if he knew anything at all about English customs. The kiss this time was prolonged only a bit beyond what etiquette called for.

But George held her a little while afterward, smiling fondly upon the small slight freckles at the top of her cheeks.

"I said," the man from outside put in, "that I'd have that message."

"So you did," George said carelessly.

He put an arm across Anne's shoulders and led her to a bink, on which they sat side by side, very close.

"Art— Art safe?" she murmured.

"Nobody's safe, just here. Now tell me," he asked of her, "hast noted anything French about this fellow? Anything he carried or used?"

"Well, he opened his wallet. He can read. He wasn't sure of thy name, and he read it out."

"And there were other papers in the wallet?"

"Oh, yes. And they were in French. I don't know much French, but I know enough to be sure of that."

"Official-looking papers?"

"Aye. Tape, sealing-wax, all the rest."

George nodded, staring at the Italian, who by this time was confronted by a determinedly polite Sir John Crofts.

Yes, he would be a French agent. George had been told there were many such on the fringes of the French court, where the queen mother, the power behind the throne, smooth and serpentine Catherine de' Medici, herself an Italian, had many uses for them, all underhanded. They would be especially bold just now in England, where arrangements for the d'Anjou match, together with the need to prevent Paris from moving to the aid of Mary Stuart, had put France in the ascendant, Spain in shadow.

George's Spanish clothes, his association with Hawkins, their visit to Cecil House, George's two trips to Spain, all had conspired to bring about in the mind of Giuseppe here—for George had so named the man to himself—the conviction that George was a Spanish spy. When George turned off the Great North Road at Biggleswade, on the first visit to Sheffield, Giuseppe had followed him, had overtaken him at the Crossed Keys, and, no doubt thinking this a brilliant stroke, had accosted him in Spanish, and received a Spanish response. Surely the man had made inquiries about George afterward, learning of his over-night stay at Okeland. Then he had trailed George all the way to Sheffield Castle and back.

Had he followed George too to the London home of Don Gerau de Spies? This was possible, even probable. And now, after the second visit to Sheffield, Giuseppe must have felt sure that George was carrying something of significance. If Giuseppe could get that piece of paper he might gain much credit and even some gold. On the highway he may have hesitated to use such a direct approach, but here in an out-of-the-way place like Okeland he thought it safe. Here, immediate might could count. Giuseppe, sure of his own strength and skill and speed, also of the length of his rapier, had assumed that he'd meet with no resistance. The reporting of so delicate a matter to the lord lieutenant of the shire or even to the sheriff was not likely. By that time anyway Giuseppe would be back in London, where he could sue for the protection of the French ambassador, a man nobody dared to offend just now.

In other words, Giuseppe knew just what he was about to do.

Yet he looked puzzled. No memory of manners impelled him to pay heed to the remarks of his host. He was worried about George, whose offhandedness might mask some subtle scheme. Crooked himself, Giuseppe searched for crookedness in others. Was George playing for time? Did George expect friends? The Italian shifted uneasily.

"I'm sorry I attracted this toad," George said to Anne. "Forgive me."

"George, art thou—"

"Diplomacy, my chuck, my dear. I've been walking a path that is not always straight, and sometimes the way is mud. Like now."

He patted her knee, and tilted her face up and kissed her.

She asked: "Will there be trouble?"

"Probably," he replied as he had replied to her father, "but not here."

He looked around. It was outrageous that violence should even be thought of in the comfortable, homely, familiar great-hall of Okeland. What was that damned foreign pimp doing here anyway? Who did he think he was, to invade the home of an English gentleman?

In any event, this was not a good place for a fight. The light was poor. The ceiling was well out of reach, but a couple of suspended coronas for candles would have hindered high strokes, and the rushes below, fresh, green, would make for slippy footing.

George was only surveying the scene, as any swordsman might. He didn't mean to engage with blades. Fighting was not for him. Fighting was only for fools, or for those who were cornered.

But was he cornered? At least Giuseppe was between him and the door of the screens. True, George knew every inch of this house, and he might flee to the kitchens and from there out into the barn or the stables, where he could graciously permit himself to be hunted down like a rat. No. He shook his head.

Anne shivered under his arm. He smiled a little when he realized that she was anxiously watching him. Giuseppe was watching him too. And so, though he strove not to, was Sir John Crofts.

George could have made everything quiet by handing over the message. He didn't know what it contained, and did not care. But he refused to give it up. This was not out of loyalty to Hawkins, to Burghley, or even to Mary of Scotland.

"Thou'rt thinking of *her?*" Anne accused, as abruptly as though the name of Mary Stuart had been written on a large sign.

"No," George said.

And he was honest here. His pause had been brought about by something quite different—a distaste of taking orders from a strutting foreigner, right here in the middle of England. Bugger diplomacy! His betters George would heed, when he had to; but a man can get tired of being pushed about.

"Darling, what wilt thou do, then?"

"Something shameful, my sweet. I'm going to run away. Scurry off like a coward. You must steel yourself for this."

"And leave us—"

"That lout won't linger. It will draw him away. I have something in my purse he seeks. Anyway, countryfolk like thee and thy father, people without court connections, they aren't for this hulking brute. Buss me again, my sweet—and trust me."

He rose languidly. He started to stroll toward the screens.

Giuseppe was up at the instant, his hand near the hilt of his sword, his eyebrows low.

George made Sir John a bow.

"I must ask your indulgence, sir. I'm about to liver-heart."

Then he spun on his heel and ran outside.

George had not seen the Italian's horse and supposed that it had been led around to the stables. His own horse he had left, saddled and untethered, just outside of the door. It was tired, the poor beast, having traveled hard, yet George reckoned that it could take him to sanctuary before Giuseppe could saddle and pursue.

As he mounted and dug spurs into an animal that deserved a rest, he heard Giuseppe bellow.

Unexpectedly, there was a thud of hooves; and George looked back to see that the Italian, now mounted, was chasing him. Giuseppe was not the dimwit he looked. He had anticipated a flight and had left his own horse saddled.

It would not be a long chase. It couldn't be. The Italian's was by far the better horse and, in addition, was less tired.

By assiduous spurring George reached the Crossed Keys. It was as dreary and drab as before. There was no one in sight around the inn itself and nobody on the road leading north to Ashby-de-la-Zouch, south to Wellingborough.

George, although not sure what to do next, didn't pause, but his horse did. Blind with fatigue, outraged, the animal stepped into a hole and with a squeal fell forward.

George saved himself a broken ankle only by jumping. Then he rose, sword in hand, and turned.

Giuseppe could have cut him down dead. He didn't. Instead he dismounted. He might have been reluctant to murder a man before an inn, even though there was no witness. Conceivably too it never occurred to him that George would resist. He had drawn, and now he moved forward, not with the wary cat-steps of a fencer but rapidly, carelessly, his point advanced.

"Hand me the letter. Nay, I don't want your money."

"It's just as well you don't," George said.

He slipped under the other's point, which however still threatened George's face, and, afraid to lunge, flicked his edge against the Italian's elbow. He sprang back.

Giuseppe roared with rage and pain.

"Porco cane!"

He charged, fully in guard position now, his sword-arm straight.

"Ti faccio a pezzi!"

It was a ferocious attack, yet not wild. George retreated before it, stepping a little right, a little left, as he fell back, not consenting to move his own steel. George wasn't flustered. He would not risk a riposte until he had studied this man's style, but he saw no reason to let Giuseppe learn the nature of his favorite parry, his instinctive one, the one he used when hard-pressed or excited. Every swordsman had such a parry, of course, and his opponent's work was half done when he learned it. George gave no clue.

It was a curious duel, and a brilliant one. It merited more appreciative spectators than two tired horses and perhaps, somewhere in the depths of his dingy inn, the boniface. It was such rapier play as seldom is seen.

The Italian, especially after suffering the first cut, might have been expected to resort to all manner of stampings and blade-beatings, snorts and violent flourishes meant to intimidate George. He was that way in everything else—his walk, his talk, and clothes. But when he wielded a sword he was another man, all efficiency and concentration. Gone was the rant, the rodomontade cast off like a cloak. After that first explosion he never made an unnecessary move. He was alert, but he saved his wind.

Each knew, each sensed, as only a swordsman can, that he was meeting a master.

They took their fighting seriously, these two.

If there had been a spectator, just at first, and if he was unlearned in the art of fence, he might have supposed that those two were afraid of one another. This of course was not the case. Neither were they wasting time. It was never well to start in a hurry—let the other fellow do that. Yet neither did it pay to prolong a duel. Once you had sized up your man and decided upon the best attack, go right in and finish the affair. Posing was for beginners—and for popinjays. When men faced one another with bare steel there were too many accidents possible, too many slips that could occur, to make safe even an extra second of combat. "Playing with" an antagonist, "cat-and-mousing it," not only was cruel: it could be damned dangerous.

The Italian was the first to disengage. Warily, making his point move in small circles, he began to feel the air with his weapon as a climber might feel for crevices in a slick high wall.

George raised his guard a trifle.

Giuseppe advanced. George fell back, making no movement with his sword. Giuseppe advanced further, using small, very fast steps. Again George retreated, having refused to parry.

But now George's left foot felt stones. It would not do to retreat among them. So he stood his ground, and even pressed forward a little, his point menacing the other's eyes. Giuseppe permitted this, seemingly intent upon learning something about George's reach and speed of disentanglement.

Suddenly the bravo undercut George's blade and, throwing his own point out of line, swept upwards with a high guard attack, a smash that was more like saber play than a *passe* with rapiers. Its unexpectedness almost caused it to succeed. George's blade was lifted, all but wrenched from his hand, and the Italian struck for the top of the head.

Unable to protect himself with his weapon in that instant, George darted back. Giuseppe, having missed, also sprang back. George had been given no time for a counterattack.

Thereafter each allowed the other plenty of room.

Giuseppe crouched. Accepting this invitation, George attacked high. By arching his body and going up on his toes in order to offset a possible riposte, he got his point to the top of the bravo's right shoulder.

It was not much of a wound, not painful. Perhaps the Italian never even felt it.

For a little while, still not panting, they regarded one another. Such was the intensity of their study that they looked not slaughterous at all, but merely preoccupied. Neither showed any sheen of sweat.

Abruptly, as though at a signal and by mutual agreement, each attacked.

They needed to know more about one another, and they were willing to risk a few cuts to learn, though neither went in full-length. Sparks flew. It must have *looked* sensational, that exploration. Yet neither man was ready to kill.

Had there been a watcher he would think that George came off second-best from that flurry, for the bravo had pinked him three times—twice in the right forearm, once in the right elbow. But these touches were trifling. There was little blood.

In fact it was George who profited from the feeling-out, or so he believed. For he thought that he had found a flaw in Giuseppe's defense.

When they did withdraw, simultaneously and even ceremoniously, stepping back, again it was as though at a signal, perfectly in accord, in time, as though they were treading the figures of some intricate dance—a pavane or a galliard.

Stolid to see, motionless, George recast his strategy.

Here in the Italian was a fencer who could lunge and parry with the speed of light. His reflexes were exquisite. In the middle line of engagement he was never at a loss: the uninitiated might have said of him that he had a wonderful wrist, though in truth all the muscles of the arm were involved, as well as most of those of the whole body. He could fight well in the high line too, and in the low line. But . . .

When he shifted from high line to low, or back again, Giuseppe was the slightest bit slow. In a less finished performer this would have gone unnoticed. It was because his swordsmanship was so sound that Giuseppe's one weakness—if it was a weakness—stood out.

There were three possible reasons, George reflected as he steadied himself for a kill.

One was that the bravo's knees were not the supple joints that his elbows were. A touch of rheumatism? Perhaps that sun-birthed frame had found England's climate hard to bear.

The second was that Giuseppe's tallness and great length of limb caused him to favor the middle line, where reach counts most, over the high and low lines of engagement, which he could have neglected.

The third possible explanation was that this dark bully was *not* slow, ordinarily, in getting into and out of the low-line position. He might have been acting this for the purpose of causing George to plan the very attack he now was planning. In that case George would catch a counter that might kill him.

It was a risk he meant to take.

He went in.

He used a long arm, as the saying is, his elbow scarcely bent, blade high. He kept his point dancing, licking in and out. He was raising it more and more, getting up on his toes, beginning to arch his body, all the while moving forward.

The bravo might think that George, having touched him from this position, was about to try the same trick twice. In that case he would counter not for the drawn-in body but for the face or the neck.

George stooped. He took no step either ahead or back, but simply bent his knees.

Giuseppe was lunging, high. George made no move to parry, for he had been prepared for this.

The Italian's sword slithered right over the top of George's head.

All of Giuseppe's right side, from the armpit down, was exposed in that split-second. It was enough. George did not even need to lunge. Giuseppe, coming in, spitted himself.

He fell forward, caroming off George's left shoulder as George started to straighten, all but knocking George down.

George jerked his sword out. It was wet halfway to the hilt.

The Italian flopped like a great fish, arms flung out. He clung to his sword. The only thing about him to move was his throat, which throbbed as great thick gouts of blood gushed out of his mouth.

Whatever else he might have done in the past, he died well, that brute. He died as a man should.

Gingerly—for the flies, attracted by the sweet sickish odor of blood, already were beginning to gather—George got down on one knee and unfastened the Italian's wallet.

Yes, he was in French pay. And the French ambassador would clamor for the punishment of his assailant. George's Spanish connection and his recent trip to Seville would tell against him. Burghley would do whatever was possible, but Burghley would be perilously embarrassed and might forswear him. The very best that George could expect was a long term in prison. More prison! And they might well rack him. Or hang him. Or both.

He looked up the road, down the road. Not a sight, not a sound. Nor did anything move along the lane that led past Okeland to Rugby. The inn too was still, though George was convinced that somebody in there stared.

His horse lay on the ground, panting heavily, perhaps not crippled but certainly exhausted. The Italian's horse too was tired. George was more than fifty miles from London. He might ride to the Great North Road, where, with the order of the lords-in-council to support him, he could command fresh mounts. He might push it all night into London, and throw himself upon the mercy of Lord Burghley. But the hue and cry would be raised behind him, and the sheriff's men too might have strong horses. George could easily be traced through the posting stations. Burghley might be out of town. And then, there was the letter.

The shadows were long, the west red. Soon it would be dark.

So still was the scene that when a sparrow landed on the small of the bravo's back, and cocked its head at George, George all but jumped. Jerkily the sparrow looked around; and when it saw nothing of interest, it flew away.

George looked again at the papers he had taken from the wallet, noting with a wry smile that the dead man's name was not Giuseppe but Antonio, Antonio Salvo.

He felt suddenly doused with shame, standing there with those papers in his hand. To kill a man in fair fight was one thing. To rifle a corpse was quite another. Impulsively George knelt again, and he replaced the wallet. What if they did find it? The thing to do was keep them from finding *him*.

He rose, and sheathed, and brushed his knees. He fetched a sigh. Head low, shoulders hunched, he started to run along the lane that led to Rugby. But he did not go as far as Okeland. Instead, about halfway there, he swerved to the right and made across a field of cut hay to a wood. There, very tired and beginning to be afraid, he lay on the ground and waited for night to fall.

14

It Was Hot in the Hole

Again it was a case of the watched pot. Would this crepuscular lull never end? What was there that made daylight cling so stubbornly?

Fear, which had come suddenly just before he entered the wood, was violent and undeniable, like nausea: it did in fact almost make him sick. Worse, it wouldn't let him rest; and tired though he was, all his muscles aching, he could not lie still on the leaves but must be up and prowling, peering cautiously now out of this part of the wood, now out of that.

The scene he surveyed was one of peace. Here and there in the distance a workman trudged in from a field and a few columns of smoke wobbled lazily against the reddened sky.

No tocsin rang. No courier, bent low in saddle, spread the hue and cry. There was nothing to indicate that a little while ago a man had been slain.

True, Antonio Salvo would not be known in these parts. It might be several days before the French ambassador, hearing of his agent's death, would pound a table and demand arrests. Yet even out here, a district seemingly so remote from international plot and counterplot, the rich doublet of Antonio, his long sword, his horse, also his foreign aspect, should cause a stir. Yet no sheriff's men were in evidence.

The wood was small, largely clear of underbrush, a neat round park rather than part of a forest. It occupied high land, as land in that part of England went, and from its perimeter George could examine all the surrounding territory.

It was not a wood favored by charcoal makers, because of its size. Neither was it an oak wood, which would have brought swineherds to pasture their charges among the acorns. As he soon saw, George had the place to himself.

Yet he walked around and around, peering out from time to time like some hunted animal.

Darkness came at last, but even then George waited for some time before he slipped out of the deeper darkness of the wood. He did not turn toward Okeland, although that had been his original thought. It would be easy to learn of his friendship with the Croftses, even supposing that nobody had seen him visit there today. Sir John and Anne surely would be questioned, among the first. They were not likely to lie, seeing no reason to. Nor would either of them have *made* a good liar, George believed, if he induced them to shelter him. It was better not to put that strain upon them.

The moon had not yet risen, and it was truly dark by the time he set forth from the wood. Nevertheless he moved from cover to cover, as careful as a stalking cat, tree to hedgerow, hedgerow to ditch, ditch to tree. And when he heard horsemen he fell flat and wrapped his head with his arms.

From the sounds there were two of them. They never spoke. They were walking their horses fast, and George sensed that except for the uncertainty of the ground on a dark night they would have urged them to a gallop. He heard the creak of their straps. Then they were gone—in the direction of Okeland.

It was some time before George rose.

Scurrying now, scuttling, bent low, he made for Weddell Lodge. He had already seen the light.

It was not customary in the country for men to stay up after dark. In the instance of Terence Weddell there were two possible explanations. He might be reading, or—he might have visitors.

The dog barked as George approached. Damn that animal! But though the turf was broken—he could smell its clean freshness—no steed was tethered there now.

George went boldly to the door and knocked.

The balk was thrown almost immediately, as though somebody inside had been waiting, and the door was opened without challenge.

"You're back sooner'n I thought, sir. If you—"

George stepped in, pushing aside a stumpy gnarled gnomelike man he hardly saw. He went to the right side of the stair and rapped with his knuckles.

"Is he still in there?"

The little man wore Weddell's cognizance on his sleeve. Clearly a servant. The way he stooped, his head cocked, and the way he squinted in that dim corridor made him seem somehow subterranean. He should have been inside a mountain. Yet he was not servile, and his voice boomed, startlingly loud.

"What the Devil are you doing here?"

George pounded the panel again.

"I'm your next guest," he announced. "That is, if the reverend father has been whisked away, as I suspect. Open this up."

Whether the little man had glimpsed George that afternoon, or for some other reason knew or could guess who he was, George did not learn. But he hesitated only an instant, keenly studying George. Then, pressing a place down near the floor, he lifted the panel out.

"There you are, sir. Since you insist. 'Tis no palace."

George was dismayed by what he saw. He had expected at least a little room in which to move around; but the closet or hole—whatever it should be called—at first glance seemed impossibly cramped. Could any man get in there? It was no more than a padded space about six feet long, possibly two feet square. It might have been a coffin, tipped up at one end; for it was at a forty-five degree angle, following the slant of the steps.

George caught up a quick breath and wriggled in. He went right side first, which meant that his sword had to follow him. He had some trouble getting the sword in.

"They don't usually carry 'em," the dwarf offered. "I'll warrant it's been through somebody lately?"

"You warrant too much," George said coldly. "Now, I want you to report me to your master as soon as he comes back."

"Aye, that I'll do, sir."

"Close the door."

There was no clack, no thud, or even a scraping sound. It was as simple as though somebody had blown out a candle.

George knew an instant of panic, but it was only an instant. Firmly and more than once he told himself that he could have no *logical* fear. Weddell, whatever he might think of the visit, would not give his guest away. The very fact that he had such a closet, clearly designed for priests, meant that he was part of a conspiracy to protect those outlaws. Such a man if nabbed would be hanged. Terence Weddell knew that. So, assuredly, did the dwarf, whom George now heard moving away.

It was hot in the hole, though the night was chill. He crossed his arms on his chest, having some trouble in doing so, and he muttered a short earnest prayer made up for the occasion. He refused to let himself twist or push. In the darkness, grimly he grinned.

He might have been half asleep when the knocking came. It was very loud. He thought at first that someone with a heavy fist was pounding on the panel beside his head.

He heard the dwarf, muttering to himself, fumble with the latch, swing open the door.

There were bootsteps, heavy, ominous.

"Where's your master?"

"Riding around his fields. He does that to clear his head, when he's been studying too hard."

"First time I've ever known Terence Weddell to take any interest in his fields, day or night."

The men were very near. There might have been four or five of them. George could hear their hangers and cross-straps creak. He could hear them breathe. Again and again they passed within inches of the place where he lay, the servant pattering after them like an importunate child.

He should have been a stage player, that servant. He made no try to keep the men away from the panel, and his voice was a whine.

The men went to the library. Probably they were afraid to range much farther without a warrant and in the absence of the owner. When they came back they stopped again by the slat of wood that blocked off George Fitzwilliam.

What were they doing there? Were they staring at that panel? Would they reach down and push it?

"Have you seen anybody go past here tonight, or heard anybody?"

"Tonight? Certainly not. Nobody ever comes here."

"You've been awake?"

"Of course. I have to wait up to unlatch the door for the master when he comes back from his ride. Who— Who is this person you're talking about? What kind of horse does he ride?"

"He'd be on foot. He hasn't got a horse, as far as we know. But he's got a sword, and it's a long one. He killed a man with it this afternoon at the Crossed Keys. He might kill another if he thought he was about to be caught. You'd best not open this door again tonight unless you're mortally sure it's your master."

"Oh, I won't! I won't, truly! And—thank you!"

The latch fell into place, and in a little while George heard them ride away. He sighed with relief and slumped a little lower.

Next thing he knew there was light slamming against his eyes, and Terence Weddell stood there.

"Here, let me help you—"

It was as well that he did. George was indescribably stiff.

"Forgive me," he muttered. "D'ye have anything to eat?"

"Come into the library. It's safe just now."

Watchful, much quieter, the dwarf trailed them.

George was smiling a little, but Weddell was frankly worried, as they sat down, facing one another.

"I don't understand. Are— Are you—"

"I'm not of your ring, no. Nor am I a member of your church. But I *did* come direct from Mary Stuart."

"And how did you know about the panel?"

"Guessed it. Sensed it. And when you went out to fetch wine this afternoon, I put my ear up against it, and I heard somebody clicking rosary beads. The rest wasn't hard. This must be simply an overnight stop. There wouldn't be a large enough congregation to justify the risk of a longer stay. So I assumed that you would be moving his reverence tonight. And I came."

"Here's your food."

George was feeling better. He ate deliberately and well, seldom looking up to smile, though he could feel Weddell's eyes upon him.

At last Weddell said carefully: "There was a man killed before the Crossed Keys late this afternoon."

"I know."

"He was the one who stopped here to ask the way to Okeland."

"Yes. He was a French spy."

"And—you?"

George opened his wallet and drew out the small balled missive that had been sneaked into a slit of his canions.

"You know her escutcheon? Mary Stuart herself handed this to me, and I shall take it to Don Gerau de Spies in London, if I ever get back there alive."

He did not say that he would take it by way of Lord Burghley.

"I believe you," Weddell said quietly. "I have no choice anyway."

"That's true. Now could I have writing materials, please?"

"Sir John?"

"And his daughter. I'd like to reassure them."

"No."

"*Eh?*"

Weddell still was pale, despite the light of the library fire that played upon his thin thoughtful face. But he shook his head.

"Your wish to tell them does you credit. But if I carry your message or if my servant does, they'll know where you are. I don't say that they'd betray you! But there could be a slip."

"How?"

"Crofts has servants too, remember. I'm not equipped here to put up a fugitive for more than one or two nights. It may be much longer than that before I can make arrangements to pass you along. And if there's a slip—any slip at all!—it might mean the lives of many, many devout persons all across the land."

"Yes . . ."

"So you see how it is? As soon as possible I will make arrangements for you to tell them you're safe. Meanwhile it would be all right for you to sleep on a trundle-bed in my room, except of course at such times as there's somebody nearby. Tonight I don't think we'd better trust it."

"I'll survive in the hole."

"Many a man has."

"I am sure of it."

"But you don't want to go back there right now. You're not tired enough to fall asleep. What about a game of chess instead?"

George Fitzwilliam put his feet up on the table.

"I'm not much good at chess," he confessed. "Let's just talk about something that interests us both much more. Let's talk about Mary Queen of Scots."

15

Stay Away from Windows

One of the reasons George preferred land to sea, the country to the city, was that he loved to live well, enjoying good clothes, good wine, company. The many months afloat in appallingly overcrowded ships, the years in a Spanish prison, had only sharpened his fondness for life's material amenities. And yet, though the routine at Weddell offered these things in abundance, days there dragged with a more pronounced bumpiness than any he had endured whilst cruising off the Main or lying in the grip of the Inquisition at Seville.

Terence Weddell treated him well. Not the trundle but the master's own magnificent four-poster was George's for sleeping. He was allowed full liberty of the library. Cider and perry, hippocras, metheglin, alicant, claret, charneco, and sherris sack were his for the asking, served too in silver goblets. Weddell's valet de chambre, the gnome Sylvestre, the only servant George ever saw inside of the house, waited upon George with skill, combing his hair, trimming his beard, perfuming his doublet, starching his ruff, and washing and mending his clothes. Weddell's cook, a wizard George was never to meet, must have spent all his waking hours in the concoction of marchpane and sugar meats, gingerbread, biscuits, candied eringo, and pastries of red deer and fallow deer, cony and goose, squirrel and swan.

Weddell himself was away in the daytime—riding off alone, returning alone, disinclined to talk about his business. But at night he was at George's service, and an accomplished host he made. Weddell's keenness to play chess had blabbed of his ability: he was much too good a player for George Fitzwilliam. But at mumchance, as indeed at all games of cards, they were evenly matched, while at the pastime George himself had first proposed, the discussion of Mary Stuart, they were one. A few times they fenced; but Weddell was as inferior to George in this as George was inferior to him in chess. Some nights they had music. Weddell played a cittern very well, Sylvestre was an adept at the curtal, and George could acquit himself tolerably well on a recorder. They sang too—"Fond Youth is a Bubble," "On Going to My Naked Bed," "Never Weather-Beaten Sail," "Green Sleeves"—the dwarf taking the countertenor, George the bass.

Nevertheless the month was the longest in George's life. There was not a pinch of danger to spice it. Though he was taught how to work the panel and the priest-hole was always at his disposal, George had recourse to it only a few times, and never for long. At first the sheriff's men and a little later some queen's men from London came calling at Weddell Lodge, but they seemed satisfied with the explanation the squire gave and did not ask to be permitted to search either house or grounds.

Of other callers there were few. Nonetheless it was advisable that George stay away from windows.

In the country even more than in the city, a man's wealth might be gauged by the number of windows he had in his house. All over England, and whether or not they could afford it, men were smashing holes in their gloomy old houses, admitting light and air, putting up costly glass panes. Weddell Lodge was modest in size, but it did boast a great many windows, having been built since the beginning of the fashion.

Fortunately the ones in the library were high. "I had 'em cut that way so's I wouldn't be distracted from my books on a beautiful day," Weddell explained. George himself spent a great deal of time over those books, out of boredom studying the art of navigation, the proper drawing of loxodromes, the handling and reporting of ring-dials, astrolabes, nocturnals, cross-staffs, and geographical planispheres.

There were many reasons why George remained at Weddell Lodge so long, but the first of these—the question of where he should go if he *did* leave—was enough in itself. George had no home, no headquarters.

His mother and father were dead, his godfather as well, while his brother, Sir William, presently the head of the house, was in Ireland. His master, John Hawkins, was either in Plymouth or in London. *His* master, and truly George's, Lord Burghley, George thought best not to mention; but Burghley would be among the first to learn of the death of Salvo, and it was likely that he would guess who had brought this about.

It was an agony to George to reflect upon the fact that Okeland was but a few miles distant, almost within sight of Weddell Lodge, yet he was not permitted to communicate with the Croftses. Here Terence Weddell, in many matters easygoing, was firm. When the questioning parties had ceased to come, Terence Weddell spent a good part of each day away, arranging stopping-places for George. Weddell would refuse to release him until a whole chain of such places had been staked out, so that George would be far away from the Lodge if caught. This took time. In no circumstances, Weddell made clear, would Okeland be one of those places, nor might George pause there even briefly in passing. Okeland was too near. Weddell liked Anne and her father —who, as George happened to know, liked him—but he pointed out that Sir John was, well, perhaps a bit puritanical in his views. George glumly agreed. He remembered the rage the very mention of Mary Stuart's name had brought about. Sir John was not a hot gospeler— no, not like that detestable little Captain Drake who had read to the released prisoners Joshua's instructions to his lieutenants—but beyond dispute a man of stern religious principles.

Once the first ado had subsided George wrote a letter to John Hawkins in which he made no mention of Salvo but hinted mysteriously at some cause for delay and in effect asked for orders. He signed it with his own name and addressed it to Hawkins at his London house. At the same time he entrusted to Weddell for delivery to the Spanish ambassador at London Mary Stuart's smuggled note; for he had read this and resealed it, and knew that it was harmless, a tester of a potential new outlet.

How these messages were carried and by whom, George never learned. He could only hope at the time that they would get to their respective destinations.

He wished now that he had done the whole thing otherwise. It was not in his nature, ordinarily, to cry over spilt milk. But perhaps he had too much time on his hands. He should either have given Antonio the message, or else he should have fought that bravo right there at Okeland, with Sir John Crofts as witness. Anne's father wasn't rich and he had no political connections, but he was a man of unimpeachable honor, and his testimony would have acquitted George at once. Instead, George had ignominiously bolted. What did Sir John think of that? What did Anne think?

Then one morning—a morning filled with rowdy-dowdy sunshine and birdsong and the buzz of bees—George was about to cross the entrance hall when he saw that the door was open. He should have jumped away, like a thief who fears detection, for this was the practice at Weddell Lodge. But he looked out—and saw Anne.

She was alone. She had tethered her horse by the gate and was walking up the alley of lime, slapping her knee with a riding rod.

Once again she was bare-headed, for she was daring that way; and the sun fleered from her honey-colored hair. The tilt of her chin, the set of her shoulders, and the way she walked, thrilled him. He gave a cry—never before had he wanted her so much—and started through the door.

He was hauled back, yanked as unceremoniously as if he were a sack of rye. Sylvestre, though so short, was strong.

"*You fool,*" he whispered.

George flung him off.

"Now this is too much, by God! Nobody's going to—"

"*Get into that closet!*"

It was as though a rabbit had transformed itself into a dragon. The little man meant it. All fire and fury, though he was fond of George, he would have slashed. His first thought was for his master.

George, who had started to draw his own dagger, clacked this back. He nodded.

"You're right," he muttered.

In agony, he snatched a glimpse of Anne, who came on. It was as though he gulped her with his eyes. Then he folded himself into the priest's hole, and Sylvestre closed the panel.

As though set off by the clicking of that clasp, hot suspicion struck the back of George's eyes. He started to sit up and was slammed back by a bump against his head.

Why was Anne coming here?

There might be a hundred reasons. Weddell Manor was not properly a farm in the working sense that Okeland was, but the two were contiguous, and many homely everyday articles might well be exchanged between them. One of the hands or Sir John himself would seem a more convenient runner of such errands, but the hands might have been busy, while the knight's feeling about papistry was so strong that he might have feared to find himself in Terence Weddell's presence. Again, Anne could merely be dropping over for a visit. Where was the harm in that?

Nonetheless George writhed. Perspiration broke out all over him. Never before in the course of an immurement—save for the first terrible instant—had he known a touch of fright. But now he verged on panic. He had all he could do to keep his fists from pounding the panel.

However, he forced himself to lie perfectly still; and he was able to hear every word, for Weddell had come out of the library and he and the visitor stood only inches away.

"Mistress Crofts! An unexpected pleasure! Will you have some cherries? A mug of cider?"

"Thank you, no; I have so much to do. I came to ask you about Master Fitzwilliam."

"Nothing's been heard of him?"

"Nothing."

There was a pause and George, though an inch of oak intervened, could all but feel the piercing intensity of Anne's eyes. They must be making Terence Weddell uneasy.

"He knows this country well, of course, and he must have learned that the man he killed had French connections. So it's best to lie low, very low indeed."

"He knew of Salvo's French connections before he fought. He didn't want to fight. He tried to run away."

"Run away? George Fitzwilliam?"

"Aye. It was best. He's not the fool he sometimes looks."

There was another pause, which Anne broke abruptly:

"Master Weddell, the sheriff's men and the queen's men must have visited this house, right after the duel?"

"Oh yes, they were here. They searched the place."

"And found nothing?"

"There was nothing to find."

"And you told them that you hadn't seen George Fitzwilliam that night?"

"I told them that, yes."

"Was it true?"

"Why, of course it's true!"

"Master Weddell, did you also tell them that George Fitzwilliam had visited you that very afternoon, just before he killed Salvo at the Crossed Keys?"

George could not hear Weddell's gasp, but he suspected it. Anne, he reasoned, had not been idle. She'd combed the countryside in search of information, and no doubt she had come upon some peasant who remembered having seen Master Fitzwilliam ride up to Weddell Lodge that fateful afternoon. There was no reason why she shouldn't; there had been nothing furtive about the visit.

"No, I did not tell them that. Their questions were sharp enough as it was. It is the custom these days to press down hard upon persons of my religious belief, no matter what the issue or how far removed from any church. If the sheriff's men were to learn that Fitzwilliam was here that afternoon they'd tear the house to pieces. They'd welcome such an excuse."

"Yet I can't help thinking that George Fitzwilliam is somewhere near here, somewhere very near, right now."

"What makes you think so?"

"His horse was tired, and he left it behind. He couldn't have gone far on foot. There's no real forest around here, only small woods that can easily be searched. He must have ducked into some house before the chase was fully up, before the hue and cry. But why hadn't he reached me with at least a word? We're betrothed, you know."

"I hadn't known that."

"Oh, no banns have been posted, and he hasn't given me a ring, but that's only because he hasn't had the time. George is very busy these days—getting into trouble."

Again there was some silence, and George was convinced that Anne had put a hand upon Weddell's arm and was looking up at him, appealing to him. George wriggled, pettishly.

"If he should chance to visit here, Master Weddell, or if you hear aught of him, please tell me, won't you?"

"I shall surely do that, Mistress Crofts."

"He may be avoiding me for fear of implicating me. He— He's foolish that way. He has old-fashioned ideas of chivalry."

"I see."

"But make no mistake about it, Master Weddell, I love that man. If it would spare him a single unhappy moment I'd let myself be thrown into a fiery furnace, like Shadrach and Meshach and Abednego. No, I won't have any cherries or cider, but thanks again. I must off."

George heard them move toward the door and pause.

"By the way,"—Anne's voice was fainter but still distinct—"*why* did George stop here that afternoon?"

Weddell never hesitated. No doubt it was his policy, as well as a personal preference, to tell the truth whenever possible.

"He had just come from Sheffield, from Queen Mary. It was my birthday and she'd remembered it, being graciousness in all her parts.

You must know that I was a page in her household once, in happier days, at Holyrood. So she took the opportunity to send me her miniature, by Master Fitzwilliam."

"I see . . . And this is it?"

"Aye. I keep it next my heart. Perhaps I too have old-fashioned ideas about chivalry."

"Does she really look like that, Master Weddell?"

"Not a bit. She's lovelier. Much lovelier."

"You and George must have discussed her. What does *he* think of her beauty?"

"Ma'am, I couldn't know. He did not seem interested in the subject, so we didn't talk about it."

George hugged himself, chuckling without a sound, and when Sylvestre opened the panel a moment later, he was all grin.

"Your honor, I'm sorry I was so urgent."

"You were absolutely right, Sylvestre. I lost my head."

Terence Weddell was thoughtful as he returned from the doorway. "She didn't believe me, that last thing I told her."

"Of course not."

"You know, Fitzwilliam, you're a very lucky man. I had never really met Mistress Crofts before today, never informally."

"You like her?"

"Let's put it this way: I think you have more reason than ever for keeping away from windows. Now, what about a game of chess?"

When a week later the answer to George's letter arrived—George, clapped into the priest's hole, never did see the messenger—it was from London, and from Burghley, being indeed in the baron's own hand. Burghley, like George, had eschewed ciphers but wrote with a careful vagueness, making no mention of the law, the duel, Salvo, the French ambassador, Mary Stuart, or anybody else excepting only George's master, John Hawkins.

Hawkins, the letter informed, was on his way to Plymouth, where George was instructed to rejoin him. Every precaution should be taken. What would happen if George was nabbed—whether these two would dare to come to his defense—the letter did not say. Neither did it say specifically what was planned for George when he got to Plymouth, though there was an implication that it might be another assignment to the New World.

Even after the letter had been received and even though George had no preparation to make, it was three days before Weddell would permit a departure. Arrangements had to be made for his reception in some house a short night's ride to the south. Also, there was the matter of the moon. On the night in question it would not rise until near midnight, when assuredly no one would be abroad. Terence Weddell had taken everything into consideration.

The parting touched them both. George was not in the least amazed when Terence Weddell guided him to the lane that led to the Crossed Keys, being careful on the way to avoid Okeland or any rise from which Okeland could have been seen; but he was shaken by the force of his own emotion.

"Go to the inn. 'Tis closed now, but there will be a man lurking in the yard. Somebody you've never seen before. Trust him utterly."

He extended a hand George could scarcely see. But George leaned past that, his throat tight, and they kissed like cousins, embracing one another. Each was sobbing.

"God bless you, Fitzwilliam!"

"Amen."

"God lead you safe out of this!"

"Amen."

Weddell, who knew every inch of the country thereabouts, rode quickly away. Despite the dark, the lane was easy to follow.

George sat silent for a moment.

The way was dappled with gently wavering starshine. A breeze soughed, and above and on either side of the lane a few leaves rustled peevishly. Somewhere low there was a guarded scurry of small feet, perhaps a fox. The thunk of Weddell's steed had long since ceased.

George turned back toward Okeland.

16

Oh, Wait for Me!

All George meant to do was look at the house. He had no thought of betraying his friend's confidence by rousing the Croftses. He would look a moment from afar, that was all.

But when he saw a blur of white nightrail at the window he knew to be Anne's, his heart was caught up. It was too much, and he rode right across the garden.

The window was old-fashioned, without glass. Anne stood alone, immersed in her private thoughts. She had been weeping, George thought, though he couldn't be sure.

How he loved her! And must he always be hurting her, always riding away? Was it his doom to skulk like an outlaw, shying from the company of decent, normal people? If only this were home, thought George, who had no home. If only he could dismount and go inside for a kiss and a good night's sleep! He sighed.

Directly under the window, he rose upright in his stirrups.

"My chuck—"

She started and leaned out, staring wildly.

"George!"

She knew him from his voice; it was too dark for her to have seen his face.

"Sh-sh!"

"I'll come down!"

"No! And thou must not tell Sir John!"

She would have been obliged to pass through her father's bedroom to get to the stair, as he knew.

"I'm off, my sweeting. I may be gone for a long while. But I'll come back. Wait for me."

She leaned out even farther, extending a hand. He could not reach it. He climbed to the horse's back and stood in saddle, and then he could reach the hand.

Her hair fell, a cascade of perfume, all around him. He kissed it. He kissed her hand.

"But—why? *Why?*"

"Sh-sh! 'Tis too long a tale for here."

"It hath something to do with that French woman!"

This he could not deny, so he only kissed her hand again. It was some time before he ventured to speak.

"My sweet, you must believe me when I say that I ran from that Italian only because I thought—"

She brushed this aside with the swift impatient gesture of one who walks into a cobweb in the dark. She was not interested in tickle points of niceness in masculine honor. She was interested in Mary Stuart.

"George, you love her!"

It was well that she couldn't see his face.

"I love *thee*," he said quietly. "If it would spare thee a single unhappy moment I would let myself be thrown into a fiery furnace like Shadrach and Meshach and Abednego."

He heard her gasp and instantly realized what a foolish thing he had done. He was no psalmsinger like her father, and it would not ordinarily be natural for him to make an Old Testament allusion. The truth is, the phrase had stuck in his memory ever since—crouched in that priest's hole—he had heard Anne Crofts utter it of him more than a week ago. It had come forth by itself, unbidden, blurted out, and it startled Anne.

George knew better than to protest. She was not easily duped, and she'd have time to think it over later. He squeezed her hand so hard that it must have hurt.

"Darling," he whispered, "thou must tell nobody! Not thine aunts, not thy father! Promise me!"

"Oh, I promise."

Once again, she was not interested. She was not thinking of Terence Weddell and the possibility that his head was in a noose. She thought only that George had told her he loved her.

He slithered down into saddle, and his feet found the stirrups.

"I'll come back," he repeated. "Wait for me."

"*George!*"

"Wait for me."

He tugged at his rein and rode off.

The manner in which George was passed along was miraculous. The organization astounded and delighted him, and sometimes it frightened him. Everything had been thought of; and he could not help wondering whether London, Burghley, the government of the realm, the queen, could have commanded so neat a performance. There was no house at which he was not expected, no groom who took his horse without appearing to know why. Nobody asked his name, or whether he had any title (he was sometimes addressed as "Father," and he never corrected this), or presumed to make any mention of where he might be going or on what manner of mission.

The houses were good, many of them palatial. The grooms were expert. The hosts, like the hostesses, quite clearly were of fine or even exalted blood. The food was excellent, as was the wine. Repeatedly he was offered money, an offer he declined. His horse, readied the night after his arrival or three or four nights later, invariably was in prime condition. Some of the holes in which he had to sleep were tight, yet none was as cramped as the one at Weddell Lodge; and the padding, the sheets, the pillows, were silken, like the mien of those who bedded and waked him.

All he lacked was exercise. He still was obliged to avoid windows; and his rides at night were short ones, customarily with a guide who insisted upon silence and no gallop. George feared that he was growing fat.

It was an extraordinary experience, and it vastly increased his respect for Terence Weddell and for the English Catholic party; but in itself it answered no question, settled no dispute. They might have been from another world, those gracious persons who wined and dined him, passing him along. They spoke English, they *were* English, yet they were more alien to George Fitzwilliam than had been the colonists of New Spain.

When at last he came to the end of the chain a bit north of Plymouth, he realized that though he had been handled by charming persons, he didn't know a single name. It had been planned that way.

Plymouth itself he entered on foot. Not masked, for that would have drawn attention to himself, but wrapped in a long dark loose cloak that hid his Spanish costume.

He made his way swiftly and without the slightest trouble to the Hawkins house. It was this trip that he had feared. He knew so many persons in Plymouth, where so many more knew him! It would have been awkward if some relative of one of the released prisoners had spotted him and pounced upon him with glad grateful cries.

The Hawkins house was in Kinterbury Street in the southwestern part of Plymouth, a neighborhood he knew well. He was surprised to see that it was lighted, for this must have been two hours after sunset.

George noted with a grin that since his last visit there had been carved into and painted on both gate posts the newly granted Hawkins arms: sable, on a point wavy a lion passant or; in chief three bezants. Ex-Mayor John, who grew paunchy, was doing himself well as a gentleman. But in all truth, a soul saw ever so many newly-granted escutcheons in the seaports, for they were fairly slubbered over with these. And all fancy, complicated. The molet of the Veres, the Percy crescent, the simple Crofts chevron, the lozenge of the Fitzwilliams, were not for these "new men."

There was a holdup at the door, the only hitch in the trip from Weddell Lodge, but when George raised his voice he was admitted. John Hawkins appeared, clad in cramoisy.

"George!"

"Sh-sh! Is that permissible?"

"Go to, lad. I don't have a servant I can't trust. You'll wash?"

"Truth is, your worship, I'm abnormally clean at the moment. But —where do I go?"

"Why, to bed, if you wish."

[99]

"Let be! We'll wade no further into that. Where do I go *tomorrow,* your worship? You have some oversea enterprise making up?"

"Well asked. I have. The admiral himself is here, by good chance. You'll meet him. Come."

"America again?" George faltered.

"America again. Till this blows over. 'Tis needful that I win back some of the losses, you understand?"

"Oh, clearly. So we—pirate?"

"Tut, lad. You'll be assigned to the admiral, and you'll watch after my affairs. All's ready. We shall have to smuggle you aboard, but smuggling you're used to by now, eh?"

"Aye."

"At this moment, a person who has in any way offended France is not a person to banquet, I can tell you. You know that there's a warrant out for your arrest on a charge of murder?"

"Those who have entertained me made no mention of a warrant, but I could guess as much."

"Aye."

"And so I must go far away?"

"Aye. And for a long time."

"Ah, well. Where's this admiral you mentioned?"

"Why, in the next room. Kin of mine. Come."

John Hawkins was kindly, and he had embraced George in a manner that left no doubt as to his relief and pleasure. Yet that "Come" stuck in George's craw.

Hawkins put an arm across George's shoulders. He led George into his solar. And the admiral rose, nodding curtly.

George bowed.

"So we will smite the Amalekites together?"

"You will smite the Amalekites as I direct," replied Francis Drake.

17

Delicate, Dangerous Too

The jungle was a maw, implacable, pitiless, in color so dark a green that it was almost black. Sunlight smashed upon the water, as dazzling as diamonds; but the shore shone with a dull cold wet gleam that made George think of Sheffield.

The men of the *Pascha,* like those of the *Swan* anchored nearby, were in frolicsome mood, what with fresh water and fresh fruits. They did not dare to dice or play cards, since any such activity was forbidden, but they fished uproariously, and now and then one would try a crossbow shot at a gull. The gulls were bewildered, never before having seen sea vessels. Their necks were far-stretched, and they screeched querulously as they circled. They were not good meat, being bitter, and it was against regulations to waste quarrels or arrows on them; but a certain amount of lenity can be allowed when you have just crossed an ocean.

None of these sounds did the jungle reflect. Rather it swallowed them, leaving no echo.

Not only was there no surf, there were not even small love-patting wavelets, for the very water seemed stricken with awe when it approached that somber beach.

Nowhere along the Main or among the West Indies, or in New Spain, or even at an earlier stop off the coast of Portuguese Guinea, had George Fitzwilliam seen so menacing, so dark a shore.

" 'Tis a little more than twenty miles, you say?"

"Aye. You should make it by Wednesday afternoon."

"Two days to travel *that* distance?"

"When you have stepped on land," Francis Drake said, "I think you will see what I mean."

Thoughtful, they went to the captain's cabin, a pretentious place paneled in oak, with high closets that housed the captain's extraordinary collection of fine bright clothes and his plate—real silver, each piece engraved as was everything else there with the Drake device: argent, a wyvern with tail nowed gules. The captain knew nothing of heraldry—probably couldn't have told a flasque from a flanch or a cross engrailed from a cross urdee—but he was fascinated by this wyvern, or dragon, that he so fondly believed to have been a grant to his ancestors, and he had planted it in every place he could find.

George was familiar with the cabin, where he spent a great deal of time, though he had never been comfortable there. While he was experienced in sailing, as a gentle it would not have behooved him to haul a sheet or help at the capstan. And on the same vessel with Francis Drake—who, whatever he might not have been, was a great mariner—it would have been presumptuous to make any suggestion about the condition or employment of spritsails, clew-garnets, leechlines, forebowlines, falls, swifters, preventers, bonnets. Consequently his duties aboard the *Pascha* were largely clerical. Besides being the representative of John Hawkins, the heaviest adventurer in this voyage, he had become a sort of secretary to Francis Drake.

Drake needed one. As George had divined in the hoy out of Seville, this cousin of John Hawkins could not read. Or rather, he read very slowly, awkwardly, uncertainly. Most of his reading had been in the Bible, which George sometimes thought the man must know by heart, not by memory which is a different thing, but by heart. But he did have other books in that splendid cabin, most of them about discovery, travel, geography, and of course navigation. Drake was extravagantly sensitive about this near-illiteracy of his, which he would not confess even to George, and often he had George read to him on the plea that his own eyes were tired. Always George pretended to believe this.

They did not like one another, these two, but they got along well enough.

Yet not even George Fitzwilliam with a secretarial exemption would have ventured to enter the captain's cabin unless he was, as now, in the captain's company or unless he had been invited. This was a stern rule. Drake, George suspected, feared being surprised in the act of strutting in his fancy clothes or perhaps with knotted brow and moving lips struggling over a letter.

So George was astonished when he found the cabin occupied.

There was only one man, but what a man! He was huge, a giant, veritably a Goliath of Gath. He was also black—not tan, or the color of chocolate, but black. He was naked to the waist, and the muscles of his magnificent shoulders and arms rippled.

"This is Diego. He is a Cimarron."

"Oh?"

George had heard of them. Members of an African tribe noted for its ferocity, brought over to New Spain as slaves, they had broken loose and taken to the hills—the word meant hill-people—where they ran wild. Understandably, they hated the Spaniards by whom they were treated like beasts to be shot on sight. But they were tough. Without arms or equipment of any kind, they kept up the struggle and pressed it. There weren't many of them, but they were cunning, fierce.

"I did a favor for Diego a few years ago," Francis Drake reported. "I believe in his gratitude. He says he will guide one of my men to Nombre de Dios. At least, I *think* that's what he said. Suppose you talk to him?"

Drake's plan was plain enough, if a breath-catcher.

Twice a year, treasures in gold and silver and pearls were shipped down the west coast of Mexico and up the coast of Peru to the far side, the South Sea side, of this isthmus of Darien to a city called Panama. From thence they were sent by muleback across the isthmus to the town of Nombre de Dios on the Atlantic side, near the mouth of the Chagres. At about the same time a *flota* or treasure fleet was on its way to Nombre de Dios from Cartagena. When these two met for a week or so twice a year, Nombre de Dios, which othertimes must have been a sleepy village, would teem with life. From there the combined fleets would move to San Juan de Ulua, the Atlantic port of Mexico and the port of George Fitzwilliam's capture, where they would join still another treasure fleet. Under very heavy escort they would start for Spain itself.

There would have been no sanity in trying to attack the various treasure fleets, separately or together. There were not enough ships and fighting men in England and France combined to make a dent in the Spanish navy.

Drake's plan was to sack Nombre de Dios while the Mexican-Peruvian treasure was there waiting to be loaded. It was as simple as that. The odds in man power would be heavily on the side of the Spaniards, but surprise might turn the trick. After all, what reason had the authorities to suppose that there was an Englishman within three thousand miles?

But now, it appeared, something had gone wrong.

Diego's Castilian left much to be desired, and it was interspersed with outlandish words that had no meaning for George, but the black was a naturally expressive man, and in time George had the story.

The treasure was in Nombre de Dios all right, but it had come from Panama with reinforcements of one hundred and fifty crack regulars and some cannons. Not because anybody dreamed that Drake was in this part of the world! Rather it was because of the Cimarrons, whose raids had been very bold.

The regulars were bad enough; they would more than double the size of the Nombre de Dios garrison. But the cannons might be worse. As nearly as George could get it from Diego, there were six of those big guns—the black of course knew no technical details as to bore, tonnage, etc.—and they had been or were being mounted on a hill on the east side of the bay.

It was not likely that these cannons would prevent a landing. But they could cut off retreat. If they were properly mounted, and manned with even a minimum of skill, they could blow the poor little *Pascha* and the poor little *Swan* out of the water.

"Um-m. Yes, that's what I thought he said."

Was Drake inhuman? Anybody else would have dropped the plan, perilous to the point of foolhardiness in the first place. Francis Drake seemed never even to have considered quitting; an obstacle to him was simply something to be pushed aside.

The only doubt in Drake's mind, George believed, pertained to his selection of a man to sneak into Nombre de Dios from the land side, from the jungle, and make a preliminary survey. George, unmarried, his face darkened by the sun, wearing Spanish clothes, speaking Spanish, was a logical choice. George, though not powerful, had powerful connections, and Drake might have been pondering whether he should risk the loss of a man like that.

" 'Twill be fraught with peril, you understand, Fitzwilliam?"

"There seems little doubt of that."

"Your first move should be to find out about those cannons. Then, where are the reinforcements housed? And where is the treasure—in the cabildo or in the governor's palace? If you know this when we land, if you meet us with this, 'twill help enormously."

"You'll invade anyway?"

"Of course."

Might the admiral of this small expedition also be influenced by the fact that George could prove an embarrassing passenger on the return if the raid was not a success? Given treasure, nothing else was needed. "Who ever heard of being a pirate for a million pounds?" Drake once had asked his secretary. And he hadn't been jesting—he never did that. If, on the other hand, something went wrong, so that the expedition's investment did not pay dividends, or some unlooked-for international event should cause France to lose favor at the English court, necessitating a switch to Spain, then this voyage would be discountenanced, and the recruiting of a fugitive from justice would prove one more count against Master Drake. But if George was killed—

George had not been asked to volunteer for this assignment, but he decided to act as if he had.

"I'll go," he said, "provided I get two extra parts in the share-out."

This was a stipulation Francis Drake could see. It made the whole thing clear to him, as John Hawkins' offer to sell out the Channel fleet had suddenly become clear to King Philip when Hawkins demanded that he be paid. So far from resenting the request, Drake welcomed it. That would make the whole business legitimate in his eyes.

"You are entitled to that. Write it, and I'll sign it."

While George wrote, Drake ignored Diego and scowled at the shore through a port.

"The men must not learn about those reinforcements. I think it would be best if you go right away."

"Yes."

"But you will need God's help, Fitzwilliam."

"Don't we all need that?"

"This is different. If you're taken it will mean more than death. It will mean an exceedingly *prolonged* death."

George smiled.

"You think that if when I'm screaming under their red-hot pincers I tell them how I got there, 'twould be a warm reception you'd meet, eh?"

"It would be the end of England's hope for empire," Francis Drake said gravely. "For each of us would be hanged, and after that the queen's majesty would permit no man to sail west. Should we give up half the world for fear, Fitzwilliam?"

"Have I said anything about fear?"

Francis Drake got to his knees.

"I think we should pray," he pronounced.

Embarrassed, yet rather touched, George got down beside him. He clasped his hands, closed his eyes.

Drake prayed at some length.

Diego watched them, wondering what they were doing.

When at last they rose, George tightened his sword-belt and grinned at Diego who grinned back, all teeth.

"Shall we be getting on our way?" George asked.

18

Through Hell with an Angel

Ships, he supposed, were the most malodorous conveyances ever devised by mankind. Yet it was true that if you could stay on deck you got fresh air. The voyage just finished, combined with the easy living in rural England, George hoped, had stiffened a frame made slack by months in prison. When he stepped ashore he felt ready for any physical ordeal.

It was amazing how quickly the jungle took away that confidence. The blood might have been drained out of him and warm soapy water substituted. It was as though the walls of his lungs came together, striving to stick to one another. His joints moved grittily. His skin itched with sweat.

It was extremely hot and close, and he kept his mouth open even when he was not moving. He panted.

It was extremely dark too. Entering that jungle was like being swallowed up by the speluncar gloom of a cave. From time to time they came upon what might have been called a clearing, a break in the vines and spiked creepers, the branches and boughs, the roots, the hanging moss, so that they could move a few steps without pushing something aside or cutting something down; but there was never any clearing in the roof that blocked the sky, and not so much as a javelin of sunlight found its way to where they were. Until his eyes adjusted, George could not even see his own feet.

More difficult still to see, even when his eyes *had* accustomed themselves to that Stygian darkness, was Diego's back.

The Cimarron went ahead, bent like a hound on scent. It almost seemed as if he snuffed the ground. Certainly there was no path or trail. Yet he never hesitated. He carried a weapon strange to George Fitzwilliam, a scimitarlike broadsword with no point, and he used this to hack vegetation, to carve a tunnel through the undergrowth. Yet even when thus engaged, Diego moved faster than George, who, from time to time touched by panic at the prospect of being lost, shouted for a stop. Diego was polite, but puzzled. He couldn't understand how anybody could be so slow.

Twenty miles? It might have been a hundred! Since there was no sun there were no hours, and night was the same as day. They never slept in the stretched-out, proper sense. Whenever they stopped for a little while, George just collapsed, careless of whether he dropped on mud or in a pool of scummy water. Diego would hunker down, his forearms on his widespread knees. As far as George could see, Diego never did close his eyes, which gleamed in the dimness as did his teeth when he smiled.

At these times, George dreamed in a kaleidoscopic fashion. The images were jerky, flighty; he might have been suffering from a touch of fever. Lying in that primeval ooze, George would see Milton in the days before the death of his father. (The seat was a ruin now, his brother's property.) He saw the Anne Crofts of childhood, and the Anne of today, with her grave gray-blue eyes and the smile that came so quickly but went quickly too, leaving her face as serious as before. He saw the prison at Tenochtitlán, also the dungeons beneath the palace of the archbishop of Seville . . . The audience hall at the

Escorial, so depressing in its grandeur . . . The look on Guy Harris'
face when they led him out to be burned alive in the marketplace . . .
The Thames as seen through a certain window at Cecil House . . . The
majesty of Scotland being brave beneath a shabby cloth of state . . .
That saucy sparrow that had landed on Antonio Salvo's back . . .

When Diego apologetically shook him, and he struggled to his feet
again, the images disappeared as abruptly as though washed off a
slate. When he walked, slogged rather, George thought about nothing
at all.

It was always George who called the halt, Diego who called for
the resumption of the journey. Diego in some mysterious manner kept
track of time. He maintained a schedule. Though he smiled, he was
insistent when he signaled that it was time to take up the trudge.

They saw no human being nor any evidence of such—footprints,
the charred remains of a fire. Nor did they hear anything that might
indicate human life. It was not probable that sound would reach
them anyway. The air was too wet, sopping up each syllable they
spoke, and multitudes of insects swarmed around their heads, humming
loudly. Diego paid no attention to these insects, which he called *mos-
quitos,* but George Fitzwilliam was tormented by them.

Once they saw a snake. Diego had just shaken George, who opened
his eyes to find himself staring at the thing. It was slender, sleek, five
or six feet long. Its back was composed of pale green, pink-edged
triangles that glowed as though from an inner light. Its head was
small, and shaped like the head of an arrow. At its throat, as George
saw when the snake lifted itself to stare at him, was a bright yellow bib.

"*Barba amarilla,*" said Diego.

"Poisonous?"

"*O, mucho, señor. Mucho muchísimo.*"

Yet though the big Negro held in his hand the chopping weapon
he called a *machete,* he made not the slightest move toward the snake,
which soon slithered away. One of his gods, perhaps? George shivered,
yet at the next stopping-place he slumped to the ground again without hesitation.

They had plunged in, but they crept out. There was nothing dramatic
about their emergence from the jungle. As much as he could be considered conscious of anything, George for some time had been aware
that they were going downhill. Gradually the roof of foliage lightened,
and there was even a spear of sunlight now and then. They began to
come upon small glades or clearings, in each of which a column of
that same sunlight, very sharp to the eyes, stood upright. Diego went
around these places.

Once they saw the sea, far off, and that was a heartlifting glimpse.

They found a path, or rather the path appeared to find them, quietly sidling out of nowhere to slip without fuss beneath their feet. It was not much of a path and didn't seem to be leading anywhere. Nevertheless Diego trod it with caution. He kept further ahead of George than he had done in the jungle, and his machete was held high, ready for action. Every now and then he would stop a moment to listen.

At one of those stops Diego turned. He went back to George and knelt, and with hands as big as hams, yet unexpectedly gentle, he smoothed George's canions and base hose, brushed his boots, flicked bits of foliage from his sleeve.

Diego wasn't even sweating, wasn't even breathing hard.

From the position of the sun and the direction of the sea vouchsafed by that one glance, George took it that this was mid-morning. They had traveled all afternoon and all night, and now they must be near Nombre de Dios. Diego could go no further; that much was clear. He would be killed like a mad dog by the first Spaniards he met.

The big Cimarron was smiling, yet at the same time there was a glint of moisture in his eye. He bobbed, nodding. He leaned over and rubbed his nose against George's nose, first on one side, then on the other. He stepped back, beaming.

"Thank you, Diego. *Gracias.* You've been an angel."

George took the savage's hand and shook it. Diego looked alarmed, shying like a pricked horse. But he grinned again, sure that George had meant him no harm and in his queer way was only trying to express gratitude.

It was the first time anybody ever had shaken hands with Diego.

He bobbed again. Then he disappeared.

There could be no other word for it. Big as he was, he seemed to have vanished like a wisp of smoke. At one instant Diego was there, at the next he was gone.

George waited a moment, thinking that Diego might come back, wishing that he would. He looked around; he felt hideously alone and more than a mite frightened. He swallowed, and marched up the path.

He came to a trail. It could hardly be called a road, but it was clearly marked, and straight. It went toward Nombre de Dios on the right, toward the South Sea on the other side.

George paused. A boy passed, whistling. A *recua* or mule train passed—perhaps thirty beasts, all heavily laden, and half a dozen drivers. There was also a considerable clump of foot soldiers, who outnumbered the drivers, and obviously had been assigned to protect the train from Cimarrons. The soldiers looked cross, but the mule-teers were bright, and they all smiled at George, three of them lifting their hats.

He made no acknowledgment. It was not the part of a minor grandee to smirk at mule drivers; a salute would have brought suspicion upon him.

He waited a little longer, not knowing what to expect. Nothing happened. Yet the trail was a well-traveled one, trampled by many feet, human and other, and stippled with the droppings of many mules.

At last he turned to the right, and in a little while he came to the south gate, the Panama Gate, of Nombre de Dios.

There was activity here—some sort of squabble between the soldiers and the muleteers, while the animals themselves, half asleep, resigned to the lack of grass, stood to one side.

The only other person in sight was a sentry, who sat under an umbrella, and who showed no interest in the spat, being concerned with keeping the flies off his face.

One of the muleteers appealed to George to intervene, but George scornfully refused even to acknowledge the request and walked past, toward the gate.

The sentry never even looked up.

George was in Nombre de Dios.

He drew a deep breath.

19

When in Doubt, Be Haughty

The policy of aloofness could prove a sound one. Nombre de Dios was a small town, just now seriously overcrowded. It had a holiday air. Informality was the watchword; and more than once George was hailed by men who would have made his acquaintance. It was always men; he never saw any women. If there were women in Nombre de Dios they were kept indoors, as was the Spanish custom in the Old World.

George made no reply to these breezy salutations. He was Señor Stiff-Neck. In Spain he would not have feared for his Spanish, but here in America there might be local expressions, an ignorance of which would set him apart. Besides, when in Darien, he told himself, do as the dons do.

His first thought was for a wet and a wash, also some food. The town was filled with strangers, many newly arrived, and whether they had come by sea from Cartagena, by boat down the Chagres, or on foot or muleback across the Panama Trail, they would be dirty, thirsty, hungry. It was an innkeeper's night.

There were three ordinaries along the beach, and he picked the least dingy. He took a place near the middle of the table, an act of seeming sociability that his manner soon belied, for he spoke to no one save in monosyllables, though he listened assiduously. There was much to hear.

The food was hot and spicy: yams soaked in molasses; a salmagundi made up in part of eggs, liquor, nutmeg, garlic, leeks, and cinnamon; a lettuce salad; and a creamed white meat of delicate flavor somewhat resembling breast of swan, though sweeter (not until later did George learn that this was iguana, a particularly repulsive lizard). The wine, a Canary, was excellent. George ate a great deal and drank as much as he dared. He loitered over the meal, for men were coming and going all the time, and they were loquacious.

There was no fumbling for money. The shillings and pence had been cleaned out of George's purse, and now he carried reals, escudos, castellanos.

When at last he quit the ordinary all weariness had gone. He felt an exhilarating sense of destiny. His position thrilled him. He was supposed to be seeking his fortune, not just risking his neck, but he believed that he would have volunteered for this errand even if Captain Drake had not agreed to grant those two extra parts of the share-out. Undeniably it made a man feel good, in his chest and clear up and down his back, to realize that he was alone in the midst of so many enemies. How he longed to tell these cocky colonists that there was an Englishman among them, that their hold upon the New World no longer would be complete! But he walked on, picking his teeth, saying nothing.

When Drake came at dawn they would learn.

George already had gathered that the town was in a state of twitchiness, fearful of attack. But this was because of the Cimarrons, who were stronger than ever and multiplying at a high rate. They had recently thrown themselves against Nombre de Dios and came within an ace of taking it. No one would have been left alive if they had succeeded. This was the reason for the reinforcements from Panama, which as Diego had reported numbered a hundred and fifty men and officers. These were quartered with the regular garrison of eighty men in a long wooden barracks near the Panama Gate at the far end of the town from the beach. In addition, no fewer than nine royal *recuas* had arrived in Nombre de Dios within the past week, and by regulation each of these was accompanied by fifteen soldiers to protect them against the Cimarrons. Many of those soldiers might still be in town. Surely there had been private *recuas* too, such as the one George saw. And it could be assumed that every male civilian was armed.

Drake would have seventy-odd seamen.

Nombre de Dios was not hard to survey. It was a square, the sea being its northern side. The three land sides were walled, a mud wall, thick, fifteen or sixteen feet high, with no rampart but some temporary plank hoardings. Since the Cimarrons did not have boats of any kind, not even the most primitive dugout, no fear was felt for the sea side. There was no palisade. The customs house was not slitted for crossbows, nor did it show strong in itself. There was a battery of four small brass pieces, more ornamental than fierce; they were probably intended only for saluting purposes. The new battery, on the hill to the east, should be his first point of inquiry, George decided.

Half an hour later, still chewing his toothpick, he was there. Nobody had turned a head. He had gone unchallenged at the east gate.

He saw right away that Drake would not have to send a squad to spike these guns, six iron eleven-pounders, for they had not been mounted on their trunnions. There was a small but strong magazine, and a long rack of ball, guarded like the guns themselves by a lugubrious pikeman. Nobody else was around.

George divined that the task of mounting these guns had been postponed in favor of erecting the hoardings on the wall, attack from one of the land sides being thought the immediate threat. Or again, it could be that the machines needed for mounting the pieces were being used on the beach for loading treasure. Whatever the reason, many hours of work must be done before these cannons could boom.

The pikeman looked hopefully at George, though he did not venture to speak first. George nodded affably, Señor Stiff-Neck forgotten.

"Get lonely, lad?"

"Now, that it does, sir. There's times I all but wish somebody would storm the town. But—not them Cimarrons!"

"Nasty fighters, are they?" George asked, adding: "I'm new here."

"Oh, terrible fighters! The saints only know what we'll do about 'em if they ever get guns. It's bad enough when they're only using sticks and stones and their bare hands."

George, bemused, looked down over the town and bay, toys from here, bright figures on the shore, the high-castled ships, the sloops with their masts waving, the pert yellow-and-pink houses. He smiled.

"Who else but the Cimarrons are likely to strike?"

"Well, there're the French, sir. They might, some say. They're pirates, you know. Hug-o-nots. They're heretics, aye, but at least they're *men*."

"The English?"

"What English, sir?"

"Well, there *are* English, aren't there?"

"Eh, I suppose so. But they'd stay home. They'd never come this far. They'd be afeared to. Ha-ha. Imagine the English here!"

"Ha-ha," muttered George Fitzwilliam. "Well, it's been a pleasant chat. *Hasta la vista, amigo.*"

"May the saints walk with you, sir."

George drifted back to the town, still unaccosted. His problem was not how to get the information Captain Drake sought—that would be absurdly easy—but how to get it without showing too busy or, contrariwise, too casual.

First he walked all over the town, fixing it in his mind. This was not difficult. Few of the streets were of any importance from a military point of view. The broadest—Avenida de la Something-or-Other—bisected Nombre de Dios neatly, running up a slight slope from the middle of the beach, the place where the brass pieces were, to the plaza, which was in almost the exact center of town. Beyond that, in a somewhat less wide form, it continued to the Panama Gate. The soldiers, stationed near the gate, would come down that avenue. Drake and his men would ascend it. Yes.

The treasure was stored in two buildings: the governor's palace, a low stone structure about seventy-five feet long, which made up the east side of the plaza; and the cabildo, a much stronger-looking pile about halfway down the Avenida, between the plaza and the customs house. Each of these buildings was full. Each was well guarded.

The only thing George was unable to learn—for he feared to probe too far—was which one contained the better part of the treasure and which the overflow.

His inspection over, George found himself faced with a predicament nobody had anticipated. What would he do with himself while waiting?

It was about half past four. Drake and the Devonshire men were not due for twelve hours.

He was tired. Though he walked a razor's edge, and with the lightnings playing about his feet, he could not help but fetch a yawn. His heart beat fast, yet he could hardly keep his eyes open.

It was in this condition that he started to look for a place to sleep. In less than an hour he knew that he would not find it. Not even a bed shared with two or three others was available. Not even two chairs pushed together, or the top of a table. Nombre de Dios was crammed. He would be obliged to stay out-of-doors.

This would not have unsettled him—most of the buildings were arcaded, so he would have protection against rain—but for one thing. What about his clothes? Aunt Jane's bounty had been well used. For all the mud and spiked creepers of the jungle, for all his sweat, and the days at sea, days of salt air and sun, George Fitzwilliam still was the most richly dressed man in the streets of Nombre de Dios. It would never do for such a one to sleep under an arcade, or on the beach.

Hungry again, he went into a tavern and ate a large supper, washing this down with wine. He bought there a small leather bottle of rum, a spirituous drink made from sugar cane. He did not like rum, but it had a stronger smell than wine, and George thought that if interrogated he could feign stupor.

He lingered as long as he dared. Then he roamed the streets for a little while, until he saw that he was alone.

There were many places to sleep if he didn't mind stone, something not likely to disconcert an old prisoner. He should think of two things: where he would be most useful when the alarm was sounded and where he would be the least conspicuous meanwhile.

The waterfront near the brass cannons would be the nearest spot, and it might prove—what with the sand—the least adamantine. On the other hand, the plaza probably would be crowded with such as him—though it was not likely that any of the others would be wearing such silk. And the plaza, after all, was not far from the beach, and the way was downhill. He chose the plaza.

As he had expected, there were others there, already asleep. Their snoring was loud in the dimness of the arcades, and they were curled up sideways on sleazy blankets, their sombreros over their faces.

George picked a secluded spot, sat down, and leaned back against the wall.

He purposely sat that way so that he wouldn't fall asleep.

It did no good.

Two men were shaking him, and he knew instantly, even before he opened his gummy eyes, that it was not dawn. Yet he knew he had been sleeping for a long while. He was very stiff.

He mumbled something, feeling for his purse. The coins still were there. These men weren't petty thieves. Groggy, George lifted his head.

They were soldiers.

"You must come with us, señor," one of them said.

He waggled his head. He managed a hiccup, and sank back.

But they were persistent. They shook him again.

"Señor, the captain of the guard—"

From what he had seen of the moon George reckoned that the time was at least two hours short of sunrise. Much could happen in two hours. If he wasn't down there on the beach when the Devonshire boys came tumbling ashore, how would they know that they didn't have to smash the east gate and climb the hill to the dismounted eleven-pounders? How would they know where the treasure was?

"Señor, it isn't right that you should—"

And if the raid was made without him, he would be left in captivity, sure to meet an investigation. It was not pleasant to think what might be done to him then.

He shook his head again. When in doubt, be haughty.

"Go away."

They started to lift him to his feet. He got up, but he pushed the soldiers off.

"*Pudendos,*" he screamed. "*Puta madres!*"

In the darkness somebody giggled.

A coin? A handful of coins? But since these men had not already robbed him they could be believed to be honest guardsmen. There *were* such things. His luck! He straightened his ruff, snorting.

"Señor, the captain of the—"

"*Mierda!*"

George drew.

They could have encircled him, one on each side. They could have yelled. But they paused, irresolute.

Then from the beach at the bottom of the Avenida came a shout.

"*Fitzwilliam! Where are you?*"

George smiled at the two soldiers, for whom he felt sorry. Sleepers were sitting up. Somebody came running from the direction of the customs house, his voice a shattering screech.

"*Piratas! Los piratas!*"

George moved his point coaxingly back and forth.

"You would fight?" he asked.

The sword was long.

"*Piratas!*"

The soldiers did a sensible thing. They turned and ran, back toward the Panama Gate.

And George ran the other way, down the hill to the customs house.

20

A Few Feet Away

Halfway down the slope he met the watchman running up, a swagbellied stumpy man, rufous of countenance, who kept yelling *"Los piratas!"* The watchman stopped, his eyes bugging out, when George lifted his sword. His lips moved as he muttered a prayer; he thought he was about to die.

George hit him only with the flat, over the left ear, a blow that sent the man spinning. Without any pause, George ran on.

But the damage had been done. Heads were popping up at windows. Back by the Panama Gate where the two soldiers had given the alarm, a drum rolled, trumpets blared.

In the light of a leprous moon intermittently besmogged by clouds, the men on the beach were a motley lot, hissing in whispers as they toiled. They were making boats fast, resetting their helmets, passing out arms, or spiking the touchholes of the brass saluting pieces, while others, grasping mauls, were knocking away the supports of the platform on which those pieces had been emplaced.

Breathless, unable to shout but seeking the admiral, George running down the slope forgot that his sword was naked in his hand, forgot too the Spanish apparel. He was astounded when two men leapt out of the shadows, their swords and targets high.

He dropped to one knee, leaning backward, and parried the first stroke, but with no time for a riposte. The second man, stooping, he touched on the kneecap, producing a squeal of pain.

"Ye fools!" he cried.

"Master Fitzwilliam!"

They were John Oxenham, an adventurer, and stout Tom Moone, the company's carpenter. They were in agony over their mistake, though they could scarcely be blamed. George had appeared so suddenly, so swiftly, in his Spanish clothes, with his sword . . .

"No matter now! Where's the admiral?"

[115]

Suddenly Drake was with them, asking questions. George gasped out his report in a few words. He told Drake that he could forget that battery of eleven-pounders. The treasure was in two buildings, but the one on the plaza should be broached first, since whoever held the plaza held the town, and the man who struck from the sea would be covering his own line of retreat. This latter point was important, as they both knew. The raid would depend for its success largely upon surprise, confusion, speed. The loot would be heavy.

"But, 'tis not dawn!"

"I started 'em early, Fitzwilliam. They twitched. There was no more to do while we lay behind that island out there, and they fell to fretting about the Spaniards. So I declared it was dawn, and we moved."

"Thank Christ you did!"

"Fitzwilliam, watch your language! I'll have no profanity in my command!"

There was no time for further reprimand. The admiral did not bustle, and though he was giving orders in a swift stream he seldom raised his voice.

"Keep to me," he told George. "We'll be making all the clamor we can, and it might be hard to talk."

The party had been broken into two groups, about equal in numbers, each containing a drummer and a trumpeter, boys. One group was in charge of the admiral, the other of his brother John, captain of the *Swan*.

Some men already were armed. Weapons were being passed to others. These were pikes and fire pikes, swords and targets, partisans, longbows, even some muskets and calivers. George's heart sank when he saw them, so inferior to the Spanish arms. Longbows! Why did England's armies drag?

The Devonshire boys were not atwitter, dancing on their toes; nor yet were they making last-minute practical preparations, as soldiers should. They were nervous. They were even frightened.

It was no way in which to leap into a lion's mouth.

Drake gave these feelings little chance to ferment. "When trouble threatens, keep the boys busy," was an old skipper's adage; and the admiral, with some reason, seemed to think that it would work on land as well.

"We'll storm the square from two directions. I'd make it three, if I could spare the men. Now how—"

George was ready.

"Along the beach until the second tavern. It has the sign of a pig before it," he told John Oxenham, who was to share command of the flanking group with the admiral's brother. "Turn left just past that. It's a wide street, like this one, and it goes up. Four-five hundred yards you come to a church on the right. Turn *left* there."

"Aye."

"That's well, off with ye," cried Francis Drake. "Trumpeter, drummer, strike up. And you others, all of you, *cheer, sing.* I don't care what it is, but make a noise. Now—come along."

He started up the slope at a trot, George behind him.

From the questions called by residents who were barricading their windows, George could deduce that, despite the "piratas" cry, most of them believed that the town was being assailed by Cimarrons. Nobody appeared in the street itself. The visitors didn't see a soul until they burst into the plaza, on the far side of which the Spanish soldiery was lined up to meet them.

Then there was an instant that appeared to last a year.

George could not help but admire the spirit of men who in the middle of the night could tumble out of their bunks and into their uniforms, gather their gear in perfect condition, array themselves as neatly as though on parade, and await an unknown enemy—all in a matter of minutes. Most of them were arquebusiers, with a few pikemen to protect them after misfires. Their weapons were supported, and obviously loaded, an elaborate process that must somehow have been done on the run between barracks and the plaza. Their matches were lit, the serpentines cocked.

This was the Spanish infantry, the best in the world.

Impassive, they waited.

There was an order. Then came the volley, one great roar, a terrible explosion that reddened the square. Chips of stone flew, chunks of plaster dribbled down to the pavement. The trumpeter, who had been standing alongside Drake after they had stopped at the entrance of the plaza, went right over backward, a Catherine wheel. Drake—as though some powerful person had pushed him in the chest—was slammed back against George, who in turn was pushed against a wall.

"You're hit!"

"Sh-sh! I'm all right. *Bows!*"

Many were fired. Some Spaniards fell. But this was not Agincourt, not Crécy. The arquebusiers started to reload, while pikemen stepped forward to protect them.

"*Pikes!*"

They got there in time to prevent a reloading, a second volley. The arquebusiers were obliged to fall back, carrying their equipment. The Spanish pikemen, though outnumbered now, clearly were prepared to stand—until they heard the drum and trumpet together with the shouts of men from the west, their left. Then their officer, not knowing how many invaders he had to contend with, wisely ordered his pikemen to fall back. This they did in perfect order, still covering the arquebusiers.

Drake asked: "Which is it?"

George pointed to the governor's house.

From somewhere a battering-ram was produced. It was a thirty-foot trunk of chestnut, each side studded with spikes of ash. It had not been built here. It had been brought. Even before he left England, Francis Drake was preparing to break down treasure-house doors.

The men who had hauled this ram up the slope were too winded to swing it at first, but Oxenham's party now burst into the plaza, and there were plenty of volunteers. George himself, forgetting his heritage, took a spike. So did Francis Drake, just before him.

"Better let me look at that leg, sir," George said.

"Sh-sh-sh!"

Thunk the thing went. *Thunk . . . Thunk . . .*

The door fell.

They poured inside. The first of them, though he was limping badly, was Francis Drake.

"The cellars," George called.

There was another door, but their shoulders took care of that. Then they stormed into the cellar.

It was only one room, albeit an enormous one, perhaps seventy-five to eighty feet long, fifteen feet wide, twelve feet high. And it was filled almost to the ceiling, almost to the last square inch of floor space, with one pile of crisscrossed metal bars.

The ingots flared like white fire in the light of the torches. Hundreds of tons. An emperor's ransom.

"Silver," cried the admiral in a tone of disgust. "Leave it here. Too heavy. Fitzwilliam, where's that other building?"

Amazingly, he was obeyed. Not one of them ever had seen anything like the heaped fortune in the cellar of the governor's house at Nombre de Dios, and nobody but Francis Drake ever could have dreamed of such a mass. Yet they turned their backs upon it.

There was no further fighting in the plaza; and the fallen Spaniards, four in number, already had been stripped, while friends were carrying the trumpeter's body down the slope to the boats. Still no face appeared at a window. The Devonshire boys might have had the town to themselves.

But they knew better. Eyes were watching them, mouths reporting their arrangement to a rally of regulars by the Panama Gate. Soon the Spaniards would know the weakness of this invading force and would stamp it out like a cockroach.

Keep the boys busy. The admiral unhesitatingly commanded that the ram be taken halfway down the slope to the cabildo, the front door of which should be smashed. Meanwhile he told off a rear guard to wait in the plaza, with orders not to battle but to return fire only when fired upon and then fall away.

Drake stood leaning against a wall of the governor's house, nursing his wound, but his voice was clear and sure, his eyes flashed, his very whiskers appeared to bristle. The man was not playacting. He *believed*. The Lord had so ordained it.

But when Drake walked off it was with a wrenching limp, and George, who followed close behind him, noticed that blood pumped out of his left boot at each step.

The cabildo was a tougher nut to crack than the governor's house. Its walls were thick, its oak door triply bolted with iron. Moreover, it was more difficult to swing the ram. Unlike the plaza, which was level and floored with flagstone, the Avenida was paved only with jagged stones. The footing was treacherous. Because of the slope, the men on one side of the ram were higher than those on the other. Worse, they had barely started to hit when the heavens, as though at a signal, opened up. None of the boys from Devonshire had known such a rainstorm. It was a cloudburst. It came down in sheets, pounding them, all but forcing them to their knees. Lightning flared and thunder banged, shuddering the town.

Francis Drake sloshed among his men, screaming encouragement.

It did little good to reason that this rain meant wetted matches on both sides. Not a musket, caliver, or arquebus could be fired now. But man for man, pike for pike, sword for sword, the Spaniards were greater; and as time passed, their organization was improving. Soon it would be light.

Men came running down the street from the plaza, yelling that the Spaniards had returned in overwhelming numbers. They were lost to decency, those deserters. George, Oxenham, John Drake, a few others, tried to stop them or even to drive them back with the flat of the sword. It was no use. In that torrential rain they slipped past, down to the shore to the boats.

Then the men who held the ram dropped it.

Drake shook his fists at them, and even above the thunder his voice could be heard.

"I bring ye halfway across the world! I bring ye within a few feet of the heaped-up treasures of America! And you—you—"

He pitched forward on his face and was still.

The Spaniards gave them a farewell salute, some time after they'd pushed out into the bay, from one of the small brass cannons they had managed to remount, but whether this was done as a chivalrous gesture or in derision or merely as a token pursuit was never known.

The rain had ceased. The sky to the east was streaked with dawn.

Many of the men rowing back were worried about the admiral, and tender after tender approached the moses boat of the *Pascha,* in the sternsheets of which sat George Fitzwilliam with the admiral's head in his lap.

"Is he— Is he dead?"

"He's not dead," George would reply, looking down at the taut small red face. "He'll never die, this man."

21

This Was the Blackest Time

Piracy was a young man's game. The admiral himself, at twenty-eight, was the oldest member of his band, many of which were in their teens. Their powers of recovery were prodigious. In truth they had not been much hurt of body—the trumpeter killed, Francis Drake with a nasty wound in the groin, Tom Moone's kneecap, an assortment of bruises and flesh cuts—and the damage was largely in confidence, in morale. They'd been beaten, and they knew it. They had quaked and quavered and had run. Now their chance was past. It was known that they were off the coast of Darien, and every post would be warned, every ship's master. They had not pressed their boldness, and they might as well go home and admit it.

For all that, the excitement of the unforgettable morning, the weather, the fresh sea breeze where they lay at anchor in the lee of a little island bunched with clean-smelling pines, and perhaps most of all the fish they caught, the fruit they picked, the fresh water they drew, combined to make them talkative again. But they would fall silent whenever they chanced to glance at the door of the cabin where

Francis Drake lay, for they dreaded the time when he would come forth to flay them.

Yet the commander-in-chief, as his secretary already knew, was not disgusted with their performance at Nombre de Dios.

"Fighting comes natural to some men, I suppose, but most of 'em have to learn. Soldiers are taught, but nobody ever expected sailors to fight. They're just laborers. They're supposed to take the real fighters, the soldiers, from one place to another—that's all."

"Well, I'll not huck with that. Now, your bandage—"

"Let be. 'Tis good enough. I tell ye, Fitzwilliam, they will show up all right, those lads out there, once they come to know that a don's mortal."

"They behaved well enough that night. The dons, I mean."

"They did. They have courage, and equipment, and good training. But we have—God."

"Um-m-m."

"D'ye doubt it, Fitzwilliam?"

"Certainly not. But even with God's help we couldn't get that treasure back here now. It's on the way to Spain."

"There'll be another along in half a year."

"You'd come back, sir?"

"No, I wouldn't be able to raise the money. No, we're going to stay here."

"For *six months?*"

"Longer, if need be. We'll not go home until the voyage has been made."

"But—*six months!* What will we do all that time?"

"Well, to start I thought we might attack Cartagena."

It was the capital of the Spanish Main, the strongest city in the New World, and George did not take this announcement seriously, supposing as he did that it was intended only for circulation among the men for purposes of enheartenment. Yet a few days later, when Drake was able to hobble about, they made a course for Cartagena.

To storm such a place with the force they had would have been suicide, but they did pounce upon one unsuspecting vessel loaded with supplies and guarded only by a single aged watchman who told them that all the others had gone ashore to fight about a woman. The next day, despite all the fury from the shore, they cut out a larger ship even more richly stocked. They tacked all that day just out of gunshot, easily fighting off attempts of small craft to board them. They took two coasters putting in from Nombre de Dios; and one of these bore official dispatches informing the governor-general at Cartagena that the pirate El Draque was loose somewhere along the coast. Alas, the poor governor knew it well!

They withdrew, on their own terms, with several well-found vessels, a large number of prisoners, all of them willing to talk, and vast supplies of food and gunpowder. It was not a history-making exploit, but it stimulated them. They had cocked a snook at the king of Spain, they'd snapped their fingers under his very nose, and they felt good when they sailed away, singing.

"You watch them next time," said Francis Drake. "It'll be another case of the sword of the Lord and of Gideon."

"Has it occurred to you, sir," George asked slowly, "that what we have just done was an act of war?"

"I'll take the responsibility for that. If you had any qualms about the justice of our cause you shouldn't have come."

"I was given no choice."

"And I," he said bitterly, "was given no choice about taking you."

"I wonder how the lawyers would handle it," George mused. "Certainly you have not acted as a *hostis humani generis,* nor yet with *animo furandi.*"

Himself unlearned, Drake always was rasped when anybody quoted Latin. He thought it was done to shame him.

"Spain is our natural enemy!"

"Yet England has not officially declared war on her. Or at least, not at the time we sailed."

For the months previous to their sailing, George, although cooped aboard the *Pascha* and not even allowed on deck except after dark, had been kept informed of political events in London. John Hawkins had seen to that. George knew about the duke of Norfolk's trial and conviction and knew too that the queen hesitated to sign the death warrant of her most exalted subject. He knew that Don Gerau de Spies had been called before the privy council, told that his treasonous connection with Mary Stuart would no longer be tolerated, and ordered to leave the kingdom forthwith. He knew that both houses of Parliament as well as the whole convocation of bishops had petitioned Elizabeth to have Mary Stuart executed. He knew that Alva's atrocities in the Low Countries had brought hatred of the don to a new pitch of intensity so that volunteers were pouring into Holland and Zealand to fight for the rebels, even without pay. He knew too that Spanish soldiery in Ireland had done anything but increase Whitehall's love for Madrid. And then, just a few days before the often postponed sailing itself, Queen Elizabeth at last made up her mind and signed her name, so that on a rainy morning on Tower Hill the duke of Norfolk's head rolled. All the same, as George had just pointed out, there had been no actual declaration of war.

"Spain is papistical!"

"So is France. So are all of the Italian states and most of the ones in Germany. We can't fight the whole world."

"Fitzwilliam, you split hairs."

"An old academic custom."

"I was wronged, I appealed to my government for redress, and redress was not forthcoming. By the law of nations, that gives me the right to collect as best I can."

"Provided your monarch has assented. Has she?"

Drake did not answer. Not even with his own confidential secretary should a man discuss such a matter. Conceivably Drake himself didn't know. Conceivably he was taking the word of John Hawkins, Sir William Wynter, and the others who had adventured in this voyage. *They* knew!

George himself believed that the queen had been aware of the purpose of this expedition and quite possibly had invested in it under another name. But he also believed that if the political situation dictated, Elizabeth would unblushingly deny everything and make scapegoats of Drake and his men.

"Home is the place for the timid," averred Francis Drake, somewhat sententiously. "He who'd cross the sea should have a heart for anything."

Quietly: "Did I cower at Nombre de Dios?"

"Forgive me!"

The admiral did not like George any more than George liked him, but they respected one another. And Drake knew George's value.

"Only mind you this," he added. "Tickle points of law won't decide it. We'll not be adjudged pirates if this voyage is made. The only way for us to be hanged is to go back empty-handed."

They sailed along the Main for some weeks, picking up all sorts of small prizes. There was no resistance, since until this time it had never occurred to the Spaniards to arm against any outsider. The prisoners were puzzled but grateful for the good treatment. Drake never held any of them for ransom or as hostages, but put them down as soon as he conveniently could. There was nothing bloodthirsty about this corsair, who seldom even punished his own men, though he kept strict discipline. He was avaricious, but not stupidly so. He took whatever he could carry, but he did not wantonly destroy that which he could not take.

This was too good, this cruise, to last. In a few months the rains came, and a terrible time set in. Food rotted, men sickened, the beer turned sour. The dons, alive at last to their danger, stayed in harbor, save when they sallied forth in specially built galleys to raid and destroy the magazines Drake had established up and down the Darien coast.

Drake changed boats as other men might change shirts. The *Swan,* which drew too much for his purposes, was stripped and scuttled, and the *Pascha* was marked to go. He was using Spanish vessels now, small, shallow-drafted, speedy.

In addition to the magazines, Drake's men had built on the shore of Port Pheasant—their secret harbor—a blockhouse they called Fort Diego after the devoted Cimarron, who had rejoined them with a sizable following.

The Cimarrons brought word that the *flota* from Cartagena was putting in at Nombre de Dios, which meant that the treasure-laden mule trains soon would be starting across the isthmus. To strike again at Nombre de Dios would have been the height of folly. The Spanish authorities had learned their lesson, and undoubtedly that battery on the east hill had been mounted and manned. To waylay the *recuas* somewhere in the jungle in the middle of the isthmus would hardly be wise. From the nature of the terrain there, they could not hope to get many muleloads in one place, and once the alarm was out a retreat might be difficult. Besides, the authorities would be most on their guard along the jungle trails, for those were the favorite lurking places of the Cimarrons, men who cared not a whit about gold and pearls but who dearly loved to slaughter Spaniards. The boldest possible strike, and therefore the best, would be just outside of the gates of Panama itself, when the *recuas* had barely started.

Accordingly, on Shrove Tuesday, February 3 of that year 1573, the English set forth. Eighteen men out of the original seventy-three were all that were available for this back-breaking trek. The others had died of wounds or of sickness, or were left behind to protect the escape route. However, a large force of Cimarrons went with them.

Those black men had noses like panthers. Time after time when the little party was near some Spanish outpost they would literally smell out a sentry, locating him exactly. They smelled the matches of the Spanish firelocks, they explained. They could sneak up on such a man and kill him with their bare hands before he could utter a sound. They did not believe in prisoners.

For days, for weeks, Drake and his men struggled through some of the worst country in the world. They viewed the great southern ocean, the first Englishmen who ever had. They descended upon the coastal plain, the *llano,* enduring a merciless heat as they crept, sometimes for miles on their hands and knees, closer and closer to the fabled city of Panama. Then they had a stroke of bad luck. An overexcited sailor who did not wait for the signal caused their presence to be betrayed so that instead of the princely treasure that had been within their grasp they got only a few armfuls of bar silver. They retreated to the interior, to Venta Cruz at the navigable head of the Chagres, a town they stormed and took and pillaged. With negligible loot and against unspeakable hardships, they fought their way back to Port Pheasant.

This was the blackest time. The Spaniards had been alerted against them; the *recuas* would be heavily guarded. And these weary flea-bitten men, most of them shoeless now, many of them sick, could not be expected even under the leadership of Francis Drake to hang onto that pestiferous coast for another half year.

It was George who proposed that they all make the same trip he and Diego had made from the mouth of the Rio Francisco, twenty-odd miles through dense jungle, to the Panama Gate of Nombre de Dios. George argued that this was the one place where an attack upon the *recuas* would not be expected. Fairly within sight of their goal, the soldiers and the muleteers would relax their vigilance. Since it was open plain there for some distance from the cover of the jungle, they would believe that any small attacking force surely would already have been seen and routed by the now large garrison in Nombre de Dios.

"God knows I don't want to make that trip again," George said, "but if Diego will guide us I'll carry my share."

This time the bag was unbelievable: three *recuas,* all royal, one of fifty mules, two of seventy mules each. There was a fight of course, but it was quickly won. There was a counterattack, an energetic pursuit. They were forced to leave behind an estimated fifteen tons of silver, which they hid in land-crab holes and shallow brooks. But they won through, staggering under the weight of pearls and gold, rich men, every one.

The *Pascha* had a rotten bottom now and was too slow for them, so they gave her to some prisoners. They sailed home with an all-Spanish fleet, good boats, fast. They did it in twenty-three days from the Cape of Florida to Scilly, a record.

The voyage had been made.

22

I'll Never Go Away Again

The house in Kinterbury Street was solid, substantial. It knew none of the damp and rottenness of the tropics. Winds couldn't shake it, suns bleach its walls, nor rain rip away the tiles of its roof. Whatever might be their shortcomings, these "new men," when they built, built to last. The walking lion and three bezants—all appropriately yellow, the hue of gold, upon a black background—had been carved or sewn, painted or etched, into every place where room could be made for them. Otherwise the house was without ostentation, being a structure to live in.

This was August, the windows were open and George Fitzwilliam's feet were on one of the sills. He wriggled his toes—tipped back in his chair, grunting, as he had the day he returned from the Spanish prison.

No crowd surged outside. Much fuss had been made at their arrival the previous day, but none of it was official. They had not been summoned to London. No plans for a banquet were announced. They had not even been greeted by the lord mayor. Indeed, after the first burst of joy, embarrassment set in; and far from being hailed as heroes, they were being treated somewhat furtively. The crewmen had been loosed upon the town and were throwing their money away with shouts. But the admiral together with John Oxenham, Ellis Hixom, and sundry other officers and gentles, had been *sneaked* into this house in Kinterbury Street, where John Hawkins greeted them with a wry smile.

The others were made uneasy by this, but George Fitzwilliam was too happy to be home to care. He was thinking of Anne.

The share-out, held on the way back, had taken George's breath away. Even after the adventurers had been accounted for, the part that remained for the officers and men was stupendous. Because of his charge from Hawkins, and through Hawkins from certain other investors, the share-out had meant a great deal of work for George Fitzwilliam; but it was gratifying to see in his own figures, especially with those two extra shares, how rich he was.

Hawkins wiped sweat from his face, though it was not a hot day.

"So there it is," he said. "You'll hear the whole tale elsewhere. And it's grisly enough, I can tell you!"

Somebody asked: "And this happened a few months after we sailed?"

"Aye. Last August. A year ago. Matter of fact, it was St. Bartholomew's Day. That's when it *started* anyway. The duke of Guise's varlets pounced upon Coligny when he was crippled in bed and couldn't defend himself. They hacked him to pieces, threw him out of a window, and cut off his head. Gallant men!"

For all his insouciance, George shivered. He could not forget that Mary of Scotland was half a Guise.

"That *started* it, as I say. Paris went mad. So did all the rest of France, catching it like fever. Mobs coursed the streets of every city and town, killing all the Protestants they could lay hands on—and not only killing them but slashing them to pieces. Men, women, children, everything, even pet cats and dogs and birds. They say it took weeks to scrub off the blood. From the pavement, I mean," Hawkins added bitterly. "It'll never be scrubbed off history."

They were silent for a while, flabbergasted to come back from savage America and hear this tale. Why, even the Cimarrons would never have behaved like that! There was nothing so beastly, they supposed, as a "civilized" man when he went mad.

"They came pouring over by every sort of boat, poor stricken souls! England was inundated with 'em. And what they said about the butchery would make your veins freeze. Everywhere you went you saw Huguenots, still in a panic, starting at every small sound, with the memory of hell in their eyes. Ugh!"

He paused, as though to apologize for his eloquence. Hawkins was normally not an eloquent man. Again he wiped his face.

"But what has all this got to do with us?" asked Hixom, who was not quick-witted.

Hawkins looked long at him, unblinking, expressionless, like some huge owl.

" 'Tis an axiom," Hawkins made known, "that England must cling to France or Spain, one or the other, for we're too weak to stand alone. That's simple, isn't it?"

"Well, I suppose so."

"A little while ago it was France. Spain waxed too strong. France was nearer. She should be placated lest she back Mary Stuart. So nothing was too good for our friends across the Channel. The queen even hinted that she might take the French king's brother, that little hop-toad D'Alençon, for her mate. France could do no wrong—then."

He looked at George.

"That was the moment you elected to skewer a French spy."

"*I* didn't elect it. *He* did."

"No matter. That was why you had to depart. And from what Captain Drake tells me, it was a good thing for us that you did. But things have changed now, and nobody cares who killed a French agent. You need have no further worry on that score, lad. I took care of it last month. The warrant hath been quashed."

He belched thoughtfully.

"Aye, now 'tis the other way 'round," he went on. "The D'Alençon match is off, France is out of favor, we're sending men and ships and arms to help the Huguenots. Even the exigencies of politics couldn't make us stomach such a shambles as that. And Alva in the Low Countries and Philip in Spain are taking advantage of this change of course. Naturally. We don't truly fawn on them, but we do favor 'em. Now it's *Spain* that can do no wrong. And what d'ye think Spain will say about your exploits?"

This time there was a considerable silence, for even Ellis Hixom saw the point. They shifted uncomfortably—all but George, who smiled out of the window, still thinking about Anne Crofts.

"If we asked the law—"

Hawkins shook a heavy head.

"There's no legal or non-legal here. The queen's majesty must do what she can for the defense of her realm, and if that means hanging a man she knows to be innocent—or even a dozen such men—why, then she must do so."

"You really think they might make us pirates?" asked Hixom.

" 'Tis possible, yes. The least they would do to placate the Escorial, to soothe the ruffled feathers of our dear cousin Philip, the very *least* would be to strip away all the treasure you've won—and hand it back to Spain."

He rose, sighing. He had hated to tell them this. For all the beauty of the day, and the glorious success of the expedition, it was a topsy-turvy world they faced. It was a world in which any man might have a hard time making an honest living.

"The lord mayor won't send word of your return until tomorrow. He's promised me that. And the messenger will lag. But—there could be other messengers, faster ones. I think that within a few days somebody will be riding here from London, and your presence will be demanded in an order we can't ignore. I'd suggest a disappearance. Things were turned upside-down while you struggled on the far side of the sea. In another year or so, if you can stay hidden that long, they may be reversed all over again. And then you could come back."

Francis Drake nodded soberly. He had worked and mucked, saved and slaved, and fought with fury for more than a year and a half, taking a tremendous gamble. And now that he'd won, he had lost. Because of something agreed upon over a conference table he was to be treated henceforth as a criminal. If he wished to keep his loot, he must fly. He must hide.

"The Lord's will be done," he muttered. "I'm to Ireland. It's a place for kites, not hawks. But nobody asks questions there."

"A good plan, Frank. And—you others?"

"The Low Countries for me," Hixom said promptly. "No matter what they might say at Whitehall there's always room for a man who is willing to fight. And somehow I've got to be like those blacks we marched with: I've got to enjoy killing Spaniards."

"For me, America again," John Oxenham said. "It'll be hard to raise the money, since now it turns out that we are all thieves. But I'll do it somehow."

"They'll hang you if they nab you," Drake warned.

"I'd rather be hanged by a foreigner than by my own countrymen."

George rose, smoothing back his doublet. Plymouth was no Madrid, but in the circumstances he had done well for himself with his new riches. He wore lugged boots, purple silk hose, an oyster-colored taffeta doublet trimmed with galloon and crystal buttons, a high-cocked black velvet bonnet with an ostrich plume. The bonnet was French, which assumedly would be out of fashion now, but he fancied it all the same. He drew a velvet rose-colored mandilion across his shoulders, and lifted a gold-filigreed pomander to his nose.

"And you, Fitzwilliam? Holland?"

"America again?"

"Ireland with me?"

George shook his head.

"I'm making for Northampton," he said.

Two days later, after riding hard, and no longer affecting foppish airs, George clasped Anne Crofts in his arms.

"My chuck, it's been so long!"

"George!"

"I'll never go away again," he said.

And over her shoulder a moment later, he grinned at Sir John Crofts who, weeping, watched them.

"These clothes I bought myself, sir," George said.

They were married that afternoon in the Church of St. Basil of

Stornaway, Rugby Town. Anne was ravishing in a gown of white-and-marigold sarsenet all trimmed with long black bugles and topped by a wide supportassed ruff; and she carried a lace fan too, a city touch. All this she had produced seemingly from nowhere, yet it fitted her.

"I knew you would come back," she said simply. "You promised me."

It was not so much the gown itself as the fact of her frankness about it that startled George Fitzwilliam.

"Oh, I'm shameless," she said, then hung her head, blushing.

The very next day George rode over to Weddell Lodge to see about buying some land.

23

You Never Know Your Wife

He had believed that he knew Anne as well as anybody on this earth. As children, wading in brooks, climbing trees, popping the popinjay, playing wild-mare or last-in-Hell or hoodman-blind, at Milton as well as here at Okeland, they had made no try to conceal or discolor their fondness for one another. They were remote cousins, and as such were permitted an intimacy that abroad or even in urban England would have been deemed iniquitous. For some years now they had been aware of one another's physical attractions. Their kisses were fiery, their trembling not that of embarrassment, and if it had not been for George's long absence in the Americas and in Spain doubtless they would have been in bed together before this, since George had been eager to marry her not only because he longed for an ordered and more quiet life but also because he wanted her body. Yet, knowing her so well, he had not supposed that marriage itself would bring many surprises. It did.

Anne Crofts had been one person. The wife of George Fitzwilliam was another.

Disconcerted, he yet was not dismayed; the changes weren't basic. If undeniably there was a certain officiousness about Anne's manner in the house and garden, after dark she had slipped none of her ardor. Aunt Helen and Aunt Sylvia—long before made patient by circumstances—and a somewhat bewildered Sir John, were the principal sufferers from the new forwardness. George himself would be absent from the house most of the daylight hours, traveling to Rugby or to Northampton in search of fodder or supplies, or to Weddell Lodge in search of fellowship, or else riding around the land he had bought, supervising its drainage and its enclosure.

Anne's chief demands were windows and finery. Neither, he supposed, should have startled him. Everybody wanted windows today; and if she was a shade peremptory in the way she ordered them put in, and if she hired workers without first consulting either her father or her husband, who would have to pay them, it was a fault easily forgiven.

The clothes she had always craved. Nothing could be more natural. She had been cooped up here for many years, far from a city, many miles from the court. A few times when the queen was on a progress in the summer, the great and glittering procession had passed through part of Northamptonshire, but Anne herself had never been presented and, worse, had never been vouchsafed a chance to note the clothes and bijouterie of those who were. Sir John was no cheese-parer, but neither was he wealthy. What peacock plumes Anne could get before her marriage she'd made fullest use of. More than once George recalled to mind the time he'd dined here on his first visit to Sheffield and the ravishing blue and yellow costume she wore, snatching the breath out of him. On that occasion he had brought her from London a bright red silk stomacher, in which she gloried.

The Plymouth shops were by no means so well stocked as those of London, and what they had in the way of expensive clothing for women was largely Spanish—being in fact the loot of pirates, whether French, Dutch, or local—and therefore dull. *Male* Spanish attire tended to brightness, and George had done himself reasonably well along those lines before his departure for Okeland. George had at the same time bought so many ruffs and rabatines, kirtles and half-kirtles, bolts of velvet and lengths of reticella lace, that he found it necessary to buy an ass upon which to load them. Though some of these articles were for Sir John and the two maiden aunts, most, understandably, he gave to Anne. He was astonished not by her delight, which he'd expected, but by the gravity and continuing joy with which she treated them. It sometimes seemed as though these objects had become not a mere addition to her wardrobe but veritably a career in themselves. Though hers was a busy life as mistress of Okeland, still she found many hours to spend making gowns and petticoats and capes—or directing her aunts and tiring-women as *they* made them—

and trimming them, altering them, most of all putting them on and taking them off. She was not flippant about this, nor even girlish. She showed none of the affectations of a flirt. She didn't pirouette; she did not make mock curtsies, or simper, or smirk; and though sometimes she would solemnly climb and then descend the staircase, studying the hang of the material on either side as she did so, or sweep back and forth across the garden, she could never be said to *strut*.

When by chance a stuffs pedlar did find his way to Okeland—there were those who, greatly daring, specialized in off-highway routes—Anne would hold him up half the day, haggling. And she'd buy without any preliminary conference with her husband, only demanding of him the price when that had been agreed upon.

"Thou must think I'm made of money," he'd grumble, but he always paid.

In truth, from the beginning he began to worry about gold, though he made no mention of this. Terence Weddell had been more than fair when he sold the land, which surely was worth what George paid for it, but George, who had spent much on clothes in Plymouth, now that he was out in the country, striving to improve the manor house and farm alike, was appalled at the prices of things. Sugar twenty shillings a pound! Salt three bushels for sixpence! Beer eighteen shillings a hogshead! Laborers one and three a day! He had been told that this was yet another reason why Spain must be restrained in the New World. The sea of gold and silver that at little cost to herself she pumped out of America and into Europe to support her wars was like the pit Abaddon guards, having no bottom. No other nation possessed anything like such a treasury. So, prices went up. And up.

George assumed that this was true, and that it made sense. He had always previously been a part of some large household, where a duly appointed official handled the purse, and as long as you didn't steal you had no reason to trouble yourself about money. It was different at Okeland.

Anne suddenly had become concerned about her complexion, an excellent one, and the preparations she bought—ceruse, madder, ocher, rose water, cherry water, brazil, cochineal—were costly. George had never seen so many bottles, jugs, jars. Anne did not dye her hair—George would not have permitted it—but she spent hours goffering and brushing it.

Inevitably the question came:

"Why can't we go to London for a visit?"

"What for?"

"To see the city. I haven't been there since I was a chick."

"Thou'lt always be a chick to me."

"Go to! What's London like now?"

"Just the same. Dirtier, that's all. Noisier."

"And John Hawkins hath a house there too? We could put up in it. Thou'rt still his man, I suppose?"

"Well . . ."

The truth is, George didn't know. Nobody knew. Progress was a desirable thing, no doubt, but there were times when a man could not help sighing for the days he had never known, the feudal days when everybody was sure of his own place no matter how lowly, no matter how high. Was George still the servant of John Hawkins? There had been no contract, not even a verbal agreement. Certainly George, though not of nature sympathetic with this merchant, must forever feel *morally* obligated to him. More, there were moments as George counted his money and cast up his accounts, shaking his head, when he wondered whether he had done the right thing, from a worldly point of view, by moving to the country. Being away from a base gave one a wobbly feeling, even a brush of nausea.

"We could go to court," Anne pursued.

"The court moves around—Nonesuch, Hampton, Windsor, Whitehall, Greenwich."

"We could go after it. Thy friend Lord Burghley could present me to the queen."

It was not like Anne to natter like this. She never reveled in clack. Her persistence this night was unsettling.

"My friend Lord Burghley," George ventured, "is a very busy man."

He swiveled his eyes toward her, where she lay. The arrowslit had been widened and paned by her orders, and another window had been built into the east wall, so that their chamber was well sprinkled with starshine. Anne looked lovely. On her back, she had her hands clasped behind her head and was gazing in thought at a ceiling she could scarcely see.

For no reason, and naughtily, George tried to imagine what Aunt Sylvia would look like in that position. It was not kind. He'd encountered Aunt Sylvia in the garden only that afternoon and had paused politely to chat and admire her needlework. He scarcely knew the small dry quick-cackling woman, there being times when he could not with confidence distinguish her from her quick-cackling dry small sister, Helen.

"Tell me, why hast thou never married?" he had asked Sylvia Crofts.

She might have been expected to slap his face, or to snub him, or burst into tears. She did none of these things, only went on stitching, her bone-white fingers agile.

"Because my father could not raise a dowry," she had replied. "And of course I wouldn't mate below my station."

"Of course. I'll warrant thou hadst many an offer?"

"I had—some."

"And thou really wanted to?"

She had looked up suddenly, smiling at him. (She must have been beautiful as a girl, he thought.)

"Doesn't every woman?"

"I suppose so."

"At first you're afraid. Then you get frantic. And after a while you become afraid again. But by that time it's too late anyway."

She returned to her work, and George, bumbling an apology, had gone away.

Helen and Sylvia . . . There but for the grace of God went Anne as well.

"Besides," he said to his wife, "why shouldst thou wish to meet the queen?"

"In order to look at her, of course."

"A cat can do that."

"It would mean more to me than to a cat."

"She, uh, she's not as fair as they say. That's a sort of figure of speech, about her beauty."

"I wasn't thinking about her face. I was thinking of what she'd have on."

"And besides, a presentation would cost a great deal of money."

"Well, we're rich, aren't we?"

He winced.

Anne was no babbler; she could be called laconic. At dinner, even when there were visitors, she listened well but seldom said a word beyond what etiquette called for. When George, having ridden in from the fields, would pause before dismounting to watch her fondly through one of the new windows as she plied embroidery or dipped candles or combed flax or bundled herbs with her aunts, he was put in mind of a couple of starlings, twittering with excitement, on either side of a staid, pensive swallow.

The only time Anne talked much was at night, like this.

"And money's not all," he went on cautiously.

"Thou fearest the city? But why? The indictment was killed, about that Italian."

"It was. But there are still dons in London, though the ambassador's not there. And they don't like what happened at Nombre de Dios. They say no alliance till they've been recompensed. And this at a time when the queen's majesty ogles Philip."

"Thou wert never a signer of that adventure!"

"On paper, no. In fact, yes. They know that. They know that I was awarded a lay and two extra shares beside. And if they see me they'll cause me to be nabbed, and the crown lawyers will make me disgorge every liard of it. Nay, chuck, 'tis better that I remain quiet for a while, till the wind veers to another direction."

"But—thou'rt no pirate!"

"That depends upon who points at me."

"And if thy business commands thee to—"

"Not business. Politics."

"Then I think that thy politics are stupid!"

"Don't call them *my* politics," he grumbled, and rolled over and pretended to go to sleep.

But she was whispering into the space between his shoulder blades. She was promising to talk no more—tonight.

Oh, she'd not nag! But from time to time, very casually, she would toss out some mention of "When I bow to the queen—" or "When we go to London—" She never puffed this. She simply sought to let George know that she had not forgotten.

24

Don't Go Near the Water

What really astounded George was to learn that Anne was jealous.

He knew little enough about love in its romantic aspects. Most of his adult life in England, brief enough, had been spent amid a mercantile atmosphere, where the figures written in ink were more important than those wrapped in a busk and silk and sarsenet. He had been much abroad; but his page days in the household of his aunt had been given over largely to lessons in fencing, dancing, languages, and the anfractuosities of court etiquette, while his more recent memories were bleak: the France of song he had never known, and Spain to him was no land of moonlight, balconies, a tossed rose, but rather cockroaches and wine that had gone sour.

In consequence he could have been matter-of-fact, lacking in the decorative details of courtship. He seldom penned a sonnet. He could strum a lute well enough, and dearly loved to join in any glee; but most of the ballads he knew were of a bawdy sort, to be sung around a campfire—provided that the vinegarish Captain Drake was not within earshot. Chrétien de Troyes was no more than a name to him, and he had always thought that the rhymed activities of Lancelot and Guinevere, Tristram and Iseult, Aucassin and Nicolette, were just plain silly. From what little he did know of conventional, traditional, poetical amorousness, Eleanor of Aquitaine's code and so forth, he saw that jealousy loomed in it as a large fact; yet to George jealousy could only be an emotion degrading to the one who felt it and an insult to the person who was its butt.

In ordinary circumstances it would have infuriated him to learn that his wife was jealous. But he knew that this was not a usual, earthy case. Anne did not hold in doubt her spouse's fidelity. Granted, there was another woman in her mind, one she feared, dreaded, and was fascinated by; but it was one who was unattainable, and who could not seduce, in a carnal sense, George Fitzwilliam or any man: Mary Stuart, queen of Scotland and the Isles.

Anne blanched and gasped, putting her hand over her heart, whenever she thought of the prisoner of Sheffield.

A woman could lie beside a man each night, a woman could have him in a cell, yet lose him. Anne knew this. Her instinct had told her. Familiarity breeds contempt, and the untasted will ever tease. A man might be of this world, eminently sensible, hardheaded forsooth, independent—yet a dream could lead him around by the nose. For dreams are exceedingly strong, at the same time being as hard to struggle against as smoke from a fire. There it was! Her helplessness! She could have done battle with a dame on the next estate. Against a princess locked in a tower far away she was lost.

George did not deride this reasoning. Rather, he sympathized. Though it was unfair to the Stuart, he refrained from any use of her name except sometimes in a slip of the tongue, treating Mary, by implication, as though she had been his partner in some vile affair of the past.

It made him feel mean, small.

In only one matter connected with the imprisoned queen did he refuse to give way. This was the tear-shaped ruby he carried in his left ear. He had few enough gauds, and what he had he wore only on special occasions; but the ruby was in his ear morning, noon, and night, as though he feared to take it out, as though he thought its removal even for an instant might destroy some spell. Anne did not fail to notice this, though she made no comment.

Knightly vows, as everyone knew, were holdovers, ludicrous relics, storybook nonsense. And yet, though he would never have admitted it, George had sworn to himself when he fastened the gem into place that it would remain there as long as he lived. He didn't know why. Certainly Mary Stuart had not asked or even suggested it. "Wear it sometimes and think of this poor caged bird," was all she had said.

More than once he wondered what he would say if Anne asked him to take the earring off. She never did.

Autumn over, winter in, he was at home more of the time, as they all were. Once the weather had become harsh the duties to be done were largely of a womanish nature, and Anne and the maidens were quite capable of taking care of them. Nevertheless George and Sir John did their part, if somewhat clumsily. The work was not simply supervisory, for the servants at Okeland expected their betters to toil beside them. George never before had been a member of so poor a household, and he was amused to find himself carving beechen spoons and platters, fitting and riveting the bottoms of horn mugs and plugging the leaks in jacks, plaiting osiers and reeds into baskets and weirs, sharpening scythes, shaping new ash or willow teeth for the harrows and hardening these in the fire, fashioning ox-bows, yokes, forks, racks, rack-staves. . . .

There were mornings, not many, when George waved aside these trivia and called for his horse, frankly announcing that he would ride over to Weddell Lodge for a chat with Terence.

Though he did not look upon this as a scandalization, Sir John disapproved of the visits. This was not because of their effect upon the neighbors but because of their possible effect upon his son-in-law's soul.

"The man's a papist, I tell thee!"

"He could be."

"Oh, he communicates now and then. Maybe once every third or fourth week. But he only does that to save himself the fine."

"Who can blame him? Ten golden guineas each month would be a strain on anybody's purse. And they say it will be raised."

"But I tell thee he's a papist at heart!"

George would shrug, for he could see no profit at any time in arguing about religion.

"I'm not calling on his heart," he would reply.

Surely Anne guessed who it was her husband and their neighbor would talk about. But she made no comment.

Anne might have been relieved but more likely would have been puzzled and further worried had she listened, hidden, to one of those conversations. After the first few, the name of Mary Stuart seldom was spoken. As in the larger world of which it could have been called a microcosm, at Weddell Lodge the Scottish queen was in many minds but few mouths.

In part this reticence, at least at Weddell, might have been brought about by fear of the captive's welfare, her very life forsooth, since her position was parlous. In Scotland the son she had scarcely seen, her only child still little more than a baby, had been proclaimed king, but he was a pawn in the hands of her enemies. The last stronghold to fly her flag, Edinburgh Castle, had recently fallen, thanks to English help; and what friends she had were scattered and presently impotent, without organization. France, out of favor with the English queen and torn by civil war, no longer could even bluster about the treatment of Mary Stuart. Her latest suitor, Norfolk, had been beheaded for his activities in her behalf. The Spain to which she had transferred her hopes muttered sympathetically but was too eager to placate Elizabeth and get a hands-off promise in the Netherlands to raise its voice for the imprisoned princess.

In the Scroll Tower at Sheffield, frowned upon by the hills of Hallamshire, feeding and in caressive tones talking to her pets, Mary Stuart might well fear that the world had forgotten her.

Or—the silence at the lodge could have meant conspiracy. This thought troubled George through the winter and spring, and as a drowsy summer set in. Was Terence Weddell involved in one of the plots to free Mary of Scotland? With his otherwise morbid craving for obscurity he was, beyond a tittle of doubt, a link in the secret Catholic chain that crisscrossed England. George would have deduced this even without his experience among those harried people. Was he more? Was he one of those fervent young men who had dedicated their lives and fortunes to the cause of a liberated Mary Stuart? George hoped not. For all the allure of this woman, George could see that her forced release could only mean catastrophe to England. Sheffield was a strong place, and George was sure that Lord Shrewsbury had orders to cut his prisoner's throat at the first threat of attack; but even assuming that some one of these groups of harebrained youngsters did succeed in bringing off such a feat, where would Mary be taken or sent? Certainly not back over the border. Unless she came accompanied by an English army the Scots would have her throat squeezed within half a day: the enemies she had made there simply couldn't afford to let her live, for Mary, though a kind friend, was relentless as a foe, and she had a long memory. France might take her, but only to immure her in some nunnery, loading her with empty honors and leaving her to rot without any touch of that which she still somehow clung to at Sheffield—hope. Spain was far away, and the Narrow Seas between were at all times crowded with rapacious Huguenots made mad by the remembrance of St. Bartholomew's Day, fanatical Puritans from the south of England, and the even more fanatical Dutch rebels, the Beggars of the Sea, to whom the only good Catholic was a dead Catholic.

No, any plot to rescue the beauty in the Scroll Tower could only have for its aim the seating of her upon a throne that from the papal point of view she had always been entitled to: the throne of England. That involved, necessarily, the killing of Elizabeth. It involved the invasion of the realm by some foreign force. It meant civil war—possibly, even probably, a whole series of civil wars, a semi-permanent state of strife such as had torn England from end to end in the bitter days when the Yorkists and Lancastrians grappled.

This troubled George's mind, but he made no mention of it. Neither he nor Terence Weddell ever referred to religion. When they met again, George had thanked him briefly though feelingly for the escape arrangements of two years before; that was all. Whatever his inner fervor, Terence must have seen that George Fitzwilliam was not a man whose beliefs could be swayed. There was an understanding between these two, the stronger since it had never been voiced. Several times when George came riding for a visit Terence Weddell in greeting him had hinted that the hour was not propitious; and George, sensing the presence of somebody underneath the staircase—all but *smelling* a priest—would excuse himself.

They needed one another, these two, yet they fumbled for a topic of talk. Religion was taboo. Terence had no interest in the land; and George's early eager prate of turfing, marling, denshiring, left him cold. Nor was he concerned with the problem of how to get workers from the village to tend the enclosures near the manor house, for indeed he seemed rather wishful of keeping such men away.

At last, there in the very middle of England, so far from any port, they settled upon navigation.

Had Anne overheard some of the talk at Weddell Lodge on a given afternoon, it most likely would have been about how to say a compass, how to feed the needle with a lodestone, why kennings and a rutter were treacherous in shoal water—and of course useless off soundings—and whether a Jacob's staff could be relied upon for getting the Mercator height.

Weddell loved geography but despised mariners, and except for a few Channel crossings he had never been to sea. Yet he was interested in George's New World travel and asked him questions about the action of the winds and sea currents, the nature of the strands along the Main and among the Indies, even the routine of a vessel under sail.

Once George chuckled. Of a sunny summer afternoon, following a chat, he was lolling toward the door.

"Two salts, eh? We arrange it all—a hundred miles from blue water!"

Terence—short, slight, jointy, with a birdlike jerkiness about him as he walked—waved his arms.

"Why not? *Somebody* has to study the sea. The mariners never will. They're too lazy, or too stupid, or maybe they're so busy picking weevils out of their biscuits or lice out of their hair that they can't find time to look around them. For hundreds of years they've been cruising in search of fish, and they never even noticed that there was another world just beyond the horizon. Or if they did notice it they forgot to mention it when they came home. Seamen are the most unimaginative men in all this world. They think of nobody else. They put down no observations. They keep no records."

"Most of 'em can't write."

"Most of 'em can't think, either. And yet they are in charge of protecting this isle. They are given a free hand, willy-nilly, in the task of doubling the size of the earth. Sailors! Sailors! I tell thee, Fitzwilliam, we simply can't leave the sea to such as them!"

George had paused in the doorway, and he watched a man who had just ridden up the avenue of lime trees and who was dismounting.

"You had best not say that to your visitor."

"Eh? Um-m. Who is he, d'ye suppose?"

"His name," George answered, "is Francis Drake."

25

Sailor on Horseback

Weddell Lodge was the only house George knew in which the entertaining was done in the library. Terence Weddell must have been near thirty, yet he was a bachelor, and a bachelor, moreover, of exceedingly studious tastes: a library was his natural habitat. The lodge boasted no gallery; it did have a solar, of course a screens, and a dining hall—it could hardly be called a great-hall—but the library was its hub.

Windows were fashionable; they permitted those inside to look out. But windows also permitted those outside to look in. Weddell Lodge was new, its mortar scarcely dry, and while it could have been that the windows of its library had been built high only to prevent a student's attention from wandering, as Terence averred, it could also have been to provide protection against the peering of some casual passer or some new arrival. George as a guest had been but clandestine, but it was safe to assume that his predecessors had been and his successors would be both clandestine *and* ecclesiastical.

In any event, Drake, when he was ushered into that library after George had introduced him to Terence Weddell, clearly was relieved to see the high windows.

This was not the tyrant George had known. The mouth that had been a steel trap twitched, and the eyes, once damn-you, warily moved back and forth. For all his psalm-singing background, Francis Drake, as George well knew, was inordinately fond of finery. He would not prink before his betters, nor yet before the members of his crew, but among friends or alone in his cabin he was as polychromatic as a pigeon's neck. He loved to wear a chain around his neck, a silver cabasset, a scabbard that was studded with rhinestones. Today it was not so. His doublet was the color of rust, his canions were black, his base-hose unclocked, his bonnet a steeple, and the spurs he wore on one-hued boots were iron. His very beard, longer than usual, did not flare with the old strident red, stabbing like an accusatory finger, but shrank against his chest. Here was a man who strove to seem commonplace. Now and then he would look over his shoulder; he had been more at home in the steamy jungles of Panama than he was here in the middle of his own native land.

Noting this uneasiness, Terence refrained from a frank study and talked trippingly of minor things. It was Drake himself who broke this.

"Master Weddell, it was not to discuss the weather that I came."

"Oh?"

"Fitzwilliam here will tell you that skimble-skamble's not my fare. Said I well?"

"I fear that you have me in the lurch, captain."

"Master Weddell, it is my plan to venture into far seas again, in search of—well, trade."

"So soon?" cried George.

"Oh, I'm still in disfavor, granted. That's why I travel with no staff, no retinue. That's why I ask you now, my gentles, if you will refrain from any reference to Francis Drake when you speak with neighbors—"

He looked from one to the other, and when each had silently assented, being in no way astonished by this request, he went on.

"The situation will change. And meanwhile, preparation's the watchword, eh? Why shouldn't an enterprise be making up? We may wait a month, we may wait a year or more, but whenever word does come we'll be off like an arrow from the bow."

"To where?" George asked.

Drake seemed not to have heard that question. He addressed himself to Terence.

"The money's pledged. And the vessels. All that remains is to get the right man. Master Weddell, you have translated Pigafetta's *First Circumnavigation of the Globe?*"

"Oh, yes. There's a copy right behind your head, captain, if you care to check something."

"And you are the author of *Paths Across the Ocean Sea?*"

"A small thing. Its success amazed us all. I mean to rewrite it some day, smooth it out."

"You studied at Mortlake under Dr. Dee, and you helped Humphrey Gilbert write his *Discourse to Prove a Passage by the Northwest to Cataia?*"

"Only as an adviser. Technical clarification. Sir Humphrey needs no one to teach him how to write."

"Master Weddell, will you sail with me on my new enterprise?"

"No."

"Eh?"

"Forgive the abruptness, captain, but may I remind you that you haven't even told us where you're going."

"No matter now. Probably Alexandria."

"You could cape-hop that. Anyway there must be almost as many pilots in the Mediterranean as there are ships."

" 'Tis possible we might go—elsewhere."

"Calais would be too far for me. Four times have I crossed the Channel, and I was sick as a dog each time."

"Let be! Three-quarters of my men are sick the first week out!

You'd not be called upon to work the ship, only to be as you were with Humphrey Gilbert—an adviser."

The host shook his head as he simulated regret.

"Captain, I fear that all my voyaging will be as it's been in the past, right here in this room, among these books."

"You'd have a share, just like one of the adventurers! Man, you'd make your fortune!"

"It could be that I don't care to make a fortune."

Drake had risen. The pose of humbleness was gone; the old arrogance flowed back. He was being refused.

"This is flying against God's very will!"

Terence permitted himself a tiny frown.

"Captain, you must permit me to judge of that myself."

The departure was strained. On his entrance Captain Drake had announced that he was in the shire as much to call upon George Fitzwilliam as to call upon Terence Weddell, so that it had been a case of well-met; and he declined a mug of wine in order to ride off with George, who had been about to go anyway. Terence, contrite, strove to help him mount, but Drake shook him off angrily, abruptly, like a dog shaking off water.

Drake would have done well to accept that assistance; he needed it. George, who had watched the man dismount and thought he never saw a clumsier performance, did not dare to watch the mounting. Neither, as they rode toward Okeland through the dusk, did George dare to look sideways at his companion, who dug knees into an unoffending beast and gripped the reins like a drowning man. This no doubt was the farthest Francis Drake ever had been from the sea; and to give him credit, he made no pretense of equestrian skill. Nevertheless, George was glad that they didn't pass anybody he knew.

Drake fairly quivered.

"The man's a fool! I tell you he's a fool!"

" 'Tis a privilege some claim."

A thought struck Francis Drake, and he reined.

"Maybe he didn't hear my name aright? Maybe he doesn't know who I am?"

"He knows who you are," George said.

They resumed their way, Drake seething.

Nobody who was acquainted with him could have felt amazement to learn that Francis Drake was plotting another foray. If his nation wouldn't go to war with Spain he would do so alone. Already, as a result of those *recuas* outside of Nombre de Dios, he was richer than any of his relatives or friends ever had dreamt of being—the extent of the captain's own dream was beyond estimate—yet that he might retire, settle down, cease to rove, was unthinkable. Nor would a place like Ireland, with its petty picking, hold him long. Ireland was for the buzzards; an eagle would try America.

That he risked seizure of all his loot by being in England while he was still under a cloud would not have fazed this peppery small man, who, for all his fulminations against dice and cards, was a gambler to the core. He knew that the queen's favor could not be counted upon to shine long in any one direction, the exigencies of politics and her own temperament being what they were, and like a good mariner he wished his vessel to be caulked and stocked, and all a-tauto, so that when tide and wind permitted he could pop out of port and scuttle over the horizon beyond the reach of law, giving Queen Elizabeth no chance to change her mind.

"I said that I came to see you as well, Fitzwilliam. I am sure that you'll not be the dunce your friend is."

George said nothing. He was praying that Francis Drake wouldn't fall off his horse.

"I'll have eight vessels, mayhap nine. Will you command one?"

"As a—*captain?*"

Easygoing, amiable George was stung this time. He wouldn't make a move to draw, for his companion merited no such move; but rage was like a gag in his throat.

"Why not? You'd have a sailing master assigned to you, of course. And gentlemen have captained vessels ere this."

"Will you name one?"

They had reached Okeland, and Drake worked his feet out of the stirrups, dropped the reins, grasped the pommel, and otherwise prepared to dismount.

"We will speak of this later," he said.

"We will not," said George Fitzwilliam.

They had a small supper served in the solar, for supper at Okeland customarily was not formal. The staff ate in the kitchen and was called in only for evening prayers. Anne shone in silver and blue, but the visitor paid her scant attention, concentrating on her father, whose opinion of church law he found well-bottomed.

Miffed by the talk in the lane, Francis Drake ignored his one-time secretary. Toward the close of the meal, however, he swung excitedly upon George.

"See here, Fitzwilliam, your father-in-law hath just told me that Terence Weddell is under suspicion of being a Roman Catholic."

"I have heard so," George murmured.

"You should have told me!"

"Why?"

"I'm lucky that he turned down my offer!"

Knowing the importance that this man put upon reading, erudition, George was mildly astonished.

"You think that his devotion to the Virgin Mary would cause his hand to wobble when he drew a rhumb line?"

"I think that I want no taint of antichrist upon our voyage!"

"To—Alexandria?"

"To anywhere! Nor do we need such fancy fripperies of learning. The Lord will guide us."

"A good astrolabe too," George muttered as he made bread crumbs, "wouldn't do any harm."

Whether she had trained herself to it during the long wait for a wedding or whether it was instinctual, Anne could do what so few wives can: she could refrain from asking questions. Her curiosity piqued, she would be watchful but silent. She'd get what she sought, if she got it at all, obliquely, fortuitously, in haphazard snatches. All things, she believed, or at any rate almost all things, come to her who waits long enough—and keeps her ears open. What George wanted to tell her he would tell, and when he didn't want to tell her she would learn gradually, by indirection.

You don't spur a willing horse; you don't goad a willing ass. Even in a matter so close to her heart as that of Mary Stuart she could make mumness her rule. Questions hurled at her husband might have barbs in them of which she herself knew nothing; they might set up wounds that festered, causing him to snarl and snap.

The case of the rejected admiral was different. Anne had heard of Francis Drake—who hadn't, since Nombre de Dios?—but his presence did not impress her, he being anything but her mind's picture of a hero, a patriot. His somewhat elephantine attempts at gallantry when first he met her disgusted even so secluded a woman as Anne, who, if she hadn't been to court, at least possessed the innate ease of her class. But soon, as abruptly as the turning-off of a beer tap, he had swung from her to her father in whom he saw a kindred spirit, and throughout the supper these two chattered, magpie-like, of candles and liturgy, baptism by immersion, the sinfulness of certain vestments, and the heinous custom of crawling to the altar on Easter eve to kiss the paschal lamb. The discourtesy—she saw of the guest during the meal only the back of his head and the back of his left shoulder—did not unsettle her; indeed, it was something of a relief. But Anne was quick to notice too the coolness between Francis Drake and her husband, and when they got to bed that night she asked him about this, though not immediately.

"Why did ever he seek to enlist Master Weddell, such a quiet gentle, so far from seeming a corsair?"

"He loves learning because he lacks it. Like every man who's never had Latin he sees something magical in it. He thinks that a given word only becomes potent when it is in print. Actually Terence might have helped him a little, if he plans to sail to far parts."

"Does he?"

"His secrecy would suggest it. Alexandria's ridiculous. He only said that because it was the first name that swam into his head."

"And—thee?"

"He offered me the captaincy of one of his vessels. Me—a captain!"

"I'm sure thou'dst make a very good captain, sweeting."

"I might make a good scullery boy too, once I got used to it."

After a while, as though in exploration:

"Thou hast no love for Francis Drake?"

"I hate him. And he hates me."

"Why?"

"I don't know. Some men are born that way, to be enemies—like the lion and the unicorn. Captain Drake and I shared a small space for long hot months. We fought side by side and suffered together. I've saved his life, as he has mine; and I'd do it over again, and I think so would he. Yet I hate him. I could put it rationally. I could cry down city chuffs who view the world in terms of shillings and pence—and also stolen golden ducats. I could wince when I see such an one representing this country in other lands. I could say that no man who quotes the Bible as if he had written it himself, who can't read without moving his lips, and not much even that way, and who sits so badly in saddle—no man like that's the man for me. But there is more to it, chuck."

"I'm sure there is. Drake's a good mariner?"

"I've never seen a better, and I doubt that I ever will. Oh, his is a dirty business, but he does it damn' well. He can look at what to thee or me would be nothing more than sky and water, and within seconds he can tell where the ship is, which way it's going and how fast, what the day will be like, and how much longer the voyage will last—and tell it more accurately than Terence Weddell with all his books. He knows the sea as a baby knows its mother. He might have been born there."

They were lying naked, for the night was hot, and as he said "born" he placed a hand, very gently, on Anne's belly, which was big.

"And thou'dst have him go back to sea?"

"No—no. It pains me to cede this, chuck, but sometimes it seems that perhaps over the long course, Francis Drake, for all his vulgarity, may prove to be a good thing for England."

"But you wouldn't go with him, even if he offered you a secretaryship? You prefer manure to roving?"

He had not taken away his hand. He paused, not from dearth of words for reply but in search of the best arrangement.

"I know my place," he said at last, slowly, thoughtfully, without anger if without any exhilaration either. "And my place is here."

26

Go Away, Galahad

Was farming, then, preferable to roving? George thought so. Certainly it was less monotonous. Even the months spent in Spanish cells counting cockroaches to keep madness off, in retrospect were not as dreary as the months at sea—the endless march of waves, the blazing sun, tar bubbling in the seams of the deck, timbers creaking as they had creaked last week and the week before and the week before that, the taste of salted food, and always inescapably everywhere the stink of bilge. Okeland by contrast offered something different every hour—from dawn, when the world lay sodden with dew, to sundown, when the birds fussed themselves to rest while creeping shadows sponged the slopes. The light changed, the colors changed, and the odors. Moreover, and most important, things *grew*. George watched them, bemused. For he moved about his property, as about that of Sir John Crofts, directing the work on the spot, not from the manor house, believing that the best manure is the foot of the master.

Sir John, especially after the birth of Janet, the delight of his life, was glad to leave most of the supervision to his son-in-law, though he was full of advice. Their talk at meals, Anne complained, was crops and costs, costs and crops.

Costs indeed made up a grim topic. Northamptonshire was mostly champian, and Sir John's fields had been devoted in large part to grain, very little to pasturage. After his first summer, that of 1574, George estimated that they had averaged less than eighteen bushels of wheat per acre, twenty-six of barley, thirty-three of oats and beans. With such fertile earth, with such good rainfall, this was poor. He had heard that in the Low Countries, where the farmers used not only animal but human dung, putting even nail parings and hair clippings into the earth, the yield was much better.

The price of wool, like the price of beef, was going up. Most of the land George had bought from Terence Weddell he put into pasturage. He bought some swine and even some bees, for he was mindful of the old rhyme:

> "He that hath both sheep, swine and hive,
> Sleep he, wake he, he may thrive."

Yet he didn't thrive. It would take time, he got to know. One year, two years, wouldn't be enough. Laborers were hard to get, for many of them were making for the cities of the south, where the work was regular—and easier. The hands he could hire were lazy, and they demanded a crushing wage. Things bought outside, such as clothing and glass, were expensive.

He even worked after supper, reading whilst yet there was light, or sometimes after dark, by candle—tallow candles, not wax, for wax cost too much. He was accumulating a library—in no way comparable to that at Weddell Lodge but suited to his own needs. His shelf held Fitzherbert's *Husbandry*, Thomas Tusser's *Five Hundred Good Points of Husbandry*, Reginald Scott's *A Perfect Platform for a Hop Garden*, Thomas Hill's *The Profitable Art of Gardening* and his *A Profitable Instruction of the Perfect Ordering of Bees*, as well as Heresbach's *Four Books of Husbandry*, as translated by Barnaby Googe; and he would pore over Mascall on pruning as a more romantic-minded man might pore over Ovid.

These and other authorities, he noted, exalted agricultural methods in the Low Countries. It was from Zealand or perhaps Brabant that there had come the practice, eagerly embraced by Sir John Crofts, of planting turnips out in the fields, thus providing fodder on less land than was required for hay.

George waxed curious about the Low Countries, which he had never visited, and one night he expressed a wish to go there.

"Praise be," was Anne's quick comment. "We can travel by way of London."

He frowned, though he turned away so that she could not see it. London, London! Sometimes it seemed to be all she could talk about;

and George hated the place, as he hated the court wherever it was.

Occasionally he would try to explain this feeling to Anne, but she was infatuated, not open to reason. Lately, discouraged, he had ceased to splutter.

It was unsettling to reflect that since the birth of Janet and even more since that of little George, he and his wife had been seeing less of one another than they had been wont to do before he first went to the Indies. An enlarged Okeland was no palace, but it called for constant cleaning, and they could not afford a full staff of maids. Nor did George skimp his duties outside. Conscientious, he rode forth every day and personally supervised all the labor in the fields. In consequence, he was not often with Anne. Their talks in bed at night were liable to interruption from one of the cradles. Sometimes after supper they would play maw or little primero; but neither had much stomach for cards, and dice was not proper for a lady.

The cider press was the place where they did most of their talking. There were good apples at Okeland, and George had figured that cider for the maids and the field hands came almost fifteen per cent cheaper than beer, so they made a great deal of it. In the life of the farm, responsibilities were carefully given out; but it had never been ruled whether the making of cider was by right a part of the mistress' work or a part of the master's, and since they both enjoyed it they both did it. George of course had seen to the gathering of the fruit in the first place, as Anne would see to the storage of the cider, but in the actual pressing and jugging they worked together. Though they didn't dally, these were pleasant times.

"They say an ambassador's an honest man sent abroad to lie for his country," George told her at one of these sessions. "If that's all there was to it, all right. Nobody *has* to be an ambassador. But the way things are now, practically everybody who has any connection at all with the court *has* to do at least a little lying—and maybe it's getting to be more all the time. I don't know why this is, but I don't like it."

"Truly, sweetard, thou dost not think of *thyself* as a liar?"

"Sometimes I almost do. It could sneak into a man, that habit. Sometimes I get afraid that I might be lying without even knowing it."

"Would that be lying, then?"

He had no answer to this, but turned the press and watched the juice flow, sniffing its cleanness, his ear cocked to its gurgle.

"Besides, it could be that thou'rt too harsh on the court. I'll reserve my own decision. When thou hast taken me there I'll make up my mind, when I can see for myself."

That was the way it always ended, on that note.

And that was why George sighed to himself, turning away, when Anne announced her intention of going to the Low Countries with him—by way of London.

He was by no means sure that such a visit could be arranged for himself alone, even if he could afford it. The Dutch and Flemings were in a more or less permanent state of revolt against their Spanish masters; half of their cities were besieged, while the countryside was overrun by soldiers. So Whitehall, being additionally moved by the fact that the Belgian provinces were hotbeds of English Catholic exiles, would issue no passport for travel there unless the applicant showed good cause. In such a matter it would be necessary to go to no less a person than the queen's first secretary. This was no longer Lord Burghley, "her majesty's housekeeper." There had been changes in high government. John Hawkins was treasurer of the royal navy now, in the place of his brother-in-law, Benjamin Gonson, and as a result he would be more often than ever in London. Burghley had been raised to lord treasurer of the realm. The queen's first secretary, succeeding Burghley, was Sir Francis Walsingham, about whom George knew nothing.

While he pondered this problem—should he write to Hawkins asking for his influence in getting a passport—a letter came from Walsingham himself.

It asked George, in effect ordered him, to appear before that personage "alone and unattended, and in the most inconspicuous manner that shall be convenient," for conference upon "something that appertaineth to the welfare of the realm."

What could that be? Certainly not turnips. George sensed the queen of Scots again.

The stipulation "alone and unattended . . . inconspicuous" irked him as sneaky, but at the same time it suggested that Spain was still in the ascendant at the English court, which in turn meant that Francis Drake's latest sea venture would remain motionless for the present. Also against such specific wording Anne had no recourse, although it caused her a great effort to contain her annoyance at not being permitted to accompany her husband to London.

In March of 1575, a scant week after he had received this letter, he set forth.

He called first upon Hawkins—a somewhat strained visit, since neither knew what attitude to take toward the other. Was the enterprise at Okeland to be looked upon as a diversion, a hobby? Was George still Hawkins' man? George had refused a personal appeal on the part of Hawkins' cousin Drake to take a captaincy in the forthcoming expedition, in which Hawkins, beyond all doubt, was interested. The older man was nettled by this. Nevertheless John Hawkins was helpful, telling George, if somewhat guardedly, whatever he knew about Sir Francis Walsingham.

This man, moderately wealthy, had traveled much on the Continent and was thought of as Italianate, though his religious views were puritanical and extremely stringent. He could speak half a dozen languages, and had read everything. He had no private life: he was all work, an unremitting conscience, a drive that never slowed. Undoubtedly it was about Mary Stuart that he wished to see George. Walsingham had never met Mary Stuart, but he had extreme ideas regarding her.

"He mislikes her?"

"He hates her. He calls her the bosom viper. More than any other man I know, more even than my Lord Burghley, he subscribes to that motto—how doth it go?—'Vita Mariae—uh—'"

"Vita Mariae mors Elizabethae; vita Elizabethae mors Mariae."

"That's it."

Soon afterward, having been admitted by a side door, George stood in the presence of the first secretary himself, Walsingham, the new master of all English spies.

And George shuddered.

Here was a man who might have had vinegar in his mouth instead of spit. He was lank and long, though as George saw when he rose behind the table, not actually tall; he was slabsided, angular. His mouth was an abrupt slit, without color. His cheek and brow were cretaceous, his eyes dark hollows of disapproval. Over those eyes, as if he feared that they might betray him, habitually he kept his lids half-lowered. This implied no sleepiness! Those heavy creased lids which never quivered, suggested rather an extra awareness, a hidden feline alertness. Velvet-muscled, this man was at all times ready to pounce. He was dressed in black, as though he had been a gentleman executioner. Not the least frightening thing about him was his voice. It was hollow, though neither deep nor notably loud, and was compounded of echoes, as though it came out of a cave.

Acidulous, saturnine, he could have been expected to give forth only harsh words; yet the first thing he said to George was praise.

"My Lord Burghley hath spoken highly of you. Your probity, your energy, your wit."

Astounded, George sat down. He swallowed.

[151]

"So too my lord of Shrewsbury, who writes that you have twice talked with his charge, and that she thinks right well of you."

This was an even greater jolt. At the same time, it flustered George, who felt his face go hot.

Walsingham leaned back a little, though not in relaxation. It was impossible to think of this man as ever being relaxed, as it was impossible to picture him playing tennis or riding to hounds or even, like Burghley, raising roses. He steepled his bone-thin fingers. His eyes were all but closed.

"Would you tell me about her, please, Master Fitzwilliam?"

This graveled George, who sat up straight. Never mind the nature of Mary Stuart's opinion of him! What Walsingham wanted was a catalogue of her weaknesses.

Cautiously he asked: "What is it you wish to know?"

"What sort of person is this schemer?"

"Why, very lovely to look at."

"So I've been told," Walsingham said dryly. "But what hath that to do with the policy of the queen's government toward her?"

"I should think it might have a great deal. *I* am not the first secretary, sir, but if I was I would surely take Mary Stuart's beauty into account. 'Tis worth a thousand pikemen."

"Um-m. What I seek is less sensational."

"Sir, when I met this lady I was stricken with bewilderment. I was dazzled."

Now the eyes came open, almost with a leathery rustling sound like that of a bat's wings.

"And has it affected your judgment, this bedazzlement?

George shrugged.

"So it has been with other messengers," Walsingham went on. "They come back yammering of that exquisite mouth, those soul-searching eyes. Bah! Even Burghley, who's not susceptible to Satan's wiles every day, I can tell you—even he babbles a bit when he recalls to mind her smile. This is not what I seek."

George had averted his head, not because he blushed any longer, nor yet from fear of Walsingham's gaze, but only in order to control his anger.

"Perhaps if your worship would ask specific questions—"

"Very well."

For some time then they were businesslike, and George was as informative as might be, never hesitating; but in time there came the question that all along had been inevitable, hanging over him.

"Master Fitzwilliam, you would seem to have this woman's confidence. There are not many such men we can trust. Can we trust you? If in the very name of the queen's highness you should be asked to take a message to Sheffield Castle—a message, I mean, that might bring out the murderousness that's in the prisoner—"

He paused.

George cleared his throat.

"If the queen's highness commanded, I should of course obey."

"'Tis not a matter of mere obedience," Walsingham pointed out impatiently. "*How* would you deliver that message? Would the Stuart believe it?"

"Does your worship mean a message calculated to enmesh her in some plot against the life of the queen's highness?"

"Yes."

"Concocting such a plot, falsely?"

"Why not?"

George rose. He walked back and forth a little, his left hand gripping the hilt of his sword.

"Sir," he said at last, "chivalry to some may mean only dragons and entranced maidens; it is a clumsy word nowadays—that I realize. But could not any healthy man gag at the thought of tricking a prisoner in order that she might be slain?"

"Not tricking her, sirrah! She needs none! Simply offering her a chance to hire an assassin, that's all."

"Your worship is sure?"

"I am. But then, I lack chivalry. Which may clarify my vision. These foes I fight for the safety of the queen, these papists, d'ye think that they know anything about knight-errantry, Fitzwilliam? When Lord Moray was slaughtered as he rode through Edinburgh, was it face to face or from behind a screen? And what about William of Orange? Did *he* have a chance to draw and defend himself when King Philip's creature shot him? And—God save the mark!—Coligny?"

George said nothing.

"I tell you it's their own weapon—to be taken as long as the fanatic who wields it can be promised eternal bliss. Murder the right person, a person picked by the pope, and Heaven's gates will be swung wide for you. D'ye believe that, Fitzwilliam?"

Still George was silent.

"Oh, I was in Paris the night of St. Bartholomew—and all the beastly days and nights that followed. I was her majesty's ambassador there, and I tell ye, Fitzwilliam, I saw such savagery as made me ashamed to call myself man. Every group that whooped past my windows had at least a leg to display, or a hand, usually a hacked-off head. Some of them waved chunks of skin, as brave as battle flags. They didn't only kill, they tore to pieces. The pavement was clobbered with blood. The Seine was so choked with bodies that it backed up over the embankment."

He too had risen now, and he leaned over the table, waggling a long lean schoolmasterish forefinger.

"And did their spiritual leader, their so-called Holy Father in Rome, did he reproach them for butchery? No! He *lauded* them! He struck a medal in honor of that glorious event!"

He sat down.

"And you would fight fair, Fitzwilliam, with people like that?"

"I— I am not informed on matters of dogma and high politics, your worship. I have never looked upon God as a member of any faction. And I fear I would make a poor messenger."

"Eh? No matter. We have no call for your services now anyway. You may go."

But as George started away: "Nay, a moment!"

He shuffled some papers, and lifted a letter.

"Near you in Northampton there lives a squire named Weddell?"

"Aye."

"We've been told that he too takes orders from the Vatican. Is that true?"

"I have heard it said so. I don't know for sure."

"You mean you won't tell?"

"I mean I don't know. I only know what neighbors say."

Walsingham turned aside. The tops of his cheeks had been touched with hectic red, but now they faded. His eyes had flared, but now he half-closed them, banking their fire.

"No matter," he said again. "You may go."

"A favor first, your worship?"

"What is it?"

"I'd visit the Low Countries."

"Why?"

"To study their methods of growing corn."

"Umph! To study at Douai, like enough!"

"Are you implying that—?"

"I'm implying nothing, save that I don't like Galahads. Your petition's denied. No passport. And now goodbye, Master Fitzwilliam. The door is right behind you."

27

Touch Not My Friend

The sun rose and the sun set, and if the days didn't march to music neither did they drag. There was always work to be done. One from the great world, visiting this part of Northampton, might have found it dull; but nobody at Okeland did.

They were not idle. Only a year after little George, Elizabeth was born. (George at first had thought to name her Mary, but decided against this without having mouthed it.) The local laborers, whey-faced under their rye-straw hats, and with sinews that might have been made of paper, demanded and eventually got a higher rate of pay. Aunt Helen died one night, very quietly. George contracted to breed a rag of colts. Sir John ailed. In the cornfields, fumiter, burdocks, nettles, and darnel flourished, despite George's cursingest efforts. The household gave up white bread when the price of wheat rose, but a drop in the price of barley and rye more than offset this. When winter came again and wages were not so high, George decided, he would, ungratefully, take down that park in which he had hidden after killing Salvo—it was part of the property he had bought from Terence Weddell —and, after raking out the leaves for compost, would cut the trees for fuel.

Okeland was not forgotten. In the chancellories of Europe the plotters and counterplotters, the counter-counterplotters as well, might have lost the name of George Fitzwilliam; but the queen's tax collectors did not. The mummers, mimes, and morris dancers, the beggars, itinerant tinkers, pedlars, avoided Okeland as a box from which few coins could be extracted; but Francis Drake remembered that address.

Twice the Plymouth skipper caused letters to be written to George, asking for his services. Each time in reply George wrote a felicitous "no."

On his visit to George and to Terence, Drake had concealed his identity. According to some reports he was in Ireland, according to others, dead. It was much the same to those who lived near Okeland. Drake had penetrated that county and returned from it without once being pointed out—a circumstance that might have miffed him.

With George it was otherwise. Nothing was known locally of his visits to the prisoner of Sheffield, but his record of enterprise under Hawkins and under Drake was public property. A man who had traveled to the New World was a sight even in Plymouth, even in London; in Northamptonshire he was unique. More, a squire who had visited in Devon came back with the story of George's freeing of the New Spain prisoners, and since it was not possible to let out the whole truth about this the tale was wonderfully embroidered. By these rustics, then, George was hailed as a hero who had bubbled the king of Spain. They never tired of asking him about this and connected exploits. "Is it true that he has horns and his teeth are black?" "These savages in the wilderness . . . Is it true that they don't wear *no* clothes *at all?*" "Master Fitzwilliam, sir, would you be good enough to tell Tim here about the time you whipped all them dons at San Juan de Ulua, if I'm pronouncing that right?"

It would never do to greet such demands with a snort. George after all was dependent upon his neighbors' good will for many things: sociability, credit, transport for his crops, the seasonal supply of labor. No matter how weary of the questions he might get he could not afford to turn away from them.

"Is it true, your worship," a clod once asked him in the taproom of The Plow at Kettering, "that the streets of the Spanish cities in America are really paved with gold?"

"I'm afraid I never saw any like that."

"But the ones you did see, what were they paved with? Only pearls?"

"Mud, as I remember it," George replied. "Mostly mud."

The puritans George had met were simple, or they were uncouth, or both. He wouldn't have told his father-in-law this, but it was true. An exception, the only one he knew, was Sir Francis Walsingham. He often thought about this man, shivering as he did so. He had told Terence about Walsingham's question concerning him.

"It was but a letter he plucked from among others. But he knew where you lived, even before he looked at it."

Terence had nodded somberly.

"Thanks, my friend. Yes, we know about Walsingham. We've been watching him for some time. He's no fool! Not that Burghley is either. But Burghley's a dutiful steward, whereas Walsingham is a flame."

"Do you think he means to get you into trouble?"

"Well, I'll leave for a while, before it can come. Could I ask you to act as caretaker here for a year or so? Of course there'd be a fee, and you could market the crops, such as they are."

"Never mind the fee—"

"I do mind. And you should."

"—but where would you go?"

"The Low Countries." He had smiled a small thorny smile. "But not to study their manuring. Bruges, Louvain, Douai. No, I'm not a priest, nor will I become one. But I have friends there, you understand."

"But you can't leave for the Low Countries without a passport, and if I couldn't get one how could you?"

"How? Why, I'll order it made for me. We have a printing press in London, you know. A very good one. And we have penmen who can sign Francis Walsingham's name better than he can."

The caretaker's fee was too much—paid in advance as it had been—and George was determined, if ever he could get that money together again, that he'd repay it when Terence came back. Going through the house now and then was a simple task. From time to time George would borrow an armful of books, as Terence had begged him. ("It keeps a book alive to be read," he had said.) And the produce of the garden, the orchards, the hay fields, more than paid George for his time and trouble.

The truth is, the two farms should have been made into one, since Weddell was by now almost surrounded by Okeland. Economy called for a merger. Some day, George decided, if it was possible, he would buy up the rest of Terence's property and combine these farms. Two houses of course would not be needed. Weddell Lodge, though the smaller, was the better built, and George had made up his mind to tear down Okeland, keep the name, and rebuild around the lodge, though not, to be sure, while Sir John lived.

All, he reflected sternly, would call for cash. And he had no cash, nor any immediate prospect of it.

The combined farms, the superimposed and rebuilt manor house—these could be classed with castles in Spain. He had best think right now of how to pay for the cows he had come to Rugby to buy. If he could only talk old Copplewait into—

His worriment was broken as he dismounted before the George and Dragon, for the door of that inn flew open and he was swept into a scene of wild excitement.

Those who first came out came backward, yet moving very fast, in full scamper, while they waved their arms, jabbering. Each held a dagger.

"*God-a-mercy!*"

"*Mind him there!*"

"Kill him! Kill the Moor!"

These were countrymen, not boys, but they looked like children when the one they fled from burst forth.

He was enormous. And his skin was black—not a dark brown, but black. His head was bare, his feet as well. His ruff was torn. His face gleamed with sweat, while his eyes rolled white, the size of tennis balls. No sword or poniard had been strapped about his red-doubleted waist, but in each hand he grasped a cudgel-like stick, the leg of a stool he had pulled apart.

"Throw something at his shins! Hit his shins!"

"Get a pitchfork, somebody!"

The giant paused, not panting like the others but blinking in the glare of the sun after the taproom's gloom. For all his bulk, there was something feline about him: his feet were spread wide, and he was ready to jump in any direction with deadly speed. He was a bull, an elephant, tormented past endurance by gadflies. George, who had never before seen him in anything but a loincloth, marveled that he did not split his clothes.

"Here's Master Fitzwilliam! Will you draw, sir? Oh, skewer him!"

"Nonsense," George said sharply.

"Eh?"

Two men came out of the inn, bent low in a crouch. Between them they carried, like a battering-ram, a long rusty-headed pike. They were about to rush the Negro and run him right through the back; but though he could not have heard them, he sensed them, jungle beast that he was, and he spun around, raising both huge hands, both cudgels. The men dropped the pike and fled back into the taproom.

The giant turned again, his mouth working, eyes rolling. Curiously crunched sounds came from his throat. He verged on panic and could think only to smash, to kill. All men were his enemies.

George started forward.

"Mind him, Master Fitzwilliam! He—"

"Go to, bum!"

George did not draw, nor did he make any sort of sudden movement.

A few feet from the wild man he stopped, smiling a mite, and in a low caressive voice as though calling a kitten he spoke one word, a name.

"Diego—"

The black dropped both stool-legs. He sprang forward, and threw his arms around George, and rubbed his thick rubbery nose against George's.

"Señor!"

Most of what he said was in his own Cimarron tongue or else in badly fractured Spanish, so that even George did not understand it; and of course it meant nothing at all to the scared countrymen. George and Diego, however, from experience could communicate by hand language and by tone of voice, and when at last they separated, each was laughing and weeping at the same time.

That his guide to the back door of Nombre de Dios was in England, George did not find extraordinary; for Francis Drake, whether out of a liking for the Cimarron or because it tickled his vanity to have so large and colorful a body servant (George believed it to be the latter) had brought him from Panama. That he was in the middle of Northamptonshire surpassed all understanding—just at first. Diego, it might be assumed, even if he was allowed ashore at all, would hardly have gone more than a few hundred feet from the edge of the sea of his own accord. He must, then, have been sent. There must be a letter.

George asked—and there was. Diego, who had forgotten it, now fetched it forth from somewhere under that straining doublet. George thrust it into his purse. It would be from Drake, of course. Knowing his fondness for Diego, Drake had sought to lure George back by this means. Which meant that the new venture must be making up again.

George was at once angry and flattered, but more immediately he was concerned about his companion. He soon had the story, as best Diego could tell it. Diego had not been turned loose upon the English hinterland alone. A sailor had gone with him, to keep him from toppling off his horse, to guide him to Okeland, to cause him to wear a riding mask and a wide-brimmed low-pulled bonnet as a screen against prying passers. After several days of travel, somewhere near at hand—Coventry? Leamington?—this companion had vanished. It might have been drunkenness, a fight, or ordinary desertion. Whatever the reason, a bewildered, frightened Diego, knowing that he was near the place where Señor Fitzwilliam lived, and in any event afraid to stay still, had floundered on. Somehow he had found his way into the taproom of the George and Dragon, Rugby, where, his fragmentary, recently acquired English having left him like his guide, he tried in vain to solicit information from the gathered clods, most of whom should have been out in the fields at that hour anyway. Flabbergasted at first, soon they had thought to make sport of him. Whereupon, an overtried Diego had gone berserker.

"I see. *Gracias*. Wait here a moment."

A thundercloud, George turned upon the others. He drew.

Half the population of the village was there by this time, crowding the narrow high street, but George addressed himself only to those who had tumbled out of the tavern. He swished his rapier, and they stepped back a bit.

"*So,* my fine bawcocks! Applause for ye! Because his words didn't come well and because his skin was dark you minded you could prick him like a chained bear, eh? You thought you'd play the dogs—aye, a part well chosen!—and you'd harry him with snaps and growls, never getting too near, and never having had to put up your tuppence to the keeper of the garden, is that it? Ballocks! You met a *man* this time, God rot ye!"

He swished the sword again, and again they stepped back, for it had a razor's edge and was very bright and long. He jerked his head to indicate Diego, who stood behind him now.

"Tosspots, pisspots, you were temerarious! You picked on a friend of mine!"

Diego grinned, all teeth. He didn't understand a word of it, but he was pleased to learn that his beloved *el señor* Fitzwilliam here in his own land was a leader, a chief, even as Diego himself had been in Darien.

"He tells me that somebody took his horse away but didn't walk it. I'll have that beast walked—aye, and head-rubbed, and its gear tightened. Then it shall be brought before this door and held until my friend and guest is ready to mount again.

"He tells me," George went on, slowly, ominously, "that somebody bobbed his bung. That will be returned too, mind ye, and instanter. And down to the last penny-piece in it, down to the last cog.

"He tells me that when he came here he was carrying his boots in his hand, for that they hurt his feet. And these too were filched, eh? Well, randyboys, these too will be straightaway brought back—but they'll be polished first so that a man can see his face in 'em. Do I make myself clear?"

He swished the sword yet again, and it glittered in the sun.

"For if this is not done, and done now, I'll flail the skin off some tobies around here."

He sheathed. He turned toward the beaming Diego, but turned back for a final shot.

"I'll do more than that. I'll loose *him* on you again!"

He threw an arm across Diego's shoulders and laughed.

"Come along, *amigo.* I'll buy you a beer."

28

Between Two Stools

The shadow loomed, swelling, seeming to lean in menace away from the wall; then it collapsed like a struck tent; but it rose again, enormous, expanding, dark as Erebus.

"I think you should go," said Sir John.

"No," said Anne.

The shadow swayed from side to side, monstrously abob. It ebbed. It stretched, straining the oak beams above.

"And you, Aunt Sylvia?"

She had no opinion. Seamed, small, crushed by many years, she must have been fifty. Since the passing of her sister she had seldom spoken, and though she went on working day after day with a birdlike doggedness, in truth she was but herself awaiting Death's embrace. Tonight, in addition, she had been badly rattled by Diego, from whom she couldn't rip her gaze. She shook a dazed head, and when she spoke it was in a voice barely audible—a voice thread-thin, as though she suffered from thirst.

"You— You must do as you think best, George."

Sideways, sympathetically, George studied a guest who might have sprung from the primordial ooze. As happy as a puppy with a shoe, seated in a thronelike chair on the dais, beaming down upon the others, who had taken more comfortable places below, Diego threw that restless shadow. A shadow distorted, a grotesque. In truth there was nothing restless about Diego himself; he could take no part in the talk, but he was having a wonderful time.

Was that a representation *in petto,* was it a symbol, of America—a glowering, huge, ever-changing shadow thrown on a wall by one who, seen from near at hand, was all amiability? George thought not; the picture was too pat. The New World, as he had reason to realize, was anything but insubstantial, a shadow. It was harsh; it could terrify. It repelled him, and he didn't want to go back to it.

Beggars cannot be choosers, men said. George was no beggar yet, but he was perilously close to the edge; he teetered on the verge of bankruptcy. On the table before him were two documents, and it was these that had brought about the discussion.

One was the message Diego had delivered. It was from Francis Drake. That some unnamed scribe had done the actual writing made no difference; the voice was that of Drake, clear, imperious. George knew well, none better, how Drake could fuss over a letter, causing his secretary to recast it many times. He had a sharp ear, an infallible memory, and he knew what he wanted. He could be tart too. On Captain Drake's ship you were not permitted to give such cries as "Devil take it!" or "God rot it!" or even the universal "Upon my shot!"—this last being taken by him, rightly or wrongly, as a euphemism for "Upon my soul!" which in the nature of it would be blasphemous. Looking down upon the letter, George smiled at the sight of an old admonition, written after Drake had warned him that farming and roving did not mix and that he who tried both might fail in both: "Between two stools the arse goeth to the ground."

Chuckling, he read this aloud.

"Sh-sh," said Anne, glancing at Aunt Sylvia; but that old woman, still under the spell of Diego's shadow, had not heard.

The other article on the table was the Okeland account book, which told a grim story. For a long time George had known that the money situation was bad, very bad; but seeing it on paper, looking at the figures themselves, somehow made it seem even worse.

This need not be a losing battle. Okeland was naturally rich, and not too far from the market. The new methods Sir John and George had introduced would eventually increase the size of the crop, the size of the herds too. But—time was required. And time was an intangible something that couldn't be whittled, condensed, or stored away for future use.

Disaster was not inevitable. Okeland *could* be made to pay. There was nothing about the tale the ledger told that couldn't be righted, and for good, by five hundred golden guineas. But—where could such a stupendous sum be raised? Every acre of Okeland-Weddell was mortgaged, as was the house itself. The furniture was negligible, Anne's jewels, like those of Aunt Sylvia, were modest. George's prize money from the Nombre de Dios venture, staggering though it had seemed at the time he brought it here, was all gone; nor did he have any inheritance to borrow against.

Five hundred guineas. It was a vast sum, twenty-five years ago all but unthinkable, while even today George didn't suppose that there were twenty men in the kingdom who could have raised it out of hand, instanter. His uncle, John Russell, earl of Bedford, was a man of wealth but a man too of many business affairs, and in person a niggard. John Hawkins had inherited much and made more, but like Uncle John he kept his money busy, and it was not likely that at a given time he could lay his hands on anything like five hundred guineas. Burghley? Here was no gambler, like the others, but a cautious adventurer, one who looked before he leapt financially, if indeed he ever leapt at all. Burghley would have a nest egg. But—would he lend this to George Fitzwilliam? Most assuredly if he did it would be with an understanding about future service. He would insist that George become his "man." And George didn't want to be anybody's man any more.

Should he consider his own private feelings? But it wasn't only that. Anne Crofts had not married a mountebank, nor yet a trained dog who at the word of command would sit up on its hind legs and beg. Her father, Sir John, the proper proprietor of Okeland, had given all he'd got and was too old to be expected to gain more, by whatever means. But George, the real master, should have other resources.

And he *did* have.

He stared at the letter.

"I would go," said Sir John.

"The waiting," George muttered. "The delays . . . the emptiness . . ."

"What's war but waiting? Three-quarters waiting and one quarter looking for something to eat."

"Perhaps I don't like war?"

"Perhaps I didn't either, but it's the only way for a young man to make money." He rapped bony, waxy knuckles against the letter on the table. "He agrees thou'lt not be called upon to be a common captain, and thou'lt have the old secretaryship back. Three whole lays of the adventure, before an anchor's up! And it should be a richer one even than before. The Mediterranean—"

"He'll not go to the Mediterranean," George said curtly.

"Why not?"

"There's too much competition."

"He *said* Alexandria, that night he stopped here. Could he be meaning to go back to the West Indies or New Spain?"

"No, not that either. Not Francis Drake. The Spaniards are no sluggards. By this time every town along the Main and in New Spain and among the islands will be cannoned and ramparted and stocked with a garrison. It would need such a fleet as the queen's self could hardly raise, to force one of them now."

"The smaller places?"

"The smaller places are for smaller men."

"The Far Indies are not. But—clear around Africa?"

George shook his head.

"The Portuguese have plugged that hole."

"Where else, then? Where else *is* there to go?"

"There is the Southern Sea, on the other side."

Sir John stared at his son-in-law.

"But—nobody's ever *been* there, except Spaniards!"

"Nobody had ever been below the Line, until a few years ago. Men used to say that whoever tried it would be burned to a crisp."

George nodded to the bobbing Cimarron.

"*He's* been there. He's paddled his feet in it. I've only seen it from afar, myself. And so has Drake. But it's there; I can vouch for that."

"How could he ever get *to* it? The Spaniards cross the isthmus and build vessels on the other shore."

"Magellan didn't."

George dipped a forefinger into his wine and started to draw lines on the top of the table.

"This is the way it was explained to me by Terence Weddell, and also by Master Hawkins from time to time, and by Richard Grenville that night we had the banquet when I brought the Spanish prisoners back. Grenville's fascinated by the scheme. I think he's behind Drake as much as Hawkins is. Look, you both have heard of the symmetry of nature, of course?"

"Well, something," ventured Sir John.

Anne only nodded. She had raised her head and was looking at George.

"Well, here's America. A great land mass like this, see? Here's Florida . . . and New Spain . . . and then it gets narrow, just north of the Line here, and that's Darien, between the two seas. That's where Nombre de Dios is, and Panama."

"Yes, I know," said Sir John.

"Then of course there's another land mass, since it is always that way—always balanced, necessarily. Here's the Main, and here's Brazil-wood Land, and then the land of the Amazons . . . But it slopes in toward Tierra del Fuego, from what we hear. This southern mass is not as large as that of the north, and what's more the Line does not divide them evenly but leaves more to the north. True?"

"Aye . . ."

"Well now, the earth is round. And it turns. It spins. We all know that, always have. But mark ye, if there was so much more land in the northern half, the upper half, why, land being heavier than water, it would wobble on its axis, is that not right?"

"Um-m. It would seem so."

"It *is* so, undoubtedly. The men who know about these things say so, the men who have studied them."

"Your friend Weddell?"

"Yes. But also Mercator. And Ortelius, Phrysius, and Finaeus. And Dr. John Dee. And many another as well. They point out that by the law of the symmetry of nature there must be a counterbalancing land mass far to the south, to offset this difference. Is that clear?"

"Well . . ."

"They call this far place Terra Incognita, which means Unknown Land, or sometimes Terra Australis, the Land of the South. It is bleak and bare, bitterly cold."

"How dost thou know?"

"It has been seen. By one man only! By Master Magellan, who found a narrow strait or channel above Tierra del Fuego, which is to say the southern part of America. He sailed through the strait and into the Southern Sea. Why couldn't Drake do the same? I don't like the man, but he's a master mariner if ever there was one."

"The men wouldn't go!"

"He wouldn't tell 'em. He would not even tell me. That's why he lets fall this foolish talk about Alexandria."

"But— But even if he got there, what would he do?"

George's was a tight smile.

"A thousand miles of seacoast, all unfortified because no enemy ever had been in that sea, treasure ships without a cannon on 'em, cities to be picked like peaches from a tree—oho, Captain Drake would know what to do! Have no fear of that!"

"He couldn't get back," Anne said suddenly.

"Why not?"

"Thou hast said that the strait is narrow, a thin place. Wouldn't the dons fortify it against Drake's return?"

"Why truly, that they would. But there might be other exits. Look—"

He wetted his finger again, and drew more lines.

"Since there is a passage between the two ocean seas at the southern extremity of America here, it follows that there must be one at the northern extremity as well. That's the way all nature is: balanced. It stands to reason."

"Has anyone ever found a northern passage?"

"Frobisher thinks he has. He's equipping right now for a deeper try. Humphrey Gilbert is interested in that route too, since it's surely there. And others. But it wouldn't attract Captain Drake, for it leads away from the Spaniards, and the Spaniards are the ones with the money.

But look: Granted that the dons would block the Magellan channel against any return—for they are no fools and they can move mighty fast when it comes to protecting their wealth—still, what's to prevent Drake from sailing on up this coast, up through the Southern Sea along the far side of the northern part of America, until he reached the other entrance of the northern passage? It *must* be there."

Sir John Crofts's eyes were sparkling.

"To sail clear around half of the known world! God's bodikins! What I wouldn't give to do that, if I were younger!"

There was some silence after that. Diego was munching an apple. Aunt Sylvia had fallen asleep. Sir John, in the candlelight, *looked,* indeed, younger. George felt somewhat ashamed of himself for failing to share that enthusiasm, yet Anne, it developed, was of his way of thinking.

"It might be a deed of derring-do," Anne said at last, "but it sounds like a sinful waste of time—to go into somebody's house by the front door and out by the back, ending at the same place."

"But ending with your arms full of plate," George reminded her. "Francis Drake never forgets his owners."

"And how can you be sure that the back door won't be locked? Or, what if you couldn't find it? What would you do then?"

George shrugged.

"The earth is round," he repeated. "There is still the long way home. It's been done once. It could be done again."

He rose.

"I don't know," he said to nobody in particular. "I'll sleep on it."

He did not. He lay awake for a long while, on his back, silent, but knowing all the time that Anne, who didn't stir, was awake beside him. He thought of the steaming jungles of Darien, the snakes, the swamps, of the maddeningly endless squeak of ship's timbers, the swish of unseen bilge, the hours and days that seemed to have no end. . . . In the darkness he shivered. After a long while he slipped his arms around Anne, and held her very tight.

"The symmetry of nature," he whispered, trying to sound playful, though in truth he was badly frightened.

Later he flopped over on his belly, his favorite position for sleep. Indeed, he pretended to sleep, even essaying a small tentative snore, as he lay listening to the dear familiar night-sounds of Okeland. It was no use. Anne never was fooled by such a performance. And when she did speak at last it was quietly, evenly, with no preliminary inquiry about his state of slumber. She *knew* he was awake.

"Thou hast made up thy mind?"

"Yes, dear."

There was an absent-minded thudding of hooves from the stables, a chorus of frogs from the duck pond, and from the wood the song of a nightingale.

"Thou art going?" she said.

"Yes, dear."

29

Watch That Man

George's fears of postponement and senseless delay were justified: he was destined to stay all summer, all autumn, in Plymouth. Nor was he kept very busy, though he had to be on hand. Drake knew his backers; his plans were well laid; and some time before George arrived the five vessels were equipped and fully victualed so that they could have sailed at once, save for two things—God and Queen Elizabeth.

The ships were *Pelican, Marigold, Elizabeth, Benedict* (a mere pinnace, for scouting purposes), and the fat storeship *Swan*. The last two had no guns, but *Elizabeth* and *Marigold* bristled with them. *Pelican,* the largest, was so cluttered with artillery that when you were aboard of her it was hard to move: seven stout demi-cannons on each side, a couple of falconets, and mounted forward two long sakers, four-pounders. This promised to be an interesting trade voyage!

First the wind and then majesty said "no"; when one would relent the other was obdurate. The mariners might wake in the morning to tumble up on deck and scan the sky, the sound, the wind ribands. They'd raise a cheer. And then—then—a courier from London would appear. The queen's highness had decided that the fleet must not sail.

Variable as the winds were, this monarch's disposition was more so; and nothing could be done except sit and wait, chafing at the consumption of hard-won rations. By the time Elizabeth Tudor had changed her mind yet again, graciously giving permission for the adventure to proceed, the weather too had yawed and the wind once more was from the south, pinning them to Plymouth.

George was comfortable enough as the guest of John Hawkins. He was not obliged to sleep aboard ship, though he was constantly on call and of course prohibited from leaving Plymouth. His temper was frayed by the delays, and he tended to be snappish; but he forgot this and everything else when he returned to the house in Kinterbury Street one afternoon to find Anne.

There was a fond, small smile on her face as she held out her arms.

"If thou hadst gone, I sought to know it. And if thou hadst not, then maybe I could comfort thee a little."

She was wearing something blue, and he wept for gladness at the sight.

"Oh, I love thee, my chuck!"

"Can I believe this?" she asked.

"Eh?"

"Hast thou not told me that lying's become a habit with thee?"

He released her, and stepped back, shocked. For he took the charge seriously. Anne was not a playful woman; levity had no part in her make-up. But now, repentant, she seized him.

"Nay, sweetard," she pleaded. "I spoke in jest."

As if to make up for his trip to London, George squired her all around Plymouth, even accompanying her into the shops. She, in her turn, did him a world of good, just by being there. But when at long last he sailed, of a cold wet morning, December 13, 1577, her presence made departure just that much harder to bear. Standing on the quay in a dismal drizzle, he clung to his wife.

At The Plow in Kettering there had been sundry who from time to time expressed to George their wonder that he, who could, was not sailing the great ocean sea. "Why?" he asked. "God-a-mercy, it gives a man the mulligrubs to be pent in a place like this," they would answer, "but out there you could be *free!*"

George would then guffaw. "Heed this," he'd reply, "there is no jail so close-confining as a ship afloat. You can't walk without lurching, and holding on to something, and stepping over somebody, and even then you can't walk more than a few feet in any one direction. You're never *alone.*"

They'd cry: "Now, is that true?"

"Heed this," George would go on, "if you sneeze at sea you joggle somebody's elbow, and if you spit you sully somebody's boot, that's how tight they pack you. You sleep, when you can, in a bunk made of boards that push against your shoulders on each side and make you bend your knees, and if you start up you bump your head. Even so, unless your birth's exalted, or your investment very, very large, you must needs share this Stygian slit, taking turns with some stranger whose bugs you also share—for there are always bugs, forsooth!"

Customarily that quieted them, but on one occasion a newcomer to the neighborhood had named another inducement:

"Yet at least you'd get away from politics, out there!"

This amused George Fitzwilliam, this memory. Get away from politics? Why, they were carrying Whitehall right along with them!

The riffraff of the forward castle, though ignorant almost beyond belief, knew when the west coast of Africa was raised that they were not bound for Alexandria. They were stupid men, but not stolid; and now they were uneasy.

The officers, hand-picked by Francis Drake, would do anything he told them to do. The gentlemen did not feel that way. The gentlemen never did believe the Alexandria story, but they had been led to suppose that this was in truth a voyage of trade and exploration. It was possible and even probable, they thought—though at first they were careful to keep this from the hands, who might panic—that the fleet would make its way into the Southern Sea. But the reason for this, they assumed, would be to plant factories on Terra Australis or in the Spice Islands. The Spanish possessions would not be molested.

These men got a shock when off Cape Blanco the admiral picked up a Portuguese vessel with some unpronounceable name, which he thereupon rechristened *Christopher*. True, he swapped the pinnace *Benedict* for this; but the small *Benedict* already had proved herself unseaworthy, and the skipper of the new vessel was not given a voice in the "bargain." More, among the Cape Verdes they halted and took over —without any pretense of giving something in return—a large Portuguese ship, *Mary,* bound for Brazil Land, together with her cargo of wines and, even more important, her pilot, the renowned Nuña da Silva.

These were plain acts of piracy, since England was no more at war with Portugal than she was with Spain. They had not even started in the direction of the New World. And the delight with which Drake greeted the short, dark, laconic, heavily bearded Da Silva, one of the few men acquainted with the South Atlantic, further troubled the gentlemen.

To make matters worse, Drake appeared to think that these gentlemen should help handle the ships. They did not like it.

There were not many of them: Thomas Doughty and his brother, John, who had known Drake in Ireland; John Winter, who was well connected and seethed with resentment because George Fitzwilliam was not obliged to command a vessel as he was; John Saracold and John Audley, who, though merchants by occupation, here represented certain investors and hence were classed with the gentles; John

Thomas, the only person in the fleet besides George who could really speak Spanish.

The Doughtys were the worst. They simply couldn't keep their mouths shut.

So it was that, all tightness, with tempers bent, they started for the Line, making a course that should take them to Tierra del Fuego, south of Brazil Land.

It was a strain. With the exception of Da Silva, a very old man, none of them ever had crossed the Equator. Even those of education, like the Doughtys, like George, quailed at the thought, though they might keep a bold face before the mariners.

What made it worse was the weather. Fury they could face, these men bred in the north, but the doldrums they had not even heard of; and days in mid-Atlantic dragged with an agonizing slowness, piling up into weeks. The sky was the same, merciless. There were no jumping fish; there were no clouds; there was nothing. Heat waves shimmered above the decks, and nobody dared to touch metal. Not even the night brought relief, for there wasn't a smitch of breeze, so that the men lay panting, wondering when this torture would cease.

Francis Drake, who never trusted anybody, and who knew or sensed the talk that was going about, used these days of no-motion to pass from one vessel to another in his brightly painted cock, inspecting, instructing, giving encouragement.

As for George, he wrote poetry to his wife.

George had a poor hand for verse—a hole in his training. Not since school had he done much with it, and he never had wooed Anne Crofts as he should have done. A triolet now and then maybe, or a roundelay. Nothing more. He was now aware of the ugly old phrase to the effect that you don't chase a horse you've already mounted; or, more mellifluously:

> *"Think ye, if Laura had been Petrarch's wife,*
> *He would have written sonnets all his life?"*

This George knew, and he didn't care. Anne might never have a chance to read what he was writing. He might tear it up; he might not get home. She had trouble with her reading anyway and in this case understandably would be loth to ask for help. But just at the time, so far away, it felt good to write it, like talking to her, the nearest thing.

This was in Drake's own cabin, a sumptuous one. The *Pelican* was still; nobody stirred. Sunlight reflected off the water smashed through the ports and against a ceiling of polished oak.

Absorbed in one of man's most absorbing sports, at first George did not hear the door open. When he did hear, and had looked up, it was with some difficulty that he repressed a frown. No man enjoys being disturbed when he is writing to the woman he loves, and George in particular disliked to be confronted with Thomas Doughty.

The man was saponaceous. His learning was genuine, his breeding (George had checked) undisputed. But he was subtle, a schemer, who seldom looked at the person he addressed. He was large, languid, light-bearded.

He threw himself into a chair, something he would never have dared to do if the admiral was present.

"Fitzwilliam, why doth Captain Drake never summon a council? Does he have some sort of commission or authorization from the queen's majesty herself that causes him to act like an unanswerable master here?"

For weeks Doughty had been probing the admiral's secretary for this information. Now he was essaying a new course, a direct approach calculated to jar loose some response.

George, however, made no reply. He himself did not know whether such a paper existed, though he doubted it. He did know—for the official correspondence was open to him—that the queen herself had a stake in this enterprise. But she would not acknowledge it; she was too shrewd to put such things on paper. If Drake succeeded she would share his profits. If he failed she'd disown him.

"You and I—Winter—Thomas—we should be called into consultation. We never are. Is this fleet going to Peru, Fitzwilliam? Will it harry the don?"

Still George did not answer. Nobody knew where they were going, nobody but the commander-in-chief. The instructions, which George had read, could be variously interpreted. Most admirals would have proceeded with care, calling a council as often as this was convenient, if only in order to protect themselves. Not Francis Drake. His arrogance, his refusal even to recognize the rights of any of the others, officers or gentlemen, had given rise to talk that he had a personal, private order from the queen; and if he had not confirmed this, neither had he denied it.

George sighed, and put his half-finished poem away in a blue envelope.

"I have not been told," he said.

"You're gentle. You're close to Drake. What do *you* think?"

George shrugged.

"Whatever I think must be my own affair," he said mildly.

[171]

"God's kidneys, man! Hast thou no heart!"

"Don't you 'thou' me!"

"Say, if we go to Peru we'll all be hanged for pirates!"

"It seems likely."

"It would take a miracle to save us!"

"I have seen Captain Drake perform miracles," said George. "This is not meant to be irreverent."

"You're Bedford's nephew, yet you let yourself be ordered about like a lackey. I don't understand it."

He had talked this way before, though never with such force.

"Are you *afraid* of Francis Drake?"

George, who sometimes wondered whether he was, only smiled. He wished that he had been allowed to finish that verse.

"Because you should know right here and now, Fitzwilliam, that there are those of us who don't see why—"

He went on, and on. Doubtless it was all very mutinous, but the heat was intense and George was not disposed to listen. George was thinking of the weeping willow by the duck pond at Okeland, the nightingale, the boxwood hedge he had caused to be planted, the great-hall, the stables.

"—and nothing less than a direct written order from her own majesty—not from any minister, mind you!—could justify it. Don't you agree?"

George was thinking of the humming of bees, the stamp of horses in their dark stalls, a crackling fire. He was remembering how on warm nights he and Anne used to lie side by side, stark naked, starfished out, enjoying themselves even during the time their bodies didn't touch.

"—and what's more, I'm not alone. I can tell you, Fitzwilliam, I've been among the men, and you can take my vow for it that—"

"You have certainly been among the men," said Francis Drake as he stepped into the cabin. "I've been there myself and I know what you told them. Get out of my cabin, Doughty."

When the visitor had gone, not shutting the door, Drake stared after him.

"I have been watching that man. We may have to try him."

George had no love for Thomas Doughty. Yet—Doughty was well born. And George instinctively took a side opposite that of the "new men," as typified here by the admiral. George frowned at the open door.

"Because he's a gentleman?"

"Because he is in my way," said Francis Drake.

30

A Question for the Courts of Love

That spat might have cleared the air, for a breeze sprang up, and there was a whole series of thundershowers, which helped to fill the casks but were hard on the navigators, making even Nuña da Silva unsure of himself. They struck every night, yet it was certain that they drifted, off course and probably too far north.

The men, who didn't mark these navigational hazards, were cheered. Not only was it cooler, but flying fishes began to appear and were easily caught. They made good eating. Also, there were birds.

The pelicans in particular fascinated George.

"They sleep up there, with their wings spread out," Da Silva said in his spaced English. "Then if they get a down-current of air and begin to approach the water, it wakes them. They hate water. It is their natural enemy. So they open their eyes and flap their wings and fly high again, and then they go back to sleep."

"Sounds like a pleasant life."

One morning the *Mary* was missed, with all its wine and its company, including Thomas Doughty. Doughty was military commander of the expedition, and his duties took him to each of the vessels in turn. However, the *Mary* turned up, unobtrusively, a few days later.

April 5 they raised land, which almost immediately was wiped from sight by the worst fog any of them ever had known. For six days they stumbled here and there, afraid of breakers, losing touch with one another, for this was a lee shore and leadsmen kept reporting that the water shoaled.

Da Silva had an explanation. The Indians who lived here, he said, were so cruelly treated by his own compatriots, the Portuguese, that they had made a pact with certain storm gods, pagan gods, to keep ships away. Whenever they sighted sail, he said, they would go to the beach and pick up a handful of sand and toss this into the air as a signal to the gods, who would then keep their part of the agreement and produce fog.

(George could not decide whether Da Silva really meant what he said or whether he was amusing himself. Anyway he was a skillful pilot. That they survived the first terrible week—a pampero, Da Silva called it—was largely due to his efforts.)

"I don't believe that," Francis Drake told his secretary. "The reason for the storm is Thomas Doughty. He's been conjuring."

George made no comment. It was true that both of the Doughtys, loose-mouthed men, more than once had boasted of supernatural powers. Yet George believed that in this case there was at work something more substantial than spells, incantations, pricked images.

It could have been meaningful that when at last the pampero subsided and they counted bowsprits, the only vessel missing—they had to comb the coast four days for her—was the *Christopher,* presently carrying Thomas Doughty.

All the vessels needed scraping. This would call for a halt, when the right place was found. Boot-topping—shifting all guns and stores to one side of a vessel so that her other side was partly exposed, scraping this, and then reversing the process—would not be advisable with vessels as beamy as these and in seas so uncertain. They would have to find a beach. This made every delay a possible disaster: the Magellan Strait, if it could be traversed at all could be traversed only in the southern summer—January, February, March—and if that season was missed they could not possibly hole up in some convenient cove for a year. This was not the Gulf of Darien, this bleak stony strand.

Thanks to their foul bottoms, they crawled; and their pace slowed even more when the admiral ordered them to keep a close formation lest once again a ship be lost.

Twice while coasting they sighted Indians, who were not giants as had been reported. One group of Indians was overtouchy and shot from the shore, killing two Englishmen. The others were friendly, if shy, and none wore any clothes.

Dragging along as a wounded animal drags itself on its belly, the ships made an anchorage at a place they called Port Desire—just before they were hit by a second pampero.

Da Silva told them that never had he known two such storms off this coast within so short a time. There must be witchcraft at work, he avowed.

"Aye," muttered Francis Drake.

Again they were scattered, not only *Christopher* but even *Pelican* being blown out to sea. It was more than ten days before the fleet could be reassembled.

Luck is luck; but this was not natural.

They put in at a place they called Seal Bay after the large herds of seals they found there. None of them ever had seen this animal, which they found so ludicrous that while they laughed they permitted hundreds to get away, seeking refuge in the sea. Hundreds of others they clubbed to death. The slaughter was horrid, messy, and very malodorous, but the meat of these beasts was good, especially the pups, and the hides were of service.

They left Seal Bay June 3, and that night *Christopher* disappeared again, both of the Doughtys being aboard. They found her two days later, and since nothing could be proved against captain or master, much less against the Doughtys, Francis Drake passed it off with a grim nod. He did, however, have the *Christopher* stripped of her metal and turned adrift, saying that she was no more than a trouble-maker.

The name of this, the first of the vessels they had seized, might have had some significance, George thought. She presumably was so called in honor of Christopher Hatton, a young man with a stake in this enterprise—as George, who kept the accounts, could testify. It was about this time too—in fact in Seal Bay—that the admiral, having vouchsafed no reason, formally rechristened the *Pelican* the *Golden Hind,* that being Hatton's hereditary device. This Christopher Hatton was not yet a major power at court, but he was a coming man. Burghley and Walsingham, though likewise investors in this enterprise, were older, warier. As for the other backers: Leicester could not be expected to do more than hold what he had; Humphrey Gilbert was in the savage, inconclusive, heartbreaking war of the Low Countries, while his half-brother, Walter Raleigh, was in the even worse war— from any courtier's point of view—of Ireland. But Christopher Hatton stayed at home, a remarkably handsome man, whose dancing the queen had praised. Already he was Captain of the Guard, a position of glitter, and at the time the expedition left Plymouth the rumor was that he'd soon be knighted. A man to be watched. Francis Drake was looking ahead.

June 20 they limped into the best bay they had yet seen. It was perfect for careening purposes, being perhaps a mile wide, two miles long, and everywhere a good four fathoms. The hills that hemmed it in were glum and rocky, but there were no boulders near the sea. The water was clear and cold, and it swarmed with fish. There could be no excuse here for the master of any ship to let her drag her anchor and be blown outside, for the hills blocked high winds, as a low sandy island blocked the mouth of the bay.

Nautically neat, spiritually the spot depressed. There was scant vegetation, only some dry, brittle, juiceless grass and so few trees that at last they broke up *Mary* for firewood. The hills glowered. The sky glowered. They never did see the sun.

It was the belief of all those who had taken part in the navigation, including George Fitzwilliam, that they were now in Tierra del Fuego, and so could expect only worse weather as they went farther south, even when summer had come back to those regions. It was also their opinion that this must be the very Port St. Julian marked on Magellan's chart, the haven where he had paused to refit. Magellan had done more. He had put down a mutiny here—if it really was Port St. Julian— and with some ceremony had executed two men. There were those among the mariners who claimed to have discovered the ruins of the gallows—unlikely, after more than fifty years in that wet country, but the rumor had its effect.

It was hardly to be expected that Francis Drake would fail to take advantage of this. The hot gospeler might look upon all actors as limbs of Satan, but he himself had a high sense of drama.

At first everything was work. Drake caused all three remaining vessels—their flyboat, like the *Mary,* had been broken up for firewood— to be hauled ashore, demasted, and overtipped. Anywhere else in the world it would have been poor policy thus to ground all ships at once; but the chance of an enemy pinning them in this remote spot was slim, and the admiral wished to leave no means of escape until he had spoken.

Even George, who did not get around among the men, knew that the situation was serious. Unless something radical was done the gentlemen would revolt. They might be followed by many of the mariners. They'd seize the first vessel put into commission again, and they would sail for England, crying piracy. Drake and even George could see this making up. But George didn't know what to do about it. Drake did.

George was more than ever in the admiral's cabin these days, and that for several reasons. He was keeping a diary for the admiral, and at the same time compiling a more formal record of the voyage, this too to be ostensibly Drake's. He was teaching Drake Spanish. Also George enjoyed the company of Diego, who was not notably happy in his role of valet to a man who wouldn't permit him to go naked. Diego never had been able to do much with his English, and George was the only person with whom he could chat.

There was yet another reason. "You're never *alone!*" George had been wont to tell the customers of The Plow. "You never get a chance to *think*, at sea!" Yet the secretary of a personage traveling in such state as Francis Drake, whose cabin was sacrosanct, did get a little privacy now and then. It was in the admiral's cabin, the only possible place, that George Fitzwilliam was wont, from time to time, to work upon that sonnet sequence for Anne.

All the same, it was not like living in the country; and once they were aground at Port St. Julian, and the vessels careened for cleaning, George put on his boots and indulged himself in a great luxury—a walk.

He went alone. He wanted to think.

Here was no Dorsetshire. The bleakness of the land all but shrieked. The very ground was harsh, unresponsive, a dirty grayish-brown. Low liver-colored clouds scuttled past, for the wind, a wet one, never paused; but there were no trees to toss their branches, no shrubs to bob and bow. Not only was there no hint of sun: this dreary landscape looked as though the sun never *had* shone upon it and never *would,* having, like God, forgotten it.

George trudged on, preoccupied with a problem that once had been sung by Bailleul, Mauléon, and the ineffable Chrétien de Troyes, and debated by Eleanor of Aquitaine, Marie of Champagne, and other ladies in the Provençal courts. But George was not interested in its historical significance, only in its immediate validity—if valid it was.

The question was: Can a man love two women at the same time?

George believed that a man could, because he believed that he did.

Okeland's chatelaine and the Strange Guest were two different persons, and why should it not be possible and even advisable to love them in two different ways? Was love indivisible? If it were split, would not each part flourish?

He loved Anne for what she was: his wife, his favorite companion. He loved Mary Stuart for what she represented. Was this weak and irresponsible, this attitude? Men laughed at chivalry, but was it, after all, dead? Was it even dying? Didn't it still make a great difference in the souls of men, even such men as denied its existence? Did a person have to wear shining armor, did he have to prance in the tiltyard, in order to know what chivalry meant? George thought not. He believed that a man might be a farmer and still have Galahad's own spirit. Not all the tortures of the Inquisition could have wrung from George any thought of a physical infidelity to Anne, yet at the same time he would always hold in his heart an image of the lovely pale prisoner at Sheffield.

But he would not mention this at home. He sometimes wondered how much physical fidelity—on the part of their husbands—meant to most women? Perhaps it was largely a male idea. Anyway it was best to be quiet about it.

Bemused, he touched the ruby in his right ear as he walked.

A flake of snow like a tiny wet rag hurled hard at him and struck his face. Then there was another, and another.

Almost immediately, as though at a signal, the snow ceased. The wind fell off. George crested a small rise and came into sight of sea and camp alike.

He saw instantly that something was wrong.

31

This Man Must Die

The three vessels, looking like great fish out of water, lay deserted along the beach. Nor were any of the tents occupied or any of the guns guarded. There were no fires. The men, in small arm-waving, gesticulating groups, strewn across the improvised bowling green, were looking toward the *Golden Hind*. The admiral was not among them—he was always easy to spot from afar because of his polychromatic clothes. Either he had ordered them to assemble on the green (which was anything but green) or else, more ominously, *they* had ordered *him* to appear there.

Either way, it spelled trouble. George started to run down to the ships.

Francis Drake was in his cabin, which was crazily aslant in this high-and-dry vessel. He was troubled about something, and mumbling to himself. George he greeted with a glad nod; but it was upon the valet, faithful Diego, that most of his preparation fell. It quickly became clear that whatever he was rehearsing in his mind, whatever it was that caused his lips to move, this man Drake was engrossed not in thoughts of what he should *do* when he faced a hundred and fifty men, but in thoughts of what he should *wear*.

It was another of his contradictions that though he might denounce the pomps and vanities of this wicked world, still he maintained a wardrobe any king could envy. When Drake conducted prayers on deck, as he did every morning and again every evening, sometimes he told the hands that a humble and a contrite heart was the greatest offering anyone could make to his Creator. Yet he ate off gold plate; he had musicians to play for him—he who couldn't even whistle the simplest air!—and he strutted in satin and silk. Had anyone found the temerity to tax him with this, and had Drake condescended to answer, that answer probably would have been that though it scraped his soul so to shine he believed he owed it to the queen's majesty, whose arm he was, whose hand. He often spoke of the queen that way, as though he was doing her a personal favor. It was one of the reasons—it and his own bland assumption that he was above any council—that gave rise to the rumor that this man did actually have a commission from Elizabeth Tudor.

Now he examined the doublets, the hose, the bonnets, the capes —fussing, clucking his tongue—holding some of them against himself or at arm's length up to the light. He brushed, smoothed, lifted off lint, fretted, and commanded Diego to work with comb and needle and goffering-iron. He polished. He laid the pieces of apparel side by side, sometimes many of them, shifting and changing them as though they were flowers he arranged in a vase.

At last a military costume was chosen: this would screen the splendor of his breast with steel. In part he made up for that coverage by selecting a doublet with parti-colored puffed silk sleeves. He wore a white wired ruff, a morion, tooled leather gauntlets, canions slashed black and red, black base hose, scarlet leather half-boots. He was brave. The breast- and backplates, like the morion, were brilliantly burnished. The breastplate was fitted with a tapul, in the Spanish fashion. He fussed about this.

When he was ready to appear he sent his trumpeter, young John Brewer, to announce him. He took a last look at himself in the mirror, not an easy task in that slanted place.

"You'll attend me, Fitzwilliam."

"Aye."

Drake looked around, saw the desk, went to it, opened a drawer.

"I need a piece of paper . . ."

He took the first thing that came to hand, not looking at it, and crammed it beneath his breastplate, on the left side.

"Very well."

The day was, for that place, bright. Body armor was not usual among the English, even at court, and Francis Drake had all eyes before he even took his stance atop a small barrel of wine.

He started mildly, protesting that he had no natural eloquence such as was given to some, nor yet any training in rhetoric, being but a plain honest Englishman.

This the men liked and cheered.

Then Drake drew a long breath—and plunged into the most moving speech that George Fitzwilliam ever had heard. George had lived close to this man for a long while and supposed he knew all his talents, but this speech was astounding.

Drake at first pointed to none, neither friend nor foe, but treated them all as though they were equally guilty. He made it plain that thereafter no one was above manual service on any ship under his command, and he would listen to no wrangles about birth or precedence.

". . . for I must have the gentlemen to haul and draw with the mariners, and the mariners with the gentlemen . . . nothing else will do."

Neither should there be any further talk, even among themselves, about a council. *He* was the council, all there would ever be. He represented her gracious majesty the queen, who had given him no instruction to seek advice. No matter what others had done! Any who opposed him now were opposing their own lawful monarch, and he'd know how to handle them.

Easily, even scornfully, he announced that he was removing all officers from their posts. They would be restored when they had done his bidding.

Was that clear?

Nobody said anything.

Drake pointed to Thomas Doughty, as though indicating a snake against whom they should protect themselves. This man, he made it known, was a traitor and a spy, and the voyage could not go on with him. In addition, Doughty was a practitioner of witchcraft, who would have doomed them all. Drake then commanded—he didn't *ask*, he *commanded*—that the man be tried, here and now. They must choose a jury amongst themselves. He, Francis Drake, agent of her highness Elizabeth, queen of England, would pass sentence. He would await their decision in his cabin; and he adjured them not to take too long about it, for the law could prove impatient.

His authorization? Did anyone question it? Well, no man might expect him to pass around a paper the queen herself had handed him. Such a paper was not for the vulgar. Yet, if they cared to hear it—

He reached under his breastplate, on the left side, the side of the heart. He drew out a blue envelope, and from this, reverently, took a piece of paper, which he unfolded.

"Know ye by these presents, that my trusted and truly-beloved servant, Francis Drake, Esquire—"

It was polysyllabic, and it was all-embracing, for it made him a little king over here at the other end of the world.

The admiral was touchy about his lack of education, and there were few, perhaps there were not any, who knew that he could not really read. If in the audience there had been some such they surely assumed that he had learned this testament by memory, as indeed he had. Only George Fitzwilliam knew that what Drake looked at as he spoke was a sonnet intended for Anne of Okeland.

When the admiral finished there were tears in his eyes, and truly most of the men were weeping too. The admiral kissed the place where the signature would have been if there had been a signature, thus making them all feel, stingingly, the presence of a woman who was in fact very far away. He refolded the paper and put it back into its blue envelope. He started to stuff this under his breastplate on the left side, from whence he had taken it; but impulsively—it appeared—he changed his mind. He went to George and thrust the envelope into his hands.

"This is too precious a paper, it is too sacred a document, to be subjected to the push and jostle of a crowd," he said in a voice the farthest hand could hear. "Master Fitzwilliam, you will return it to my cabin, and wait for me there."

George saw the trick, but he had no choice. If he remained on the bowling green it was probable that he'd be picked as a juror. And it was unlikely that he would vote for the conviction of a gently born person on the evidence at hand. For as one of twelve, George would have dared—and surely none of the others would have dared—to stand out against the admiral.

With a sob Drake said: "Guard this as though it were your own baby. Now, go."

George was to be eliminated. He bowed his head in grave acknowledgment, took the envelope, and went back to the *Golden Hind,* where he rejoined Diego, who was putting away the rejected garments. George helped him.

"What they doing out there?"

"A little thing called murder. But they're doing it legally."

"Señor?"

"Never mind."

Part of the proceedings—when they were finished with the wardrobe—they watched from the deck. A jury was empaneled, a certain amount of evidence was heard, and another speech was made. Then the admiral returned to his ship.

"I hope that the absence of that particular paper from our desk didn't inconvenience you, Fitzwilliam," he said while Diego was unstrapping his armor.

"That's all right," George answered.

"It was part of the work of the Lord," Francis Drake pointed out. "And now, if you two will leave me for a while—"

He was getting down on his knees as they went out.

He called them back a little later and made known that he would remain in the cabin.

"I must not do anything to influence their decision," he said.

Two hours and fifty-four minutes later the men on the beach sent a committee to notify the admiral that Thomas Doughty had been duly tried by a jury, which had found him guilty as charged. What was the wish of the queen's representative?

"Death," said Francis Drake.

32

Diego Was Bewildered

August 17 they sailed from that abode of gloom and on the 24th they arrived at the eastern mouth of the passage between the seas. The men were to call this—though never within the admiral's hearing—the Tunnel to Hell.

It is notable that this name was applied *afterward,* for the Hell was not the strait but its western end. Magellan Strait itself they found a not unpleasant place. The first few days it was wide, and if the hills on either side were stark there were sometimes fires and once they saw a few Indians fishing. The second afternoon they stopped at an island they called Penguin Island after the curious bird they found there in great numbers. The penguin walked upright, and it appeared to wag its absurd stubs of wings only for comic effect, as a jester his bauble. It had no feathers, only a thick black and white down, like that of a gosling. It was slow, and easily slaughtered. In that one afternoon the mariners estimated that they had clubbed to death two thousand— the smallest being about ten pounds in weight—yet the beach was still black with them.

Two days later they rounded a bend and the strait narrowed at some points to not more than a mile and a half across.

It made for silence, that closeness, and the men had time to reflect upon what had happened to Thomas Doughty.

They had to proceed with caution; they always hove-to at night. Still, the strait was passed through in sixteen days.

They came out into the great, the fabled South Sea—and were hit by what could only have been the wrath of God. For a month the water was mad, the air in a frenzy. Spray stung them like the studs on a scourge. They shortened so much canvas that by the third day and for all the rest of that terrible time they were being driven under bare sticks.

It was the *direction* in which they were driven that frightened them. The wind was north-northwest, and they were helpless before it, three cockleshells implacably pushed south. This was the end of the world, down here. The only thing below them was Terra Incognita Australis, upon the spikes of which they might at any moment be pounded to pieces.

Marigold vanished one night. They never did learn what had happened to her.

Drake had prepared a stone monument for the western end of the Magellan Strait, meaning with this to claim all that country for Queen Elizabeth. He never had a chance to erect it. Even after *Golden Hind* and *Elizabeth* had staggered back to the place from whence they had emerged, the weather still was so bad that this ceremony had to be postponed. Another storm struck them. *Golden Hind* rode out this second blow, but *Elizabeth* took refuge in the strait and was never seen again. They waited for more than a week, keeping watch. At last they set a northern course. The fleet of five that a year ago had sailed out of Plymouth now was one. The men, who had numbered more than a hundred and sixty, were less than eighty.

The weather cleared, and the wind steadied, blowing clean from the south, so that they fairly bowled along. The health of the crew, badly strained in those weeks of storm, waxed better every day. Other than ships and fighting men, the only thing they lacked was water. They had wine, but they craved water, which proved to be hard to come by in this wild country where the rivers sank into the sand before they could reach the sea.

They lost their master gunner, Great Nele, a Dane—as distinguished from Little Nele, who was a Fleming—on one of their attempts to fill the casks. It was at an island named Mocha, and the landing party was attacked by Indians. Great Nele was killed without linger, an arrow through his breast. The giant Diego, struck in the side of the neck, was whirled completely around and slammed against George, who half-hauled and half-carried him back to the boat, where he fainted from loss of blood as George clucked over him like a mother.

The admiral himself was hit in the face, just beneath the right eye. They were lucky to get away.

Again, near La Serena, a party of Spanish horse captured one of their number, a lad named John Minivy, who was slow about getting back to the boat. The Spaniards cut off Minivy's head and paraded it on the end of a pike up and down the beach until sunset, when they carried it away. The admiral sent a party ashore after dark to bury the headless corpse.

In neither of these cases did they get a drop of water.

It would seem that the incident near La Serena was not reported overland, for when they arrived at Valparaiso they astounded everybody, and took over the one vessel there, a coaster named *Capitana*, with the greatest of ease. In the *Capitana* were 1,770 jars of wine, a large number of cedar boards, and 24,000 pesos of gold from Valdivia. They took it all, including the vessel itself. However, one seaman had escaped and swum ashore to give the alarm, so that when they looted the village they did not get much.

They sailed December 6.

From December 22 to January 19, as George duly noted in Francis Drake's diary, they watered, wooded, and generally recovered at Salada Bay. They brought up from below and mounted several brass culverins. They also brought up the parts of a pinnace, which was assembled and launched. Their chief purpose in putting in at Salada Bay, however, and their only purpose in remaining there so long, was the hope of being rejoined by either *Marigold* or *Elizabeth*. But nothing like this happened.

They resumed their northward course.

At Tarapaca, in an unlocked storehouse, they found two men asleep with three thousand pesos of silver just brought down from Potosi on llamas. These llamas were the funniest beasts yet: bushy things with long skinny necks, an expression of perpetual astonishment on their faces. Also in the storehouse was a large quantity of *charquí,* beef that had been cut into long thin strips and dried in the sun. They took it and later ate it, as they did the llamas.

February 5 they dropped in at Arica, where they seized thirty-seven bars of silver, five hundred pesos in silver coins, and three hundred jars of wine. Always wine!

Callao, the port of Lima, was a sleepy little place, though the harbor was crowded with ships. These were small ships, all of them empty. The governor made a great ado about pursuit, but Drake shook him off.

It was at Callao that they heard about the *Cacafuego*.

Cacafuego was not her real name, Heaven forbid. Spanish is a language that cultivates its obscenity to such an extent as to make much of it untranslatable. "Spitfire" was as near as George could get, and nobody thought that amusing. The Spaniards were indefatigable nicknamers, and since each vessel should have a formal title, preferably religious, it was expected that each should also have a playful one. Columbus' *Niña* was properly the *Santa Clara,* while his flagship, *Santa Maria,* more often was called by the men *La Gallega.* The *Cacafuego's* real name was *Nuestra Señora de la Concepción.*

This ship, privately owned, bound for Panama, was said to bulge with treasure. For more than two weeks they stalked her, passing smaller prizes, and late in the afternoon of March 1, on a flat sea, they raised her. Before full darkness—what resistance could she make without so much as a pistol on board?—they took her.

Though there had been no fighting, the confusion was great. Mariners were whooping with joy after a glimpse of the treasures below. Passengers and officers of the Spanish ship were pleading for their lives.

Amid all the commotion there were two men who were silent, below deck on the *Golden Hind.* George Fitzwilliam, who would be responsible for the classification, evaluation, and stowage of all those immense riches, took no part in the celebration, for Diego was dying.

That Cimarron was a bewildered man. He had been struck by an arrow shot by some red man he never saw; this was graspable: Diego's whole life had been a fight. But the later part of that life—the years in England and Ireland as Drake's valet, the months at sea—were beyond his understanding. Nor could he love his master, though he conscientiously tried to do so; for he had been a chief, a sort of king, among his own people, and he was not attuned to act as lackey. Drake had tired of him, for though Diego was picturesque he was also stupid. It had been tacitly agreed that if Diego survived the Mocha wound, and if *Golden Hind* should go anywhere near Panama, he might be put ashore and given a chance to seek out his own savage hill-people. Perhaps that was why Diego had lasted so long. He had been very sturdy, and he took a long time dying.

His friend George Fitzwilliam was with him. Nobody thought of these two, the excitement being so great. The shouts and stamping, the thud of money chests, came faintly from above.

George had tried to persuade the Cimarron to think about the welfare of his soul, the future life; but Diego shook a feeble head. The savage had been converted to Christianity largely because of politeness—it had seemed to mean so much to the admiral!—and he never had made any try to survey its mysteries. He knew now that he was about to die and that he would not see his own people again, and his eyes begged George not to spend the last precious hours talking about transfiguration and things like that. So George had fallen silent.

The hilarity on deck continued until almost dawn. Diego did not. *"Hasta luego,"* he whispered at last, a little after midnight. His eyes rolled up, and he was done.

The men sang up above, and they talked exultantly of the things that they would do when they got home, as they passed jacks of rum back and forth. For they were very happy: the voyage had been made.

But George Fitzwilliam, down below, wept by the side of his dead friend's hammock.

33

Hangover and Hard Work

It was a godlike occupation—or so some men would have esteemed it—to sit in judgment over such a mass of treasure: to count and recount, stack and restack, the 1,300-odd bars of silver, to seal the fourteen huge chests after attesting to the weight of their contents, to class according to size the pearls, nuggets, opals, diamonds, rubies, and to pile the plate in great, glowing, exact stacks. It was also tiring. The air below deck was fetid; the light was poor. They had run out of wax candles, and George had only tallow ones. The realization that if he desired he could mount these in priceless gem-studded candlesticks did not in any way lessen their stink or the strain that they caused his eyes.

The admiral positively forbade that the performance of George's other routine duties, the keeping of the diary and the teaching of Spanish, be conducted on deck, where George might get some fresh air. Drake's reason, it could be supposed, was reluctance to let the hands see that somebody else did his writing or that he needed instruction in anything at all.

However, he prized George; and he was not a cruel man, so he promised readily enough to throw George's way whatever outside chores might present themselves. This was why they called George from the counting-house when a bark was sighted moving south.

She was slow, and looked heavy, and she hugged the shore.

After a few days in the company of the *Cacafuego*—days of hang-over and hard work—they had turned that vessel loose, together with her crew and passengers, though with very little of her original rich cargo. They had not then made a course for the Gulf of Panama, as no doubt the Spaniards would expect them to do, but instead had headed for the coast of Nicaragua, which they raised March 16. They could hardly hope to gain more riches. Their concern now was to get away.

Drake ordered around the pinnace and put George in charge. Then he went back to his cabin.

Four hours later George confronted him there.

"She's a coaster. Belongs to a man named Rodrigo Tello. She wouldn't be of any use to us."

"Gold?"

"None. No silver either."

"We don't have room for any more silver anyway."

"No pearls, no plate."

"What *is* she carrying? She looks crank in the bows."

"She's out of a place called Nicola, on the Rio de Pamar, and she's headed for Panama with a cargo of lard."

"Ugh!"

"Also sarsaparilla. That might be good for the men."

"All right. But don't be long about it."

"Also a large supply of honey and of dried maize."

"Bah! Is that all?"

"That's all in the hold, sir. But in the cabin—"

"What about the cabin? We don't need any prisoners."

"These two might interest you; they come from Acapulco."

"Um-m. I know all I need to know about that port. I'd like to burn the shipping there, to prevent it from chasing us across the sea, but the officers of the *Cacafuego* said it's too strong."

"Aye. These two men were waiting there for a new governor of the Philippines to come up from Panama, but it seems that this personage —his name, by the way, is Don Gonzalo Ronquillo—has elected to sail directly from Panama, so these two are on their way—"

Drake sprang to his feet.

"You mean they're—*pilots?*"

George nodded, grinning.

"The best in this part of the world. Alonso Sanchez Colchero and Martin de Aquirre, complete with charts."

Francis Drake rolled his eyes up and threw out his arms.

"Prayers! We must thank God for this!"

"A good idea," George agreed. "But it's near sundown, and we don't want those pilots to drift out of sight, now do we?"

In his triple capacity—historian, interpreter, navigator—George sat in at each of the conferences that followed. He was an admirer of Nuña da Silva—that caustic, cantankerous old Portugee who had been sent ashore with the *Cacafuego,* being of no use in this ocean. And he found Colchero and De Aquirre of the same class: men learned and at the same time practical, and stubbornly independent. Spain and Portugal for many years had striven to keep their sea lore to themselves. De Aquirre and Colchero, like Da Silva, belonged to a privileged group: artists who were at the same time adepts, holders of secrets, nautical high priests. Theirs was a knowledge that properly should have been universal, and they knew this. They might serve an enemy of their country, but they could not be forced. Drake was anxious to have one or both of them accompany the expedition west, and he offered large cash sums, also privileged positions in England afterward. Baffled by their bland refusal, furious because he couldn't get his way, he turned to threats, and blustered in such a manner as to disgust his secretary, who had never before seen him so wild, so vulgar. Colchero and De Aquirre remained unmoved.

Yet these pilots were not mum, especially with George in whom they recognized a kindred spirit. And all their maps, charts, and rutters or coast-books, together with their sealed sailing directions, were legitimate loot, to be held for reference. When at last, after several days of abuse, these inflexible men were put aboard of a Panama-bound coaster, hailed for that very purpose, the officers of *Golden Hind* had a much better idea of where they were and how they might get out.

It would not be the part of wisdom to spread sail for the other side of the South Sea at this time, since such a voyage would mean arrival in the Spice Islands at the height of the typhoon season. Several months should be allowed to elapse. Here was an opportunity to search the coast of California for the western end of that interoceanic passage, the other end of which Frobisher already had found—or thought he had found. This was a project close to George Fitzwilliam's heart, though the admiral seemed indifferent. As George had told Sir John Crofts, Drake never was interested in any enterprise that led *away from* the Spaniards and their accumulated gold, his lodestone. Nevertheless, and since there was no other way of passing the weeks, they turned north.

First, almost as though absent-mindedly, they took the town of

Guatulco, Guatemala. It was a miserable, flea-bitten place; and George could see no reason for molesting it, since they didn't even need wood or water. They picked up no shipping, neither did they get any news. Most of the inhabitants had decamped, and the few they captured—government officials who had refused to fly—stolidly resisted all questioning, howsoever streaked with threat. Drake was red with rage and indignation.

The mariners remained three days in Guatulco, and it was not likely that any of them ever would boast to his grandchildren about this feat-at-arms. The sole reason for it that George could see—and George was outspoken in his dislike of the deed, further irritating the admiral—was its effect upon the hands, who had been waxing restless. Things, in truth, had come *too* easily: there had been no fighting, and the men yearned for violence as they might have yearned for women. So they were permitted to sack the town.

Poor grubby sunbaked little Guatulco! They all but pulled it to pieces. Though they already had too much and though it wasn't very good, being somewhat sour, they took all the wine that they could find. Though they had no use for the bell from the church tower, and the labor was considerable, they unhitched and carried it off—only to throw it overboard a few days later. The church itself, easily the most pretentious building in town, they ransacked. They slashed the paintings and the altar cloth, and spat upon them. They splintered each saint's image. Using a maul, they battered the crucifix, and with this same tool they cracked the altar stone. One wag donned the chasuble, in which he paraded, now and then blowing his nose upon it. He was loudly cheered.

George, sickened by this exhibition, appealed to the admiral; but Francis Drake was curt, cold, and refused to interfere.

"They need the exercise," he said cynically.

California was a disappointment, as were the Californians—a glum unresponsive pack of beggars, drooping, dirty, not at all like the savages of Patagonia.

Though the mariners lived in such close quarters, and though they were farther from home than ever before, discipline was not relaxed: the admiral saw to that. Yet George himself, in the privacy of the cabin, and now that Diego was gone, became increasingly critical of the chief. Thus, when after only a few weeks of scouting the California coast the admiral gave orders to make about in search of a haven, George noisily remonstrated. George knew he couldn't win—for by this time Francis Drake thought himself infallible—but he believed that he should at least put himself on record as having been opposed to turning away from the first chance anybody had known to seek out the far end of Frobisher's passage; and when Drake suggested that he write into the record that the swing-around had been forced upon them by snow and adverse winds, George flatly refused.

"I had to do that sort of thing when I was a diplomat. Not now."

"You know, of course, that I can have some scribe rewrite the thing? Scribes are cheap."

"They always have been."

"You should think about when we get back."

"*If* we get back."

"That's a harsh word, Master Fitzwilliam."

"One of the harshest in the language. A truly *laconic* word. You've heard the story of the laconic reply?"

Guardedly: "Well . . ."

George went ahead all the same.

"Old Philip of Macedonia, the father of Alexander the Great, was a very fierce fighter. He didn't care for quarter. Once he was trying to bully the people of Laconia with an army at their borders. 'If I enter Laconia you shall all be exterminated,' he wrote. And they replied with that one famous word: 'If.' That's what we mean when we say that a thing is 'laconic.'"

Sensitive as he was about classical references, Drake could appreciate this story; and he came as near as he was ever likely to come to smiling. Nevertheless they continued south. Drake had no intention of getting beyond the range of the Spanish charts simply for the sake of a possible alley among the icebergs.

They found a fine bay, guarded on the north by a long rocky point, and there they remained for some weeks, refitting, careening. There was a great deal of fog, also many seals. They were comfortable there, but the labor took a long time. In order that the *Golden Hind* might be beached for scraping, every scrap of water, wine, food, and treasure had to be hauled out of her, also all the guns; and afterward, of course, it all had to be put back.

They broke up for firewood a small vessel they'd brought from Guatulco, having scarcely enough hands left to man *Golden Hind* herself.

They left the magnificent bay July 23, 1579.

None of them questioned the existence of Frobisher's northwest passage, but only George had been eager to seek it out for the sake of science. The others, after long exposure to tropical suns and at the first touch of chill, were glad to hear a southing order for the Moluccas, sometimes called the Spice Islands.

The trip was long, hot, and uneventful, the wind being with them all the way, the sea smooth. They saw no other vessel, and only faintly glimpsed a few flat scorched atolls.

The sultan of Ternate was a grumpy man, very fat, with a disagreeable expression. George would not have trusted him as far as he could spit, but Francis Drake appeared avid for some sort of contract or treaty, and they arranged at last to buy, with silver, six tons of cloves.

Repairing always, patching, scraping, laboriously holding themselves together, they built a fort on a place they called Crab Island; and there they lived, somehow, for a little while.

They did not seek new scenes; rather they avoided them. The men were weak, worn, and they had very little powder left.

George figured out—from the investments, the number of individual lays, including two of his own, and the value by his own estimate of the treasure, minus the pay of the crew—that *if* they got back (that laconic word again!) the voyage would prove to have paid about 4,700 per cent.

Already they had done what the maddest men never dreamed of. What if they had passed the land of Lochac? What if they did miss Ophir? They couldn't conceivably carry anything more.

They were wary. They tiptoed, avoiding all passers.

The night of January 9, 1580, far from any inhabited place, they struck a reef. Wind and seas were driving them farther on. They prayed, and some swore. Wildly they dumped cannons, also three tons of cloves. Then the wind fell off, the sea subsided, and *Golden Hind* slithered back into deep water.

March 26 they set a course for the Cape of Good Hope.

By the end of June they were back in the Atlantic.

September 26, 1580, they sailed into Plymouth Sound.

For months they had been as furtive as thieves, hailing no sail; for they were no longer armed, and they were very weak, slow too, their bottom being slubbered over with barnacles, their hold crammed with metal.

Any pirate could have snapped them up, the greatest prize in history.

Even when they entered the English Channel they remained coy. Yet the boat they encountered as they started into Plymouth Sound was no enemy. She was small, fat, clumsy, capacious: a fisher.

"Ahoy!"

"Ahoy yourself! What ship is that?"

Drake made no answer, being too eager to ask his own questions. With hands cupped, he called:

"Does the queen's majesty still live?"

"The— The queen?"

"Queen Elizabeth, dolt! She's alive?"

"Why shouldn't she be?"

Drake exhaled and leaned against the rail, relieved. That was all he needed to know. He never had sweated or trembled like this in battle. He was as weak as a baby, and could scarcely stand.

But another thought struck him, and his hands went to his mouth again, while to his face came the frown so many men had learned to fear.

"Tell me, what's Devonshire coming to when men make sail with nets on the Lord's day? You should hang your heads in shame!"

Those in the crumster were puzzled.

"This ain't the Sabbath, if your worship please."

"Don't call it that!"

("Sabbath" Captain Drake scorned as Jewish, while "Sunday" he believed to be of classical origin.)

"Well, it ain't the Lord's day either, then."

"Why, you fools! This is the twenty-fifth of September."

"No, sir. It's the twenty-sixth, and it's a Monday."

They might have gone on for some time this way, had not George intervened.

"The man's right, sir. We went around the world from east to west, and when we crossed the one hundred and eightieth meridian of longitude, a day dropped out of the calendar. That was last year, September 2, by my calculations. I told you at the time, sir, but you tut-tutted it."

"And—this is truly—"

"Monday, September 26, sir."

"Blessings be! I do not have to come back to England and see men setting forth to fish on the Lord's day. Call the hands together, Fitzwilliam. We'll have a service."

"Aye, aye, sir."

"But first get them to grease the anchor cables. And I want my plum-colored doublet laid out, and the dark blue velvet bonnet. You understand?"

"Aye, aye, sir."

34

Home Is the Hero

If the oyster could be defined as a fish built like a nut, Sir Laurence Godden might be called a man built like an apple. He was round; he was red, yet cool; he gleamed. He had taken some time to ripen, and might also take a long while rotting, for he would do this only in spots at first. He was bland, but he could be mildly acidulous. He even had, in the middle of an otherwise bald head, a stiff up-twisted fillup of hair that suggested a stem.

He smiled soapily.

"You must find it very tame here now, Master Fitzwilliam?"

George shrugged, a movement made supple by practice. Sir Laurence—attended by three other neighbors, each appropriately obsequious—was first cousin and political secretary to the earl; and since he would not call at Okeland merely to congratulate Sir John on the return of his son-in-law, and since he had already hinted at a soon-to-occur vacancy in Parliament, there seemed no shadow of doubt that he was feeling out Anne's father for the post. Now that George was back, Sir John had both the time and the money to go to Parliament, something that for years he had dearly wished to do. George summoned a deprecatory grin.

"Oh, not so tame," he murmured.

It was good to be rich. George had noted the change right away. More caps and bonnets were lifted to him—and lifted higher. From the lowest laborer grumbling over his wage, which had never before been half so high, to the very earl himself who had sent his own kinsman, the attitude of others was different. Even his wife, though never a natterer, was hushed in his presence if others were about. Just now, for instance, though she bent over her embroidery at the far end of the great-hall, a picture of ladylike industry, George had no doubt that she heard every word.

Sir John Crofts leaned forward.

"But—Wentworth?"

Peter Wentworth of Lillingstone-Lovell might be a hard man to dislodge. He was a rabid puritan, eloquent, troublesome, tiresome, tart. A champion, and surely fearless, he sometimes embarrassed his fellow members of the House of Commons by the stridency of his speech, as he nettled his neighbors here in sleepy Northampton by the fervor of his religious views.

"We hope to persuade Wentworth to resign on the ground of ill health."

"Why, the man's as strong as an ox!"

Sir Laurence still smiled, but his gooseberry eyes had gone opaque.

"There are, uh, ways of doing this," he said.

He finished his brandy and smacked his lips. It was good French brandy, though not as good as they should have had in their new circumstances, George reflected. George hoped to lay down a truly great cellar.

"It would in part depend," Sir Laurence continued, "on what substitute we had. If this was a man who'd have the confidence of every gentleman in the district, a man of outstanding integrity and ability, why, Peter Wentworth might be ousted. And we think we have found such a man. That's the reason we have come here this afternoon."

He turned full upon George.

"Master Fitzwilliam, would you consent to stand for the seat?"

The slow hum of an Okeland afternoon did not for an instant cease, but George's breathing did. There had been no hint of this, no clue previously given by the visitors.

Sir Laurence when he spoke for his cousin did not look for a refusal. He stared fixedly at George.

George had to think fast. If he refused the offer or even appeared to pause, he would incur the displeasure of the shire's hereditary nobleman, a displeasure that could mean shillings and pence, privileges too. On the other hand, if he accepted, it would break Sir John's heart.

Anne's hands as she leaned over the embroidery frame had ceased to move. Her maids, no doubt so instructed, worked on without a whisper. Anne's breath, George was sure, was caught up like his own. Her father, blinkless, had not yet fully realized what it was Sir Laurence said.

George smiled a little. He fished a letter from his purse. It had come by royal messenger that morning, and George had not intended to tell of it until he was ready to depart for London. But here was an emergency.

"I am most deeply touched." He was urbane, resuming his Madrid manner. "But when the queen's majesty speaks, even though it be through one of her ministers, a good subject's days are not his own. I

have been summoned to London, sir, by Master Secretary Walsingham."

"Ah?"

"He urges haste, in the name of his august mistress. It could be that
all they wish is mine own account of the late circumnavigation,"
went on George, who knew that they ardently desired to get their
hands on the diary he had kept for Francis Drake. "On the other hand,
it may be their wish to send me somewhere on a mission. I must hold
myself open for such an assignment. His lordship your cousin, sir, I
am sure will understand."

"Um . . . Yes. In that case . . . Well."

With the stirrup cup—it was served in glasses and deeply impressed
the visitors—they were more relaxed, talking amiably. Anne and Aunt
Sylvia came out and curtseyed. It was all very nicely done. Sir John
had recovered and was the good host again, though it was George who
helped Sir Laurence into saddle.

"Aye, tame, I should think," Sir Laurence wheezed. "I could certainly think it would seem so, after all you've been through."

As George had expected, the moment the men were gone Anne
pounced upon him, demanding that she be taken to London too. This,
curtly, he refused. The argument was suspended at supper, largely
out of respect for Sir John Crofts, but it was renewed as soon as they
were in their bedchamber.

Anne did not even pause long enough to praise him for having won
the offer of a seat. All she could think of was London, and she actually
scolded him—she who in ordinary circumstances was careful to keep
her voice down—for having failed to tell her about that letter from
Francis Walsingham.

She brushed aside his cavil that he might not be able to attend her
for more than a few hours once the city was reached, and that she,
having no relatives there, would be unguarded.

"I'm unguarded here!"

"Save for thy father, a steward, two assistant stewards, two garden-
ers, and four field hands, besides the women."

"Pooh!"

"Also, London's a much more perilous place than Northampton."

"Pooh!"

He pointed out that he might be sent away immediately, even somewhere abroad. He was a public figure now. He was available.

"But thou'lt see the queen, at least?"

"It seems likely."

"Then why shouldn't I?"

"Because thou hast not been commanded to appear. 'Tis not the custom to drop in on an anointed monarch as though she was a neighbor in the country. She— Well, she's not much to look at anyway."

"Not like the French woman at Sheffield, I take it?"

It was the first mention of Mary Stuart since George's return, and it came explosively—a shock. He had kept his ears open to little avail: England appeared to have forgotten "the strange guest" although George sensed that she was, as the saying went, in every man's mind, in no man's mouth.

Anne must have been overwrought to let slip that name. It was dark, and he could not see her.

But he could see, by the side of the bed where it rested on a stool, the December 1577-September 1588 diary of Francis Drake. A scrupulously honest narrative, signed at several of the more telling places by the admiral himself—for he could write his name, though with difficulty—it would be found to differ in sundry important respects from the official version of the voyage as compounded of the carefully pruned reports of the admiral and his officers. In the hands of Spanish spies it could be a bombshell. Spain and England were still, on paper, at peace; and Spain had a strong claim for the recovery of the loot, a claim that it might be hard to deny before the world *if* it was bolstered by such a document as this. The treasure was immense, and undoubtedly Elizabeth and her ministers would do everything possible to keep it in England, among themselves. But they wouldn't risk war —or at least the queen wouldn't, Burghley wouldn't, or Walsingham. The diary assuredly should have been sent to Whitehall by messenger immediately after the *Golden Hind* had dropped anchor at Plymouth. That this had not been done, that in the excitement George Fitzwilliam had been permitted to slip away with it under his arm, surely must have brought about a shrill scolding; and George suspected that Captain Drake, hero though he was, had had his ears boxed. The summons of that morning had been peremptory. George was to prepare himself instanter and was directed to wait only for one thing: the arrival, soon after the messenger, of a band of men-at-arms. Nothing else should delay him. He had not told Anne of this.

Now she stirred.

"But *why?*" she whispered fiercely. "Why should one piece of paper be permitted to stand against the word of many men?"

"'Tis more than one piece of paper. There's hundreds there."

"Well then, why should hundreds?"

"Because, my sweet, there are so many men who believe that ink can't lie. This is absurd, but they do. Their fellow men they might not credit, even in chorus—well, *especially* in chorus—but if it's writ on paper, they think, it simply must be true."

"Nonsense! Now if you'd only—"

"Sh-sh-sh!"

George had felt no fear of a thief while he slept, for the window was too high to be entered from the back of a horse, even if the rider stood in saddle, as once George had done; and though many things had lately been planted in the garden there was no vine set to climb this particular wall. The only way to enter the room he shared with his wife was through that in which her father bedded, and Sir John was a light sleeper.

But Sir John was not asleep now. The sobbing was so low, so slight, that they barely heard it. No doubt Sir John had supposed *them* asleep, and even so he was holding in his grief as best he could, being ashamed of himself.

It was an eerie sound, that sobbing. Utterly still, they lay for a long while listening to it. Parliament had meant a lot to Sir John Crofts.

35

All of Impulse

Anne was silent all the next day, and it was a silence that perturbed her husband. Though he had many things to look after, having been home for such a short time, George did not venture far from the house, for he was conscious of the diary in the bedroom. He wished that the soldiers would come and he could be on his way. The sooner he went the sooner he'd get back, and the sooner he got back the better. There were preparations for winter that clamored to catch his attention. There were, too, neighbors who pressed invitations upon him: they were eager to hear the tale of the voyage from his own lips. There was Terence Weddell, who had returned from the continent. Most of all, there was that never-failing wonder to be enjoyed: his wife.

So he fretted. And when no men came he announced angrily that he would depart at dawn, alone.

Anne made no comment at supper, nor yet later in bed. This in itself was odd, a disturbing circumstance. George did not sleep well that night.

The morning was different. It was all sparkle and nip, with smoke columns, straight-stripped, standing without wobble against a cobalt sky, a morning so still and clear that your throat caught at the feel of it against your face and you half believed you could hear God breathe.

George bussed his wife. He noted with some concern that she wore a brown cheverel dress, short in the skirt, a hat that matched, no ruff but a simple white fall, and shoes, as though she too was about to depart. Did she mean to be prepared, in case he changed his mind and asked her to go with him? Was she, who so seldom wept, intent upon trying tears? Would she storm?

Nothing happened. She only smiled up at him, bidding him to ride with care.

He bowed before Aunt Sylvia, shook hands with Sir John, and said a grateful farewell to the servants, every one of whom was out to Godspeed him.

Carefully he worked the diary, the sheets of which had been bound between stiff leather boards, into the right saddlebag.

He mounted, waved, and was off:

> *"Come away, come sweet love!*
> *The golden morning breaks.*
> *All the earth, and all the air,*
> *Of love and pleasure speaks."*

Just before he reached the edge of the small wood he must rim before he came to the Crossed Keys, he turned in saddle. This was the highest point of land for many miles around.

There were not many in the group before the door of Okeland now, and he was disheartened to see that Anne no longer was there. Of course she had many household duties, but he had hoped that she would remain for that final wave.

But it didn't matter, he told himself.

He tried the lay again:

> *"Come away, come sweet love!*
> *Do not in vain adorn*
> *Beauty's grace that should rise*
> *Like to the naked morn—"*

It was no use. Even with a lute he would have been in poor voice. Perhaps the wood by his side depressed him. It was the same in which he had hidden after skewering Antonio Salvo, and the fright that he

[198]

felt that early evening sometimes would come back to him, chilling his blood. He owned that wood now, having bought it from Weddell, and for years he had meant to cut it down, to use the land for pasture, enclosing it. Farmers, he supposed, like housewives, always had things they *planned* to do. If ever by chance they did get them all done they wouldn't be housewives any longer—or farmers.

The wood was at his east, so that it blocked the early sun, making the track dark. A breeze moved through it, stirring the leaves—still on the trees but sered at the edges—so that they whispered together, a susurrant sound.

As by instinct, George's hand went to the right saddlebag, just forward of his knee. Once the hand was there, he consciously used it, undoing the flap, half-withdrawing the diary, patting this, carefully replacing it.

He was worried about Anne. He'd been churlish. Should he turn back, even now? No. If there was to be trouble on this trip—and he felt in his bones that there would be—he should take it alone, not dragging in his wife.

Perhaps he should have waited for the men-at-arms? Then he might have brought Anne who could have one of her women with her, probably Helen, her favorite.

But—turn back before all those servants?

To his right, fields fell away to the west, bright with dew, an opalescent sheen. But to the left was the wood, its leaves sibilant, shadows close-packed. Queerly, as his steed paced past, George had the conviction that he was being watched from that wood. He could see nothing there and he could hear nothing but the furtive conference of leaves, yet he loosed the sword in his scabbard and once again he felt for and assured himself of the safety of the diary.

Clear at last of the shadow of the wood, and about to get upon the Market Harborough road—no highway, but better than the track he presently followed—he heaved a sigh of relief. For he no longer felt that he was being watched.

Surely, at least, there was nobody in the Crossed Keys. That shabby inn had been closed for more than two years, he had heard, though from its look it might have slumbered for twenty. How could any building in so short a time get to look so desolate? It had fallen apart bit by weary bit, crumbling to the soft sponginess of rot.

Even decay can fascinate. George reined, shaking his head. He had no fondness for the Crossed Keys, but he felt impelled to pay it the tribute of a sigh. Slowly he rode around it. And slowly he went away, shaking his head again, along the route to Biggleswade.

He had gone no more than a mile from the inn when he rounded a curve to find himself confronted by two men. They were mounted, facing him; and so narrow was the way that they blocked it. One held a drawn sword, a very long one. The other held a pistol, which he pointed at George.

"Here it is," George muttered, almost pleased to see that his presentiment had been well based.

He came to a halt, perforce.

"What the Devil do *you* want?" he cried.

In the course of his travels, as in the course of many hours spent riding over his fields, George Fitzwilliam's face had come to look as though it had been stained with walnut juice, and there was little that sun and dust and rain could do to it now. Nevertheless he had not even thought of undertaking a journey without his loo or half-mask. He no longer needed this, as when he'd just come out of a Spanish prison; but it remained a habit, as also perhaps a mark, an outward sign, of his gentility.

The men who confronted him also were masked, but their masks were large and long, covering the whole face: all George could see was eyes.

Their clothes, he was quick to note, were not cut in Spanish fashion. Moreover, the one who held the sword, and who now spoke, had no trace of Spanish accent. Foreigners, George supposed, would attract too much attention out here in the country. King Philip's spy-master in London, whoever he was, controlled a large purse, and he could afford the service of natives.

"Get down," the swordsman said.

So that was it? They wanted the horse, not George himself? They knew what was in the right-hand saddlebag?

For a wild instant George cursed his servants. They had all been there to bid him farewell, true, but it was the previous night that he'd disclosed his plan to start for London at dawn, and one of them could have slipped this snippet of news to somebody who lurked out of doors. However, that wouldn't account for this accoster's knowledge that the diary was in a saddlebag. Until just before he mounted, George had meant to stuff the thing under his doublet.

He'd been seen, then. And a message had been flashed, somehow, to these skulkers.

The wood! Some member of the band who had climbed a tree, and who was possessed of sharp eyesight, could have overlooked the scene before the Okeland Manor door, drawing his own conclusions. These conclusions such a man might well have verified when George, riding past the wood, had taken another peek at the diary. And he could have signaled this information to the men who now confronted George.

George didn't stir, but continued to regard the two coldly, his lip curled. As in Nombre de Dios, he reckoned, arrogance was the best policy.

They looked formidable. George had little knowledge of *mounted* swordplay, as the man who addressed him might have. The other, the one with the pistol, seemed less sure of himself. The pistol was heavy: he held it in both hands. The barrel was made of iron, very thick, very wide, a small cannon. The match was lighted, burning well in the crisp morning air, while the striker was drawn back. The man's forefinger was on the trigger.

They were fallible, those machines, and this one did not faze George. At least half the time they failed to fire. At best they wouldn't shoot more than a few yards. At worst, what with their huge touchholes, they were likely to flare back into the face of the man who held them —a possibility of which this particular scoundrel seemed well aware. George believed that the pistol was shown largely in the hope of intimidating him, and that the man with the drawn sword was capable of dealing with this situation by himself. Even so, George would have wheeled and galloped back toward Okeland, except for two things.

His mare, Alberta, was fresh but not fast, whereas these robbers were extremely well mounted; and since there was a third one back in the wood it could be assumed that part of the beauty of their plan lay in the fact that this man could cut off George's retreat.

At that very moment George heard hoofbeats behind him.

"I said 'dismount.'"

"Why, so you did," George agreed.

Alberta was a willing beast, but as she was no racer neither was she a hunter. He did not know how she might respond if he rode her across fields. In any event, he must not let himself be struck from behind. That approaching horseman sounded very close, back there. George turned.

He saw Anne. She smiled radiantly; and she was followed, on an ass, by Helen her maid, and two large hampers of clothing.

"Stop there!" George yelled.

She had seen the men now, and she no longer smiled. She reined to a halt, obedient. Helen too stopped. Probably they were out of the range of the pistol, but he couldn't be sure.

It had been his thought to draw sword and charge, but the presence of his wife changed that. A madheaded scheme anyway, he nodded thoughtfully, grimly. He started to dismount.

His foot slipped in the stirrup. Alberta, always a twitchy steed, shied. And the pistoleer fired.

Whether that man, like Alberta, had acted from nervousness, or whether he truly thought that George was about to resist, made no difference. That shot for an instant obliterated the rest of the world. A mass of gray-white smoke filled the air, which was made acrid with the smell of gunpowder. George felt as though he had been hit in the chest with a pike. He went backward, over Alberta's rump, to the ground.

The mare reared, screaming, made panicky by the shot.

Stunned, but retaining his senses, George scrambled to his feet. He drew sword and slapped Alberta's flank with the flat.

"*Away,* girl! *Away!*"

The mare wheeled, jumped a hedge, bolted across a hayfield.

And the robbers did just what George had hoped that they would do. They went after Alberta.

George brushed himself. He did not sheath. He made a brief bow to his wife. He rather admired her daring and ingenuity, for it was clear that she thought that if she surprised him from behind, dressed for travel, and packed and attended, he would let her come along rather than go back to the manor house and face all those servants. But of course he couldn't let this admiration show. A lesson was called for.

"Well met, my dear. This makes me more than ever determined that thou'lt not go with me until proper preparations can be made. We'll return now, and I'll wait for the escort, as I should have done in the first place."

"Art— Art thou all right?"

"I'm jarred, no more. Here, let me go first. There's another of these rascals back in the wood—if that shot hasn't frightened him away."

"But— Alberta! The diary!"

"Alberta will find her way back to the stables. Everybody around here knows her. As for the diary, I hid that in another place while I rode around the old Crossed Keys. An impulse."

He lugged the thing out from under his doublet. That doublet was ripped, a little to the right of the breastbone, and the stiff leather cover had been gashed by lead.

"A *lucky* impulse," George amended. "Now let's get back."

The queen's men-at-arms arrived at Okeland the next morning; and three days after that, in London, George delivered the diary to Sir Francis Walsingham.

He wondered if he would ever hear of that diary again—if anybody ever would. He doubted it. The thing would be lost to history, alas. The queen's majesty, though she had but lately learned of the existence of the diary and its whereabouts, had been in closet for many long hours and even days with Francis Drake, whom she knighted. She would have sopped up details, descriptions, figures; and she had the memory of an elephant. Already she knew everything that George had written; the diary itself could give her no news. Her only interest in it was to see it destroyed—to see this with her own royal eyes—lest it fall into the hands of the Spaniards and be of incalculable value to them in a lawsuit to recover the treasure. She must protect her investment. She might be doing it at that very moment.

In his mind's eye George could picture her: her accipitrine face lit by the red flames, she leaned over a fire in one of the remoter chambers at Hampton Court or Nonesuch, gloating, as with her own hand she fed the diary, page by torn page, to oblivion. She would probably stir the ashes afterward; she wanted to be sure of her money.

Well, that was high politics, George supposed. He shrugged. After all, he had done *his* part.

36

How Many Women?

George's wrists rested upon his knees. Exasperated, he waggled his hands, so that the reflection of the gemmery in his rings flecked the ceiling.

"But—why *me*? With all the well-mounted men you have at your command, why pick one who hates this service?"

"There are various reasons," replied Sir Francis Walsingham, who, long and dour, drably dressed, fitted that lugubrious place. "One is that you have done it several times. You know the way."

"So would a professional courier."

"A professional courier would expect to be paid. Not so you."

"Why not?"

"Look at the money you've made! It puts you into a different class. The queen's highness likes to have her errands run by men who can pay their way."

"I see."

"There are inconveniences about being rich, as you will learn."

"I think I am learning it."

"And there are other reasons. You will be well received, for Shrewsbury likes you and so doth Mary Stuart."

Fatuously, George was thrilled. His heart skipped like that of some smitten boy, and his mouth went dry.

"Then too, you have been away, and so you're not involved in Shrewsbury's domestic wrangles."

"Eh?"

"You see? You've never even heard of the strife with his wife! But everybody else in England has. Their feud may yet affect governmental policy. I'd like a report on this too."

"*You* would?"

"The queen's majesty would."

"Oh? She's interested in such petty matters?"

"Master Fitzwilliam, when the premier peer of the realm and its richest countess—who happen also to be host to the world's most embarrassing visitor—when *they* call one another names it is not a petty matter: it is an affair of state."

"I see."

"There is yet another reason why you'll make the ideal messenger just now, Master Fitzwilliam. You are one of the Argonauts. You've been near to the captain who is being called the master thief of the unknown world. You have a tale to tell and all the world wishes to hear it."

Miserably: "I know."

Walsingham looked like a man who looks older than he is. It was a characteristic he had in common with Lord Burghley, who, however, could never have known youth, and might almost have been born with a long beard and a wrinkled brow. Walsingham harrumphed, sourly eyeing his protégé.

"Thus you have an entertainment value, like some fine poet."

"Sing for my supper, eh?"

"It could be called that. To select an Argonaut is subtly flattering. It is like sending Shrewsbury a brace of gerfalcons or a prime stallion. Except that *you* can keep your eyes open."

"And you want me to tell my story to Mary Stuart? Damn it, man, I've just told it to one queen!"

He had indeed spent most of the morning in a private chamber with her majesty of England, who asked him many questions about the circumnavigation, questions that hit like pellets. He could still see her thin small face as she leaned toward him, intent upon his words, her small dark cold eyes not unlike the eyes of a snake, bloodless lips, knife-edged nose, waxy oval mustard-colored freckles, stringy reddish hair. He still could hear the squeak of her querulous voice.

Walsingham frowned. For all his scorn of the bright and gay, at heart he was the perfect courtier and it smarted him to hear an anointed monarch lightly named. He harrumphed again, this time with a note of disapproval.

"Not unless she asks for it. She may know nothing about the trip around the world. She gets only what Shrewsbury elects to feed her, and this he might have thought to withhold. For Mary has connived in secret messages with the king of Spain. She would make him her heir. She'd send him her son, the king of Scotland, whose title she does not recognize. Her French cousins have all but repudiated her, so she casts her lot with Spain. A desperate thing to do."

"She's a desperate woman."

"Perhaps not desperate enough. It could be that Shrewsbury guards her *too* carefully. It could be that she should be given more rope."

"To hang herself with?"

"What else?"

The man was shameless, as he was implacable. He had been trying for years to get Mary Stuart legally killed, and he would continue to try, using any means at hand. He made no bones about this, for he esteemed it a patriotic duty, a duty as well to his puritanical God. Whatever else he might be, Francis Walsingham was no hypocrite: he was so powerful that he could afford to be honest.

"You ask me to help you betray a prisoner? You ask me to rig some trap into which an unsuspecting woman will stumble, just because she has expressed a fondness for my company?"

"No. There are limits to what any man can be commanded."

"It gladdens me to hear you concede that."

"What I *do* expect you to do is examine the situation at Sheffield Castle. See what precautions are taken against the French woman's escape. They may be overrigorous. See what state of health she's in, and what state of mind too. The place may be too strong. We may have to move her."

"And what card would you play for that? The queen?"

Sarcasm never had an effect upon this saturnine man.

"I expect you to deliver me a report on the conditions of her captivity."

"Oh, she's a captive now? I had thought she was still a guest?"

"We have official reports, of course. But they lack certain details. And I know of no man better equipped to carry out this task than you, Master Fitzwilliam. I cannot sympathize with your softness toward an unscrupulous conspirator, but I have nothing but applause for your integrity."

"Why, thank you!"

"If you don't wish to accept this commission at my hands, I can of course arrange to have the queen herself ask you. That would be a command, then."

George sighed. He waggled his hands again, and again those flecks of colored light rioted across the ceiling.

"All right," he said. "Now, could you be more specific? Just what lies am I expected to tell this time?"

George brought a bolt of sarsenet, a roll of whipped reticella lace, and sundry sweetmeats, such as sugar sops and eringo, to Anne and Aunt Sylvia; but he was reluctant to talk about the trip. Oh, yes, he had seen the queen. For a long while? Too long. What did she look like? Oh, about the same—maybe a little skinnier, a little more shrewish. What was she wearing? To tell the truth, he had not noticed, excepting that it was something blue.

None of this was very satisfactory, and silence fitted down like a lid on Okeland after Anne had asked him outright where he was being sent this time.

"Oh, north."

"To see whom?"

"Why," he answered carelessly, "the other queen."

She looked at him a moment, then turned sharply and went back to the kitchens.

He felt sorry for her. Like everybody else—everybody who hadn't met her—Anne thought of Mary Stuart as a schemer of no conscience, to face whom was fatal for any man, for she ruined them simply in order to feed her own lascivious delight. Anne could not be expected to know how gentle and sweet the Scottish queen was, how thoughtful, how kind. True, she had been brought up in the rottenest court in Christendom, the court of France, but that did not necessarily make *her* rotten. If only she could be taken out of that great gloomy pile and allowed to move about, smiling that inimitable smile of hers! But

—she had *too* much charm. She was too lovely. They were afraid of her, so they kept her locked up.

Anne was a woman, and she took it like a woman, personally. He didn't blame her, but in this one matter he avoided her. He hated to see her suffer.

No doubt Anne, like everybody else, believed that the trouble between the Shrewsburys—a widely discussed tiff, George had learned —could be pointed back to Mary of Scotland, who had led the nobleman astray. This was nonsense. Dry, cautious George Talbot, sixth earl of Shrewsbury, was not one to be led astray by anybody, least of all by someone under his own roof: he took his responsibilities much too seriously. And Mary of Scotland took her royal position too seriously to be guilty, even absently, of flirtation. Why, she was the most *un*flirtatious woman imaginable! Anybody who knew her knew that; just as anyone who knew Bess of Hardwick, old Hatchet-Face, would know that she'd cause trouble in Heaven itself, if ever she got there.

George was glad when the time came to ride north.

Anne permitted herself to be kissed, but there was nothing more than that. For a fleet moment George thought of digging out those sonnets, which he had never mentioned to her; but he passed this plan, being too shy.

Aunt Sylvia, who was very old, and Sir John, who was both old and ailing, might not have noticed that there was anything wrong; but certainly the servants did.

Dumpy inside, George rode first to Weddell Manor, which was on his way anyway. It would be good to see Terence again, after so long. But Terence wasn't there, and the stupid retainers appeared to have no notion of where he was or when he would come back. Sylvestre the short, the bass-voiced, was not there either. Nobody seemed to know what had happened to Sylvestre. George nodded, and went on.

It was a morning of glint and flare, colored like a huge pearl, chill yet dry. After a while, as he rode north, his spirits revived. For—this was England. Where else was there a country so clean, so pleasant to the eye? He began to hum, and then to sing:

> *"God save our gracious sovereign,*
> *Elizabeth by name,*
> *That long unto our comfort*
> *She may both rule and reign."*

Well, he subscribed to that sentiment. Elizabeth Tudor was truly the sovereign, and he would fight for her title at any time, no matter what he thought of the lady herself. She was England, as this was England around him. That he went to call on another queen did not make him a traitor. And as for Anne . . .

Somewhere in Derbyshire, when it was getting late and he should have begun to think about an inn, three glass balls bounded out before his path.

It was odd, he thought as he reined. He had not passed so much as a wattle-and-thatch hut for some time. But here were these glass balls.

One was bright green, one blue, the other the yellow of buttercups, a frivolous color.

They had come out of the wood on his left, where stealthy shadows congregated now.

He dismounted and picked the things up. It so happened that he had to relieve himself anyway, so he turned to the left and walked a little way into the wood.

Immediately he came upon a glade, where the sun still shone. There were eight or nine men there, most of them hunkered down on their heels, all of them ragged. There was a small fire, which he had not sniffed because the wind was adverse.

A large man, a veritable Goliath of Gath, bearded like a Visigoth, hair everywhere, and no doubt lousy as well, held an exquisite Toledo rapier, a sword any duke might have envied. With the flat of it, viciously he slapped the bare back of a smallish, hunched man, who was whimpering under the chastisement. The welts appeared long and red, angry. The other men watched.

Here was a band of ruffians, George assumed, and they had their own discipline, their rules, their convictions, and punishment. Ordinarily he would have turned away.

But that was a memorable piece of steel. How had the rascal got it?

"You could put that to better use," George said coldly.

Absorbed until that moment, none of them had seen him. Now they gasped, their jaws dropping. The humped small one, flat on the ground, only went on moaning; but the giant who held the rapier whirled upon George.

"God's cullions! Who art thou?"

It was much to be thou'ed by such slime, yet George remained equable.

"It was made for a gentleman," he pointed out. "It should be used in a gentlemanly fashion. That's good steel, you clod."

Breathing heavily, as much from astonishment as from his recent exertions, the giant regarded George for a long minute. George of course wore his loo. His bonnet was bright, but no aigrette fastened it. The rings on his fingers were covered with thin red leather gauntlets. The gaze of the giant instantly centered upon the ruby in the lobe of George's left ear.

"Um-m," he said.

Inwardly George boiled. Who was this blob of ordure that dared look upon an earring Mary Queen of Scots once had owned?

George should have bowed and backed away; it was none of his affair; but that stare infuriated him. It was as though the filthy fellow actually had reached out and laid a hand upon Mary Stuart. It was sacrilege!

"A better use for it, popinjay? Mayhap thou'rt right. A better use for it might be to run it through thy guts."

"Good," said George. "Why don't you try?"

He drew.

37

Artists in the Moonlight

The light was good, though it would not remain so. The ground was level and dry, and moreover it was uncluttered. The fire, with a pot hanging from a tripod, was off to one side of this clearing. The beaten man had crawled or been dragged away from the center; and the others, all eyes, had simply shuffled back a bit.

The hairy man, the big one, stared. He was not fazed, only flabbergasted; he had not expected defiance. For he was, evidently, an upright-man: a chief or crownless king of the underworld of the road. Such complete ruffians had absolute command over their own gang of nips and foists, dummerers, Abraham-men, hookers, fraters, whatnot. Such a personage stayed undisputed among his followers. He had all power of punishment, even to life and death. This he kept, of course, only because he was so strong, so violent, and desperate. Already marked, probably branded as a thief, so that the next time he was napped it would mean a noose, he had nothing to lose but his life. And he would brook no wisp of disagreement; he couldn't afford it.

The upright-man, an utter outlaw, always was a brute, though sometimes he was a cunning brute.

This one was different from most, not in the matter of ferocity but because of his weapon. A cudgel would have been more usual, or if a sword, then a heavy old-fashioned broadsword. A rapier in the hand of such a ruffian was like a bracelet around the neck of a bull.

Yet this Visigoth at least knew how to hold it. After his first eye-popping amazement he smiled—a rather mean, side-slanted smile. He started toward George.

He did not move like a fencer—right foot forward, left arm back, the point threatening. Instead he *strolled,* superbly confident, while he swished the blade before him as though he would knock the heads off daisies.

George retreated.

It has been said that the best fencer in the world would not be afraid to face the second-best fencer, but he might well be afraid to face the fifth- or sixth-best. However many treatises might be written, or diagrams drawn, however many lectures might be given about the punta riversa, the stoccata, the incartata, the volte, all the rest of it, there remained the fact that swordplay was dangerous even for the adept. You never knew what might happen. You never could be sure what the other man might do; and the scantier his training, the greater this uncertainty.

George retreated a little farther.

Scornfully, Goliath fell into guard position. He cut high for the head. George ducked, and half-lunged, pinking the right kneecap.

The upright-man bellowed. It must have been hideously painful, like being touched with a red-hot poker. It would not cripple him, but it caused him to pause for a moment.

Then George went in.

George would have preferred a feeling-out period, would have liked to wait for the other to attack. But what with the failing light and the possibility of interference if the upright-man shouted for it—George could have been tripped—he deemed it best to get the business over with right away.

He feinted high, then feinted low. Then he slipped under the Visigoth's guard and touched the right forearm, drawing blood. He menaced the eyes, steadily advancing. The giant, bewildered, fell back.

George held his blade in the high line, circling the point. The giant fell farther back. George dropped his guard suddenly, and went in low—to slap with the flat the pricked kneecap. There was another screech of pain.

George moved ahead, not smiling, making no unneeded motion. He had scant respect for bravado. Flourishes were for fencers who didn't know better; George was not performing for the benefit of spectators. His object was to win. This bout should be an easy one, but he would not relax until it had been finished.

Had he dared, the giant would have turned, would have run away. As it was, he retreated until his back was against a tree at the edge of the glade. There, trapped, his eyes enormous, face wet with sweat, he perforce paused. He lowered his point.

George took this for surrender. Disgusted, he turned away.

"You may keep your sword," he muttered.

It might have been the intake of breath from those who watched, or perhaps the prompting of his own protective instinct. Whatever it was, without conscious reasoning he threw himself flat. And the Visigoth, who had been about to run him through as his back was turned, stumbled over him, cutting only air.

George leapt to his feet.

"Now you may *not* keep your sword!"

Their positions were reversed, and George again had the length of the glade in which to pursue. He did this, never giving the upright-man a chance to make a stand, while he pinked him in three places and sliced a chunk of skin from the right shoulder.

It was too much. The ruffian, whimpering in fright, dropped his rapier and ran into the wood.

George sheathed. He looked around. Save for the beaten man, who lay face down, they were all staring at him, wondering who he was.

He jerked his head to indicate the darkening wood.

"Will he come back?"

They chinned an emphatic no. The upright-man should have stood his ground. Once he had shown the white feather he need hope for no further obedience—unless he got control of another such group elsewhere. Meanwhile, the men who regarded George Fitzwilliam were leaderless, and they looked a little lost.

George smiled at them.

He went to where the stumpy small man lay, and gravely he studied a back that might have been a mass of raw beef. There was, oddly, something familiar about this man, who lay, his face buried in the grass, semiconscious, sometimes moaning a little. But George had no acquaintances among strolling players, and the hideously slashed back and the failing light did not encourage a close inspection. He shook his head.

"Better do something. Anybody got butter?"

Someone tittered. In the half-darkness George could not see which it was.

"Anybody got any French brandy?" a voice asked. "Anybody got any peahen cooked in Burgundy? Anybody got any marchpane?"

George grinned.

"Well, what about bear grease?"

"I have that," said the man next to him. "I'll take care of him."

"Good. Give him these again, when he recovers."

George put the three glass balls on the ground before the lashed man.

"A juggler, eh?"

"Aye, your worship. And a good one."

"But I take it not good enough to please old Fusty-Whiskers, the personage who has just departed? He dropped his tossers, and Fusty-Whiskers kicked them aside and started to lam him, eh?"

"Aye. He was often that way. Impulsive."

They spoke of the upright-man as though he were dead. As far as they were concerned he was.

George ambled over to the pot.

"Smells good. What is it?"

"Cony."

"Seems more like chicken."

"It's cony. You can't catch chickens running wild in the wood."

"You can catch 'em running tame in a farmyard, after dark."

"Cony. Would your honor like to try some?"

"Supernaculum!"

"Again, please, sir?"

"Go to! What I meant was that it would be a delight. Thanks."

They served him in the upright-man's bowl, a silver one: all the rest were treen. They seated him upon the upright-man's stool.

"Excellent chicken," he pronounced.

He stretched his legs, wiped his mouth, and contentedly belched.

"Come now," he said. "You have been kind to this wayfarer. But I must give you good even, if I'm to get to Whittington before midnight."

"The Cock and Pyenot?"

"Aye."

"That's full of fleas, your honor."

"Oh? I had not heard so. I've never slept there, but it's only a few miles from the place where I mean to go, and—"

"Why not spend the night here, sir? There's God's plenty of water" —and indeed before this George had heard the important pitter of a brook near at hand—"and we could have berries for breakfast and perhaps more of that, uh, cony."

George paused. The night was mild, and he had ridden hard.

"Mighty Mitch won't come back," another said, clearly referring to the upright-man. "You could use his blankets. They're cleaner'n the ones at the Cock and Pyenot."

This, following the offer of the stool and the silver bowl, had about it a suggestion of investment in the robes of some abdicated king; and George was wary about getting involved with strangers. Nevertheless these men were quiet, not ruffianly, though surely in rags; and they seemed sincere, being grateful. Before George could make up his mind, an old man spoke. He was the oldest of them all, and the most dignified.

"If your worship will loiter here we'd be pleased to regale you with an exhibition of our art."

George swallowed, uncertain whether he had heard aright.

"You— Well then, you are artists?"

"Oh, truly, sir! You didn't take us for vagabonds, did you?"

"No, no! Of course not!"

"Most of us have played in London. Or at least *near* London. Southwark. I myself have been a member of the earl of Leicester's company."

"Have you, now?"

"Yet too much of the city, you see, sir, it cramps the free spirit. A player can't go on giving of his best every morning and every afternoon unless he make contact with the people—the everyday people, I mean, the *working* people, the *common* people."

"Yes, I can see that that might be so."

The old man clapped his hands and called an order, and they unpacked their baggage, with extraordinary results. They must have planned to spend most nights in barns or stables rather than in the open air, for they had pitifully few camping utensils. But they did have many cloaks and robes, crowns and scepters, spangles, musical instruments, hoops—all of them, at least in the light of an emergent moon, looking very rich indeed, very brave.

It was startling. These ragamuffins, clad in false finery, glittering, were skilled. They danced, they played, they tumbled. Two put on a truly hilarious burlesque wrestling match: they had George roaring with laughter. The wee juggler with his glass balls was excused from performing tonight, though George again and again was assured that he was brilliant, a true artist.

The old man himself was the most impressive. Radiantly robed, his chin high, he spoke one of George's favorites:

> *"The rugged Pyrrhus, he whose sable arms,*
> *Black as his purpose, did the night resemble*
> *When he lay couched in the ominous horse—"*

The old man's beard gleamed white in the moonlight. He had a resonant baritone, and he rolled the accents—yet not mouthing them, for they never tangled in his teeth.

> *"But, as we often see, against some storm,*
> *A silence in the heavens, the rack stand still,*
> *The bold winds speechless and the orb below*
> *As hush as death, anon the dreadful thunder*
> *Did rend the region—"*

It was magnificent. It was English. The old man's face, as he looked up, was lit with glory. The syllables rang.

> *"Out, out, thou strumpet, Fortune! All you gods*
> *In general synod, take away her power;*
> *Break all the spokes and fellies from her wheel,*
> *And bowl the round nave down the hill of heaven,*
> *As low as to the fiends!"*

George was weeping long before the end; they all wept, though the others must have heard it before. George wrung the old man's hand.

"God's mercy! I wish I could do that!"

"Thank you kindly, sir." The old man himself was weeping. "To the performer, praise is salt."

This was too solemn a note on which to end the evening, so at George's request they passed him the lyre, which was in tolerably good tune. There were also a recorder and a lysarden, and every one of the men had a good voice and knew all the airs.

When he unsaddled and rubbed down his horse—he did not permit any of the artists to do this for him—George had fetched out of a saddlebag a flask of brandy, which he now passed around. It wasn't much, but they did not need much to fight the gathering chill.

They sang then. They sang "Kiss Me, Alice, Let Me Go" and "Green Sleeves," and "Never Weather-Beaten Sail," and many another popular one. They did it well, too. If a fussy old owl was the only creature to hear, it made no difference there under the moon. And when at last they rolled up in their blankets or rags on a bed of plucked moss, they were sleepy and happy.

"You have never been members of the queen's own company, any of you?" George asked in the darkness.

"Oh, no, sir," several whispered.

"I have been approached," the old man said. "I have taken it into consideration. Perhaps I should have accepted, if only to be able to say that I had."

"I see. But then none of you has ever performed before a queen?"

"Why, no, your worship."

"Tomorrow," George promised, "you will do so."

38

The Gilt Was Wearing Thin

He had spoken too soon. The players could not get to Sheffield the next day if they had to go by foot.

"If we'd had a horse we'd've et it," one of them pointed out.

So George rode ahead, the agreement being that they would present themselves at the gate the following morning. This would give George a chance to prepare Lord Shrewsbury.

Though the weather was mild, the sight of the castle struck a chill to George's breast. Rain better suited Sheffield; sunshine seemed afraid to fall on those gray grim walls. It was the most *relentless* building George ever had seen. That scummy moat could have been Styx; the guard, in chat with a slattern from the village, many-headed Cerberus and his mistress Hecate; whilst those who plodded back and forth across the draw suggested the Erinyes. George looked up, half expecting to see carved in the stone above the gateway the words of the Italian poet: *Lasciate ogni speranza voi ch'entrate*—All hope abandon, ye who enter here.

As each time before, he skipped when he passed under a portcullis that dangled like some Damoclean sword; yet his mien when he demanded entrance was supercilious. He would not even consent to see John Bateman the secretary, but insisted that he be taken instanter to my lord of Shrewsbury himself. And this was done.

Shrewsbury's eyes darted back and forth, and his voice was more fretful than ever, but his manners remained fine and it was with warmth that he greeted George Fitzwilliam, rising to shake George's hand, calling for wine. Bateman he waved away.

Shrewsbury, since Norfolk's execution the premier peer of the realm, held most of his properties in the north of England, far from any seaport. He had not been an investor in the voyage of circum-navigation: this George knew. All the same, and like everybody else in England, noble or common, he was fascinated by the affair. He would have many questions to ask. Pent in this dreary grand place, laden with responsibilities, aware that men were sniggering behind his back about his effort to divorce his wife, he had been highly unhappy; and he looked upon George with relief. He even started to talk about Drake before the arrival of the wine.

"Um, to be sure, aye," murmured George, looking away.

He had a pearl of great price here, and he knew it. Sing for his supper, forsooth? Why, he'd sing for more than that!

"The man himself I'm unacquainted with, of course. One of that Plymouth crowd, and clearly a pusher. They do say that the queen's highness bestowed the accolade upon him by reason of these monu-mental robberies. Oh, I cry your pardon, Master Fitzwilliam!"

George smiled.

"Not a bit. I call them robberies too."

He sipped his wine, a full-bodied red Beaune, very good.

"So I wondered if perhaps you—"

"Forgive me, my lord, but were it not meet that the queen's concern come first?"

"You have some word from her majesty?"

"Only indirectly. I saw her, last week. I talked long with her, as I shall tell you anon. But just now—it was Master Secretary Walsing-ham's suggestion, as you can see in his letter—if you can promise me an audience—"

"Surely! I'll write right now!"

He did so, with an almost undignified haste, his hand shaking.

"Oh, she'll consent! She hasn't had a visitor in four months! And she always did like you, Master Fitzwilliam."

"If she consents, I take it that I might be permitted to wear my sword on that occasion?"

"Well . . . After all, we do know you well by this time, eh? Ha, ha! Aye, I think we could make that small privilege."

"Gramercy."

But George, who knew he had a good thing, would not be rushed. He had been bored by that business, three years of ennui, yet it was as though he were the only man ever to reach the moon and return to tell his tale. From the lousiest oaf who loafed outside of The Plow, up to her royal majesty Elizabeth, by grace of God queen of England and Ireland, queen of France, etc., they hung on his every word.

"There's another matter, my lord. Or rather, an extension of the first. Master Secretary Walsingham gave me to understand that it was his wish—so far of course as this concurred with your own convenience, my lord—that Scotland's grace should be amused in some manner, or diverted."

"Frank Walsingham said that?"

It bumped George to hear the lank vinegarish secretary called "Frank." But he was dogged. If he was to tell a lie at all, it might as well be a big one.

"Nay, I know not his reason. Something devious, no doubt."

"No doubt," darkly.

"And it was because of this that I brought a troupe of players."

If he had said that he brought a coopful of tigers Shrewsbury could not have been more astounded.

"Players! Good God, man, you mean that the queen lent you her own?"

"Oh, no. Not those."

"Leicester's, then?"

"Not his either. No, these have no sponsor, and they, uh, they really have no name. But talent they do have, as my lord will see tomorrow morning when they come knocking at the gate."

"But— But look here, Fitzwilliam, unlicensed players are forbidden by law!"

"So many things are forbidden by law, my lord."

"But such men are rated as vagabonds, criminals. I can't allow them inside my castle."

"Not even to entertain Scotland's monarch? Not even to please Sir Francis Walsingham? Oh, the lady's your charge, sir, and you are to be the judge of her security, but doesn't that include her bodily well-being? It would be most embarrassing if she died. Everyone would say that she had been assassinated. Now—couldn't a circus be called a health measure?"

He spread his hands.

"After all, the outer bailey is large, and the portcullis could be lowered, the bridge raised. Your own soldiers, your own townspeople —what have you to fear from a handful of mummers?"

In any other circumstances, he was sure, he would not have won his petition. As it was, Shrewsbury agreed only with many complicated qualifications. But he did agree.

Then, and not until then, George told his tale. It was interrupted only once, and then by a messenger from Mary Stuart's own apartments in the Scroll Tower. Shrewsbury read the note with impatience, then shoved it aside.

"Scotland pleads her stomach. She's abed. But she sends a greeting to you, sir, and will receive you tomorrow morning at eleven. Now, as to the time when you went ashore at—"

"Forgive me, my lord, but did you tell her anything about the players?"

"No, no. Now if—"

"Good. Then I shall break these news to her."

He did so next morning on the ground floor of the Scroll Tower, which was as dim as ever. He had kept the earl of Shrewsbury's own valet de chambre busy for more than three hours the previous evening, after the besought tale had been finished at last, and he looked his best, well rested, the dust of the journey wiped away.

He knew the same sensations that he had felt the first time he entered this chamber: tightening of the throat, airiness of the knees and feet, inability to turn his head, or even to swerve his eyes. Though he could not see her distinctly, when first he came in, she caught him as before; and she held him.

"We are happy to greet you again, Master Fitzwilliam."

It was the same voice, limpid, not chill, not caressive either, the voice of a fond faithful friend. Yet . . . something was different.

"So much has happened in the world since last we met, Master Fitzwilliam. But none of it happened to me. I simply stay here. So I have nothing to tell you. But surely *you* have something to tell *me?*"

He did not believe that she was hinting for the tale of the circumnavigation, of which it was unlikely that she had heard; and in any event, George had promised Shrewsbury not to mention this.

"Immediately, ma'am. Aye. Not of the past."

"Who cares for the past, sirrah? Rise, rise."

It was not until he got to his feet that he had a real look at her. She had much declined. She would always be beautiful, and her voice was a young woman's; but the years of confinement had taken their toll. The face was pasty, and even its delicate heart-shape was somewhat marred by flabbiness under the chin. The eyes remained enigmatic, and George couldn't even have named their color, though he knew that they were dark; but the hair was much thinner than it had been, and he suspected that it was braced and laced with switches, and possibly touched with dye. The gown was very long, so that George was not vouchsafed a glimpse of the ankles, which he had heard were swollen now with dropsy. The gown itself was in good condition, but the draperies over Mary Stuart's head, her royal hangings, had faded; and the gilt was wearing off, for now George could scarcely read those curious words: *En ma fin est mon commencement.*

These things did not matter. She was Mary Stuart. That was all he needed to know, or cared to.

Shrewsbury and only three gentlemen were ranged behind George, though the guards at the door were four. The master of the household, that same aged man George had seen twice before, was impeccably dressed, and his air was one of distinction, but he no longer had a sword at his side. Behind the throne, where there should have been scores, there were but eight attendants, male and female alike.

George noted that young Anthony Babington was not one of these, and he asked about him.

"He has inherited," Queen Mary replied. "He has an estate in Northumberland, near Chartley."

"He would do well to stay there," put in the host. "He's a fanatic, that lad."

"My lord Shrewsbury always fears ardor, in any form," Mary said with a small thorny smile. "He dreaded that one of his too-ready men-at-arms would cut down poor little Tonino. So he sent him away. Tonino had no right to such fervor."

Shrewsbury muttered something, but did not otherwise speak.

Queen Mary asked about Terence. There was not much that George could tell her, for he had not seen Terence Weddell in more than three years, and the rumors of the countryside were hazy.

She understood, and gave him a chance to change the subject.

"You mentioned some *immediate* news, Master Fitzwilliam?"

"Ma'am, 'tis of a frivolous nature."

"And who is Scotland to be above frivolity? Pray proceed."

"Ma'am, there is a company of strolling players clamoring for admittance, and my lord of Shrewsbury has agreed that they may be permitted to give their show in the lower bailey this afternoon, provided that your majesty will consent to honor it with her presence."

Tears leapt to her eyes, and she clapped her hands in joy and amazement. It had been so long!

George too wept, nor did he seek to conceal this, for he continued to look straight at her, which was something like staring at the sun.

"You are kind," she whispered at last, after swallowing. "I'll consent to see this on two conditions."

"And they are, ma'am?"

"First, that my servants also be permitted to watch."

"'Tis granted in advance. My lord of Shrewsbury already promised that."

He heard the earl behind him gasp, but there was no interposition. Mary Stuart reached out to touch George's forearm.

"The other condition, Master Fitzwilliam, is that you stay by my side and help me to laugh and to cheer."

"*Majesty!*"

He dropped to both knees, passionately kissing the hand. For a moment he could not trust himself to move.

"Methinks there may be more than one Anthony Babington," muttered the earl of Shrewsbury.

39

"The Show Is Over!"

That false St. Martin's summer was gone. Winter had its foot inside the door. Clouds loured. The air smelled of rain, or even snow. The sky rumbled.

None of this damped the spirits of the visitors, who might have been unaware of it, so great was the excitement. Lord Shrewsbury could shake his head at ardor, fervor; but he had a townful of it beyond his moat. When word sped that a company of players was to hold forth in the outer bailey, old and young, weak and strong, came from every direction. The bridge was black with them.

Each as he entered was searched. This precaution, like the posting of so many guards—every one of the thirty soldiers was on duty, while each member of the castle staff of more than forty had been assigned to sentry duty—seemed to George unnecessary. There was after all nobody to impress, save only George himself, and he could not believe that he meant so much. Was the earl *twitchy?* And had his state of high nerves communicated itself to his retainers? Here was an edgy situation.

Yet it could not be denied that Mary Stuart, when she threw herself on the mercy of her cousin Elizabeth, had a record of swift movement, quick thinking, disguise, and escape. Her brilliant exit from water-girt Lochleven Castle showed that she was most marvelously hard to hold. More, she was designed to turn young men's heads; this too she had proved, and many times. She needed but to smile, no matter where the place, and some featherbrained but athletic champion would plead for the privilege of risking life and limb, braving the rack, the pilliwinks, the gallows itself, in her service, howsoever illicit. It made her a woman to be watched, in every sense of the word.

Also, not only the man who sought by any wile to rescue her, but also the man who sought to slay her, must be forestalled. As she had the gift of plunging some into lunatic love, so also she could drench the souls of others with a hate as black and bitter as gall. This was especially true in recent years, what with the mounting anger against Spain, the rise of the puritan party, the machinations of Catholic seminarists. George had seen how the mere mention of Mary Stuart's name could send such a temperate soldier as Sir John Crofts into a spasm of rage. If to thousands the lady was persecuted Purity, to thousands of others she was Jezebel, Lucifer's lieutenant, Antichrist himself, to be stamped out at all costs. These men too, like the Babingtons, were unaccountable yet cunning.

So all were examined before being admitted, and passed one by one. They took this in good part, each patiently awaiting his turn.

They had three good reasons, besides a natural willingness to drop work for any holiday.

First, there were the players. The profession being in disrepute, Sheffieldians never had seen mummers of any sort, and many may never even have seen acrobats or listened to a minstrel.

Then there was the queen. She had been twelve years in captivity now, ten of them here in Sheffield; yet few of the residents had viewed her. When their business took them to the castle, it was only to the outer bailey, a semipublic yard in which Mary was not allowed. On the rare occasions when she rode forth for a canter in the park—Shrewsbury's own jealously policed enclave—that outer bailey first was cleared; and in any event she would be so hedged by soldiery as to be scarcely glimpsed by the nimblest. All sorts of stories—it was but human—were told about her. Actually seeing her would be like catching sight of a myth, or having a fairy story come true.

Finally, there was his lordship. He was not a "popular" earl, and knew no obligation to show himself in public. Though he could not be called an absentee landlord, there being scarcely a day when he was not at either the castle or the nearby lodge—he had not been to London or indeed more than a few miles from his estates since Mary Stuart like an Old Man of the Sea had been fastened upon his back—still he was aloof, remote, preoccupied with personal affairs, a conscientious housekeeper but not one to mix. He had been especially reserved of recent months, since the break with his countess, the redheaded Bess of Hardwick, who was cordially disliked in the town.

And this too added to the eagerness to see him again, for the people dearly loved a marital spat in high places, and they would study their earl, speculating on how he was "taking it."

It was little enough they learned from his appearance that afternoon. George Talbot, sixth earl of Shrewsbury, wore clothes that befitted his station—a lilac doublet of silk, purple canions with blue-gray slashes, white gauntlets, a scarlet velvet bonnet, even his Garter—but his face might have been congealed in some colorless paste for all the emotion it showed. He was cool, correct. He never pointed, never raised his voice. The people were disappointed.

They were not disappointed in the queen.

A fanfare—it must have been her first in many years—announced her. When she came under the archway between the two courts her step was light. She had pleaded illness only the previous day, and even now she was supported by her handsome distinguished master of the household and a lady-in-waiting, both of them persons she towered over; yet she all but skipped.

A cheer went up. She paused, lifting a tiny white hand. Then she smiled; and they were hers.

There might have been eight hundred persons in the outer bailey, all crowded against the walls. There were no other spectators, for the ramparts above, like the towertops and arrowslits and windows, had been cleared. George noted that about a quarter of the persons went to their knees, and some began to cross themselves; but nobody reproved them.

Mary Stuart did not sag, anywhere. Her hair was caught under a blue caul embroidered with gold and surmounted by a red cloth, yellow-plumed cap. A tight-fitting blue bertha covered her bosom. Her stomacher—it was one of the new French V-shaped ones—was scarlet. Her petticoat was purple, her kirtle black. There was a crucifix hung by a chain around her neck, and from her waist was suspended a mirror; but she did not touch these.

She stood a long moment, as more and more persons fell to their knees.

You can dress a dummy in glittering garb, but a dummy cannot turn its head, and neither can it speak. Mary Stuart was every inch a queen, trained to such scenes as this; and even the men who stood closest to her did not see any sign that while with majestic mien she surveyed those before her she was carrying on a conversation with George Fitzwilliam.

"You have a message?"

"Ma'am, only my own."

"And—that?"

George paused. His ostensible mission—to give Scotland an account of his adventures—he had already promised Shrewsbury not to mention. What the queen's secretary really sought—more detailed information about Shrewsbury's precautions, should Mary of Scotland be given less freedom, or more—George could not divulge. But he could warn her!

Now he bowed. Like her, he spoke without seeming to move his mouth. He was not as adroit in this as was the queen; but then, fewer were watching him, and even to those he was turned sidewise.

"Perchance there are too many Babingtons?"

"He hasn't pounced."

"He will. He or somebody like him. I fear for your life, ma'am."

"I don't. When every night you lie down wondering whether you'll ever get up again, then you cease to fear. All I dread is that they may do it in the dark, with a dagger, before I can make my peace with God. For years I have dreaded this. I must hold myself prepared."

"To escape, ma'am?"

"Prepared to appear before the Heavenly Throne was what I meant."

More and more of the spectators were dropping to their knees. The queen stood there, a superb figure of a woman, slowly turning her head, acknowledging this obeisance, talking all the time from a corner of her mouth.

"Your warning then, sirrah?"

George whispered: "I have carried messages for your highness, and this might give me the right to point out that if only you would refuse to countenance plotters—"

"Not beat against the barred window? Have you ever lived in a cage, Master Fitzwilliam?"

"Ma'am, I have met Francis Walsingham. You haven't. He hates you."

"For that I forgive him. But I tell you—"

She saw Shrewsbury take a step toward her. She crooked her arm at George.

"Would you help me?" she asked. "I don't walk well, these days."

It had been planned that the queen of Scots should go directly from the outer bailey to a throne that had been set out for her. It was not veritably a throne, only a large X-chair set upon a small square dais, cushioned with velvet. There was no overhang.

She would have none of this. The soldiers waited, and those who immediately flanked her tried to push her, if apologetically, toward the X-chair; but she shook her head. These people had come to see her, and see her they should. Though it caused her pain—as George, who held her arm, could know—she insisted upon circling the yard, smiling here, waving there, nodding. She accepted none of the gifts offered—this had been agreed upon in advance—and several times she refused to lay hands on a diseased petitioner, but she demurred so graciously that all were charmed.

George glanced sideways at Lord Shrewsbury. He was impassive. He must have been troubled inside. It was plain why Shrewsbury was reluctant to expose his prisoner. If he allowed Mary Stuart to smile as she was smiling now, Queen Elizabeth wouldn't have a friend left in Sheffield. Additionally, Shrewsbury was vexed about the circuit, a violation of orders. But he said nothing. There was a halberdier on either side of him; and these men stood erect, statues, their weapons upright before them, razor-edges out.

The master of the household made some ado about arranging the cushions, but Mary Stuart brushed him away and sat down, thanking George.

After seating her, George knelt, his heart beating fast, for he knew the value of every split-second here.

"I tell you this," she went on, as smoothly as though their talk never had been broken, "that I'll heed no harebrained scheme."

His head of course was bowed, but he could be sure that Mary Stuart spoke smilingly, for the benefit of others, as though she said something gracious, formal, courtly.

"It must be real," she pursued. "I'll slip through no smashed door. When I leave this prison, Master Fitzwilliam—if ever I do—it will be as queen of England."

He swallowed.

"Then Elizabeth Tudor would be dead, ma'am?"

"She is not likely," in a silken whisper, "to step from that throne and invite me to take her place—now, is she?"

"Ma'am, if—"

In a louder voice: "Nay, rise, rise, Master Fitzwilliam, and stand here, so that we can enjoy this performance together."

She waved to her right side, and he went there. How many men would have been willing to die for the privilege? The dais was small, and by standing off it and by bending a little toward the queen he would keep his head lower than hers, yet at the same time virtually lean on the arm of the chair.

She smiled at him, very close.

Then, facing the populace, she smiled again, and all but laughed. She clapped her hands.

"Let the show begin," she cried.

As though it had picked up a signal the sky was split with lightning, and there was a crash of thunder. Nobody looked up.

A morris dance was first.

A few times during this past hour George Fitzwilliam had felt misgivings about these players and about the impulse that had caused him to bring them here. After all, they *were* a rabble. But when he saw Mary Stuart's delight his fears evaporated. Even if the players were poor the queen would enjoy them.

They were not poor. The morris dance went off well, and then there were some instrumental pieces, and a minstrel with a lute sang several lays. They were light airs, those lays, and amusing, though perhaps in deference to the presence of royalty they were not bawdy. Yet the crowd liked them. And Mary Stuart, who could hardly have understood every word, clapped with enthusiasm.

"He's an angel," she cried to George.

"A rather mangy one, ma'am."

"You're too fussy!"

The burlesque wrestlers, clowns, were extraordinarily funny. Mary, queen of Scotland and the Isles, laughed so hard that she had to hold her sides, leaning back, while tears streamed down her cheek. As for George, he almost collapsed over the arm of her chair.

On the other hand, the old man's recital was not the high point of the program, as it had been in the moonlight. The old man was superb, true:

> *"But if the gods themselves did see her then*
> *When he saw Pyrrhus make malicious sport*
> *In mincing with his sword her husband's limbs—"*

He missed no nuance; his frenzy was flawless; yet it was patent that he would win but moderate applause. George supposed this was but natural. What was Pyrrhus to these louts? And what Hecuba?

> *"The instant burst of clamor that she made,*
> *Unless all things mortal move them not at all,*
> *Would have made milch the burning eyes of heaven,*
> *And passion in the gods."*

Shrewsbury, a halberdier on either side of him, was much too concerned with the temper of the crowd to catch any classical reference. As for Mary Stuart, her hearing disappointed George. Though she did

[225]

not throw the old man a purse—this too had been forbidden—she did lean forward to applaud him. She knew that it had been art, but her ear for English was not yet trained to the point where it could seize upon the magnificence of those lines. She was of course kind, but she would have preferred to have the burlesque wrestlers back.

The sky spoke again, and it grew dark in the court.

Each of the other performers had been ambulatory, favoring the queen but with trained persistence moving around the courtyard, facing now this way and now that, as they worked. The next one, however, the juggler, confronted the queen and the queen alone, being, it would appear, spellbound.

This juggler did not even see George Fitzwilliam. But George saw him—saw his face for the first time—and it was all George could do to keep from crying out.

The juggler was small, with enormously broad shoulders, not a hunchback but suggestive of that. His was extremely dark hair.

He was Sylvestre, Terence Weddell's valet.

Had this been planned? Had the glass balls, the beating, been arranged as George rode that lonesome road? Did these mummers know that he was on his way to Sheffield, that he would surely gain admittance to the castle?

It was a wild thought, but that was a wild moment.

Should he call to Lord Shrewsbury? Should he stop the show? Terence Weddell was a sincere Catholic, and it stood to reason that his valet was the same. Sylvestre might in addition be rabid, a fanatic. Would he go to any lengths in order to get into the presence of Mary Queen of Scots? Why else was he here? Was there some frenzied hysterical plot to seize her, take her away? It would have been futile, and would mean much killing. Should George speak?

If Sylvestre was a designer he was maladroit. He could hardly hold his glass balls, much less toss them into the air, he was so fastened to the sight of the queen. He moved a step toward her.

Shrewsbury said something to a halberdier, who raised his weapon.

Sylvestre did not see this. He moved another step toward Mary Stuart.

George started forward, meaning to get between them. He feared that the dwarf might try to kiss Mary's feet or embrace her ankles. No physical contact with the players or anybody in the audience was to be permitted: this was part of the contract.

Sylvestre broke into a run. Now he was saying something, babbling something rather. Nobody could make out what it was.

He put one hand under his parti-colored shirt. He might have been replacing the balls. George at least knew that he was not reaching for a weapon.

Lord Shrewsbury spoke again.

The thing that was thrown caught Sylvestre underneath his raised left arm. It was heavy and exceedingly sharp. It all but cut the little man in half. It spun him around, and he fell on the pavement, splattering George's base-hose with blood.

"You—might—have—waited," George sobbed.

He stepped directly before the dead figure, to shield it from the sight of Mary Queen of Scots.

George Talbot, earl of Shrewsbury, raised both arms, and the soldiers began to close in, shoving the crowd toward the main gate, obliquing their pikes to do so.

"The show is over," Lord Shrewsbury cried. "You must all go home. The show is over."

It began to rain.

40

Good-by, This World

His wife was pregnant, his father-in-law in dubious health, so George should have hurried home; but curiosity in part, though even more, to give him credit, an urgent sense of fear for the safety of his friend, prompted him to stop a few miles away at Weddell Lodge. Maybe Terence would be home now. Or if he wasn't, his absence could be taken as a hint of guilt.

The parklike approach of Weddell Lodge, its townhousey appearance, originally had puzzled George. Now he knew that Terence preferred to have his visitors obliged to dismount at the gate, some distance away, and open this for themselves. It never was attended, even in the daytime. The gate was noisy, heavy, clumsy, and its opening, and the subsequent remounting, would give the dog or one of the inhabitants of the house some warning of approach. At least, nobody could dash up to the door.

It was late when George arrived, yet there was a light in the library. Terence had a visitor?

George did not open the gate, but climbed over it, leaving his horse outside, a beast much too tired to wander. He walked up the avenue of lime trees and was within a few feet of the door before the dog in back heard or smelled him and began to bark furiously, fighting its chain.

Instantly the light in the library went out.

A moment later the door was opened a few inches, and a cocked pistol appeared, the muzzle toward George.

"Don't come nearer, but explain yourself."

"Tut, tut," said George. "Such rudeness to an old companion!"

"George!"

After these two had embraced, and while Terence was relighting the candles, they nattered on like a couple of girls, for the reunion was good. But seriousness came soon, George introducing it. He told Terence about Sylvestre.

He did not try to trap his friend. He asked no preliminary questions, but plunged right into the tale.

Terence was touched. Tears rolled down his face and his mouth quivered, while the knuckles of his pressed-together hands went white.

"He left me almost a year ago. You weren't back yet. I begged him to stay, but the call of the road was too strong. He went to London—or said he was going there. I gave him money, much more than the wage I owed him, and I got him a let-pass to protect him on the way. He said he knew where he could get a place with a troupe of players. I haven't heard from him since."

"That had been his occupation before?"

Terence nodded.

"Aye. It was on the road that I met him. He was sick of the life then, and we fell to talking, so that I learned he was of my own faith. That makes a difference, you know. It's a bond."

"I can believe it."

"Sylvestre was very devout. It's important to think of that, in this traffic. He was not intelligent, but he was strong, he was faithful. Thank God he never did have to endure the rack, but I had to take the possibility into consideration when I trusted him."

Yes, thought George, *I* am hailed as a hero, while *you* all the while risked torture and death. *I* had a few touchy times, but *you* walked the edge of a cliff every day all day, year after year. *I* stood a chance of wearing out my fingernails counting money, or choking on a biscuit weevil, or being bored to death, but *you* might at any time have your joints pulled open one by one, and your testacles clipped, your guts yanked out, your head cut off.

But he said nothing of this. Neither did he mention the priest who must have been hiding under the stair, where, George hoped, being an old hand at that sort of thing, he wasn't too uncomfortable. The less George knew the better. There was always the possibility that they might some day take *him* to London Tower, and lay him on La Gehenna, that ingenious table-machine of little cranks and pulleys, and stretch him until he screamed—by the hour. He preferred to be as ignorant as possible.

"Why did he go back to the road?"

Terence shrugged, shaking a sad head.

"Had it in his blood, I suppose. He was forever fetching out those ridiculous glass balls, until I simply couldn't pretend any longer to be interested. He craved a real audience. A different audience every time. I paid him well and never beat him. I was fond of him. And he got a great spiritual satisfaction from being able to help me in my, well, 'calling.' But still—he went away."

"Will his death bring the bailiffs?"

"I don't see why. He wouldn't have spoken to his companions about me, lest he slip some reference to what went on here. And you say that he was killed instantly?"

"Oh, instantly. He didn't know what hit him."

"Wasn't there any sort of trial or inquiry?"

"Yes, but it didn't last long. Sylvestre was already buried by that time—just outside the castle grounds, only a few hours after it happened. There was a hearing, and the soldier made a statement; but after all, the order had been heard by hundreds—and it was given by the high steward of England, lord lieutenant of the county, and a man who was acting in defense of what I suppose could be listed as the queen's own property. Not much to be done there, eh? The other players were paid and dismissed. They'll talk, of course, but who believes what a strolling player says?"

Terence looked into the fire, again shaking his head.

"The oddest part," he whispered, "is that poor Sylvestre should be accused of trying to murder her."

"*I* believed that he was about to throw himself at her feet," George said, "and so did most of the others, and it was certainly proved afterward that he had no weapon. But Lord Shrewsbury thought otherwise. And the official record will bear him out."

"He worshipped that woman," Terence whispered. "He adored her as though she was a saint. She *was,* to him. He was always getting me to tell about the time I was one of her pages, and when you were here he'd hide outside the door by the hour in the hope that you'd talk about her too. That miniature you brought me: he all but groveled before that, as if it was an icon."

[229]

"But the law says that he tried to kill her."

In the screens again, before the door, George picked up the pistol. He noted that it wasn't loaded, and put it aside.

"You should certainly get another dog," he said in a feeble try at jocularity.

"Yes."

George put a hand upon his shoulder.

"Because I don't want thee to be napped. Thou'rt a good neighbor, and I'd mislike to lose thee."

"Thanks," Terence muttered.

There were lights too in the Okeland windows, which alarmed George, for it was near to midnight. He cursed himself for having broken the trip, and spurred his tired horse.

There was some stir in the stables, and he went there first, surprising a groom.

"What?"

"Thank the Lord you're back, sir. Sir John's very ill."

"And you're going for a leech?"

"For a minister, sir. To Rugby."

"H-m-m. He's that bad?"

"He'll not last the night."

"Wait here. I'll go instead. But I'd speak with my wife first. Saddle Alberta for me, and rub this one down."

With death itself George had been long familiar, and it held no horrors for him. Sir John was old and had been failing. It was the effect upon his wife that George was most concerned about, his wife and the child she carried.

Nevertheless the sight of Sir John was a shock. George had been gone only five days, but it might have been five years. The knight's face was as colorless as the pillowcase behind it. It was seamed like an old rock, and might have been sanded. The eyes, only half open, were lusterless, glazed. The upper lip sometimes twitched; yet this was the only sign of life, and without it George would have said that the man was already gone.

They were all there: Anne with the baby in her lap; Aunt Sylvia, herself more than half dead; the house servants, hushed, frightened. It was clear that they had some time since given up hope of communicating with Sir John.

He showed no sign that he recognized George, who spoke to him. The lip did not twitch again for a while.

"The last thing he said," Anne whispered, "he asked for a priest."

[230]

"He knows how bad it is, then?"

"He knows all right."

By "priest" Sir John had meant a minister of the state church, the Church of England. In London such a person might have been called a pastor, since tending his flock would be more apparent in that crowded place. In the smaller seaports, with their puritanical sects, which favored extemporizing and long sermons, he would have been called a preacher. To Sir John Crofts he was still a priest.

The country in general, at least the hinterland, was not well provided in this respect. The church was a new thing, only recently established, or, as some insisted, restored; and the authority of the bishops differed from place to place, from time to time as well, which made for confusion. Discipline was lax, standards uncertain. Elizabeth Tudor, a puny woman at best, nearing fifty, and still, despite her flirtations, determinedly unwed, might at any time die—or be killed. In that event the "strange guest" at Sheffield almost certainly would ascend to the throne, and the old religion would be more or less forcibly reinstated. It was a prospect that didn't please young men who might otherwise have been ecclesiastically inclined. And so, as the older ministers died off there were few to take their places.

Conditions in this part of Northampton were especially bad. The nearest Anglican divine, so far as George knew, was at Rugby, several hours ride each way over abominable roads, and he was a "sporting" minister, unrestrained, utterly unreliable.

"I have sent for Gates."

George shook his head.

"I stopped that. It would take all the rest of the night to get Gates here. *If* he could be found and *if* he was sober."

"But what—"

"Maybe I can find a nearer one."

Lest he never see his father-in-law alive again, though he would be gone but a short while, George knelt by the side of the bed and said a prayer. Sir John's hand moved a little. Then George went out.

He made no try for silence this time when he rode up the avenue of lime trees to the door of Weddell Lodge, and a mystified Terence was waiting for him in the library. George explained.

"Wouldn't that be fraud?"

"I'm not asking that he be given extreme unction. Just that he see a man in black standing there, praying for him. If he *can* see any longer. Aren't they allowed to do that, as a simple act of compassion?"

"I'll ask him. Wait here."

A few minutes later the priest entered the library. He was young, a mere beardless boy, yet he was thoughtful, ascetic of appearance, an aristocrat, and, more important, a man of common sense, a man of good will. George liked him instantly, and trusted him. He wore clerical garb, but his head had not been shaved. He was introduced simply as Father Smith, though his real name, George guessed, might have been a noble one.

He was crisp, asking few questions, listening attentively to the answers.

"I realize that there is a certain amount of risk involved, and for the benefit of a man who isn't of your faith," George said impatiently. "I'll answer for my wife, but of course the servants will see you. But as far as your cassock's concerned, it could be an Anglican one—"

The priest smiled.

"It once was," he murmured.

"—and if only you remember not to cross yourself—"

"Master Fitzwilliam, you misunderstand. It is not the danger of arrest and death that I fear, but rather the danger of craving these things too warmly."

"Eh?"

"That my work will be cut short by the public hangman I don't doubt. But it's my duty to put off that day as long as possible, so that I can serve my communicants. They taught us at the seminary, Master Fitzwilliam, that a craving for martyrdom is something that should be suppressed."

"I see. And—you don't think my father-in-law's worth the risk?"

"I didn't say that. Any man who is about to die, no matter what his faith, deserves the services of such as I. But I've got to think of the good of the greater number. In this case I believe we are all right. I was to move out of here tonight anyway."

"In a little while," Terence put in. "That's why you see us up so late, George. The horses are already saddled."

"If I got away before dawn, and you were waiting for me, d'ye think we could make it to where we're going before there was traffic on the road?"

"We could if we pushed."

"Good. You won't go into the house with us, since you're already suspect?"

"No," said Terence. "I'll wait at the edge of that little wood on the rise toward Biggleswade."

The priest nodded. He pulled on a hood, designed to protect his head from the night air. He unlooped the crucifix from around his neck and kissed it, and put it into a pocket.

"Your wife's father may be able to see better than you suppose, and after all it's *his* spiritual welfare that we're thinking of, eh?"

Okeland must have seemed small and mean by comparison with some of the houses this young priest had visited, had indeed been raised in, but his manner, George was sure, would have been the same in any place—palace or shepherd's hut. Wall hangings, coronas of candles, teakwood chests, meant nothing to him. Neither did those who stood about, any one of whom could have betrayed him. He scarcely nodded to Anne and to Aunt Sylvia, and it could be that he never even saw the servants. He went right to the bed. He knelt.

There was no need to lie, none to practice deceit. If nobody was told that here was a Jesuit missionary from the Continent, neither was anybody told that here was an Anglican minister. His name was not mentioned, nor did George call him "Father," while he himself remembered not to make the sign of the cross, nor yet to rattle his rosary beads. He talked in a low steady vibrant voice, in English, sometimes with his head bowed, his eyes closed, praying, at other times directly addressing Sir John, whose face was so close to his own. The words were measured, but without pattern, of a consolatory nature. They were generalized, not particular, having to do with the goodness of God, Christ our Redeemer, the forgiveness of sins, and such. There was about them nothing set or sectarian. Whether the knight was aware of this talk they were never to know. A few times the lips twitched.

Death came early, and very quietly. There was no stiffening of the limbs, no throat rattle, and the eyes remained the same, half open, expressionless.

How the priest sensed it, would be hard to tell. He looked up, stared hard at Sir John for a moment, then took from his purse a small mirror, which he held before the knight's open mouth. He sighed a little, put the mirror away, and crossed Sir John's arms on his breast. Then he went on with his prayer.

The others got down on their knees and prayed with him, and afterward Anne and Aunt Sylvia found that they could weep again.

The priest refused all refreshment, but he was glad to have George ride a little way with him, to the wood, since he did not know this shire, never having seen it in daylight.

"Thank you, Father," George said. "Here's a purse for your poor. And thank *thee* too, Terence, my true friend."

They nodded, then rode rapidly away, for the sky to the east was lightening.

"My God, I hope they aren't caught," George whispered.

[233]

Aunt Sylvia and the steward and Anne's tiring-women from time to time after that, circuitously—for they wouldn't dare to be direct in such a matter, George being the master of the household now—strove to learn from him where he had found that charming priest who attended Sir John at his death. He only shook his head in reply.

Anne never asked him at all. Perhaps she was afraid to learn.

41

Memento Mori

The day the news came that they had killed the queen of Scots church bells were rung and bonfires built, while laborers ran in from the fields, glad of an excuse to take a holiday.

Yet the deed was not unexpected.

At first the government had juggled this monarch as the late Sylvestre might have juggled one of his balls, hustling her from Carlyle Castle to Lowther, to Bolton, to Tutbury, a glum place, from whence she was shipped to Wingfield Manor, a rather pleasant one. But soon they moved her back to Tutbury, and when the northern earls rose in revolt in 1569 her guards took Queen Mary farther south, lest she be freed. She spent some time at Coventry. After the rebellion had been quashed she was shifted to Tutbury again, then Chatsworth. From Chatsworth, November 28, 1570, while George Fitzwilliam still lay in a Spanish prison, they had moved her to Sheffield, where she was to remain for fourteen crushingly unhappy years.

All this time, and while her friends in France systematically robbed her of her dowry, her household was whittled down, her living allowance reduced. Thanks to my lord of Shrewsbury, a kind man, she was not publicly humiliated; but she was not allowed the exercise she needed, so that her health failed.

Toward the end this rigor was abated for a few weeks in the summer, when she was permitted to go to Buxton to take the waters, or to Chatsworth or Worksop or Wingfield, Shrewsbury properties; but Sheffield remained her real jail.

Plot after rescue plot, exploded, could not be traced to her. Besides, many might sympathize with her wish to break that odious prison, for wasn't it any captive's instinct to escape? It would be different if she could be proved to have plotted against the life of Queen Elizabeth. To get her head—and Walsingham, like Cecil, was determined to get it—the ministers would find it necessary to tie her directly to some such scheme. Meanwhile, as Walsingham had learned at least in part from George Fitzwilliam, her confinement was oversevere. Mary Stuart could no longer walk alone, and she had to be helped to mount—she who had been one of the great horsewomen of her time! who after the battle of Langside had ridden nineteen hours without pause!—so that no such display of suppleness as had marked the escape from Lochleven could be looked for again. That is, it would no longer be helpful to give her enough rope, since she didn't have the strength to hang herself.

Some new policy was called for. Shrewsbury was *too* efficient, *too* conscientious, and Walsingham, at long distance, started a campaign calculated to get him relieved.

Shrewsbury for years had been pleading for just that, yet when the time came he balked.

Mary had cost him money and infinite anxiety. She tied him down, preventing travel. Innocently enough, no doubt, she yet had been the means of bringing about his rift with his wife. But he was a stubborn man; he did not wish to let Mary go. He wouldn't confess failure.

In part this could be because in spite of himself Lord Shrewsbury had fallen in love with his charge. In part also it could be a matter of prestige. For all his wealth and high place, *politically* Shrewsbury was not a power. He was not "of the court," and no good at manipulation. When he came to grips with a master like Francis Walsingham his defeat was sure. It took time, but it was done. September 7, 1584, Shrewsbury was replaced by Lord Somers and Sir Ralph Sadler, who resigned a year later in protest against the way they were obliged to treat their ward, and were succeeded in turn by Sir Amyas Paulet, a hot gospeler, fiery of eye if toothless.

Now they were moving her again: Sheffield to Wingfield to Tutbury; then Wingfield again, Chartley, Tixall, back to Chartley; and at last Fotheringay, the end of the line.

George knew Fotheringay Castle, which was not far from Milton, his own ancestral seat. A royal property, though by no means as large or as strong as Sheffield, like Sheffield it was a depressing place. George had played there as a boy. Indeed, his older brother, Sir William Fitzwilliam, the present head of the family, once had been its castellan. George shuddered when he thought of Mary Stuart at Fotheringay.

Yet it was not there but at the next-to-the-last stop, the comparatively cheerful Chartley, that the trap had been sprung. George learned many of the details from Terence Weddell, who had been approached by the conspirators but because of the essential part that the killing of Queen Elizabeth must play in this plot had refused to join. Yet Terence was suspect. Even while he told George how it had happened he was packing his bags, a passport in his pocket.

"There was this brewer in the village. Mary's household was being allowed one hogshead of beer a week, on Saturday. A courier from the French embassy would call and hand over a message, which the brewer would give to one Thomas Phelippes, a professional forger in Walsingham's pay, who was living in the village under another name. It would be in cypher, but Phelippes knew the cypher. He'd copy the letter and give it back to the brewer, who would roll it up and stick it into the hollowed-out bung-stopper of the hogshead, which would be delivered next morning to the queen's apartments at Chartley. The old one, the empty, would be taken away, of course, and in the bung-stopper of that there'd be a message from Mary Stuart. Phelippes would copy this and then give it back to the brewer, who would give it to the ambassador's courier, who would give it to the ambassador, who would give it to Babington or to whomever it was addressed. They kept this up for months."

"Would that be young Anthony Babington?"

"Aye. He lives near there. Or did. He's like me, a harborer of priests, which is bad enough. But Babington wanted to go further— an invasion of the realm, an uprising of Catholics here, and a quick end to Elizabeth. Six young fools like himself had pledged themselves to kill Elizabeth. They were arrested with Babington, night before last, in St. James's Wood. They're in the Tower. And I'm for Douai."

He went to a window. It was late August, and the country drowsed, drenched in sunlight. He sighed.

"They'll expropriate, I'm sure. I'd make thee a deed, George, save that it might stir suspicion. You could buy in easier. It's a logical addition to your place. And there won't be any other bidders, not after the way you refused to stand for Parliament against Wentworth."

"I didn't do it for that reason."

"No, no!"

Terence was about to back away from the window, when something caught his eye, and he showed like a man whose heart had been snicked out.

"I waited too long. Look: two sheriff's men. I know from here."

They had come through the gate at the end of the lime-tree avenue. They remounted, and started toward the house.

"Run for it!"

"How?"

"My horse out there! She's saddled!"

"That would get you into trouble."

"I could say you'd stolen it! No, wait! *Stroll* out! But first—"

Crouching, his shoulders high, bonnet low, he ran outside and leapt upon Alberta's back. He heard the sheriff's men hallo, but he kept going. He went around the manor house, across a meadow, over a ditch, past a wood. It was rough, but they stayed close behind him, as he could hear. Not until they were out on the Market Harborough road, eight miles from Weddell Lodge, did George look back. Then, seeming astonished by what he saw, he came to a halt.

"Why the Devil didn't you tell me you were sheriff's men?" he demanded. "I was there to collect a debt, and I thought you were some of his damned papist friends, so I ran."

That such a hero should fly so readily might have been hard to believe, but the sheriff's men were short of time.

"Where is *he?*"

"Now how should I know?"

Master Fitzwilliam was owner of Okeland, son-in-law of the late Sir John Crofts, intimate of Sir Francis Drake, and locally vouched for by Peter Wentworth. It would not do to question him too hard. They wheeled and on tired horses raced back toward Weddell Lodge. They did not catch Terence. Terence never was seen in Northampton again.

Whether he had been involved, even if remotely, in that plot the exposure of which shook England, George did not learn. It was possible. For Anthony Babington had chosen to confess. "Why, for that lady, sir, I swear, I'd let myself be torn to pieces, limb from limb!" he had cried to George, some ten years ago, when he was a stripling of fourteen or fifteen, a page at Sheffield. "Let's hope you never have to," George had replied. The memory was ironic. Babington of Dethick and six other well-born young hotheads quite literally were torn limb from limb, after being hanged, one morning on Tyburn. The others all had said, "Damn your eyes, no!" whereas Babington had talked.

Mary Stuart, not knowing all this, was moved from Chartley to Tixall, ostensibly for an outing, and while she was away her apartments at Chartley were ransacked, the very paneling being ripped out, the very mattresses chopped, and all her letters and papers—also her cash—taken. Soon after that she was moved to Fotheringay. They were almost ready.

[237]

She was tried, as all the world knew, by an extraordinary commission of peers and knights. She was allowed no lawyer, nor was she confronted with her accusers or permitted to see the letters that were used in evidence against her.

There was Babington's confession, a telling instrument. There were statements by her two secretaries, Curle, a Scot, and the Frenchman, Nau. Nobody could be sure that the secretaries had been tortured—the authorities insisted that Babington had not—but it was certain at least that they were led to the small low-ceiled chamber in London Tower where the rack was kept, and the workings of this apparatus explained to them. That was sometimes enough. Nau and Curle did not appear in person at the trial. No witness did.

Mary, without a friend there, defended herself magnificently. But she was convicted. She was sentenced to die.

It was weeks, it was more than three months, before Queen Elizabeth could find courage to sign the death warrant of her cousin and rival, a woman she never had met. When this had been done the rest followed quickly, for the ministers could not run the risk that Elizabeth might change her mind yet again. Mary Stuart was executed in the great-hall at Fotheringay the morning of February 8, 1587.

That was why the church bells rang.

A midland farmer, troubled about dung and fumiter, about the corn being inned, the sarclers paid, is unlikely to hear "inside" stories of statecraft. George had been told by Terence the reason for the Babington Plot's exposure. He was to hear details of the death of Mary Stuart from a man he never saw.

It was at The Plow one early spring afternoon, and George had stopped not because he craved company—the contrary was true—but because he was thirsty. He never did reach the common room. Just outside the door, a hand raised to the latch, he stopped, overhearing through an open window the voice of a stranger.

"Aye, I was there. All the time. I was in the service of Lord Huntingdon, and I was just off the platform, so close that a couple of drops of blood got splashed onto my jerkin. I can tell you they scrubbed that, afterward! They wouldn't let any get away!"

He cleared his throat, then coughed a little.

"Oh? You'd hear about this? Well—"

There was a splash and a gurgle. It was clear even to George outside that the speaker, scarcely six weeks after the event, had become a past-master of pauses, an expert at hesitation, who could cast a most marvelously rueful glance at his mug.

He took up the tale, a moment later, in practiced terms.

"They had this platform, I'd say about twelve feet each way, made of wood, and it was maybe two feet high, and covered with black cloth. That was at the end of the great-hall, where the fireplace was. Three sides of it they had a small low railing, and that was covered with this same black cloth. On the fourth side were a couple of steps. That was all I saw when I first came in, except that there was a fire in the fireplace, but it was chilly there just the same.

"Well, they lined us up around all four sides, and we were supposed to stand facing *out*—I mean, away from the platform—but naturally we had plenty of chance to look over our shoulders."

"What'd you carry?"

"Halberds. But we never had to use 'em. And we could rest the butts on the floor—I mean, we never had to hold 'em obliqued, which can make your arms mighty tired."

"Go on."

"I was wondering if—"

"Here."

"Thankee. Well, I'd been standing there a little when the soldier next to me, name of Hal Garth, he pushed me and told me to look around, and I did, and there was the executioners. It gave me a jump. I'd never seen or heard 'em come in. They must have walked like cats. They were both dressed in tight black, with white aprons."

"Like butchers?"

"Yes, like butchers. Which of course they were, really. One had an axe, and it was a big one, though the shaft was short. You wouldn't have wanted to cut down a tree with it. Heavy. That was the chief executioner, and Hal Garth whispered to me that his name was Bulle. I don't know that for a fact; it's just what Hal told me. They both had black masks over their faces."

George Fitzwilliam's hand fell to his side, but he did not otherwise move. That lady! That kind lovely lady! He bowed his head.

"So then the lords started coming in. Never saw so many. Might have been Parliament, except that they didn't have any place to sit. They just stood there. There was a crowd outside too. You could hear 'em, but you couldn't see 'em, the windows were too high."

"No place to sit down at *all?*"

"Only for her. There was a stool on the platform. Then there was the block itself, but nobody'd want to sit on *that,* ha-ha! Could I have— Ah, thankee."

The gurgle again.

"There was more on the platform next time I looked. One was Lord Shrewsbury. I knew him. And another I heard afterward was

Lord Kent. Then there was a preacher, come from Peterborough, dean of the cathedral there."

"They didn't allow her a Roman priest?"

"No. She asked for one. I heard it. But they said no. Then there was another man there; I guess he was the sheriff. He was all in black. But he didn't do anything, just stood there. He had a white stick in his hand. And when *she* came in I couldn't see her at first because just then the sergeant was standing right there. But I could *hear* her, and I could tell two or three people were helping her to walk."

"She weeping?"

"Never a tear! No, she sat as quiet as could be. In black. That's what I saw when I got a chance to turn my head. But she had a white ruff and a long white veil from the top of her cap, like a bride at a wedding. She was holding a cross in both hands, in front of her. Then another man come up, I don't know who he was, but he unrolled a piece of paper and he read out of it for a long time. Lawyer stuff. I couldn't make any sense out of it."

"The death sentence," somebody offered.

"That must have been what it was. I was watching Mary at the time. She'd put the cross down into her lap, but she didn't seem to be listening much, and when he was all through—the man who'd been reading—and we'd all yelled 'God save the queen,' why, then she took the cross up again, and she asked once more if she couldn't please have a priest, but they said no. Well then, my Lord Shrewsbury said to her 'Ma'am, you hear what we are commanded to do?' And she just nodded, as if he had no more than said it was a nice day—which it wasn't. She just said 'You must do your duty.' And then she got up. She had two women on the platform with her now, and they had to help her, but once she got up she shooed them away and stood there by herself. And she made a speech. I don't know . . . I suppose I should have listened to it more. It was in English, and it wasn't very long, something about her being an anointed queen that had never planned to kill anybody anywhere at any time. That was the gist of it anyway."

A pause. A plash. A long wet sigh of contentment.

"After that this man from Peterborough started to pray at her, and everybody repeated what he said, but she wouldn't listen. She got down on her knees and started to pray all by herself. *He* was praying in English, in a loud voice, but *she* was praying in something else, I guess it was Latin, very quiet. That went on for some time. Then the executioner went over to her and started to take a chain from off her neck, because he said that that was his by right, which as you know they always are. But she said no. She said he'd be paid properly—the money was all laid out—and she'd promised that chain to somebody else. They pulled it back and forth a little while, but finally Bulle gave up. But he didn't like it. So he began taking off her dress and her ruff, which would have got in the way of the axe. But she stopped him. 'Let me do this,' she said. 'I understand it better than you,' she said. But she couldn't seem to raise her arms high enough—rheumatism, I suppose—and those two women had to help her again. *They* was weeping like fountains, but Mary Stuart herself didn't let go a tear. I'll swear to that. I'd have seen it if she had.

"Anyway these two women, they did manage to get the dress off, and there she was in bright red underwear. No, you couldn't see much skin. But everything was very clean and neat, I'll say that.

"Then these women, they tied a fancy lace kerchief around her eyes, and she sat down and picked up that cross again, and said 'All right.' She must have thought Bulle would do the job sideways, the way I hear they do it in France, only they use a sword there. He went to her, him and his assistant, and they helped her over to the block—she couldn't see then because of that bandage around her eyes—and she got to her knees there. But even then she didn't put her head down. She didn't seem to think she was supposed to. Bulle had to do that for her."

George thought: Yes, Mary Stuart was not accustomed to stooping.

"He did a bad job. Maybe he was nervous. The first time he hit her he hit her over the right ear. She made a little groan-sound, but she didn't move. And he hit her again, this time getting in a pretty fair one across the neck, though even then it didn't quite take the whole head off, the way it should. But it must have killed her. But he had to hit her a third time afore he could get the head free. Then everybody yelled 'God save the queen,' and Bulle he got out his platter and reached down to pick up the head to show it, the way he's expected to. But he took hold of it by the hair—and that all came off! See? She was as bald as an egg, and she'd been wearing a wig!"

He laughed; but nobody else laughed.

"Well, he carried this around to each window, holding it up, and there was blood running over the sides and down both of his arms. You could hear everybody out there yelling 'God save the queen' and then— Look: I wonder if I could—"

"Here—"

"Aye. It was the second one that splashed the blood on me. Right here, aye. My, how they scrubbed it! But that's the very spot. You want to put your hand there? Well now, how much would you—"

George went away, for he feared that if he entered the taproom he might kill that man.

Grief had scant chance to coast. There was a message from Hawkins waiting for him. It said to report in Plymouth immediately. It was not a request but a command. The Spaniards were coming.

42

"If It's a Fight You Want—"

No man ever had seen a sight like this. A nation, complete with brass and banners, rose out of the dawn. On right, on left, as well as ahead, the horizon was studded with sails that gleamed in the early light; and though already there were more vessels than George Fitzwilliam had supposed to exist in the world, others, perversely, were appearing all the time.

The noises they made were multitudinous, and seemed everywhere. Trumpets greeted the day; and the roll of drums, changing the watch, was as ubiquitous as thunder—and almost as loud. Stern lanterns were being doused, twitching out as did the stars in an oily green sky, and doubtless there were shouts exchanged from vessel to vessel, but these were not to be distinguished aboard the ketch *Anne*. Bells rang; sea and sky alike, in every direction, seemed to be filled with the clang of bells.

For a moment George feared that he had somehow stumbled into the very middle of the Spanish fleet. And indeed, if he didn't put about, that's where, in a matter of minutes, he might be. Yet he stood like a man spellbound, paralyzed.

More and more of them loomed into sight. They were perfectly spaced, mathematically exact, military in the precision with which they moved, beautifully handled. They formed an enormous crescent, the tips of which, on either side, could scarcely be seen, they were so far away.

Right between those tips was the tiny six-gun *Anne;* and it was headed for the center. It drifted, mainsail flapping like a lame duck. Nobody even held the tiller, which swung back and forth, for the helmsman, like everybody else aboard, stood stunned by the sight of the Armada.

More and more sails appeared, as the last of the stars went away and the moon faded. The hulls too could be seen now. They were huge. There were some pinnaces or dispatch boats, and perhaps twenty caravels, but the greatest number of the vessels, the overwhelming majority, were high-sided and many-decked, built with enormous castles fore and aft. At least a dozen, all near the center of the line, were twice as big as any vessel those aboard the ketch ever had seen.

It is small wonder that they doubted their eyes.

The reds and pastels lent by a lightening sky weren't needed by this fleet. The vessels themselves were straked with gilt, their bows carved and painted, their aftercastles a miracle of fretwork. Few sails, even the smallest, but bore some sort of device. Most of those sails, all the biggest ones, showed a colossal red cross, the Crusaders' cross, testifying that this was designed as a holy war rather than a mean expedition of conquest, avarice. Also there were, literally, thousands of silken streamers, banners, oriflammes, ensigns, pennants, and pennoncels, some of them many yards long, all sewn with threads of white, yellow, orange, crimson, azure, green.

For George it was agony to tear his gaze away.

"Hard larboard! Grommets, break out that spritsail! And two bonnets on the course!"

The spell was split. They were mariners once more, not children peering at a fairy-story pageant. Yet—they would never be the same again.

This was somewhere between the Lizard and Guernsey, at the very entrance of the English Channel. The Spanish ships, as well they might, were closing their ranks. Now there was a call for nearness, whatever the danger of collision. The maneuver was complicated, albeit exquisitely performed, and it would take time; yet somebody had noted the little scouting vessel and had gone to the trouble of sending a pinnace after her. The farther up the channel the Spaniards got before the fleet at Plymouth came swarming out, the harder it would be to stop them from making contact with their invasion forces in the Low Countries.

"Put on the last bonnet! And hoist that topper!"

"We're being chased, sir," said young Cornelius van Doorn.

"So it would seem."

Fishermen in those waters say that in fine summer weather—this was July 19—the wind customarily "goes around with the sun." It will blow from the north at night, edging toward northeast as the dawn spreads. By noon it would come clear around and be blowing from the south. In the afternoon it would be from the southwest. There is usually a lull at sundown, they say, but when the wind picks up again, after dark, it is once more from the north.

It was ahead of schedule this morning. Though none of the body of the sun yet had shown, the wind was blowing from the southeast. The ketch's new course was north, and it was moving fast. But the pinnace was fast too. George watched her. Foam creamed at her bows, and she had cracked on everything but the cook's shirt. She was gaining on them.

"Master gunner!"

"Sir?"

"Load that saker in the stern. And do you, Doorn, rig the whipstaff to get the helmsman out of the way of the kick."

Doorn was extremely young, still in his teens, but he was a veteran of these troubled waters, being one of that company of nautical rebels who called themselves the Beggars of the Sea. As such, his life was forfeit if the Spaniards caught him. Recently he'd had a close shave. The *Anne*, then called the *Kabbeljaw*, had been surprised and captured by a patrol boat near Flushing. The skipper and most of the crew had been killed when they resisted, and only Doorn—the mate then as he was now—and a few hands were left. He fully expected death, probably a prolonged one. The chance arrival of one of the earl of Cumberland's private pirate vessels alone had saved him. The ketch had been brought into Plymouth, where George Fitzwilliam, who had been on the lookout for some such small fast vessel, bought her from Cumberland's agents and renamed and refitted her, retaining of the crew only the mate, young Doorn.

George had no dislike of Dutchmen, but for his present purpose he thought them too passionate in their hatred of Spaniards to be counted upon to keep their heads. Doorn, however, he did hire for his knowledge of the sailing points of this ketch.

The Nombre de Dios expedition, like the voyage of circumnavigation, had been, on paper at least, a mercantile adventure. This was war now, real war, and George had not the slightest objection to taking an active command at sea—indeed, he had insisted upon it. He was not only captain and owner of the *Anne;* he was also her sailing master.

The dons, who always moved slowly—King Philip was famous for his *pie de plomo,* his foot of lead—had taken a long while to come. For years this invasion had been threatened, as the Spaniards were barbed by the behavior of just such swashbucklers as Francis Drake —*Sir* Francis Drake now—and his cousin John Hawkins. Philip didn't want to do it, for he had more than he could handle with the rebellious Low Countries, the recently snatched Portugal, and the New World; but he saw no alternative.

Don't wait for them to come—break them before they get started! was the Hawkins-Drake counsel. Hit 'em at home! But Queen Elizabeth preferred to keep her ships near her own shores, where she could control them. The army, under Leicester, was pitifully unprepared, a joke. If ever the crack Spanish troops did come pouring ashore there would be no stopping them. It was up to the navy to prevent that. After much wrangling and political maneuvering, the war party had prevailed at least enough to get the queen to consent to an off-balance blow. That had been the previous year, 1587, when George was called to Plymouth to assist in the preparations. After months of outfitting, victualing, restocking, recruiting, the actual thrust was something of a lark. With George commanding a small bark he had bought for the occasion—he was to sell her later at a profit—they had met with no mentionable resistance when they sailed into the harbor at Cadiz, chief supply port for the fleet that was being assembled at Lisbon, the greatest fleet in the history of mankind. They burned as many of the storeships as they could reach—more than ten thousand tons, plus cargo—and there and along the coast in the form of supply vessels meant to converge upon Cadiz, they seized vast amounts of dried fruit from Andalusia, olive oil, flour, wine, salt, gunpowder, pike staves, breastplates. The venture had been commissioned "to prevent or withstand such enterprises as might be attempted against her Highness' realm or dominions," but the men called it "singeing King Philip's beard." It was reckoned that this raid—if so massive a movement could be called a raid—had set back by a full year the invasion of England.

It had set it back; it had not killed it. The Spaniards, though dismayed, were not discouraged. They started all over again, assembling another enormous fleet.

Drake pleaded to be permitted to smash that one too, in its place of birth, as he had done before. The queen's chief objection to war was known to be its expense; and Drake pointed out that by taking the fight to the enemy, *his* way of waging war, the institution actually could be made to show a profit. It was of no avail. Elizabeth was frightened by this time, and the ships were commanded not to stir from the Channel.

So there was the long and tedious task of keeping the narrow seas, holding warships and men in readiness, with wages and supplies furnished on a weekly basis and never liberal. It was the kind of work George did well, and hated. He got home very little that winter.

"I thought you'd have more time to spend here, once you were rich," Anne said.

"I thought so too. But it seems we were wrong. It seems that the more money a man has the more time he is expected to give to the public service—free."

"I might as well be a mariner's wife."

"Aye. But it can't last forever."

Remembering this, he eyed the Armada, which was making up-Channel on a course about northeast by east; and he admired the seamanship. The ketch's course, almost due north, was taking it away from that glorious sight. The pinnace, pressing on every inch of canvas, was creeping up.

George shook his head. He knew what van Doorn was thinking. Doorn would have turned to fight. That's the way they were, those Dutchmen: emotional. But as George saw it, it was his duty to get to Plymouth with the news of the arrival of the Armada, not to turn aside for a duel. He saw no shame in running away; there would be plenty of time for fighting later.

George did, however, consent to tell his reason for loading the stern gun.

"They're touchy. They have old-fashioned ideas. The captain of that craft, if we fire at him—even if we don't reach him (and we probably won't)—he'll feel himself in honor bound to fire back four or five times. He believes that the admiral's watching him, but he'd do it anyway."

He pointed to the pinnace, where they could see in the light of the rising sun a glint of brass far forward.

"He'll fire from the bow, and every time he does there'll be a recoil. And every recoil will slow him a bit. Oh, not much! But inches could count in a chase like this, I think. If the fleet's bound up in Plymouth Sound, England's lost!"

The gunner worked out the tompion, a plug that had been placed into the muzzle of this small brass stern saker for the purpose of keeping out spray and sea water. He mopped the inside, which proved to be perfectly dry. He weighed powder, and cut a ball. He loaded, rammed home the wadding, and goosed the touchhole with a wire, having first fastened a strip of tin around that part of the gun so that the loosened powder wouldn't be whuffed away. He stepped back and picked up a match that one of his mates had lighted. He regarded the pinnace.

"I don't think it will," he muttered.

"Fire anyway," said George.

Timing it for a rise of the stern, the gunner put the match to the touchhole. Though they were firing back into a following wind, there was very little flare. The powder burned briskly, almost with a *poof,* and the gun went off.

They saw the plash. It had been only a few yards short of the pinnace, and perfectly in line.

"A bigger charge?" George suggested.

"Wouldn't be safe," the gunner said. "I used all I dared that time, more'n I should've."

"They're loading, back there!" van Doorn cried.

The bit of brass at the pinnace's bow coughed, and a round white-gray cloud of smoke came out of it, tumbling over and over as the wind took it toward *Anne.* When it enveloped them for a moment it was streaked and thin. Before this time they had seen the ball hit, woefully short. But still the pinnace gained on them.

"Better load it again," said George, troubled.

The helmsman, the only man in the ketch who was facing forward, let out a great yell. He pointed exultantly.

Those aboard the pinnace had of course all been facing forward—and the pinnace put about.

The chase was ended.

For somebody else had got in with the news before George could do so, and now from out of Plymouth Sound, under the shadow of Mount Edgecombe, around Rame Head, English ships were being painfully warped—Lord Howard's, the queen's, John Hawkins', Martin Frobisher's, Francis Drake's.

Here were not gaudy galleons. They showed no gilt, blew no trumpets. No banners streamed from their mastheads. They were pygmies compared with the giants from Spain; but they were handsomely gunned, as they were vigorously manned, and ready for anything. They made a course due east, meaning to close with the Spanish flank.

"Yonkers aloft! Put her over! Smart there! Take in that spritsail! And, master gunner—"

"Aye, aye, sir!"

"Load everything!"

"Aye, aye!"

"Our course is due east," George Fitzwilliam told his mate. He dropped a hand on the lad's shoulder. "And if it's a fight you're yearning for, *mijnheer,* I think you are going to get it."

[247]

43

Conclave of the Besmudged

For two weeks he had not taken off his clothes, and if he had slept at all it was in snatches, so that when the order was flown for him to report immediately aboard the flagship, he cursed with a bitterness that bubbled out of his heart. Dizzy, perhaps made lightheaded by the cannonading, he went so far as to shake a fist at the *Ark Royal,* where the admiral was. Nevertheless he prepared to obey.

Those preparations were not elaborate. When he had sailed from Plymouth it was for the purpose of making a two-day scouting cruise, and he had with him no other clothes than those he wore, encrusted now with dirt and with unburned gunpowder: "Cudgel me and you'd bat out enough to fire another broadside," he had said only that morning. Neither could he wash. As there was no gunpowder left so was there precious little water, and what there was—there being no beer at all—must be saved for drinking purposes. George's beard was black, as was his face. He had lost his bonnet. His hose were ripped, his boots scuffed and scorched. His mouth tasted like a blacksmith's bib.

"You're in command," he muttered to Cornelius van Doorn.

"Aye, aye, sir."

The Dutcher too had a face as black as any Senegambian's, so that he crickled when he smiled or even spoke—the red eyes and the tear-washed skin around them, together with the extruded wet lips, touching up that negroid appearance. He too had lost his bonnet; but his hair, determinedly yellow, was finer than George's and had not caught so much grit.

This was his first command, and he was very serious about it.

It was not the ketch *Anne.* The second night of the running battle, when the Spanish fleet, still keeping its formation, was assembled in the tricky waters off Portland, the *Anne* had stumbled upon a caravel that was dragging its anchor. Without grappling hooks or boarding nets, they had swarmed all over her in a matter of minutes, and that for two reasons: her skipper and more than half of the crew of forty-odd were violently sick from some kind of food poisoning, and the others, confused, had been so busy trying to cut the cable of the offending anchor and to make about that they did not realize how far from formation they were. It was a great stroke of luck. The caravel, *San Juan de la Purificación,* commonly called *El Chico,* was a well-found vessel, in no way damaged, carrying two extra suits of sails, a chest of gold and silver coins for pay purposes, and a large supply of provisions and gunpowder, both of which would command fabulous prices anywhere along the south shore of England just then. By the rules of warfare, cargo and caravel alike went to George as a private adventurer. It would be a tidy fortune, and almost any other skipper would have headed for shore to take advantage of it. George never even considered this course. Instead he stripped his own *Anne* of her six guns, her provisions, and all her canvas save a small topsail, and loaded her—overloaded her, rather—with Spaniards, whom he told to find their way to shore as best they could, praying meanwhile that they would not be murdered when they got there. He retained only a handful of powder-boys.

He liked the *Anne*—she was smart—but she was too small. He hoped that she would survive, somehow. He couldn't worry; there was too much to do.

This feat he had supposed would pass unnoticed, but he was mistaken. It was several days before he could be sure that any English ship he neared wouldn't open fire on him, but the word at last had been spread, and instead of being cannonaded when she hove into sight *El Chico* was cheered. And George, who already had the distinction of having discharged the first shot in this greatest of sea fights since Lepanto, now had the added distinction of being the only man to board an enemy vessel.

For it had been a standoff fight, contrary to all the rules of sea warfare. The Spaniards had the best soldiers in the world, and if they could ever come to grips with the enemy, as they hoped to do, the result would not be in doubt. But the English were nimble, and they were alert. *Fight the ships!* was the Hawkins-Drake dictum.

Those ships were fast. When they moved in together for the first time, the morning of the 21st—it was a Sunday but for once Francis Drake didn't seem to mind—it was not in battle spread-formation, Mediterranean style, but as a single line, one following the other. The Spaniards, bracing themselves, could hardly believe their eyes, and when the first vessel had wheeled, fired a broadside, and fallen off, and the second had done the same, and the third, the Spaniards had given a great cheer, for they thought, poor fools, that their enemy was in retreat! It must have bewildered them when the English returned almost immediately to do the same thing over again, in reverse. And then do it again. And again.

After all, why *should* they close? Why should they risk an embrace almost certain to crush them, for they were like dogs yapping and snapping around a chained bear—for all their show of ferocity, careful not to get too close.

Spanish soldiers lined the rails, six deep, their helmets gleaming, pikes or swords in their hands, tears in their eyes as they screamed to the heretic dogs to stand up and fight like men. But the heretic dogs only fired their cannons and fell back, reloading for the next run. Never had so much gunpowder been burned as in these past two weeks. Yet they begged for more. They would have paid anything for powder with which to finish the fight. It was not to be. Fortunately the don too was out of the stuff, so that now, battered, reeling, the winds denying him any chance of a return to the sands of Gravelines, he could only continue to run.

This was in the North Sea somewhere off Tynemouth, at the end of that five-hundred-mile fray.

As his cock was being brought around, George studied the Armada. Its course, he reckoned, was northwest by west. Their own course for the past half hour had been almost due west. They planned to put in somewhere, maybe the Firth of Forth. They had perforce broken off the pursuit.

Close-up, as he had so many times seen it, the Armada at that moment no doubt presented a pitiful sight. She had been mauled—spars shot away, anchors lost, rudders damaged, scarcely a hull that hadn't been holed. Her sails were shredded, coming apart. Always slow, now she could barely move: she staggered like a man in the last stages of exhaustion.

From where George stood at the head of the Jacob's ladder she seemed glorious still. The wrecked rigging, the severed lines, did not show, and the sails looked whole, full-bellied, their red crosses defiant in the light of the setting sun.

Those Spaniards were brave men. Their world was dead around them; they had been passed by, for they represented a way of life that already was gone. Yet when they died, when their fond foolish ideas of chivalry at last were exploded, something of Romance would expire at the same time, as something had done last year when the men at Fotheringay hacked off the head of Mary Stuart.

George Fitzwilliam knew that. He was too weary to be sure of much else, but he did know that.

"Have we got a man left who can still row?" he asked.

He was too tired to ponder the purpose of the call. It could hardly be a council. Why a council? There was no question of tactics. The only thing they could do was limp to the nearest port and get something to drink. Besides, by no means all of the captains were being summoned, in fact only a few.

"Here we are, sir. Should I help you?"

William Howard, earl of Effingham, lord high admiral of England, was tall, lank, slabsided, blunt. He was that rarity, an aristocratic mariner. He might have been spotted anywhere as a seafaring man. He held his position because of his birth; but though an accomplished courtier when he condescended to be, he preferred the poop deck to an armchair in some palace; and though he could hardly be expected to have the nautical knowledge of his vice-admiral, Drake, or his rear-admiral, John Hawkins, yet he was nobody's fool.

"Ah, Beeston . . . and Hawkins . . . and our old pirate friend Martin Frobisher . . . come aboard, sirs, come aboard!"

He had a voice that might have been caked with chalk.

"Captain Fitzwilliam, sir! You're most welcome!"

It was jolting to be greeted thus, right in the waist, by a man who, like all the rest of them, resembled an African slave. For though my lord had retained his bonnet and his sash of authority as the queen's personal representative on the sea, and also his fine long Spanish rapier, he was as shabby as any, and his face too had been blackened with smoke.

Even a Howard, George marveled, can get dirty.

He led them to the poop.

There were drummers, rigid at attention, and a couple of trumpeters who sounded a fanfare. There was a clump of officers and gentlemen-adventurers: they all looked alike.

"What's this mean?" George whispered to his old master.

"Don't you know? Didn't they tell you?"

"If they did I didn't hear it. My ears have been ringing so—"

He broke off, for he had seen a friend. Despite the charred clothes, the charcoal face, there could be no mistaking him.

"*Terence!*"

"Sh-sh! Thou'rt part of a ceremony. And that's not my name here." But he squeezed George's elbow, trying to turn him. "It's good to see thee and know that thou hast survived."

"I thought thou'd gone to the Continent!"

"I came back when I heard of the Spanish fleet. I—I'm going to take holy orders at Douai, George. Next time thou seest me, and pray

God it be soon, I'll be in priest's garb. But I couldn't let them invade England—and me sitting off to one side."

He pushed George forward, toward the center of the deck.

"There, they called thy name," he whispered. "Good luck!"

George stumbled toward Lord Howard, who stood with bare sword. It was not until then that George realized what was happening. Here was an investiture! a field-of-battle accolade, the finest kind!

"Well, I'll be damned," he muttered as he went to one knee.

The blow on his shoulder was no formal tap. It was sound and firm, even harsh, a man's greeting. It rocked him, clearing his head.

"Rise, Sir George!"

Then Lord Howard, beaming, thrust the sword beneath his left arm and shook George by the hand.

And George, a little out of breath, rejoined John Hawkins, who had just become Sir John Hawkins. Terence, perhaps not trusting himself to control his emotions, had disappeared. Hawkins was watching Martin Frobisher, George Beeston and Roger Townsend become knights. George was watching the red sails of the Armada as they slid away.

Yes, something had died. . . .

But something too had been born.

"This, uh, this'll be confirmed by the queen?"

"Oh, aye. At a big function in London. A splendid court affair."

"Good," said George. "I'll bring my wife."

Stories
for a
kindred
Heart

Over 100 Stories Celebrating
Friendship, Family, and Love

COMPILED BY ALICE GRAY &
BARBARA BAUMGARDNER

Guideposts ®

CARMEL, NEW YORK 10512

www.guidepostsbooks.com

This Guideposts edition is published by special arrangement with Multnomah Publishers, Inc.

STORIES FOR A KINDRED HEART
published by Multnomah Publishers, Inc.
© 2000 by Alice Gray and Barbara Baumgardner
International Standard Book Number: 1-57673-704-7

Cover illustration by Georgie Mize
Background image by Photodisc

Scripture quotations are from:
The Holy Bible, New International Version (NIV)
© 1973, 1984 by International Bible Society,
used by permission of Zondervan Publishing House
Also quoted:
The Message © 1993 by Eugene H. Peterson
The Holy Bible, New King James Version (NKJV) © 1984 by Thomas Nelson, Inc.
The Living Bible (TLB) © 1971. Used by permission of Tyndale House Publishers, Inc.
All rights reserved.
The Holy Bible, King James Version (KJV)

Library of Congress Cataloging-in-Publication Data:

Stories for a kindred heart: over 100 stories celebrating friends, family, and love / compiled by
Alice Gray and Barbara Baumgardner.
    p.cm.
    ISBN 1-57673-704-7 (pbk.)
    1.Christian life. I. Gray, Alice. 1939– II. Baumgardner, Barbara, 1931–
    BV4515.2.S835 2000
    242—dc21

                                                                    00–008678

FOR KINDRED HEARTS...

*There is no greater joy
than having hearts entwined with others
through time, laughter, and tears.*

A Special Thank You to:

Doreen Button, Jennifer Gates,
Karen Jamison, Casandra Lindell, Teri Sharp.

Thank you for sharing your love of wonderful stories

and for your sweet friendship.

We are kindred hearts…bound by God's love.

Blessings,

Alice

My Love and gratitude to those too-numerous-to-name

kindred friends who encouraged me, prayed for me,

and kept asking, "Is it a book yet?"

Finally, dear ones, it is. Let's go to lunch!

Hugs,

Barbara

Encouragement

Friendship

CONTENTS

CONTENTS

CONTENTS

Life

Faith

CONTENTS

Encouragement

WHEN THE WINDS ARE STRONG

If your life is windy these days—
winds of change, winds of adversity,
or maybe the constant winds of demands and expectations
that leave you feeling, well…
windblown—take heart.
As my mother used to say,
"The roots grow deep when the winds are strong."

CHARLES R. SWINDOLL

THE GIFT

GARY SWANSON

FROM *FOCUS ON THE FAMILY* MAGAZINE

*T*he mother sat on the simulated-leather chair in the doctor's office, picking nervously at her fingernails. Wrinkles of worry lined her forehead as she watched five-year-old Kenny sitting on the rug before her.

He is small for his age and a little too thin, she thought. His fine blond hair hung down smooth and straight to the top of his ears. White gauze bandages encircled his head, covering his eyes and pinning his ears back.

In his lap he bounced a beaten-up teddy bear. It was the pride of his life, yet one arm was gone and one eye was missing. Twice his mother had tried to throw the bear away, to replace it with a new one, but he had fussed so much she had relented. She tipped her head slightly to the side and smiled at him. It's really about all he has, she sighed to herself.

A nurse appeared in the doorway. "Kenny Ellis," she announced, and the young mother scooped up the boy and followed the nurse toward the examination room. The hallway smelled of rubbing alcohol and bandages. Children's crayon drawings lined the walls.

"The doctor will be with you in a moment," the nurse said with an efficient smile. "Please be seated."

The mother placed Kenny on the examination table. "Be careful, Honey, not to fall off."

"Am I up very high, Mother?"

"No dear, but be careful."

Kenny hugged his teddy bear tighter. "I don't want Grr-face to fall either."

The mother smiled. The smile twisted at the corners into a frown of concern. She brushed the hair out of the boy's face and caressed his cheek, soft as thistledown, with the back of her hand. As the office music drifted into a haunting version of "Silent Night," she remembered the accident for the thousandth time.

She had been cooking things on the back burners for years. But there it was, sitting right out in front, the water almost boiling for oatmeal.

The phone rang in the living room. It was another one of those "free offers" that cost so much. At the very moment she returned the phone to the table, Kenny screamed in the kitchen, the galvanizing cry of pain that frosts a mother's veins.

She winced again at the memory of it and brushed aside a warm tear slipping down her cheek. Six weeks they had waited for this day to come. "We'll be able to take the bandages off the week before Christmas," the doctor had said.

The door to the examination room swept open, and Dr. Harris came in. "Good morning, Mrs. Ellis," he said brightly. "How are you today?"

"Fine, thank you," she said. But she was too apprehensive for small talk.

Dr. Harris bent over the sink and washed his hands carefully. He was cautious with his patients but careless about himself. He could seldom find time to get a haircut, and his straight black hair hung a little long over his collar. His loosened tie allowed his collar to be open at the throat.

"Now then," he said, sitting down on a stool, "let's have a look."

Gently he snipped at the bandage with scissors and unwound it from Kenny's head. The bandage fell away, leaving two flat squares of gauze taped directly over Kenny's eyes. Dr. Harris lifted the edges of the tape slowly, trying not to hurt the boy's tender skin.

Kenny slowly opened his eyes, blinked several times as if the sudden light hurt. Then he looked at his mother and grinned. "Hi, Mom," he said.

Choking and speechless, the mother threw her arms around Kenny's neck. For several minutes she could say nothing as she hugged the boy and wept in thankfulness. Finally, she looked at Dr. Harris with tear-filled eyes. "I don't know how we'll ever be able to pay you," she said.

"We've been over all that before," the doctor interrupted with a wave of his hand. "I know how things are for you and Kenny. I'm glad I could help."

The mother dabbed at her eyes with a well-used handkerchief, stood up, and took Kenny's hand. But just as she turned toward the door, Kenny pulled away and stood for a long moment looking uncertainly at the doctor. Then he held his teddy bear up by its one arm to the doctor.

"Here," he said. "Take my Grr-face. He ought to be worth a lot of money."

Dr. Harris quietly took the broken bear in his two hands. "Thank you, Kenny. This will more than pay for my services."

The last few days before Christmas were especially good for Kenny and his mother. They sat together in the long evenings, watching the Christmas tree lights twinkle on and off. Bandages had covered Kenny's eyes for six weeks, so he seemed reluctant to close them in sleep. The fire dancing in the fireplace, the snowflakes sticking to his bedroom windows, the two small packages under the tree—all the lights and colors of the holiday fascinated him. And then, on Christmas Eve, Kenny's mother answered the doorbell. No one was there, but a large box was on the porch wrapped in shiny gold paper with a broad red ribbon and bow. A tag attached to the bow identified the box as intended for Kenny Ellis.

With a grin, Kenny tore the ribbon off the box, lifted the lid, and pulled out a teddy bear—his beloved Grr-face. Only now it had a new arm of brown corduroy and two new button eyes that glittered in the soft Christmas light. Kenny didn't seem to mind that the new arm did not match the other one. He just hugged his teddy bear and laughed.

Among the tissue in the box, the mother found a card. "Dear Kenny," it read. "I can sometimes help put boys and girls back together, but Mrs. Harris had to help me repair Grr-face. She's a better bear doctor than I am. Merry Christmas! Dr. Harris."

"Look, Mother," Kenny smiled, pointing to the button eyes. "Grr-face can see again—just like me!"

THE RED PURSE

LOUISE MOERI
FROM *VIRTUE* MAGAZINE

I know we are not supposed to judge people, but where Kennie Jablonsky was concerned, I found it impossible. I decided he was the wrong person in the wrong kind of work.

I'm a swing-shift nursing supervisor and it's my job to evaluate workers' performances at Homeland Convalescent Hospital.

Kennie Jablonsky was a new employee, tall and very strong, not bad looking with his blond hair cut to the collar and dark green eyes. After a few weeks' probation, I had to admit he was clean, punctual and reasonably efficient. But I just didn't like him.

Kennie Jablonsky looked like a hood. I knew the neighborhood he came from—a cesspool of gangs, drugs and violence. His language was street talk, his manner wry, his walk springy and controlled like a boxer's and his expression closed-off like the steel door on a bank vault. He seemed too large and carefully controlling of a powerful will to be able to fit into a highly specialized teamwork of a convalescent hospital.

The vast majority of our patients come to us in the final stages of terminal disease or with the most terminal of all diseases—old age. They come to us crippled, weakened, confused and defeated, no longer able to function out in the world. Many have lost the faculty of rational thought, a casualty of failing health and a world that often seems brutal and indifferent.

Mary B. was one of those. Attendants call her Mary B. because she was one of four Marys in the West Wing. At ninety-four years, Mary B. was frail as a cobweb. She outlived her husband and sisters, and if she had any children they had long since abandoned her. She was in almost constant motion as long as she was awake.

Mary B. had an obsession that someone had taken her purse. She searched for it all hours of the day and night. Unless tied to her bed or wheelchair, she would go through the door onto the street, into the men's wards, through the laundry room and into the kitchen, mindlessly searching and never giving up. When restrained, she wanted her wheelchair in the hallway, where she stopped everyone who came near.

"Can you lend me a comb?" she asked. "I've lost mine. It was in my red purse. My money is gone, too. Where is my purse? Where is my purse?"

Every day it was the same, until Mary B.'s queries became background noise, like the sound of hot carts loaded with trays rumbling down the halls, the hum of air conditioning or the static of the intercom.

We all knew Mary didn't have a purse. But on occasion someone would stop to listen to her out of kindness and concern, although we were furiously busy. Still, most of us maneuvered around her with, "Sure, Mary, if I see your purse I'll bring it back."

Most of us—but one.

The last thing I expected of Kennie Jablonsky was that he would listen to Mary B., but strangely, he always had a word for her.

What is he up to? I wondered, watching him. My first suspicion was that he might be working here to steal drugs. I thought I had spotted a potential troublemaker.

Every day as Mary B. stopped him to ask about her purse, and as Kennie promised to look for it, my suspicions grew. Finally I concluded that Kennie was planning something involving Mary. He's going to steal drugs, I told myself, and somehow hide them around Mary. Then some accomplice will come in and sneak them out of the hospital. I was so sure of all this that I set up more security systems around the drug dispensing department.

One afternoon, just before supper, I saw Kennie walking down the hall with a plastic grocery bag in his hand. It was heavy.

This is it, I told myself, scrambling from behind my desk. I started after him, but realized I needed more evidence. I halted behind a laundry cart, piled high with baskets.

It was tall enough to conceal me, but I still could see Kennie clearly as he strode down the hall toward Mary B. in her wheelchair.

He reached Mary and suddenly turned, looking over his shoulder. I dodged out of sight but I could still see him peering up and down the hall. It was clear he didn't want anyone to see what he was doing.

He raised the bag. I froze…until he pulled out a red purse.

Mary's thin old hands flew up to her face in a gesture of wonder and joy, then flew out hungrily. Like a starved child taking bread, Mary B. grabbed the red purse. She held it for a moment, just to see it, then pressed it to her breast, rocking it like a baby.

Kennie turned and glanced sharply all around. Satisfied no one was watching, he leaned over, unsnapped the flap, reached in and showed Mary a red comb, small coin purse and a pair of children's toy spectacles. Tears of joy were pouring down Mary's face. At least, I guessed they were. Tears streaked my face, too.

Kennie patted Mary lightly on the shoulder, crumpled the plastic grocery bag, threw it into the nearby waste can, then went about his work down the hall.

I walked back to my desk, sat down, reached into the bottom drawer and brought out my battered old Bible. Turning to the seventh chapter of Matthew, I asked the Lord to forgive me…

At the end of the shift, I stood near the door used by the aides coming to and leaving work. Kennie came bouncing down the hall carrying his coat and radio.

"Hi, Kennie," I said. "How's everything going? Do you think you'll like this job?"

Kennie looked surprised, then shrugged. "It's the best I'll ever get," he grunted.

"Nursing is a good career," I ventured. An idea was growing. "Uh, have you ever thought of going on to college for a registered nursing degree?"

Kennie snorted. "Are you kidding? I ain't got a chance for anything like that. The nurse's aide course was free or I wouldn't have *this* job."

I knew this was true. Kennie set down his radio and pulled on his coat. "Take a miracle for me to go to college," he said. "My old man's in San Quentin and my old lady does cocaine."

I clenched my teeth but still smiled. "Miracles do happen," I told him. "Would you go to college if I could find a way to help you with the money?"

Kennie stared at me. All at once the hood vanished and I caught a glimpse of what could be. "Yes!" was all he said. But it was enough.

"Good night, Kennie," I said as he reached for the door handle. "I'm sure something can be worked out."

I was sure, too, that in Room 306 of the West Wing, Mary B. was sleeping quietly, both her arms wrapped around a red purse.

ICE CREAM PARTY

ROCHELLE M. PENNINGTON

I stopped at Dairy Queen, purchased a sandwich, and sat down in the crowded dining room next to a family celebrating their son's basketball game over an ice-cream cake. Since the aisles were especially narrow, I soon felt like I was a part of the party.

"So, your team must have won this afternoon," I commented.

The little fellow smiled and wholeheartedly announced, "No, we lost twenty-four to two!"

"Well, you must have made the only basket then," I said.

"No, I missed all of the eight shots I took, but three of them did hit the rim."

This child was elated. I was confused. They were celebrating because his team lost the game and because he had missed eight baskets! Seldom am I at a loss of words, but the only response I could muster up at that moment was a blank stare and a very large, insincere looking smile. Absolutely no clue.

After another mouthful of cake, and still grinning ear to ear, he added, "We're having a party because last week I missed nine shots and none of them even came anywhere near to the backboard. Dad says that all of my practicing this week really paid off. I'm making progress."

THE BUNNY AND
THE EGGHEADS

TED MENTEN
FROM *GENTLE CLOSINGS*

One of my groups of kids is bald from either chemotherapy or radiation therapy. The children range in age
from seven to thirteen. When they're alone they walk around without hats
on—at least the boys do. The girls are embarrassed about losing their hair
and tend to wear their hats.

Children adapt quickly and form tight circles from which outsiders
are excluded. Although I'm an outsider who has all his hair, I'm not
excluded from their games and their humor. In fact, I'm often the butt of
their hairy jokes.

Among themselves the kids are called Eggheads. Of course I'm not
supposed to know this because it's a secret and exclusive clan. Eggheads
support and reassure one another as no outsider can. I consider it an
honor even to be tolerated by them.

As Easter approached, the little girls were feeling some anxiety about
wearing Easter hats. Bonnets were suggested but rejected as too babyish.
None of them even considered wearing a wig. It was declared yucky.

As the time grew closer I decided on a plan that I thought they all
would enjoy.

I checked around and found some water-base paint that could be used safely on skin, and then rented the most awful rabbit costume I could find. It was a terrible fluorescent pink and very, very tacky. The Saturday before Easter, I arrived at the hospital dressed in the bunny suit and made my way to where the kids were waiting for me. When I came in they got hysterical and it took quite a while to get them settled down. Then the fun began.

One by one I decorated their heads in bright colors like Easter eggs—flowers and butterflies and stars and dots and stripes. The more garish the better. At first only the boys let me paint them, but eventually the girls took off their hats and I painted their heads with ribbons and flowers and tiny hearts. We laughed as each head was painted until everyone had a colorful dome. Then I took off my bunny head and revealed by own bald pate. Of course it was a fake, but it could be painted and all the kids got to draw something on it.

Later, when the nurse came in, she nearly had a heart attack. The doctors didn't find it at all funny but the kids loved it. The next week they voted me an honorary Egghead.

The Noble Art of Turning

The weathercock on the church spire,
though made of iron,
would soon be broken by the storm-wind
if it did not understand the noble art of turning
to every wind.

HEINRICH HEINE

MOLLY

BARBARA BAUMGARDNER
FROM *HUMAN SOCIETY OF CENTRAL OREGON* NEWSLETTER

hen I take Molly for a walk, I frequently get way-laid by people who "once had a golden retriever." I call them *kindred hearts* because they don't seem to object as Molly leaves hair and drool all over their pant legs whenever I stop to chat. *Kindred hearts* are a lot more tolerant of things like shaggy, shedding, slobbering dogs—and of people, too, in general. Molly is learning to pick out those *kindred hearts* when we go visiting the nursing homes, assisted living centers and hospitals.

At eighteen months old, I wasn't sure she would be able to calm down enough to be a "visiting dog" under the Humane Society program. She is a typical golden: affectionate but active, tail-wagging, always ready to play. Tom Davis described her well in his book, *Just Goldens,* when he said, "Goldens are imaginative, mellow, enemies of routine…quirky, fun-loving and full of surprises…you'd want a Golden to throw a party. A couple of hours into the festivities, it's the one wearing the lampshade."

That's Molly: the one wearing the lampshade.

She wasn't sure what her role was when we began to make our sched-uled visits. She'd wiggle and whop everyone around her with her tail; the tail that wags with such force it can hurt or it can clear the coffee table.

She thinks she is still a lap dog but we weren't visiting anyone healthy and big enough to hold her. However, like all goldens, she has that innate desire to please me. As I coached, she finally figured out that if she would sit, someone would pet her or better yet, hug her. And sometimes she would lay her head in a willing lap.

Recently on one of our visits, she performed like a pro. We were at a health care center, in the section where people need a lot of care. A woman, secured to a wheelchair, seemed so unaware that we nearly passed her by. Her hands were crippled and bent under; her head had fallen to one side, eyes closed. Molly paused and so did I.

The woman responded to my touch when I put my hand on her arm so I grasped a gnarled hand and touched it to Molly's soft fur. As her hand in mine stroked Molly's head, the woman opened her eyes and began to laugh. Soon she was alert, but giggling like a child as I continued to move her hand around the golden's body. Molly sat close, and soon put her head on the lap in the wheelchair. Then with her own strength, the woman managed to bend forward enough to push her arms around Molly's neck, her excited giggles catching the attention of the nurses close by. The woman couldn't speak, but she communicated her kindred heart: giving love through touch, in the same way Molly does.

My dog and I will return to visit the woman again. I think Molly finally understands that when she's on assignment, she must give up the lampshade and just be the light.

WE ALL NEED TO BE
LOOKED AFTER

MAX LUCADO
FROM *IN THE GRIP OF GRACE*

*G*ood, I'm glad you're sitting by me. Sometimes I throw up."

Not exactly what you like to hear from the airline passenger in the next seat. Before I had time to store my bag in the overhead compartment, I knew his name, age and itinerary. "I'm Billy Jack. I'm fourteen, and I'm going home to see my daddy."

I started to tell him my name, but he spoke first. "I need someone to look after me. I get confused a lot."

He told me about the special school he attended and the medication he took. "Can you remind me to take my pill in a few minutes?" Before we buckled up he stopped the airline attendant. "Don't forget about me," he told her. "I get confused."

Once we were airborne, Billy Jack ordered a soft drink and dipped his pretzels in it. He kept glancing at me as I drank and asked if he could drink what I didn't. He spilled some of his soda and apologized.

"No problem," I said, wiping it up.

When he started playing his Nintendo Game Boy, I tried to doze off. That's when he started making noises with his mouth, imitating a trumpet. "I can sound like the ocean, too," he bragged, swishing spit back and forth in his cheeks.

(Didn't sound like the ocean, but I didn't tell him.)

Billy Jack was a little boy in a big body. "Can clouds hit the ground?" he asked me. I started to answer, but he looked back out the window as if he'd never asked. Unashamed of his needs, he didn't let a flight attendant pass without a reminder: "Don't forget to look after me."

When they brought the food: "Don't forget to look after me."

When they brought more drinks: "Don't forget to look after me."

When any attendant passed, Billy Jack urged: "Don't forget to look after me."

I honestly can't think of one time Billy Jack didn't remind the crew that he needed attention. The rest of us didn't need it. We never asked for help. We were grown-ups. Sophisticated. Self-reliant. Seasoned travelers. Most of us didn't even listen to the emergency landing instructions. (Billy Jack asked me to explain them to him.)

An epistle to challenge the self-sufficient, the books of Romans was written for folks like us. Confession of need is admission of weakness, something we are slow to do. I think Billy Jack would have understood grace. It occurred to me that he was the safest person on the flight. Had the plane encountered trouble, he would have received primary assistance. The flight attendants would have bypassed me and gone to him. Why? He had placed himself in the care of someone stronger.

I ask, have you?

One thing's for sure: You cannot save yourself. God has sent His firstborn Son to carry you home. Are you firmly in the grip of His grace? I pray that you are. I *earnestly* pray that you are.

One last thought. Billy Jack spent the final hour of the flight with his head on my shoulder, his hands folded between his knees. Just when I thought he was asleep, his head popped up and he said, "My dad is going to meet me at the airport. I can't wait to see him because he watches after me."

The apostle Paul would have liked Billy Jack.

LOVE LETTERS

BOB WELCH
FROM *WHERE ROOTS GROW DEEP*

*N*ear as anyone can tell, Sally's grandmother never touched a computer keyboard. She didn't particularly like talking on the phone. Instead, she communicated with her extended family through something far superior to anything high technology could offer, something better than even e-mail.

She reached out and touched us all with g-mail—Gram Mail.

Gram Youngberg, who died in the fall of 1997 at the age of ninety-five, wrote letters. Thousands of letters spanning decades and decades, many of which my wife has saved. Part of Gram's legacy was how she lived her life, but part of it, too, was the words she left with us all—words that became an extension of the woman who penned them. Words that helped sustain and link the interdependent parts of her legacy tree.

They tell us of a simple, salt-of-the-earth woman who noticed the daily comings and goings of people with detailed enthusiasm. Like Emily, the young girl in *Our Town* who wonders if anyone but the "saints and poets" really notice the nuances of life around them, Gram, too, noticed the "clocks ticking, and Mama's sunflowers and new-ironed dresses and hot baths…" Mainly, she noticed her extended family and friends.

"Bud Payne," she wrote in one letter, "is still housebound with his severed knee ligament… Max Coffey plans on going to Haiti as a mechanic on the medical team the last of November… My, but Brad and Paul have grown!…"

The letters tell of someone for whom people were the utmost priority. She always wrote more about others than herself. She gloried in her family's victories, commiserated in our defeats. She welcomed in-laws into the family as if we were long-lost friends who, despite no blood links, belonged. She was always more amazed at the accomplishments of others than of her own, though she had many.

"Sally: We are so proud of you and Ann for doing your bit for others in Haiti…

"Today, I've been painting the little wooden fire trucks, eleven of them, for needy children. Then sand them and paint again. Takes almost twenty minutes to do one."

The letters tell of someone who had a special heart for children.

"I'm enjoying my Sunday school class. I have eight five- and six-year-olds and they are nice little kids."

"Your boys' drawings are something. Ryan's cows are an active, happy bunch, and show such action."

The letters tell of someone who reveled in the bounty of God's earth, in weather and soil and seasons and sunsets. "I'm busy with Indian summer crops," she wrote. "I love this time of year. Freezing corn, drying prunes, and finishing up on canning. The apple crop—pears also—were nothing and the few on the trees were wormy and scaly. But there are peaches. And how we enjoyed them!"

In another letter: "Thermometer showed twenty degrees and white frost. Snow in the hills but not here—yet." And still another: "Have you been seeing the glorious sunsets: one last night—and then sunsets during the week. They are gorgeous to behold—to appreciate the handiwork of the Lord."

Her letters were full of recipes and news of chickens and cows and gophers and sewing and church potlucks and, of course, Pop. She always took time to ask about how your family was doing. She was fond of exclamation points and, for rare occasions (like when noting a granddaughter's husband was home from the service), used happy faces.

She seldom complained. Oh, a few letters included touching lines in the years after Pop died; she was lonely. But for the most part, she had an uncanny ability to see silver linings in the darkest of clouds, to accept that pain and loss were part of life, much as drought and hail were part of farming.

"Pop is tired," she once wrote, "but we can't complain."

From another letter, extolling the accomplishments of other family members: "Aren't we lucky."

Were Gram alive today, I know how she would respond to such glowing accounts of her life. She would react the same way she reacted after I told her what an inspiration she was and that I felt fortunate to be part of her family, even as an adjunct.

"Thanks for the complimentary letter, Bob, but to be honest, I'm very undeserving of such noble motives. For I'm doing what comes naturally. In my growing-up years, I learned to make do, to make use of what is on hand, so I do it."

Decades of letters. Letters whose stamps, in just the last twenty-five years, went from eight cents to thirty-two cents. Letters that, for a while, after Gram broke her arm, were written left-handed. Letters first signed "Gram and Pop" then just "Gram," then finally stopped coming altogether—but only when she physically could no longer write.

Letters reminding us that, over the years, Gram really had two gardens: one with carrots and peas and tomatoes and corn. And one with a son and two daughters and grandchildren and great-grandchildren and nieces and nephews.

In addressing the church at Corinth, Paul writes, "You yourselves are our letter, written on our hearts, known and read by everybody." In a sense, Gram's life was one long love letter to her family and friends and God. A ninety-five-year-long letter.

Nothing would make her prouder than to know that we had tucked that letter in our wallets and purses—better yet, hidden it in our hearts— and lived the same kind of other-oriented life she had lived. She would want us to look for the best in one another. To "make do" with what circumstances we've been given. And, of course, to stop and look at the sunrises and sunsets, for, as she wrote, "They are gorgeous to behold…the handiwork of the Lord."

Kind words are the music of the world.
They have power that seems to
be beyond natural causes,
as if they were some angel's song
that had lost its way and come to earth.

FREDERICK WILLIAM FABER

GOD DOESN'T
MAKE NOBODIES

Ruth Lee
From *Touch 1* magazine

t was the last day of an extremely beneficial Christian writers conference. Someone suggested we should gather that night in the prayer rooms of our dormitories for a time of sharing.

After the banquet was over, the ladies gathered in the second-floor chapel of my dormitory. In nightgowns and pajamas, we all seemed much alike. Someone suggested introductions, but I interrupted.

"Please," I said, "let's not just say our names. Share something about yourself."

By the time three people had responded, I knew I should have kept my mouth shut! One lady was a director of nursing, another taught English on the college level, and the lady next to her had just received her doctorate! There I sat, halfway around the room, and what was I?

Nobody. Oh, yes, a wife, mother and grandmother, but nothing important.

After the introduction of two authors with published books, and other women with other claims to fame, it was my turn.

"My name is Ruth," I said, "and I feel so inferior I think I'll just go back to my room."

Everyone laughed, so I plowed ahead. "I guess you could call me a producer. In thirty years I've produced a well-adjusted respiratory thera-pist, a machinist and another happy homemaker. And I'm involved in the coproduction of seven grandchildren."

I told them how full my life is. Full of checking on cows, helping fix fences, praying for rain and then praying it will stop raining. I told them of busy hours spent baby-sitting and contending with my household.

And then I told them how hungry I was. Hungry for the type of spiri-tual and emotional food I had received at this conference.

From the far corner of the room a quiet young girl spoke up. "Would you please turn so I can look at you?"

I did as she asked, and she continued to speak. "I want to remember your face when I write," she said. "I want to write for women just like you."

Suddenly I had no need for title or degree. I served a purpose. With her words, she had helped me realize what I should have known all along. God doesn't make nobodies. Everybody is somebody important to God.

Heart Friends

A friend will strengthen you with her prayers,
bless you with her love,
and encourage you with her heart.

AUTHOR UNKNOWN

OVERNIGHT GUEST

HARTLEY F. DAILEY
FROM *SUNSHINE* MAGAZINE

Greenbriar Valley lay almost hidden by the low-hanging clouds that spilled intermittent showers. As I plodded through the muddy barnyard preparing to do my afternoon chores, I glanced at the road that led past our place and wound on through the valley. There was a car parked at the side of the road a little way beyond the pasture corner.

The car was obviously in distress. Otherwise, no man so well-dressed would have been out in the pouring rain, tinkering with it. I watched him as I went about my chores. It was evident that the man was no mechanic—desperately plodding from the raised hood back to the car seat to try the starter, then back to the hood again.

When I finished my chores and closed the barn, it was almost dark. The car was still there. So I took a flashlight and walked down the road. The man was sort of startled and disturbed when I came up to him, but he seemed anxious enough for my help. It was a small car, the same make as my own but somewhat newer. It took only a few minutes for me to spot the trouble.

"It's your coil," I told him.

"But it couldn't be that!" he blurted. "I just had a new one, only about a month ago." He was a young fellow, hardly more than a boy—I should have guessed twenty-one, at most. He sounded almost in tears.

"You see, mister," he almost sobbed, "I'm a long ways from home. It's raining. And I've just got to get it started. I just *got* to!"

"Well, it's like this," I said. "Coils are pretty touchy. Sometimes they'll last for years. Then again sometimes they'll go out in a matter of hours. Suppose I get a horse and pull the car up into the barn. Then we'll see what we can do for it. We'll try the coil from my car. If that works, I know a fellow down at the corner who'll sell you one."

I was right. With the coil from my car in place, the motor started right off, and it purred like a new one. "Nothing to it," I grinned. "We'll just go see Bill David down the road. He'll sell you a new coil, and you can be on your way. Just wait a minute while I tell my wife, Jane, where I'm going."

I thought he acted odd when we got down to David's store. He parked in the dark behind the store and wouldn't get out. "I'm wet and cold," he excused himself. "Here's ten dollars. Would you mind very much going in and getting it for me?"

We had just finished changing the coil when my little daughter, Linda, came out to the barn. "Mother says supper's ready," she announced. Then turning to the strange young man, she said, "She says you're to come in and eat, too."

"Oh, but I couldn't," he protested. "I couldn't let you folks feed me. I've got to get going anyway. No, no, I just can't stay."

"Don't be ridiculous," I said. "After all, how long will it take you to eat? Besides, no one comes to Jane's house at mealtime and leaves without eating. You wouldn't want her to lie down in mud in front of your car, would you?"

Still protesting, he allowed himself to be led off to the house. But it seemed to me as if there was something more in his protests than just mere politeness.

He sat quietly enough while I said the blessing. But during the meal he seemed fidgety. He just barely picked at his food, which was almost an insult to Jane, who is one of the best cooks in the state and proud of it.

Once the meal was over, he got quickly to his feet, announcing that he must be on his way. But he had reckoned without Jane.

"Now, look here," She said, and she glanced at me for support. "It's still pouring rain out there. Your clothes are all wet, and you can't help being cold. I'll bet you're tired, too; you must have driven far today. Stay with us tonight. Tomorrow you can start out warm and dry and all rested."

I nodded slightly at her. It isn't always advisable to take in strangers that way. Unfortunately, there are many who cannot be trusted. But I liked this young man. I felt sure he would be all right.

He reluctantly agreed to stay the night. Jane made him go to bed and hung his clothes to dry by the fire. Next morning she pressed them and gave him a nice breakfast. This meal he ate with relish. It seemed he was more settled that morning, not so restless as he had been. He thanked us profusely before he left.

But when he started away, an odd thing happened. He had been headed down the valley toward the city the night before. But when he left, he headed back north, toward Roseville, the county seat. We wondered a great deal about that, but decided he had been confused and made a wrong turn.

Time went by, and we never heard from the young man. We had not expected to, really. The days flowed into months, and the months into years. The Depression ended and drifted into war. In time, the war ended, too. Linda grew up and established a home of her own. Things on the farm were quite different from those early days of struggle. Jane and I lived comfortably and quietly, surrounded by lovely Greenbriar Valley.

Just the other day I got a letter from Chicago. A personal letter, it was, on nice expensive stationery. "Now who in the world," I wondered, "can be writing me from Chicago?" I opened it and read:

> Dear Mr. McDonald:
>
> I don't suppose you remember the young man you helped, years ago, when his car broke down. It has been a long time, and I imagine you've helped many others. But I doubt if you have helped anyone else quite the way you helped me.

You see, I was running away that night. I had in my car a very large sum of money, which I had stolen from my employer. I want you to know, sir, that I had good Christian parents. But I had forgotten their teaching and had got in with the wrong crowd. I knew I had made a terrible mistake.

But you and your wife were so nice to me. That night in your home, I began to see where I was wrong. Before morning, I made a decision. Next day, I turned back. I went back to my employer and made a clean breast of it. I gave back all the money and threw myself on his mercy.

He could have prosecuted me and sent me to prison for many years. But he is a good man. He took me back in my old job, and I have never strayed again. I'm married now, with a lovely wife and two fine children. I have worked my way to a very good position with my company. I am not wealthy, but I am comfortably well off.

I could reward you handsomely for what you did for me that night. But I don't believe that is what you'd want. So I have established a fund to help others who have made the same mistake I did. In this way, I hope I may pay for what I have done.

God bless you, sir, and your good wife, who helped me more than you knew.

Robert Fane

I walked into the house, and handed the letter to Jane. As she read it, I could see the tears begin to fill her eyes. With the strangest look on her face, she laid the letter aside.

"For I was a Stranger, and ye took Me in," she quoted. "I was hungered, and ye fed Me; I was in prison, and ye visited Me."

UNTHANKED PEOPLE

STEVE GOODIER

When William Stidger taught at Boston University, he once reflected upon the great number of unthanked people in his life. Those who had helped nurture him, inspire him, or cared enough about him to leave a lasting impression.

One was a schoolteacher he'd not heard of in many years. But he remembered that she had gone out of her way to put a love of verse in him, and Will had loved poetry all his life. He wrote a letter of thanks to her.

The reply he received, written in the feeble scrawl of the aged, began, "My dear Willie." He was delighted. Now over fifty, bald, and a professor, he didn't think there was a person left in the world who would call him "Willie." Here is that letter:

> My dear Willie,
>
> I cannot tell you how much your note meant to me. I am in my eighties, living alone in a small room, cooking my own meals, lonely, and, like the last leaf of autumn, lingering behind. You will be interested to know that I taught school for fifty years and yours is the

first note of appreciation I ever received. It came on a blue-cold morning and it cheered me as nothing has in many years.

Not prone to cry easily, Will wept over that note. She was one of the great unthanked people from Will's past. You know them. We all do. The teacher who made a difference. That coach we'll never forget. The music instructor or Sunday school worker who helped us believe in ourselves. That scout leader that cared.

We all remember people who shaped our lives in various ways. People whose influence changed us. Will Stidger found a way to show his appreciation—he wrote them letters.

Kind words can be short and easy to speak but their echoes are truly endless.

MOTHER TERESA

ANGELS ONCE IN A WHILE

BARB IRWIN

In September 1960, I woke up one morning with six hungry babies and just seventy-five cents in my pocket. Their father was gone.

The boys ranged from three months to seven years; their sister was two. Their Dad had never been much more than a presence they feared. Whenever they heard his tires crunch on the gravel driveway they would scramble to hide under their beds. He did manage to leave fifteen dollars a week to buy groceries. Now that he had decided to leave, there would be no more beatings, but no food either. If there were a welfare system in effect in southern Indiana at that time, I certainly knew nothing about it.

I scrubbed the kids until they looked brand new and then put on my best homemade dress. I loaded them into the rusty old '51 Chevy and drove off to find a job. The seven of us went to every factory, store, and restaurant in our small town. No luck. The kids stayed, crammed into the car, and tried to be quiet while I tried to convince whoever would listen that I was willing to learn or do anything. I had to have a job. Still no luck.

The last place we went to, just a few miles out of town, was an old Root Beer Barrel drive-in that had been converted to a truck stop. It was called the Big Wheel. An old lady named Granny owned the place and she peeked out of the window from time to time at all those kids. She needed someone on the graveyard shift, eleven at night until seven in the morning. She paid sixty-five cents an hour, and I could start that night.

I raced home and called the teenager down the street that baby-sat for people. I bargained with her to come and sleep on my sofa for a dollar a night. She could arrive with her pajamas on and the kids would already be asleep. This seemed like a good arrangement to her, so we made a deal.

That night when the little ones and I knelt to say our prayers we all thanked God for finding Mommy a job.

And so I started at the Big Wheel. When I got home in the mornings I woke the baby-sitter up and sent her home with one dollar of my tip money—fully half of what I averaged every night.

As the weeks went by, heating bills added another strain to my meager wage. The tires on the old Chevy had the consistency of penny balloons and began to leak. I had to fill them with air on the way to work and again every morning before I could go home.

One bleak fall morning, I dragged myself to the car to go home and found four tires in the back seat. New tires! There was no note, nothing, just those beautiful brand new tires. Had angels taken up residence in Indiana? I wondered.

I made a deal with the owner of the local service station. In exchange for his mounting the new tires, I would clean up his office. I remember it took me a lot longer to scrub his floor than it did for him to do the tires.

I was now working six nights instead of five and it still wasn't enough. Christmas was coming and I knew there would be no money for toys for the kids. I found a can of red paint and started repairing and painting some old toys. Then I hid them in the basement so there would be something for Santa to deliver on Christmas morning. Clothes were a worry too. I was sewing patches on top of patches on the boys' pants and soon they would be too far gone to repair.

On Christmas Eve the usual customers were drinking coffee in the Big Wheel. These were the truckers, Les, Frank, and Jim, and a state trooper named Joe. A few musicians were hanging around after a gig at the Legion and were dropping nickels in the pinball machine. The regulars all just sat around and talked through the wee hours of the morning and then left to get home before the sun came up. When it was time for me to go home at seven o'clock on Christmas morning I hurried to the car. I was hoping the kids wouldn't wake up before I managed to get home and get the presents from the basement and place them under the tree. (We had cut down a small cedar tree by the side of the road down by the dump.) It was still dark and I couldn't see much, but there appeared to be some dark shadows in the car—or was that just a trick of the night? Something certainly looked different, but it was hard to tell what. When I reached the car I peered warily into one of the side windows. Then my jaw dropped in amazement. My old battered Chevy was full—full to the top with boxes of all shapes and sizes.

I quickly opened the driver's side door, scrambled inside and kneeled in the front facing the backseat. Reaching back, I pulled off the lid of the top box. Inside was a whole case of little blue jeans, sizes two through ten! I looked inside another box: It was full of shirts to go with the jeans. Then I peeked inside some of the other boxes. There were candy and nuts and bananas. There was an enormous ham for baking, and canned vegetables and potatoes. There was pudding and Jell-O and cookies, pie filling and flour. There was a whole bag of laundry supplies and cleaning items.

And there were five toy trucks and one beautiful little doll. As I drove back through empty streets as the sun slowly rose on the most amazing Christmas Day of my life, I was sobbing with gratitude. And I will never forget the joy on the faces of my little ones that precious morning.

Yes, there were angels in Indiana that long-ago December. And they all hung out at the Big Wheel truck stop.

MRS. WARREN'S CLASS

COLLEEN TOWNSEND EVANS
FROM *START LOVING*

One of the great joys in life comes from watching a troubled person turn and go in a new—and better—direction. What causes such a thing to happen? A miracle? Sometimes. Forgiveness? Always!

Tom was a charming child, as most rascals are—but he was rebellious, a prankster, a rule breaker, a flaunter of authority. By the time he entered high school, his reputation had preceded him and he filled most of the teachers with dread. He took a special delight in disrupting classes and driving teachers to the limits of their patience. At home, he also was a problem. There were frequent confrontations between parents and child, each one seeking to prove he was more powerful than the other.

So many complaints were filed against Tom that the high school principal decided he would have to expel him—unless a teacher named Mrs. Warren agreed to take him into her class. Mrs. Warren was an exceptionally capable English teacher, but she also was a loving, endlessly patient woman who seemed to have a way with problem students. Yes, Mrs. Warren said, she would find a place for him in her eleven o'clock English Literature class, and also in her home room. She listened calmly as the principal read from a list of Tom's misdemeanors—a long list that had the principal shaking his head as he read. No, Mrs.Warren said, she wouldn't change her mind. She knew what she was getting into—she had heard about the boy.

When Tom was transferred to Mrs. Warren's class, he behaved as he always did upon meeting a new teacher. He slouched in his seat in the last row and glared at her, daring her—by his attitude—to do something about him. At first Mrs. Warren ignored him. Then, as the class began to discuss the reading assignment, Tom whispered a joke to the boy in front of him, making the boy laugh. Mrs.Warren looked up. Then she closed her book, stood and placed another chair at the desk, next to hers.

"Tom, come up here and sit with me for a while," she said—not as a reprimand, but as a friend. It was an invitation she was offering, and her manner was so sweet that Tom couldn't refuse. He sat next to her as she went on with the lesson. "Tom is new to our class and hasn't had time to read the assignment, so if you'll bear with me, I'll read it aloud to him."

With Tom next to her, sharing her book, Mrs. Warren began to read from *A Tale of Two Cities*. She was a fine reader and captured Dickens' sense of drama magnificently. Tom, for all his determination to be an obstruction, found himself following the text, losing himself in the unfolding of a great story, sharing the excitement of it with a woman who really seemed to care about his interest in the book. That evening he startled his parents by sitting down without any prodding to do his homework—at least the assignment for Mrs. Warren's class.

That was only the beginning... Tom never missed a day of school after that first day in Mrs. Warren's class. Sometimes he cut other classes but never hers. He sat in the front row, participated in discussions, and seemed to enjoy reading aloud when he was called upon to do so. His appetite for reading suddenly became ravenous, and he asked Mrs. Warren to make up a list of books she thought he might enjoy in his free time. After school he stayed in the classroom when the other students went home and had long talks with Mrs. Warren about the things he had read and the ideas they stimulated.

Tom wasn't exactly an angel in other classes, but the effect of his behavior in Mrs. Warren's class began to rub off a little—for which the other teachers were most grateful.

Tom didn't finish high school. In his junior year, after an angry outburst at home, he defiantly joined the Navy. He didn't even say good-bye to Mrs. Warren, who was very sad to see him leave school, because she thought she had failed in her attempt to reach him.

Seven years later, when Mrs. Warren was closing up her desk one afternoon before leaving for home, a young man came to the doorway and stood there, smiling. He was much taller and more muscular now, but Mrs. Warren recognized him within seconds. It was Tom! He rushed to her and hugged her so hard her glasses slid down her nose.

"Where have you been?" she said, adjusting her glasses and looking at him intently. My—he was so clear-eyed, so happy and self-confident!

"In school," he said, laughing.

"But I thought—"

"Sure, you thought I was in the Navy... Well, I was, for a while. I went to school there."

It was a long story he had to tell. Thanks to the Navy he was able to finish high school...and then he went on to college courses. When his enlistment was up, he got a job and continued his education at night. During that time he met a lovely girl. By the time he graduated he was married and had a son. Then he went on to graduate school, also at night.

"Well, what are you doing with your fine education?" Mrs. Warren asked.

"I'm a teacher—I teach English...especially to kids who disrupt other classes."

Tom had never forgotten the feeling of acceptance he had had from that first day in Mrs. Warren's class. More than all the threats, all the arguments and confrontations he had known, her forgiving love got through to him. And now he was passing that love on to other young people. He had learned the give-and-take of forgiveness.

THE OTHER SIDE
OF THE CURTAIN

RUTH LEE
FROM *TOUCH 1* MAGAZINE

*F*oolish. That's the way I felt. I didn't know the name of the woman on the other side of the curtain. Couldn't even see her, and still we were having a rather personal conversation.

My mother, in a semiconscious state as a result of a stroke, lay in one hospital bed, and on the other side of the curtain was a stranger—a woman I'd heard the nurse refer to as "Claudine."

The doctor had advised us to stay with Mom and keep her stimulated by talking to her.

From the other side of the curtain, Claudine answered each query I made.

"Can you hear me, Mom?"

"Yes, Dear. I can hear you," Claudine answered.

"I love you, Mom."

"That's nice, Honey. I love you, too," Claudine replied.

A nurse told me Claudine was terminally ill. A brain tumor was claiming her life. She suffered severe depression and cried most of the time. Some days she was irrational.

Before long, I learned there were other days when she regained partial control of her life. On good days, she told me about her son who lived too far away for visits. We talked about his farm, his dogs.

"Hunting dogs," Claudine said. "Beagles. Good rabbit dogs."

During the bad times, Claudine would cradle the telephone in her lap, crying out for contact with old friends.

"Would you dial for me," she'd ask. But the numbers were gone from her mind. She couldn't remember.

Without hesitating, I would punch in the number of the hospital, and say, "Listen. The number is busy right now. You can try later." She would rest, comforted by the buzzing signal.

The floor nurse began to notice my involvement with Claudine. She told me, "I can have her moved if she's becoming a problem."

I shook my head. "She's no trouble. Leave her be."

Even Mom felt I was becoming too involved. Mother was much stronger now and no longer required constant attention, but each day Claudine grew weaker.

"She needs my friendship," I explained, and they could not deny the truth of what I said.

"You'll end up getting hurt," the nurse cautioned. "Why do you think their families stay away?" I knew she referred not just to Claudine, but to all the terminally ill patients in her care.

Then one day the son came to visit. Claudine's boy. His mother had been heavily sedated just prior to his arrival, and all she could do was cling to his hand and cry. The young man wept openly.

I closed the curtain, allowing him privacy.

When visiting hours were over, I kissed Mom's forehead in farewell and, crossing the room, made a decision.

"Bruce?" The young man turned at the sound of his name. "You are Bruce?" I confirmed.

"Yes," he answered. "But how did you know?"

"I know a lot about you. About your farm, your hopes and dreams." Astonishment was written on his face.

I smiled. "I even know about your beagles. One is named Dolly; the other one is Cookie."

"But how...?"

The young man looked at the figure curled into a ball on the bed.

"She's not always like this," I said. "There are moments of happy memories." I knew instinctively what he wanted to hear.

"You will be able to visit with her, Bruce. She'll know you next time you come."

Tears coursed down his face. I held out my arms and he rushed to them.

The time of feeling foolish was gone. Holding and comforting a stranger seemed the natural thing to do.

Reaching out and sharing with others has a way of bringing its own reward.

Laughter is the sun that drives winter from the human face.

VICTOR HUGO

Friendship

THE HEART OF A FRIEND

I breathed a song into the air,
It fell to earth I know not where…
And the song from beginning to end,
I found again in the heart of a friend.

HENRY WADSWORTH LONGFELLOW

MRS. HILDEBRANDT'S GIFT

ROBERT SMITH
FROM *COUNTRY* MAGAZINE

*I*t's been thirty years since I last saw her, but in memory she's still there every holiday season. I especially feel her presence when I receive my first Christmas card.

I was twelve years old, and Christmas was only two days away. The season's first blanket of white magnified the excitement.

I dressed hurriedly, for the snow was waiting. What would I do first—build a snowman, slide down the hill, or just throw the flakes in the air and watch them flutter down?

Our station wagon pulled into the driveway, and Mom called me over to help with the groceries. When we finished carrying in the bags, she said, "Bob, here are Mrs. Hildebrandt's groceries."

No other instructions were necessary. As far back as I could remember, my mom shopped for Mrs. Hildebrandt's food and I delivered it. Our ninety-five-year-old neighbor who lived alone, was crippled from arthritis and could take only a few steps with her cane.

Even though she was old, crippled and didn't play baseball, I liked Mrs. Hildebrandt. I enjoyed talking with her; more accurately, I enjoyed listening to her. She told wonderful stories of her life—about a steepled church in the woods, horse and buggy rides on Sunday afternoon, and her family farm without running water or electricity.

She always gave me a dime for bringing her groceries. It got so that I would refuse only halfheartedly, knowing she would insist. Five minutes later, I'd be across the street in Beyer's candy store.

As I headed over with the bags, I decided this time would be different, though. I *wouldn't* accept any money. This would be my Christmas present to her.

Impatiently, I rang Mrs. Hildebrandt's doorbell. Almost inaudible at first were the slow, weary shuffles of her feet and the slower thump of her cane. The chain on the door rattled and the door creaked open. Two shiny eyes peered from the crack.

"Hello, Mrs. Hildebrandt," I said. "It's me, Bob. I have your groceries."

"Oh, yes, come in, come in," she said cheerfully. "Put the bag on the table." I did so more hurriedly than usual, because I could almost hear the snow calling me back outside.

As we talked, I began to realize how lonely she was. Her husband had died more than twenty years ago, she had no children, and her only living relative was a nephew in Philadelphia who never visited.

Nobody ever called on her at Christmas. There would be no tree, no presents, no stocking.

She offered me a cup of tea, which she did every time I brought the groceries. Well, maybe the snow could wait.

We sat and talked about what Christmas was like when she was a child. We traveled far away and long ago, and an hour passed before I knew it.

"Well, Bob, you must be wanting to play outside in the snow," she said as she reached for her purse.

"No, Mrs. Hildebrandt, I can't take your money this time. You can use it for more important things," I resisted.

She looked at me and smiled. "What more important thing could I use this money for, if not to give it to a friend at Christmas?" she asked, and then placed a whole *quarter* in my hand.

I *tried* to give it back, but she would have none of it.

I hurried out the door and ran over to Beyer's candy store with my fortune. I had no idea what to buy—comic books, chocolate, soda, ice cream. Then I spotted something—a Christmas card with an old country church in the woods on the cover. It was just like the one she'd described.

I handed Mr. Beyer my quarter for the card and borrowed a pen to sign my name.

"For your girlfriend?" he asked. I started to say no, but quickly changed my mind. "Well, yeah, I guess so."

As I walked back across the street with my gift, I was so proud of myself I felt like I had just hit a home run to win the World Series. No, I felt *better* than that!

I rang Mrs. Hildebrandt's doorbell. The almost inaudible sounds of shuffling again reached my ears. The chain rattled and the door creaked open. Two shiny eyes peered from within.

"Hello, Mrs. Hildebrandt," I said as I handed her the card. "Merry Christmas!"

Her hands trembled as she slowly opened the envelope, studied the card and began to cry. "Thank you very much," she said almost in a whisper. "Merry Christmas."

On a cold and windy afternoon a few weeks later, the ambulance arrived next door. My mom said they found her in bed; she had died peacefully in her sleep. Her night table light was still on, illuminating a solitary Christmas card.

THE LOVE SQUAD

VIRELLE KIDDER
FROM *DECISION* MAGAZINE

"Oh, no! Not company!" I groaned the moment that my car rounded the corner and our house came into full view. Usually I'd be thrilled to see four cars lined up in our driveway, but after I spent a weeklong vigil at the hospital with an ill child, my house was a colossal mess. Turning off the car engine, I dragged myself to the front door.

"What are you doing home so soon?" my friend Judie called from the kitchen. "We weren't expecting you for another hour! We thought we'd be long gone before you got home." She walked toward me and gave me a hug, then asked softly, "How are you doing?"

Was this my house? Was I dreaming? Everything looked so clean. Where did these flowers come from?

Suddenly more voices, more hugs. Lorraine, smiling and wiping beads of perspiration from her forehead, came up from the family room where she had just finished ironing a mountain of clean clothes. Regina peeked into the kitchen, having finished vacuuming rugs and polishing and dusting furniture in every room in the house. Joan, still upstairs wrestling with the boys' bunk-bed sheets, called down her "hello," having already brought order out of chaos in all four bedrooms.

"When did you guys get here?" was my last coherent sentence. My tears came in great heaving waves. "How come...how come...you did all this?" I cried unashamedly, every ounce of resistant gone.

I had spent the week praying through a health crisis, begging God for a sense of His presence at the hospital. Instead, He laid a mantle of order, beauty and loving care into our home through these four "angels."

"You rest a while, Virelle," Lorraine said firmly. "Here's your dinner for tonight—there are more meals in the freezer." The table was set with flowers and fancy napkins, and a little gift was at my place. A small banquet was arranged, complete with salad and dessert.

"Don't you worry. We're all praying," my friends said. "God has everything under control."

After my friends left, I wandered from room to room, still sobbing from the enormity of their gift of time and work. I found beautiful floral arrangements in every room...and little wrapped gifts on each bed. More tears.

In the living room I found a note under a vase filled with peonies. I was to have come home and found it as their only identity: "The Love Squad was here."

And I *knew* that God had everything under control.

Friends are lights in winter;
the older the friend, the brighter the light.

ROGER ROSENBLATT

LUTHER'S LUMBER

JOE EDWARDS

Luther had been home from the war nearly four months, now, and worked at the Carnation Milk plant in Mount Vernon where his wife, Jenny, worked.

This morning he was in the little Miller Café next door to the post office waiting for the mail to be "put up." Sitting across from him in the booth was his old friend, Fred Hill. They were discussing the war which was still going on in the Pacific Theatre. Recruitment posters still lined the walls of the little café.

Fred had not been in the service, because when the war started in 1941, his parents had been in very poor health; his father with a bad heart, and his mother with cancer. He was needed at home to care for them and operate the farm. His parents had since died, and the farm was now his— his and Maggie's.

When Luther, Fred's best friend since childhood had flown over Miller in the B-17, and when the bodies of the Hobbs boys and Billie Martin had been shipped home, and when Perry came home with hooks where his hands should have been, Fred felt guilty. He felt he had not done his part for the war effort, and in his own eyes, he was diminished.

But today, it was Luther who seemed depressed. Fred asked him what was bothering him. "You seem down in the dumps today, Luther," he said. "I can't see what could be botherin' you. You came through the war without a scratch; you got a beautiful wife and a baby on the way; you got a good job. What's the problem?"

"Jenny's mother is in bad shape," said Luther, "We're going to have to take her in, and with the baby coming we don't have the room."

"Can't build a room on?" asked Fred.

"No lumber available," said Luther. "I've tried here. Mount Vernon, Springfield, Joplin, and there won't be any more shipments for the duration. Who knows how long that will be?"

"Tried Will's sawmill?"

"Yeah, but he just saws oak, and it's green. The baby'll be here in August, and we can't wait for the lumber to dry. Besides, you can't build a whole room out of oak, anyway."

"Wouldn't want to," said Fred, "Reckon the mail's up?"

"Probably."

The two young men left the café and went into the post office next door. Buford Patten, the postmaster, had raised the door to the service window, signaling that the mail was in the boxes. Luther and Fred retrieved their mail and left—Luther to work at Mount Vernon, and Fred back to the farm.

That evening, Fred finished the milking and sat on the front porch with Maggie. "Days are getting longer," he said, "Man could get half a day's work done after five o'clock."

"Better put your pa's car up," said Maggie. "Radio says rain tonight."

Fred's father had bought a new 1941 Ford just before his first heart attack, and the car was now Fred's. He had built a new garage for it just before Christmas, and tonight he congratulated himself on getting it built before the lumber ran out. He didn't even know it had until Luther told him this morning.

Fred drove the car into the new garage and latched the door. He walked back around the house to the front porch. Something was nagging at his mind, but he couldn't define it. He shook it off and sat on the porch with Maggie until darkness fell. They could see heat lightning in the west, and the wind started to rise. They went in the house to listen to the news of the war on the radio, and shortly went to bed.

The next morning, Fred again drove his pickup into Miller for the mail. The air was fresh and clear now, the rain having washed it clean. The sun was shining, and he felt good. When he reached the café, Luther was there ahead of him.

"Still haven't found any lumber, I guess?"

"No, I asked everybody at work, and nobody knows of any. I don't know what we'll do."

Now the nagging in Fred's mind defined itself. "I found the lumber for you," he said.

"You did? Where?" Luther was delighted.

"Fella I know. He'll let you have it free, you bein' a veteran and all. He doesn't seem to want you to know who he is, so I'll have to haul it in for you. It's good lumber, fir and pine, cut different lengths and got nails in it, but that's no problem. Tell you what, you get your foundation poured, and I'll bring you a pickup load every day and help you build it. We'll have it done before the baby gets here."

"That's a friend for you," Luther said to himself, as he drove to Mount Vernon. That evening he came home with sacks of cement in his pickup.

Luther dug and poured the foundation, and when it was ready for the footings, he told Fred.

"Fine," said Fred. "I'll bring the first load over and be there when you get home from work."

Fred appeared every evening with a load of lumber, and the two men worked until it was too dark to see. Sometimes Maggie came too, and the women sat in the house listening to the radio or talking about babies or Jenny's ailing mother, their sentences punctuated by the sound of the hammers outside.

Over the next few weeks the new room took shape and was finished and roofed. "Where did you get the shingles?" asked Luther.

"Same fella," answered Fred. "He's got all kinds of stuff."

Luther didn't push. Lots of older folks liked to help out the young veterans anonymously. It was common.

It was done! The women fixed the room up inside, and moved Jenny's mother in. The men went back about their business.

At supper one evening, Luther told Jenny he would like to do something nice for Fred and Maggie, since they had been so helpful with the new room.

"I know," said Jenny brightly. "Maggie likes those big wooden lawn chairs like Aunt Birdie has in her lawn. Why not get them a couple of those?"

"Good idea," agreed Luther, and the next Saturday he bought a couple at Callison's hardware and loaded them into his pickup.

When he got out to Fred's farm, there was no one home, Fred and Maggie having gone into Springfield, shopping. *That's okay,* Luther thought, *I'll just put them in the garage in case it rains.*

He drove around the house and into the driveway that led to Fred's new garage.

The garage was gone. Only the foundation remained to show where it had been.

Luther put the chairs on the front porch and drove home, tears in his eyes.

The two men are now in their midseventies and are still the best of friends. They never spoke of the incident.

How could they? There was nothing to say.

TREASURE

PAUL KORTEPETER
FROM *INTERART*

Years ago I found a solitary tea cup at an antique shop with a gorgeous pattern. I fell in love with it on the spot. From then on, I searched high and low for the rest of the set: in china shops, at auctions, flea markets, rummage sales…

Alas, without success. Not even a saucer!

Just as I was beginning to suspect that the cup wasn't part of a set at all, but a one of a kind, never-to-be-found-again treasure, I was served tea on the very same china at the home of a friend!

Well, I stared with wide eyes until my friend said, "Isn't it beautiful? I found it at an estate sale. Unfortunately one of the cups is missing."

With a twinkle in my eye, I knew that my precious cup would soon have a new home.

Count your blessings by smiles, not tears;
Count your age by friends, not years.

AUTHOR UNKNOWN

REPLY TO BOX 222B

BARBARA BAUMGARDNER

*W*as it loneliness, the call of adventure, or just plain insanity that made me answer that newspaper ad? I paced back and forth through my house, telling myself it was a really stupid thing to do. But like a jeweler crafting a priceless, one-of-a-kind brooch, I composed my reply to the tantalizing ad.

For a moment I hesitated. *Am I actually answering a lonely hearts ad?*

I'd always believed that only those who are desperately lonely advertised for a companion or answered the ads of those who did.

That's what I am, I thought, *desperately lonely.*

What would my children think? Would they understand that the bold, black letters just leaped out at my unsuspecting eye? *Christian rancher, 6' tall, 180 pounds, 50+. Hardworking, clean-cut, healthy, good physical condition. Enjoys fishing, camping, cross-country skiing, animals, dining out. Wants to meet sensible and sincere lady, 40–50, attractive, neat, loving, honest, for meaningful relationship. Box 222B.*

Mama mia! What loving, sensible, honest, and *lonely* woman could resist? Well, maybe not sensible.

"Fifty-plus what?" my letter began. "I'm a healthy, hardworking woman who loves to cook, sew, travel, pray, and walk in a desert sunset or barefoot on the beach."

I didn't say I could meet all the requirements in his ad, but I didn't give him any reason to think I couldn't. But could I?

I was already past fifty, questionably attractive, not always neat and very uncertain about pursuing a meaningful relationship. What I really wanted was a friend. Had I been dishonest not to tell him so?

Holding the letter heavenward, I asked God, "If you want me to meet this man, will you bring him to me?" Then I set the stamped envelope on the desk for the following day's mail.

During the next few weeks, I found my hands getting sweaty every time the phone rang. Could it be him? What if he didn't like me? What if he showed disappointment as soon as he set eyes on me? Could I handle that?

One day while dressing before the mirror, I turned from side to side, surveying the ravages of fifty-plus years on this earth. I studied my face, hollow and gaunt, perched atop muscular shoulders and arms. Large, sturdy hands that never knew what to do with themselves. Twenty extra pounds, a thick waist, stalwart thighs above husky calves and large, scrawny feet. I remembered the boy in the fifth grade who told me I was built like a brick outhouse: strong and useful but not much class.

Tears began to flow freely as I slumped to my knees beside my bed. "Oh, God, look at me; I'm a mess. Why did I send that letter? Please forgive me for misleading that man, for communicating the woman I want to be, not the woman I am."

It was Sunday evening a few weeks later when I invited my friend, Jeanette, for waffles after church. As we were leaving the service, she introduced me to a friend from the singles group she sometimes attended. Impulsively, I asked him if he'd like to join us for waffles and he said yes.

We spent the next three hours stuffing ourselves, laughing and talking. Jim was divorced, had several grown children and raised alfalfa for cattle feed. He was a likable man, tall and handsome, considerate, and seemingly ambitious. I felt sad for him as he talked about his loneliness.

Shutting the door behind them after a delightful evening, I began to clear up the clutter. I'd dumped my past few days' mail on the big maple desk in the dining room, and it seemed like a good time to sort it out. I tossed the junk mail in the trash and filed some bills for payment. Then I stared in astonishment. There was the letter! My reply to "Christian Rancher" had never been mailed. All that emotion and self-doubt for nothing.

Then a suspicion crept into my thoughts. Pieces started to fall into place. Jim wore cowboy boots and a western shirt; he was a rancher; he was lonely. Could he and the Christian rancher possibly be one and the same?

I rushed to the phone to call Jeanette. "Do you think he ever put an ad in the newspaper for a woman? Do you suppose he'd call himself a Christian rancher?"

Jeanette roared with laughter. "Yes, everybody at the singles group knows he did that. I guess he's gotten some seventy or eighty answers by now. Some real lulus, too."

I hung up the telephone feeling a trace of excitement, a bit of foolishness and a lot of awe at a God who would arrange for a letter that I never mailed to receive an answer. And God and I were the only ones who knew about it.

Several days passed before I picked up the telephone to hear Jim's voice suggesting that we go to the state fair for the day. "I'd love to," I said. *Wow! A real live date with a guy who had seventy or eighty women to choose from!*

A warm toastiness cradled me as I hung up the telephone. Then I raced to the bedroom, my heart pounding with excitement. What would I wear? In front of the mirror once more, I observed a middle-aged woman, still awkward and overweight, with a skinny face and bony feet, but she wasn't afraid anymore. "What you see is what you get," I chuckled.

The next day I stepped out into the sunshine to begin a new friendship with a Christian rancher.

What happened that day at the fair? We had fun together. Did we see each other again? Yes. Did we marry? No. But that didn't matter. My self-confidence soared, and I learned something else too: If you're destined to meet a particular person, whether future friend or spouse, it *will* happen, as surely as the sun rises every morning. And it'll happen even if your perfectly crafted letter sits gathering dust on an old maple desk.

Embracing

We are like angels with just one wing:
We fly only by embracing each other.

AUTHOR UNKNOWN

SAVING THE BEST
FOR LAST

ROCHELLE M. PENNINGTON
FROM *GOD'S MATH*

*S*aving the best for last." The old cliche crossed my mind as we waited for dessert to be served. Undoubtedly, it would be wonderful; worth the wait.

Tonight was our annual ladies Christmas party, and the evening had been a delight. The meal, preceded by a short program, was followed by a gift exchange.

One by one we stood up to open the present which had been placed on the table before us. Small gifts. Simple gifts. Candles, stationery, bubble bath. Polite applause responded to each.

It was not until this orderly process had made a full circle to the last person remaining that anyone noticed that she didn't have a gift to open...and then everyone noticed at once.

Her name was Dorothy, our older—and newest—member. Having joined us nearly a year ago after moving to the community, this was her first Christmas party.

An awkward silence fell upon those gathered as we waited for someone to think of something—and to think of it quick—to save Dorothy from embarrassment. And then someone did. It was Dorothy.

Standing up, she reached for her purse and removed a brown paper grocery sack. Unfolding it, she looked inside the seemingly empty bag, then looked at us.

"Let me tell you about my gift," she said. "I received love and kindness and friendship from you. For these, I am grateful. Thank you."

Dorothy sat down to a roar of applause.

And for the second time, the old cliche crossed my mind. The best, again, had indeed been saved for last.

If instead of a gem, or even a flower,
we should cast the gift of a loving thought
into the heart of a friend—
that would be giving as the angels give.

GEORGE MACDONALD

MY CHILD, MY TEACHER, MY FRIEND

GLORIA GAITHER
FROM *CHRISTIAN HERALD* MAGAZINE

*F*rom the moment I first held you—still drenched in birth—until now as I watch you drive away to the appointments you've made with life, mothering you has been my life's most awesome, fearsome, and joyful adventure. I didn't know that first day what mothering would mean, though I was eager to begin. You seemed so fragile, so small and trusting, depending on me for every life-sustaining need. I thought at first you'd break. "Be sure to support the little head," they told me. But I soon learned you were tougher than you looked, and could out-squeal, out-sleep and out-endure me ten-to-one. In fact, those first three months, I wondered if I'd ever again finish a meal or a night's sleep.

The teaching began immediately. I had studied to be a teacher, but never was there a student as hungry to learn as you. Before you could speak, your eyes asked questions, and your tiny hands reached to touch and learn, taste and see. It wasn't long, though, until your cooing turned inquisitive, with every babbled sentence ending with a question mark. Your first words were: "What's that? What's that?" Soon your questing vocabulary grew, and you were begging, "Teach me something, Mommy. Teach me something."

And I would stop to teach you: numbers, names of things, textures, shapes, sizes, foods, furniture, pets, trees, flowers, stars and clouds. But soon you were teaching me…teaching that when the lesson stopped, the learning kept on going.

You taught me to see the miracles I'd stumbled over every day. You taught me trust and delight and ecstasy. You held a mirror before my attitudes, and role-played all my reactions. You taught me what it meant to live what I verbalized, to believe what I preached, to internalize what I lectured.

You taught me what Jesus meant when he said we must become like children if we are to enter the kingdom of heaven. Through you I understood why he used the metaphor of birth for the truth of conversion. For you, who came to me all wet from birth, baptized the common things with natural freshness, and, with the shower of your laughter, washed away the barnacles of grown-up cynicism and the dust of dull routine. You made things new. You gave me an excuse to be myself again, to skip down forest trails or sled the frozen hillsides clean with snow, to splash through springtime puddles, barefoot glad, and guess at where the shooting stars must go.

You gave me eyes to see the realness of people once again, to look beyond their faces' thin facades. You saw the child inside the aged, the longing and the passion long entrapped by gnarled joints and failing eyesight. You recognized profundity and wisdom in the giggly teen-age baby sitter, beauty in the plain, and creativity in the timid. You showed me that the generation gap is the artificial invention of our culture and bigotry a sick perversion of God's celebration of variety.

I have helped you learn to crawl, toddle, walk, run, swim, dance, ride bikes and drive the car. I have encouraged you to stand tall, walk alone, run from evil, dance for joy, ride out the hard times and drive yourself on when you felt tempted to give up. I have been there waiting when you crossed the road, climbed off the school bus, came in from dates and returned home from college. In fact, now about all I can do for you is *be there*, because gradually you have become your own person—not so much my child, but my friend.

GOD, A DOG, AND ME

DEBORAH HEDSTROM

*D*ogs and I never got on well. They barked; I feared. They slobbered; I shuddered. They wanted petting; I fretted about fleas. So it came as a total surprise when God used one in my life.

It all started when my married daughter came over and blurted out, "Don't say no until you've heard me out."

Having been the mother of four children for more than twenty years, I knew a wheedling plea was on the way. I looked at my daughter who was fidgeting in her chair. "Okay, I'll listen."

Given her chance, the words tumbled out on top of each other. "You know the dog Nathan and I bought? We can't keep it at our apartment. We thought we could because other tenants had dogs, but we got a notice saying dogs must be at least a year old." Pausing only for a brief breath, she cinched her plea with, "We just need a place until we move in a few months. You can leave him in the backyard. We'll bring food over for him and do everything."

I'm not sure why I agreed. Maybe it was the fact my daughter was pregnant. Whatever the reason, "Perry" ended up in my backyard.

At this point, dog lovers might think they know what happened next.

But it didn't. A black, velvet nose and wagging tail at my screen door every day did not win me over. I fed him in the morning, made sure he had water, and once in a while petted him. But I didn't do much more.

After forth-five years of keeping dogs at a distance, I had little doubt my treatment of Perry would change. To deal with the empty house left by grown children, I had started putting my energy into having a perfect looking home. Knowing that "perfection" would never fill the void in my heart, God pushed Perry into my life.

When I'd only had the puppy a couple of weeks, I noticed he'd stopped eating his food. Later I saw he'd been sick in the yard. I called my daughter and her husband, but knew with their jobs and finances, they couldn't help. As we tried to decide what to do, they confessed they'd forgotten to get the dog his puppy shots. I feared the worst but said, "He'll probably get better in a few days."

He didn't. Instead, I woke up one day to a dog so weak he could hardly stand. When he tried, his fluffy malamute tail that normally curled up over his rump, sagged between his back legs. Though he meant nothing to me, his illness tugged at my heart. I found myself remembering my husband's illness and death ten years earlier and I knew I just couldn't let this dog die. Crying, I picked him up and put him in the car.

My tears made the veterinarian think I was deeply attached to the dog. "He has parvovirus," he said. "It attacks the dog's digestive system and often ends in death."

I asked him what I should do but he said that was up to me. Torn by my memories and the awareness that it was my daughter's dog, I agreed to three days of veterinary care.

Three days later Perry came home with me, improving, but his ribs were clearly showing through his sagging skin. He wasn't well enough to put outside, but I was still bothered by thoughts of germs and fleas. Looking at the weak dog, I said, "I have to give you a bath."

I'd never washed an animal in my life and didn't have a clue how to begin, but I did have a shower stall with a sprayer on a long hose. Opening the stall door, I called to Perry. He walked in and submitted to a shampoo, rinse, and towel dry without an ounce of opposition.

Relieved that fleas wouldn't be deposited in my house, I felt better about having the dog inside. But that night I worried that Perry would jump up on my bed. I told him it was off limits. He went to the entrance of my bedroom and lay across it. When I woke up the next morning, Perry was still there, guarding my doorway. I was surprised at how safe I felt. Since my husband's death and my children leaving home, I'd never felt overly fearful, but I was aware of being a woman alone. Perry's presence made me feel less vulnerable.

Though I knew nothing about the care and training of dogs, suddenly I was thrust into the middle of it. When I had a big question, I'd call my son-in-law, but for the most part I just tried to figure things out. I often found myself talking to the dog. "Think you could handle some chicken today?" "Shall we add another block to our walk?" "See this jar of treats. Every time you go potty outside, I'll give you one."

Every few days my daughter and her husband came over, but the arrival of their baby, being unable to move from their apartment, and their alternate-shift jobs kept Perry with me. More and more, he became my companion. He'd lie nearby as I worked at home in the mornings and then eagerly look forward to our afternoon walks.

I felt pleased when my bony puppy filled out into a handsome dog that many people stopped to admire. Though his Alaskan malamute father dominated Perry's looks, his shar-pei mother gave him his gold color and expressive face.

But Perry wasn't the only one who had changed. One day I noticed I no longer raced to wash my hands every time I petted Perry. I played fetch with him and even roughhoused once in a while. I couldn't believe it. I laughed out loud the day I realized I no longer took pride in the unmessed vacuum trails in my carpet. Perry obliterated them as quickly as I made them. My once immaculate house had rubber toys lying around and dog dishes in the kitchen.

By now my daughter and her husband knew Perry was as much or more my dog as theirs. But though they still could not take him, my son-in-law struggled to let go of his dog. I understood but it shook me. Putting Perry on his leash I headed out for a walk. "God, I can't keep falling in love with this dog. It will hurt too much when I've got to give him up. I'm going to put him back in the yard. I have to get used to having an empty house again."

When my words ended, God seemed to whisper, "Will you let fear of pain keep you from the joy I've brought into your life through this dog?"

Perry turned around and looked at me when I started to cry. Regaining control and wiping my eyes with the sleeves of my sweatshirt, I told him, "It's okay. Don't worry. I'm going to keep you as long as the Lord lets me—even if that means some pain in the end."

Four years later, I still have Perry. Given more time, my son-in-law finally realized a large dog just didn't fit in their apartment. One day he told me, "He's your dog, Mom."

I don't know the exact moment I realized that God understood and helped fill the void in my heart left by an empty home. But when I think of how He orchestrated events to get past forth-five years of "Go away, doggie," I appreciate even more the wagging tail that greets me each morning.

*One of the most difficult things
to give away is kindness—
it is usually returned.*

CORT R. FLINT

74

Friendship Is a Diamond

Friendship is a diamond
buried in the earth;
a treasure of great worth.
But first it must be mined
then faceted and shined.
It takes pick and shovel and strain,
encompassing time and enduring pain,
until its grace is seen;
a glittering gift of love
that's shared between we three:
First God,
and you,
then me.

SALLY J. KNOWER

THE COMFORT ROOM

MAYO MATHERS
FROM *TODAY'S CHRISTIAN WOMAN* MAGAZINE

s your Comfort Room available next weekend?" The voice of my friend on the telephone sounded weary and faint. "I could sure use a respite."

I smiled, assuring her it was. Hanging up the phone, I walked down the hall to the room she'd inquired about. The Comfort Room developed quite by accident, but there is no doubt in my mind that the people who stay here are no accident at all. God brings them to us when they're most in need of comfort.

I looked around the room, running my hand lightly across the soothing pattern of the wallpaper. Walking over to the antique bed, I stretched out across the quilt with its blue and white wedding ring pattern and luxuriated in the familiar sense of comfort that settled over me like a feathery eiderdown.

My earliest memory of the bed goes back to when I was three years old. My parents had just brought my new baby sister to Grandma's house where I'd been staying. As Mom laid her on the bed, I stood on my tiptoes, eagerly peeking over the high mattress to catch a glimpse of her.

For as long as I can remember, the bed and its accompanying dresser and dressing table occupied what had once been the parlor of my grandparents' large Missouri farmhouse. During those long-ago summers, when all the grandchildren visited, "taking turns" was the order of the day. We took turns on the porch swing, took turns on the bicycle, and even took turns at the chores. But there was no taking turns when it came to sleeping in Grandma's bed. Even on hot, smothery, summer nights she let us all pile in around her at once. Our sweaty little bodies stuck happily together as we listened to Grandma's beloved stories of the "olden days" until one by one, we fell asleep.

Those well-spun tales gave me a strong sense of family identity, pride, and comfort. And I needed plenty of comfort when clouds started building in the summery blue skies that stretched over the corn fields surrounding the farm. How I dreaded the wild, crashing, earsplitting midwestern thunderstorms that resulted from those massive clouds!

Standing at the window, I'd watch the lightning flashes intensify across the sky and count the seconds until I heard the low growl of thunder. Grandma told me that was how to tell how many miles away the storm was.

I hated nighttime storms the most—when I'd have to go upstairs to my bedroom, up even closer to the storm. Sleep was impossible. As the jagged slashes grew more brilliant, the time between the stab of lightning and the crash of thunder grew less and less.

Then suddenly, FLASH! KA-A-A-BOOM! The light and sound came as one! *The storm was here! Right on top of me!* At that point, I'd leap from the bed, and with my sister close behind, we'd slam into our brother in the hallway. The three of us tore down the stairs as one.

Hearing our pounding feet, Grandma would already be scooted over in bed with the covers thrown back for us. We plowed beneath them, scrunching up as close to her as we could. While the thunder shook and rattled the house, she'd jump dramatically and exclaim, "Whew! That one made my whiskers grow!" And from under the pillows where we'd buried our heads, we couldn't help but giggle. In Grandma's bed we were always comforted.

There I found comfort not only from thunderstorms but from lifestorms as well. Hurt feelings, broken hearts, insecurities—all were mended there. When I was lucky enough to have Grandma to myself in her bed—which wasn't often—I'd tell her all my deepest secrets, knowing she took them very seriously.

When my father, her son, died of cancer, I was eight years old. On that last night of his life, instead of spending those moments with him in the hospital, Grandma gathered me into her bed. Curling her body around mine, she infused me with comfort I didn't yet know I needed.

In college, when a broken engagement had crushed my heart and hopes, she comforted me by saying, "The pathway to love never runs smooth, honey, but you'll find your way when it's right." Four years later, her prediction came true.

Shortly after my wedding, Grandma died, bringing an end to the unlimited source of love and comfort that I knew could never be replaced, the kind that only comes from a grandmother. When my aunt called to tell me the beloved bedroom set was mine, I immediately drove to Missouri to pick it up. Although the beautiful pieces had to be placed in storage, I hoped that someday I'd have room for them in our home.

The years melted away with startling speed. Caught up in the happy frenzy of raising our two sons, I rarely thought of the bedroom set stuck away in the attic. There was too much present to think of the past. Before I knew it, our firstborn was packing his belongings to move on to a new phase of life.

The day Tyler left, I went into his empty room and sat down in the middle of the floor while memory after memory scurried up to tap me on the shoulder. His leave-taking had been more wrenching than I had anticipated. Inside the echoes of the room I tried to come to grips with the door that had just closed on my life.

Quite abruptly, a thought came to mind. I raised my head and looked around my son's room with new eyes. I finally had room for Grandma's bedroom set!

For the next two weeks I worked on the room, lovingly choosing paint, wallpaper, and pictures. Frequent tears splashed into the paint tray as I pondered all the different seasons one passes through in a lifetime. When the painting and papering were done, my husband lugged the bedroom set down from the attic and helped me arrange it in the room. I stopped to consider the completed result and was drawn to the bed where I let my fingers trace around the grooves in the curved footboard of the wonderful old treasure. As I sat quietly, a familiar feeling begged to embrace me—the same feeling I'd had as a child with Grandma beside me in the bed. It was as if she were in the room with me right then comforting me in this new stage of life I was entering.

Right then I christened it the "Comfort Room." From where I sat I prayed, "Lord, I hope everyone who stays in this room feels the comfort I'm feeling now. Bring people to us who need the comfort."

Our first guest in the Comfort Room was a friend who'd just lost her brother and two close friends to death. Next was a couple who were at a transition point in their life, not sure which direction to go. Then a young cousin arrived in need of a temporary home and an out-of-town uncle whose wife was flown to our medical center following a severe heart attack. From the day it was completed, God has seen to it that the Comfort Room is well used.

There is one guest, however, whose arrival I most anticipate. I'm waiting for the day when my son will return and bring with him a grandchild. Then I will be the grandma snuggling up with my grandchild in that old bed. I'll be the one spinning stories of the "olden days." And I'll offer to them what my grandma gave to me—unending comfort, unlimited love.

SOMEONE TO DIVIDE WITH

FROM *TEA TIME WITH GOD*

t the turn of the century, a man wrote in his diary the story of a young newsboy he met on a street near his home in London. It was well known in the neighborhood that the boy was an orphan. His father had abandoned the family when the boy was a baby, and his mother had died shortly after he began selling newspapers.

All attempts to place the boy in either an institution or a foster home were thwarted, because the boy refused each offer of help and ran away when attempts were made to confine him. "I can take care o' myself jest fine, thank ye!" he would say to kindly old ladies who questioned whether he'd had his porridge that day.

Indeed, he never looked hungry and his persistence at selling papers, load after load, gave the impression he spoke the truth.

But the streets are a lonely place for a child to live, and the man's diary reflects a conversation he had with the child about his living arrangements. As he stopped to buy his paper one day, the man bought a little extra time by fishing around in his pocket for coins and asked the boy where he lived. He replied that he lived in a little cabin in an impoverished district of the city near the river bank. This was something of a surprise to the man.

With more interest, he inquired, "Well, who lives with you?"

The boy answered. "Only Jim. Jim is crippled and can't do no work. He's my pal."

Now clearly astounded that the child appeared to be supporting not only himself but also someone who was unable to contribute any income, the man noted, "You'd be better off without Jim, wouldn't you?"

The answer came with not a little scorn—a sermon in a nutshell: "No, sir, I couldn't spare Jim. I wouldn't have nobody to go home to. An' say, Mister, I wouldn't want to live and work with nobody to divide with, would you?"

Go oft to the house of thy friend,
for weeds choke the unused path.

RALPH WALDO EMERSON

EMPTY PLACES FILLED

CHRIS FABRY

FROM *AT THE CORNER OF MUNDANE AND GRACE*

Life without Jim has been hard. I realized that when we saw him last week. Jim is six years old and tall for his age. He has sandy hair and bright blue eyes, I think.

Before he moved at the end of the last school year, he played with my son Ryan. Ryan is a year and a half younger, but they got along well.

After kindergarten Jim would come over to our place. He and Ryan would play with Jim's cars or set up a McDonald's by our fireplace. They were good for about two hours together. Then they would fight, yell a couple of times, then make up.

I noticed a change in Ryan the first week after Jim moved. He didn't mope or hang his head, but there was something missing. Jim was missing.

A couple of days later the outburst came. Something was thrown, or someone was hit, and there was crying and wailing.

I remember my wife saying, "You miss Jim, don't you, buddy?" Those are the times you thank God for a wife and not a spoon. Ryan nodded and buried his head in her chest. A few minutes later he was back to normal.

The summer went by and talk of Jim subsided. He was out there somewhere. Wisconsin was what they called it, but it was China for all my son knew. A four-hour drive is an eternity when you're four.

But a few weeks ago we heard Jim was coming for a visit. The excitement steadily built.

"When is Jim coming? Is it tomorrow? Can he come over?"

"Next week, bud, next week."

On the night I said, "Jim comes tomorrow," Ryan's eyes widened. He smiled and scrunched beneath the covers and shook with anticipation. It was one of those involuntary reactions that spreads to everyone in the room. I went to bed smiling, remembering my own childhood friend.

His name was Johnny, but we called him Little Johnny, because his older brother was also named John. Little Johnny came to our house, and we dug holes in the earth simply because we could. We stood on an old basketball backboard and pretended the hoop was the hatch to our spacecraft. If you fell off you would be lost forever with only enough oxygen to last five minutes. If your fellow astronaut didn't help you get back on quickly, you would swell up, turn blue, and eventually pop like a balloon. The search-and-rescue missions on that backboard were better than any film I've ever seen.

Somewhere in my elementary years Little Johnny moved.

I never heard from him again. His friendship left an empty hole in my life, with the memories piled up like dirt alongside the edges. I hadn't thought about Little Johnny for a long time, but Jim's return brought the memories back.

In the morning Ryan was up extra early wearing one of my long-forgotten T-shirts that dusts the floor. After a bowl of cereal he was dressed and at the window.

"Remember, buddy," I said, "they're going to call after lunch for you to come over."

Questions persisted before and during lunch. I kept his coat off him as long as I could. We were about an hour away from Jim-down. The baby was asleep. Ryan had eaten lunch and cleaned his room. Barney was finished for the day. We sat and waited.

I got a cover and stretched out on the couch. He came with a couple of books, leaned against my chest, and we read *Hippo Lemonade*. When we got to the scary part, he drifted off. His breathing slowed, his eyes drooped, and soon we were both asleep.

The phone woke us and we both jumped. Jim was on his way. He would pick Ryan up at the corner, and they would walk back together, just like old times. We put our coats on and watched the street for any sign of him. It was a gray day and the street was wet. I heard an old muffler coming and soon a station wagon chugged by our house. When the smoke cleared I saw a blond head and some feet bouncing down the street.

"There he is!" Ryan said.

I crossed with him, and we waited a few inches past the street. Ryan wanted to walk as much sidewalk as he could with his friend. Jim was taller now, his shoulders wider. He cracked chewing gum and his cheeks were red from the cold.

"Hi, Jim," I said enthusiastically. "Boy it's been a long time since we've seen you. How are you doing?"

"Okay," he said softly. He looked at Ryan. "Are you ready?"

"Yeah."

Ryan's turtle tennis shoes scooted along the sidewalk, pushing at the leftover leaves. Hands in pockets. Head straight. No conversation.

They were nearly to the corner when Jim's head turned and he said something. Ryan looked up at him, his hair fluffy in the back, and laughed. They picked up the pace, heads bobbing. I would have given a fair amount of money to hear that conversation. To walk with them and listen to the musings of two friends. But there are some places you cannot go, and there are conversations you cannot hear. I crossed the street alone, and when I turned, they were running.

There are empty places where friends should be. We don't realize it until we find a friend to fill them. The sight of those two rounding the corner was enough to create my own hunger, to make me want to dig a hole or stand on an old backboard again. As I went back to the house, I think I saw the sun peek through the clouds.

Love

ON AN OLD SUN DIAL

Time flies,
Suns rise,
And shadows fall.
Let time go by.
Love is forever over all.

AUTHOR UNKNOWN

THE WALLET

ARNOLD FINE

*A*s I walked home one freezing day, I stumbled on a wallet someone had lost in the street. I picked it up and looked inside to find some identification so I could call the owner. But the wallet contained only three dollars and a crumpled letter that looked as though it had been in there for years.

The envelope was worn and the only thing that was legible on it was the return address. I started to open the letter, hoping to find some clue. Then I saw the dateline—1924. The letter had been written almost sixty years ago.

It was written in a beautiful feminine handwriting on powder blue stationery with a little flower in the left-hand corner. It was a "Dear John" letter that told the recipient, whose name appeared to be Michael, that the writer could not see him anymore because her mother forbade it. Even so, she wrote that she would always love him.

It was signed, Hannah.

It was a beautiful letter, but there was no way except for the name Michael, that the owner could be identified. Maybe if I called information, the operator could find a phone listing for the address on the envelope.

"Operator," I began, "this is an unusual request. I'm trying to find the owner of a wallet that I found. Is there any way you can tell me if there is a phone number for an address that was on an envelope in the wallet?"

She suggested I speak with her supervisor, who hesitated for a moment then said, "Well, there is a phone listing at that address, but I can't give you the number." She said, as a courtesy, she would call that number, explain my story and would ask them if they wanted her to connect me. I waited a few minutes and then she was back on the line. "I have a party who will speak with you."

I asked the woman on the other end of the line if she knew anyone by the name of Hannah. She gasped, "Oh! We bought this house from a family who had a daughter named Hannah. But that was thirty years ago!"

"Would you know where that family could be located now?" I asked.

"I remember that Hannah had to place her mother in a nursing home some years ago," the woman said. "Maybe if you got in touch with them they might be able to track down the daughter."

She gave me the name of the nursing home and I called the number. They told me the old lady had passed away some years ago but they did have a phone number for where they thought the daughter might be living.

I thanked them and phoned. The woman who answered explained that Hannah herself was now living in a nursing home.

This whole thing was stupid, I thought to myself. Why was I making such a big deal over finding the owner of a wallet that had only three dollars and a letter that was almost sixty years old?

Nevertheless, I called the nursing home in which Hannah was supposed to be living and the man who answered the phone told me, "Yes, Hannah is staying with us."

Even though it was already 10 P.M., I asked if I could come by to see her. "Well," he said hesitatingly, "if you want to take a chance, she might be in the day room watching television."

I thanked him and drove over to the nursing home. The night nurse and a guard greeted me at the door. We went up to the third floor of the large building. In the day room, the nurse introduced me to Hannah.

She was a sweet, silver-haired old-timer with a warm smile and a twinkle in her eye. I told her about finding the wallet and showed her the letter. The second she saw the powder blue envelope with that little flower on the left, she took a deep breath and said, "Young man, this letter was the last contact I ever had with Michael."

She looked away for a moment deep in thought and then said softly, "I loved him very much. But I was only sixteen at the time and my mother felt I was too young. Oh, he was so handsome. He looked like Sean Connery, the actor."

"Yes," she continued. "Michael Goldstein was a wonderful person. If you should find him, tell him I think of him often. And," she hesitated for a moment, almost biting her lip, "tell him I still love him. You know," she said smiling as tears began to well up in her eyes, "I never did marry. I guess no one ever matched up to Michael…"

I thanked Hannah and said good-bye. I took the elevator to the first floor and as I stood by the door, the guard there asked, "Was the old lady able to help you?"

I told him she had given me a lead. "At least I have a name, but I think I'll let it go for a while. I spent almost the whole day trying to find the owner of this wallet."

I had taken out the wallet, which was a simple brown leather case with red lacing on the side. When the guard saw it, he said, "Hey, wait a minute! That's Mr. Goldstein's wallet. I'd know it anywhere with that bright red lacing. He's always losing that wallet. I must have found it in the hall at least three times."

"Who's Mr. Goldstein?" I asked as my hand began to shake.

"He's one of the old-timers on the eighth floor. That's Mike Goldstein's wallet for sure. He must have lost it on one of his walks."

I thanked the guard and quickly ran back to the nurse's office. I told her what the guard had said. We went back to the elevator and got on. I prayed that Mr. Goldstein would be up.

On the eighth floor, the floor nurse said, "I think he's still in the day room. He likes to read at night. He's a darling old man."

We went to the only room that had any lights on and there was a man reading a book. The nurse went over to him and asked if he had lost his wallet. Mr. Goldstein looked up with surprise, put his hand in his back pocket and said, "Oh, it is missing!"

"This kind gentleman found a wallet and we wondered if it could be yours?"

I handed Mr. Goldstein the wallet and the second he saw it, he smiled with relief and said, "Yes, that's it! It must have dropped out of my pocket this afternoon. I want to give you a reward."

"No, thank you," I said. "But I have to tell you something. I read the letter in the hope of finding out who owned the wallet."

The smile on his face suddenly disappeared. "You read that letter?"

"Not only did I read it, I think I know where Hannah is."

He suddenly grew pale. "Hannah? You know where she is? How is she? Is she still as pretty as she was? Please, please tell me," he begged.

"She's fine...just as pretty as when you knew her," I said softly.

The old man smiled with anticipation and asked, "Could you tell me where she is? I want to call her tomorrow." He grabbed my hand and said, "You know something, mister, I was so in love with that girl that when that letter came, my life literally ended. I never married. I guess I've always loved her."

"Mr. Goldstein," I said. "Come with me."

We took the elevator down to the third floor. The hallways were darkened and only one or two little night-lights lit our way to the day room where Hannah was sitting alone watching the television. The nurse walked over to her.

"Hannah," she said softly, pointing to Michael, who was waiting with me in the doorway. "Do you know this man?"

She adjusted her glasses, looked for a moment, but didn't say a word. Michael said softly, almost in a whisper, "Hannah, it's Michael. Do you remember me?"

She gasped, "Michael! I don't believe it! Michael! It's you! My Michael!" He walked slowly toward her and they embraced. The nurse and I left with tears streaming down our faces.

"See," I said. "See how the Good Lord works. If it's meant to be, it will be."

About three weeks later I got a call at my office from the nursing home. "Can you break away on Sunday to attend a wedding? Michael and Hannah are going to be married!"

It was a beautiful wedding with all the people at the nursing home dressed up to join in the celebration. Hannah wore a light beige dress and looked beautiful. Michael wore a dark blue suit and stood tall. They made me their best man.

The hospital gave them their own room and if you ever wanted to see a seventy-six-year-old bride and a seventy-nine-year-old groom acting like two teenagers, you had to see this couple.

A perfect ending for a love affair that lasted nearly sixty years.

*If I could reinvent the alphabet,
I would put U and I together.*

AUTHOR UNKNOWN

THE BUS PASSENGER

AUTHOR UNKNOWN

*T*he passengers on the bus watched sympathetically as the attractive young woman with the white cane made her way carefully up the steps. She paid the driver and, using her hands to feel the location of the seats, walked down the aisle and found a seat he'd told her was empty. Then she settled in, placed her briefcase on her lap, and rested her cane against her leg.

It had been a year since Susan, thirty-four, became blind. Due to a medical misdiagnosis she had been rendered sightless, and she was suddenly thrown into a world of darkness, anger, frustration, and self-pity. Once a fiercely independent woman, Susan now felt condemned by this terrible twist of fate to become a powerless, helpless burden on everyone around her. "How could this have happened to me?" she would plead, her heart knotted with anger.

But no matter how much she cried or ranted or prayed, she knew the painful truth—her sight was never going to return. A cloud of depression hung over Susan's once optimistic spirit. Just getting through each day was an exercise in frustration and exhaustion. And all she had to cling to was her husband, Mark.

Mark was an air force officer and he loved Susan with all of his heart.

When she first lost her sight, he watched her sink into despair and was determined to help his wife gain the strength and confidence she needed to become independent again. Mark's military background had trained him well to deal with sensitive situations, and yet he knew this was the most difficult battle he would ever face.

Finally, Susan felt ready to return to her job, but how would she get there? She used to take the bus, but was now too frightened to get around the city by herself. Mark volunteered to drive her to work each day, even though they worked at opposite ends of the city.

At first, this comforted Susan and fulfilled Mark's need to protect his sightless wife who was so insecure about performing the slightest task. Soon, however, Mark realized that this arrangement wasn't working—it was hectic and costly. Susan is going to have to start taking the bus again, he admitted to himself. But just the thought of mentioning it to her made him cringe. She was still so fragile, so angry. How would she react?

Just as Mark predicted, Susan was horrified at the idea of taking the bus again. "I'm blind!" she responded bitterly. "How am I supposed to know where I'm going? I feel like you're abandoning me."

Mark's heart broke to hear these words, but he knew what had to be done. He promised Susan that each morning and evening he would ride the bus with her, for as long as it took, until she got the hang of it. And that is exactly what happened.

For two solid weeks, Mark, military uniform and all, accompanied Susan to and from work each day. He taught her how to rely on her other senses, specifically her hearing, to determine where she was and how to adapt to her new environment. He helped her befriend the bus drivers who could watch out for her and save her a seat. He made her laugh, even on those not-so-good days when she would trip exiting the bus, or drop her briefcase.

Each morning they made the journey together, and Mark would take a cab back to his office. Although this routine was even more costly and exhausting than the previous one, Mark knew it was only a matter of time before Susan would be able to ride the bus on her own. He believed in her, in the Susan he used to know before she'd lost her sight, who wasn't afraid of any challenge and who would never, ever quit.

Finally, Susan decided that she was ready to try the trip on her own. Monday morning arrived, and before she left, she threw her arms around Mark, her temporary bus riding companion, her husband, and her best friend.

Her eyes filled with tears of gratitude for his loyalty, his patience, his love. She said good-bye, and for the first time, they went their separate ways. Monday, Tuesday, Wednesday, Thursday… Each day on her own went perfectly, and Susan had never felt better. She was doing it! She was going to work all by herself!

On Friday morning, Susan took the bus to work as usual. As she was paying for her fare to exit the bus, the driver said, "Boy, I sure envy you." Susan wasn't certain if the driver was speaking to her or not. After all, who on earth would ever envy a blind woman who had struggled just to find the courage to live for the past year?

Curious, she asked the driver, "Why do you say that you envy me?"

The driver responded, "It must feel so good to be taken care of and protected like you are."

Susan had no idea what the driver was talking about and asked again, "What do you mean?"

The driver answered, "You know, every morning for the past week, a fine looking gentleman in a military uniform has been standing across the corner watching you when you get off the bus. He makes sure you cross the street safely and he watches until you enter your office building. Then he blows you a kiss, gives you a little salute, and walks away. You are one lucky lady."

Tears of happiness poured down Susan's cheeks. For although she couldn't physically see him, she had always felt Mark's presence. She was lucky, so lucky, for he had given her a gift more powerful than sight, a gift she didn't need to see to believe—the gift of love that can bring light where there had been darkness.

LEVI'S VALENTINE

J. STEPHEN LANG
FROM *THE CHRISTIAN READER* MAGAZINE

hen Levi Carpenter proposed to Letitia (Letty) McCluskey on New Year's Eve 1919, he said, "Pick a day [for our wedding], and make it one I can always remember." She chose February 14.

That year, 1920, a foot of snow fell in Fayetteville, Tennessee, on Valentine's Day. Letty said, "Let's put it off a week, to make sure all the guests can arrive." Levi wouldn't hear of it. He was convinced the day was right, snow or no snow. The wedding was hastily moved from the church to the minister's parlor, with five people present.

Because the roads were impassible, all arrangements for flowers, refreshments, and formal wear had been scrapped. Yet, as if by magic, Levi arrived with a bouquet of pink roses for his bride. When prodded, he said he "had connections." Forty-some years later, he confided to me (his great-grandson) that the minister's wife brought them from her own greenhouse.

By the time I came into the world, Levi and his Valentine wife were well past sixty. Living only a few miles away, I saw them almost every weekend. After Valentine's Day, without fail, I knew a huge bouquet of pink roses would be on the mahogany table in the foyer. But that wasn't all.

Somewhere near the vase was Levi's one annual attempt at artistry: a large snowflake intricately cut from paper. Attached to it was a note: "To Letty, my Valentine lady these forty-four years." The words never changed from year to year, just the number. Yet true to nature, the snowflakes were always a different design.

At age nine, I discovered a nook in the china cabinet where every anniversary snowflake had been placed, lovingly and dearly, starting with the first one inscribed, "To Letty, my Valentine for a whole year." Levi, a carpenter who was considered "tight-lipped" and unemotional, showed his heart to everyone once a year.

One day Levi sat me down and patiently showed me, step-by-step, how to fold and cut paper snowflakes. But it didn't take long before I became more frustrated than artistic. My efforts resulted in things that looked more like rat's nests than snowflakes. It made me wonder: *Does Great-Granddad really want me to know the secret?*

He seemed to delight in being the only one in the family with an artistic gift. He knew his wealthy brother Claude had taken his wife on a Valentine jaunt to the Caribbean, giving her a pearl necklace on the way. But Claude could only *buy* gifts. Levi could *make* snowflakes. And every one was a reminder of his wedding day, and of the girl he married.

No one ever said to me on February 14, "This is a big day for your great-grandparents." But I knew it was. The only time I recall them kissing was on a Valentine's Day, when my parents and I just happened to arrive at the moment Levi gave Letty her annual snowflake and roses.

When she realized we were watching, Letty's cheeks flushed as she scurried from the room, shrieking, "Levi, you wicked thing!" She wasn't convincing at all.

A few years afterward Levi gave Letty a snowflake on which he had written, "To Letty, my Valentine lady these fifty-six years." No one was sure if Letty saw this one. She was alive, and conscious, but so heavily medicated that she could only nod faintly when Levi held the snowflake in front of her. He placed it on her bedside table in the nursing home, beside the vase of pink roses.

He turned to Letty and said, "I'll be in tomorrow, early, Letty." Then after a pause, he added, "my love." She nodded faintly again.

Levi took my arm—a rare occurrence—as we left the room. A few feet down the corridor he said, "Boy, go get that snowflake. Them nurses or cleanin' women may throw it out with the garbage."

I retrieved it, knowing Levi intended to take it home to the china cabinet with the others. If Letty ever came home, he would show it to her then.

The following Valentine's Day, Levi and I made our way to the cemetery, bringing a bouquet of pink roses. There was a light dusting of snow, and he brushed it away from the double headstone. He placed the roses in the headstone's vase, hesitated, then put them back in the glass vase he'd brought them in.

"This is foolish, boy," he said. "No point in leavin' these here where no one'll see them."

He let out a deep breath, then said, "She'll see 'em, anyway, wherever they are. We'll come back in April. I'm thinkin' of plantin' a rose bush here, if the church won't mind."

"Pink roses?" I asked.

"Sure, pink's a nice color. Here, go put these flowers back in the car."

I took the vase, trying not to look at his face, knowing that stifling a tear was even harder if he knew I was watching him. I sat in the car, the motor running, holding the vase of roses. Then I saw Levi take something from his coat pocket and tuck it down inside the stone vase. It appeared to be a piece of paper, though I couldn't be sure.

The snow had started to fall in earnest and Levi shuffled back to the car. "Gonna be a big snow this time, I think. Let's get going."

I knew that the one thing he wouldn't discuss was the one thing on his mind. How could the heavy snowfall not remind him of this day fifty-seven years earlier? At fifteen, I hadn't yet experienced a broken heart, but sitting with my great-granddad, I was near enough to feel it.

The following year I got my driver's license. It was my first time to drive to the family cemetery by myself. There was no snow this Valentine's Day, just a gray, dull chill.

The rose bush Levi and I had planted in April had bloomed beautifully through the summer. It looked rather somber now, as did the entire cemetery. The date of Levi's death had been carved on his stone four months earlier.

My parents had placed some silk poinsettias on the grave at Christmas, and they were still there. *Out of season now,* I thought.

As I pulled them from the stone vase, something caught my eye. Barely visible in the pebbles at the bottom of the vase, I saw a corner of white paper. Somehow, after a year of snow and rain and wind, Levi's last paper snowflake was still intact.

I reached for it, thinking I would put it with my great-grandparents' other belongings in my parents' basement.

But the paper wasn't a souvenir for me. It was Levi's anniversary gift. It needed to stay exactly where it was.

Love comforteth like sunshine after rain.

WILLIAM SHAKESPEARE

I LOVE YOU ANYWAY

DR. JOE HARDING

It was Friday morning and a young businessman finally decided to ask his boss for a raise. Before leaving for work, he told his wife what he was about to do. All day long he felt nervous and apprehensive. Finally in the late afternoon he summoned the courage to approach his employer, and to his delight, the boss agreed to the raise.

The elated husband arrived home to a beautiful table set with their best china and lighted candles. Smelling the aroma of a festive meal, he figured that someone from the office had called his wife and tipped her off! Finding her in the kitchen, he eagerly shared the details of his good news. They embraced and danced around the room before sitting down to the wonderful meal his wife had prepared. Next to his plate he found an artistically lettered note that read, "Congratulations, darling! I knew you'd get the raise! This dinner is to show you how much I love you."

Later on his way to the kitchen to help his wife serve dessert, he noticed that a second card had fallen from her pocket. Picking it up off the floor, he read, "Don't worry about not getting the raise! You deserve it anyway! This dinner is to show how much I love you."

Total acceptance! Total love. She stood behind him no matter what—softening the blows, healing the wounds, and believing in him. We can be rejected by many if we're loved by one.

Grow old along with me!
The best is yet to be,
The last of life for which the first was made.

ROBERT BROWNING

CRUMBLING SANDCASTLES

SUE MONK KIDD
FROM *TODAY'S CHRISTIAN WOMAN* MAGAZINE

ne mild summer day beside the sea, my husband and I were lying on our beach towels, reading, each locked in our own separate worlds. It had been like that a lot lately. We'd been busy, preoccupied, going in different directions. I'd hoped the leisure of vacation would be different, but so far we'd spent most of it marooned in silence.

I looked up from my book at the ceaseless roll of the waves, feeling restless. I ran my fingers through the sand. "Wanna make a sandcastle?" I asked my husband.

He didn't really, but he humored me. Once we got started, though, he became surprisingly absorbed in the project. We both did. In fact, after a while we were working over that heap of beach sand like it was about to be photographed for Sandcastle digest. Sandy made bridges across the moat, while I crowned the top of the castle with spires. We made balconies and arched windows lined with tiny angel-wing shells. It looked like Camelot.

Neither of us noticed when the tide changed. We never saw the waves slipping up until the first swish of water gnawed a little piece of our castle away. Indignant, we shored it up with sand and patted it down. But as the waves returned with monotonous regularity, our hands grew still and our eyes drifted off toward the horizon. Sandy got on his beach towel. I got on mine. We went back to our silence.

The next time I looked around, the sandcastle we'd labored over was awash in the shifting tide. The bridges were washing away and the spires were starting to lean.

I gave it a soulful look, an inexplicable sadness coming over me. And suddenly in the midst of that ordinary summer, I had a moment of pure, unbidden revelation. There sits my marriage, I thought.

I looked at my husband. The soundlessness between us seemed to reach clear to the sky. It was the hollow silence of a mid-life marriage, a marriage in which the ceaseless noise of everyday living threatens to drown out the music of intimacy.

Dear God, when had the tide shifted? When had mortgages and laundry and orthodontist appointments become more important than those unspeakably long looks we used to exchange? How long since we'd shared our hidden pain or stumbled together upon a joy that was round with wonder and laughter? How had it happened that two people who loved each other could allow such distance to creep in?

I thought of the attentiveness we'd lavished upon our relationship in the beginning, and how, eventually, the endless demands and routines of running a household, raising two children, and juggling two careers had stilled our hands and averted our eyes.

That night, after the children were asleep, my husband found me standing in the shadows on the porch, staring into the night. "You've hardly said two words all evening."

"Sorry," I muttered. "I've just got something on my mind."

"You want to tell me what it is?" he said.

I turned around and looked at him. I took a deep breath. "I'm thinking of us," I said. "I'm thinking that our relationship is being drowned out by the demands of day-to-day living. We've taken our marriage for granted."

"What are you talking about? We have a very committed marriage!" He was indignant.

"Of course we have a committed marriage," I told him. "But sometimes it seems commitment is all we've got. Sometimes we are two strangers existing under one roof, each going separate ways."

He didn't say a word. Now I've done it, I thought. I've rocked the boat to the point of tipping over. I've told my husband our marriage is bordering on empty commitment. Good grief!

We stared at each other. It was like we were stuck inside some big, dark bubble of pain that wouldn't pop. Tears welled up in my eyes and started down my face. To my amazement, tears started down his face, too.

And suddenly, in what is surely the most endearing moment of my marriage, Sandy took his finger and traced the path of tears on my cheeks, then touched his own wet face, blending our tears together.

Strange how such things can begin to re-create the mystery of relatedness between two people. Sandy and I walked down the porch steps onto the beach under the blazing stars. Slowly we started to talk. We talked a long time. About the small agonies of being married, about the struggle of it all. We talked about the gnawed and fraying places in our marriage and how they'd happened. We spoke aching words about the unmet needs between us.

We were whirling the darkness that had settled in our relationship. And yes, it was uncomfortable and scary, like bobbing around in the ocean without a boat. But trading chaos and braving pain is often the only way to come upon a new shoreline. For God is in dark water, too.

Finally with the hour late and a sense of deepening and newness growing between us, I said rather dreamily, "It might be nice someday to say our wedding vows to each other again."

"What's wrong with right now?" my husband said. I swallowed. Was there no end to the surprises this man would spring on me tonight?

"B-but what would we say? I mean, I can't remember the vows exactly."

"Why don't we simply say what's in our hearts?"

So out there beneath the light of the stars, with the crash of waves filling the night, we took each other's hand and tried to put words to the music we had begun to recapture between us.

"I promise to listen to you," he said. "To make time for genuine sharing…"

"And I promise to be honest, to work at creating more togetherness between us," I began.

I don't remember all the words; mostly I remember the feelings behind them, the way my voice quivered and his hand tightened over mine. Mostly I thought what we were doing was rebuilding the castle, restoring the bridges, raising the spires.

The next morning we left the children stationed in front of the television with their breakfast cereal and went walking along the ocean edge. The sun poured a golden dial of light across the water that seemed to point us on and on. We talked as we went, a little awed by the events of the night before—knowing in the harsh light of day that saying words is one thing, but living them is another. We couldn't leave our newly spoken vows back there dripping in the moonlight. We had to take them home to the frantic schedules and the broken dryer and the Dorito crumbs under my son's bed.

Miles down the beach we waded knee-high into the surf and stood soaking up the turquoise sky and jade water. We were about to turn back to the condo when it happened. A huge, bottle-nosed dolphin came splashing out of the water a mere twenty yards away, startling us so badly we fell backward into the surf.

Sitting in the water fully clothed...a dolphin diving and surfacing before us in a spinning silver dance, was such an unexpected and exhilarating wonder, the two of us laughed until our insides hurt. I cannot remember a joy ever so plump and full.

At last we picked our delirious selves up and walked in our soggy shorts back up the beach where a few crumbling sandcastles dotted the shore. I took note of each one of them.

And I began to hear a voice deep inside me whispering: "When tomorrow comes and life beats upon your castle walls, remember the power of honest pain and blended tears. Remember the healing of laughter deeply shared. Remember what's important. Hold onto it always."

TITANIC LOVE

JIM PRIEST
FROM *THE DAILY OKLAHOMAN/OKLAHOMA CITY TIMES*

*T*hey were the picture of romance as they strolled the deck of the luxury ocean liner.

Arm and arm they walked, heads together, sharing stories and secrets and smiles.

From what people could see, they seemed very much in love. But beneath the surface, where no one could see, there was something else. Something that eyes could not behold, that ears could not hear and that minds could not grasp.

Beneath the surface was a deep and abiding commitment to one another that welded them together stronger and tighter than the rivets holding the unsinkable ship they were aboard.

Their names were Isidor and Ida Strauss.

Immigrants to America, they had scratched and scrapped their way in the new world and made a name for themselves.

With sweat and smarts, they had been able to build a little merchandise store in New York City: they named it Macy's. As they walked the decks of the HMS Titanic that April day in 1912, they were enjoying a much deserved vacation. They were enjoying each other's company. Unknown to them they were enjoying their last day together.

It was April 14, 1912, late in the evening, when the Titanic—the unsinkable ship crossing the Atlantic on her maiden voyage—struck an iceberg and started to sink. Icebergs, of course, only show a small part of themselves, most of the imponderable chunk of ice is below the ocean's surface.

Beneath the surface where no eye could see, no ear could hear, no mind could grasp its depth and size. As the ship began to list and take on water the lives of those on board began to change.

Some fearfully scrambled for safety. Some valiantly helped those in need. Isidor and Ida Strauss walked calmly on the deck, assessing the situation before finally approaching a lifeboat. Mrs. Strauss began to climb into the lifeboat, but changed her mind at the last minute.

She turned to her husband and said, "We have been living together for many years. Where you go, I go."

Members of the crew overheard her and tried to get her to change her mind. She would not listen.

A crew member turned to old Mr. Strauss and said, "I'm sure no one would object to an old gentleman like yourself getting in."

But Mr. Strauss was as stubborn as his wife.

"I will not go before the other men."

So the issue was settled. Neither would go without the other, and neither one would go.

Mrs. Strauss turned to her maid, now safely on board the lifeboat and said, "Here, take my fur coat. I won't be needing it."

Then the old couple walked a few steps to some nearby deck chairs and sat down together to await the inevitable.

Like the iceberg, the Strausses had more beneath the surface than could be seen by a casual observer. True enough, they showed their love for one another, but that was just the part that was visible. Beneath the surface was a solid commitment to one another that nothing, not even the threat of death could shake.

WHERE I BELONG

BOB WELCH
FROM *MOODY* MAGAZINE

*W*ith the freeway ahead of us and home behind, the photographer and I left on a three-day newspaper assignment.

We were bound for the Columbia Gorge, where the Columbia River carves a mile-wide path between Washington and Oregon; where windsurfers come from across the country to dance across waves created by "nuclear winds"; where I would be far from the world of nine-to-five and deadlines and routines and errands and rushing kids to baseball practices and having to make sure I hadn't left my socks on the bedroom floor.

Frankly, it had not been the perfect farewell. Our family was running on empty. Our '81 car was showing signs of its age. We were all tired, cranky and, spiritually, about a quart low.

My eight-year-old son tried to perk us up with his off-key version of a song from the musical *Annie:* The sun will come out tomorrow; bet your bottom dollar that tomorrow there'll be sun....

It didn't work.

I had been busy trying to get ready for the trip; my wife, Sally, had been fretting because my three days of freedom were going to mean, for her, three days of extra responsibility.

"Daddy, are you coming to hear my class sing Thursday night?" Jason, my eight-year-old, asked amid the chaos of my departure.

Bill Cosby would have gotten a funny expression on his face and said, "Well, of course," and everyone would have lived happily ever after.

I didn't feel much like Bill Cosby that morning. "I'm going to be out of town," I said. "Sorry."

Giving Sally a quick kiss, I was on my way. Now, hours later, I was far away from my family—free from the clutter, the runny noses, and the demands on my time.

The photographer and I shared a bit about ourselves as we drove. Roughly my age—mid thirties—he was married but had no children.

He told me how he and his wife had recently taken a trip to the gorge by themselves. My mind did a double take. By themselves? I vaguely remembered what that was like. Taking off when the mood hits. No pleas for horseback rides about the time you're ready to crash for the night. No tornado-swept rooms. No meet-the-teacher nights.

Besides having no children, the photographer had no six-month-old french fries on the floor of his car, no legs of Superman action figures on his dashboard, and no road maps on which most of Idaho had been oblit-erated by a melted Snickers bar.

For the next couple of days, despite a threat of rain, we explored the gorge: thousand-foot walls of basalt rising on either side of the Columbia; fluorescent-clad sailboarders, like neon gnats, carving wakes in the water.

If the land and water were intriguing, so were the windsurfers. There were thousands, nearly all of them baby boomers, spending their days on the water, their nights on the town, their mornings in bed.

Every fourth car had a board on top. License plates from all over the country dotted the streets. Some of these "boardheads" were follow-the-wind free spirits who lived out of the back of vans; others were well-established yuppies here for a weekend or on vacation.

Seeing this group was like discovering an ancient tribe. While I was busy trying to put on jammed bike chains, my generational brothers were jamming to the rock beat of dance clubs every night. While I was deposit-ing paychecks that were spent on groceries and orthodontia bills and college funds, these people were deciding what color sailboards to buy.

Where had I gone wrong?

On our last night, the cloudy weather continued, which irked the photographer and mirrored the mood that had overcome me. We both needed sunshine, only for different reasons.

As I stared from the motel window at the river below, I felt a sort of emptiness, as if I didn't belong. Not here. Not home. Not anywhere. Just as the winds of the gorge were whipping the river into whitecaps, so were the winds of freedom buffeting my beliefs. God. Marriage. Children. Work. I had anchored my life on such things, and yet now found myself slipping.

Had I made a mistake? Had the boundaries of Scripture become a cage around me? Had I sold out to the rigors of responsibility? Someday, when I was older, would I face the brittle-cold reality of regret, wishing I would have gone with the wind?

I was getting ready for bed when I spotted it—a greeting card in my suitcase, buried beneath some clothes. It was from Sally. The card featured cows—my wife's big on bovines—and simply said, "I'll love you till the cows come home."

I stared at the card for minutes. I repeated the words to myself. I looked at the same handwriting I'd seen on love letters in college, on a marriage certificate, on two birth certificates, on a will. And something inside me melted. My wife's promise bored through my hardened heart, refocusing my blurry perspective. In an instant, I knew exactly where I belonged.

The next day, after a two-hour interview, a six-hour drive, and a three-block sprint, I arrived at my son's school, anxious and out of breath. The singing program had started twenty minutes before; had I missed Jason's song?

I rushed into the cafeteria. It was jammed. Almost frantically, I weaved my way through a crowd of parents clogging the entrance to where I could get a glimpse of the kids on stage. That's when I heard them: twenty-five first-grade voices trying desperately to hit notes that were five years away.

The sun will come out, tomorrow; bet your bottom dollar that tomorrow there'll be sun...

My eyes searched this collage of kids, looking for Jason.

Finally I spotted him: front row, as usual, squished between a couple of girls whose germs, judging by the look on his face, were crawling over him like picnic ants. He was singing, but with less enthusiasm than when he's been told to clean his room.

Suddenly, his eyes shifted my way, and his face lit up with the kind of smile a father gets to see only in a grade-school program when his eyes meet his child's. He had seen me, a moment that will forever stay frozen in my memory.

Later, through a sea of faces, I caught sight of Sally and my other son. After the program, amid a mass of parent-child humanity, the four of us rendezvoused, nearly oblivious to the commotion surrounding us. I felt no emptiness, only connectedness.

In the days to come, I would resume my part in life as a bike-fixer, nine-to-fiver, Sunday school teacher, and husband—roles that might cause a windsurfer to yawn.

But I decided that for all the temporal freedom of skimming across a river, I'll take the eternal freedom of a faithful God. For all the luxury of a spotless car interior, I'll take the front-row smile of my eight-year-old. And for all the carefree living in the Columbia Gorge, I'll take the responsibility of caring for the woman who has vowed to love me till the cows come home.

A happy marriage is the union of two good forgivers.

ROBERT QUILLEN

THE SPIRIT OF SUNSHINE

AUTHOR UNKNOWN

FROM *LADIES HOME JOURNAL* MAGAZINE

ow's business, Eben?"

The old man was washing at the sink after his day's work.

"Fine, Marthy, fine."

"Does the store look just the same? Land, how I'd like to be there again with the sun shining in so bright! How does it look, Eben?"

"The store's never been the same since you left it, Marthy." A faint flush came into Martha's cheeks. Is a wife ever too old to be moved by her husband's praise!

For years Eben and Martha had kept a tiny notion store, but one day Martha fell sick and was taken to the hospital. That was months ago. She was out now, but she would never be strong again—never more be partner in the happy little store.

I can't help hankering for a sight of the store, thought Martha one afternoon. *If I take it real careful I think I can get down there. 'Tisn't so far.*

It took a long time for her to drag herself downtown, but at last she stood at the head of the little street where the store was. All of a sudden she stopped. Not far from her on the pavement stood Eben. A tray hung from his neck. On this tray were arranged a few cards of collar-buttons, some papers of pins and several bundles of shoe-laces. In a trembling voice he called his wares.

Martha leaned for support against the wall of a building nearby. She looked over the way at the little store. Its windows were filled with fruit. Then she understood. The store had gone to pay her hospital expenses. She turned and hurried away as fast as her weak limbs would carry her.

It will hurt him so to have me find it out! she thought, and the tears trickled down her face.

He's kept it a secret from me, and now I'll keep it a secret from him. He shan't ever know that I know.

That night when Eben came in, chilled and weary, Martha asked cheerily the old question:

"How's business, Eben?"

"Better'n ever, Marthy," was the cheery answer, and Martha prayed God might bless him for his sunshiny spirit and love of her.

❧

In this life we cannot do great things.
We can only do small things with great love.

MOTHER TERESA

NEW BEGINNINGS

PATRICIA WYMAN
FROM *VIRTUE MAGAZINE*

ee you tonight, Lee." This morning, Mark's perfunctory kiss didn't even reach my cheek. Starting toward the door, he turned, "Oh, I may have a meeting tonight. I'll call if I do."

I had not returned his "kiss" nor did I respond to his comment. Oblivious to my lack of response, Mark closed the door behind him.

On impulse, I grabbed my cup of coffee, hurried to the door and reopened it. I watched Mark wind his way around the azalea bushes, losing sight of him when he entered the garage. In the early years of our marriage, this had been a morning tradition. I would stand in the doorway until he backed the car out, tooted the horn and waved good-bye. No wave met my gaze this morning; he no longer expected me to be there.

Returning to the kitchen, I refilled my cup, threw a sweater over my shoulders and went into the back yard to sit on the old glider. Our back yard had always delighted me. I hoped that being there would help me capture memories of happier times.

Although it was only April, the sun warmed my face. The maple trees were beginning to sprout buds, and the morning dew on the yellow wisps of the forsythias reflected the sun's rays.

I looked at the spot where the flowering Japanese cherry tree used to stand. Mark and I had planted it when we moved into the house nearly twenty years ago. As the tree flourished, it came to represent much more than beauty and shade to me. The tree's maturing paralleled the growth of our three children.

The near-hurricane winds had blasted through our region last fall, toppling the tree. When the landscapers dug up the roots, I felt as if my own roots were being torn from me.

Staring at the bare patch that remained, I couldn't help but remember the day I'd learned that we were going to move here.

Married for six years, Mark and I had three small children—Mark Jr., Becca and Emily. All of us were crammed, like an overstuffed suitcase into an incredibly small apartment. I was mashing potatoes for supper when Mark literally bounced into the house.

"Everyone in the den," Mark ordered. "I've got something to tell you." He paced the floor impatiently while waiting for us to get settled. "I've found us a house! It needs all kinds of work, but it's sound—and best of all, it has a huge back yard. No, best of all, we can afford it!"

Sitting in that same back yard on a sunny April morning, I realized all I had left was the house.

The children were off on their own. Even though I held a rewarding job as a nurse for a local pediatrician, I found myself facing hours that I didn't know how to fill, hours when I found myself fighting feelings of desolation and uselessness.

I had always taken my job as a mother seriously. Determined to raise our children in a spiritual home, I had spent vast amounts of time instilling values. I had driven them to practices, games and lessons. I had helped with homework and had filled my days with the 101 other things that children require—the things no one seemed to need anymore. True, Mark's body still lived in our home, but, emotionally, he had moved continents away.

What bothered me most was not knowing when it happened. By the time I recognized his distance, the chasm between us felt too deep and too wide to be crossed.

"Enough of this," I said, and headed for the house. The telephone rang just as I entered the kitchen—Becca's Wednesday morning phone call, right on schedule.

"Mom," she began abruptly, "I know you absolutely despise surprise parties, so I'm not giving you one."

"That's sweet of you to be so thoughtful, Becca. But even if I did like surprise parties, why would you be giving me one?"

"Mother!" In her exasperation she sounded more like my mother than my daughter. "For your twenty-fifth anniversary next month."

"Save the big bash for our fiftieth, honey." *If there is one,* I added silently.

After filling me in on all the amazing things my grandson was doing, Becca said good-bye. As I dressed for work, I continued wondering what hidden ailment was destroying my once-strong marriage.

The thought that I'd refused to dignify with conscious consideration kept poking at me until I said, "No. It can't be someone else. Oh, please, God, please don't let it be someone else."

The next few weeks passed with little change in our relationship. We were painfully polite to one another. Perfunctory kisses became our morning ritual and Mark continued to have periodic, late appointments.

When Mark suggested we go out to dinner one Saturday, I found myself hoping, against all reason, that our "date" would revive something in both our hearts. In anticipation, I pampered myself with a facial, a shampoo, a bubble bath, a manicure and an hour's rest.

I decided on a beige, silk shantung suit that I hadn't been able to fit into in three years. Apparently, my apathy about so many things must have included food.

As he helped me into the car Mark said, "You look...lovely, Lee."

Sadly, the date went downhill from there. After we finished discussing the children and work, our conversation became stilted, awkward.

Over dessert, my hopes rose again when, once more, he said, "You really do look lovely tonight, Lee." But we fell asleep that night in our usual position—back to back—with an ocean of space between us. When I accidentally touched him, I immediately drew away. It seemed indecent—as if I had touched a stranger.

My mind kept whispering, "It's all the fault of that storm," but I knew that whatever was wrong with our marriage couldn't be blamed on a felled tree.

I awoke at six and quietly eased out of the bed. Wrapped in an old, cuddly robe, I took my coffee out into the back yard and sat amid the chirping of sparrows and chickadees.

"It's over," I muttered. "Our marriage is truly over...but I don't want it to be over! I can't let it be over!"

My gaze turned to the spot where the tree had been, and I saw something poking up from the ground. Setting down my cup and wrapping the robe tightly around me, I walked over and knelt down.

Little shoots were pushing their way through the hard earth. I recognized them as lilies of the valley. Perhaps they had been there all along, hiding among the roots of the trees, and I just hadn't noticed. Maybe they had been forced to lie dormant all these years, yielding their space to the overwhelming needs of a growing tree.

Regardless of how they got there, a few little plants stretched toward the sky and the sun.

My thoughts returned to the back yard of my childhood home, filled with lilies of the valley. As my mother stood on our porch admiring them and inhaling their sweet scent, her face would have the same peaceful expression as when she was in church.

"Those little bell-shaped flowers may look delicate," she would say, "but they're as strong as can be. No matter how harsh the winter; they pop right up each spring."

Then, she'd spread her arms as if she could grasp the yard and all it contained. "Can you believe that this abundant growth of beauty started from a few plants? I do believe that they're a message of hope from our Lord."

I went back inside, cooked Mark's favorite breakfast, fixed a tray, and carried it to the bedroom.

Bending down, I gave him a kiss and whispered, "Do you have any idea how much I love you?"

Startled out of a deep sleep, he peered out of heavy lidded eyes and hoarsely asked, "What is it? What's wrong?"

"I'm not sure," I said. "But I'm willing to work on fixing whatever it is. Are you?"

"Lee, there's something that I want to tell you."

"Not now, Mark. Right now, let's plan our trip."

"What trip?" he asked, propping himself on one elbow.

"Our twenty-fifth anniversary trip. Where would you like to go?"

"Lee—it isn't what you think—I never…"

"I didn't think you had," I said.

As I stood there with my tousled hair, swaddled in my old robe, Mark took my hand and said, "You're so beautiful."

And the new beginning promised by the lilies took root in my heart.

All, everything that I understand,
I understand only because I love.

LEO TOLSTOY

The Secret

*E*ven the most devoted couple will experience a storm once in a while. A grandmother, celebrating her golden wedding anniversary, once told the secret of her long and happy marriage.

"On my wedding day I decided to make a list of ten of my husband's faults which for the sake of our marriage, I would overlook," she said. "I never did get around to listing them. But whenever my husband did something I didn't like, I would say to myself, 'Lucky for him that's one of the ten.'"

AUTHOR UNKNOWN

THE GOLDEN CRANE

PATRICIA LORENZ

s a teacher of origami (the ancient Japanese art of paper folding) at the LaFarge Lifelong Learning Institute in Milwaukee, Wisconsin, Art Beaudry was asked to represent the school at an exhibit at a large mall in Milwaukee. He decided to take along a couple hundred folded paper cranes to pass out to people who stopped at his booth.

Before that day, however, something strange happened—an inner voice told him to find a piece of gold foil paper and make a gold origami crane. The urging was so strong that Art actually found himself rummaging through his collection of origami papers at home until he found one flat, shiny piece of gold foil. "Why am I doing this?" he asked himself. Art had never worked with the shiny gold paper; it didn't fold as easily or neatly as the crisp multicolored papers. But that little voice kept nudging. Art harrumphed and tried to ignore it. "Why gold foil anyway? Paper is much easier to work with," he grumbled.

The urging continued. "Do it! And you must give it away tomorrow to a special person."

That evening Art very carefully folded and shaped the unforgiving gold foil until it became as graceful and delicate as a real crane about to take flight. He packed the exquisite bird in the box along with about two hundred colorful paper cranes he'd made over the previous few weeks.

The next day at the mall, dozens upon dozens of people stopped by Art's booth to ask questions about origami. He demonstrated the art. He folded, unfolded, and refolded. He explained the intricate details, the need for sharp creases.

Then there was a woman standing in front of Art. The special person. Art had never seen her before, and she hadn't said a word as she watched him carefully fold a bright pink piece of paper into a crane with pointed, graceful wings.

Art glanced up at her face, and before he knew what he was doing, his hands were down in the big box that contained the supply of paper cranes. There it was, the delicate gold-foil bird he'd labored over the night before. He retrieved it and carefully placed it in the woman's hand.

"I don't know why, but there's a voice inside me telling me I'm supposed to give you this golden crane. The crane is the ancient symbol of peace," Art said simply.

The woman didn't say a word as she slowly cupped her small hand around the fragile bird as if it were alive. When Art looked up at her face, he saw tears filling her eyes, ready to spill out.

Finally, the woman took a deep breath and said, "My husband died three weeks ago. This is the first time I've been out. Today..." She wiped her eyes with her free hand, still gently cradling the golden crane with the other. She spoke very quietly. "Today is our golden wedding anniversary."

Then this stranger said in a clear voice, "Thank you for this beautiful gift. Now I know that my husband is at peace. Don't you see? That voice you heard, it's the voice of God and this beautiful crane is a gift from Him. It's the most wonderful fiftieth wedding anniversary present I could have received. Thank you for listening to your heart."

And that's how Art learned to listen very carefully when a little voice within him tells him to do something he may not understand at the time.

ROSES FOR ROSE

JAMES KISNER

Red roses were her favorites, her name was also Rose.
And every year her husband sent them, tied with pretty bows.
The year he died, the roses were delivered to her door.
The card said, "Be my Valentine," like all the years before.

Each year he sent her roses, and the note would always say,
"I love you even more this year, than last year on this day.
My love for you will always grow, with every passing year."
She knew this was the last time that the roses would appear.

She thought, he ordered roses in advance before this day.
Her loving husband did not know, that he would pass away.
He always liked to do things early, way before the time.
Then, if he got too busy, everything would work out fine.

She trimmed the stems, and placed them in a very special vase.
Then, sat the vase beside the portrait of his smiling face.
She would sit for hours, in her husband's favorite chair.
While staring at his picture, and the roses sitting there.

A year went by, and it was hard to live without her mate.
With loneliness and solitude, that had become her fate.
Then, the very hour, as on Valentines before,
The doorbell rang, and there were roses, sitting by her door.

She brought the roses in, and then just looked at them in shock.
Then, went to get the telephone, to call the florist shop.
The owner answered, and she asked him, if he would explain,
Why would someone do this to her, causing her such pain?

"I know your husband passed away, more than a year ago,"
The owner said, "I knew you'd call, and you would want to know.
The flowers you received today, were paid for in advance.
You husband always planned ahead, he left nothing to chance.

"There is a standing order, that I have on file down here,
And he has paid, well in advance, you'll get them every year.
There also is another thing, that I think you should know,
He wrote a special little card…he did this years ago.

"Then, should ever, I find out that he's no longer here,
That's the card…that should be sent, to you the following year."
She thanked him and hung up the phone, her tears now flowing hard.
Her fingers shaking, as she slowly reached to get the card.

Inside the card, she saw that he had written her a note.
Then, as she stared in total silence, this is what he wrote…
"Hello, my love, I know it's been a year since I've been gone,
I hope it hasn't been too hard for you to overcome.

"I know it must be lonely, and the pain is very real.
For if it was the other way, I know how I would feel.
The love we shared made everything so beautiful in life.
I loved you more than words can say, you were the perfect wife.

"You were my friend and lover, you fulfilled my every need.
I know it's only been a year, but please try not to grieve.
I want you to be happy, even when you shed your tears.
That is why the roses will be sent to you for years.

"When you get these roses, think of all the happiness,
That we had together, and how both of us were blessed.
I have always loved you and I know I always will.
But, my love, you must go on, you have some living still.

"Please…try to find happiness, while living out your days.
I know it is not easy, but I hope you find some ways.
The roses will come every year, and they will only stop,
When your door's not answered, when the florist stops to knock.

"He will come five times that day, in case you have gone out.
But after his last visit, he will know without a doubt,
To take the roses to the place, where I've instructed him,
And place the roses where we are, together once again."

LIFE'S FINEST HOUR

Eugene S. Geissler
From *The Best Is Yet To Be*

o you remember, Jo, when you first called me "Friend Husband"? It was many, many years ago, early in our marriage. I don't think it struck me as particularly extraordinary at first to be called that name. After all, what else is expected from a husband or wife? But now that I am old and you still say it, it has grown into considerable significance for me.

We have been through a lot together and having survived it all we look forward to continued care for each other. Our tenderness is more precious than ever because of our greater need for each other.

Thirty-five years into our marriage you wrote, "Friend Husband was twenty when I met him—so I have no first-hand knowledge of his early years. The person he was at twenty-eight commanded my immediate interest—there was no strangeness, no tension—and we were friends from our first meeting. And we remain friends together."

Short days ago we quietly celebrated forty-five years of marriage. It was indeed one of our finest anniversaries, wasn't it? The next day you took me aside though there was nobody around that could see or hear us. You confided: "Ever since we've been married and then when you were overseas, and all these years since, I've wanted to buy you a gold wedding band. Would you wear it?"

So I sit here with my golden wedding band shining at me. I've had it on less than forty-five hours, but it fits and feels like it has been there for forty-five years. The next time I left a note for you on the kitchen counter, I delighted in signing it: "Friend Husband w/ the gold ring."

Am I just talking trivia? Or is it perhaps not necessary to say anything? A husband and a wife, friends together for forty-five years, might just know what the other is thinking. At the end of such a long period of time, sitting silently together becomes a kind of virtue, a pleasing sound, a language of presence. Would you say that every now and then we are inclined to call it "life's finest hour"?

Five years ago our children decided to redo our family room into a room for just the two of us. We were caught by surprise, not feeling secure about the offer. You know how people growing older don't like things being changed around. But it was a Christmas present, lovingly signed by our children.

It is a rather long but somewhat narrow room, facing south and front, with a large picture window. On the narrow east end of the room is the library. There you have the wing chair you have always wanted, and there you spend a lot of time reading. Reading is your pastime, much of your entertainment, your therapy and refuge.

My wing chair, matching yours across the room, sits in the corner next to the stove. It's my home base. A couch against the wall opposite the window allows for some good company now and then.

So here we are, daily facing each other across the room—you in the library most of the time, and myself, an up-and-down, in-and-out person, only half as much. But much happens between us here. We say prayers together; we often eat our breakfast and lunch here. We interrupt each other with things to tell, insights to offer, deep thoughts to share, jokes to laugh at, even disagreements to start and stop.

We are aware of our need for each other, our concern for each other, our promises to take care of each other, whichever one is able to do so when that time comes. Sometimes we ask the Lord if we might die close together. Every day we thank God for our being together.

Among the people we seem to pray for more often now are "the old and the infirm," and the other morning we had to add: "among whom we class ourselves." Neither of us is either that old or that infirm to be talking much about it. Still we know it to be coming—the end of those things we have cherished together. To be honest about what lies hidden before us doesn't distract us from those fleeting moments of peace and quiet of soul, which are a foretaste of the good things that wait us in the presence of the Lord.

*The way to love someone is to lightly
run your finger over that person's soul
until you find a crack, and then gently
pour your love into that crack.*

KEITH MILLER

RUDY'S ANGEL

WILMA HANKINS HIAWICZA

I walked into the grocery store not particularly interested in buying groceries. I wasn't hungry. The pain of losing my husband of thirty-seven years was still too raw. And this grocery store held so many sweet memories.

Rudy often came with me and almost every time he'd pretend to go off and look for something special. I knew what he was up to. I'd always spot him walking down the aisle with the three yellow roses in his hands.

Rudy knew I loved yellow roses. With a heart filled with grief, I only wanted to buy my few items and leave, but even grocery shopping was different since Rudy had passed on.

Shopping for one took time, a little more thought than it had for two. Standing by the meat, I searched for the perfect small steak and remembered how Rudy had loved his steak. Suddenly a woman came beside me. She was blond, slim, and lovely in a soft green pantsuit. I watched as she picked up a large pack of T-bones, dropped them in her basket, hesitated, and then put them back. She turned to go and once again reached for the pack of steaks. She saw me watching her and she smiled.

"My husband loves T-bones, but honestly, at these prices, I don't know."

I swallowed the emotion down my throat and met her pale blue eyes. "My husband passed away eight days ago," I told her.

Glancing at the package in her hands, I fought to control the tremble in my voice. "Buy him the steaks. And cherish every moment you have together." She shook her head, and I saw the emotion in her eyes as she placed the package in her basket and wheeled away.

I turned and pushed my cart across the length of the store to the dairy products. There I stood, trying to decide which size milk I should buy. A quart, I finally decided and moved on to the ice cream section near the front of the store. If nothing else, I could always fix myself an ice cream cone.

I placed the ice cream in my cart and looked down the aisle toward the front. I saw first the green suit, then recognized the pretty lady coming towards me. In her arms she carried a package. On her face was the brightest smile I had ever seen. I would swear a soft halo encircled her blond hair as she kept walking toward me, her eyes holding mine. As she came closer, I saw what she held and tears began misting in my eyes. "These are for you," she said and placed three beautiful long stemmed yellow roses in my arms. "When you go through the line, they will know these are paid for." She leaned over and placed a gentle kiss on my cheek, then smiled again.

I wanted to tell her what she'd done, what the roses meant, but still unable to speak, I watched as she walked away as tears clouded my vision. I looked down at the beautiful roses nestled in the green tissue wrapping and found it almost unreal. How did she know? Suddenly the answer seemed so clear. I wasn't alone.

"Oh, Rudy, you haven't forgotten me, have you?" I whispered, with tears in my eyes. He was still with me, and she was his angel.

Inspiration

Twenty years from now you will be more disappointed
by the things you didn't do than by the ones you did do.
So throw off the bowlines.
Sail away from the safe harbor.
Catch the trade winds in your sails.
Explore.
Dream.
Discover.

MARK TWAIN

OL' ED NEVER FORGOT

MAX LUCADO
FROM *IN THE EYE OF THE STORM*

*T*o the onlookers, some things seem like an empty ritual, when to the person who is informed, they seem more significant than life itself. Take ol' Ed down in Florida. Every Friday evening about the time the sun is the size of a giant orange just about to dip into the water, ol' Ed comes strolling along the beach to find his way to his favorite pier. He's carrying in his bony hand a bucket full of shrimp. The shrimp are not for him. The shrimp are not for the fish. Strangely, the shrimp are for the seagulls. Ed, alone with his thoughts, walks out to the end of the pier with his bucket, not saying a word. But that's where the ritual begins.

Before long the sky becomes a mass of little dots screeching and squawking, making their way to ol' Ed there on the end of the pier. They envelope him with their presence. Their fluttering wings sound like a roar of thunder. Ed stands there and sort of mumbles to them as they're feeding on the shrimp. In fact, he reaches in his bucket and he throws a few up to them. You can almost hear him say, "Thank you. Thank you." Within minutes, the bucket is empty. And Ed stands there, almost as if raptured, in his thoughts of another time and another place. Then, without a word being spoken, he quietly makes his way back home.

Who is ol' Ed anyway? His full name is Eddie Rickenbacker. He was a captain in World War II. He flew a B-17 Flying Fortress. He and seven other men were sent on a mission across the Pacific to locate General MacArthur; however, their plane crashed in the water. Miraculously, they all made it out of the plane into a life raft.

Aboard their life raft, they fought the sun and the sharks. Most of all, they fought hunger, as all eight of these men ate and drank very little, until finally by the eighth day their rations ran out. No food. No water. They needed a miracle for them to survive.

After an afternoon devotional time, the men said a prayer and tried to rest. As Rickenbacker was dozing with his hat over his eyes, something landed on his head. It was a sea gull. That gull meant food…if he could catch it. And he did.

He tore the feathers off and they shared a morsel of it together. Then they used the intestines for fish bait. They were able to survive until they were found and rescued, almost at the end of their lives.

Later, Billy Graham asked Captain Rickenbacker about the story, because he heard that that experience had been used to lead him to a saving knowledge of Jesus Christ. Rickenbacker said to Billy, "I have no explanation except God sent one of His angels to rescue us."

Ol' Ed never forgot. He never stopped saying, "Thank you." Every Friday evening for years until he died, he would go to that old pier with a bucket full of shrimp and a heart full of gratitude for the rescue to say, "Thank you. Thank you. Thank you."

BETTER THAN
A TROPHY

GRACE WITWER HOUSHOLDER

$\mathcal{E}$arly in the season my husband told me this would be his last year coaching baseball.

After ten years he had learned he loved the sport and the kids so much that he couldn't do it halfway. The one hundred percent dedication and many extra practices were taking an emotional and physical toll. He said it was time for him to become a spectator again.

Going into the tournament his team of ten- and eleven-year-olds had the best record in the league. They had gone from 3 to 3, to 10 to 3. It looked like his players would be bringing home trophies.

But flu struck that night.

In the last inning one of the sick players, the best hitter on the team, was unable to bat. Tears streaming down his face, he told the coach he couldn't stand up. He could only lie down. The team would have to bat out of order and receive its third and final out.

Only I knew how hard it was for my husband to end his coaching career with a loss.

Three days later this letter from one of the game's umpires appeared in the local newspaper:

In the post-season tournament of the Youth Baseball Major League, I witnessed a wonderful example of what youth sports are all about. Before the game one team had two players that were feeling sick but still wished to play. The coach granted their wishes and inserted them in the lineup.

In the bottom of the last inning the team was trailing by two runs and had two outs when the next batter was slated to be one of the flu-stricken players. Despite his gutsy play to that point he simple could not fight off his illness anymore. He could not bat. Under strict rules of baseball, which were being played, this resulted in the team batting out of order and committing the third and final out.

The coach could have chosen to fight the rule and try to persuade the other coach to grant his team one more out. But he chose not to. His players could have chosen to look down on their ailing teammate, but they comforted him instead. The fans could have chosen to plead with the officials and prod the coach to action but chose to console their sons.

In an age when winning seems to be the bottom line nobody on the losing side made any excuses or outraged appeals. They accepted their defeat according to the rules of the game.

Baseball can be viewed as a microcosm of real life. Sometimes the breaks go your way; sometimes they don't. You can abide by the rules and face the consequences, or you can break them and possibly cheat someone else. The coach showed that although the rules might not always be in your favor, they are still the rules, and obeying them is better than losing your dignity and compromising the spirit of the game. The children may have cried because their season had ended, but what they accomplished on that evening will forever outlive the tears.*

The day after the letter to the editor, my husband got this letter from one of his ten-year-old players:

Thanks for being my coach. You improved us all. I know it was a bummer to lose because you have won two years in a row. But you never lost your temper, and when you almost did you smiled.

My husband and his team entered the tournament wanting a trophy. They left with something better.

---

*The name of the umpire writing the letter was Brian Allen.

LOVE AND
THE CABBIE

ART BUCHWALD

I was in New York the other day and rode with a friend in a taxi. When we got out, my friend said to the driver, "Thank you for the ride. You did a superb job of driving."

The taxi driver was stunned for a second. Then he said, "Are you a wise guy or something?"

"No, my dear man, and I'm not putting you on. I admire the way you keep cool in heavy traffic."

"Yeah," the driver said and drove off.

"What was that all about?" I asked.

"I am trying to bring love back to New York," he said. "I believe it's the only thing that can save the city."

"How can one man save New York?"

"It's not one man. I believe I have made that taxi driver's day. Suppose he has twenty fares. He's going to be nice to those twenty fares because someone was nice to him. Those fares in turn will be kinder to their employees or shopkeepers or waiters or even their own families. Eventually the goodwill could spread to at least one thousand people. Now that isn't bad, is it?"

"But you're depending on that taxi driver to pass your goodwill to others."

"I'm not depending on it," my friend said. "I'm aware that the system isn't foolproof so I might deal with ten different people today. If out of ten I can make three happy, then eventually I can indirectly influence the attitudes of three thousand more."

"It sounds good on paper," I admitted, "but I'm not sure it works in practice."

"Nothing is lost if it doesn't. It didn't take any of my time to tell that man he was doing a good job. He neither received a larger tip nor a smaller tip. If it fell on deaf ears, so what? Tomorrow there will be another taxi driver I can try to make happy."

"You're some kind of a nut," I said.

"That shows how cynical you have become. I have made a study of this. The thing that seems to be lacking, besides money of course, for our postal employees, is that no one tells people who work for the post office what a good job they're doing."

"But they're not doing a good job."

"They're not doing a good job because they feel no one cares if they do or not. Why shouldn't someone say a kind word to them?"

We were walking past a structure in the process of being built and passed five workmen eating their lunch. My friend stopped. "That's a magnificent job you men have done. It must be difficult and dangerous work."

The workmen eyed my friend suspiciously.

"When will it be finished?"

"June," a man grunted.

"Ah. That really is impressive. You must all be very proud."

We walked away. I said to him, "I haven't seen anyone like you since *The Man from LaMancha.*"

"When those men digest my words, they will feel better for it. Somehow the city will benefit from their happiness."

"But you can't do this all alone!" I protested. "You're just one man."

"The most important thing is not to get discouraged. Making people in the city become kind again is not an easy job, but if I can enlist other people in my campaign..."

"You just winked at a very plain-looking woman," I said.

"Yes, I know," he replied. "And if she's a schoolteacher, her class will be in for a fantastic day."

The grand essentials of happiness are:
Something to do,
Something to love
And something to hope for.

ALLAN K. CHALMERS

The two most beautiful things in the universe
are the starry heavens above our heads
and the feeling of duty in our hearts.

JACQUE-BÉNIGNE BOSSUET (1627–1704)

WE COULD HAVE
DANCED ALL NIGHT

GUY DOUD
FROM *MOLDER OF DREAMS*

s adviser to our high school student council I worked
with the leadership to encourage projects that
involved student service. I was impressed with my students' enthusiasm
for helping with local canned-food drives and other events to aid charity.

Our "Adopt-a-Grandparent" program had been rewarding for the students who had been involved. They had grown as people by discovering the worth of others. I believe that the true leader is the true servant, and I tried to convey that message to my students. But it never got through to them as clearly as it did the night of the prom.

Tom Rosenberger had given me a call. A friend, and one of the local elementary principals, Tom had heard of an idea at a conference he had attended and called to share the idea with me. I fell in love with it and soon shared it with my student council.

"Mr. President?" I asked.

Mike, the president of the student council, acknowledged me. "Yes, Mr. Doud?"

I started gradually. "I've been thinking of an idea, and I want to bounce it off everyone."

"What's the idea?" asked Mike.

"I think we should host a prom." I said.

"We already have a prom!" answered about thirty students all at once, who seemed to wonder if I had lost my mind. They knew that organizing the prom was the responsibility of the junior class cabinet.

"Oh, I don't mean a prom for eleventh and twelfth graders," I said.

"We're not going to include sophomores!" said one senior boy.

"No. I want to have a prom for senior—" but they didn't let me finish.

"Seniors can already go to the prom," Mike answered, wondering what had gone wrong with his adviser.

"No, for senior citizens. People fifty-five years of age and over. Let's hold a prom for them."

"Why would we want to do that?" asked Mike.

"Let's take the money we've earned this year," I said, "and let's give it back to the community in the form of a gift. That gift will be a prom. We'll invite all senior citizens to come. We'll decorate the gym, hire an orchestra, have corsages for the ladies...." I was beginning to show some real excitement.

"If we spent money doing that, does that mean we wouldn't take our usual spring trip?" asked one girl, putting down the mirror she held in her hand.

"We would spend as much of the money as necessary to make this a most special evening for the senior citizens. The orchestra we hire will play the big band sounds of the twenties and thirties and other dance music. I've already contacted an orchestra, and I've talked with our principal, who thinks it's a great idea. I told him that I thought you guys would think it's a great idea, too." I can be pretty persuasive sometimes.

After much discussion, the council voted to form a committee to plan the senior citizen prom. In the weeks to follow, I watched my students become excited about the prom. Some of the young men in the council decided to order tuxedos so they would look nice as hosts. The girls planned to wear their long dresses to serve as hostesses.

All of Brainerd got excited the week before the prom. Paul Harvey began page two of this national daily broadcast his way: "In Brainerd, Minnesota, the student council is planning a prom...for senior citizens.

That's right! A prom…for senior citizens. The Brainerd students are going to provide an orchestra, corsages, valet parking, free hors d'oeuvres and…they are also going to do the chaperoning!"

I had been somewhat concerned about the lack of advertising. My students had contacted the senior citizen centers in the area and had sent out invitations, but when I heard it announced by Paul Harvey, my fears of poor publicity died.

The night of the prom finally arrived. The students had decorated our gym more beautifully than I had ever seen it. It was like the gym I had seen in my dreams when I had been in high school. The floral department at the vocational school had donated corsages, some of the local banks provided the hors d'oeuvres, the bus company that contracts with the school district provided free transportation to any senior citizen needing it. My students had tried to cover all the bases. We sat back to wait and see how many seniors would attend. The prom was to begin at six-thirty. At four o'clock, they started to come!

One of the first to arrive was an older lady with a cane. She stopped inside the door and looked around.

"Oh," she said, "so this is the new high school."

I didn't remind her that the high school was more than fifteen years old.

"I've never been in here before," she said.

Mark Dinham, one of the main organizers of the prom, grabbed a corsage and asked her if he could pin it on her. She readily agreed.

"The prom doesn't begin until six-thirty," Mark said.

"I'll wait," she said. "I want to get a good seat."

"I hope you'll do some dancing!" I said.

"I'll dance if you dance with me!" she replied as Mark finished pinning her corsage.

He turned a bit red. "Sure, I'll dance with you, but I've got to go home and change clothes," he said.

A few moments later, a couple walked up to the table. "Is this where the prom is being held?" they asked.

"That's right," I said.

I could hardly believe what they had to say: "We're from Oregon, and we're on our way to Wisconsin. We heard it on Paul Harvey yesterday, so we looked up Brainerd on the map and decided to go a little out of our way so we could come to your prom. Are we welcome?"

And people kept coming. By 6:30 when the prom began, more than five hundred senior citizens packed the transformed gymnasium.

But we had developed one major problem. Mike was the first to call it to my attention. I had noticed him dancing with one lady after another. He wasn't able to take a break.

"Mr. Doud," he said, "we have a serious male shortage here."

"What are you going to do about it, Mike?" I asked.

"I know where some of the hockey team is tonight, and I think I could call them and tell them to go home and get their suits on and get over here."

"Good plan," I said.

Soon some of Mike's friends started to arrive. I watched as the lady who had been the first to come walked up to one of the sophomores who had just entered the gym.

"You come dance with me," she said, grabbing his hand before he was sure what had happened.

Mike came up to me. "This is fun. Where did they learn to dance like this?"

Mike and many of my students were amazed that some dances actually had set steps and patterns. I joined in as the senior citizens taught us to waltz and polka. I had never learned to dance, either.

One of the seniors who had dressed up for the occasion had on a beautiful long dress with sequins, and the mirrored ball in the middle of the dance floor reflected light off her dress. We danced. She led.

"If I were about sixty years younger, I'd go after you," she said.

I laughed.

"What grade are you in?" she asked.

I laughed harder. "I'm a teacher here. I'm in charge of these kids."

"Oh," she said, "you're so young and handsome."

I didn't laugh. "And you are very beautiful," I said.

"Oh, come on now...."

The orchestra began to play a song from *My Fair Lady,* and as I followed my partner, I thought of Eliza Doolittle. Henry Higgins saw an elegant woman when everyone else saw a peasant.

"I could have danced all night...." My partner sang along with the music. "That was a good movie," she added, "but I bet it's before your time."

"No, I remember it well." I looked about at my students, every one of them dancing with a senior citizen.

One older man was teaching a sophomore girl how to waltz. I watched her. I was used to seeing her in torn blue jeans. She was beautiful in a long dress.

When the evening finally came to an end, no one wanted to leave.

Mike walked up to me. "That was the most fun I've ever had in high school."

"You mean that was more fun than your junior-senior proms?" I asked.

"No question about it." Mike was definite.

"What made this so much fun?" I asked.

Without thinking for even a moment, Mike answered, "It really feels good to do something for somebody else."

The following Monday, Paul Harvey, who must have spies all about, concluded his broadcast with this story: "Remember last week I told you about how the Brainerd, Minnesota, student council was going to host a prom for senior citizens? Well, they did...and more than five hundred senior citizens showed up. The high school students danced with the seniors, and the chaperons report no major problems.... Oh, there was a little smooching in the corner, but no major problems. Paul Harvey, good day!"

TURN ABOUT

STEVEN J. LAWSON
FROM *ABSOLUTELY SURE*

soldier who was a Christian made it his practice to conclude every day with Bible reading and prayer. As his fellow soldiers gathered in the barrack and retired for the night, he would kneel by his bunk and offer prayers to the Lord.

The other soldiers saw this and began to mock and harass him. But one night the abuse went beyond verbal assault. As the soldier bowed before His Lord in prayer, one antagonist threw his boot through the dark and hit him in the face. The other soldiers snickered and jeered, hoping for a fight.

But there was no retaliation.

The next morning when the taunting soldier awoke, he was startled to discover something at the foot of his bed. For all to see, there were his boots, returned and polished.

JOHNNY

Barbara A. Glanz
From *Care Packages for the Workplace*

ast fall I was asked to speak to three thousand employees of a large supermarket chain in the Midwest on building customer loyalty and regenerating the spirit in your workplace.

One of the ideas I stressed was the importance of adding a personal "signature" to your work. With all the downsizing, re-engineering, overwhelming technological changes and stress in the workplace, I think it is essential for each of us to find a way we can really feel good about ourselves and our jobs. One of the most powerful ways to do this is to do something that differentiates you from all the other people that do the same thing you do.

I shared the example of a United Airlines pilot who, after everything is under control in the cockpit, goes to the computer and randomly selects several people on board the flight and handwrites them a thank-you note for their business. A graphic artist I work with always encloses a piece of sugarless gum in everything he sends his customers, so you never throw away mail from him!

A Northwest Airlines baggage attendant decided that his personal signature would be to collect all the luggage tags that fall off customers' suitcases, which in the past have been simply tossed in the garbage, and in his free time send them back with a note thanking them for flying Northwest. A senior manager with whom I worked decided that his personal signature would be to attach Kleenex to memos that he knows his employees won't like very much.

After sharing several other examples of how people add their unique spirit to their jobs, I challenged the audience to get their creative juices flowing and to come up with their own creative personal signature.

About three weeks after I had spoken to the supermarket employees, my phone rang late one afternoon. The person on the line told me that his name was Johnny and that he was a bagger in one of the stores. He also told me that he was a person with Down's syndrome. He said, "Barbara, I liked what you said!" Then he went on to tell me that when he'd gone home that night, he asked his dad to teach him to use the computer.

He said they set up a program using three columns, and each night now when he goes home, he finds a "thought for the day." He said when he can't find one he likes, he "thinks one up!" Then he types it into the computer, prints out multiple copies, cuts them out, and signs his name on the back of each one. The next day, as he bags customers' groceries—"with flourish"—he puts a thought for the day in each person's groceries, adding his own personal signature in a heartwarming, fun and creative way.

One month later the manager of the store called me. He said, "Barbara, you won't believe what happened today. When I went out on the floor this morning, the line at Johnny's checkout was *three times longer* than any other line! I went ballistic yelling, 'Get more lanes open! Get more people out here,' but the customers said, 'No no! We want to be in Johnny's lane. We want the thought for the day!'"

The manager said one woman approached him and said, "I only used to shop once a week. Now I come here every time I go by because I want the thought for the day!" (Imagine what that does to the bottom line!) He ended by saying, "Who do you think is the most important person in our whole store? Johnny, of course!"

Three months later he called me again. "You and Johnny have transformed our store! Now in the floral department, when they have a broken flower or an unused corsage, they go out on the floor and find an elderly woman or a little girl and pin it on them. One of our meat packers loves Snoopy, so he bought fifty thousand Snoopy stickers, and each time he packages a piece of meat, he puts a Snoopy sticker on it. We are having so much fun, and so are our customers!"

That is spirit in the workplace!

*Wisdom is oft times nearer when
we stoop than when we soar.*

WILLIAM WORDSWORTH

THE AROMA OF CHRISTMAS

BARBARA BAUMGARDNER
FROM *LOOKOUT* MAGAZINE

*S*ometimes I tried to recall the first Christmas. Most of it was a blank. The fragment I could remember included forced laughter, fake smiles, and trying desperately to have a good time.

Christmas had come, right on schedule, only three months after my husband's untimely death. There were no tears or discussion of his absence...only empty festivities. Occasionally I'm glad I don't remember more. "Widow's shock" someone had called it, and they told me I would heal.

Twelve months later that healing was evidenced by the excitement welling up within me as I prepared for a grand and glorious holiday. The kids were coming! Two daughters, a son-in-law and two grandchildren had all agreed to spend Christmas at my home.

I decorated everything I could reach. Glass balls of many colors hung from the leaves of the rubber plant in the entryway and tinsel icicles waved lazily to and fro from branches of the weeping fig tree. Christmas cassettes filled the air with "Joy to the World" and "O Little Town of Bethlehem."

Poinsettias, holly, and mistletoe decorated bedrooms, living room, and over the bathtub. Even the dog diligently guarded the gingerbread boys hanging on the Christmas tree and growled each time the cat walked near.

The aroma of Christmas was the best part because it deliciously replaced the aroma of death that had hung heavily in my home for so long. Spicy snickerdoodles and chewy lemon sugar cookies produced a spirit-lifting, pungent fragrance.

Sticky cinnamon rolls, butter-filled bread twists, and golden brown pumpkin pies found their way out of the busy kitchen of spicy holiday scents and into the freezer to await a celebration of our Savior's birthday and a reunion of family and friends.

The aroma of Christmas was free to soar to the rafters, unhampered this year by an estate to settle, a business to close down, or clothes and tools to dispose of. This year, I could hardly wait to have the family gather for Christmas in my home.

But at 7:00 A.M. three days before Christmas, the first telephone call came. "Mom, I hope you'll understand. The weather here is below zero, and I've been up all night with freezing, breaking water pipes. There's no way I can leave this mobile home to the elements and come for Christmas. Are you going to be OK with that?"

"Of course!" I knew the weather in Portland had been a record-breaking cold, and Jeri's mobile home was old and not well insulated. Jeri was still single, and to go off and leave could cost her so much in storm-damage repairs. "We'll have Christmas later," I told her. "You take care of that home."

The second call came only twenty minutes later. "Mom, with the wind-chill factor, it's forty-five below. We can't leave the sheep and the water pipes to come home for Christmas. Is there any way you can come here?"

"I don't see how I can get away, honey. That's all right. You and Gregg and the kids have a good Christmas and I'll put your packages on the bus to you."

As I hung up, I felt very, very alone. I lived only one hundred thirty-five miles away from this daughter and my only grandchildren, but I couldn't go there for Christmas because I was committed to some people here in town.

I had invited my brother-in-law, who was a widower, and his eighty-four-year-old mother to come for Christmas dinner, and a young man from the singles group at church had already accepted too. *I sure wouldn't have invited them if I had known my family wasn't going to be here.*

And I had told the old man across the street that I would bring him a plate of dinner at two o'clock on Christmas Day. He was a blunt old codger in his eighties. He always smelled like stale cigars and had brown goo running down his chin, matting his unkempt beard. I hadn't wanted to invite him over, so I offered to bring his dinner to him. "Me and Tish" (his dog) "don't need anything," he had told me. But it soothed my conscience to promise him dinner.

And I had invited a single lady friend with an eight-year-old boy to spend Christmas Eve with me and my family. And now my family wouldn't be here.

"Why, Lord?" I protested aloud. "Why can't I be with my family on Christmas? You knew they weren't going to be able to come; why didn't You stop me from becoming committed to all these others?"

The widow next door had come home from the hospital recently, and her family had left to have Christmas out of town because I had promised to check on her, get her mail and feed the dog. *Boy, am I stuck here!*

I would miss seeing my grandchildren open their beautiful packages and hearing their gleeful cries. And my daughter wanted a food dehydrator so badly. "Lord, You know I got her one; why don't I get to see her open the box and hear her squeal? Lord, it's Christmas!"

Unexpectedly, an awesome humility silenced my complaining heart. Without utterance or movement, the Lord began to answer me: "I know it's Christmas, Barbara; it's *My* birthday. What did you get Me?"

"What do You mean, what did I get You, Lord?"

"Whose birthday is it?" He insisted. "What did you get Me?"

It was at that moment that the expensive gifts around the Christmas tree didn't seem to matter anymore.

"What shall I get You, Lord?" There was only silence. "Could I start by inviting *more* folks to Your birthday party? Perhaps I could take care of my neighbor lady a bit more willingly? I could even invite the old guy from across the street to bring his dog and sit down to the dinner table with us."

My heart began to flutter with anticipation. "There's that man from the gospel mission that I fired last summer while he was trimming my trees because I didn't like his attitude." I began to laugh. "Wouldn't it blow his mind if I'd call and invite him to dinner?

"And the checker from the grocery store who shoveled my driveway out the last time it snowed—he's alone now and will probably eat in a restaurant."

My joy soared! *What a menagerie of misplaced mortals; an ingenious assembly of aristocrats and renegades!*

The list began to grow as I telephoned people who would be alone for Christmas. Soon my table was filled, but not as full as my heart.

The old man across the street could hardly talk, he was so choked with emotion when I invited him to come over and join the crowd for dinner.

"Oh, come all ye faithful," I sang at the top of my lungs. "Come, even if you're not faithful! Y'all come!" And I punched down the last of the bread dough.

I do not remember ever having so much fun preparing Christmas dinner as the day I gave my Christmas to Jesus as a birthday gift. The aroma of the holiday filled my home as I'd planned. And the meaning of Christmas penetrated my heart in a way I'd not anticipated.

Never have I received such a precious gift as when I watched the man from the gospel mission fill his plate five times and I sensed the Lord's nod of approval.

"Alone at Christmas? Never! It's Jesus' birthday, and I'm having a party. You want to come?"

Glory in the Morning

It's 5:30 A.M., and Day knocks at the dark doors of Night. I sit on my porch swing under a dark-green umbrella of maple leaves that hover maternally over the porch roof. And I wait for Sun.

A thin wisp of steam hovers expectantly over the coffee cup I hold. The air vibrates with ecstatic birdsong. Cat curls beside me for her final nap before breakfast. Morning-glories prepare to unfurl the blue trumpets. Then it happens, and I am as awestruck as if I had never seen a sunrise.

Curtains of Night draw back silently, and Sun bursts merrily over the blue haze of distant hills, painting earth in green and brown stripes. It is morning…and it is glorious!

I listen, and hear Sun whistle a song of new opportunity. I hear Nature's first day-song waiting to be sung, and am reminded that "this is the day the Lord has made." And I decide to "rejoice and be glad in it."

LINDA ANDERSEN
FROM *SLICES OF LIFE*

A LITTLE GIRL'S DREAM

JANN MITCHELL
FROM *HOME SWEETER HOME*

*T*he promise was a long time keeping. But then, so was the dream. In the early 1950s in a small southern California town, a little girl hefted yet another load of books onto the tiny library's counter.

The girl was a reader. Her parents had books all over their home, but not always the ones she wanted. She would make her weekly trek to the yellow library with the brown trim, the little one-room building where the children's library actually was just a nook. Frequently, she ventured out of that nook in search of heftier fare.

As the white-haired librarian hand-stamped the due dates in the ten-year-old's choices, the little girl looked longingly at *The New Book* prominently displayed on the counter. She marveled again at the wonder of writing a book and having it honored like that, right there for the world to see.

That particular day, she confessed her goal.

"When I grow up," she said, "I'm going to be a writer. I'm going to write books."

The librarian looked up from her stamping and smiled, not with the condescension so many children receive, but with encouragement.

"When you do write that book," she replied, "bring it into our library and we'll put it on display, right here on the counter."

The little girl promised she would.

As she grew, so did her dream. She got her first job in ninth grade, writing brief personality profiles, which earned her $1.50 each from the local newspaper. The money paled in comparison with the magic of seeing her words on paper.

A book was a long way off.

She edited her high school newspaper, married, and started a family, but the itch to write burned deep. She got a part-time job covering school news at a weekly newspaper. It kept her brain busy as she balanced babies.

But no book.

She went to work full time for a major daily. Even tried her hand at magazines.

Still no book.

Finally, she believed she had something to say and started a book. She sent it off to two publishers and was rejected. She put it away, sadly. Several years later, the old dream increased in persistence. She got an agent and wrote another book. She pulled the other out of hiding, and soon both were sold.

But the world of book publishing moves slower than that of daily newspaper, and she waited two long years. The day the box arrived on her doorstep with its free author's copies, she ripped it open. Then she cried. She waited so long to hold her dream in her hands. Then she remembered that librarian's invitation, and her promise.

Of course, that particular librarian had died long ago, and the little library had been razed to make way for a larger incarnation.

The woman called and got the name of the head librarian. She wrote a letter, telling her how much her predecessor's words had meant to the girl. She'd be in town for her thirtieth high school reunion, she wrote, and could she please bring her two books by and give them to the library? It would mean so much to that ten-year-old girl, and seemed a way of honoring all the librarians who had ever encouraged a child.

The librarian called and said, "Come." So she did, clutching a copy of each book.

She found the big new library right across the street from her old high school, just opposite the room where she'd struggled through algebra, mourning the necessity of a subject that writers would surely never use, and nearly on top of the spot where her old house once stood, the neighborhood demolished for a civic center and this looming library.

Inside, the librarian welcomed her warmly. She introduced a reporter from the local newspaper—a descendant of the paper she'd begged a chance to write for long ago.

Then she presented her books to the librarian, who placed them on the counter with a sign of explanation. Tears rolled down the woman's cheeks.

Then she hugged the librarian and left, pausing for a picture outside, which proved that dreams can come true and promises can be kept. Even if it takes thirty-eight years. The ten-year-old girl and the writer she'd become posed by the library sign, right next to the reader-board, which said:

WELCOME BACK, JANN MITCHELL.

One can never consent to creep
when one feels an impulse to soar.

HELEN KELLER

YOU DON'T BRING ME FLOWERS ANYMORE

AUTHOR UNKNOWN
FROM *MORE OF BITS AND PIECES*

The elderly caretaker of a peaceful, lonely cemetery received a check every month from a woman, an invalid in a hospital in a nearby city. The check was to buy fresh flowers for the grave of her son, who had been killed in an automobile accident a couple of years before.

One day a car drove into the cemetery and stopped in front of the caretaker's ivy-covered administration building. A man was driving the car. In the back seat sat an elderly lady, pale as death, her eyes half-closed.

"The lady is too ill to walk," the driver told the caretaker. "Would you mind coming with us to her son's grave—she has a favor to ask of you. You see, she is dying, and she has asked me, as an old family friend, to bring her out here for one last look at her son's grave."

"Is this Mrs. Wilson?" the caretaker asked.

The man nodded.

"Yes, I know who she is. She's the one who has been sending a check every month to put flowers on her son's grave." The caretaker followed the man to the car and got in beside the woman. She was frail and obviously near death. But there was something else about her face, the caretaker noted—the eyes dark and sullen, hiding some deep, long-lasting hurt.

"I am Mrs. Wilson," she whispered. "Every month for the past two years—"

"Yes, I know. I have attended to it, just as you asked."

"I have come here today," she went on, "because the doctors tell me I have only a few weeks left. I shall not be sorry to go. There is nothing left to live for. But before I die, I wanted to come here for one last look and to make arrangements with you to keep on placing flowers on my son's grave."

She seemed exhausted—the effort to speak sapping her strength. The car made its way down a narrow, gravel road to the grave. When they reached the grave, the woman, with what appeared to be great effort, raised herself slightly and gazed out the window at her son's tombstone. There was no sound during the moments that followed—only the chirping of the birds in the tall, old trees scattered among the graves.

Finally, the caretaker spoke. "You know, Ma'am, I was always sorry you kept sending the money for the flowers."

The woman seemed at first not to hear. Then slowly she turned toward him. "Sorry?" she whispered. "Do you realize what you are saying—my son..."

"Yes, I know," he said gently. "But, you see, I belong to a church group that every week visits hospitals, asylums, prisons. There are live people in those places who need cheering up, and most of them love flowers—they can see them and smell them. That grave—" he said, "over there—there's no one living, no one to see and smell the beauty of the flowers..." he looked away, his voice trailing off.

The woman did not answer, but just kept staring at the grave of her son. After what seemed like hours, she lifted her hand and the man drove them back to the caretaker's building. He got out and without a word they drove off. *I've offended her,* he thought. *I shouldn't have said what I did.*

Some months later, however, he was astonished to have another visit from the woman. This time there was no driver. She was driving the car herself! The caretaker could hardly believe his eyes.

"You were right," she told him, "about the flowers. That's why there have been no more checks. After I got back to the hospital, I couldn't get your words out of my mind. So I started buying flowers for the others in the hospital who didn't have any. It gave me such a feeling of joy to see how much they enjoyed them—and from a total stranger. It made them happy, but more than that, it made *me* happy.

"The doctors don't know," she went on, "what is suddenly making me well, but I do!"

I'm not afraid of storms,
for I'm learning how to sail my ship.

LOUISA MAY ALCOTT

THE CELLIST
OF SARAJEVO

PAUL SULLIVAN
FROM *HOPE* MAGAZINE

s a pianist, I was invited to perform with cellist Eugene Friesen at the International Cello Festival in Manchester, England. Every two years a group of the world's greatest cellists and others devoted to that unassuming instrument—bow makers, collectors, historians—gather for a week of workshops, master classes, seminars, recitals and parties. Each evening the six hundred or so participants assemble for a concert.

The opening-night performance at the Royal Northern College of Music consisted of works for unaccompanied cello. There on the stage in the magnificent concert hall was a solitary chair. No piano, no music stand, no conductor's podium. This was to be cello music in its purest, most intense form. The atmosphere was supercharged with anticipation and concentration.

The world-famous cellist Yo-Yo Ma was one of the performers that April night in 1994, and there was a moving story behind the musical composition he would play:

On May 27, 1992, in Sarajevo, one of the few bakeries that still had a supply of flour was making and distributing bread to the starving, war-shattered people. At 4:00 P.M. a long line stretched into the street. Suddenly,

THE BABY BLANKET

WINONA SMITH

It was a spring Saturday, and though many activities clamored for my attention, I had chosen this time to sit and crochet, an activity I enjoyed but had once thought impossible.

Most of the time I don't mind being a "lefty"—I'm quite proud of it, actually. But I admit, it did cause me a few problems three years ago, when I wanted to help out with a project at church.

We were invited to crochet baby blankets, which would be donated to a local Crisis Pregnancy Center at Christmas. I wanted to participate but I knew nothing about how to crochet, and my left-handedness didn't help. I had trouble "thinking backwards."

I suppose where there is a will, there is a way, because a few of the ladies got together and taught me one stitch. That's all I needed. I learned that granny stitch, and before long I had a blanket made. I was so proud of my little accomplishment and it seemed, inexplicably, so important, that I made quite a few more that same year. I even included in each blanket, as a note of encouragement, a poem I had written that read:

Little girls are sweet in their ruffles all pink.
Little boys in overalls look divine.

But no matter which one that the Lord gives to you,
A better "Mom" he never could find.

All of a sudden, my thoughts were interrupted by the ringing of my telephone. I hurried to answer it, and to my surprise and delight, on the other end of the line was Karen Sharp, who had been one of my very best friends ever since elementary school. Karen, her husband, Jim, and their daughter, Kim, had moved away a few years ago. She was calling to say that she was in town for a couple of days and would like to come by. I was thrilled to hear her voice.

At last the doorbell rang. As I flung open the door, we both screamed, as if back in junior high. We hugged each other. Then questions began to fly. Finally, I guided Karen into the kitchen, where I poured a cool glass of tea for both of us and the conversation slowed.

To my delight, Karen seemed to be calm, rested and, most of all, self-assured, which were a few qualities that she had seemed to lose during the last few months before they moved away. I wondered what had caused the positive change.

As we talked and reminisced, Karen began to explain to me the true reasons for her family's move a few years ago. The original reason they had given me was that Jim had a job offer in another city, which they could not afford to pass up. Even though it was Kim's senior year in high school, they still felt it necessary to make the move. Apparently, that had not been the biggest reason.

Karen reached into her purse and pulled out a photograph. When she handed it to me, I saw it was a beautiful little girl—maybe about two or three years old.

"This is my granddaughter, Kayla," Karen said.

I couldn't believe my ears. "You're a *grandmother?*" I asked. "I don't understand."

"You see," Karen went on, "Kim was a few months pregnant when we moved away. We had just found out, and Kim was having a really rough time dealing with it—she even talked about suicide. We were frantic. So we decided to move away, hoping that she would adjust more easily.

When we finally settled in our new home, we hoped that Kim's outlook would begin to improve, but she became more and more depressed. No matter what we said, she felt worthless and like a failure. Then we found a woman named Mrs. Barber, a wonderful pregnancy counselor. She got Kim through some very tough times.

"As the time for delivery came closer, Kim still had not entirely made up her mind about whether to keep the baby or not. Her father and I prayed that she would. We felt prepared to give the baby a loving home— it was, after all, our first grandchild!

"Finally, the day came, and Kim had a six-pound, six-ounce baby girl. Mrs. Barber came to visit her in the hospital. She hugged Kim and told her how proud she was of her. Then she gave Kim a pastel-colored package containing a hand-crocheted baby blanket inside."

At this point, I felt a huge lump come into my throat, and I felt rather limp all over, but I tried not to show my feelings and kept listening to Karen's story.

Karen must have noticed the look on my face. She asked if I was all right. I assured her I was fine and asked her to please continue.

"As I said," she went on, "there was a baby blanket and a little personal note, something about little girls and their ruffles, little boys and their overalls, and a word of encouragement about becoming a new mom.

"We asked who made the blanket, and Mrs. Barber explained that some of the pregnancy centers have people who donate these blankets to new mothers and their babies. Her center was given the surplus from one of the other centers in the state, and she was glad to have one for Kim.

"Kim was so moved by the fact that a total stranger had thought enough to put this much time and effort into a blanket for her baby. She said it made her feel warm all over. She later told her dad and me that the little poem gave her a boost of confidence and helped her to make up her mind to keep little Kayla."

Karen's story had an even happier ending: A year later, Kim was married to a young man who loves both her and Kayla with all his heart. Karen grinned as she told me, then sobered. "My only regret is that I did not feel close enough to our friends here to have been able to lean on you all for support and comfort, instead of turning away.

"We are so thankful for so many things—especially the way everything turned out; but I think the one thing that we are the most thankful for is that kind person who made that little baby blanket for our daughter and her baby. I just wish I could give her a big hug and tell her how much she is loved and appreciated by our family."

I looked again at the photo of the sweet child in my hands. Then I leaned over to Karen and gave her a big hug.

*Not a sigh is breathed, no pain felt,
not a grief pierces the soul,
but the throb vibrates to the Father's heart.*
AUTHOR UNKNOWN

Family

TRIBUTE

My father never talked to me about how to treat people.
Every act of kindness I have ever shown another person
was because I was trying to imitate him.

PAMELA MCGREW

THE NIGHT THE STARS FELL

ARTHUR GORDON

FROM *A TOUCH OF WONDER*

One summer night in a seaside cottage, a small boy felt himself lifted from bed. Dazed with sleep, he heard his mother murmur about the lateness of the hour, heard his father laugh. Then he was borne in his father's arms, with the swiftness of a dream, down the porch steps, out onto the beach.

Overhead the sky blazed with stars. "Watch!" his father said. And incredibly, as he spoke, one of the stars moved. In a streak of golden fire, it flashed across the astonished heavens. And before the wonder of this could fade, another star leaped from its place, and then another, plunging toward the restless sea. "What is it?" the child whispered. "Shooting stars," his father said. "They come every year on certain nights in August. I thought you'd like to see the show."

That was all: just an unexpected glimpse of something haunting and mysterious and beautiful. But, back in bed, the child stared for a long time into the dark, rapt with the knowledge that all around the quiet house the night was full of the silent music of the falling stars.

Decades have passed, but I remember that night still, because I was the fortunate seven-year-old whose father believed that a new experience was more important for a small boy than an unbroken night's sleep. No doubt in my childhood I had the usual quota of playthings, but these are forgotten now. What I remember is the night the stars fell…

*Children will not remember you
for the material things you provided
but for the feeling that you cherished them.*

RICHARD I. EVANS

THE JEWELRY BOX

FAITH ANDREWS BEDFORD
FROM *COUNTRY LIVING* MAGAZINE

onight is our anniversary and my husband is taking me out. I look through my closet and pick out a deep green velvet dress with long sleeves and a high neck. It looks wonderful with my mother's seed pearl necklace and my grandmother's tiny pearl earrings.

As I sit at my dressing table, my daughter, Eleanor, perches beside. She loves to watch me get dressed for special occasions. "Mama," she addresses my reflection in the mirror, "may I pick out your jewelry?"

"Of course," I reply.

She opens the drawer where I keep my jewelry box and begins to sift through the contents. There are the macaroni necklaces she made me in kindergarten and the locket my husband gave me when we were engaged. In a little box Eleanor finds my old Girl Scout pin and some badges.

She holds several pairs of earrings up to her small ears, then discards them. She tries on several necklaces, and shakes her head. At last, with a little cry of delight, she pounces on a pair of long, dangly earrings from Ceylon. They are set with flashing mirrors, obviously left over from the seventies. I wore them with bell-bottoms and tunics. In another box she finds two long ropes of beads from the same era.

She drapes the beads around my neck and hands me the earrings. I put them on and give my head a little shake. The earrings glitter brightly. "Perfect!" She sighs with pleasure. We grin at each other in the mirror.

As Eleanor twirls out of the room to tell her father that I am almost ready, I remember how, when I was Eleanor's age, I used to watch, entranced, as my own Mother prepared for an evening out.

While she pinned up her French twist, I would ask her to tell me where each piece had come from.

In a velvet case lay a beautiful garnet necklace and matching earrings. Mother told me that they belonged to her grandmother who wore them to Boston, where she had seen the famous Sarah Bernhardt perform.

The seed pearl necklace had been given to Mother by her godmother as a wedding present. Like me, she always wore it with the tiny pearl earrings her grandmother left her. Now I have inherited both.

My favorite things in the drawer were the gifts my Father had given her. In a velvet box was a necklace of rhinestones that glittered with the brilliance of real diamonds. Mother told me they were not diamonds at all, but I thought she still looked like a princess.

When Father went on a business trip to Arizona, he brought Mother back a ring with a big square piece of turquoise. It just fit her ring finger; it was too big for my thumb.

For her fortieth birthday, he presented her with some earrings from India. The black enamel had been cut away to reveal silver figures of dancing women bent into impossible positions. My sisters and I tried to imitate them. We couldn't.

The Christmas I was ten I had saved up enough money to buy Mother some earrings at the five and dime: two red plastic bells hung from tiny bows. The edges had been sprinkled with silver glitter. Mother wore them all Christmas day. She shook her head frequently to show us how they actually made a tinkling sound.

A few days later, I came into her room just in time to help zip up her black and white taffeta evening dress.

"Will you pick out some earrings for me, dear?" she asked.

Opening her drawer I sorted through the options. Her dress was pretty,

I thought, but it needed a bit of color. I proudly pulled out the little red plastic bells.

"Just the thing." She said, putting them on. I looked at her and thought no one ever was more beautiful.

My husband's voice pulls me back to the present. "Ready?" he asks.

"Almost," I reply, putting Mother's pearls and Grandmother's earrings back into my jewelry box.

As I come down the stairs, my beads swinging and the brass earrings flashing in the light, I look down and see Eleanor's proud face. "You look beautiful," she sighs.

"Only with your help," I reply as I kiss her good night. She will be asleep by the time I return.

The mother's heart is the child's schoolroom.

HENRY WARD BEECHER

THROUGH A
FATHER'S EYES

LONNI COLLINS PRATT
FROM *MOODY* MAGAZINE

I saw the car just before it hit me. I seemed to float. Then darkness smashed my senses.

I came to in an ambulance. Opening my eyes, I could see only shreds of light through my bandaged, swollen eyelids. I didn't know it then, but small particles of gravel and dirt were embedded in my freckled sixteen-year-old face. As I tried to touch it, someone tenderly pressed my arm down and whispered. "Lie still."

A wailing siren trailed distantly somewhere, and I slipped into unconsciousness. My last thoughts were a desperate prayer: "Dear God, not my face, please...."

Like many teenage girls, I found much of my identity in my appearance. Adolescence revolved around my outside image. Being pretty meant I had lots of dates and a wide circle of friends.

My father doted on me. He had four sons, but only one daughter. I remember one Sunday in particular. As we got out of the car at church, my brothers—a scruffy threesome in corduroy and cowlicks—ran ahead. Mom had stayed home with the sick baby.

I was gathering my small purse, church school papers, and Bible. Dad opened the door. I looked up at him, convinced in my seven-year-old heart that he was more handsome and smelled better than any daddy anywhere.

He extended his hand to me with a twinkle in his eye and said, "A hand, my lady?" Then he swept me up into his arms and told me how pretty I was. "No father has ever loved a little girl more than I love you," he said.

In my child's heart, which didn't really understand a father's love, I thought it was my pretty dress and face he loved.

A few weeks before the accident, I had won first place in a local pageant, making me the festival queen. Dad didn't say much. He just stood beside me with his arm over my shoulders, beaming with pride. Once more, I was his pretty little girl, and I basked in the warmth of his love and acceptance.

About this same time, I made a personal commitment to Christ. In the midst of student council, honor society, pageants and parades, I was beginning a relationship with God.

In the hours immediately after my accident, I drifted in and out of consciousness. Whenever my mind cleared even slightly, I wondered about my face. I was bleeding internally and had a severe concussion, but it never occurred to me that my concern with appearance was disproportionate.

The next morning, although I couldn't open my eyes more than a slit, I asked the nurse for a mirror. "You just concern yourself with getting well, young lady," she said, not looking at my face as she took my blood pressure.

Her refusal to give me a mirror only fueled irrational determination. If she wouldn't give me a mirror, I reasoned, it must be worse than I imagined. My face felt tight and itchy. It burned sometimes and ached other times. I didn't touch it, though, because my doctor told me that might cause infection.

My parents also battled to keep mirrors away. As my body healed internally and strength returned, I became increasingly difficult.

At one point, for the fourth time in less than an hour, I pleaded for a mirror. Five days had passed since the accident.

Angry and beaten down, Dad snapped, "Don't ask again! I said no and that's it!"

I wish I could offer an excuse for what I said. I propped myself on my elbows, and through lips that could barely move, hissed, "You don't love me. Now that I'm not pretty anymore, you just don't love me!"

Dad looked as if someone had knocked the life out of him. He slumped into a chair and put his head in his hands. My mother walked over and put her hand on his shoulder as he tried to control his tears. I collapsed against the pillows.

I didn't ask my parents for a mirror again. Instead, I waited until someone from housekeeping was straightening my room the next morning.

My curtain was drawn as if I were taking a sponge bath. "Could you get me a mirror, please?" I asked. "I must have mislaid mine." After a little searching, she found one and discreetly handed it to me around the curtain.

Nothing could have prepared me for what I saw. An image that resembled a giant scraped knee, oozing and bright pink, looked out at me. My eyes and lips were crusted and swollen. Hardly a patch of skin, ear to ear, had escaped the trauma.

My father arrived a little later with magazines and homework tucked under his arm. He found me staring into the mirror. Prying my fingers one by one from the mirror, he said, "It isn't important. This doesn't change anything that matters. No one will love you less."

Finally he pulled the mirror away and tossed it into a chair. He sat on the edge of my bed, took me in his arms, and held me for a long time.

"I know what you think," he said.

"You couldn't," I mumbled, turning away and staring out the window.

"You're wrong," he said, ignoring my self-pity.

"This will not change anything," he repeated. He put his hand on my arm, running it over an IV line. "The people who love you have seen you at your worst, you know."

"Right. Seen me with rollers or with cold cream, not with my face ripped off!"

"Let's talk about me then," he said. "I love you. Nothing will ever change that because it's you I love, not your outside. I've changed your diapers and watched your skin blister with chicken pox. I've wiped up your bloody noses and held your head while you threw up in the toilet. I've loved you when you weren't pretty."

He hesitated. "Yesterday you were ugly—not because of your skin, but because you behaved ugly. But I'm here today, and I'll be here tomorrow. Fathers don't stop loving their children, no matter what life takes. You will be blessed if life only takes your face."

I turned to my father, feeling it was all words, the right words, spoken out of duty—polite lies.

"Look at me then, Daddy," I said. "Look at me and tell me you love me!"

I will never forget what happened next. As he looked into my battered face, his eyes filled with tears. Slowly, he leaned toward me, and with his eyes open, he gently kissed my scabbed, oozing lips.

It was the kiss that tucked me in every night of my young life, the kiss that warmed each morning.

Many years have passed. All that remains of my accident is a tiny indentation just above one eyebrow. But my father's kiss, and what it taught me about love, will never leave my lips.

*The heart of every child beats
to the rhythm of a father's love.*

STEVE CURLEY
FROM *STORIES FOR A DAD'S HEART*

A GOOD HEART
TO LEAN ON

AUGUSTUS J. BULLOCK
FROM *THE WALL STREET JOURNAL*

When I was growing up, I was embarrassed to be seen with my father. He was severely crippled and very short, and when we would walk together, his hand on my arm for balance, people would stare. I would inwardly squirm at the unwanted attention. If he ever noticed or was bothered, he never let on.

It was difficult to coordinate our steps—his halting, mine impatient—and because of that, we didn't say much as we went along. But as we started out, he always said, "You set the pace. I will try to adjust to you."

Our usual walk was to or from the subway, which was how he got to work. He went to work sick, and despite nasty weather. He almost never missed a day, and would make it to the office even if others could not. A matter of pride.

When snow or ice was on the ground, it was impossible for him to walk, even with help. At such times my sisters and I would pull him through the streets of Brooklyn, New York, on a child's sleigh to the subway entrance. Once there, he would cling to the handrail until he reached the lower steps that the warmer tunnel air kept ice-free. In Manhattan the subway station was the basement of his office building, and he would not have to go outside again until we met him in Brooklyn on his way home.

When I think of it now, I marvel at how much courage it must have taken for a grown man to subject himself to such indignity and stress. And at how he did it—without bitterness or complaint.

He never talked about himself as an object of pity, nor did he show any envy of the more fortunate or able. What he looked for in others was a "good heart," and if he found one, the owner was good enough for him.

Now that I am older, I believe that is a proper standard by which to judge people, even though I still don't know precisely what a "good heart" is. But I know the times I don't have one.

Unable to engage in many activities, my father still tried to participate in some way. When a local sandlot baseball team found itself without a manager, he kept it going. He was a knowledgeable baseball fan and often took me to Ebbets Field to see the Brooklyn Dodgers play. He liked to go to dances and parties, where he could have a good time just sitting and watching.

On one memorable occasion, a fight broke out at a beach party, with everyone punching and shoving. He wasn't content to sit and watch, but he couldn't stand unaided on the soft sand. In frustration he began to shout, "I'll fight anyone who will sit down with me! I'll fight anyone who will sit down with me!"

Nobody did. But the next day people kidded him by saying it was the first time any fighter was urged to take a dive even before the bout began.

I now know he participated in some things vicariously through me, his only son. When I played ball (poorly), he "played" too. When I joined the Navy, he "joined" too. And when I came home on leave, he saw to it that I visited his office. Introducing me, he was really saying, "This is my son, but it is also me, and I could have done this, too, if things had been different." Those words were never said aloud.

He has been gone many years now, but I think of him often. I wonder if he sensed my reluctance to be seen with him during our walks. If he did, I am sorry I never told him how sorry I was, how unworthy I was, how I regretted it. I think of him when I complain about trifles, when I am envious of another's good fortune, when I don't have a "good heart."

At such times I put my hand on his arm to regain my balance, and say, "You set the pace. I will try to adjust to you."

Comfort

The best place to be when you are sad
is in Grandma's lap.

AUTHOR UNKNOWN

A MOTHER'S PRAYER

MARGUERITE KELLY
FROM *THE MOTHER'S ALMANAC*

HELP ME give my children the best—not of trappings or toys, but of myself, cherishing them on good days and bad, theirs and mine.

TEACH ME to accept them for who they are, not for what they do; to listen to what they say, if only so they will listen to me; to encourage their goals, not mine; and please, let me laugh with them and be silly.

LET ME give them a home where respect is the cornerstone, integrity the foundation, and there is enough happiness to raise the roof.

MAY I give them courage to be true to themselves; the independence to take care of themselves and the faith to believe in a power much greater than their own.

SEE THAT I discipline my children without demeaning them, demand good manners without forgetting my own and let them know they have limitless love, no matter what they do.

LET ME feed them properly, clothe them adequately and have enough to give them small allowances—not for the work they do but the pleasure they bring—and let me be moderate in all these things, so the joy of getting will help them discover the joy of giving.

SEE THAT their responsibilities are real but not burdensome, that my expectations are high but not overwhelming and that my thanks and praise are thoughtful and given when they're due.

HELP ME teach them that excellence is work's real reward, and not the glory it brings. But when it comes—and it will—let me revel in each honor, however small, without once pretending that it's mine; my children are glories enough.

Above all, let me ground these children so well that I can dare to let them go.

And may they be so blessed.

Most of all the other beautiful things
in life come by twos and threes, by dozens and hundreds.
Plenty of roses, stars, sunsets, rainbows,
brothers and sisters, aunts and cousins,
but only one mother in the whole world.

KATE DOUGLAS WIGGIN

NEW GROUND

MARGARET BECKER
FROM *WITH NEW EYES*

I remember how thick the air felt in my room when I awoke that morning. The month of July in this bedroom was always sticky. For a moment I lay and adjusted to the sounds of the creek, the birds, the cicadas. I thought about how different these sounds were from what I was used to—car horns and the dull whine of rubber on pavement.

At my house in Tennessee, the sounds were of struggle: people rushing from here to there in pursuit of the ever elusive dollar; people hurrying anywhere for a few precious moments of peace. They were sounds of a journey in heated progression.

Here at my parents' retirement home, the sounds were of arrival; of a journey well taken. There were no neighbors shouting to children, no traffic at 8:30 A.M., just the occasional pickup truck on its way to the local store for a paper. I guess that's why the clanking I heard caught my ear. *That's strange,* I thought, glancing at the clock. *It's only nine. What is that?* I listened for a moment. It was a methodical sound whose rhythm I soon recognized. I brushed my curtains aside to see my father.

His reddened face beaded with perspiration, his expression taut with determination, he stood in the middle of the yard pushing a rusty hoe deep into the hard ground. Ten feet around him, in a perfect square, lay dark red, freshly overturned topsoil. It took me a moment to realize what he was doing. The year had been a dry one and the grass, once a carpet of green, now receded into small, disconnected patches of brown stubble. It was not the first time I had seen him turn over topsoil before planting new seed.

He was a diligent worker and I was evidence of it. He had taken a hoe to my life on many occasions, breaking up the fallow ground of my heart, assessing my needs and planting seeds of truth along the way. When I was overwhelmed, he reminded me of my strength. When I was wrong, his correction came swiftly and ended with a hug of assurance: it was forgotten. When I needed his advice, he gave it with respect and caution. He even allowed me a few "weeds" along the way to show me the cost of freedom and the importance of choosing wisely.

As I watched him, my mind slipped back through the years. I remembered curling up in the warmth of his lap where I would hear magnificent stories of kings and princesses from far-off places. I remembered his strong hands playfully whisking me off my feet into his safe embrace. I remembered his inexhaustible patience with my endless questions…the shadow of his body on the dining room table as he checked the answers to my homework…the cool of the evening air fresh on his hand as he lay it on my fevered brow…the gentleness of his step at the yearly father-daughter square dance. I had so many wonderful memories.

As I looked at him that sticky summer morning, it was as if I saw him for the first time: This was my father, an honest man, a kind man, a man who had spent his entire life giving to others.

The tears that brimmed my eyes were a surprise. I wondered what memory had passed my mind and pierced my heart unbeknownst to me. Surely these were all happy memories, nothing to cry over. Nothing that would justify the gnawing in the pit of my stomach.

Looking around my room, my eyes resting on nothing, I searched myself for an answer. Seconds later I looked back out at my father. The warm explosion in my chest felt so unexpected yet so familiar. With stinging clarity the truth revealed itself: How many Saturday mornings had I heard these very same sounds—the dull thud of a shovel, the whir of the lawn mower, the terse clipping of the shears—how many times had I rolled over for another half hour of sleep? How many late Sunday afternoons had I watched my father stiffly lower himself onto the couch, more exhausted from the weekend's chores than he ever was from his normal eight-to-seven workday?

How many times had I told him that I love him? How many times had I assured him that he was an excellent father, generous in the needful things like love and attention—and time? How many opportunities had I let slip by to show him, the way he showed me every day of his life, that I cared?

In that moment I understood the broad scope of love that is the back bone of fatherhood: the constant unnoticeables, the many details that are silently taken care of. I thought about how God, in His fatherly provision, had taken such care in this detail for me—providing this man. Few things have ever made me as thankful as the simple act of breathing did in that moment. I was here, he was here—there was still time.

Hurriedly I slipped out of bed. I put on shorts and sneakers and wiped the tears from my chin. I bowed my head for just a moment. "Thank You, Lord, for the wonderful man You have given me for a father."

I'll never forget the look on his face when I came around the corner with the metal rake in my hand.

"What are you doing up so early, Maggie?" he asked.

"I came out to help you, Dad."

He smiled warmly, with an expression I'd seen only a few times over the years—the kind that hears the unspoken regrets, senses the rawness of the moment, and allows it to pass graciously—the kind that only someone with a parental bond can give. We began to turn over new ground, and with each pull of the ancient rake, I felt a joy and excitement that only comes from reconciling a long overdue debt of love.

THE COSTUME

BILL BUTTERWORTH
FROM *MOODY* MAGAZINE

*P*art of the success that Rhonda and I enjoy in our marriage is in a freedom to explore aspects of life that defy traditional gender roles.

I cook—no big deal.

She fixes leaky faucets—no problem.

I do grocery shopping—so what?

She works well with her table saw, jigsaw, and router—who cares?

This is the stuff that's made our marriage strong.

So I couldn't believe what came from my lips when Jesse came up to me one afternoon last week and said, "Dad, I need a costume for the play I'm in."

"Don't ask me. Go ask your mother."

We both sat there in mild shock.

"Why, Dad?"

"I…I don't know," I stammered. Then I added, "Unless it's because I don't know the first thing about costumes or because I know nothing about sewing or because you've always asked Mama for help with the costumes. Why would you suddenly turn to me for help?"

After a long pause, my son made his reluctant admission. "Mom's not here, and I need it…for tonight."

"Tonight?"

"Yeah…" He forced a laugh. "It kinda snuck up on me."

This is always a toss-up for a parent: Do I lecture him on the peril of procrastination, or do I run to his rescue as the Father of the Year?

After a quick prayer for wisdom, I opted for Father of the Year.

"Okay," I began slowly. "What's the first thing we need to do?"

Jesse just sat there for a second and smiled. It was his nonverbal thank-you for helping him out.

"Well, first we need to go to the thrift store to get an old pair of pants that look like burlap."

"Burlap?"

"Yeah…I'm a woodsman in medieval times."

Why couldn't you be Moses—or Dick Tracy—or Bozo? I pondered. *Bathrobes, overcoats, or even clown suits are readily available.*

"All right. Thrift store here we come."

So we drove down and purchased one fine pair of burlap trousers. While we were driving home, Jesse filled me in on the rest of the duties. "Now we gotta make the pants look real old and tattered—you know, holes and jagged cuts on the bottom."

Once home, Jess collected his shirt, boots and hat while I retrieved the sewing kit from Rhonda's side of the master bedroom closet.

Meeting Jesse in the family room, I pulled out a pair of scissors and began to cut up pants and shirt. While I sliced, Jesse and I talked, laughed, and had a great time. It was highly ironic, this male bonding over a sewing kit.

Fortunately, the costume had to look "trashed," as Jesse put it. This was to be no ordinary woodsman. He also doubled as a pauper.

"Your dad's pretty good at rippin' up stuff," I bragged as Jesse tried on his newly old pants.

"Yeah, Dad—this is perfect!"

So this is how moms feel when they complete one of their many tasks for their kids! I couldn't contain my pride. During a dress rehearsal, I leaned over to one of the moms and said, "I ripped those pants he's wearing!"

She looked at me kindly, yet quizzically. She couldn't know that I had discovered how to be Father of the Year: be like Mom.

THE REDHEAD AND
THE BRUNETTE

JOHN WILLIAM SMITH
FROM *HUGS FOR MOM*

They sat right in front of me on a Southwest flight. Those of you who have flown on Southwest know how close that is—I could smell their perfume. I think they were about the same age and the same build—but all similarity vanished at that point.

The brunette arrived first. She was beautifully, stylishly, immaculately dressed. Everything matched. Her hair was radiant, there were subtle changes of color when she moved her head, and the light shone from any angle with vibrant intensity. Every strand was in place. Her nails were long and manicured, her lipstick and makeup were flawless, and she was breathtakingly beautiful. She carried a very smart-looking, soft-leather briefcase, which must have cost a small fortune, and inside it, she had a powerbook. She was also carrying an exclusive looking shopping bag that had "Macy's" written in large letters on one side.

She had a beautiful smile—a radiant smile that lit up her whole face. She parted her lips slowly, invitingly, and revealed perfect, white, even teeth. It was a deliberate smile—one that she had practiced before the mirror a thousand times. She wore three rings. They weren't the large, gaudy kind, they were the stylish, expensive-looking kind. Two of the rings were on her right hand, and one was on her left. There was no ring on her "ring finger." She placed the shopping bag in an overhead compartment, and sat down in the window seat with her briefcase.

The redhead was carrying a huge diaper bag, a fold-up stroller, and a baby. Her hair was all over her head, not unkempt, but frazzled. Her clothes were modest, they fit loosely on her spare frame, and they had "K-Mart" written all over them. She wore no makeup, and she carried no shopping bag. Her nails were so short that they couldn't be manicured, and she only wore one ring. It was on her "ring finger"—and it wasn't expensive. She smiled at the brunette and asked if she could sit next to her. She had a great smile. It was one of those smiles that just explodes—nobody could ever hope to practice a smile like that. It happened so quickly that you couldn't tell where it started, but before it was over, it had gotten into her eyes, magnified the dimples in her cheeks, wrinkled her nose, lifted her eyebrows, raised her ears, showed the filling in her teeth—and whether you wanted to or not, you found yourself smiling back.

At first, you could tell that the brunette didn't want to be bothered, but the smile did it. She couldn't possibly resist that smile. She smiled back, a little stiffly, and said she would be glad for her to sit next to her. And she said it with so much friendly enthusiasm that I think she surprised herself.

We hadn't seen the baby yet, but as soon as the mother sat down, the baby stuck her head out from under the blanket. She was (I say "she" because she "looked" like a she) about nine months to a year old, I think, and she was the absolute image of her mother—I mean there was no doubt whose baby this was—she even had the same explosive smile.

The redhead was bubbly and excited. I picked up enough of the conversation to know that she had been to see her mother, who had never seen the baby, and she had had a great visit, but she was anxious to get home and see her husband. The brunette was all business. She wasn't unfriendly exactly, but she spoke in clipped, precise tones. She stated her name, her company, her position, the colleges she had attended—told the redhead that her baby was cute—opened her briefcase, took out her powerbook, turned it on, and began scanning some documents in a way that was calculated to let the redhead know that the conversation was over.

But the redhead didn't take the cue.

The redhead was cute, really cute, and she possessed an innate type of enthusiasm and innocence that unsettled the brunette. She chatted easily and naturally about her husband, her house, and her neighbors, and she told the brunette all the plans she had for the baby's room. She was breast-feeding the baby, and it came time to eat. The brunette watched in absolute amazement as the redhead very easily and modestly made arrangements for feeding the baby. While the baby was eating, the mother needed something and asked the brunette if she would mind getting it for her out of the diaper bag. The brunette closed the powerbook, placed it in the leather briefcase, zipped it up, and reached for the diaper bag.

Ten minutes later, the baby was through eating and was ready to play. The mother placed the baby over her shoulder and patted her on the back until she burped. The brunette watched. After the burp, the baby sat on the redhead's lap and cooed, gurgled, grabbed everything in sight, and tried to stuff whatever she grabbed into her mouth. The brunette never took her eyes off of the redhead and the baby.

The baby, smiling at the brunette, was captivated by her dangling, colorful earring and reached for it. The mother grabbed the hand just in time and said, "No! No!" The brunette assured her it was all right, took the earring off, and handed it to the baby—who immediately put it in her mouth. The mother rescued the earring, gently mentioned that it wasn't good to give the baby articles that could be swallowed, and handed the earring back.

"Would you mind if I held her?" I couldn't believe my ears. It was the brunette. ("This ought to be good," I said to myself.)

"My goodness, no. I don't mind at all, but are you sure you want to? She squirms a lot, and she will wrinkle your clothes—and," she added, with a touch of admiration in her voice, "your clothes are so beautiful."

The brunette tentatively held out her hands toward the baby, absolutely convinced, I'm sure, that the baby would reject her. I thought she would too. It was an important moment, a critical moment, and more was riding on it than anybody who was watching could possibly be aware of. The baby looked hesitantly at the extended hands, then looked tentatively at the mother, who smiled reassuringly, then that smile exploded all over the baby's face, and she reached out both of her hands toward the brunette. It was great.

The brunette placed the baby's face right next to hers and held her so tight I thought the baby would cry. She was a little stiff at first, but it didn't take her long to get the hang of it; and before long, she was doing it like an old pro. I couldn't see the brunette's face, but I knew the look of peace and joy that was on it. For the next twenty minutes, this perfectly dressed woman cooed, baby talked, patted, played "patty cake," bounced, and entertained the baby.

After about ten minutes, the baby threw up—I think "spit up" is more accurate. The redhead was horrified and tried to clean it up with a diaper. She apologized all over herself and reached to take the baby back. The brunette—to her credit—was gracious and assured her that she didn't care, and she insisted on keeping the baby.

When the captain announced that we were on our final approach, the redhead took the baby back, and the brunette got out her makeup kit and spent the rest of the time restoring her businesslike, pristine appearance. When we got off the plane, the brunette offered to carry the baby to the baggage claim area, and the redhead said she would be grateful. The redhead put the Macy's shopping bag, the diaper bag, and the leather briefcase in the fold-up stroller, and they chatted on the most intimate terms all the way to baggage claim. I followed closely, determined to see how this was going to play out.

The redhead's husband was waiting for her at baggage claim, and after they had kissed and hugged each other for an inordinately long time, she introduced the brunette, who reluctantly handed the baby to the father. As they waited for their luggage to come, the redhead and her husband stood close together, with their arms around each other—the father holding the baby. Once, the baby reached for the brunette. She started to reach back, but checked herself, and with some effort, deliberately placed her hands at her sides.

The redhead's luggage came first. The husband picked up the bags, and the redhead turned to say goodbye. The brunette and the redhead hugged each other in a genuine, spontaneous display of emotion. Then the brunette picked up the Macy's bag and handed it to the redhead, pleading with her to take it. I couldn't hear all of the conversation, but it was obvious that they were both embarrassed. The brunette won, and the Macy's bag was added to the other luggage. Then the brunette reached out, placed her fingers softly on the cheek of the baby, and whispered some parting affection to her.

Just before they disappeared, she waved goodbye to the baby, whose face was toward her, and the baby made a gesture that might have been interpreted as a farewell wave. When the brunette turned back toward the luggage carousel, there were tears and makeup smudges on both cheeks. She made no attempt to wipe them away. Her luggage came. She got a cart and placed her luggage on it.

She stood a long moment, wiped the tears and smudges with her fingers—making them worse, of course—gathered herself, grabbed the cart handles, and walked determinedly toward the exit.

The redhead, I imagine, went back to her home and the brunette back to her office—both, I feel quite sure—feeling more keenly the value of mothering.

Old Doors

The auction at a quaint old farm
brought many folks that day.
Most items sold for less than half
of what we thought we'd pay.
New owners did not care for old.
So on that day in June,
disinterested, they watched the sale
until the afternoon.
Then as the dusk of evening summoned
farmers to their chores—
the auctioneer began his bid
on beautiful old doors.
The bidding started at a price
below what they appraise.
But every time I gave my bid—
a frail hand would raise.
So back and forth we both would bid
past what I could afford.
Although I wanted those old doors,
I stopped when prices soared.
Then as the sale ended and
I started out to leave,
I met the frail woman with
the doors she did retrieve.
"Why did you pay so much for them?"
Her answer was precise.
"My children's heights are on those doors—
for which there is no price."

CARLA MUIR

AWARD CEREMONY

P. R.

FROM *SONS: A FATHER'S LOVE*

For years I had poked and prodded Gordon, my oldest son, to be a better student, to get higher grades, to get better scores on his exams. I was always a little disappointed in him because he never quite measured up to my standard of excellence. I knew he wasn't stupid, but I wasn't satisfied with his B-average academic performance. It wasn't that I had been such a great student, it's just that I expected better things from him.

When Gordon was a senior in high school, the student body decided to invite parents to an awards assembly so that we could see our kids honored for their various accomplishments. I was rather puzzled by the invitation. Clearly, Gordon was going to be awarded for something, but I couldn't imagine what.

We received a program when we got inside, and I didn't see any possible award that would fit Gordon. I began to feel annoyed. Had they just invited us to fill seats? I would have to sit there and see every straight-A student marching up the aisle, getting applause, while my son sat in the back of the room. Why didn't he try harder? Why was he so mediocre? My attitude grew steadily worse as the ceremony went on.

By the end, I was fuming. But then the principal went to the microphone and made an announcement: "For the first time this year, I am presenting a special award to a young man who has been so exceptional that we could not overlook his accomplishments..."

He called Gordon to the front, and then spent several minutes describing my son's fine character, kindness toward others, trustworthiness, and quiet leadership. "We have never had a student quite like Gordon in our school," he said. "And there may never be another. So we're giving you, Gordon, the first and possibly the last Principal's Cup award for integrity, diligence, and decency. Thank you for what you've brought to our school. No one who has really gotten to know you will ever be quite the same again."

In that moment, I realized that he was talking to me. I had never really gotten to know my son—much less appreciate him for who he was. And I knew that once I did, I—his father—would never be the same again.

*To understand your parents' love
you must raise children yourself.*

CHINESE PROVERB

DADDY HANDS

SUSAN FAHNCKE

I awoke in the night to find my husband, Marty, gently rocking our baby son, Noah. I stood for a moment in the doorway, watching this amazing man with whom I was so blessed to share my life, lovingly stroking Noah's fat pink cheeks in an effort to comfort him. I felt in my heart that something was seriously wrong with Noah. This was one of several nights that Noah had been up, burning with a high fever.

Tears filled my eyes as I watched my beautiful husband move Noah's little cheek up against his own chest, so that Noah could feel the vibrations of his voice. Noah is deaf. Learning to comfort him has brought on a whole new way of thinking for us. We relied on our voices, a soothing lullaby, audio toys, and music to comfort our other children. But with Noah, we need to use touch, his soft blankie, sight, the feel of our voices, and most importantly, the use of sign language to communicate emotions and a sense of comfort to him.

My husband made the sign for "I love you" with his hand and I saw a tear roll down his cheek as he placed Noah's tiny, weak hand on top of his.

We had taken Noah to the doctor more times than I can remember.

It had been a week and a half and Noah's fever remained very high and very dangerous, despite everything the doctor or we had tried. I knew in my soul the way only a mother can know, that Noah was in trouble.

I gently touched my husband's shoulder, and we looked into each other's eyes with the same fear and knowledge that Noah wasn't getting any better. I offered to take over for him, but he shook his head, and once again, I was amazed at this wonderful man who is the father of my children. When many fathers would have gladly handed over the parenting duties for some much needed sleep, my husband stayed stubbornly and resolutely with our child.

When morning finally came, we called the doctor and were told to bring him in again. We already knew that he would probably put Noah in the hospital. So, we made arrangements for the other children, packed bags for all three of us, and tearfully drove to the doctor's office once again. Our hearts filled with dread, we waited in a small room, different from the usual examining room we had become used to. Our doctor finally came in, looked Noah over, and told us the news we expected. Noah had to be admitted to the hospital. Now.

The drive to the hospital in a neighboring town seemed surreal. I couldn't focus on anything, couldn't think, couldn't stop crying. My husband reassured me that he felt in his heart that Noah would be okay. We admitted Noah and were taken to his room right away. It was a torturous night, filled with horrible tests that made my son's tiny little voice echo through the halls as he screamed over and over.

I felt as if I were shattering from the inside out. My husband never wavered in his faith. He comforted me and Noah, and everyone who called to check on Noah. He was a rock.

When the first batch of tests were done, the nurse informed us that a spinal tap would be performed soon. Meningitis was suspected. Marty and I had a prayer together with Noah. Our hands intertwined, we held our son, and the love of my life lifted his voice to the Lord, telling him how grateful we were for this awesome little spirit with whom he had entrusted us. With tears streaming down his face, he humbly asked the Lord to heal our son. My heart filled with comfort and gratitude.

A short time later, the resident doctor came in. He told us that Noah's first results were back, and that he had Influenza A. No spinal tap was needed! Noah would recover and soon be back to his zesty, tornado little self. And Noah was already standing up in the hospital crib, bouncing like he was on a trampoline. My husband's talk with the Lord was already being answered.

Marty and I grinned at each other through our tears, and waited for Noah to be released from the hospital. Finally, in the middle of the night, our own doctor came in and told us that it was fine to take Noah home. We couldn't pack fast enough!

A few days later, I was cooking dinner. Noah was healing, slowly but surely. I felt at peace and knew my husband was the greatest father I could ever want for my children. I peeked around the corner into the living room, and chuckled at the picture I saw. There was my husband, sitting in his "daddy chair," Noah in his lap. They were reading a book, dad taking Noah's teeny hands to help him form the signs for the words in the book. They both looked up and caught me watching them, and my husband and I simultaneously signed "I love you" to each other, then to Noah. And then Noah put his little arm up, trying to shape his chubby hand in his own effort to sign "I love you" to his daddy. I watched with tears in my eyes as my husband carefully helped him form his tiny fingers into the sign with his own gentle hands. Daddy hands.

A MATTER OF PRIDE

Terry L. Pfleghaar
From *HomeLife* magazine

ell, she did it! She accomplished the dream of her life, her three-and-a-half-year-old life. She cut her hair!

Her father and I were sitting in our favorite chairs in the living room having a discussion. It was an intense dialogue, at times bordering on becoming a heated debate. On occasion, I would stare out the window and survey our land, a few acres of beautiful winter radiance, a delight to my eyes. My eyes would then return to my man, and I again would join in the conversation.

A hush permeated the room, and we could hear once again the faint sound that had been intermittently peppering our ears for the past few minutes. What was that sound? I cocked my ear. Oh sure, it was the familiar sound of the bathroom cupboard door clicking shut, the cupboard where I kept the garbage can. I turned back to my husband.

There was that sound again! *Wait a minute!* I thought. *I can understand opening it once or twice to throw in a tissue if she were blowing her nose, but what is she doing?*

"Sweetheart," I called. "What are you doing in there?"

She came out to the living room and stood by my chair, a radiant grin on her face. At first I didn't see why she was so delighted. All I could see was my good pair of hair-cutting scissors clutched in her left hand.

Her eyes lit up as she fingered her dark locks. "Look at my hair, Mama!"

I looked. I lifted my eyebrows. I closed my eyes and took a deep breath. Holding my breath. I looked again. No, my eyes were not deceiving me. She had cut it!

In my shock, I gently turned her around. She had cut the sides up to her ears, with a few spots close-cropped to the head. Consistent with today's styles, she had permitted a swath of long hair to remain intact, waving down the length of her small back.

Her father and I marched her to the bathroom. There it was, layered in the garbage can. A collection of elegant eight-inch fragments of wavy chocolate-colored hair. I covered my horror-stricken face with my hands. The little darling was chattering, so pleased with herself. After all, she had been wanting it cut since she was two years old! Unfortunately, mother was not so pleased. In my pregnant state of hormonally controlled emotions, I ran to my bedroom, threw myself onto the bed, and cried.

Didn't she know what a priceless treasure she had in that hair? Didn't she realize what she had just lost? It was thick, the envy of her little friends, and admired by mine. "Oh, she's so beautiful! You should model her!" complete strangers would exclaim. Yes, I had to agree, the way those luxurious chestnut locks framed her dark eyes and long, dark eyelashes, she was the portrait of loveliness.

I always encouraged her to thank others for the compliments, afraid she would become prideful. Of course, I didn't consider that perhaps I was the one who was prideful! No, I couldn't be! It wasn't *my* hair.

As I lay on my bed feeling sorry for myself, I could hear her excited prattle in the hall. "Do you like my short hair, Daddy? I love it!" Then it dawned on me. She was happy! I was feeling sorry for me, not her! She had become my own living dolly, my personal creation that I had manipulated and used for my secret glory. She had been pleading for a haircut for a year, and cried almost every time I combed her hair. Nevertheless, I had forced her into the mold I had fashioned for her. I had to suck up my pride, and let her be a person with her own ideas and desires. After all, that was the way God made her!

So I dried my tears, and straightened out my rumpled clothes. Pulling my shoulders back, I walked out into the hall. There was my little darling, her shining brown eyes staring up into mine with expectancy.

"Mama, don't you just love my hair? I cut out all the tanglies!"

I smiled and reached down to pick her up. I kissed her pink cheek and fingered the remains of those soft, long locks that had been the source of my pride. "Yes, honey, I love your hair, and I love you!"

Memories

*God gave us memories so that
we might have roses in December.*

AUTHOR UNKNOWN

THEIR BEST

CONNIE LOUNSBURY
FROM *LIFEWISE* MAGAZINE

We still talk about that frigid January morning in 1950 when I was eight years old.

I was brushing my hair, huddled close to the wood stove along with my older brother and three little sisters, trying to keep warm while Mom cooked oatmeal. We heard sounds upstairs like marbles rolling across the floor, so Dad went upstairs to check. Halfway up the stairs he yelled, "The house is on fire!"

We lived way out in the country near Orrock, Minnesota, with no telephone, so the house and most of our belongings burned to the ground before help arrived. Family photographs, Mom's treadle sewing machine and a few other personal belongs were all they could pull from the house while we girls ran to the neighbors.

Dad had been unemployed that winter, and we had neither money nor insurance with which to replace anything we lost in the fire. After we stayed a few days with relatives, Dad borrowed money to rent an old farmhouse nearby. Mom set up housekeeping with furniture, bedding and kitchen utensils relatives and friends donated.

We didn't have much before the fire, but I hadn't felt our poverty before. Now I stood in someone else's too-large dress, in a colorless, bare-windowed house, looking at a paint-spattered table, mismatched chairs, worn towels and a spatula with a broken handle, and I couldn't keep from crying. We had become paupers who didn't deserve better. While we were extremely grateful for everything we were given, it was a difficult, dreary time for us.

Then a neighbor came with a gift. She handed my mother a set of brand-new, beautifully hand-embroidered pillowcases. The sight of the pure white cotton cases, folded to display the bright, hand-stitched pink, lavender and green floral design, almost took my breath away. I could hardly believe she meant for us to keep them. Others had given us what they least wanted themselves, but this neighbor gave us the best she had!

We hadn't lived in that community very long before the fire, and we soon moved away and lost touch with the neighbors. Now, almost fifty years later, I no longer remember who gave us that gift, but I do remember the sense of self-worth it restored to me. *We must be okay for someone to give us such a beautiful and precious handmade gift.*

It is one of my favorite memories and many times it has been the example that directs my own actions. They gave the best they had.

Our todays and yesterdays are the blocks
with which to build tomorrow.

HENRY WADSWORTH LONGFELLOW

A PAIR OF
WORN-OUT SHOES

THELDA BEVENS

his morning it was his shoes. I was rounding up the garbage and sorting the recycle items, carrying them down to the street and looking around the place for any I had missed. Since the garbage can was only half full (another reminder of how much has changed), I wandered into that place where junk abounds—the garage.

The first item I tossed away was the broken snow shovel, then the hammer claw without a handle, then rusty nails in an old torn paper sack, and two small empty boxes tools had once occupied. And then—there they were. His old shoes. Nike sneakers. Once, a long time ago, white—now red with dirt from our undeveloped, unlandscaped yard. Dotted with splashes of dark paint the color of the trim on our old house. Splotched with blue from painting the porches on our new house. Matted with sawdust and mud from building steps and handrails in December to please the county inspector. Filthy, ugly, worn-out shoes that I had asked him to throw away a dozen times, but which he kept and wore and cherished. I think he never threw anything away. He was one of those you-never-know-when-you-might-need-it persons. But now he was gone and he didn't need these shoes and I could throw them away right now. Into the garbage. Poof!

Then I looked at them, and saw the years of work—the painting, the remodeling, the building, the repairing, the digging, the sawing, the installing, the creating. So much of what he was and how he lived, and all the things he could do and loved to do were in those old shoes. And now nobody was in those shoes. And no one, I thought, could ever be in those shoes. He walked in them strong and able and confident. How ironic that these ugly old shoes were still here and he who walked in them was gone.

But—the decision was mine; I could throw them away now—if I wanted to. I *should* throw them away. Nothing was stopping me.

I set them carefully on top of the garbage and shut the lid. I waited. But I could not do it. I lifted them out and held them and loved them and cried for the man who had walked in them.

As I hugged those worthless shoes, I tipped them slightly and a tiny stream of what I thought were pebbles flowed downward from the toe of one shoe. The shoes had little rocks in them, I thought, from past digging and gravel spreading. I looked more closely. No. Not rocks at all, but pine nuts deposited by one of the squirrels in our woods—quite a lot of nuts—enough to last a frugal squirrel several days, perhaps a week.

Well—did I think those shoes worthless? Ha! Dar and the squirrels knew better! The shoes usefulness was never questioned by my husband. And now his view was born out by nature.

I set the shoes back where I had found them. They were much more needed as a safe place to stash a squirrel's winter food than to adorn a smelly garbage dump. And somehow I am less sad, more reassured by this connection with nature. It pleases me, and I know it would please Dar, to know that a beautiful wild gray creature now walks in his beautiful old shoes.

THE RICH FAMILY

EDDIE OGAN
FROM *VIRTUE* MAGAZINE

'll never forget Easter 1946. I was fourteen, my little sister Ocy, twelve, and my older sister Darlene, sixteen. We lived at home with our mother, and the four of us knew what it was to do without many things.

My dad had died five years before, leaving Mom with seven school kids to raise and no money. By 1946 my older sisters were married and my brothers had left home.

A month before Easter, the pastor of our church announced that a special Easter offering would be taken to help a poor family. He asked everyone to save and give sacrificially.

When we got home, we talked about what we could do. We decided to buy fifty pounds of potatoes and live on them for a month. This would allow us to save twenty dollars of our grocery money for the offering.

Then we thought that if we kept our electric lights turned out as much as possible and didn't listen to the radio, we'd save money on that month's electric bill. Darlene got as many house and yard cleaning jobs as possible, and both of us baby-sat for everyone we could. For fifteen cents, we could buy enough cotton loops to make three pot holders to sell for one dollar. We made twenty dollars on pot holders.

That month was one of the best of our lives. Every day we counted the money to see how much we had saved. At night we'd sit in the dark and talk about how the poor family was going to enjoy having the money the church would give them. We had about eighty people in church, so we figured that whatever amount of money we had to give, the offering would surely be twenty times that much. After all, every Sunday the pastor had reminded everyone to save for the sacrificial offering.

The day before Easter, Ocy and I walked to the grocery store and got the manager to give us three crisp twenty-dollar bills and one ten-dollar bill for all our change. We ran all the way home to show Mom and Darlene. We had never had so much money before.

That night we were so excited we could hardly sleep. We didn't care that we wouldn't have new clothes for Easter; we had seventy dollars for the sacrificial offering. We could hardly wait to get to church!

On Sunday morning, rain was pouring down. We didn't own an umbrella, and the church was over a mile from our home, but it didn't seem to matter how wet we got. Darlene had cardboard in her shoes to fill the holes. The cardboard came apart and her feet got wet. But we sat in church proudly. I heard some teenagers talking about the Smith girls having on their old dresses. I looked at them in their new clothes, and I felt so rich.

When the sacrificial offering was taken, we were sitting in the second row from the front. Mom put in the ten-dollar bill, and each of us girls put in twenty dollars. As we walked home after church, we sang all the way. At lunch Mom had a surprise for us. She had bought a dozen eggs, and we had boiled Easter eggs with our fried potatoes!

Late that afternoon the minister drove up in his car. Mom went to the door, talked with him for a moment, and then came back with an envelope in her hand. We asked what it was, but she didn't say a word. She opened the envelope, and out fell a bunch of money. There were three crisp twenty-dollar bills, one ten-dollar bill and seventeen one-dollar bills.

Mom put the money back in the envelope. We didn't talk, we just sat and stared at the floor. We'd gone from feeling like millionaires to feeling like poor white trash.

We kids had had such a happy life that we felt sorry for anyone who didn't have parents like ours and a house full of brothers and sisters and other kids visiting constantly. We thought it was fun to share silverware and see whether we got the fork or the spoon that night. We had two knives, which we passed around to whoever needed them.

I knew we didn't have a lot of things that other people had but I'd never thought we were poor. That Easter Day I found out we were. The minister had brought us the money for the poor family, so we must be poor. I didn't like being poor. I looked at my dress and worn-out shoes and felt so ashamed that I didn't want to go back to church. Everyone there probably already knew we were poor! I thought about school. I was in the ninth grade and at the top of my class of over one hundred students. I wondered if the kids at school knew we were poor. I decided I could quit school since I had finished the eighth grade. That was all the law required at that time.

We sat in silence for a long time. Then it got dark, and we went to bed. All that week, we girls went to school and came home, and no one talked much. Finally on Saturday, Mom asked us what we wanted to do with the money. What did poor people do with money? We didn't know. We'd never known we were poor.

We didn't want to go to church on Sunday, but Mom said we had to. Although it was a sunny day, we didn't talk on the way. Mom started to sing, but no one joined in, and she only sang one verse.

At church we had a missionary speaker. He talked about how churches in Africa made buildings out of sun-dried bricks, but they needed money to buy roofs. He said one hundred dollars would put a roof on a church. The minister said, "Can't we all sacrifice to help these poor people?"

We looked at each other and smiled for the first time in a week. Mom reached in her purse and pulled out the envelope. She passed it to Darlene, Darlene gave it to me, and I handed it to Ocy. Ocy put it in the offering.

When the offering was counted, the minister announced that it was a little over one hundred dollars. The missionary was excited. He hadn't expected such a large offering from our small church. He said, "You must have some rich people in this church."

Suddenly, it struck us! We had given eighty-seven dollars of that "little over one hundred dollars." We were the richest family in the church! Hadn't the missionary said so?

A PERFECT GIFT

AUTHOR UNKNOWN

*I*t's just a small, white envelope stuck among the branches of our Christmas tree. No name, no identification, no inscription. It has peeked through the branches of our tree at this time of the year for the past ten years or so.

It all began because my husband Mike hated Christmas. Oh, not the true meaning of Christmas, but the commercial aspects of it. You know, the overspending, the frantic running around at the last minute to get a tie for Uncle Harry and the dusting powder for Grandma, the gifts given in desperation because you couldn't think of anything else.

Knowing he felt this way, I decided one year to bypass the usual shirts, sweaters, ties, and so forth. I reached for something special just for Mike. The inspiration came in an unusual way.

Our son Kevin, who was twelve that year, was wrestling at the junior level at the school he attended. Shortly before Christmas, there was a non-league match against a team sponsored by an inner city church. The kids were mostly black.

These youngsters, dressed in sneakers so ragged that shoestrings seemed to be the only thing holding them together, presented a sharp contrast to our boys in their spiffy blue and gold uniforms and sparkling new wrestling shoes.

As the match began, I was alarmed to see that the other team was wrestling without headgear, a kind of light helmet designed to protect a wrestler's ears. It was a luxury the ragtag team obviously couldn't afford. Well, we ended up walloping them.

We took every weight class. And as each of their boys got up from the mat, he swaggered around in his tatters with false bravado, a kind of street pride that couldn't acknowledge defeat.

Mike, seated beside me, shook his head sadly. "I wish just one of them could have won," he said. "They have a lot of potential, but losing like this could take the heart right out of them." Mike loved kids—all kids. He understood kids in competitive situations, having coached Little League football, baseball, and lacrosse. That's when the idea for his present came.

That afternoon, I went to a local sporting goods store and bought an assortment of wrestling headgear and shoes and sent them anonymously to the inner city church. On Christmas Eve, I placed the envelope on the tree, the note inside telling Mike what I had done and this was his gift from me.

His smile was the brightest thing about Christmas that year and in succeeding years. For each Christmas, I followed the tradition—one year sending a group of mentally challenged youngsters to a hockey game, another year a check to a pair of elderly brothers whose home had burned to the ground the week before Christmas—on and on...

The envelope became the highlight of our Christmas. It was always the last thing opened on Christmas morning and our children, ignoring their new toys, would stand with wide-eyed anticipation as their dad lifted the envelope from the tree to reveal its contents.

As the children grew, the toys gave way to more practical presents, but the envelope never lost its allure. Still, the story doesn't end there.

You see, we lost Mike last year due to cancer. When Christmas rolled around, I was still so wrapped in grief that I barely got the tree up. Yet Christmas Eve found me placing an envelope on the tree, and in the morning, it was joined by three more. Each of our children, unbeknownst to the others, had placed an envelope on the tree for their dad.

The tradition has grown and someday will expand even further, with our grandchildren standing around the tree with wide-eyed anticipation, watching as their fathers take down their envelopes.

Mike's spirit, like the spirit of Christmas, will always be with us.

You will find as you look back upon your life,
that the moments that stand out are the
moments when you have done things for others.

HENRY DRUMMOND

WHEN STRANGERS PASSED THROUGH

RUTH LEE

FROM *LIVE* MAGAZINE

At the age of seven, not having a mother caused me to spend a lot of time with my friends. Their mothers wore smiles while correcting my manners, and sewed ruffles where ruffles had no need to be.

I heard their words. I knew what they were doing. They were attempting to fill the "no-mother-emptiness" in my life by treating me like one of their own.

"Girls! Girls! Where are you? Come now, hurry along into the house." We knew what the call from someone's mother signaled.

When we were securely inside we were allowed to watch from behind lace curtained windows as the man in raggedy clothes with a burlap sack thrown over his shoulder shuffled his worn-out shoes down the sidewalk.

Steel tracks carried a steady procession of trains through the small Midwestern town where I grew up. While some of the passengers rode plush seats in deep maroon comfort, others hunkered small in corners of empty box cars.

The Depression was drawing to a close, or so the newspapers said, but in our rural community we had little evidence to support the claim and itinerant men continued to knock on doors asking for food in exchange for chores.

After the stranger had passed, we were allowed to go back to our play, but many times playing was no longer on my mind. I would say good-bye and walk towards home.

More often than not, when I reached our home at the edge of town, the man I had watched through the curtains of lace at my friend's house would be sitting with my father on the back doorstep outside our kitchen. On his lap would be a blue willow plate, heaped full of last night's leftovers.

Once, when I had asked in front of the stranger, "How come that old tramp gets to eat off our best dishes?" my father had reprimanded me with his we'll-talk-about-this-later look.

"Child," he'd explained, "most of the men you see come passing through town are just going through hard times. Many of them are family men, trying to earn a dollar to send on, or maybe trying to get home to those they love."

My father didn't have a degree to frame and hang on the wall, but he was a scholar, a student of human nature. He looked at people in a different way than most folk did, always reaching for a reason that might make an individual act in a certain way. And once he'd found what lay inside, he'd take an even closer look to see what that person could become, if given half a chance.

I'm grown up now, and many things have changed. Our government takes care of the handouts and I guess that's just as well. I still see a lot of people who remind me of those mothers who called us in from play, but I don't see many who remind me of my dad.

THE LITTLE APRON

CHARLENE ANN BAUMBICH
FROM *MAMA SAID THERE'D BE DAYS LIKE THIS*

ach of us possess items with no real earthly value, but the minute we see them, memories flood our minds. I have many such items; I keep them in my view. Some comfort me, some make me laugh. They range from rocks to photos.

Recently I lost one of those items: a pocket knife with a green cover, not more than two and a half inches long. Its blade was shaped like a saber, and it was incredibly sharp. The knife belonged to my grandmother, and I loved using it.

I often imagined what Grandma might have sliced, diced, screwed, slit, or stuck with it. George and I used it just before it disappeared. We were on vacation, sliced a beef salami, and then the knife was gone.

Another of my favorite items is a five-inch diameter rock on a pedestal in our living room. Mom fished it out of the bottom of a lake the last time we caught a fish together.

Several months after Mom's death, I went through her belongings. I sifted through her closet, hanger by hanger. Certain events and outings were triggered by familiar dress clothes, and suddenly, there it was: the apron. It's a pinafore type and ties in the back, with one pocket on the right front. It's probably all cotton, but I don't know for sure. Instantly, I was weeping. I could hardly look at it. The pain was too close, instant, and piercing.

Mom loved to entertain, she loved her home, her duties, and her agenda; but most of all, she loved us. She loved doing for us. And she often wore that apron during the doing. The apron seemed to be a beacon flashing reminders that would nevermore be.

The worn apron now hangs on the wall in my office, a silent reminder of time well spent: peeling potatoes; making her specialty pineapple cream pie with meringue; planting pumpkin seeds in her hand-shoveled mounds of rich black earth; running her Electrolux in a complete panic before company arrived; gifting us with country fried chicken, mashed potatoes, corn on the cob (out of the garden, of course), and the best white chicken gravy laced with crunchies from pan drippings that any human ever put to palate.

The apron also elicits memories of her spunk: how she stood up to a shoe salesman who tried to tell her it was our fault her little girl had blisters on her feet; shooting a fox in our basement; driving a delivery truck to Chicago when she was nine months pregnant to help my father's new business stay afloat; becoming a business woman for the first time, after age fifty; and emptying a punch bowl over the head of a blond bombshell who had flirted once too often with my father....

The apron represents hot tea and cold watermelon. Ironing and wash on the line. Popsicles when we were sick, and Sunday evening popcorn and fresh squeezed lemonade when we were well. It reminds me of the scent of Lilies of the Valley, with which mom slathered herself once a year when Coty released its new batch. It conjures up images of Mom holding her first-born grandson close to her breast and weeping.

And laughter. Endless peals of laughter so quick to pour from her bountiful and overflowing joy-filled spirit.

I thank God for this symbol of motherhood. And, like the knife, should the apron disappear on one of *those* days, although I'll be sad, I know I'll never lose the glorious memories given to me from my "no earthly value," but "all that matters" items.

A thing of beauty is a joy forever;
Its loveliness increases;
It can never pass into nothingness.

JOHN KEATS (1795–1821)

THE ETCHING

BARBARA BAUMGARDNER

I was barely eighteen when my future husband took me fishing from the banks of the Williamson River in southern Oregon. We picnicked at Collier Park where he carved my initials deep into the bark of a birch tree. I took a photo for my album.

More than forty years later, I returned to Collier Park, a widow hungry for a hug from the past. The park had been expanded, lawn planted, and modern restrooms installed. Longingly, my eyes searched the numerous carvings chiseled into the bark of the only small grove of white trees on site. I photographed the trees from all sides, hoping one chance shot would show me some remaining record of the leafing out of love in this place.

I found the park host to ask for help. "Would the tree have grown too high for me to identify my initials?"

"Oh, no," he replied. "But by now the injured bark would be healed and the carvings significantly stretched out as the tree grew so they'd be pretty difficult to read."

Undaunted by his discouraging words, I stifled a couple of girlish giggles as my search continued for my very own tree-tattoo. How ridiculous I must have looked pointing my camera at all the silent, jagged scars in the tree trunks.

A poem crept into my mind:

Forty-three years ago, my husband to be
carved my initials upon a tree.
Today I return to find his mark
in a lovely place named Collier Park.

A week later when my roll of film was developed and I compared it with the forty-three year old photo, I knew I had found the etching. It was the only double tree trunk in the small grove of now large birches. I laughed. And then I cried. And I remembered.

I suppose now, a generation later, those who play in the park might wonder about the origin of the etchings or perhaps chastise the person who used a sharp pocketknife to record his love for a young girl. However, for me, the deep scars in the tree trunk are a reminder of the scars in my own heart, put there by the sharp blade of death. And like the small grove of large birches, I too have been marvelously healed and stretched.

*Enjoy the little things
for one day you may look back
and realize they were the big things.*

ROBERT BRAULT

LILACS TO REMEMBER

FAITH ANDREWS BEDFORD
FROM *COUNTRY LIVING* MAGAZINE

*T*he soft spring air is full of the fragrance of the year's first mowing. Neat golden bales dot the meadow, and the fruit trees look as though they've been frosted with vanilla icing. As I stand on my porch and look out across the valley to the mountaintops beyond, I can see that the light green of new leaves has pushed up the slopes and almost reached the peaks. It is time for the first wildflower walk of the season.

My husband and I take our pickup along an old logging trail that winds its way up the mountainside. As we bounce over rocks and displace loose gravel, pale pink mountain laurel branches brush against the windows. The road ends beneath a tangle of wild rhododendron. We lace up our hiking boots and fill our water jugs from a spring that burbles up from beneath a mossy rock.

As we walk, we spot trillium and lady's slippers, false Solomon's seal and dogtooth violets. Sun-warmed pine needles release their pungent fragrance as we maneuver beneath the drooping boughs of the tall trees.

A faint path leads off into a hemlock wood. We have passed it before but never taken it; this time, we decide to explore. Presently, the forest begins to open up and ahead we can see the light of a clearing. In the center rises a stone chimney, a remnant of an abandoned homestead.

I smell the lilacs before I see them. The breeze is suddenly rich and sweet. Beside the chimney we find an old root cellar ringed with periwinkle; blue blossoms pale against shiny green leaves. Next to a broad flat rock, which must have served as a front step, stands a lilac bush, its thick, gnarled branches laden with deep purple spires. I draw some to me. The scent envelops me and, for a moment, I am no longer in a forest clearing but in my grandmother's garden.

Lilacs were her favorite flower; her yard was ringed with them. But it was not until I was nine or ten that I discovered that one of the shrubs was mine. On a soft spring afternoon much like this one, Grandmother and I were gathering flowers for her dining room. As I reached up to clip the white lilac she said, "That's *your* lilac, you know." I turned around in surprise.

She smiled. "Yes, I planted that in your honor the year you were born." I regarded the lovely shrub, which was far taller than I was, and felt very important.

Then Grandmother took my hand and introduced me to all of the other lilacs in her garden. As we stood beneath the largest one she said, "I planted this one the year Jimmy was born." ("Jimmy" was my father. It always startled me to hear anyone call that tall, balding man Jimmy. Mother called him Jim.)

We moved on to a wine-red lilac. "And this one I planted in memory of your grandfather the year he died." Her smile faded for a moment, then she led me toward the front yard. By the gate was a deep-pink lilac just a bit taller than mine.

"This one I planted the year your parents were married," Grandmother said. "It certainly has thrived."

Indeed it had. Several boughs were so heavy with blooms that Grandmother had to prop them up with forked branches pruned from her apple tree.

Behind the flower bed were two small lilacs, one light lavender and one pale pink. "These I planted for your sisters," she said, clipping a sprig from each and placing them in her basket. "The lavender one is Ellen's; it is called 'Minuet.' The little pink one is called 'Moonglow'; I planted it three years ago for Beth."

My little sisters were only six and three, but I couldn't wait to tell them that they had their very own lilacs in Grandmother's garden—lilacs with beautiful names.

As we drew close to the terrace, I saw a small lilac bush with just a few tiny blooms. They were the blue of an evening sky and their scent was exotic, almost spicy. I had not seen the bush before. I looked up at Grandmother.

"That one is called 'Nocturne,'" she said, "and I planted it for myself last fall in honor of my retirement from the library." She laughed and added, "I thought I deserved it."

For years, Grandmother had helped the children of our village find the perfect book. Now she would be able to spend her days doing what she loved best: reading and gardening.

For many years, our lilacs, as I came to regard them, filled both her house and ours with fragrant arrangements. At my wedding, I carried a bouquet that Grandmother had fashioned from my lilac bush.

By the time my first child was born, Grandmother could no longer garden. When I told her of Drew's birth she said, "Plant a lilac for him, won't you, dear?" And I promised that I would.

But it was many years before we had a home of our own. Though I planted lilacs for my children, we kept moving and leaving their lilacs behind. By the time we settled down, my firstborn was in high school. I had forgotten about the lilacs.

Now, surrounded once again by the sweet scent of a lilac in bloom, I remember Grandmother and my promise to her. Drew became a father last month; his new daughter, Carter Elisabeth, has his pale hair and blue eyes. I resolve to plant a lilac in honor of her birth and in memory of her great-great grandmother.

As we turn to walk back, I break off a small branch from the lilac bush and tuck it into my hatband. The earthy dampness beneath my feet mingled with the scent of lilac is like a garden after rain.

When I get back home, I shall take down my gardening books and find just the right lilac for my new granddaughter and my grandmother. Perhaps "Vestale," a white one like the one Grandmother planted for me, or maybe "Primrose," an outstanding pale-yellow lilac just the color of Carter's hair.

It must be perfect, this lilac for a first grandchild. It will grow and flourish and then, some spring when she comes to visit, I will pluck for her a bouquet of sweet-scented blossoms from her very own lilac bush. And she will feel very important.

Life is made up, not of great sacrifices or duties,
but of little things in which smiles and kindnesses,
given habitually are what win and preserve the heart.

SIR HUMPHREY DAVY

MY MOTHER'S GLOVES

SHARRON DEAN McCANN
FROM *VIRTUE* MAGAZINE

hey were probably made from a fabric called lisle. I know they were black, white or navy and smelled like cold cream and face powder. Mom wore them all the time but I liked my Mother's gloves best on Sunday mornings during church. I loved the slippery feel of them squished inside my fist. I pulled them on and pretended I was a lady, tucking in the ends where my stubby fingers didn't fill them out.

But once I grew up, Mother's gloves might have been forgotten had I not as a little girl grumbled about all the good things boys got to do. I always wanted to be one of them.

"Boys get to follow in their father's footsteps," I muttered. "What do girls ever get to do? Probably just follow in their mother's gloves."

I put that thought aside, but the idea came back years later as I watched my own children playing dress-up, pretending to be grown. What had I learned with my little hand tucked in Mother's gloved one?

The tips on Mom's left glove were empty and one gloved finger was hollow halfway down. Long before I was born, when she helped on the hay wagon, her fingertips were cut off in a hayfork accident. To me, they were just her fingers, but she always hated the nubbed ends. She may have worn the gloves to cover her shame. But through them, I learned an awful lot about life.

My first memories were amid Mother's life transitions: She had seen three sons off to war—one never came home—tended an invalid husband, sent her oldest daughter to college, raised a teenage son; and held me, her tag-along baby girl.

When her husband died, she moved us to town, restored old houses—transforming them into homes, then sold them and bought others to fix. She also had a job outside our home, working her way up from a seamstress for a state mental institution to its head housekeeper.

I didn't realize all that I learned from those years until I faced divorce. Crying in the shower one morning, I leaned against the wall with uncontrollable sobs. Thoughts began to tumble out of me. *I can't go on.*

Then: *Yes, I can.* And *How do I know this? Where did I learn how?*

Immediately I knew I'd learned how to survive in hardship by walking, hand in glove, with Mom. We went to church, the market, Grandma's, school events, work parties. And even though Mother had a full-time job, she made time to bake: plump golden loaves of bread, bubbly pies and soft, warm beans filled our kitchen every Saturday. I rarely remember a week that she didn't make extras.

She'd drop these off to the elderly, ill or handicapped. I was taken along to sit quietly listening. The conversations, I've forgotten. But I remember the feather ticks, the sounds of Tigers baseball on the radio, lemonade, cookies, and "how good that was for Mrs. Whoever" and "how little it cost."

Sometime in the summer of 1945 or '46 Mom called me from play to go for a walk and we started around the block with a basketful of food. I thought we were going on a picnic. I badgered Mom with questions: Why were we taking a basket? Who was it for? Where were we going?

At first, she just replied, "To that house down there."

I continued my questions. Finally, she said: "A friend of your brother, Garnett, married a Japanese girl and brought her home to live. No one in town will sell them anything so we are taking them some food." I knew that it was in the war with the Japanese that my brother had been killed.

It took me a lot longer than my Mom to learn forgiveness, but I learned "give-ness" on that short summer walk.

Mom is ninety-two now. Her gloves lay waiting on the table. Until she was eighty-five, she still drove to church in them, the car always filled with "old ladies who can't drive." And she went to feed her oldest brother every day.

Forty-five years ago, I may have doubted the joy in being female, but now I know for sure: A little girl can hardly go wrong if she grows up to follow in her Mother's gloves.

*It is when we forget ourselves
that we do things that will be remembered.*

AUTHOR UNKNOWN

PORCH SWING

BRENDA A. CHRISTENSEN

I was six months pregnant with our first child when we bought our house—our very own home.

It was small, but almost storybook perfect. Its early twentieth-century charm didn't hit me the first time we looked at it, as the heat of August aggravated my all-day morning sickness, and the mosquitoes were on the offensive.

My husband liked it immediately. Somehow we were brought back when the real estate company held an open house. After dragging both our families through it, I changed my mind. Suddenly, I saw the hundreds of flowers surrounding the entire yard, including the flower box that was actually the front wall of the front porch.

There was a giant maple tree which must have witnessed every storm our small city had ever encountered and still managed to hold its own. The enormous windows, though stained with years of tobacco smoke and layers of paint, drew me in further, as did the two window seats I had longed for as a young girl, to sit in and dream and wish, or write in my diary. It would be perfect for my little girl.

But the thing that convinced me this was our new home, was the porch swing. It was all I had wanted as we combed the city for a house: No porch for a swing, no deal.

I had such fond memories of sitting on my grandparent's swing. All this place needed was a white picket fence and we were set.

Our baby girl was born and our house seemed to be coming along— it did need some work done—and we spent much of our time outside when the weather began to warm. Walking around the block, playing chase in the grass, and of course, swinging on the porch occupied much of our day. I can't think of the countless times I rocked her to sleep on that swing, and with my second daughter as well.

We learned our ABCs and other charming songs and rhymes, including some we made up. The swing was frequently sticky from the popsicles melting in our hands on a hot summer evening. We played and swung wildly. We watched the traffic go by or the moon drift through the branches of the maple tree as we rocked softly. I sat on that swing and watched my girls play in the yard, jump in the leaves, or run through the sprinkler and smile in delight. I was in heaven.

From the day we bought our little "doll house" as our realtor referred to it, we were planning to sell it. My husband and I worked so hard to make necessary repairs and update the decorations. After five years and two children, we had outgrown our home. The time came to move out into the country where I had always dreamed of raising my children. All I could do was cry the whole day.

We went back to the house one more time to make one final go-round, one last quick meal in the old place, and one last sit on the swing.

I think the last five years of my life in that house flashed before me, sort of like some people say it does before they near death. I cried so hard I could barely see to leave. We all waved good-bye and drove away with tearstained faces.

It had been over two months and I hadn't driven by, even once, until recently. I really wanted to visit the elderly neighbor lady whom I had befriended.

When I pulled up there was a young woman, about my age when I had my girls, sitting on my porch swing playing with her toddler behind the flowers I had planted earlier this spring. I hollered hello to her as I knocked on the neighbor's door.

I couldn't take my eyes off them. Nor could I hold back the tears that began streaming down my face. My friend wasn't home and I was tempted to go over and introduce myself to the woman but decided not to since I knew I couldn't dry my eyes long enough to so much as say my name.

So I got into my car and pulled away, watching them play on the front porch through my rearview mirror.

I cried in sadness for my loss, and I cried in happiness for their gain. I cried in joy for the fate of my porch swing, making happy memories, as I am sure it did before me, and as I have now seen, it will continue to do without me.

THE BARN

Sharron Dean McCann

My favorite winter place as a child was the barn at twilight. Not our barn but Uncle Ernie's barn. Uncle Ernie and Aunt Audie, and their collie, Mutty, were neighbors who took care of me. Mutty and I romped through our first seven years of life together.

I always knew when it was time to go to the barn because Mutty would come nuzzle me from whatever I was doing. After pushing and pulling me to the door she waited impatiently while I struggled into leggings, boots, coat, hat, and mittens.

It wasn't far from the house to the barn, but between the two was a fence, a big gate, and a dog gate. We always crawled through the dog gate and stayed together until we got to the barn door. Mutty then scooted through another gate into the barnyard and gently moved through the animals using all her instincts to get them inside.

While she did that I ran through the side door into the main barn floor and up onto the hay mow. Uncle Ernie said the animals came in easier if no one was in their way. I didn't mind hiding because I loved to lay in the dusty hay to look, listen, feel, and smell.

My barn was not a fancy milking parlor. It wasn't scrubbed and clean.

It wasn't a proper red barn with high mows reached by big forks and lifts. The center barn roof was just high enough for a team of horses and a wagon full of hay. The sides sloped down low, to just above Uncle Ernie's head. On one side there were two stalls for the horses, Lady and Tony, and four stanchions for the cows, Bess, Elsie, May, and June. The other sloped side was the sheep barn.

I knew everyone was in the barn when I heard the munching begin. Munching and puffing and lowing. They really did low. Uncle Ernie said it couldn't be called mooing or neighing because the sound was too soft and quiet.

As the stanchions clanked shut, Mutty came to the mow to get me. The barn was steaming with a mixture of cold night air and warming bodies. Uncle Ernie was settled down on his little stool encouraging the big Jersey quartet to give him their cream. While he did the milking, I was suppose to get my chores done.

I ran to the buckets he had fixed for me to give to the animals. I never did much with the manger by the cows because I didn't like cow's faces. Besides, they were already chewing and slurping. The clanging of their stanchions and gurgling water cups was part of the music of the barn.

I dumped the buckets into the sheep mangers quickly and quietly. They were so quiet I thought I should be quiet. The manger was long and narrow and crowded with woolly bodies. Gently they nudged their way in and peacefully munched my little offering to them.

I hurried through pans of milk for the cats and Mutty so that I could have lots of time with the horses. I loved them. Grabbing their bucket of oats I climbed up on the manger in front of Lady and Tony. After I dumped the oats in one end I got more hay and shoved it in their faces. They munched and puffed and didn't seem to mind if I wanted to sit on their manger and rub their noses.

When all the mangers were licked clean, the milking was done, and the lights were out, we were ready to head for the house. Uncle Ernie and I stood in the dark silence and savored the moment. It was a delicious time for me: of sound, and sight, and scents.

I grew up and left the barn. I hadn't seen a manger for years when a nurse laid my firstborn son in my arms. He was wrapped in a big sheet that had a tiny hole for his face and bound him like a papoose. I was told not to unwrap him. The big city hospital rules said that wasn't clean or safe for him.

Not clean? The thought shook loose my memories. I remembered a girl named Mary who had laid her firstborn son in a manger. I recalled the mangers in Uncle Ernie's barn. Not white and sterile. If they were ever clean, it was from being scrubbed by the long, thick, rough tongues of Tony, Lady, Bess, Elsie, May, and June. I knew the manger Mary had to use was even rougher than those in my memories.

Not safe? God come to earth as a baby didn't get a blue bassinet in a glass-enclosed nursery, away from the touch, feel, or smell of his mother. He got straw, in a manger, cleaned by animal tongues. Jesus, who came to be the Savior of the world was born in a barn steamy with the warm bodies of animals and filled with the sounds of munching, puffing, and lowing.

I waited until the nurse was gone. Then I unwrapped my firstborn son. I counted his fingers and toes. I held him close to my body and said thank you to that one who long ago slept in a manger, in what is still one of my favorite places, a winter barn.

Life

STEPPING STONES

Dear Lord—
I do not ask to walk smooth paths
Nor bear an easy load.
I pray for strength and fortitude
To climb the rock-strewn road.
Give me such courage that I can scale
The hardest peaks alone,
And transform every stumbling block
Into a stepping-stone.

GAIL BROOK BURKET

A LIGHT IN
THE WINDOW

FAITH ANDREWS BEDFORD
FROM *COUNTRY LIVING* MAGAZINE

oving day was drawing to a close. The van rumbled down the lane leaving us with three hungry children, a frightened cat, and a mountain of boxes to unpack. Our new home seemed vacant and lonely; the nearest neighbor was about a mile down the road. I could see a faint light glimmering through the woods.

Presently I heard the crunch of tires on gravel; a small pickup truck pulled in beside the barn. When I opened the door, I was greeted by a warm smile. Our new neighbor, Marian, had brought us dinner, friendship and advice.

My little red address book, full of all the names and numbers a family needs to function, was of no use in this new place. I peppered Marian with questions. Who was a good vet? Where could I find aged manure for the garden? Was there a good plumber in town?

I learned with dismay that the nearest dentist was thirty miles away. But Marian assured me that the drive was beautiful.

She was right. As we drove down the valley, the hills were ablaze with autumn colors. Sugar maples bordered the old stone walls and yellow willows hung over the stream that meandered alongside the road. In the golden meadows, cows contentedly grazed. We all decided that our favorites were the belted Galloways, whose wide band of white in the middle of their black bodies made one think of Oreo cookies.

By the time we left Dr. Thomasson's office, dusk was beginning to settle. As we passed the edge of town, Drew asked, "Why does each house have a Christmas candle in the window when it isn't even Halloween?"

I remembered that the Syndersville Apple Festival was slated for the coming weekend; we planned to help with the cider pressing. Perhaps this was some sort of tradition, part of the festivities.

That evening, when I called the cat in, she did not come. Kate had been confused ever since the move, meowing forlornly as she wandered through the unfamiliar house. The following morning she was still missing.

Then winter closed in. The children worried about Kate and I tried to reassure them that she had probably found a nice warm barn to stay in for the winter. She was hibernating, I said, like a bear.

Mud season delayed the plowing. Spring chores piled up. Finally, one warm March afternoon as the first daffodils were blooming, the children and I headed back to Syndersville to buy new shoes. Sarah couldn't decide between the red sneakers or the white, and Eleanor took a long time just finding the right pair of party shoes. It was late by the time we left for home. Dusk was beginning to fall.

"Look," said Eleanor as we neared the outskirts of the village, "those houses still have lights in the window."

We saw that four or five houses on the left side of the road and three on the right all had a single candle lit.

I asked Marian if she knew why and she answered, "It's the way it's always been." Then she laughed. "That's a common answer to a lot of questions around here."

The following month, while the children were being seen by Dr. Thomasson, I asked his nurse if she knew the answer to the mystery.

She just shrugged and replied, "That's the way it has always been."

I hid a small smile.

"Excuse me," a voice behind me said. I turned around. An elderly lady in a green print dress motioned to me from a sofa in the waiting room.

"Come sit by me," she said, patting the seat beside her. "I'd be happy to tell you about those candles. I'm Grace Harding and I live in the last house on the left. You know, the little red one?"

"Yes," I said, "I admired your beautiful bank of forsythia on the way into town."

"Forty years ago, when I married Henry and came to Syndersville, the first people to welcome us were the Johnsons, Clem and Anna. They had the farmhouse set back from the road."

I had seen the neat, white frame building set among its barns and outbuildings. It looked sort of like a mother hen surrounded by her chicks.

"They had two sons, Arthur, the elder, a strong helpful boy who took after his father, and James, a quiet sort. He liked to read books. He's a professor over at the state college now." She smiled at Sarah, who was sitting beside me, listening intently. "When we began to have children, their daughter, Mary, used to mind them if we went to the cinema.

"Well, the war came along and Arthur signed up. It nearly tore Anna apart, him being her firstborn and all. But he wouldn't be dissuaded. James stayed home and helped his father run the farm." She sighed. "A lot of the village boys went off to war."

Drawing herself back to her story, she continued, "Arthur wrote home regularly and Anna used to read his letters to all the neighbors. She was very proud of him but worried, nonetheless. Mothers do that."

I nodded in agreement.

"About a year after he'd left, the letters stopped coming. Anna was just frantic. Then a man from the war office came by to tell them that Arthur was missing in action. They didn't know if he had been taken prisoner or..." Her voice trailed off as she looked at Sarah, who was holding my hand tightly.

"That evening, Anna left the porch light on all night. Told Clem that she wouldn't turn it off until Arthur came home. A few days later I noticed that Ella Winter, down the road, had left her light on, too. So had the Moores. At twilight, I turned on a small lamp in my front window. It was the least I could do."

"How long did she have to leave the porch light on?" I asked, half dreading her response.

"Until she died," she answered in a soft voice. "After Arthur had been reported missing, I went to pay a visit. When I turned to go, I noticed a big piece of tape over the switch to the porch light. Anna looked at it. 'No one touches that switch,' she said to me. 'Clem tried to turn it off one morning but I stopped him. Told him I didn't care about the electricity.'"

Mrs. Harding looked at Sarah and continued. "A few years later, those little electric Christmas candles came out and the neighbors and I began burning them in our windows. We left them on for Arthur." She paused and then added, "And for all the others."

"The farmhouse still has its porch light on, doesn't it?" asked Sarah.

"Yes, dear," Mrs. Harding replied. "James lives in his parents' house now. The tape is still over the switch."

"Do you think that Arthur might come back someday?" asked Sarah quietly, her face full of worry.

"He might," Mrs. Harding said quietly.

"But he'd be very old, wouldn't he?" said Sarah.

That evening after supper, I heard noises in the attic and felt the cool draft that always means someone has left the door at the top of the stairs open.

"Who's up there?" I called.

"Just me," Sarah's muffled voice responded.

She came down the stairs with one of our window candles in her hand.

"I know it isn't Christmas yet, but I really want to put this in my window," she said, with a look that was at once hopeful and resolute.

"For Arthur?" I asked.

"Well, sort of," Sarah said. "But mostly for Kate. Maybe she's lost and just needs a light to guide her home."

I could not say no.

After I tucked her in, I stood in the doorway and looked at the candle.

Two weeks later, Kate returned followed by three kittens. Where she'd been, we'll never know. We were just glad to have her back.

"Can we leave the light on?" asked Sarah when we settled Kate into her basket. I nodded. For Arthur. And for all the others.

CREATURE COMFORT

BILL HOLTON
FROM *PETLIFE* MAGAZINE

*I*n his forty-five years as proprietor of Cooke's Funeral Home in Nitro, West Virginia, Fred Cooke has comforted thousands of bereaved parents, children and spouses. But four years ago when his wife died of cancer, Cooke needed comforting himself. His daughter suggested he get a dog, thinking it would help him feel less alone, and Cooke adopted a rambunctious golden retriever pup and named her Abigail.

At the time, Cooke was living in an apartment above the funeral home. "Most days I'd take Abigail downstairs with me and let her play in my office while I worked," he says. But then one day Abigail got out and went looking for new friends to play with.

Cooke discovered Abigail in the chapel, curled at the feet of a woman seated in a chair near her husband's casket. Cooke apologized profusely for the intrusion, and made as if to lead Abigail away.

"Does she have to go?" the grieving widow asked him. "It's such a comfort, having her here."

Soon, Abigail was sneaking out of Cooke's office regularly and heading straight for one of the funeral home's visitation rooms. "She seems to sense who is most distraught, and that's the person she'll go to first," says

Fred. "She'll sit at their feet, perfectly still, and gaze up at them with those compassionate brown eyes of hers, and within minutes they've stopped crying and started stroking her fur."

Off-duty, you won't find a more playful pup than Abigail. She loves to romp and chase sticks and mooch treats from Cooke's dinner plate. "But the moment she steps into that chapel she turns into a completely different dog," says Cooke. "She's quiet and respectful. I think she must have a sixth sense of how to behave."

Abigail's only misstep happened back when she was still a puppy, and even that turned out well. "She ate somebody's carnations," Cooke explains simply.

Cooke rushed out to replace the flowers, but the family wouldn't let him bring them in. "Aunt Mary was a real dog lover," they told him. "You can't imagine how it would have make her smile to see those chewed-up flowers."

A MAILBOX MERCY

NANCY JO SULLIVAN
FROM *MOMENTS OF GRACE*

*I*t was late afternoon, Valentine's Day. I was mad at my mom. Though it had been weeks since the argument, a silly argument, I still found myself brooding.

"Why should I be the one to apologize?" I told myself as I signed my name to a Valentine I had bought out of obligation.

"No 'I love yous' from me," I said as I smacked a stamp on the red envelope.

Moments later, I drove to the post office. Amid the pink shadows of a February sunset, I steered my van into a line of cars waiting at the drop-in mailbox.

Minutes passed. The post office traffic remained at a standstill. Rolling down my van window, I noticed a rusted station wagon at the front of the car line.

Was the car stalled at the mailbox?

Soon, a well dressed woman in a red Cavalier became impatient with the wait. She honked at the station wagon, loudly, holding her horn down in anger.

Startled by the horn, an elderly man hobbled from the rusted sedan. Holding a cane to balance his uneven gait, he shuffled to the mailbox, clutching a stack of red-enveloped Valentines.

"I'm sorry," he called out to the woman, his voice soft and trembling.

In an instant, the woman opened her car door and rushed to the old man's side, throwing her arms around his shoulders.

"I'm sorry," I heard her say.

In the last sunlit rays of the day, the man gently patted her on the back, resting one hand on his cane.

As I watched from my windshield, I realized that these two strangers had given me a fresh perspective on a passage I had long since committed to memory: "If you forgive others, your heavenly father will forgive you."

Suddenly, I realized that I had been wasting my time, harboring unforgiveness in my heart, waiting for my mother's apology.

While honking the "horn" of anger, I had placed all the blame for the argument on my mom, refusing to acknowledge the hurtful words I had spoken to her.

I needed to ask for her forgiveness.

I also needed to offer her the same kind of mercy I had just witnessed at the mailbox: the unconditional mercy of God.

As the old man and the well-dressed woman parted, the line of cars began to move in a steady pace towards the mailbox.

With one hand on the steering wheel, I carefully reopened my mother's card.

Now one car away from the drop box, I quickly rewrote a new Valentine's greeting:

"I'm sorry—I love you, Mom."

Front Porch Swing

Gently swinging. Quietly creaking. Back and forth. Back and forth. Here I sit. Here I listen. Listening to the music of the front porch swing.

The weathered wood all laced with stains speaks clearly. It talks of cold snow, warm hugs, and hot summer nights. It tattles of spilled lemonade, it whispers of tipped tea cups, and shares of precious tears. This is a sacred place. A place where conversation and emotion grace the air. A place where dreams are free to dance. A place where finding oneself is possible.

Gently swinging. Quietly creaking. I keep listening to the music of the front porch swing.

I hear it speak of hands. Many hands. Smooth hands. Wrinkled hands. Muddy hands. Gloved hands. Helping hands. Holding hands. Hands in love. It is here I fold my hands, and it is here I talk to God. He holds my hands, and it is here that He talks to me.

Gently swinging. Quietly creaking. Back and forth. Back and forth. Here I sit. Here I listen. Listening to the music of the front porch swing.

KIM ENGSTROM

LAUGHTER AND LIFE JACKETS

N. C. HAAS

ho is this?" my friend asked, pointing to the snapshot of the little boy looking back from my refrigerator door.

"Oh, he's a child we know," I answered, smiling.

When she had gone, I looked again at the picture and laughed. He was such a captivating little boy, with a brightly impatient look that commanded, *Hurry with that camera! I have adventure to live and treasure to find, giants to capture and pirates to hunt!* Who knew what great heroic plan his imagination had concocted the day that picture was taken! Whatever it was, he was completely prepared to accomplish it in the outrageous outfit he had rigged for himself: a baseball cap, oversized sunglasses, bedroom slippers and—last but not least—a life jacket! How could I help but laugh? His energy bounded from that snapshot as though it were going to vault him right off the refrigerator and into my kitchen!

I could hardly believe he was already three years old, though I remembered his beginnings as though they were yesterday. His father and mother, Scott and Lisa,* were young and unmarried when he was conceived. While Lisa was still making college choices, Scott was already a sophomore thinking ahead to graduate school. Too frightened to share their "secret," they guarded it as long as they could, groping alone for a solution, any way out of their painful predicament.

They knew as soon as their secret was told, they would face the overwhelming reality of crushed dreams and agonizing decisions. They wanted a family, but not this way. They believed children needed the solid foundation of a strong marriage, but didn't know if they could build one together.

They could have ended the pregnancy. Others had. No one would know. It would be so simple to start again as though nothing had changed. But, simple as it seemed, God would know. Whatever the consequences, they chose to give their baby life.

Finally, they braced themselves for what their news might bring. Disappointment and hurt from parents, shock and whispers from church friends—and more paralyzing questions. How would they afford medical care when Lisa had no insurance? How could she raise a child and return to school if she and Scott didn't marry? How would Scott manage the financial responsibilities of pregnancy and parenting?

They moved robotically through the next weeks. Scott left college, unsure if he would ever return. He found work as a waiter, while Lisa trudged from door to door looking for anyone who would hire a young pregnant girl with little experience and no degree.

Their list of options grew more complicated. Should their parents raise the child? Should they consider adoption? Nothing seemed ideal. Meanwhile they continued through their bittersweet moments of pregnancy—the sonogram that showed they had a son, the first sounds of his heartbeat, his first rustling movements.

But, as Lisa grew larger, their deadlines pressed on them with relentless urgency. Staggered by decisions only they could make, they pored over detailed files of hopeful adoptive couples, searching for one to whom they might entrust their child. How could they choose?

Their parents struggled, too, smiling bravely at pictures of other people's grandchildren, stifling tears at baby showers. Worrying first that Scott and Lisa wouldn't marry, then worrying they would. Uncertain how to parent—holding too tight, then forcing themselves to let go. Wondering where they had failed. Always asking God to be present with his love and his will.

Finally one bright summer morning, Scott and Lisa's beautiful son was placed in their arms. Clinging to his soft warmth, they were torn again. But there was no time left; they had to decide. The next days were the most painful of all. While their parents asked God for his perfect will, Scott and Lisa struggled tearfully.

Then, bravely determining what they believed was right for their son, they dressed him, took him to a small church to dedicate him to God, then to the agency to give him to the couple they had chosen to parent him.

The terrible conflict of letting go and holding tight ripped through their hearts. They faced moments of heartache, endless moments of wondering.

Time moved them all back to life's healing routine. All that remained was a chapter of memories and a closet full of ongoing prayers. And occasionally a picture and letter from the agency updating Scott and Lisa.

It was an extra picture they had given me that hung now on my refrigerator and made me laugh each time I saw it. It was much too small to contain this three-year-old package of comical energy bursting with so much busy excitement. He really did look as though, at any moment, he would leap right into my morning, scoop me into his adventure, and dare me to keep up.

Oh, yes, I laughed back at his eager face, how I would love it if you did! I would catch you up in my arms and twirl you around and around—life jacket, baseball cap, sunglasses, and all! We would spin and laugh together—at the giants you had conquered and the pirates you had caught. We would spin, spin, and laugh again—at the fading memory of the pain that birthed you, at the wonder of the world before you. We would laugh until we cried in raucous celebration of your life.

And when we had spun ourselves dizzy, I would put you down, kneel in front of you and tell you this: Right now you can't see, but God has built bigger plans into your heart and promises into your soul than you can ever imagine. Your life is his, and your greatest adventure will be to discover him and go with him to find his plans and purposes for you. They are exciting plans, I promise, full of wonderful hope and purpose. Go and capture them. Go and live them. And don't forget your life jacket—Nathaniel, my first grandchild.

How far you go in life depends on your being tender with the young, compassionate with the aged, sympathetic with the striving, tolerant with the weak and the strong— because someday you will have been all of these.

GEORGE WASHINGTON CARVER

*Names have been changed.

GROWING OLDER

DALE EVANS ROGERS
FROM *TIME OUT, LADIES!*

ord, thou knowest better than I know myself, that I am growing older, and will someday be old.

Keep me from getting talkative, and particularly from the fatal habit of thinking I must say something on every subject and on every occasion.

Release me from the craving to try and straighten out everybody's affairs.

Keep my mind free from the recital of endless details—give me wings to get to the point.

I ask for grace enough to listen to the tales of others' pains. Help me endure them with patience.

But seal my lips on my own aches and pains. They are increasing, and my love of rehearsing them is becoming sweeter as the years go by.

I dare not ask for improved memory, but for a growing humility and a lessening cocksureness when my memory seems to clash with the memories of others.

Teach me the glorious lesson that occasionally I may be mistaken.

Keep me reasonably sweet. I do not want to be a saint—some of them are so hard to live with—but a sour old woman (or man) is one of the crowning works of the devil.

Make me thoughtful, but not moody; helpful, but not bossy.

With my vast store of wisdom, it seems a pity not to use it; but thou knowest, Lord, I want a few friends at the end.

Give me the ability to see good things in unexpected places, and talents in unexpected people. And give me, Lord, the grace to tell them so.

Some people, no matter how old they get,
never lose their beauty—
they merely move it from their faces
into their hearts.

AUTHOR UNKNOWN

THE FAITH OF
A CHILD

DEBORAH HAMMONS
FROM *VIRTUE* MAGAZINE

hen my sister-in-law, Carla, had her brain tumor, I took care of her boys, Bobby and Pete.

For me, twice as many kids not only meant twice as many sweatshirts to wash and socks to sort, but twice as many problems to carry and things to worry about.

I guess I worried most about Bobby. Our oldest son, Jeremy, was self-sufficient and Andrew and Pete played together and shared Andrew's bed at night, but Bobby was left bouncing from person to person for contact and support. I made a sleeping corner for him on Andrew's floor, piling up thick blankets for padding and making an envelope out of a fuzzy quilt. He fit perfectly there.

Everyone thought the boys would have a hard time with their parents' long absence, but after a while anything becomes normal.

Each night, with our shutters closed to the cold, we went through the routine of making sure everyone was clean, teeth were brushed, pajamas on, clothes put away and homework done. Carla or my brother phoned each night to visit with Bobby and Pete. In the middle of a wrestling match, laughing and hollering, they'd be called to the kitchen, and across the distance, through the pin-size holes of the phone's receiver, hear their mother's voice. The questions—What did you do today? How are you feeling?—from faraway Minnesota, were met by small voices.

Boys, who seconds before had been full of life, shrank to the size of a whisper. The pain and loneliness in their voices astonished me. I wanted to grab the phone and say: "No, this isn't the way it is. They're playing and laughing and sleeping through the night. They're eating and reading and we're all just fine." But for those few moments the boys did speak the truth. They were alone, suspended in that half-life of separation.

Carla's daily radiation treatments at the hospital brutalized her body until she spent every waking moment vomiting. She held herself together for those few minutes on the phone with her boys, so they knew she was all right. She told them she was bald now just like Daddy. But Mom would be home, she promised, not soon, but she would be home.

As soon as the phone was hung up, they turned back to our world with a run and a leap, piling on top of each other in physical assault. Like puppies rolling across the floor, they lived each second for itself.

But if every conscious second can be a prayer, our life was a prayer for those three months.

One evening, Bobby announced he had a project due at school. Perched on a stool at the dinner table, he told us of the annual egg drop, a contest where each student invents a way to protect an egg from breaking when it is dropped from an opening in the school's attic.

We all called out ideas as Bobby watched, eyebrows up, eyes wide.

"What do you think?" my husband asked Bobby.

"I think you could fill a milk carton with water and put the egg in that and it wouldn't break."

Our ideas had to do with things we'd seen others try like Styrofoam carved to hold the egg or parachutes attached to cartons filled with popcorn, the egg nestled inside. None of us had thought of water.

Jeremy asked, "What does an egg do in water? Does it sink?"

"Go see," said my husband.

Everyone left their plates and went to the kitchen to drop an egg in water. Everyone except Bobby. He remained at the table.

"I could use rubber bands to hold the egg in the middle of the water," he said.

"You could put salt in the water," Jeremy suggested.

"It's my project. I'm doing it the way I want," Bobby declared from the dining room.

Everyone in the kitchen stopped. My husband said, "You're right."

The boys returned to the table and finished their dinner.

With the help of Jeremy and his Uncle Steve, Bobby somehow rigged an egg suspended between rubber bands surrounded by water inside a cardboard milk carton. That Saturday, Bobby and Steve went out on the balcony in front of the house while the rest of us watched from the patio below. Bobby's grin was huge as he held the heavy carton high in the air. He was sure his idea would work.

"One, two, three," counted Bobby. "Drop off!"

The carton hit the concrete. It split open and water spread from the bottom. Bobby rushed down the stairs and out the door. He looked at the broken carton and the water as he knelt beside his project. Inside, the egg was whole, intact. Bobby lifted it and examined it closely. A string of clear liquid seeped from it.

"One crack," he said.

"Amazing," Steve said, grinning. "I didn't think it would work."

I don't think any of us did. But the results weren't good enough for Bobby. He stuck with his original idea of protecting the egg, but he wanted no damage whatsoever.

"I need a balloon," he said, "one of those balloons you get for your birthday."

"Helium balloons?" I asked.

Bobby nodded.

"But then you won't need the water," said his brother Pete.

"You need it all," said Bobby.

The day of the big egg drop, I took Bobby, his egg, new milk carton, rubber bands and helium balloon to school. He hadn't tried them all together, but he was certain it would work. I stayed to watch.

Bobby's teacher took her class to the lunchroom where a ladder led to the school's attic. One by one, the students climbed the ladder and dropped their eggs from the opening. Some eggs broke, some made it, some cracked. The kids seemed as excited by the failures as the successes.

Bobby's turn finally came. He put his project in the basket rigged to carry it to the attic, then started to climb the ladder. His fingers couldn't reach around the wooden steps. He readjusted his grip and watched his feet. Cautiously, he moved up to the opening. The night before, he'd decorated his milk carton with blue and red stars. At the top, he held it out from him, arms straight and sure, the balloon waving above.

For a second, I couldn't breathe. The strings were crooked. What if it broke? The carton could slip. I wanted it to float gently, slowly to the floor, but for a second all I could imagine was the carton crashing on its side, the egg smashed. With my whole being, I wanted it to work. It had to work, because Bobby believed it would.

He let go. The carton wobbled, then fell swiftly and it was over. The balloon had not made it waft slowly, but the carton landed erect. Bobby rushed down the ladder and ran to pull off the tape sealing the milk carton. He reached in and held up the egg. It was whole. Not one crack. Bobby laughed in triumph, and the class cheered.

That night, after dinner, the dishes, the picking up, the baths, the teeth brushing, hair combing and book reading, the phone rang.

Bobby ran to pick it up. "Hello?" he answered. "Mom? Guess what. My egg didn't break!"

It's been three years now since the doctors found Carla's tumor, its appearance and disappearance equally rare. She drives back to the hospital every six months for a check-up. We pretend it's routine, but breathe more easily once she returns home.

The boys are growing older, our families' lives more separate. I'm busy hauling Andrew and Jeremy to soccer, scouts, Sunday school.

That winter is a dim memory for Pete and Bobby, a time their mom and dad were gone and they slept at their cousins' house. But for me, it remains the winter Bobby showed us the faith of a child. It was the winter we layered around each other so none of us would break.

As the Colorado summer progressed, I would stand in my driveway and whistle; on command, the three handsome young foxes came bounding across the ravine. They stalked butterflies in a patch of wildflowers. They gave futile chase to wily squirrels. They stood on their hind legs and lapped water from our birdbath—once jumping back in alarm when a skim of ice reflected their own images.

In order to keep the deer, elk, and rabbits out of flower gardens, we have connected water hoses to sprinklers activated by motion sensors. Walk in front of the sensor, and water sprays out with a loud, startling noise. (Neighborhood kids love to introduce their unsuspecting friends to this technology.) The first time the foxes wandered in front of the motion sensor, setting off the water, they high-tailed it, literally, all the way back to their den. Soon, though, they were playing games with the sensor, dashing in front of it to see if they could set it off without getting wet.

If I threw a tennis ball, one would chase it down and run, with the other two in hot pursuit. Like some dogs, though, they never learned to relinquish the retrieved object.

The three had very different personalities. We named the bravest Mr. Bold, the most fearful Shy Guy, and the third Black Socks because of his distinctive leg markings. If I put out food, I started with one pile, which Mr. Bold immediately gobbled up, then moved a few feet away and put down another pile, which Mr. Bold dashed over to investigate.

By the time I set out a third pile, Shy Guy would cautiously approach the dregs left in the first pile—until Mr. Bold charged over to chase him away. Poor Shy Guy—his personality kept him in a state of perpetual hunger.

In animals as in humans, cleverness can help one surmount personality obstacles. Shy Guy prevailed after I started putting food in a metal dog dish. Foxes track food with their noses, not their eyes, and the three could not seem to distinguish the food from the dish. They would smell the food and bite the dish, which didn't taste at all like cat food or lamb bones. Plus, the sound of the metal dish scraping across gravel startled them. They would stare at the dish and circle it for half an hour, smelling the food but not knowing how to get it.

Shy Guy, however, mastered the dish, assuring that from then on he got a fair portion, I would put down two piles of food and leave some in the dish. The other two might chase him away, but, unable to solve the mystery of the dish, they ultimately left its contents to a grinning Shy Guy.

All summer I had three constant companions. As I weeded the garden, cut the grass, or read the mail in a hammock, they followed my every move. If I ate lunch on our wooden balcony, they would climb the steps to join me.

Mr. Bold, especially, seemed without fear. On fine summer days I tote my laptop computer outdoors and sit on a lounge chair in the shade. Mr. Bold would observe me for a while, then curl up, his white-tipped tail folded across his eyes, and go to sleep.

At such moments I felt a thrilling flashback to Eden, when the barrier of fear had not yet arisen between the species, and a flash-forward to heaven, when the lion shall lie down with the lamb and the fox shall curl up with the writer.

Naturalist John Muir once sighed, "It is a great comfort...that vast multitudes of creatures, great and small and infinite in number, lived and had a good time in God's love before man was created."

It can still happen, John.

TO GOD
FROM BEN

GLENDA BARBRE
FROM *CHRISTIAN READER* MAGAZINE

o help our five-year-old son with the trauma of his pet goldfish's demise, I agreed he could "send the goldfish back to God" any way he wanted. Expecting him to give the goldfish a proper burial in our flower garden, I was surprised to receive a call from our rural area's postmaster.

"Could you come over?" she asked. "I have something to show you." I headed right over.

"A lot is expected of the post office," she said, laughing, "but this is the most amazing delivery we've ever been asked to make!"

On the outside of a business-sized envelope, printed in big blue capital letters I recognized Ben's printing: TO GOD FROM BEN. Inside the envelope was a very flat, dead goldfish.

CHOIRS OF ANGELS

CHERYL GOCHNAUER

er first Christmas at the nursing home wasn't so bad—she was making new friends. When the school children came to sing carols, she used her cane to carefully maneuver her way to the lunchroom to hear their vivacious, if slightly flat, music.

She loved watching their shining faces, brilliant reminders of youth and energy. In the days to follow, she would replay the scene to herself, humming the tunes as she prepared to celebrate her Lord's birth.

A few years passed, and her nurse wheeled her into the lunchroom to hear the little angels sing. Like so many others at the home, she looked forward to the children's annual visit. For weeks, she had her nurse hand her the calendar so she could painstakingly mark off the days until their arrival. She was not disappointed; the faces were different and the songs were familiarly off-key, but affection poured from the young people's hearts. She soaked it all in, savoring their smiles long after they had left.

Each year, she asked the nurse to push her closer to the choir as their voices became more and more distant. Then came the program where she would not hear them at all, but she still enjoyed reading their lips, their expressive faces forming the words to carols she sang inside her head.

But as time continued to pass, even the children's faces became dim.

Her eyes failed her, and she was lost in a fuzzy world of indistinct sounds and sight. One day, her nurse shouted in her ear—it sounded dim and muffled, but she could just make out an invitation to the children's Christmas program.

Oh, no, she responded. I don't want to go.

I don't want those kids staring at me, she thought. *I can't walk; I can't hear; I can't see. They'll ignore me for the useless old thing I am, just sitting here in a wheelchair. No, I don't want to go.*

Dismayed, she felt herself being wheeled out of her room. She felt like yelling, Take me back! But she remembered the spectacles she had witnessed before her eyes gave out, other old folks like herself making fools of themselves, hollering in the halls. She pulled her shawl around her tighter and helplessly hung her head.

She sensed the expanse of the large lunchroom, felt her wheelchair locked into place. In spite of herself, after a few moments, she began to visualize a choir, a conglomeration of hundreds of children's faces, each singing their songs or carefully playing their instruments.

Sweet voices long stilled filled her head, and she caught a tune in her memory. Softly humming to herself, she smiled as her heart swelled with emotion. Before she could stop it, a tear escaped her sightless eyes. And then, it happened.

A tiny hand slipped into hers and squeezed. With that precious touch, it was as though her Lord Himself had transformed once again into the Christ child. She reached out and swept her fingers gently over the child's face, touching the upturned bow of a smile.

Embracing him, she cried, God bless you! Merry Christmas!

And it was.

TORNADO WARNING

SARAH ELIZABETH FARROW
FROM *VIRTUE* MAGAZINE

*W*hen I set aside my career as an advertising copy-writer to be an at-home mother, I felt I had to justify my decision by becoming the best of all possible mothers. I began to live by the motto on my favorite coffee mug: "God can't be every-where—that's why He created mothers." I never questioned its message until a violent summer storm hit.

It was a particularly sultry afternoon, and all four of my boys were flopped in front of the TV watching a video I'd rented to alleviate their summer boredom. "I have a few errands to run," I said. "Come along, and we'll get some ice cream."

My suggestion brought only groans of protest. "It's too hot, Mom. We want to stay home and finish watching the movie." I thought it over for a moment and decided the oldest, who was twelve, could supervise his brothers for the short time it would take me to go to the bank, the dry cleaners, and the grocery store.

"Chris is in charge. Be good, and I'll bring home ice cream," I said as I headed for the car. Absorbed in the movie, they hardly acknowledged my leaving.

I'd rather veg out this afternoon, too, I thought, scanning the heavy gray sky. *Maybe we'll get a cooling rain by evening.*

Although I rarely left the boys for even a few minutes, I reassured myself they'd be fine and attributed the uneasy feeling in my stomach to the hot and humid weather.

Big spatters of rain had indeed begun to fall while I was at the bank, and the sky was getting darker. Suspecting a thunderstorm might be coming, I decided to skip the dry cleaners and streamline my grocery shopping to get home before the brunt of it hit. I hurried up and down the aisles and was just finishing up when the storm broke. Thunder rumbled and sheets of wind-driven rain slashed against the store windows. While I waited in the checkout line, I began to fret.

At first my worries were more about the household than the children. Would they think to let the dog in? Did they close the windows? Were they still watching the movie oblivious to the storm? My husband and I have a standing joke that a bomb could go off when the TV is on and our kids wouldn't notice. Today, however, I wasn't laughing.

After I paid for my groceries, I tried to make a run for my car. The windswept rain soaked me in seconds and huge hailstones drove me shivering back into the store. While the storm got worse, I paced and chatted with other stranded shoppers to ease my tension.

Air-raid sirens began to wail, signaling this was more than a standard summer storm and that a tornado warning was in effect. I began to worry about the boys in earnest. They didn't even know where I was, and my attempt to call home was thwarted by downed phone lines. *And I always yell at them when they leave without telling me where they're going,* I thought. Were they frightened? Worried about me? Had they thought to switch from VCR to TV to get the news about the tornado warning? *Some mother I am,* I chastised myself.

In the midst of my rising panic, a single line from the psalms popped into my mind: *Be still and know that I am God.* I wasn't even sure which psalm it came from until I had a chance to look it up later (Psalm 46:10), but that line acted on me like a tranquilizer. Somehow deep inside I felt assured the boys and our household would be all right.

When the sirens stopped, I headed for my car. The rain had barely let up. Visibility was poor, the streets were slick, and cars were stalled in deep puddles and drifts of hail; but every time I started to panic, that line would come back into my mind: *Be still and know that I am God.* The main street I normally would have taken home looked like a river, so I headed for higher ground. I had a near miss with another car when its driver failed to see my car, even though I had the headlights on! Finally, I pulled up in front of my house, left the groceries in the car, and ran inside.

Everything was dark and quiet. I was afraid the boys had panicked and left, but where would they have gone? Then I heard the radio in the basement. All four were in the laundry room; the dog and cats were with them. "Wow, Mom!" Chris said. "What a storm!"

"Yeah," the twins chimed in. "We were watching that movie when it got really dark."

The youngest hugged me tight, while Chris continued. "The sky turned a creepy color, and we thought we'd better let Shadow in and start shutting windows. When we switched over to TV and heard there was a tornado warning, we all came down here."

A quick check revealed they'd not only remembered the safest place in the house, but they'd closed all the windows, turned off lights, and even unplugged the computer and the television. *Be still and know that I am God...*

Later, as I mopped up the water that had come through the kitchen window before the children could get it shut, examined my hail-devastated garden, and borrowed a neighbor's phone to report ours out of order, I felt strangely relieved rather than depressed. I'd been cramming my children's heads with instructions and warnings almost from their births. "Stay away from tall trees and water in thunderstorms." "Look both ways before crossing." "Never leave home without telling me where you're going." I'd never really trusted them, however, to follow through on their own. Yet when danger threatened and I was away, they kept their heads and remembered just what to do.

As my boys have grown into young men, the lesson of that storm has stuck with me and helped me to "be still" and know that God is God through many more of life's storms. My job, I learned, is to teach and to be a good example; their job is to learn and to follow through; and God's job is to hold us all in the palm of His hand.

I no longer use the "God can't be everywhere…" mug. I replaced it with one that says, "This is the day the LORD has made; let us rejoice and be glad in it" (Psalm 118:24). Now when I drink my morning coffee I'm reminded to take my focus off me and put it where it belongs—on God the Father! I rejoice that He is God, and that He *can* be everywhere.

SHARING

AUTHOR UNKNOWN
FROM *YOU GOTTA KEEP DANCING*

There isn't much that I can do, but I can share my bread with you, and sometimes share a sorrow, too—

There isn't much that I can do, but I can sit an hour with you, and I can share a joke with you, and sometimes share reverses, too—

There isn't much that I can do, but I can share my flowers with you, and I can share my books with you and sometimes share your burdens, too—

There isn't much that I can do, but I can share my songs with you, and I can share my mirth with you, and sometimes come and laugh with you—

There isn't much that I can do, but I can share my hopes with you, and I can share my fears with you, and sometimes shed some tears with you—

There isn't much that I can do, but I can share my friends with you, and I can share my life with you, and oftentimes share a prayer with you.

Faith

TRUSTING GOD

When I doubt His love, I hold to His wisdom.
When I can't understand His justice, I cling to His mercies.
When I wonder about His faithfulness, I cherish His grace.
When I fear His sovereignty, I bow to His holiness.
And in that my heart can rest.

VERDELL DAVIS
FROM *LET ME GRIEVE, BUT NOT FOREVER*

HEAVEN'S GOLD

RHONDA REESE
FROM *CHRISTIAN READER* MAGAZINE

I could barely get my request out. "Lord," I asked one December afternoon two years ago as loneliness and worry knocked me breathless again, "please show me something special I can do to help Mom."

Dad was gone. When he died one month before the holidays, I felt so drained that I considered skipping Christmas. But my grieving, depressed mother needed support. She and Dad were four days shy of celebrating their fifty-fifth wedding anniversary when cancer snatched my father away.

A week passed. Then one afternoon while I listened to a talk radio program about money, the show's host read a fax sent to him by a disgruntled shopper. Seems this tired consumer spent an afternoon tromping through stores, growing more exhausted with every step. She resented the pressure of purchasing gifts for mere acquaintances.

"I stayed in that mall for hours," the woman said. "My head pounded. My feet hurt. My stomach swirled. I developed a rotten attitude and just wished Christmas would hurry up and get over."

That's a familiar feeling, I thought. *I wanted to hurry the holiday away, too.*

"I fought my way through the crowds and finally got ready to pay," the woman continued. "As the line moved forward, I watched babies cry, couples argue, and a toddler throw a terrible tantrum. I felt so disillusioned that I almost walked out of the store.

"But then I noticed two children standing in line ahead of me. The boy looked about nine years old. The girl, maybe five. Neither child wore clothes warm enough for the day. Their hair was uncombed, and well, honestly, both kids smelled awful."

My dad grew up poor. I wondered if anyone had ever felt that way about him.

The lady's saga continued. "The boy clutched some one dollar bills in his skinny hand. Coins poked from between the girl's clenched fingers. As the children approached the cash register, the girl plopped the gaudiest pair of sparkly, gold high-heeled shoes I'd ever seen up onto the counter. When the clerk rang them up, the children looked ready to burst into tears. They didn't have enough money. Suddenly I heard myself offer to pay their shortage."

My mind flashed back to a time I saw Dad give two dollars to a shaky old man in the grocery store line. We never discussed it, but I'd never forgotten the scene.

The tale teller's voice broke as she told how both kids beamed. "The little boy explained that the shoes were for his mother. Then the girl piped up, 'My mamma has 'kemia. Daddy said she's going to Heaven soon. In Heaven they have gold streets. We're getting Mama shoes to match.'"

In stunned silence I realized God had spoken. He was reminding me where Dad now walked—on streets of gold. Would gold shoes help my heartbroken mother?

Before I finished my thought, the storyteller made one last comment. Something about Christmas being the way God wrapped up a love gift and sent him from Heaven.

The gift of God. A baby Savior. The Savior who made it possible for loved ones to walk on the streets of gold.

At home I found a pair of small doll shoes. After coating them with gold glitter and clear paint, I mounted them onto a mahogany plaque. With a burst of energy, I shuffled through a drawer to find my calligraphy pen and a piece of gold parchment. My hands trembled as I wrote: *Departed to Walk on Streets of Gold.* After gluing the parchment to the wood, I smiled at the finished project.

On Christmas Mom's face brightened when she unwrapped the gold shoes and my handwritten explanation. Even though the season still held sadness, the days brought joy as we talked about Pa plodding down gold pavement. I knew the Lord would guide Mother and me as we began taking steps in a healing direction.

Cast all your cares on God;
that anchor holds.

ALFRED, LORD TENNYSON (1809–1892)

AN EMPTY CHAIR

WALTER BURKHARDT
FROM *TELL THE NEXT GENERATION*

his was the experience of an old man who lay dying. When the priest came to anoint him, he noticed an empty chair at the man's bedside and asked him who had just been visiting. The sick man replied, "I place Jesus on that chair and I talk to Him." For years, he told the priest, he had found it extremely difficult to pray until a friend explained that prayer was just a matter of talking with Jesus. The friend suggested that he imagine Jesus sitting in a chair where he could speak with Him and listen to what He said in reply. "I have had no trouble praying ever since."

Some days later, the daughter of this man came to the parish house to inform the priest that her father had just died. She said, "Because he seemed so content, I left him alone for a couple of hours. When I got back to the room, I found him dead. I noticed a strange thing, though: his head was resting not on the bed but on an empty chair that was beside his bed."

SPIRIT RENEWED

BARBARA BAUMGARDNER
FROM *RV COMPANION* MAGAZINE

*I*t was a hard summer. My sister had a stroke; my mom was in and out of the hospital; and I sold my big house, opting for a small one in a gated community where someone else mows the lawn. Caregiving, selling and moving takes its toll, and I was exhausted: physically, mentally, emotionally and spiritually.

Even through the busy times of that summer, I recognized my simmering hostility toward the circumstances that were keeping me from a fling in my new motor home. I kept telling myself that my attitude was selfish, but I just couldn't shake those feelings.

When a few days finally opened up on my calendar, I e-mailed a friend:

"I'm leaving in the morning for a couple days on the coast. I'm tired. I feel so spiritually drained; God seems very far away. Hopefully, I can use these days to be still and find an answer…somewhere on the beach, or in a sunset, or even in the stillness of my own heart. Please pray for me."

Taking only my dog, Molly, I ran away from my troubles.

Parking the motor home at a beachfront campground near Lincoln City, Oregon, I kicked off my shoes and ran barefoot on the sand. Frolicking child-like with Molly filled me with invigorating feelings of release. I gratefully inhaled the salty air and the cool, earthy smell of wet sand. The seagulls filled the moist air with chattering noises, sometimes swooping and dipping overhead, sometimes standing in a row on a piece of driftwood like wooden soldiers at attention. Captivated by my surroundings, it felt like Molly and I, and those noisy birds, were the only living creatures on the face of the earth.

The next day I sat for hours watching the gray-green mounds of water rise and fall, like heavy breathing entities from the ocean floor. The sky changed colors and hues, as a coastal storm swept through the cove. Rain pelted against the metal shell of my motor home. Yes, yes! This is what I came for. How wonderful to finally reach those moments of sorely needed rest and healing.

Later that evening, I watched a brilliant, fuchsia sunset change to pink, then melon and gray; too soon, it was replaced by a pitch-black wall of nothingness.

The next morning was the seventeenth anniversary of my husband's death. I marveled at my new experiences and how far I'd come from that devastating, stormy time of my life. And I wondered, "Should I head for home or extend this get-away for one more day?"

Glancing out the front window, I was startled to see a piece of a rainbow hanging over the rock-lined cove. The top of the brilliant streams of color disappeared into puffy clouds, and the bottom seemed to have been snipped across by a giant pair of scissors. Framed in my front windshield, it reminded me of God's promise...the one that said He would never send such a violent storm again.

He had rescued me from the raging waters of new widowhood; why should I doubt that He would not rescue me now? As quickly as that thought came to me, the rainbow disappeared, and with it, my hopelessness and self-pity.

As the sand began to dry, I raced down the beach filled with joy, with Molly at my heels...renewed in mind, body, and spirit. We dug holes in the sand and took turns chasing the ball. God had given me this day, just as He gave me this beach, the sand...and a golden, brown dog who loves me almost as much as He does.

TOMMY

JOHN POWELL
FROM *THE CHALLENGE OF FAITH*

ome twelve years ago, I stood watching my university students file into the classroom for our first session in the Theology of Faith. That was the first day I saw Tommy. My eyes and my mind both blinked.

He was combing his long flaxen hair, which hung six inches below his shoulders. I guess it was just coming into fashion then. I know in my mind that it isn't what's on your head but what's in it that counts; but on that day I was unprepared and my emotions flipped. I immediately filed Tommy under "S" for strange...very strange.

Tommy turned out to be the "atheist in residence" in my Theology of Faith course. He constantly objected to, smirked at, or whined about the possibility of an unconditionally loving Father-God. We lived with each other in relative peace for one semester, although I admit he was for me at times a serious pain in the back pew. When he came up at the end of the course to turn in his final exam, he asked in a slightly cynical tone: "Do you think I'll ever find God?"

I decided instantly on a little shock therapy. "No!" I said very emphatically.

"Oh," he responded, "I thought that was the product you were pushing."

I let him get five steps from the classroom door and then called out: "Tommy! I don't think you'll ever find him, but I am absolutely certain that he will find you!" He shrugged a little and left my class and my life. I felt slightly disappointed at the thought that he had missed my clever line: "He will find you!" At least I thought it was clever.

Later I heard that Tommy had graduated and I was duly grateful. Then a sad report, I heard that Tommy had terminal cancer. Before I could search him out, he came to see me. When he walked into my office, his body was badly wasted, and the long hair had all fallen out as a result of chemotherapy. But his eyes were bright and his voice was firm, for the first time, I believe.

"Tommy, I've thought about you so often. I hear you are sick!" I blurted out.

"Oh, yes, very sick. I have cancer in both lungs. It's a matter of weeks."

"Can you talk about it, Tom?"

"Sure, what would you like to know?"

"What's it like to be only twenty-four and dying?"

"Well, it could be worse."

"Like what?"

"Well, like being fifty and having no values or ideals, like being fifty and thinking that booze, seducing women, and making money are the real 'biggies' in life."

I began to look through my mental file cabinet under "S" where I had filed Tommy as strange. *It seems as though everybody I try to reject by classification God sends back into my life to educate me.*

"But what I really came to see you about," Tom said, "is something you said to me on the last day of class." *He remembered!* He continued, "I asked you if you thought I would ever find God and you said, 'No!' which surprised me. Then you said, 'But he will find you.' I thought about that a lot, even though my search for God was hardly intense at the time." *My "clever" line. He thought about that a lot!* "But when the doctors removed a lump from my groin and told me that it was malignant, then I got serious about locating God. And when the malignancy spread into my vital organs, I really began banging bloody fists against the bronze doors of heaven. But God did not come out. In fact, nothing happened. Did you ever try anything for a long time with great effort and with no success? You get psychologically glutted, fed up with trying. And then you quit. Well, one day I woke up, and instead of throwing a few more futile appeals over that high brick wall to a God who may or may not be there, I just quit. I decided that I didn't really care...about God, about an afterlife, or anything like that.

"I decided to spend what time I had left doing something more profitable. I thought about you and your class and remembered something else you had said: 'The essential sadness is to go through life without loving. But it would be almost equally sad to go through life and leave this world without ever telling those you loved that you loved them.'

"So I began with the hardest one: my Dad. He was reading the newspaper when I approached him."

"Dad?"

"Yes, what?" he asked without lowering the newspaper.

"Dad, I would like to talk with you."

"Well, talk."

"I mean...it's really important." The newspaper came down three slow inches.

"What is it?" he asked.

"Dad, I love you. I just wanted you to know that."

Tom smiled at me and said with obvious satisfaction, as though he felt a warm and secret joy flowing inside of him: "The newspaper fluttered to the floor. Then my father did two things I could never remember him ever doing before. He cried and hugged me. And we talked all night, even though he had to go to work the next morning. It felt so good to be close to my father, to see his tears, to feel his hug, to hear him say that he loved me.

"It was easier with my mother and little brother. They cried with me, too, and we hugged each other, and started saying real nice things to each other. We shared the things we had been keeping secret for so many years.

I was only sorry about one thing; that I had waited so long. Here I was just beginning to open up to all the people I had actually been close to.

"Then, one day I turned around and God was there. He didn't come to me when I pleaded with him. I guess I was like an animal trainer holding out a hoop. C'mon, jump through. C'mon, I'll give you three days...three weeks.' Apparently God does things in his own way at his own hour. But the important thing is that he was there. He found me. You were right. He found me even after I stopped looking for him."

"Tom," I practically gasped, "I think you are saying something very important and much more universal than you realize. To me, at least, you are saying that the surest way to find God is not to make him a private possession, a problem solver, or an instant consolation in time of need, but rather by opening to love. You know, the Apostle John said that. He said God is love, and anyone who lives in love is living with God and God is living in him.

"Tom, could I ask you a favor? You know, when I had you in class you were a real pain. But you can make it all up to me now. Would you come into my present Theology of Faith course and tell them what you have just told me? If I told them the same thing it wouldn't be half as effective as if you were to tell them."

"Oooh...I was ready for you, but I don't know if I'm ready for your class."

"Tom, think about it. If and when you are ready, give me a call."

In a few days Tommy called, said he was ready for the class, that he wanted to do that for God and for me. So we scheduled a date. However, he never made it. He had another appointment, far more important than the one with me and my class. Of course, his life was not really ended by his death, only changed. He made the greatest step from faith into vision. He found a life far more beautiful than the eye of man has ever seen or the ear of man has ever heard or the mind of man has ever imagined.

Before he died, we talked one last time. "I'm not going to make it to your class," he said.

"I know, Tom."

"Will you tell them for me? Will you...tell the whole world for me?"

"I will, Tom. I'll tell them. I'll do my best." So to all of you who have been kind enough to hear this simple statement about love, thank you for listening. And to you, Tommy, somewhere in the sunlit, verdant hills of heaven: "I told them, Tommy...as best I could."

Who is Christ?
He is the Truth to be told.
The Way to be walked.
The Light to be lit.

MOTHER TERESA

Little faith will bring your soul to heaven;
great faith will bring heaven to your soul.

CHARLES H. SPURGEON

GIVING GOD PLEASURE

RUTH BELL GRAHAM
FROM *LEGACY OF A PACK RAT*

randmother's brother, Uncle Eddie McCue, lived on the old pre-Civil War home place, "Belvidere," in the Shenandoah Valley of Virginia.

One day, while working on the farm, he discarded his coat and told his collie dog, Chunk, to watch it.

That night, when Uncle Eddie got back to the house, he missed Chunk. No one had seen him. They called, but there was no response. Distressed, they ate supper, then continued searching. Bedtime came and still no Chunk. The next morning they looked outside hopefully. No sign of the old collie.

Time came for Uncle Eddie to return to the fields to work. There, in a distant field he saw something lying on the ground—his forgotten coat. And beside it lay Chunk, head and ears up, his plumed tail thumping the ground in the eager welcome.

That was years ago.

Tonight, as I sit on the porch, our old German shepherd is lying at my feet. He lifts his great head as a low mutter of thunder rumbles in the distance, and gives a deep warning bark. Then as the storm nears he rises with a lurch and tears into the front yard to meet it. The yard is a brief ledge confined by an old rail fence, beyond which it falls precipitously down a bank and is engulfed by the encroaching woods.

The storm is on us, the great dog furiously doing battle with it. As it passes, he returns to the porch, settling contentedly at my feet convinced he has driven it away.

He is a German guard dog, given to us years ago by concerned friends. He had been carefully trained in search and rescue, attack, and obedience.

Search and rescue in these mountains can come in handy. Previous dogs of ours had been used successfully for that purpose.

I cannot imagine an occasion when we would give the order to attack. But a well-trained dog can sense hostility or spot a weapon (or even what resembles a weapon), in which case it's a wise person who freezes in his tracks.

But it's the obedience training that gives us real joy. To stop, to sit, to lie down, to go away, to search, to stay, to heel. A disobedient dog is not only a headache; he can be a liability. Obedience makes a dog a joy.

Is it less so with God and His children?

There are some I know who have been trained in attack. We will not mention names. You may know a few. But they are skilled at it.

Then there are those trained in search and rescue. (I'd put the Salvation Army in this group.)

And there are those who have been trained in obedience.

I think this, more than anything else, must give the Lord pleasure. Simple obedience. Joyful, eager, unquestioning obedience; to be able to say with the psalmist, *"I delight to do thy will, O my God,"* would be the height of training for the Christian.

For it is this that gives God the greatest pleasure.

HONEY, I'M PROUD OF YOU

LYDIA E. HARRIS

For twenty-six years I saw my husband, Milt, as quiet and unassuming, so it surprised me when he announced his plan. "I'm going to organize a prayer gathering at work for the National Day of Prayer."

I was proud of his courage to try something new; proud of his bold allegiance to God; and proud of his example for our children.

He chose the time—noon, the place—the flagpole outside his six-story building. He advertised the event, pinning computer-made flyers on the bulletin boards throughout the building. Together we prayed that others would notice the posters and join him to pray.

"Who are the Christians at this large company?" we wondered. "With hundreds of employees, surely there are other Christians who want to participate. Could this be the beginning of a regular prayer time or Bible study?"

The National Day of Prayer arrived. Throughout the morning I prayed, "Lord, please send others to pray with Milt. Don't let him stand there alone. I don't want him to feel discouraged or embarrassed."

As Milt walked through our front door that evening, I greeted him with eager questions. "What happened? How many came?"

"There were three besides me," he replied with a grin.

"That's great! Who were they?"

His answer startled me, "The Father, Son, and Holy Spirit."

I was proud of my husband that day and still am. I admire him for praying alone in a public place while others scurried by. His insight taught me a valuable lesson: We are never alone. The triune God is always with us.

A weary Christian lay awake one night
trying to hold the world together by his worrying.
Then he heard the Lord gently say to him,
"Now you go to sleep, Jim, I'll sit up."

RUTH BELL GRAHAM
FROM *PRODIGALS AND THOSE WHO LOVE THEM*

TURNING POINT

BILL BUTTERWORTH

FROM *WHEN LIFE DOESN'T TURN OUT LIKE YOU PLANNED*

Without question, a real turning point for me in my spiritual journey came the Sunday of the first Christmas I was single again. What had always been the highlight of the year, December 25, was now an awkward occasion of negotiating 'who had whom' from 'when to when' and how to best handle the minutiae of keeping Christmas special to the kids when inside I was a broken-hearted wreck.

As I walked into the sanctuary that Sunday before Christmas, the room was warmly decorated with wreaths and ribbons and lanterns. The central focus, however, was a life-size manger, placed on the floor in front of the pulpit. Real straw was brimming from the four sides of the manger, and it wonderfully recreated what the Christ-child must have lain in on that cold winter's night.

When Ed stood up to preach that morning, I had already wept quietly several times as we sang a procession of well-known Christmas carols. Each song was pregnant with memories of Christmases past, when everything in the world was so much better.

I wonder what Ed will say this year? I found myself thinking before he began. There are only so many ways you can find meaning in gold, frankincense, and myrrh, for example, and no room at the inn only can go so far in its practical application.

Ed chose to go deeper into Luke's gospel account, later in the life of Christ. He chose as his text a verse from the fourth chapter, when Jesus was actually a grown man. But it was a verse that was especially relevant to the Christmas season.... Isaiah had spoken those words centuries before in prophecy of the coming Messiah.

The Spirit of the Lord God is upon me,
Because the LORD has anointed me
to bring good news to the afflicted;
He has sent me to bind up the brokenhearted,
To proclaim liberty to captives,
And freedom to prisoners.

ISAIAH 61:1, NAS

When Ed finished reading Isaiah's words, it was as if there was no longer anyone else in the worship service. I felt as if he were speaking directly to me and me alone. He chose to zero in on a key-phrase—"He sent me to bind up the brokenhearted."

"Is this year a difficult Christmas for you?" Ed asked. "Are you brokenhearted over a circumstance that has left you in great pain?"

Tears were streaming down my cheeks as I knew that this was a message from God for me. All that moisture dripping down onto my lap was silently answering Ed, "Yes...yes...I am brokenhearted."

Meanwhile Ed had moved from his position behind the pulpit to a place in front of it. Standing over the manger, he crouched down and said, "If you're here in deep pain, I want you to do something for me. I invite you to leave your burden here in the manger. For remember, Jesus Christ has come to mend that which is torn inside of you. He has come to bind up your broken heart."

I don't remember much of what happened after that, except that in my soul, I gave Christ all the pain my crisis had created. It wasn't the sort of thing that was accompanied by harps, strings, or chills up the spine, but it was an awesomely moving encounter for me. In many ways, it was like nothing I had ever experienced.

Christmas was bearable, thanks to Him who had come to bind up my broken heart. I was so grateful that I had made this discovery at what could have been the most awful time of the year.

A coincidence is a small miracle
where God chose to remain anonymous...

HEIDI QUADE

WHEN THE LORD SAYS PRAY!

CHERI FULLER
FROM *WHEN FAMILIES PRAY*

*T*he missionary rose from his campsite where he had spent the night enroute to a city for medical supplies. He extinguished his small campfire, pulled on his canvas backpack, and hopped on his bicycle to continue his ride through the African jungle. Every two weeks he made this two-day journey to collect money from a bank and purchase medicine and supplies for the small field hospital where he served. When he completed those errands, he hopped on his bike again for the two-day return trip.

When the missionary arrived in the city, he collected his money and medical supplies and was just about to leave for home when he saw two men fighting in the street. Since one of the fighters was seriously injured, the missionary stopped, treated him for his injuries, and shared the love of Christ with him. Then the missionary began his two-day trek home, stopping in the jungle again to camp overnight.

Two weeks later, as was his custom, the missionary again made the journey to the city. As he ran his various errands, a young man approached him—the same man the missionary had ministered to during his previous trip. "I knew you carried money and medicine with you," the man said, "so my friends and I followed you to your campsite in the jungle after you helped me in the street. We planned to kill you and take all the money and drugs. But just as we were about to move in and attack you, we saw twenty-six armed guards surround and protect you."

"You must be mistaken," said the missionary. "I was all alone when I spent the night in the jungle. There were no guards or anyone else with me."

"But sir, I wasn't the only one who saw the guards. My five companions saw them, too. We counted them! There were twenty-six bodyguards, too many for us to handle. Their presence stopped us from killing you."

Months later, the missionary related this story to the congregation gathered at his home church in Michigan. As he spoke, one of the men listening stood up and interrupted him, wanting to know the exact day the incident in the jungle had occurred. When the missionary identified the specific month and day of the week, the man told him "the rest of the story."

"On the exact night of your incident in Africa, it was morning here in Michigan, and I was on the golf course. I was about to putt when I felt a strong urge to pray for you. The urge was so strong, I left the golf course and called some men of our church right here in this sanctuary to join me in praying for you. Would all you men who prayed with me that day stand up?"

One by one the missionary counted the men. There were twenty-six of them, the exact number of "armed guards" the thwarted attackers had seen guarding him!

YOU'LL FIND PATIENCE

CLARK COTHERN

FROM *AT THE HEART OF EVERY GREAT FATHER*

urle ducked his head a bit and fiddled with his ever-present white handkerchief as he responded to the pastor's request. The proposition now on the table wasn't at all what the sixty-five-year-old retiree had in mind.

"Yeah, I know I told you I'd help anywhere I could," Murle admitted, "but…" he left the sentence unfinished, flapping his arms in consternation, unaware that he was waving the hanky like a flag of surrender.

"Pastor, I brought up a couple of *girls*—grown-ups now. I'm not sure I'd know what to do with a bunch of these little fellers."

His eyes had that trapped-animal look. He was obviously searching for a way out of the cage in which he suddenly found himself.

Pastor Jim, however, wasn't about to let his friend off the hook. "All you have to do," he said, "is treat those boys like you were treated by your dad when he took you fishing. C'mon, Murle. What'dya say?"

"There's not enough room in my boat for very many." Murle wiped his forehead, casting this one last excuse as bait, hoping the pastor would bite.

No sale.

"Just take 'em two at a time," Jim said without hesitation.

"Dang it, you've thought of everything, haven't you?" Murle chuckled in spite of himself.

"Well? Will you do it?"

"Oh shoot, Pastor, I *suppose* so—for what good it might do." And then he threw in, "All except that Sammy kid." Murle felt sure the pastor would understand about him.

Jim flashed a knowing grin. He knew about Sammy.

"You just start taking them two by two, and we'll pray about little Sammy," said the younger man with a twinkle in his eye.

*M*urle made good on his promise. He began taking the boys out, two at a time. Many of the young fishermen had very little dad influence in their homes. Murle provided a touch of manhood in the lads' lives.

Six weeks after he began filling his Saturdays with bluegill, bass, and boys, Murle stood in the church office, nervously swiping the beads of perspiration on his forehead as he spoke to the pastor. "He just came runnin' up after church this morning."

"Who did, Murle?" asked Jim, watching the hanky dab at the old gent's shiny head.

"That Sammy kid! He said the other boys had all got a chance and could he please have a chance, too?" Up went the handkerchief.

Pastor Jim raised an eyebrow and smiled. "Oh, the fishing trips. And Sammy wants to go, too, huh? Well...what do you think?"

Down went the hanky, crumpled into a ball. Murle shook his head. "I dunno, Pastor. You know this one. He's enough trouble by himself to sink two boats!"

"You pray about it and then do what you think best, Murle." Jim smiled as he gave his friend a couple of solid pats on the shoulder. He turned to walk away.

"Pastor!" Murle called, stuffing the hanky in his back pocket.

"Yes?" Jim stopped in the doorway.

"Okay, Okay, I'll take him...but by himself. With him, one's enough!"

"Good, Murle. Good."

*S*aturday morning a screech of tires sent Jim bolt upright in his chair at the church office.

He left his sermon notes and was headed toward the parking lot when Murle burst through the door at the end of the long hallway, huffing and puffing. All the way down the hall, he kept muttering, "He did it. He *did* it!"

"Who did what, Murle?" Jim knew his friend was flustered because he'd left his pickup truck so fast he had forgotten his handkerchief.

"Little Sammy. He DID it. I can't believe it." The old man was pacing back and forth, rubbing his hands up and down the sides of his jeans.

"Murle, take a couple of nitros and calm down. What did he do? You haven't even gotten out of the parking lot yet."

"I know, I *know*. The little minnow just blurted out and asked me *how does a kid get saved?* You know—as in eternal life!"

"And…what did you say?"

"Well, I told him you have to tell Jesus you're a good-for-nothin' sinner and ask forgiveness for your sins and ask Jesus to come into your life and be the Boss."

"That's fine, Murle. You told him the right thing. But I don't understand —why did you slam on the brakes?"

"Well, the little rug rat got right down on his knees on the floorboard of my truck and started confessin' every bad thing he's ever done since he can remember! He's still at it out there!" Murle waved his hand vaguely toward the parking lot.

Pastor Jim laughed as he walked Murle out to the parking lot, where, together, they knelt with little Sammy and gave thanks to God that he had found a family. The little lad without much dad influence had just become the Father's child. And all because Murle gave a sacrificial gift of time to a young boy.

*L*ittle Sammy grew up to become a sportswriter for a prominent Florida newspaper. Years after his parking-lot confession, Sammy wrote a special column for the paper's Father's Day issue.

It was a tribute to a man named Murle.

Later still, after many such fishing trips, Murle entered eternity. At his memorial service, Sammy, now grown and with kids of his own, stood behind a pulpit and read a tribute to his friend.

It was the article he had written years earlier for a certain Father's Day. The title? "Change a little boy's life. Take him fishing."

Murle's life demonstrated that patience has its rewards.

It is the essence of faith to let God be God.

JON SOBRINO

A RESTING PLACE

MAYO MATHERS
FROM *TODAY'S CHRISTIAN WOMAN* MAGAZINE

The headlights of my car were overpowered by the dense black night as I crept along the mountain road. I peered through the rain-splattered windshield, unsure if my tears or the rain were making visibility so difficult.

Oh, God, why did this happen? I cried. I was returning from a visit with my parents and single younger sister who live several hours away. My sister had been severely brain-injured in a drunk driving accident eighteen months ago. Since then, I'd grabbed at every tiny sign of progress, full of irrational hope for her recovery. But on this visit, I was forced to face reality. My sister would never recover. For the rest of her life, she would require constant care.

Grief consumed me as I twisted my way through the mountain pass. Shifting to a lower gear, I heard a loud *thunk*. Startled, I tried to shift into a different gear, but nothing happened. The car slowed to a standstill along the edge of the road.

Swallowing back fear, I locked the car and walked toward a gleam of light tucked back in the towering pine trees. It turned out to be the window of a small cottage. I approached the porch cautiously, hesitant to knock on an unfamiliar door late at night.

In response to my timid rap, the door swung open to reveal a middle-aged man. "Come in!" he welcomed. I hovered near the door, explained about my car, and asked to use his phone. When I dug out my calling card, he objected. "Your call's on me. I get lots of stranded people knocking on my door out here. It's my way of helping."

My phone call to my husband went unanswered, so I asked the man if he knew of a motel nearby. "No motels," he said, "but I have an idea."

Before I knew it, I was handed over to the elderly owner of a nearby fishing lodge who had a room available. She, too, refused to take money from a stranded traveler.

The "room" actually was a cabin with one entire wall of glass overlooking a magnificent rushing river. A plump couch and chair faced a fireplace where a fire was laid, just waiting for me to strike a match.

Sitting there, warmed by the fire and relaxed by the sound of tumbling water, I opened my Bible to Psalm 139. By the third verse, my tears splashed onto the page. "You chart the path ahead of me and tell me where to stop and rest. Every moment you know where I am" (TLB).

As I contemplated the words, God spoke to my heart. *From the beginning, I knew everything that would be in your path. I'll give you the strength to endure your sister's tragedy, and I'll guide you through your sorrow—but tonight, stop and rest with me.*

Before I fell asleep, I called home to leave a message on the answering machine for my husband. "The car broke down on the mountain tonight. Please come and get me—but don't hurry. God and I are resting."

Those who hope in the LORD will renew their strength.
They will soar on wings like eagles;
they will run and not grow weary,
they will walk and not be faint.

ISAIAH 40:31

ANGEL AT WORK?

BILLY GRAHAM
FROM *UNTO THE HILLS*

*T*he British express train raced through the night, its powerful headlight piercing the darkness. Queen Victoria was a passenger on the train.

Suddenly the engineer saw a startling sight. Revealed in the beam of the engine's light was a strange figure in a black cloak standing in the middle of the tracks and waving its arms. The engineer grabbed for the brake and brought the train to a grinding halt.

He and his fellow trainmen clambered down to see what had stopped them. But they could find no trace of the strange figure. On a hunch the engineer walked a few yards further up the tracks. Suddenly he stopped and stared into the fog in horror. A bridge had been washed out in the middle and ahead of them it had toppled into a swollen stream. If the engineer had not heeded the ghostly figure, his train would have plummeted down into the stream.

While the bridge and tracks were being repaired, the crew made a more intensive search for the strange flagman. But not until they got to London did they solve the mystery.

At the base of the engine's head lamp the engineer discovered a huge dead moth. He looked at it a moment, then on impulse wet its wings and pasted it to the glass of the lamp.

Climbing back in to his cab, he switched on the light and saw the "flagman" in the beam, seconds before the train was due to reach the washed-out bridge. In the fog, it appeared to be a phantom figure, waving its arms.

When Queen Victoria was told of the strange happening she said, "I'm sure it was no accident. It was God's way of protecting us."

No, the figure the engineer saw in the headlight's beam was not an angel…and yet God, quite possibly through the ministry of His unseen angels, had placed the moth on the headlight lens exactly when and where it was needed. Truly "He will command his angels concerning you to guard you in all your ways" (Psalm 91:11, NIV).

AN ICE CREAM SOLO

BARBARA BAUMGARDNER

I flunked my first night out alone—my first solo movie since I'd become a widow. It wasn't too hard buying the ticket and the popcorn. Even sitting alone in the big theater was all right. I became so engrossed in the movie that it surprised me when the lights came on and I discovered I was all by myself.

On my way to the car, the tears welled up. I didn't have anyone to have an after-the-show ice cream cone with. Suddenly that seemed very, very important.

I stepped through my garage door into the kitchen and burst into tears. Loudly, I wailed to God. "When is it going to end? How much longer, God, until I can learn to enjoy doing things without having a companion?" The waves of loneliness again washed over me and for a few minutes, I gave in to an incoming tide of sorrow.

When I stopped crying, I felt better but I still wanted some ice cream. Feeling a little foolish, I offered an invitation, "Lord, will you have some ice cream with me?"

Feeling even more foolish, I piled two cereal bowls high with rocky road ice cream from my freezer, and through the giggles asked myself, "I'm really doing this, aren't I?"

Outside on my deck, under a million blinking stars, I leisurely consumed the entire contents of both bowls, savoring each bite in the companionship of the Lord. And I was reminded of His promise, *"I will not leave you comfortless: I will come to you."*

In times of affliction
we commonly meet
with the sweetest experience
of the love of God.

JOHN BUNYAN

YOUR ABBA'S ARMS

MAX LUCADO
FROM *THE GREAT HOUSE OF GOD*

*S*ome time back, my daughter Jenna and I spent several days in the old city of Jerusalem. One afternoon, as we were exiting the Jaffa gate, we found ourselves behind an Orthodox Jewish family—a father and his three small girls.

One of the daughters, perhaps four or five years of age, fell a few steps behind and couldn't see her father.

"*Abba!*" she called to him. He stopped and looked. Only then did he realize he was separated from his daughter.

"*Abba!*" she called again. He spotted her and immediately extended his hand. She took it and I took mental notes as they continued. I wanted to see the actions of an *abba*.

He held her hand tightly in his as they descended the ramp. When he stopped at a busy street, she stepped off the curb, so he pulled her back. When the signal changed, he led her and her sisters through the intersection. In the middle of the street, he reached down and swung her up into his arms and continued their journey.

Isn't that what we all need? An abba who will hear when we call? Who will take our hand when we're weak? Who will guide us through the hectic intersections of life? Don't we all need an abba who will swing us up into his arms and carry us home? We all need a father.

There's a God in heaven who wants you to call him your *abba*.

CIRCLE OF FAITH

DICK EASTMAN
FROM *EVERY HOME FOR CHRIST* MAGAZINE

Little ten-year-old Maria lived in a rural village in central Chile. When her mother died, Maria became the "woman of the house," caring for her father who worked the night shift at the local mine. Maria cooked and cleaned and made sure her father's lunch was ready when he left the house for work each evening.

Maria loved her father and was worried by how despondent he had become since her mother's death. Maria went to church on Sundays and tried to get her father to go with her, but he refused. His heart was too empty.

One evening, as Maria was packing her father's lunchbox, she slipped a gospel booklet inside that she had received from a missionary worker who had been distributing them home to home in the area where they lived. Maria prayed that her father would read the booklet and find the comfort she had found in God's great love.

It was 1:10 A.M. when Maria was suddenly awakened by a horrible sound—the emergency whistle at the mine was blaring through the darkness, calling the townspeople to come running with shovels and willing hands to help dig for miners caught in a cave-in.

Maria made her way through the streets to the mine in search of her father. Scores of men were frantically pulling debris away from the collapsed tunnel where eight men were trapped. One of the men was Maria's father.

Emergency crews worked through the night and finally broke through to a small cavern where they found the miners. Sadly, they were too late. All eight men had suffocated.

The rescue workers were devastated, but as they surveyed the scene, they noticed that the men had died, seated in a circle. As the workers looked closer they discovered Maria's father was sitting with a small gospel booklet in his lap opened to the last page where the plan of salvation was clearly explained. On that page, Maria's father had written a special message to his daughter:

> *My darling Maria,*
>
> *When you read this, I will be with your mother in heaven. I read this little book, then I read it several times to the men while we waited to be rescued. Our hope is fading for this life, but not for the next. We did as the book told us and prayed, asking Jesus into our hearts. I love you very much, Maria, and one day soon, we will all be together in heaven.*

God not only hears our words,
He listens to our hearts.

AUTHOR UNKNOWN

ACKNOWLEDGMENTS

A diligent search has been made to trace original ownership, and when necessary, permission to reprint has been obtained. If we have overlooked giving proper credit to anyone, please accept our apologies. Should any attribution be found to be incorrect, the publisher welcomes written documentation supporting correction for subsequent printings. For material not in the public domain, grateful acknowledgment is given to the publishers and individuals who have granted permission for use of their material.

Acknowledgments are listed by story title in the order they appear in the book. For permission to reprint any of the stories please request permission from the original source listed below.

ENCOURAGEMENT

"When the Winds Are Strong" by Charles R. Swindoll from the July 1996 *Insight for Living* ministry letter. Used by permission of Insight for Living, Anaheim, CA 95806.

"The Gift" by Gary B. Swanson. Reprinted from the December 1997 issue of *Focus on the Family* magazine. Used with permission of Joe Wheeler, editor/compiler of *Christmas in My Heart Vol. 6* and Review and Herald Publishing. Permission also granted by author, Gary B. Swanson.

"The Red Purse" by Louise Moeri. Reprinted from the July/Aug 1991 issue of *Virtue* magazine. Used with permission of the author who lives in Manteca, CA.

"Ice Cream Party" by Rochelle M. Pennington, freelance writer, newspaper columnist, and contributing author to *Stories for the Heart, Chicken Soup for the Soul,* and *Life's Little Instruction Book.* You may contact her at N1911 Double D Rd., Campbellsport, WI 53010, (920) 533-5880. Used with permission of the author.

"The Bunny and the Eggheads" by Ted Menten. Excerpt reprinted with permission from *Gentle Closings* by Ted Menten, © 1991 by Ted Menten, published by Running Press, Philadelphia and London.

"Molly" by Barbara Baumgardner. Reprinted from the December 17, 1999 Humane Society insert in *The Bulletin* newspaper, Bend, OR. Used by permission of the author.

"We All Need to Be Looked After" by Max Lucado from *In the Grip of Grace*, © 1996, Word Publishing, Nashville, Tennessee. All rights reserved.

"Love Letters" by Bob Welch from *Where Roots Grow Deep*, © 1999 by Bob Welch (Harvest House Publishers, Eugene, Oregon 97402). Used by permission.

"God Doesn't Make Nobodies" by Ruth Lee. Reprinted from the March 1998 issue of *Touch 1* magazine. Used by permission of the author. Ruth Lee writes fiction, poetry, and personal essays. Her work has been shared in a variety of publications.

"Overnight Guest" by Hartley F. Dailey from the February 1963 issue of *Sunshine* magazine. Used by permission.

"Unthanked People" by Steve Goodier © 1999. Used by permission of the author. Steve Goodier is the author of a free internet newsletter called *Your Life Support System* at www.lifesupportsystem.com.

"Angels Once in a While" by Barb Irwin who is a freelance writer. Used by permission of the author.

"Mrs. Warren's Class" by Colleen Townsend Evans. Reprinted from START LOVING: THE MIRACLE OF FORGIVING by Colleen Townsend Evans, © 1976 by Colleen Townsend Evans and Laura Hobe. Used by permission from Doubleday, a division of Random House, Inc.

"The Other Side of the Curtain" by Ruth Lee. Reprinted from the March 1998 issue of *Touch 1* magazine. Used with permission of the author. Ruth Lee writes fiction, poetry, and personal essays. Her work has been shared in a variety of publications.

FRIENDSHIP

"Mrs. Hildebrandt's Gift" by Robert Smith. Reprinted from the Feb/Mar 1994 issue of *Country* magazine. Used with permission of the author.

"The Love Squad" by Virelle Kidder © 1999 Virelle Kidder; printed in *Decision* magazine, October 1999; published by the Billy Graham Evangelistic Association. Virelle Kidder is a full time writer, conference speaker, and host of a daily radio show. She is also the author of three books and a contributing writer for *Today's Christian Woman* magazine. Used by permission of the author.

"Luther's Lumber" by Joe Edwards, freelance writer in Springfield, MO. Used by permission.

"Treasure" verse by Paul Kortepeter. Used by permission of InterArt® Holding Corporation, Bloomington, IN.

"Reply to Box 222B" by Barbara Baumgardner. Reprinted from *Chicken Soup for the Single's Soul.* Used by permission of the author. Barbara has written two books, *A Passage Through Grief* and *A Passage Through Divorce,* both published by Broadman and Holman, Nashville, TN.

"Saving the Best for Last" by Rochelle M. Pennington, freelance writer, newspaper columnist, and contributing author to *Stories for the Heart, Chicken Soup for the Soul,* and *Life's Little Instruction Book.* You may contact her at N1911 Double D Rd., Campbellsport, WI 53010, (920) 533-5880. Used with permission of the author.

"My Child, My Teacher, My Friend" by Gloria Gaither. Reprinted from the May/June 1990 issue of *Christian Herald* magazine. Used with permission of Gaither Copyright Management, Alexandria, IN.

"God, a Dog, and Me" by Deborah Hedstrom who is the author of ten books and numerous articles. She lives in Salem, Oregon, and teaches writing at Western Baptist College. Used by permission of the author.

"Friendship Is a Diamond" by Sally J. Knower, © 1985. Used by permission.

"The Comfort Room" by Mayo Mathers. Reprinted from the Nov/Dec. 1997 issue of *Today's Christian Woman.* Used by permission of the author.

"Someone to Divide With" from *Tea Time with God,* © 1996 (Honor Books, Tulsa, OK 74155). Used with permission of the publisher.

"Empty Places Filled" by Chris Fabry. Reprinted from *At the Corner of Mundane and Grace,* © 1999 by Chris Fabry. Used by permission of WaterBrook Press, Colorado Springs, CO. All rights reserved.

LOVE

"The Wallet" by Arnold Fine who is the senior editor of *The Jewish Press.* Used by permission.

"Levi's Valentine" by J. Stephen Lang, reprinted from *Christian Reader,* March/April 2000. Used by permission of the author.

"I Love You Anyway" by Joe A. Harding. Used by permission of the author.

"Crumbling Sandcastles" by Sue Monk Kidd, reprinted from the July/Aug 1989 issue of *Today's Christian Woman.* Used with permission of the author. Sue Monk Kidd has authored six books, including *When the Heart Waits* and *The Dance of the Dissident Daughter* as well as other works of both fiction and nonfiction.

"Titanic Love" by Jim Priest, reprinted from *The Daily Oklahoman/Oklahoma City Times* where he is a newspaper columnist. This story won an outstanding merit award in the 1998 Amy Writing Awards. Used with permission of the author who has published a book, *Family Talk.* He and his wife, Diane, have two children and reside in Oklahoma City, OK.

"Where I Belong" by Bob Welch, reprinted from *Moody* magazine, September 1999. Used with permission of Bob Welch who is the author of *Where Roots Grow Deep* and *A Father for All Seasons,* both published by Harvest House.

"The Spirit of Sunshine" reprinted from *Ladies' Home Journal.*

"New Beginnings" by Patricia Wyman, reprinted from *Virtue* magazine, Mar/April 1997. Used with permission of the author who is retired after working as director of a school for handicapped children. She lives in Leominster, Massachusetts, with her two dogs.

"The Golden Crane" by Patricia Lorenz who is an internationally known inspirational, art-of-living writer. She is the author of *Stuff That Matters for Single Parents* and *A Hug a Day for Single Parents* and has had over four hundred articles published in numerous magazines. For speaking engagements contact Associated Speakers, Inc. in Milwaukee, Wisconsin at 800-437-7577 or write to *Lorenz and Friends,* 7457 S. Pennsylvania, Oak Creek, WI 53154. Used by permission.

"Roses for Rose" by James A. Kisner, who is the author of *Sweet Dreams and Tender Tears*. He is a modern-day poet who writes about life and the joys and tribulations along the way. You can read many of his award-winning poems on his Internet pages. For Web site address and book information, e-mail POPPYK1@aol.com. Used with permission.

"Life's Finest Hour" by Eugene S. Geissler, reprinted from *Ave Maria Press* © 1988 which drew the material from Eugene S. Geissler's book, *The Best Is Yet to Be*. Used by permission of the author.

"Rudy's Angel" by Wilma Hankins Hiawicza, reprinted from *Chicken Soup for the Single Soul*. Used with permission of the author, © 1999.

INSPIRATION

"Ol' Ed Never Forgot" by Max Lucado from *In the Eye of the Storm*, © 1991 Word Publishing, Nashville, Tennessee. All rights reserved.

"Better Than a Trophy" by Grace Witwer Housholder (www.funnyKids.com) is an author, journalist, and mother of four. She lives in Kendsville, Indiana. The umpire in the story is Brian Allen. Used by permission.

"Love and the Cabbie" by Art Buchwald, © 1992. Used by permission of the author.

"We Could Have Danced All Night" by Guy Doud from *Molder of Dreams*, a Focus on the Family book published by Tyndale House, © 1990 by Guy Doud. All rights reserved. International copyright secured. Used by permission.

"Turn About" by Steven J. Lawson from *Absolutely Sure*, © 1999 by Steve Lawson. Used by permission of Multnomah Publishers, Inc.

"Johnny" is from *Care Packages for the Workplace—Dozens of Little Things You Can Do to Regenerate Spirit at Work* by Barbara A. Glanz, CSP, McGraw-Hill, © 1996. She is also the author of *CARE Packages for the Home*, Andrews McMeel, © 1998. Barbara is an international speaker and uses "Johnny" as one of the signature stories in her presentations. You can reach her at 6140 Midnight Pass Road #802, Sarasota, FL 34242; phone (941) 312-9169; fax (941) 349-8209; bglanz@barbaraglanz.com; www.barbaraglanz.com.

"The Aroma of Christmas" by Barbara Baumgardner, reprinted from the December 9, 1984, issue of *Lookout*. Used with permission of the author who lives in Bend, Oregon. Her book, *A Passage Through Grief: An Interactive Journal* is a journaling program for the bereaved.

"Glory in the Morning" by Linda Andersen who is an inspirational author published in three hundred articles and is the author of three books. She is the editor of *Stillwater Sampler* newsletter. Linda lives with her husband, Roy, in Hamilton, MI. Used by permission, © 1986.

"A Little Girl's Dream" by Jann Mitchell, *Oregonian* columnist, lecturer, and author of *Home Sweeter Home* and *Love Sweeter Love*. Reach her at 503-221-8516 or jannmitchell@news.oregonian.com.

"You Don't Bring Me Flowers Anymore" from *More of Bits and Pieces*.

"The Cellist of Sarajevo" by Paul Sullivan, pianist and composer, Blue Hill Falls, Maine. Reprinted with permission of the author and the November 1996 *Reader's Digest*.

"The Baby Blanket" by Winona Smith. Used with permission of the author, © 1998

FAMILY

"Tribute" by Pamela McGrew. Used by permission of the author, © 2000.

"The Night the Stars Fell" by Arthur Gordon. Reprinted from *A Touch of Wonder* by Arthur Gordon, Fleming H. Revell, a division of Baker Book House Company, © 1974. Used with permission.

"The Jewelry Box" by Faith Andrews Bedford who writes for numerous magazines, especially *Country Living*, where her column, "Kids in the Country" appears regularly. She is the author of *Frank W. Benson: American Impressionist* and *The Sporting Art of Frank W. Benson*. Used by permission.

"Through a Father's Eyes" by Lonni Collins Pratt, reprinted from *Moody* magazine, September 1992. Used with permission of the author.

"A Good Heart to Lean On" by Augustus J. Bullock from *The Wall Street Journal*, June 11, 1997. Used by permission.

"A Mother's Prayer" by Marguerite Kelly from THE MOTHER'S ALMANAC by Marguerite Kelly and Elia Parsons, © 1975 by Marguerite Kelly and Elia Parsons. Used with permission from Doubleday, a division of Random House, Inc.

"New Ground" by Margaret Becker from *With New Eyes*, © 1998 by Margaret Becker, published by Harvest House Publishers, Eugene, OR 97402. Used by permission.

"The Costume" by Bill Butterworth. Reprinted from *Moody* magazine, June 1991. Used by permission of the author.

"The Redhead and the Brunette" by John William Smith from *Hugs for Mom*, © 1997 by Howard Publishing Co., Inc., West Monroe LA, 800-858-4109.

"Old Doors" by Carla Muir. Used by permission.

"Award Ceremony" by P. R. from *Sons: A Father's Love* by Bob Carlisle, © 1999, Word Publishing, Nashville, Tennessee. All rights reserved.

"Daddy Hands" by Susan Fahncke. 1325 North Highway 89, Suite 315F, Farmington, UT 84025. Web site: www.fawnkey.com, e-mail: xoxosooz@fawnkey.com. Used by permission of the author, © 1999.

"A Matter of Pride," by Terry L. Pfleghaar, reprinted from the February 1995 issue of *HomeLife* magazine. Besides writing and parenting, Terry works at her local public library and is attending a university. Anna, now ten years old, is trying to grow her hair out. Used by permission of author.

MEMORIES

"Their Best" by Connie Lounsbury from the Oct/Nov. 1999 issue of *Lifewise* magazine. Connie Lounsbury is a freelance writer who frequently writes for *Guideposts*. She lives in rural Monticello, Minnesota, with her husband David. They have four daughters and nine grandchildren. Used with permission of the author.

"A Pair of Worn-Out Shoes" by Thelda Bevens who lives in Bend, Oregon. Used by permission of the author.

"The Rich Family" by Eddie Ogan, reprinted from April/May 1999 issue of *Virtue* magazine. Used with permission of the author.

"When Strangers Passed Through" by Ruth Lee, reprinted from *Gospel Publishing*, January 25, 1998. Used with permission of the author. Ruth Lee's essays, fiction and poetry, have appeared in a variety of publications. She is a seven times first place award winning member of Missouri Writer's Guild.

"The Little Apron" by Charlene Ann Baumbich from *Mama Said There'd Be Days Like This*, © 1995 by Charlene Ann Baumbich. Published by Servant Publications, Box 8617, Ann Arbor, Michigan 48107. Used with permission.

"The Etching" by Barbara Baumgardner. Used with permission from the author.

"Lilacs to Remember" by Faith Andrews Bedford who writes for numerous magazines, especially *Country Living*, where her column, "Kids in the Country" appears regularly. She is the author of *Frank W. Benson: American Impressionist* and *The Sporting Art of Frank W. Benson*. Used by permission.

"My Mother's Gloves" by Sharron Dean McCann, reprinted from the Sept/Oct 1992 issue of *Virtue* magazine. Used by permission of author who lives in Grand Marais, MN.

"Porch Swing" by Brenda A. Christensen. Used by permission.

"The Barn" by Sharron Dean McCann. Used by permission.

LIFE

"Stepping Stones" by Gail Brook Burket. Used by permission of the estate of Gail Brook Burket.

"A Light in the Window" by Faith Andrews Bedford who writes for numerous magazines, especially *Country Living*, where her column, "Kids in the Country" appears regularly. She is the author of *Frank W. Benson: American Impressionist* and *The Sporting Art of Frank W. Benson*. Used by permission.

"Creature Comfort" by Bill Holton, reprinted by courtesy of *PetLife* magazine, published by Magnolia Media Group, Fort Worth, TX.

"A Mailbox Mercy" by Nancy Jo Sullivan from *Moments of Grace,* © 2000 by Nancy Jo Sullivan. Used by permission of Multnomah Publishers, Inc.

"Front Porch Swing" by Kim Engstrom. Used by permission of the author, © 1999.

"Laughter and Life Jackets" by N. C. Haas. The author, writing under the pen name N. C. Haas, is a freelance writer living in Southern California. She can be contacted through WORDable SOLUTIONS, (714)775-6705, or by e-mail at: armhumber@aol.com.

"Growing Older" by Dale Evans Rogers from *Time Out, Ladies!* Fleming H. Revell, a division of Baker Book House Company, © 1966. Used by permission.

"The Faith of a Child" by Deborah Hammons, reprinted from the Sept/Oct 1994 issue of *Virtue* magazine. Used with permission from the author who currently teaches high school English. Deborah has written and produced over seventy TV shows on the extraordinary people of Wyoming.

"Breaking Up Grandma" by Marjorie Maki from *For She Is the Tree of Life* by Valerie Kack-Brice, © 1995 by Valerie Kack-Brice, by permission of Conari Press.

"The Fox and the Writer" by Philip Yancey, reprinted from the September 7, 1998, issue of *Christianity Today.* Used by permission of the author.

"To God from Ben" by Glenda Barbre from *Christian Reader* magazine, September/October 1996. Used by permission of the author.

"Choirs of Angels" by Cheryl Gochnauer who is the author of *So You Want to Be a Stay-at-Home Mom.* She also writes *Homebodies,* a weekly newspaper column and online ministry (www.homebodies.org) for family-focused women.

"Tornado Warning" by Sarah E. Farrow, reprinted from the June/July 1999 issue of *Virtue* magazine. Used by permission of the author who lives with her husband of thirty-two years in Colorado.

"Sharing," author unknown. Reprinted from *You Gotta Keep Dancin'* by Tim Hansel.

FAITH

"Trusting God" by Verdell Davis from *Let Me Grieve, But Not Forever,* Word Publishing, Nashville, Tennessee. All rights reserved.

"Heaven's Gold" by Rhonda Reese from *Christian Reader* magazine, Nov/Dec 1998. Used by permission of the author.

"An Empty Chair" by Walter Burkhardt from *Tell the Next Generation,* Paulist Press, Ramsey NJ, © 1982. Used by permission.

"Spirit Renewed" by Barbara Baumgardner from *RV Companion* magazine, November/December 1999, P.O. Box 174, Loveland, CO 80539. Used by permission.

"Tommy" by John Powell from *The Challenge of Faith,* Thomas Moore Press, © 1998. Used by permission.

"Giving God Pleasure" by Ruth Bell Graham from *Legacy of a Pack Rat,* Thomas Nelson Publishers, Nashville TN, © 1989. Used by permission of the author.

"Honey, I'm Proud of You" by Lydia E. Harris, MA, who is a freelance writer living in Seattle, Washington, with Milt, her husband of thirty-two years. She has two adult children and one grandson.

"Turning Point" by Bill Butterworth, from *When Life Doesn't Turn Out Like You Planned,* Thomas Nelson, Nashville TN, © 1995. Used with permission from author.

"When the Lord Says Pray!" by Cheri Fuller from *When Families Pray,* © 1999 by Cheri Fuller. Used by permission of Multnomah Publishers, Inc.

"You'll Find Patience" by Clark Cothern from *At the Heart of Every Great Father,* © 1998 by Clark Cothern. Used by permission of Multnomah Publishers, Inc.

"A Resting Place" by Mayo Mathers reprinted from the Sept/Oct 1995 issue of *Today's Christian Woman.* Used by permission of the author who lives in Bend, Oregon, with her husband, Steve. They are the parents of two sons.

"Angel at Work?" by Billy Graham from *Unto the Hills,* © 1996, Word Publishing, Nashville, Tennessee. All rights reserved.

ACKNOWLEDGMENTS

"An Ice Cream Solo" by Barbara Baumgardner who is a hospice volunteer which laid the foundation for her first book, *A Passage Through Grief: An Interactive Journal*. A year later, *A Passage Through Divorce* was published. She can be contacted by e-mail at barbarab@empnet.com. Used by permission of the author.

"Your Abba's Arms" by Max Lucado from *The Great House of God*, © 1993, Word Publishing, Nashville, Tennessee. All rights reserved.

"Circle of Faith" by Dick Eastman from the August 1999 issue of *Every Home for Christ*, P.O. Box 35930, Colorado Springs, CO 80935-3593.

WEST GERMAN POLITICS IN THE MID-EIGHTIES

Crisis and Continuity

edited by

H.G. Peter Wallach
George K. Romoser

PRAEGER SPECIAL STUDIES • PRAEGER SCIENTIFIC

New York • Philadelphia • Eastbourne, UK
Toronto • Hong Kong • Tokyo • Sydney

Library of Congress Cataloging in Publication Data
Main entry under title:

West German politics in the mid-eighties.

Includes index.
1. Germany (West)—Politics and government—
1982–   —Addresses, essays, lectures.   I. Wallach,
H.G. Peter   II. Romoser, George K.
JN3971.A91W475   1985   324.943'0878   84–18071
ISBN 0-03-001658-4 (alk. paper)

Published in 1985 by Praeger Publishers
CBS Educational and Professional Publishing
a Division of CBS Inc.
521 Fifth Avenue, New York, NY 10175 USA

56789 052 987654321

Printed in the United States of America
on acid-free paper

ACKNOWLEDGMENTS

The original essays that make up this volume were prepared by scholars ready to make changes as events dictated and conversant with many nuances of West German affairs. Many constructively criticized the essays of colleagues. None were afraid to make suggestions to the editors, and all made efforts to communicate in order to clarify issues that arose. The result is that this book is a truly cooperative effort.

Much of this cooperation rests on collaborative efforts over the years under the rubric of the Conference Group on German Politics, an independent voluntary organization of scholars. Thus, when George K. Romoser spent three semesters in Germany, in 1982–83, filling in for Professor Rudolf Wildenmann at the University of Mannheim, it was possible for him and H.G. Peter Wallach to plan the current volume fairly quickly. The events of the period, especially the departure from power of Chancellor Helmut Schmidt, and the emergence of a new governing coalition in the Federal Republic, provided the immediate stimuli, but the intention was to examine these events in a longer-range context.

A number of persons besides editors and authors contributed to the completion of the book and each chapter. Financial and clerical aid in the production of the work was provided by the Central Connecticut State University Foundation and the Department of Political Science at the same institution. Political Science Chairman C. William Kerr arranged financial help, and Lorraine Jurgiliewicz provided secretarial support.

Many of the authors received research materials, gained interviews with politicians and access to meetings, and had their ways smoothed for travel to Germany with the aid of the German Information Center in New York and its parent organization in Bonn, the Federal Press and Information Office (Bundespresseamt). Election observation tours over the years—including 1983—were organized by these offices for a number of the authors in this volume and carried through with the help of the federal government's efficient organization for international communication, *Inter Nationes*. No favors have been asked, and scholarly independence has been retained. Thus, thanks are due to a number of directors of the German Information Center in New York: Helmut Rückriegel, Rüdiger Freiherr von Wechmar, Julius Hoffmann, Carl-Heinz Neukirchen, and Heinz Schneppen, as well as Winfried Bonse and earlier chiefs of the United States section of the Bundespresseamt in Bonn.

The First Pacific Coast Workshop on German Affairs, organized at California State University, Long Beach, in April 1983 by Christian Søe, Wilm Peters, and George Romoser, with the support of President Steven Horn of that university and of foundations in the area, provided an opportunity for many of the authors represented in this volume to exchange views and compare notes after the West German election of March. The New England Workshops on German Affairs, a regional offshoot of Romoser's long association with the Conference Group on German Politics, have provided another venue for discussion.

Romoser would like especially to thank Professor Ruldolf Wildenmann for the recent opportunity to teach in Germany, and among many other colleagues and associates in that country to whom he is indebted, would mention especially Professors Hans Maier and Kurt Sontheimer of the University of Munich, who arranged for an earlier extended stay at their institution.

Wallach received critical encouragement from Professors G. Lowell Field and Stuart Colie. The Zentralarchiv für Empirische Sozialforschung at the University of Cologne consistently made it possible for him to carry out research in West Germany, and for his essay in this volume he received support as a Mellon Visiting Faculty Fellow at Yale University.

Russell J. Dalton received support from the Council on Research and Creativity at Florida State University.

Arthur M. Hanhardt, Jr., wishes to thank Craig Stauffer, Frau Marianne Strenger, and Frau Gisela Fisher for their help in providing resources, and the Battelle Human Affairs Research Centers in Seattle for support to observe the 1983 elections.

Christian Søe received grants from the National Endowment for the Humanities and the German Academic Exchange Service (DAAD), as well as from the California State University at Long Beach.

CONTENTS

WEST GERMAN
POLITICS IN THE
MID-EIGHTIES

1

INTRODUCTION

H.G. Peter Wallach
George K. Romoser

West German voters had reason for confidence on the warm, bright, and cloudless October election Sunday of 1980: confidence enough to be the only Western democratic nation to return an incumbent from that day until they themselves voted again, in 1983.

Their confidence reflected the international respect in which Chancellor Helmut Schmidt was held, the stability of their currency, and the requests German managers had been receiving from throughout the world for lessons on effectiveness. It was a comfort derived of a strong social safety net and some relief that the Russians were confronting the experiments with freedom in nearby Poland cautiously.

Thus on that Sunday many voters went to church before voting (and some no doubt heard a priest ask them to cast a ballot for the Christian Democratic parties) and others simply walked to the school or town hall where they placed checks on the two-part voting form. Indeed, calm was the order of the day.

This did not mean citizens were passive or unconcerned about the election. Two days earlier, when the last debate was aired, nearly three-quarters of them had watched the full two and a half hours; and the numerous street placards, television advertisements, and news articles had drummed party slogans into their minds. The faces of Schmidt and Franz-Josef Strauss were familiar to them, as were those of some less well known figures. For in West Germany, where 80 percent turn out for elections, voting is taken seriously.

The voters knew that their country was starting to suffer from the same economic malaise that affected all industrialized nations: The deficit financing introduced by Schmidt had become a campaign issue. Increasing

1

unemployment and bankruptcies were leading to nervousness in a nation that had starved in 1920, suffered rampant inflation a few years later, and been rescued by currency reform in 1948. International finances were putting pressure on the Deutsche Mark.

There were other problems. The new Green party had gained representation in one state parliament, and with creative posters and demonstrations it threatened to be a force for the future. Allies were becoming more shrill about the role they expected of Germany in future relations. In the United States the beginnings of what would be a "bad press" were appearing.

These issues might have been addressed by an election, but the political parties of 1980 had not focused on them. Having allowed the boisterous minister-president of Bavaria, Franz-Josef Strauss, to run as candidate for chancellor, the Christian Democrats were undecided about their future leadership. Meanwhile, the strong left wing of the Social Democratic party, which opposed capitalist policies and a variety of NATO programs, was making it difficult for Schmidt to maintain an even course.

So on that October Sunday in 1980 German voters returned the incumbent coalition, while not increasing support for the Social Democratic party. They gave an additional edge to the junior partner, the Free Democratic party. Germans seemed to want the Free Democratic party to hold the left wing of the Social Democratic party in check.

That check would become a veto power. As unemployment continued to rise, as bankruptcies and the federal debt continued to increase, and as the Bonn government was put under increased pressure to support the international policies of the new Reagan administration, the Social Democrats found it impossible to process the resulting divisions. The Social Democrats lost more and more power, while the Greens gained seats in one state parliament after another. Hardly two years from the date of the 1980 election the Free Democratic leadership decided to leave the coalition. They blamed differences within the Social Democratic party and immorality within the government for their decision. In return, there was Social Democratic talk of Free Democratic party "treason" to the coalition.

Thus, the Free Democrats joined with the Christian Union parties to form a new government as doubts unique to Germans, though having their parallel in every advanced democracy, became explicit. Could popular government withstand economic division? Would diversity fracture unity in the absence of the resources that ameliorate demands? Was a strong leader necessary? What about the impact of radicalization, polarization, increased international competitiveness?

How would West Germany adjust to the future?

Moreover, Germany still suffered from suspicions based on the past and on its power that continued to hamper it in international affairs. At the same time, domestically, under the Social-Liberal regime, a new egalitarianism had been institutionalized but not fully accepted, and some students and citizens had programmatic visions more closely related to romanticism than to pragmatism.

What might happen? For a few months doomsayers in the United States predicted the worst for the Central European ally. The governments of both the United States and the Soviet Union seemed to feel that the internal doubt implied the possibility for wielding greater influence themselves. There was even talk of "ungovernability." In Hamburg and Munich, no less than Siegen and Langenburg, there were people urging a new election so the Federal Republic once again might demonstrate responsibility and capability.

Obviously, the internal reasons for calling the election involved all the usual ambitions of politics and politicians. All the parties once again predicted vindication.

Thus, an election was called for March 6, 1983.

It was the first one requiring special interpretation of the postwar constitution, and for a while it seems to have established a new stability for West Germany.

These are the topics of this volume: recent West German politics and the import of those politics for the eighties. So that the past is understood, and the present perceived appropriately, scholars who have written seminal works on the Federal Republic of Germany here provide contemporary analysis. They also point out the import of recent events for the future.

In the first chapter, George K. Romoser, long time chairman of the Conference Group on German Politics, describes the events and presents the conditions that have brought Germany to its current point. The second chapter is an empirical explication of West German public opinion by two of the authors of *Germany Transformed,* Russell J. Dalton and Kendall L. Baker. Then William E. Paterson, the noted British writer on political parties, provides a chapter on the Christian Union parties. This is followed by a chapter on the Social Democrats by Gerard Braunthal, author of *The West German Social Democrats, 1969–1982.* On the unique role of the Free Democrats there is a chapter by the U.S. chronicler Christian Søe. The newest West German political party, the Greens, is described by a scholar who has assiduously followed their rise, Wilhelm P. Bürklin.

Two chapters that examine the most important of the policy implications of these changes in recent West German politics follow. Arthur M.

Hanhardt, Jr., a student of international and strategic affairs in both East and West Germany, writes on international relations. On the economic issues there is a section by H.G. Peter Wallach, who has written on the linkages between elections and economics throughout Europe.

In conclusion, central themes are reassessed. These provide a guide for examining future developments in the Bonn republic.

The 1983 election, and the events leading to it, are the starting point for this book. That is the election that was to confirm the government of the near future. It was held early in the spring, on a cloudy day.

2

GERMANY AND THE GERMANS—
A REPORT FROM THE EIGHTIES

George K. Romoser

Seated in the Reichstag—now reconstructed in a curious mixture of old pomposity and contemporary functionalism—12 West Germans of various persuasions debated in January 1983 how well the postwar Germans had "come to terms" with Hitler's regime in the 50 years since its beginnings.[1] For any foreigner it was a fascinating moment, heavy with symbolism. The "overcoming" of the Nazi period became a matter for concentrated discussion. For a foreigner who has spent much time attempting to comprehend linkages and breaks between German history and the German present, the meeting in Berlin that frosty afternoon raised once again the problem of how to clarify the relationship between "the German question" of the past and the German reality of today. For—merely to take one example—less than two months after the weighty and somewhat agonized Berlin discussions marking the anniversary of Hitler's accession to power on January 30, 1933, the West Germans demonstrated once again a solid pattern of democratic performance. On March 6, 1983, they went to the polls and confirmed the establishment of a new governing majority in Bonn—without revolution, without riots, without the extremism or unpredictability thought by many to be at the root of "the German question" in politics.

This theme of relationships between the historical record and the contours of practical politics in today's West Germany lies at the heart of most discussions of Germany and the Germans—whether such discussions be learned or popular, wide ranging or based on momentary impressions of foreign visitors. No other people is viewed from abroad in such a manner, and perhaps no other people is so involved with a conscious or unconscious confrontation with its past. Are the West Germans now truly democratic?

What of a possible return to nationalism, or a movement away from the West? Is not West Germany becoming fragile in its politics? These and similar questions may not dominate everyday political conversations, but they tend to be the questions raised when the discussion outside the country turns to West Germany and the West Germans.

In truth, it will be many, many generations—and understandably so— before many persons are able to think of Germany and the Germans without associating country and people with the crimes of the Hitler period. Moreover, the legacy of authoritarian politics well into the twentieth century is also not forgotten.[2] The resulting psychological set often helps engender evident suspicion toward today's social and political developments in West Germany. It is a mood emphatically present among the West Germans themselves: Much of the Green and peace movements are based on psychological efforts to "come to terms with the past."

Such considerations form the backdrop for this book and for the reflections in this opening chapter. Regarding the latter, numerous disclaimers are in order. In these reflections, only the Federal Republic—West Germany—is under review. Moreover, the brush strokes are broad in the present chapter: The effort is to set forth basic contours of the changes in the Federal Republic's political life and values in the early 1980s, leaving to others more detailed examination of events, personalities, and institutions. The emphasis here is on those "general ideas" of which Alexis de Tocqueville wrote:

> Among all civilized peoples, the study of politics creates, or at least gives shape to, general ideas; and from those general ideas are formed the problems in the midst of which politicians must struggle, and also the laws which they imagine they create. Political theories form a sort of intellectual atmosphere created by both governors and governed in society, and both unwittingly derive from it the principles of their action.

Ideas, however, as Tocqueville also realized, neither are identical with political reality nor fully explain it. The distinction is especially important when studying Germany. For the reasons set forth earlier, there is a tendency, when studying that country, to view the present through the filter provided by the past. This creates the danger of missing current realities entirely. Thus, not simply ideas about Germany's wayward past are important to understanding the present, but evidence of how the political system actually functions today.

Intensified protest on the one hand and calm and normalcy on the other—this apparent paradox highlights basic features of the West German political system. A thorough discussion of past and present in German political experience cannot rest at only a few themes. The values and ideas expressed in political and cultural criticism—especially the view that postwar Germany is merely a "restoration"—have both a theoretical and a practical aspect, and both must be considered. Protest behavior, demonstrations, and the rise of the Green political movement are efforts at practical politics, but so too is the actual functioning of the political institutions. The ability of these institutions to channel and dampen protest accompanies the belief systems and attitudes of mass publics which support the postwar institutions and policies of the Federal Republic. The overall picture is diverse and seemingly contradictory.

To recite these seeming contradictions does not resolve them, but it does caution us to avoid overdramatization of single elements in West German society and politics. Study of the Federal Republic and its policies involves consideration of a regime and society with strong pragmatic qualities and with a diversity of interest groups and political movements. Moreover, West Germany has a demonstrated record for combining political stability with tolerance for protest and dissent. The country cannot be described with only a few generalities or historical parallels.

The present volume aims to contribute to a thorough discussion, beginning in this chapter with an introductory sketch of continuing as well as new elements in West German politics, ideas, and political culture. The chapter's conclusion has already been broached: Elements of change coexist with elements of stability, both in governmental policies and in fundamental political values. A new governing majority emerged in 1982 and was confirmed emphatically by the federal election of March 6, 1983. Yet simultaneously, dissenting behavior—especially in the peace movement and in demonstrations against the placement of U.S. Pershing II and Cruise missiles—seemed to reach more segments of the population. Conservatives spoke confidently in 1983 of a *Wende,* a change in the climate of opinion—and not without some evidence—while at the same time, as pointed out in other chapters in this volume, indications of dissent from the system, especially among young persons, were strong.[3] Truly, it seems, one might adopt the phrase of Hans Magnus Enzensberger, even if for different reasons, and write of "the ongoing effort to explain the mysteries of German Democracy."[4]

A tension between innovation and change, on the one side, and permanence and continuity, on the other, may be a phenomenon of all politics, not to speak of many other areas of human life. It has been given a special weight in Germany by the historical memories already mentioned and by

the position of the Germans in the center of a still-divided Europe. The record since 1945, or since the founding of the Federal Republic in 1949,
shows a central, strong, and continuing concern of the West German
populace for security. This concern embraces a range of values and attitudes, including interest in economic security and in a politics and way of
life which avoid risks and "extremism." It was perhaps best summed up in
election slogans from the fifties and sixties such as "no experiments" and
"safety first," but it has extended well beyond political campaigns and well
beyond the sixties.[5]

The years well into the sixties, however, were devoted most of all to
physical reconstruction, to the emergence of a West German affluent society, and to a remarkably noncontroversial social and political life. The term
restoration was early on used by those critical of postwar developments,
and even in the fifties there were voices of dissent—protest at the Western
Allies, especially the Americans, for their alleged role in placing economic
prosperity in West Germany ahead of "real reforms," protest at German
rearmament, protest at the alleged fact that the past was *unbewältigt* (not
overcome). These were minority views, especially cultivated by a segment
of the literati and intelligentsia, but they foreshadowed broader movements
beginning in the mid-to-late sixties. Such movements, in turn, were related
to cultural and social changes associated with the development of an
affluent society itself.

The phenomena which began to emerge in the sixties ranged from the
"student revolt" starting around 1965 to basic changes in *Alltagskultur*—
the daily way of life of substantial segments of the populace—to alterations
in occupational patterns, with the prominence of a "new class" of professional or semiprofessional white-collar employees in the service industries, to the appearance of "postmaterialist" values as distinct from the
"materialist" values which had guided the era of economic reconstruction,[6] to the establishment of a new governmental majority after years of
dominance by Konrad Adenauer and the conservative Christian Democratic Union and (in Bavaria) Christian Social Union coalition parties
(CDU/CSU).

Difficult as it is to summarize these changes in a few words, one
would not go far wrong by labeling more democracy and more reform as
central notions. Two influential and symptomatic books of the mid-sixties
articulated these ideas: Ralf Dahrendorf's *Society and Democracy in Germany* and Karl Jaspers's *Where is Germany Heading?* The first stressed
the importance of discussion—conflict-laden discussion—in a democratic
polity and argued that the Germans were not yet "modern" enough because

they were still too oriented to paternalistic patterns of authority. Conflict was too often avoided or controlled rather than moderated through the participatory give-and-take of confident democracy. Dahrendorf's sociological essays were echoed or accompanied by other, more pointed appeals for "more participation" and more dissent from authority.[7]

As for Karl Jaspers, many might say that he represented the ideal reformer for Germans: a renowned philosopher who yet argued for political commitment, a writer who also warned of nuclear dangers, a moralist who soon after the war had raised *The Question of German Guilt*[8]—and withal one who was truly without limitations in his somewhat vague hopes for a different kind of postwar Germany:

> One speaks of a vacuum of our political consciousness. In truth, we do not yet have a political aim deeply engraved in our hearts. Indeed, there still is for us no source of a political ideal, no consciousness of tradition, and no consciousness of a goal. There is for us hardly any other "present" than that of the will to private life, to living well, and to security.[9]

This kind of unease was repeated in numerous and increasing numbers of ways after 1965, and it remains a hallmark of protest attitudes today. Indeed, with the rise of the peace movement in the early eighties, Jaspers's works have enjoyed something of a revival.

"To dare more democracy" and "to create a modern Germany" were the catchwords of the Social Democratic party in the elections of 1969. This election brought to an end the period of somewhat uncertain direction which commenced with the decline of Adenauer's influence after 1961 and extended through the uncertain chancellorship of Ludwig Erhard (1963–66) to the period of the Grand Coalition of the major Christian Democratic and Social Democratic parties under a sort of interim chancellor, Kurt-Georg Kiesinger, between 1966 and 1969. It also marked the creation of a stable governmental majority (now of Social Democrats and Free Democrats, under Willy Brandt and Walter Scheel)[10] and the unleashing of a "reform euphoria." In short, change, reform, and "modernization" were now to have their day after the years of conservative attention to economic reconstruction and caution about "experiments."

Be it noted, however, that this opening of the possibilities for change was always within the framework of a stable political system, that is, an alternation of governments with secure majorities, and a continuation of basic patterns of "orderly" social and political behavior by the vast majority of the population. The student unrest of the late sixties, the rise of an extraparliamentary opposition, the emergence of various forms of direct democracy through citizen initiatives (*Bürgerinitiativen*) and other methods, the sensational emergence of political terrorism in the seventies—all these evidences of change were accompanied by an ongoing stability in the fundamental political institutions of West Germany and in fundamental patterns of political behavior, such as participation on behalf of moderate parties in elections by the vast majority of the population.

Indeed, even the preparation of the change in governing majority required a long period and was approached gingerly on all sides. Konrad Adenauer's political power was waning considerably as early as 1961, but he did not leave office till the fall of 1963. For three more years Ludwig Erhard engaged in what might be termed a confused attempt to transform the CDU/CSU forces into more broadly anchored parties "of the people"; he ultimately fell from power because he was neither able to project an image of sovereign competence (which has consistently been an important qualification for high office in the eyes of the voters in the Federal Republic) nor build a broad enough base of popular support. Change was in the air, both in the political system and in social reality. It was not only the small Free Democratic party (FDP)—until then (and again after 1969) the "tongue on the scales," helping to create a governing majority through alliance with a major party—which realized this and moved away from Erhard and the CDU/CSU. Voices of dissension were substantial inside the latter parties. Meanwhile, the Social Democratic party (SPD) had been moving since at least 1959—the date of its Godesberg Program, which turned the party away from what may be called militant opposition to moderate opposition—toward participation in a government.

For three years of the Grand Coalition, certain cautious initiatives foreshadowed steps of the future Social-Liberal coalition, but it was also a period of frustration for the exponents of change. Chancellor Kiesinger functioned as a sort of professional seminar leader in the cabinet and was known for avoiding decisions. This approach, however, reflected more than Kiesinger's personality. It showed a characteristic feature of the West German political system: ensuring stability and security before essaying change. Certainly, at least part of this caution reflected conservative doubts about the governmental competence (*Regierungsfähigkeit*) of the SPD. In this respect, strong historical traditions of suspiciousness in the German bourgeoisie undoubtedly continued to have influence.[11]

The result of this extended interlude, however, was to dam desires for reform and thereby to further exaggerate the hopes for such changes once initiated. One expression among many—and by far not the most pointed— may be cited, from a volume published in 1970 by the respected (not "fringe") publishing house of R. Piper in Munich, which addressed the question in the title "Departure from Authoritarian Democracy?—The Federal Republic in Transformation":

> More quickly than some observers of the political scene expected, there followed upon the prelude of the "revolutionary year of the youth" 1968 the long-postponed—far too long-postponed—change of government in the autumn of 1969. The seething youth, whose intellectual potential the ruling bourgeoisie for a long time thought it could downplay and ignore, suddenly—and noisily—broke through in action the arena which had been "taboo"—that of the claims of the State to authority. It articulated the concealed class contradictions in the society, not only *verbally,* as in the "left salons" of the fifties, but through *concrete action.* That this concretization partly became lost in blind actionism and in an elitist jargon related to it, is the object of criticism of almost all authors in this book. But there can be no way in which one can avoid the fact that . . . the revolt of the young has brought the society into movement. In the governmental declaration of the present "small coalition" of SPD and FDP, this has found expression, even if at first very cautiously, and up till now in many respects very indirectly formulated and merely reflected in statements of "purpose." In the seventies, a program of internal reform should be realized—for this, there is certainly still much, perhaps everything, to do.[12]

The level of expectation of reform advocates or sympathizers was thus rooted in a complex of political, psychological, economic, and demographic trends. Most striking about this level of expectation was its close association with generalized cultural criticism about the style of life in West Germany, and in Western societies altogether. The postmaterial value syndrome involved criticism of materialism at the same time that it incorporated notions of self-realization—self-realization in ways other than material possession.[13] Quality-of-life began to emerge as a new political program, providing for the future a direct link to the Green and peace movements of the present day.

It is probable, however, that the specific emergence of a quality-of-life approach already reflected a certain disenchantment with the achievements of reform politics after 1969. The policies of the Social-Liberal coalition indeed improved the social welfare system, reflected the loosening of traditional mores with regard to sex and the family, and achieved changes in the Federal Republic's relations with its eastern neighbors—the famous new *Ostpolitik* aimed at reaching a *modus vivendi* with East Germany (the

"German Democratic Republic") and Poland above all. But no revolution in political institutions took place, and the basic patterns of governmental activity and economic life continued. Indeed, by the election of 1976, Chancellor Helmut Schmidt and the SPD could conduct an election on the basis of a supposed model (*Modell Deutschland*) of political-economic management which was a hybrid of both Christian Democratic and Social Democratic ideas and policies.[14] At that time the repute of the Federal Republic as the model of an advanced industrial nation stood at its high, at least outside Germany. But reformers were disappointed, to say the least.

If there were only one central point to make about views on stability, harmony, and consensus versus change, reform, and innovation in the Federal Republic since the late sixties, it would be that it is the SPD which has disappointed many of the would-be innovators. This central role of the SPD was already clear at the time of the developing uneasiness of segments of the populace with the CDU state, as it was termed by opponents, in the fifties and early sixties. Social democracy stood for the possibility of changes and reform, and for many had a much more unblemished record on the issue of complicity in the Nazi past than did "bourgeois" parties. However, the SPD was able to break through its limited voter support of some 30 percent only by broadening its appeal to wider segments of the populace.

Given the increasing affluence of the West Germans in the late fifties and in the sixties, and the development of a new class of professionals oriented to mobility both in a literal sense and in ways of thinking, the party did this by stressing the modernization theme: "We will create a modern Germany." Eventually, however, the very vagueness or ambiguity of such appeals caught up with the SPD. It appears that the general tenor of West German political life—the effort to combine and balance the desire for stability and the desire for innovation—has been mirrored in the internal history of the SPD. The very approaches and slogans which made it possible to expand voter support for the SPD militated against changes of a drastic kind in the society, for these might be seen (at least by some) as threatening stability and economic security. Thus, at least as far as its public appeals and image are concerned, the party appears to have moved more and more in a direction away from specific class-oriented notions of reform and change to general and relatively unthreatening "postmaterialist" formulations. This is true even with respect to the latest tendency in the party—the opposition to new American missiles and the identification with the peace issue. Indeed, it is especially true with regard to such issues. Peace, for instance, appears to have a universal human meaning unthreatening to any specific interest other than that, presumably, of arms makers, aggressive militarists, and

American Reaganites. It—and the environmental issue—is thus perfectly compatible with generalized notions of democratization and modernization and reform, for to solve this issue would be the highest achievement of all modernity, all democracy, all reform.[15]

The constellation of interests supporting the SPD at the start of the Social-Liberal coalition in 1969 was, of course, more complex than can be reviewed in this brief chapter. But the general line of development was clear. Responding to the social and value changes which expanded the horizon of expectations, the coalition tended to inflate that horizon further through its rhetoric. Since few wished to purchase modernization or reform at the expense of stability, an orderly life, or expectations of continuing affluence, the coalition governments under both Willy Brandt (1969–74) and Helmut Schmidt (1974–82) sooner or later responded primarily to the latter inclinations. This happened with ever-increasing emphasis under Schmidt, though he was ultimately unable to continue balancing the forces in a sovereign "managerial" fashion. The combination of new social programs and efforts at stability through managerial skills led to a mixed result which itself contained the seeds of a Wende (new direction) and a change of government.[16]

Increased social programs led to increased size and complexity in bureaucracies, thereby identifying the SPD in West Germany with an increased presence of the state—a major point of attack for the small-is-beautiful, antisystem forces which emerged in the seventies and eighties. The SPD in particular was responsible for developing and implementing various crackdowns on dissidents—not only on terrorists following the serious incidents of the mid-seventies, but also on alleged radicals entering the civil service.[17] A more powerful state apparatus seemed to develop at the same time that the notion of a greater freedom was writ large on the agenda of change, modernization, and reform.

Moreover, it has been commonplace to say that a prospering economy in West Germany could place all tensions and difficulties in the shadows, or even more sharply, that the true test of the postwar German democracy would come when and if it had to face serious economic difficulties. The pattern of the years since the first oil crisis of 1973 confirmed the high priority given to economic stability within the West German political and social systems. As indicated earlier, this pattern is rooted in the essential characteristics of political and economic management by elite groups no less than in the attitudes of a mass citizenry toward expectations of future prosperity and personal income. Strong *gouvernmental* orientations by voters—that is, attitudes focused on issues of the presumed competence of political leaders to effectively manage government and economy—thus are perhaps the deepest reason for the sense of frustrated reform which began to spread after the first few years of the Social-Liberal coalition.

The managerial approach of the Social-Liberal coalition was challenged both from within that coalition and from without. Changes in party membership and in the roster of activists in both the SPD and FDP reflected an influx of new elements from the professional classes and service industries, weakening the influence of the trade union and gouvernmental forces among the Social Democrats and of the laissez-faire business interests among the Free Democrats. In both parties, "frustrated reformers" helped undermine the coherence of party programs and party actions. Outside these governing parties, the "conservative alternatives" marked time, being aided in undermining the image of governmental competence by the multiplication of new forms of political activity related to the "alternative cultures" which had emerged in the mid-sixties. While the consequences of "new politics" and "new left" positions of the sixties in the United States have frequently lain primarily in "cultural" and "lifestyle" phenomena (a tendency certainly not absent in West Germany either), the Federal Republic has also seen definite political consequences.

Quite early during the Social-Liberal coalition, there was a noticeable movement in the direction of new forms of political action to parallel the cultural changes which had begun in the sixties. The most striking new form was that of the *Bürgerinitiativen*—usually local citizen action groups outside the framework of the parties—which focused on a great variety of issues, with environmental concerns being one of the most prominent.[18] Parallel to the varied effects of the alternative or counterculture emerging from the sixties—ranging from various forms of sexual permissiveness or exhibitionism to dress styles to music to the "drop out" syndrome, to terrorism in a few cases—alternative politics developed, leading to what has already been referred to as the mixed character of West German democracy; a remarkable stability and yet remarkable protest, and a cultural-political dichotomy not unknown in other countries[19] and yet thought by many to be particularly unsettling in Germany. For alienation from "normal politics and from political parties, and the presumption that a healthier polity would exist if nonpoliticians determined affairs, raises negative associations drawn from German history.

It is likely that this mixed picture will dominate West German society for a considerable time, however. The Greens and the peace movement activists are the direct outgrowth of dissension within the SPD and FDP and of the new forms of political action outside the party sphere. While the mixed picture of stability and protest in West Germany has similarities and differences with analogous situations in other Western democracies, in an important sense the West German resolution of the tensions between cultural change and political stability has been more effective than that in the United States, for example. The latter country has seen gyrations in the occupancy of the highest political office accompanied by drastic decline in party efficacy, the proliferation of "one-interest" groups, and an avoidance of overall policy direction which has practically become an endemic avoidance of real issues. Partly because of the much smaller size of the West German polity and the tight formal and informal communications networks, the citizens experience political issues in a much more direct way. This can lead outsiders to think that the political climate is more "overheated" than is actually the case; in fact, contrasting trends can coexist. Moreover, despite some appearances to the contrary, West Germany society has shown a consistent strengthening in the quality of tolerance, as a recent important study shows.[20]

The process through which a new government emerged in the Federal Republic in October 1982—and was confirmed by the election of March 1983—was in its own way as lengthy and complicated as the earlier transition from Adenauer's "Chancellor Democracy" to the Social-Liberal coalition. In the federal election of September 1980, the CDU/CSU was not well-enough organized to take advantage of the erosion of the Social-Liberal coalition's strength. The nomination of Franz-Josef Strauss as chancellor-candidate of the CDU/CSU—a long-sought goal by that durable politician—made personality issues the underlying basis of the 1980 campaign.[21] For while many persons—especially in Bavaria—were devotedly loyal to this talented but rough-and-tumble figure, he also aroused dislike among many Germans, particularly from the north. Against Schmidt, who carefully sought to project the image of managerial competence, he was probably a predestined loser, given German political patterns. Again in 1980, the propensity of the West German voter to avoid risks was displayed.

Moreover, in 1980, the diffuse protest movement had not yet organized successfully in the form of a national party. The Greens, from the very beginning basically a decentralized movement growing out of local citizen initiatives, were not even organized to the loose extent possible by 1983. And, of course, Strauss's candidacy tended to divert protest votes to the SPD, thus temporarily concealing the splits in that party and in its sources of support. The economic situation gave only early signs to the public of the coming budgetary and unemployment problems.

In the chapters that follow, the course of events between 1980 and 1982 is illuminated from more detailed perspectives. What is important to note here is the conjunction of economic recession, inter- and intraparty disagreements among the parties of the ruling coalition, leadership weariness in the SPD,[22] the spread of a certain mentality of crisis and depression, and the reorganization of the forces of cultural criticism around the Green political movement and the antimissile and peace issues. Especially significant for an overview of relationships between values and the functioning of the political system is that the process of changing the governing coalition again took place so gingerly, and that the voices of protest against "the system" played only a marginal role in the decisive events. After various interludes and alarums, the FDP has been reconstituted with many of its left liberals gone, (some absorbed by the SPD) and with a more dependent relationship to the Christian Democratic party than in the past. The Social Democrats face an uncertain number of years sorting out relationships within the party and to various potential constituencies outside it—especially the Green constituency, which attained some 6 percent of the votes in the federal election of 1983, but has a slightly larger presence or potential in some regions, and the peace constituency.

Neither the coalition leadership, the economic situation, the social consensus, nor the skill in the area of political-economic management seems to be as solidly based now as in the earlier era of CDU/CSU-FDP government in the fifties and sixties. Yet it is well to recall that several earlier assessments of crisis in the West German system were wrong. Even during the Adenauer years, which especially in retrospect appear as a time of extraordinary stability, if not immobility, alarms were sounded abroad about imminent dangers to internal stability, or imminent dangers from West Germany because of its unresolved situation as part of a divided country torn between East and West. Such assessments were faulty because they gave inadequate attention to the actual functioning of the West German political system and to the support for that system arising from the German desire for security. Particular events could not be placed in perspective because there was inadequate understanding of the country's fundamental politics.

It is the potential for change in the basic parameters of West German policies, domestic or foreign, which interests most observers, and at the present time it is changes in values which seem to many to presage changes in political life. The dichotomy between a stolidly normal political system and those who long for change and a different way of living need not, however, lead to a fundamental change in those basic parameters. Even the latest movement of dissent, the peace movement, does not appear to be an exception to the pattern of stability combined with dissent. For one thing, the past history of peace movements is quite volatile, and such movements have been susceptible to internal dissension. The current movement is partly a revival of earlier antinuclear attitudes, and partly represents a new awareness of the level of arms development. However, it is also, as alluded to earlier, partially a product of frustrated reform in the domestic arena. It is certain too that sentiments in West Germany which express a moral engagement for peace and against new weapons as a sort of expiation for the Nazi period help feed support into the peace movement. The result of all these inputs, however, is that the movement is broad, diffuse, and volatile. It is not simply, or even primarily, directed at change in the West German political and social systems, and it is subject to crises of morale if its demonstrative actions have relatively weak impact.

To be sure, the value question in West Germany concerns more than the issue of system change. Long-range trends may be underway, think some, raising specters of an unpredictable West Germany in the future, especially of one not oriented to the West. What seems certain, however, is that any process of change which would affect the basic parameters of West German policies would be much more complex and hesitant than one might imagine by focusing upon some more or less sensational protests or upon dubious historical parallels.

Several reasons influence this observation. Richard Löwenthal, a perceptive commentator with long experience of European events, has argued that issues of communal values lie at the root of legitimacy problems, and that elites must "succeed in accepting the kind of value change required by the changed conditions of existence and . . . [keep] it within the limits of a continuity of basic Western values . . . if anomie is not to spread, with the ultimate result in the Western world . . . [of] a sequence of praetorian regimes based on naked force."[23] There are important questions about the accuracy of Löwenthal's alternatives—either acceptance of "value change" or rule by "naked force." He writes, after all, from the perspective of a convinced Social Democrat, even though on the right of that party in Germany, and presumably would not wish simply to deny the merit of longings for reform and value change. It is possible that value change in any politically focused sense may be limited to a relatively small minority, but that nevertheless systems less alarming than "praetorian regimes based on naked force" may exist. It is certainly correct, however, that environmental and peace movements have a dual character: They claim to speak for a merging of the fields of politics and cultural criticism, and by so doing they deny that the system or the government or the state stands for moral communal purposes.

Some studies of what may be termed establishment elites in the Federal Republic indeed show a lack of concern with "universal and humane values . . . [as contrasted with] issues of economic and national concern."[24] There are indications, in other words, that the "no-future" mentality which exists in a segment of dissident West German youth may not be as totally distant from self-absorbed attitudes of certain establishment groups as some of the latter would have one believe. Moreover, West German governmental elites have been relatively slow to respond either to participatory pressures or environmental concerns. This has been partly because of the legalistic and administrative approaches to public policy of these elites, and partly because of the ineptness of the environmental and participatory groups in knowing how to influence policy outputs, at least at the national level.[25]

The Green and peace movements have sought to appropriate the theme of communal values by pointing to dangers to the Germans and to humanity generally from environmental damage and from nuclear arms. Their references to "the Germans" have, in an important sense, been more or less confused reflections of an urge to appeal to communal values, rather than indications of nationalism in any conventional sense. They were paralleled in 1983 by strong indications that West Germans for the first time were viewing the Hitler period in its relationship to the lives of Germans, rather than as a series of events which primarily affected other peoples. A veritable spate of books, pamphlets, exhibits, and media presentations sounded this theme of Nazism and everyday life, indicating perhaps a strain of self-pity and self-preoccupation.

The appeal to communal values thus conceals, it can be hypothesized, a variety of ambiguities which may hamper concerted action against the existing political and social systems or the fundamental policies associated with those systems. The movements under discussion seek to articulate new values, but they are themselves movements closely following upon triumphant material progress. Liberating and self-expressive values are not unambiguously communal values as distinct from individualistic concerns. As movements of modern Western industrial society, the dissident or protest movements are products of that society and, particularly because of the emphasis on freedom, self-realization, and self-expression in these approaches, are actually linked with the very materialist, freedom-oriented society they criticize. They wish a different lifestyle but that lifestyle may be possible only on the basis of the choices afforded by the materialist society.

It is precisely at this juncture of ambiguity that conservatives or neoconservatives have been able to strike, insofar as they too begin to speak of communal values. The CDU/CSU electoral campaign of 1983 stressed what may be termed the communal values of hard work, economic performance, and achievement and family and charged that the Social-Liberal coalition, along with the dissidents, had deemphasized those virtues, resulting both in economic stagnation and in uncertainty (*Unsicherheit*) concerning goals. Such views have been accompanied by a substantial number of writings by conservative publicists and professors. The new government has moved in the direction of stressing conventional values against "alternative culture." In short, the appeal to communal values does not necessarily lie in only one direction of a conventional political spectrum.

Moreover, the cries in the Green and peace movements for humanity and a tearing down of the "life-threatening" apparatus of the state are at least implicitly accompanied by demands for yet more control, in order to enforce protection of the environment and the achievement and maintenance of peace. This characteristic dilemma of ideas for those who hold on the one hand to values of the individual and spontaneity and on the other to Rousseauistic notions of communal virtue are pronounced in the Green movement, but also in the diffuse dissident "scene" as a whole in the Federal Republic. Such tensions in ideas reflect the diversity of approaches in protest movements, hamper effective concerted action, and enable "the system" to defuse protest.

On the basis of some of the value ambiguities in the protest movements, it would be possible to speculate with seeming plausibility that "value changes" in the Federal Republic might ultimately lead in a rightist direction rather than remain at the left of the political spectrum, which would appear to be their starting point. After all, rightist movements in the twentieth century appear to have been more successful than those of the left in combining elements of protest and dissatisfaction with calls for a rebirth of community. The conservative revolution of the Weimar period in Germany, intimately associated with helping to prepare the way for the emergence of a regime combining revolutionary tactics in governing with appeals against modernity, its technology, "superficiality," and "corruption," is a startling example. What may be termed cultural pessimism has made tremendous inroads on ideas which seem to be in other respects leftist, and it provides a breeding ground for attitudes of actionism and vitalism as countermovements. Combined with important aspects of socioeconomic reality, such as continued high unemployment, especially among younger cohorts of the West German population, and the very low birth rate (now lowest in the world), this might create the impression of a society in anomie, with the possible threat of a sort of populist actionism as a way of revival.

Such speculations are intriguing, and the German experience encourages one to make them. The streak of antimaterialist, antimodern thought in Germany, no less than the notion propagated by some German thinkers and writers in earlier days of a special German way of politics different than that of the West,[26] makes all sorts of historical analogies tempting. However, at present they are only speculations and analogies, not clearly rooted in the way the West German political and social systems actually function. In assessing such speculations one must note that these systems mold the movements of dissent and change, rather than merely being affected by the latter. For example, the emphasis of dissident groups on influencing public policy has been hampered not only by governmental crackdowns or conservative reactions against protest but also by the incoherence of the tactics followed by these groups to influence policy making. Frequently, they have not understood how to use the participatory opportunities open to them in order to effect policy changes and pressure officials accustomed to dealing only with established interests. The current struggle between pragmatists and idealists in the Green movement may indicate an effort by some of the former to remedy this situation; the mere fact that they seek more effective forms of participation in the system is itself a check on system change.

In general, caution and pragmatism are likely to remain hallmarks of the West German polity as long as the political and social systems remain in their postwar patterns. Longings for "national identity"—a topic which began to emerge as a focal point for the latest readings of the German mood in late 1983 and in 1984—are likely to be affected no less than is protest behavior by this caution and pragmatism.

It is certainly correct to conclude, with an astute researcher of belief systems in Western societies, that the impact of notions of de-legitimation on political and social systems cannot yet "be answered systematically because of lack of empirical evidence."[27] Indications of the decline of political parties as instruments of political socialization and arenas for political action raise, as Max Kaase recognizes, the issue of what "other mechanisms of integration" in political and social systems exist, or might develop. Yet evidence must be evaluated as it becomes available, even though social science may not be able to speak the final word of systematic evaluation. This assessment of the available evidence is a central intention of the present book, and the resulting picture from the Federal Republic is by no means alarming.

NOTES

1. At the International Conference on the National Socialist Assumption of Power, titled "1933—Germany's Way into Dictatorship," held January 13–15, 1983, in the Reichstag, sponsored by the Historical Commission of Berlin, the Institute of Contemporary History, and the German Association for Parliamentary Questions.
   Proceedings published in Martin Broszat et al., eds., *Deutschlands Weg in die Diktatur* (Berlin: Siedler Verlag, 1983).

2. One of the most balanced recent treatments is Gordon Craig, *The Germans* (New York: G.P. Putnam's Sons, 1982).

3. Compare, for example, the essay in this volume by Wilhelm Bürklin.

4. Hans Magnus Enzensberger, "Unentwegter Versuch, einem New Yorker Publikum die Geheimnisse der deutschen Demokratie zu erklären," in *Kursbuch,* no. 56 (June 1979): 1–14.

5. Summary material appears in Richard Löwenthal and Hans-Peter Schwartz, *Die Zweite Republik: 25 Jahre Bundesrepublik Deutschland-Eine Bilanz* (Stuttgart: Seewald Verlag, 1974), and in David P. Conradt, *The German Polity,* 2nd ed. (New York & London: Longman, 1982).

6. Ronald Inglehart, *The Silent Revolution* (Princeton, N.J.: Princeton University Press, 1977); Kendall L. Baker, Russell J. Dalton, and Kai Hildebrandt, *Germany Transformed: Political Culture and the New Politics* (Cambridge, Mass., & London: Harvard University Press, 1981); Samuel Barnes et al., *Political Action* (Beverly Hills: Sage, 1979).

7. Ralf Dahrendorf, *Society and Democracy in Germany* (Garden City, N.Y.: Doubleday, 1967); Karl Jaspers, *Wohin Treibt Die Bundesrepublik?* (Munich: R. Piper, 1966).

8. (New York: Dial Press, 1947).

9. Karl Jaspers, *Wohin Triebt,* pp. 177ff.

10. Compare Arnulf Baring, *Machtwechsel: Die Ära Brandt-Scheel* (Stuttgart: Deutsche Verlags-Anstalt, 1982).

11. Compare the discussions in Andrei Markovits, ed., *The Political Economy of West Germany: Modell Deutschland* (New York: Praeger, 1982).

12. Lothar Romain and Gotthart Schwarz, "Introduction," in their edited volume *Abschied von der Äutoritaren Demokratie: Die Bundesrepublik in Ubergang* (Munich: R. Piper, 1970), pp. 7–8.

13. The essay by Kim Holmes, "The Origins, Development, and Composition of the Green Movement," in Robert L. Pfaltzgraff, Jr., et al., *The Greens in West Germany* (Cambridge, Mass., & Washington, D.C.: Institute for Foreign Policy Analysis, 1983), pp. 15–46, contains considerable information on these themes. See also Richard Löwenthal, "Political Legitimacy and Cultural Change in West and East," *Social Research* 46, no. 3 (August 1979): 401–435.

14. Markovits, *Political Economy,* passim.

3

THE CONTOURS OF WEST GERMAN OPINION

Russell J. Dalton
Kendall L. Baker

West Germany has become a nation known for its economic and political development during the postwar era. Its economy is the largest and one of the strongest in Western Europe and has displayed considerable resilience even during the worldwide economic recessions of the 1970s. In terms of foreign policy, the nation has evolved into a respected member of the international community and has become an influential voice in East-West relations. A variety of other political indicators—the political culture, government stability, and partisan continuity—signal the maturation of West German democracy (Baker at al., 1981; Conradt, 1980).

The 1980 election typified the expected style of West German politics. Faced with the choice between Helmut Schmidt and Franz-Josef Strauss, the public chose the moderate alternative and returned Schmidt to the chancellorship. Voter turnout was high, and most voters were supportive of the government and its policies. Both governing parties—the Social Democratic party (SPD) and the Free Democratic party (FDP)—consequently increased their vote shares over the 1976 election results; the strength and continuity of the government seemed assured (Baker, 1982).

It is against this backdrop of continuity and moderate politics that many analysts have viewed the events of the last few years with surprise (or alarm). In the short time between 1980 and 1983 the political landscape underwent dramatic changes. The SPD-FDP coalition eroded, and the Free Democrats joined with the Christian Democratic Union/Christian Social Union (CDU/CSU) to replace Schmidt through the first successful use of the constructive vote of no confidence. The new government called for early elections to legitimize its position. In the March 1983 election the CDU/CSU nearly captured an absolute majority of the parliamentary seats, while the SPD vote share sank to its lowest level in over 20 years.

Moreover, the interelection period was marked by frequent discussions of declining public confidence in politics and the ungovernability of the political system. Debates on the lessons of Weimar and the imminent breakdown of the political system appeared in the media (Dahrendorf, 1981; Raschke, 1982; Zundel, 1983). These concerns gained credence as a new protest party, the Greens, won representation in six state legislatures and eventually in Parliament following the 1983 election.

This chapter examines the trends in public opinion during the early 1980s, up to the 1983 election and beyond.[1] We first determine the characteristics of West German public opinion. Descriptions of the contemporary political culture have stressed the democratic values and system support of the West German public (Baker et al., 1981, chaps. 1–2; Conradt, 1980). Has there been a fundamental change in these traits as some observers have argued, or are we merely observing the inevitable shifts in political fortunes that occur in any democratic political system?

In addition to these general political trends, we also examine voter attitudes during the 1983 election. Public opinion surveys conducted during the campaign enable us to explain the substantial shifts in party support between 1980 and 1983. Finally, we take a brief look toward the future and describe public attitudes on some of the major political issues which face the new Christian-Liberal government.

THE INTERELECTION PERIOD, 1980–83

The governing parties, the SPD and the FDP, entered the 1980 election in a strong position. The economy had sustained some damage from the oil shocks of 1973 and 1979, but the West German system had weathered these storms in far better shape than most of its European neighbors. In September 1980, most West Germans (64 percent) were positive about their own economic situation, and a plurality (46 percent) were positive about the national economy. The government was, of course, quick to take credit for the nation's relatively good economic performance.

Both coalition parties also benefited from the positive images projected by their leaders (Berger et al., 1983a). The SPD leader, Helmut Schmidt, was viewed as an intelligent, experienced, and capable chancellor. Over 80 percent of the public liked Schmidt, and even a majority of the CDU/CSU voters were positive about him. The FDP leader, Hans-Dietrich Genscher, received almost as much support. In contrast, the CDU/CSU labored under the burden of a controversial and unpopular chancellor-candidate, Franz-Josef Strauss.

This imbalance in candidate images was reflected in general political orientations. More voters had a favorable image of the SPD than of the CDU/CSU. And while 72 percent of the public expressed satisfaction with the performance of the SPD-FDP government, only 51 percent were satisfied with the actions of the CDU/CSU opposition.

The SPD-FDP coalition rode this tide of public support back into office. The SPD vote in the 1980 elections increased slightly over 1976, while the FDP made large gains. The governing parties had promised to continue working together, and the electorate had voted for four more years of Social-Liberal rule.

Given the strength of the SPD-FDP coalition at the 1980 election, many observers were surprised at how quickly the new government was overtaken by events. On the economic front, a spreading worldwide recession soon enveloped the West German economy (Markovits, 1982). The gross domestic product (GDP) stagnated in 1980 and actually declined in 1981; unemployment rates increased by almost half from 1980 to 1981.

Public opinion mirrored the worsening economic situation (see Figure 3.1).[2] By January 1981 only a quarter of the public gave positive ratings to the national economy; by the end of the year even this number had been cut in half. At the same time, positive ratings of personal economic circumstances dropped by 20 percent between September 1980 and September 1981. Moreover, other survey questions showed that the public's economic expectations for the future were even more pessimistic than their evaluations of the present.

Economic problems were not the only difficulties facing the government. For example, environmental activists challenged government policy on several large projects which they felt threatened the environment. Protestors marched on the nuclear energy plant being built at Brokdorf in the north, and demonstrators attempted to prevent environmentally damaging airport expansions near Frankfurt and Munich. Other conflicts arose over energy and defense policies.

Many of these economic and environmental issues also evoked policy disagreements within the government, which extended to other issues

Figure 3.1 Evaluations of Present Economic Conditions, 1980–83

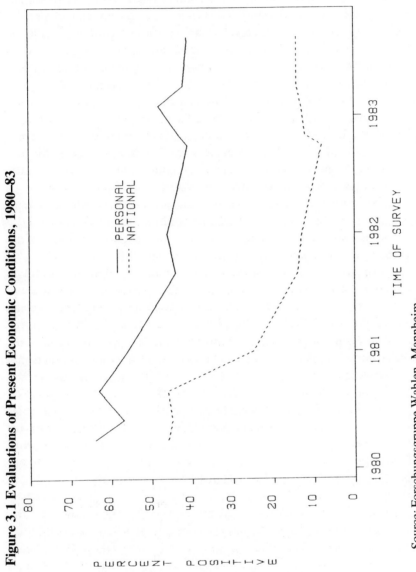

Source: Forschungsgruppe Wahlen, Mannheim.

27

(codetermination, defense policies, agricultural policy, and so forth). Faced with a deteriorating economy and public dissatisfaction, the coalition parties could not agree on how to address the nation's problems. The Social Democrats favored state intervention and government deficits in order to maintain employment levels and social programs. The Free Democrats proposed cutting social benefits and increasing investment incentives for businesses as an economic solution. These policy disagreements straightjacketed the government and led to piecemeal actions which satisfied no one. Not only were the SPD and FDP often at odds, but the SPD was itself internally divided on many of these issues (Braunthal, this volume). For example, labor union leaders within the SPD favored development projects such as Brokdorf and the Frankfurt airport expansion because the projects provided jobs and strengthened the economy. At the same time, other SPD members supported the environmentalists.

Information from several sources indicates that the social, economic, and political problems of the Federal Republic produced a pessimistic mood among the West German public. For example, the *Angst* index of the INFAS-Report asks survey respondents whether "political conditions in West Germany make you anxious." In the months preceding the 1980 election, confident replies were more common than pessimistic ones by a significant margin (INFAS, 1983, p. 67). A precipitous decline in confidence quickly followed; by the beginning of 1981 the public had settled into a prolonged period of political anxiety. Similarly, the December 1981 responses to the Allensbach Institute's annual question, "Is it with hopes or fears that you enter the coming year?" described one of the gloomiest moods that had ever been registered (Noelle-Neumann, 1983a).

This general feeling of anxiety and pessimism was reflected in attitudes toward the government and political process. The indecisive and ineffective style of the SPD/FDP coalition in dealing with the nation's problems lowered public evaluations of the government by a substantial margin (see Figure 3.2).[3] In the 1972 through 1980 elections, roughly 70 percent of the public was satisfied with the performance of the government (see Baker et al., 1981, chaps. 1, 11). By November 1981 the number of satisfied citizens decreased to a bare majority of the public, and further declines were ahead. Evaluations of the opposition parties, the CDU and CSU, were not improving in absolute terms, but beginning in 1981 the public was more satisfied with the opposition than with the government. Overall, however, neither the government nor the opposition was viewed very positively.

The public's political dissatisfaction went one step further. A more broadly framed question measured satisfaction with the political system

Figure 3.2 Satisfaction with Performance of Government and Opposition, 1980–83

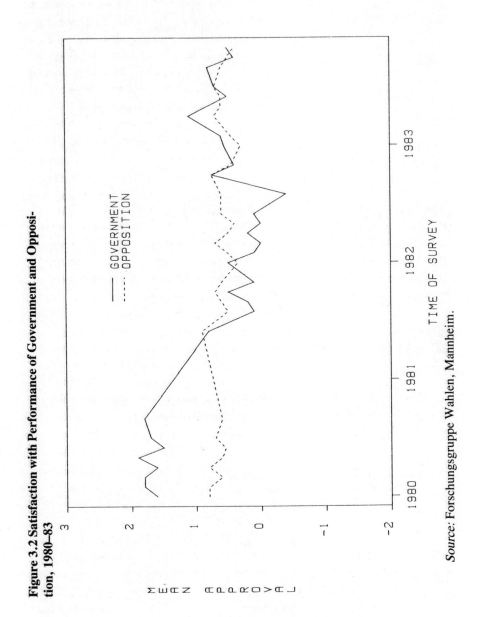

Source: Forschungsgruppe Wahlen, Mannheim.

Figure 3.3 Satisfaction with Performance of Democratic System, 1980–83

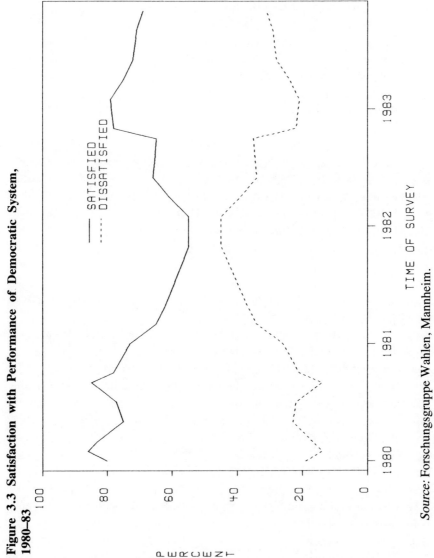

Source: Forschungsgruppe Wahlen, Mannheim.

30

and the political process—the functioning of democracy (see Figure 3.3).[4] During the 1980 election roughly 80 percent of the public was satisfied with the operation of the political system; this was similar to the levels found in 1972 and 1976. However, by the end of 1981 barely more than half of those surveyed expressed satisfaction.

The considerable declines in satisfaction with the government and the political process were a major cause for concern. Yet, they did not necessarily signal a breakdown in the democratic political culture. These questions measure evaluations of performance, which most observers admit was not very satisfactory; they do not focus on commitment to, or belief in, the democratic process. In addition, there are indications that in 1981 and 1982 these measures of political support became even more dependent on performance criteria. In previous years the satisfaction levels of the various party groups fell within a reasonably narrow range. The party gap widened considerably following the 1980 election (Küchler, 1982, pp. 42–45). For CDU and CSU voters, growing dissatisfaction with "the system" was probably due largely to dissatisfaction with the SPD-led government.

It should also be noted that other evidence indicates a strong continuing commitment to basic democratic values on the part of the West German public. A 1982 survey found that West Germans were more positive than most other Europeans in rating their nation's freedom of speech, personal freedoms, judicial equality, and respect for minorities (Eurobarometer 17, 1982, pp. 15–20). In addition, the spring 1982 *ZUMA ALLBUS* survey found widespread support for most elements of a democratic-values scale. For instance, the public overwhelmingly believed that the citizen has the right to disagree with the majority's opinion (94 percent), that each political party should have the chance to govern (93 percent), that democracy without opposition was unthinkable (92 percent), that political issues could be decided without violence (83 percent), and that citizens had the right to demonstrate in the streets (78 percent).

In sum, in 1981 and into 1982 the public was becoming more critical of the performance of the political system, though not necessarily the political system itself.[5] Increasingly, the government was seen as unable to govern. As evident from the discussion in the other chapters in this volume, these perceptions may have been correct.

The public's growing mood of economic and political dissatisfaction inevitably manifested itself in partisan preferences. Voter support for the Social Democrats declined from 42.9 percent in the 1980 election to roughly 30–35 percent in 1981 (see Figure 3.4). The SPD reached a nadir in the polls of 27.5 percent in August of 1982. Perhaps more significant, the

Figure 3.4 Party Preferences, 1980–83

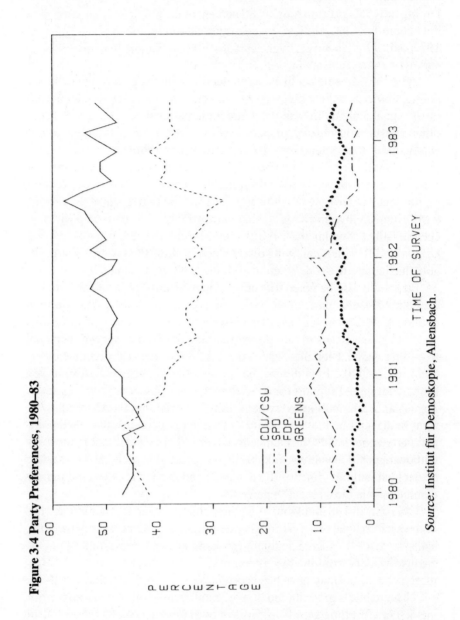

Source: Institut für Demoskopie, Allensbach.

32

FDP's support gradually declined until by mid-1982 the party was perilously close to the 5 percent level necessary to win party seats in an election.

Defections from the SPD and FDP strengthened opposition parties on both the right and left. From its defeat in 1980, the conservative CDU/CSU quickly rose in opinion surveys to capture the support of a majority of the electorate throughout most of 1981 and 1982. The new environmental party, the Greens, also benefited from the public's dissatisfaction with the government. The Greens received less than 2 percent of the vote in 1980; however, by mid-1981 they regularly stood above 5 percent in the polls and by mid-1982 they routinely surpassed the FDP in voter preferences.

These national trends in party support also appeared in the off-year state elections. The combined SPD and FDP vote dropped by nearly 7 percent in West Berlin (May 1981), by 4 percent in Lower Saxony (March 1982), and by over 8 percent in Hamburg (June 1982). In each of these elections the Greens won new representation in the respective state parliaments, and their vote share exceeded that of the FDP. Clearly, political tides were running strongly against the government. In mid-1981 there was widespread speculation about the imminent demise of the coalition. By mid-1982 the question was *when* the government would fall, not *if* it would fall.

The collapse of the SPD government resulted from a rapid series of events in August of 1982, in which the public looked on as spectators. After the change was an accomplished fact, the public's reaction was mixed. On the one hand, a slight plurality favored the *Machtwechsel,* and most voters tended to believe the new government would improve conditions (*Der Spiegel,* 1982, pp. 35–38). On the other hand, two-thirds of the public disagreed with the style and manner of the coalition change; most voters felt that the Free Democrats had betrayed their former coalition partner (Forschungsgruppe Wahlen, 1983a, pp. 70–73). As a result of their actions, the FDP and Genscher suffered a dramatic loss of standing in the public's eye. Suddenly, the very existence of the FDP was in doubt. New federal elections were planned for March 1983, and the Free Democrats were clearly below the 5 percent threshold in national opinion polls (see Figure 3.4). Indeed, the FDP failed to surmount the 5 percent hurdle in a series of state elections in Hesse (September), Bavaria (October), and Hamburg (December).

The SPD also capitalized on the manner in which it was forced from office. Charges of FDP treason and broken promises produced some sympathy for the Social Democrats. These feelings intensified when the popular Schmidt stepped down from the party leadership in reaction to the no confidence vote. The SPD's standing in the polls consequently rose during the latter half of 1982.[6]

While these partisan trends were important, the parallel changes in the public's general mood of anxiety and dissatisfaction were of potentially greater importance. For example, the pattern of worsening economic pessimism reversed with the change in government (see Figure 3.1). Perceptions of current economic conditions improved slightly between October 1982 and February 1983; questions which measured economic expectations for the future displayed an even sharper increase in optimism. In November, 36 percent of the public thought economic conditions would worsen over the next year; only 15 percent were so pessimistic in February 1983 (Forschungsgruppe Wahlen, 1983b, pp. 85–90). Similarly, the Allensbach "hopes and fears" question displayed growing optimism as 1983 began. By mid-January hopes exceeded fears by a 41 to 24 margin. The election, therefore, was clearly accompanied by a dramatic shift in popular sentiments about the economy.

The public's evaluation of the government and political process also improved with the change in government control. Satisfaction with the performance of the government improved dramatically between August and October 1982 (see Figure 3.2). Evaluations of the political process displayed an even more stunning recovery. In early 1982 barely half of the public was satisfied with the functioning of the political system. As an eventual change in government became apparent, the number of satisfied citizens increased to about two-thirds of the public in mid-1982. By February 1983 a full 79 percent expressed satisfaction, a figure comparable to the data for 1980 and earlier.

Thus, on the eve of the 1983 elections the West German public had emerged from the valley of pessimism and dissatisfaction which had characterized the 1981–82 period. The CDU/CSU was clearly in ascendence, but party fortunes were changing quickly and the exact results of the election were uncertain.

PUBLIC OPINION AND THE ELECTIONS

The March 1983 election was a stunning victory for the CDU/CSU, which recorded its second-best vote share. At the same time, the SPD suffered its worst showing since 1961. The FDP and the Greens also surprised many observers when both parties gained admission to the Bundestag.

The campaign was filled with complexities and seeming contradictions. If 1983 marked a conservative trend, how does one explain the success of the Greens? Throughout the campaign the SPD leaders debated over which image the party should project; how did voters finally perceive the party? These questions have complicated attempts to interpret the election and explain its larger meaning for observers of West German politics. This section attempts to clarify this situation by examining several possible explanations of the election in the context of public attitudes during the campaign.

Ideology

Perhaps the most common interpretation of the election is that it represented a basic ideological shift in West German politics. That is, after years of liberal social policies and the growth of government, the public was reacting against the welfare state and becoming more conservative. For some analysts, Helmut Kohl's victory in West Germany, Margaret Thatcher's in Britain, Ronald Reagan's in the United States, and right-of-center victories in Denmark, Norway, and The Netherlands suggested the arrival of a new conservative era in the 1980s.

A second general explanation of the 1983 results revolves around the policies of the SPD. The Social Democrats were campaigning against the Christian-Liberal alliance to their right, and the Greens to their left. Since the chances for victory against the CDU/CSU were limited, the SPD apparently concentrated on defending its left flank. During the campaign, Hans-Jochen Vogel espoused policies on NATO missiles, environmental protection, and education that were intended to undercut support for the Greens.[7] Critics argue, however, that these policies radicalized the SPD in the eyes of many people and resulted in a loss of support among moderate voters.

While both these explanations contain some truth, neither is a generally accurate description of the actual patterns in 1983. This conclusion is based on a comparison of public attitudes in the 1980 and 1983 campaigns. In both elections voters were asked to position themselves, the parties, and major political leaders on a left-right scale.[8] This scale acts as a summary of contemporary-issue concerns and taps the overall lines of political conflict in the party system (Inglehart, in press, Bürklin, 1982).

Figure 3.5 compares the perceptions of party and candidate positions on the left-right scale in 1980 and 1983. These data indicate that the public's ideological self-placement was virtually unchanged between the two elections (6.3 in 1980, 6.2 in 1983). In both years, the average voter is located at almost the center of this 11-point scale.

Figure 3.5 Left-Right Placement of Parties and Candidates, 1980 and 1983

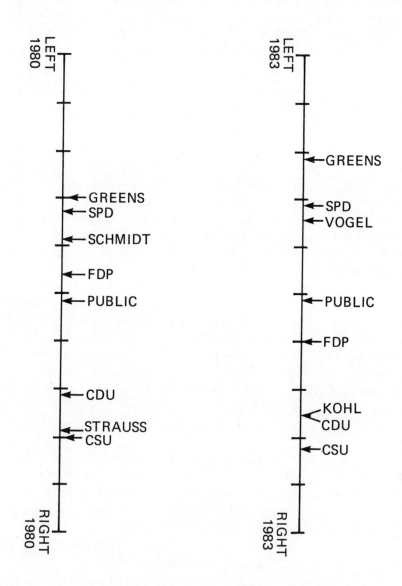

Source: 1980 and 1983 West German Election Studies, Zentralarchiv für empirische Sozialforschung (nos. 1052 and 1276).

Images of the major parties are also quite stable across this pair of elections. The SPD moved very slightly to the left in 1983, but the CDU and CSU moved rightward by an equal margin. Overall, these changes in party images are barely visible, and the distances between the public and the major parties are almost unchanged between 1980 and 1983. If one compares party leaders, however, then there is some evidence of a leftward shift by the SPD. In 1980 Helmut Schmidt was considered a moderate liberal, while in 1983 Hans-Jochen Vogel was perceived as substantially more leftist. Conversely, the CDU/CSU replaced the conservative Franz-Josef Strauss in 1980 with the more centrist Helmut Kohl in 1983. Still, even in 1983 the voters positioned themselves closer to Vogel than to Kohl. Indeed, in late 1982 and very early 1983, the Mannheim election surveys consistently found that Vogel was more popular than Kohl (Forschungsgruppe Wahlen, 1983b, p. 292; Infas, 1983, p. 79; Noelle-Neumann, 1983a; Compare Kaltefleiter, 1983; *Der Spiegel,* 1983a, pp. 88–89).

Public images of the two minor parties (the FDP and the Greens) changed substantially between 1980 and 1983. Reflecting their change of coalition partners, the Free Democrats jumped from left-of-center in 1980 to the conservative side in 1983. This dramatic ideological shift caused severe strains within the party (Søe, this volume). The public also perceived a clear shift to the left by the Greens.

In sum, these data discredit broad ideological interpretations of the 1983 election. The election produced more votes for the conservative parties, but this did not mean that the electorate itself had become more conservative. Both the voters' self-placement and their perceptions of the SPD and CDU/CSU were essentially unchanged between 1980 and 1983.

The data in Figure 3.5 also raise some more general questions about the role of ideology in the 1983 campaign. For example, in relative terms the voters actually were slightly closer to the SPD in 1983 than they were in 1980.[9] Similarly, the public positioned itself as closer to the SPD candidate than to the CDU/CSU standard bearer. Despite both of the above patterns, the SPD lost in 1983. Another paradox in these data concerns the performance of the Greens. Traditional models of rational voting imply that if a party moves to an ideologically extreme position, its support should decrease. In 1983 the voters perceived the Greens as significantly more leftist than in 1980, yet the party garnered considerably more votes. In short, while left-right self-placement was a very important influence on voting choices in 1983, the interelection shifts in voting patterns suggest that other factors affected changes in voting behavior.

Issues

Some observers have attributed the CDU's voting strength in 1983 to the changing issue interests of the voters. The public appeared to be more concerned with economic issues, and less interested in social policies, *Ostpolitik* (relations with the East), and social equality issues. Such a shift in issue interests might have benefited the CDU/CSU because of its conservative policies.

Table 3.1 presents the public's issue interests in 1980 and 1983. Economic issues ranked at the top of the list in both elections. However, the interelection shifts in issue concerns do not suggest the emergence of a "CDU agenda" in 1983. Unemployment increeased its lead as the dominant issue of the 1983 campaign, while the salience of inflation declined from 1980 to 1983. Traditionally, rising unemployment has helped the SPD, while inflation has led to gains for the CDU (Baker et al., 1981, p. 103). Similarly, interest in relations with the East (an issue normally benefiting the SPD) declined almost as much as concern with U.S. relations (normally a CDU/CSU issue). One also should note that public interest in environmental issues was relatively high in both 1980 and 1983. In sum, in normal times the changing issue interests between 1980 and 1983 would not have greatly benefited the CDU/CSU; in fact, the agenda may have changed slightly in favor of the SPD's traditional strengths.

If we probe further, however, issue opinions may hold the key to explaining the CDU/CSU's victory over the SPD. Table 3.2 presents the public's perceptions of whether either of the two major parties was more competent to deal with each of these contemporary issues. On the issue of unemployment, for example, a plurality of the public (41 percent) thought a SPD-led government could best deal with the problem in 1980, while only 25 percent believed a CDU/CSU government would be more competent. Three years later, the Christian Democrats were viewed as more competent on unemployment and all other economic issues (also see INFAS, 1983, p. 107; Kaltefleiter, 1983). Moreover, the CDU's lead on economic issue competency had increased substantially between November 1982 and the February 1983 survey (Forschungsgruppe Wahlen, 1983a). In 1983 the SPD continued to be perceived as significantly more capable only on the issues of Ostpolitik and citizen participation. Similar issue-competency questions were asked in a survey conducted for *Der Spiegel* magazine (1983b, p. 36) before the election. The CDU government was viewed as better able to deal with economic issues and most social problems. On only 4 of 13 issues was the SPD perceived as more competent.

TABLE 3.1. Issue Salience in 1980 and 1983 Elections

	June 1980	February 1983
Fight unemployment	76	88
Protect security	69	64
Lower budget deficit	—*	57
Fight inflation	70	53
Protect environment	52	48
Ensure law and order	57	41
Maintain good relations with the U.S.	37	27
Increase citizen influence in politics	32	25
Improve relations with East Europe	31	23
(N)	(1,620)	(1,197)

*Question not asked.

Note: Table entries are the percentage describing each issue as very important.

Source: West German Election Studies, Zentralarchiv für empirische Sozialforschung (nos. 1052, 1276).

The higher competency ratings for the CDU/CSU did not imply complete public support of government policies. Data from January 1983, for instance, show that disapproval of Kohl's policies exceeded approval by a slight margin, an unusual reversal of the normal advantage a chancellor enjoys (Noelle-Neumann, 1983a). In addition, the satisfaction ratings of the new CDU-led government were substantially lower than SPD governments had received in the 1972, 1976, and 1980 elections. Thus, rather than reflecting the strength of the CDU/CSU, these issue-competency questions probably represented the SPD's weaknesses.

TABLE 3.2. Perceptions of Issue Competency in the 1980 and 1983 Elections

| | June 1980 | | February 1983 | |
	SPD	CDU	SPD	CDU
Unemployment	41	25	27	45
Social security	35	28	28	41
Budget deficit	—*	—	13	51
Inflation	37	28	22	43
Environmental protection	30	16	24	23
Law and order	27	33	18	39
U.S. relations	27	27	15	45
Citizen influence	30	12	28	15
East relations	47	9	42	16

*Questions not asked.

Note: Table entries are the percentage naming the SPD or the CDU as most competent to deal with each issue.

Source: West German Election Studies, Zentralarchiv für empirische Sozialforschung (nos. 1052, 1276).

Taken as a whole, the findings in this section suggest an explanation for the CDU/CSU victory which also clarifies many of the voting paradoxes noted above. The SPD and its chancellor-candidate were slightly more compatible with the ideological position of the overall electorate in 1983. However, the Social Democrats could not campaign effectively and claim to have solutions for unemployment, budget deficits, an overextended welfare state, and other pressing problems. These were, after all, problems which had emerged under the previous Social Democratic government. Although many voters had mixed opinions of Kohl and the policies offered by the CDU/CSU, the SPD lacked credible alternatives.[10] Given the choice between uncertainty and SPD policies which had already failed, the public supported the CDU-led government. It was the public's lack of confidence in the SPD which paved the way to the CDU/CSU victory in 1983.

Undoubtedly, the Greens also benefited from the SPD's electoral weakness. The West German public has generally had difficulties differentiating the environmental policies of the SPD and CDU/CSU (Dalton, 1985). Thus, environmentalists could justifiably be skeptical of Vogel's newfound environmental concern during the 1983 campaign and continue to support the Greens. Similarly, since the SPD had failed to provide jobs and sufficient training positions for younger workers while in power, it is not surprising that many young unemployed voters preferred the Greens (*Stern*, 1983, pp. 176–178). The Greens provided an alternative for leftist voters dissatisfied with the SPD.

Party Coalitions

One way to clarify the shifts in voter preferences that occurred between the 1980 and 1983 elections is to examine the electoral coalitions of the parties. By studying the group bases of party support, we can determine which groups each party appealed to, and depended on, for its support (also see Berger et al., 1983b; Veen and Gluchowski, 1983).

Tables 3.3 and 3.4 present the social composition of party voters in the last two elections. The CDU/CSU's support in both elections is largely drawn from the conservative sectors of society—the middle class, Catholics, and religious and rural voters. For example, 50 percent of the CDU/CSU voters in 1983 were Catholics, although Catholics constituted only about 41 percent of those surveyed. In addition, about two-thirds of the CDU/CSU voters were from middle-class households. The CDU/CSU is still the primary representative of business and religious interests and depends on these groups for its financial and voting support.

Despite the CDU/CSU's distinctly conservative image, a comparison of the 1980 and 1983 surveys indicates that the Christian Union parties were partially able to broaden their base of support in the latter election. For example, in 1980 only 31 percent of CDU/CSU voters were from working-class families; in 1983, however, 37 percent were working class. Similarly, in 1983 the Christian Union parties were able to capture a significantly larger share of the non-Catholic and nonreligious vote. The CDU/CSU's success in appealing to these voters was a major factor behind the party's improved electoral showing in 1983.

The SPD's traditional base of group support is virtually a mirror image of the CDU/CSU's. A large share of the Social Democratic voters come from the working class or households with a union member. The party's strength is concentrated in central and northern Germany, especially in the cities. Protestant and nonreligious voters also give disproportionate support to the party. The SPD's electoral coalition in both tables shows surprising continuity; this indicates that the party's vote losses in 1983 were fairly uniform and not limited to one particular sector of the party.

From a long-term perspective, the 1983 election continues the convergence of group differences in SPD and CDU/CSU support which has typified the postwar period (Baker et al. 1981, ch. 7; Dalton, 1985). Both parties gradually have broadened their electoral base, producing a substantial overlap in the coalition each represents. For example, 37 percent of the CDU/CSU voters in 1983 were from the working class and 25 percent were from union households. The majority of SPD support now comes from middle-class voters, especially members of the new middle class (civil servants and white-collar employees).

TABLE 3.3. The Electoral Coalitions of the Parties, 1980 (in percentage)

	CDU/CSU	SPD	FDP	Green	Total
Occupation					
Old middle class	14	6	12	7	9
New middle class	55	49	62	71	53
Workers	31	45	26	22	38
Union member in House					
Yes	22	41	28	28	32
No	78	59	72	72	68
Education					
Primary	69	73	56	22	69

Secondary	23	18	29	34	21
Advanced	8	9	15	44	10

Religion

Catholic	62	35	33	28	45
Protestant	35	57	58	45	48
Other, none	3	8	9	27	7

Church attendance

Frequent	37	11	15	11	22
Occasionally	40	46	46	27	43
Seldom, never	23	43	39	62	35

Region

North	18	24	24	32	22
Central	40	47	46	41	44
South	42	29	30	27	34

Size of town

Under 20,000	44	31	30	20	37
20–100,000	26	26	25	30	26
Over 100,000	28	41	45	50	37

Age

Under 40	33	41	45	90	40
40–59	36	36	35	9	35
60 and over	31	23	20	1	25

Source: The 1980 West German Election Study, Zentralarchiv für empirische Sozialforschung (no. 1052), combined results from the June, July, and September surveys.

Despite the recent renewal of ideological rhetoric by the two major parties, the broadening social bases of both parties generally has been reflected in their policy actions. In expanding their voting base, both parties have added new social groups which have forced them to moderate their policy differences. Party positions occasionally overlap as they vie for the same voters, especially in their appeals to the new middle class. At the same time, a heterogeneous electoral base increases political tensions

TABLE 3.4. The Electoral Coalitions of the Parties, 1983 (in percentage)

	CDU/CSU	SPD	FDP	Green	Total
Occupation					
Old middle class	14	5	22	4	9
New middle class	49	48	50	53	49
Workers	37	47	28	43	42
Union member in House					
Yes	25	40	27	41	33
No	75	60	73	59	67
Education					
Primary	68	70	50	36	68
Secondary	24	21	38	33	22
Advanced	8	9	12	31	10
Religion					
Catholic	50	36	38	29	41
Protestant	46	56	56	59	52
Other, none	4	8	6	12	7
Church attendance					
Frequent	29	15	22	0	21
Occasionally	44	47	49	37	45
Seldom, never	27	38	29	63	34
Region					
North	19	23	20	23	21
Central	43	51	45	44	46
South	38	26	35	33	33
Size of town					
Under 20,000	42	32	33	41	37
20–100,000	28	27	28	18	27
Over 100,000	30	41	39	41	36
Age					
Under 40	32	40	33	90	38

40–59	35	36	44	7	35
60 and over	33	24	23	3	27

Source: The February 1983 West German Election Study. Zentralarchiv für empirische Sozialforschung (no. 1276).

within both major parties. In terms of group voting patterns, therefore, the 1983 election continues the long-term development of the CDU/CSU and SPD into broad-based electoral coalitions representing a collection of diverse interests, what the Germans term *Volksparteien.*

The data in Tables 3.3 and 3.4 also indicate that between 1980 and 1983 the FDP was able to redirect its electoral coalition to reflect its new conservative emphasis. For example, while the Free Democrats continue to be a predominately middle-class party, the proportion of old-middle-class voters (professional and the self-employed) increased substantially between the two elections. Similarly, the party's voting base became more religious and rural in 1983. The greatest change in support occurred in the age composition of FDP voters. In 1980 the party projected itself as a modern, liberal, and progressive force; almost half of the party's voters were under the age of 40. With its renovated conservative image in 1983, the young declined to only a third of the FDP voters.

The party with the most distinct electoral base is the Greens. Party voters are drawn heavily from groups identified with the New Politics movement (Hildebrandt and Dalton, 1978). The party is a representative of the better educated and the new middle class. For instance, while only 10 percent of the 1983 sample had an advanced education, this group accounted for 31 percent of Green voters. The Greens also are linked to secular and urban interests. Even more striking are the age differences in party support: An astounding 90 percent of Green voters are under the age of 40.

Although the Greens retained a distinct electoral base in 1983, the data in Tables 3.3 and 3.4 indicate a broadening of the party's group support. Between the two elections the party increased its support among working-class and less-educated voters; its electoral base also became more geographically balanced. These findings are probably another indication of the Greens' ability to attract dissatisfied SPD voters and capture a larger share of the leftist protest vote in 1983.

OPINIONS AND POLICY

The 1983 election is history. The CDU/CSU-FDP coalition now faces the task of running the government and attempting to resolve the political problems that the Social Democratic government could not manage. The new government's success in resolving these policy problems will depend, in part, on the public's reaction to new policy proposals. Many observers have interpreted the 1983 election results as a popular mandate for sweeping policy changes. Does such a mandate exist, or must it be created?

A survey conducted immediately after the 1983 elections assessed public opinion on many of the issues the new government is likely to face in the years ahead (Forschungsgruppe Wahlen, 1983c). Using this information, we will look toward the future and attempt to anticipate public reactions to the prospective policies of a CDU-led government.

Economic Issues

One of the central concerns of West Germans during the remainder of this decade will be, just as it was during the election, economic conditions. Writing in the *Economist* shortly after the 1980 election, Sara Hogg predicted that the 1980s in West Germany would be characterized by "overall economic stagnation, in which modest growth is intermittently offset by a series of minor recessions" (1980, p. 38). There seems little reason to question this judgment at this juncture. In spring 1983, for example, the annual report of the economics institutes indicated that the recession had ended but forecast only a 0.5 percent real growth in GNP for the year. Although real growth was actually a bit higher than this, unemployment swelled to 2.5 million. Moreover, Count Otto von Lambsdorff, the federal minister of economics, argued that high unemployment will continue for the next several years, in part because of the high birthrate of the 1960s and 1970. The data in Figure 3.1 indicate that the public's economic evaluations remained mixed throughout the latter half of 1983.

Chancellor Kohl and his government have proposed to stimulate the economy through the revival of the social market concept with its emphasis on free enterprise. One of the important components of this program is tax incentives for business, and on this issue Chancellor Kohl seems to have relatively widespread popular support. In the March 1983 survey conducted by the Mannheim Institute, about 60 percent of the respondents regarded this as a "good" or "very good" goal for the nation to pursue (see Table 3.5). Support for this measure was strongest, as one would expect,

TABLE 3.5. Public Opinion and Perceptions of Party Positions on the Issues, March 1983 (in percentage)

		Perceptions of[b]			
	Public[a]	CDU/CSU	SPD	FDP	Greens
Tax incentives for business	60.6	85.9	31.4	74.8	8.4
Reduce national debt	53.8	84.6	24.7	66.3	10.4
Increase medical payments	9.3	74.7	21.0	54.8	2.4
Measures to limit unemployment compensation	54.0	79.4	24.2	61.2	8.6
Relax rent controls	24.0	77.9	15.1	55.0	2.7
Increase taxes of wealthy	65.4	44.3	63.8	28.6	60.7
Stronger environmental laws	80.3	58.8	61.7	54.6	82.8
Continue building nuclear plants	30.5	82.4	32.0	63.6	1.6
Initiate referendum	42.8	12.2	20.0	12.0	57.6
Stronger abortion laws	35.4	71.5	12.1	31.6	4.8
Longer alternative service	29.6	75.6	16.0	47.5	3.4
Limit number of guest workers	63.5	86.3	34.7	57.3	14.7
Stationing NATO missiles	25.2	82.6	20.5	57.6	1.8
Work closely with U.S.	43.8	82.1	31.1	67.3	3.5

[a]Entries are the proportion of the population that considered each issue a "good" or "very good" one for the nation to pursue.

[b]Entries are the proportion of the population that perceived each party "favored" or "strongly favored" each issue.

Source: West German Election Study, Zentralarchiv für empirische Sozialforschung (no. 1276).

among coalition supporters, with about three-quarters of the CDU/CSU and FDP voters endorsing it. Yet, support was strong even among opposition voters; for example, about half of the SPD partisans also thought it was a good or very good idea.

Another important component of Kohl's program, reduction of the national debt, also received at least passive popular support. Overall, almost 55 percent of the respondents in the March survey thought this was a good goal for the nation to pursue. Among CDU/CSU voters, support for this policy reached 70 percent, and less than a quarter of the SPD and Green voters voiced opposition. Drawing upon this popular support, the new government has been able to halve the annual national deficit by mid-1984.

Chancellor Kohl has also proposed to cut federal spending on social services and benefits, and this was clearly reflected in the 1984 budget. In this area, however, popular acceptance is substantially more tenuous. For example, almost three-quarters of the March sample felt that the CDU/CSU favored increasing individual contributions to medical costs; yet, more than two-thirds of the respondents themselves were against this policy. Opposition was strongest, of course, among supporters of the SPD and Greens, but more than 60 percent of the coalition's own supporters objected to increasing personal medical costs. Indeed, on this issue, popular sentiments appear to be much closer to the perceived positions of the opposition parties than they are to the position of the governing coalition. For example, while only 21 percent of the respondents in the March survey believed the SPD favored this goal, almost three-quarters were convinced that the CDU endorsed it (see Table 3.5). It seems likely, therefore, that efforts by the coalition to implement substantial health-care changes—and thus savings—could evoke strong objections.

Efforts to strengthen the criteria for unemployment compensation are likely to meet less resistance, but problems could occur even in this area. Almost 80 percent of the respondents in the March 1983 survey thought that the CDU/CSU; was in favor of this policy, but only 54 percent saw this as a goal the nation should pursue. Among CDU/CSU voters support for this policy was quite strong—almost two-thirds characterized this goal as good or very good—but among all other voters, skepticism was common. In the face of continually high unemployment rates and public skepticism, significant cuts in unemployment benefits may not be politically feasible.

Hence, the Conservative-Liberal coalition's efforts to resolve the Federal Republic's economic problems through reductions in federal spending on social programs apparently lacks widespread public support. Moreover, as noted above, unemployment, which Kohl has designated as West Germany's chief problem, is unlikely to disappear any time in the near future. There seems little doubt, therefore, that economic issues will be important and potentially divisive components of the political agenda in the next few years.

New Politics Issues

A second set of issues involves noneconomic domestic topics. These issues typify the problems and issues of advanced industrial societies and have been described as new politics issues (Hildebrandt and Dalton, 1978; Baker et al., 1981). Several of these issues have been championed by the Green party because the established political parties have not been responsive to new politics concerns (Bürklin, 1981, this volume).

While new politics issues were less important than economic matters in 1983, they are issues which remain on the Federal Republic's political agenda. Two environmental issues probably top the list of new politics concerns: environmental protection and nuclear energy. Acid rain, water pollution, waste disposal, nuclear safety, and similar problems have been receiving increasing public attention in recent years. Table 3.5 indicates that the vast majority of West Germans (80 percent) favor stronger environmental standards, and only a minority favor construction of more nuclear energy plants (31 percent). The public's strong environmental orientation contrasts with its images of the governing parties. Only small majorities believe the CDU/CSU and FDP favor stricter environmental regulations, and most people feel that these parties favor nuclear energy. Public preferences on these two issues actually are more compatible with the public's images of SPD and Green policies, although the previous SPD government struggled unsuccessfully with environmental problems during its tenure in office. The new environmental consciousness of CDU leaders such as Zimmermann and Spaeth may improve the party's image, but environmental matters will probably constitute a continuing controversy for the new administration.

Another aspect of the new politics involves the opening of society to greater citizen participation in the decisions affecting their lives. Students, for example, call for the "democratization" of university administrations, workers want more say in the management of their company, and opposition movements want an opportunity to appeal for public support. As one example of these issues, a plurality (43 percent) of the respondents in the postelection survey favored the use of a referendum to decide important national issues instead of relying solely on the Bundestag. While this seems like an entirely democratic procedure, all three of the established parties were perceived as opposing this reform. Only the Greens, who have favored the referendum as a means of tapping the public's strong support for environmental protection, were seen as endorsing the public's position. The referendum issue itself is not likely to become an important political controversy, but it suggests a public longing for a more open political process that might challenge the conservative political style of the Christian Democrats.

Two other issues at least partially involve new politics values: abortion and the conditions of nonmilitary national service. Although abortion is basically a moral issue, abortion legislation affects the freedom of individual choice and lifestyle preferences. The choice between military and nonmilitary national service touches on similar themes. About three-quarters of the public perceive the CDU as favoring conservative policies on both issues which some members of the party have proposed. However, public opinion is divided on the abortion issue and relatively liberal on the national service issue. The government is not required to act on these two policies, and avoidance may be the best strategy, for new conservative initiatives on abortion and national service could potentially evoke widespread public opposition.

Foreign Policy Issues

A final important and potent source of policy debate is the defense issue and the "two-track" decision on NATO arms. These issues have generated enormous controversy in the Federal Republic in recent years, culminating in massive peace protests throughout 1983. The March survey asked respondents to indicate whether the deployment of U.S. missiles in the Federal Republic, in the event the United States and the USSR are unable to come to an agreement in Geneva, was a goal the nation should pursue. Only about a quarter characterized this goal in positive terms, and almost 45 percent were negative (see Table 3.5). Opposition was strongest, as one would suspect, among Green and SPD voters, with about 60 percent of the latter voicing negative feelings about this proposal. Even among coalition voters, however, skepticism was pervasive: Less than one-quarter of the FDP supporters and less than 40 percent of the CDU/CSU partisans regarded the stationing of American missiles on German soil as a positive goal.

Other data suggest similar conclusions (*Public Opinion,* 1984, pp. 38–39). For example, the results of an Allensbach survey conducted in December 1982 indicated that only a bare majority of 51 percent favored the two-track decision, that is, the "station[ing] of missiles in Europe to offset Soviet medium-range missiles and on the other hand to take the initiative in disarmament talks with the Soviet Union." Moreover, only 28 percent were in favor and 47 percent were opposed when the Allensbach Institute in late 1982 posed a question that focused exclusively on the deployment of nuclear weapons in the Federal Republic. According to a fall 1983 survey conducted by Allensbach, these sentiments remained essentially unchanged.

These data indicate that there was considerable opposition to the deployment of nuclear weapons in the Federal Republic. This is in sharp contrast to the population's perception of the government's position. In the March survey conducted by the Mannheim Institute, more than 80 percent of the public indicated that the CDU/CSU favored stationing medium-range nuclear weapons in Germany. The public's perception of the FDP's support for this proposal was considerably less, at about 58 percent. Nevertheless, it would appear that the public's views on this issue are considerably more compatible with those of the opposition than they are with those of the government. Only about 20 percent of the respondents believed that the SPD favored the deployment of nuclear weapons, and only 2 percent had a similar image of the Greens.

In view of these sentiments about U.S.-backed nuclear missiles, it is not surprising that less than half of the respondents in the March survey thought West Germany should try to achieve the greatest possible agreement with the United States on important political questions. In this regard, however, CDU/CSU supporters differed from all other parties. While nearly two-thirds of them endorsed this proposal as a good or very good goal, only about 34 percent of the FDP voters, 30 percent of the SPD partisans, and 13 percent of the Green sympathizers took this position.

Hence, while other public opinion data indicate that most West Germans continue to hold positive attitudes toward the United States as a nation and a people, it appears that an increasing number of them—with the exception of CDU/CSU voters—are questioning U.S. political leadership. Data recently reported by Elisabeth Noelle-Neumann (1983b) suggest a similar conclusion. When asked who the Federal Republic should cooperate with in foreign policy in February/March, 1983, 49 percent of the respondents said the nation should cooperate *equally* with the Soviet Union and the United States; in contrast, only 40 percent thought it should cooperate more closely with the United States. This is a dramatic change since

May 1981, when 56 percent had said the Federal Republic should cooperate more closely with the United States in foreign affairs. Noelle-Neumann
also indicated that as recently as January 1980 only 16 percent of the West
German population believed that the Soviet Union was "basically committed to seeking a reconciliation with the West." However, by July 1981 the
proportion expressing this point of view had jumped to 36 percent and by
mid-January 1983, it was 45 percent. Indeed, this last time more people believed that the Soviet Union was interested in reconciliation with the West
than did not, and this was the first time this pattern had emerged in the 24
years that the question had been asked.

Overall, then, it appears that West German attitudes toward the Soviet
Union have changed and that the public is increasingly skeptical about U.S.
political leadership and deeply concerned about the deployment of nuclear
weapons on German soil. These sentiments undoubtedly underlie the widespread public demonstrations against the deployment of NATO Cruise and
Pershing II missiles in fall 1983. By one account, almost three million West
Germans participated in these protests in some manner. Although the deployment is past, the public's basic concerns probably still remain—the re-
verberations of the missile decision are likely to be heard for several more
years.

In our judgment, these analyses of opinions on current issues provide
evidence that the CDU-led government enjoys less than overwhelming
support in many areas. A comparison of the entries in Table 3.5 provides a
succinct summary of this evidence. On many issues, the public's policy
views are more compatible with those of the SPD than they are with those
of the CDU/CSU. If we compare the policy preferences of the public with
their perceptions of the CDU/CSU and the SPD on all 14 issues, a rather
startling finding emerges: The public's policy preferences are closer to the
SPD on 11 of the issues, closer to the CDU/CSU on only 3 issues. In fact, if
all four parties are compared, the CDU/CSU is most proximate to the electorate on not a single issue. Even the Greens are seen as the most representative party on three issues—medical care, the environment, and referen-
dums. To see the 1983 election as a mandate for sweeping policy changes is
difficult, at best.

CONCLUSION

The paradox of the 1983 West German election was that although the
electorate's positions on the issues and the left-right continuum seemed to

match the positions of the SPD more than those of the CDU/CSU, the governing Conservative-Liberal coalition received a resounding endorsement at the polls on March 6. We have explained this paradox, and thus the outcome of the election, by pointing to the importance of issue competence and the convergence in the partisan preferences of various social groups. The implications of these findings deserve some attention.

As noted elsewhere in this volume (Braunthal), the SPD is currently involved in a debate about its electoral future and its position on the crucial socioeconomic and international issues facing the Federal Republic. On the left wing of the SPD are those who are convinced that the party must adopt policies that will enable it to regain the support of voters who favored the Greens during the recent election. In essence, the members of this group advocate that the party continue to pursue the strategy it adopted for the 1983 campaign, including strong support for environmental programs and opposition to the deployment of U.S. medium-range missiles. The SPD formally endorsed this group's position on the missile issue at the special party conference in November 1983—even though Helmut Schmidt was one of the chief architects of the two-track decision in 1979. At the other end of the spectrum are those party activists who are convinced that the SPD must concentrate its energies on solidifying its support among the working class. They point to the party's loss of working-class voters during the recent campaign and insist that the SPD pursue socioeconomic policies that benefit these individuals. They are, of course, also much more supportive of the "two-track" decision than is the left wing.

This internal partisan conflict is not new for the SPD. On the contrary, the party has had to balance the interests of its traditional voters with those of its new supporters for more than 20 years, and at no time has this been easy. In the interests of carrying out its governmental responsibilities, the party leadership could insist that internal factional disputes be kept to a minimum while the party was in power. In opposition, however, this argument is not nearly as viable. Consequently, the debates between the wings of the party, which had become increasingly divisive after the 1980 election, are currently quite intense.

The tasks of developing an effective opposition to the Conservative-Liberal coalition and convincing the voters that the SPD is a viable alternative to the government will not be easy for the current leadership triumvirate of Willy Brandt, Hans-Jochen Vogel, and Johannes Rau. Indeed, several commentators have speculated that because of the disarray in which the party presently finds itself, a decade or more may pass before the SPD will be competitive in a national election (Kaltefleiter, 1983). This would not be unusual, since it took the CDU/CSU many years to recover from its fall from power, adapt to the role of opposition, and make itself a viable governmental alternative.

Yet, if the SPD is able to develop an effective strategy, the task may be easier for it than it was for the CDU/CSU. As we have emphasized, the electorate is generally closer to the position of the SPD than to the CDU/CSU on most of the issues currently facing the Federal Republic. Similarly, the public's ideological position is consistent with its perception of the SPD's orientation. On the surface, therefore, it would seem that the SPD is in a position to rally support among the electorate if the CDU-led government implements distinctly conservative policies. Yet, there is pressure within the SPD to go the way of the British Labour party after its defeat at the polls in 1979. The left wing of the party has been quiet for many years and is stronger now than it once was; consequently, it will not be surprising if there are efforts to move the party closer to its ideological roots. Perhaps the party will learn from the experience of the British Labour party and recognize that positions that depart significantly from the prevailing sentiments of the public can lead to electoral disaster. The one advantage the SPD has is that these divergent political interests may be more easily reconciled while the party is in opposition. Freed from the responsibility of governing, the Social Democrats can promise support to all wings of the party without having to deliver.

As we and others have demonstrated, the Federal Republic has been transformed in the postwar period (Baker et al., 1981). There has been a tremendous expansion of the tertiary sector of the German economy and the corresponding emergence of groups like civil servants and salaried white-collar workers who have no clear or predetermined place in the old class structure. In addition, new values which emphasize open access to political means and resources and quality-of-life issues have developed and cut across previous class lines. The Germany of 1984, therefore, is different, both in structure and values, from the Germany of 1945. The SPD has been quite successful in gaining the support of these new components of the German society. Indeed, we feel this is clearly reflected in the similarity between the electorate's ideological and issue positions and its perceptions of the SPD's current ideology and positions on the issues. To take a dramatic turn to the left, therefore, would be to seriously jeopardize the support of these groups that increasingly dominate German society.

If this were to occur, the SPD's support among wide segments of the population could be transferred to other parties. At present, the electorate perceives the Greens as advocating extreme positions on most issues. For example, they are seen as substantially more opposed to the deployment of missiles, the construction of new nuclear plants, and the increase in personal costs of medical insurance than any other party. In contrast, they are perceived as considerably more in favor of environmental regulation than the CDU/CSU, the FPD, or the SPD. Yet, while analyses of the election indicate that the Greens were successful among individuals who advocate the values of the new politics and oppose the present socioeconomic and political system, they also indicate that the Greens were successful among a rather disparate group of voters. Unlike 1980, in other words, they were viewed by many in 1983 as a protest party that constituted an alternative to the current system parties. This is, of course, a very unstable base upon which to build a major national party. Moreover, a year after the election the Greens are still debating what kind of party they want to be. This debate focuses on the question of whether the party should continue to be a radical alternative, to seek a reconciliation and working relationship with the traditional left, or to make an effort to expand its base by courting more middle-of-the-road voters. In addition, the Greens must make fundamental organizational decisions; for example, the issue of rotation of its Bundestag delegation every two years, so that it will not be infected by the perquisites of parliamentary life.

One cannot argue at this point that the Greens constitute a viable electoral alternative to either of the major parties for most Germans. Moreover, it is far from clear that they have any desire to be anything more than a protest movement. Yet, if the SPD were to move dramatically left, a vacuum would be created, and pressure would build in West Germany, as it did in Great Britain, for something to fill it. The intensity of this pressure and the size of the vacuum, however, will depend, in part, on how the Conservative-Liberal coalition interprets its victory on March 6 and the extent of intragovernmental tensions.

We have noted that in some ways the success of the CDU/CSU and the FDP in the election was surprising. Neither the issues, their positions on them, nor the population's perception of their current ideological stance augured well for electoral success for these parties. Nevertheless, they received what appeared to be a ringing popular endorsement. It would certainly be tempting for the government to see the outcome of the election as a mandate for its policy proposals. Our analysis, however, suggests that such a conclusion could be seriously mistaken. There are significant differences between the electorate and the government over the policies and goals the nation should pursue. As noted, there were only three issues—unemployment compensation, limiting the number of guest workers (*Gastarbeiter*), and tax incentives—on which the population's position was closer to that of the CDU/CSU than to that of the Social Democrats. Moreover, the government party with which the public was in greatest agreement was the FDP, *not* the CDU/CSU. Indeed, on 5 of the 14 issues included in the postelection survey conducted by the Mannheim Institute, the electorate was closer to the position of the FDP than it was to any other party.

The CDU/CSU's position is, therefore, somewhat complicated. On the one hand, the party faces a skeptical electorate; on numerous issues its position was in conflict with that of the public. On the other hand, it must attempt to govern with a coalition partner whose positions on the issues are often divergent. The possibilities for confrontation and intragovernmental tensions, therefore, are considerable. In fact, the latter has already occurred in the debates that accompanied the coalition's efforts to strengthen the demonstration law, cut social spending, and provide amnesty for violators of the political contributions laws.

Because of the conflict between the CDU/CSU and the electorate and the sympathy of the public for many of the positions of the SPD and the FDP, it is difficult to regard the 1983 election as a general mandate for policy change. Indeed, data presented in Figure 3.2 show that public evaluations of the CDU/CSU-led government and the SPD opposition have remained nearly equal throughout the latter half of 1983; this is a dramatic change from the normal popularity bonus an incumbent government receives. This narrow base of public support may explain the conciliatory, and sometimes liberal, policies the new government has followed on relations with East Germany, acid rain, and other issues. Moreover, the actual cuts in social services often have been less than the CDU/CSU's conservative campaign promises. Having won the election, the CDU/CSU is now attempting to win the policy support of the West German public.

NOTES

1. Much of the data in this chapter is drawn from the 1980 and 1983 West German Election Studies, conducted by the Forschungsgruppe Wahlen, Mannheim. We would like to thank Manfred Berger, Wolfgang Gibowski, and Dieter Roth for providing us with early access to the 1983 study. These studies were acquired from the Zentralarchiv, University of Cologne.

2. The trends in Figure 3.1 are based on the following questions: How would you, quite generally, evaluate the present economic situation in the Federal Republic (very good, good, part good/part bad, bad, very bad)? How do you evaluate

your own financial situation today (very good, good, part good/part bad, bad, very bad)? The figure is based on the percentage responding "very good" or "good."

3. The trends in figure 3.2 are based on the following question: Are you more satisfied or more dissatisfied by what the (SPD or CDU) government has accomplished so far? How satisfied are you with the performance of the (CDU/CSU or SPD) opposition in Bonn? The figure presents the mean scores of an 11-point scale ($+5$ = completely satisfied, -5 = not at all satisfied).

4. The question was worded as follows: What would you generally say about democracy in the Federal Republic of Germany, that is, about our political parties and our entire political system? Are you satisfied, somewhat satisfied, or not satisfied with it?

5. Data collected in February 1983 suggests that West Germans distinguish between regime and authorities in a way quite reminiscent of David Easton's arguments of almost two decades ago (1965). While 51 percent of the sample said the present government was fair and just, about 83 percent gave this answer when asked about the political system as a whole.

6. In fact, in mid-January the Allensbach Institute found nearly a dead heat between the parties when voters were asked their intended second vote: CDU/CSU received 43.6 percent, SPD 41.6 percent (Noelle-Neumann, 1983a). The February 1983 Mannheim election study actually found the SPD ahead of the CDU/CSU.

7. Some observers have argued that Vogel and the SPD had been "captured" by a young, leftist, middle-class core of party activists who had little in common with the SPD's traditional working-class base. (See the data presented in Feist et al., 1978).

8. The question was worded as follows: In political discussions one always hears about the concepts of left and right. We would like to know whether you place yourself more to the left or more to the right. Please indicate on this scale where you place yourself.

9. The following table presents the difference between the electorate's average self-placement and their placement of the SPD and CDU:

	1980	1983
SPD	2.0	2.1
CDU/CSU	1.9	2.3

10. In many ways, these patterns are very similar to Jimmy Carter's weaknesses in the 1980 American presidential elections; although many voters supported Carter's issue positions, he was generally seen as lacking the capacity to govern (see Petrocik, Verba, and Schultz, 1981; Abramson, Aldrich, and Rohde, 1982).

REFERENCES

Abramson, Paul, John Aldrich and David Rohde. 1982. *Change and Continuity in the 1980 Election.* Washington, D.C.: Congressional Quarterly Press.

Baker, Kendall L. 1982. "The 1980 West German Elections and Foreign Policy." *International Studies Notes* 9: 16–24.

Baker, Kendall, L., Russell J. Dalton, and Kai Hildebrandt. 1981. *Germany Transformed.* Cambridge: Harvard University Press.

Berger, Manfred, et al. 1983a. "Stabilität und Wechsel." In *Wahlen und politisches System,* ed. Max Kaase and Hans-Dieter Klingemann. Opladen: Westdeutscher Verlag.

_____. 1983b. "Regierungswechsel und politische Einstellungen." *Zeitschrift für Parlamentsfragen* 13: 556–582.

Bürklin, Wilhelm. 1981. "Die Grünen und die 'Neue Politik.'" *Politische Vierteljahresschrift* 22: 359–382.

_____. 1982. "Konzept und Fakten." *Politische Vierteljahresschrift* 22: 359–382.

Conradt, David. 1980. "Changing German Political Culture." In *The Civic Culture Revisited,* ed. Gabriel Almond and Sidney Verba. Boston: Little, Brown.

Dahrendorf, Ralf. 1981. "Es ist nicht alles Weimar, was bunt ist." *Die Zeit* 28:3.

Dalton, Russell J. 1985. "The German Party System between Two Ages." In *Electoral Change in Advanced Industrial Democracies,* ed. Russell J. Dalton, Scott Flanagan, and Paul Beck. Princeton, N.J.: Princeton University Press.

Der Spiegel. 1982. "Stirbt die FDP, überlebt Kohl? no. 41 (October 11): 34–40.

_____. 1983a. "Quaelt die FDP sich doch noch über die Hürde?" no. 6, (February 7): 84–92.

_____. 1983b. "Zweifeln zu viele SPD-Wähler an der SPD?" no. 7 (February 14): 34–37.

Easton, David. 1965. *A Systems Analysis of Political Life.* New York: John Wiley.

Eurobarometer 17. 1982. Brussels: Commission of the European Communities.

Forschungsgruppe Wahlen. 1983a. *Mannheimer Wahlstudie 1982/1983.* Mannheim: Forschungsgruppe Wahlen.

_____. 1983b. *Politik in der Bundesrepublik, February 1983.* Mannheim: Forschungsgruppe Wahlen.

_____. 1983c. *Politik in der Bundesrepublik, March 1983.* Mannheim: Forschungsgruppe Wahlen.

Hildebrandt, Kai, and Russell J. Dalton. 1978. "The New Politics." In *Elections and Parties,* ed. Max Kaase and Klaus von Beyme. Beverly Hills: Sage.

Hogg, Sara. 1980. "West German Economy, A Survey." *Economist* (November 8): 38.

INFAS. 1983. *Politogramm: Bundestagswahl 1983.* Bonn-Bad Godesberg: INFAS.

Inglehart, Ronald. 1985. "The Changing Structure of Political Cleavages in Western Society." In *Electoral Change in Advanced Industrial Democracies,* ed. Russell J. Dalton, Scott Flanagan, and Paul Beck. Princeton: Princeton University Press.

Kaltefleiter, Werner. 1983. "Eine kritische Wahl." *Das Parlament* (Beilage 14, April 9): 3–17.

Küchler, Manfred. 1982. "Staats-, Parteien-, oder Politikverdrossenheit?" In *Bürger und Parteien,* ed. Joachim Raschke. Opladen: Westdeutscher Verlag.

Markovits, Andrei, ed. 1982. *The Political Economy of West Germany.* New York: Praeger.

Noelle-Neumann, Elizabeth. 1983a. The Voter Decides. Mimeo, Allensbach Institute.

_____. 1983b. German-American Relations and Public Opinion. Paper presented at the Pacific Workshop on German Affairs, California State University, Long Beach.

Petrocik, John, Sidney Verba, and Christine Schultz. 1981. Choosing the Choice and Not the Echo. Paper presented to the annual meetings of the American Political Science Association, New York.

Public Opinion. 1984. "Question Wording Makes a Difference." (December/January): 38–39.

Raschke, Joachim, ed. 1982. *Bürger und Parteien.* Opladen: Westdeutscher Verlag.

Stern. 1983. "Wie die Arbeitslosen Wählen Wollen." No. 7 (February): 176–178.

Veen, Hans-Joachim, and Peter Gluchowski. 1983. "Wählerschaften von CDU/CSU und SPD, 1959–1983." *Zeitschrift für Parlamentsfragen* 13: 530–555.

Zundel, Rolf. 1983. "Parteien in der Krise." *Die Zeit* 24: 14.

4

THE CHRISTIAN UNION PARTIES

William E. Paterson

INTRODUCTION

The crushing victory of the Christian Union parties in the election of March 6, 1983, has ensured their dominance in the foreseeable future. The scale of their victory and the nature of the Social Democratic party (SPD) defeat has led Professor Werner Kaltefleiter to refer to it as a "critical," that is, realigning, election.[1] In his view, the real strength of the Christian Democratic Union/Christian Social Union (CDU/CSU) result was better expressed in the 52.7 percent of the first votes gained by the CDU/CSU than by the 48.8 percent of second votes, since a percentage of second votes was "lent" to the Free Democratic party (FDP); that is, Christian Democrats voted for the FDP to ensure that it cleared the 5 percent hurdle.

In order to understand how this victory came about, how the CDU/CSU reestablished the primacy lost in 1969, we must begin by looking at the history of the CDU/CSU.

HISTORY

The total collapse of the Hitler regime in May 1945 was followed fairly closely by the creation of Christian Democratic groups at various centers throughout Germany. Initially the two major poles of attraction were the CDU of the British zone grouped around the former center-politician Konrad Adenauer and the CDU of the Soviet zone led by Jakob Kaiser. The onset of the cold war and the division of Germany with its consequent reduction of Berlin to a marginal status in the politics of the Western zones meant a continued loss in influence of the Soviet-zone CDU and the emergence of Adenauer, the most prominent leader in the Western zones, as the undisputed leader of the CDU. In Bavaria the need to combat Bavarian particularism led to the creation of the Christian Social Union. This party inherited the function of the Bavarian People's party, which lay in reconciling Bavarian Catholics to a wider political grouping than Bavaria.

By the time of the establishment of the Federal Republic, the Christian Democratic parties had established themselves as the major political force in postwar Germany. This was in itself surprising, since both the Social Democrats themselves and their bourgeois adversaries had expected the Social Democrats to triumph. However, the Christian Democrats were possessed of a number of advantages.

Firstly, they offered a fresh start. They claimed like the Social Democrats that they were untainted by Nazism, but they had the added advantage of being able to distance themselves from the discredited politics of Weimar, unlike the Social Democrats, who asserted continuity. It was this factor that made a successful relaunch of the Center party impossible, since the Center party had been compromised by its acquiescence to the Enabling Bill granting Hitler dictatorial powers in March 1933.

Secondly, the CDU/CSU had a double advantage in its adherence to Christian principles. These principles allowed the parties to take advantage of the religious revival after 1945.

> The religious revival in postwar Germany runs like a bright thread through most of the distinctive phenomena of the intellectual and political scene: the spontaneous foundation of a great "Christian" party encompassing both major faiths, the new appreciation for democracy and the dignity of the individual, the anti-Bismarckian reappraisal of German history, the return to federalism within and hope for federal union with other European countries in place of nationalism, and the high prestige of the churches, which more than any other German institution had emerged untarnished from the Nazi era.[2]

The rejection of altruistic, materialistic values contained in the espousal of Christian values enabled the Christian Democrats to attack at one and the same time the Nazi regime and the emerging communist regime in East Germany. It was thus a set of ideas which was better attuned to the mood of the postwar population in the western part of Germany than social democracy.

The division of Germany also contributed to the success of the CDU/CSU. It cut off the overwhelmingly Protestant areas of East Prussia from western Germany. Catholics formed slightly less than a third of the prewar German population but 45 percent of the inhabitants of postwar West Germany. The loss of the territories in the east deprived the Social Democrats of some of their strongest areas of support. The division of Germany also destroyed the territorial base of Protestant conservatism in Prussia.

The last major advantage of the CDU/CSU was provided by the Allied occupation policies. The refusal of the Allies to grant licenses to regional parties was one which worked to the advantage of the CDU/CSU, since it was their clientele rather than that of the SPD who might have been attracted by particularist, conservative parties. By the time regional conservative parties were licensed, the CDU was well established and firmly in the position of an embryo *Volkspartei* (catchall party) appealing to a wide range of groups and classes. More decisively, the U.S. occupation authorities made plain their preference for the Christian Democrats. In the reactive political climate of occupied Germany, this worked greatly to the advantage of the CDU/CSU, particularly after the advent of Marshall aid in 1947.

THE GOLDEN YEARS OF THE CDU/CSU

Although the CDU/CSU was the major political force by 1949, it was very far from exercising the dominance which became so marked in the 1950s. Ten parties were returned in the first Bundestag election, and the CDU/CSU secured just under a third of the votes. By 1957 the CDU/CSU had absorbed the support of most of these groups and won an absolute majority in the Bundestag election of that year.

The consolidation of the party system and the accompanying dominance of the CDU/CSU was very much identified with Konrad Adenauer's performance as first chancellor of the Federal Republic. His foreign policy priorities of anticommunism and solidarity with the Western democratic allies corresponded to the views of most West Germans and were calculated to ensuring the speedy international acceptance of West Germany. Internally, the success of the social market economy helped ensure the popularity of the CDU/CSU. A possible source of disaffection, the refugees were satisfied by the "economic miracle" and the so-called equalization of the Burdens Law. The key point for the future was that different and substantial groups were drawn to support the CDU/CSU by Adenauer and the role of the party in government.

The dominance of the CDU/CSU was further enhanced by two factors. One factor was a change in the laws governing the conduct of elections. In 1949 a party needed only to achieve 5 percent of the list vote in any one Land or one directly contested constituency seat to gain representation in the Bundestag; in 1953 this was raised to 5 percent of the federal vote or one constituency seat; and in 1957, to 5 percent of the federal vote or three constituency seats. As many of the smaller rivals of the CDU/CSU like the Bayernpartei (Bavarian party) were regionally based, this barrier greatly reduced their electoral chances and discouraged their supporters from wasting their votes.

The last factor was the cohesiveness of the Catholic vote, which provided support for the CDU/CSU across class lines and constituted a major challenge to the SPD. The fact that Catholics made up nearly half the population of the Federal Republic and overwhelmingly supported the CDU/CSU provided a solid driving core of CDU/CSU electoral support.

THE DISSOLUTION OF THE CDU/CSU ASCENDANCY

In retrospect the seeds of the decline of the CDU/CSU ascendancy were already contained in its success. The overwhelming success of the CDU/CSU in the 1950s persuaded the SPD to drop its character as a "class party" and to adopt the Volkspartei model. This process culminated in the 1959 Godesberg Program, which ushered in a period of electoral gains for the SPD, the so-called *Genosse Trend,* culminating in the 1972 elections when it overtook the CDU/CSU and for the first time became the largest party in the Bundestag.

The dependence on and identification with Adenauer, the CDU/CSU's greatest advantage in the 1950s, began to be a handicap. The struggle to push Adenauer into retirement, which began with the presidential election of 1959, ended with his unenthusiastic retirement as chancellor in 1963. He continued, however, as chairman of the party. His retirement as chancellor followed on Franz-Josef Strauss's enforced resignation as defense minister in the wake of the Spiegel affair in 1963. Strauss continued as chairman of the CSU. In their position as chairmen, Adenauer and Strauss carried on intensive warfare with Chancellor Erhard and his ministerial team. After 1965, when it became evident that Erhard would not survive as chancellor, the struggle for the succession became extremely intense and publicly damaging.

The collapse of the Erhard government led not to another CDU/CSU-led bourgeois coalition but to the formation of the Grand Coalition between the CDU/CSU and the SPD. Although this temporarily arrested the decline of the CDU/CSU, it established the SPD as *koalitionsfähig* and broke the mold of postwar German party politics. The prevailing pattern of bipolarity in the party system, of an antisocialist bourgeois bloc led by the CDU/CSU on one side and the SPD and minor allies on the other, was shattered; it was succeeded in 1969 by a new pattern of SPD-FDP reform government against the CDU/CSU.

The difficulties this gave rise to can best be analyzed by looking at a number of different areas.

ELECTORAL CONNECTIONS

The CDU/CSU electoral success of the 1950s and early 1960 was built on the core support of Catholics and middle- and upper-class Protestants. This support began to weaken in the 1960s for a number of reasons. These included a general trend toward secularization, the changing age structure of the population, and the emergence of a new middle class, often employed in the public sector, who were much more open to appeals from the SPD than in the past.

The CDU/CSU were able to dismiss the 1969 election, since they emerged as the largest party, though the FDP's decision, unjustified in their eyes, to go into coalition with the SPD forced them into opposition. They had great difficulty in adjusting to the opposition role, and their opposition to the overwhelmingly popular policy of *Ostpolitik* (relations with the East) led to a crushing defeat in 1972.

The CDU/CSU recovery really began in 1976 when they polled 48.6 percent. They did better only in Adenauer's *annus mirabilis* of 1957, when they polled 50.2 percent. It was by far the best result for a party in opposition in the Federal Republic, a country in which governmental office is normally an advantage. Indeed, the CDU/CSU vote was greater than the 48.2 percent that enabled the SPD-FDP to form a government in 1969.

The most striking feature of the results from a CDU/CSU point of view was the disparity evident in the so-called *Nord-Süd Gefälle* (north-south cleavage), a feature already marked in 1972. The overall swing in the Federal Republic was 3.7 percent to the CDU/CSU, but this concealed marked differences (see Table 4.1). These differences were, of course, partly related to the denominational balance: There are more Catholics in southern Germany than in the north. Further, partial explanations relate to the activities of the Young Socialists in the urban centers in Bavaria and Hesse and the dynamic and prosperous nature of industrial development in the south.

TABLE 4.1. Swing to the CDU/CSU by Land in 1976 (in percentage)

Bavaria	4.9	South Germany	4.3
Hesse	4.5	Middle Germany	3.5
Rhineland-Palatinate	4.0	North Germany	3.0
Baden-Württemberg	3.5		
Saar	2.8		
North Rhine–Westphalia	3.5		
Lower Saxony	3.0		
Bremen	2.9		
Hamburg	2.6		
Schleswig-Holstein	2.1		

Source: Compiled by author.

The CDU/CSU made gains in all social groups but were particularly successful in areas directly dependent on the performance of the economy.

The 1980 election result posed serious problems for the CDU/CSU. Whilst the Christian Union remained the largest part of the Bundestag, it had polled only 44.5 percent, its lowest percentage since 1949. This poor result had not been unexpected. In 1976 the CDU/CSU had polled 48.6 percent, having achieved an average of 51.4 percent in the Land elections between 1974 and 1976. At Land elections between 1978 and 1980, the CDU/CSU had only polled 48.8 percent. Thus, allowing for the "antigovernment effect" of Land elections, the prospects for the CDU/CSU in 1980 looked considerably less favorable than in 1976.

These prospects were further diminished by the adoption of Franz-Josef Strauss as chancellor-candidate for the Christian Union parties. His adoption threw into sharp relief the dilemma for the CDU/CSU identified by Werner Kaltefleiter. Writing on the 1976 election, he made the point that the CSU took 60 percent of the total vote in Bavaria, but the CDU/CSU failed to gain a majority in the country as a whole.[3] Clearly, the CDU/CSU had to improve its position in the north. The fact that the party could win majorities in these regions as well had been demonstrated in the Land elections between 1970 and 1975. The implication was that the CDU/CSU would win a majority in the whole country only through a northern strategy, where "northern" included the central regions. The question for the future development of the party was, given the overwhelming importance of the Catholic south to the party, would be internal decision-making process permit such a northern strategy? If not, the CDU/CSU might win a few more Land elections but never a national victory.

The adoption of Strauss as chancellor-candidate represented a triumph for the southern Catholic conservative section of the CDU/CSU and, as Kaltefleiter predicted, not only did this ensure a very bad result for the CDU/CSU as a whole but it affected the CDU in northern Germany most severely.

This north-south cleavage is associated with the underlying socio-structural characteristics of West German society rather than with any regional consciousness. In particular, it reflects the influence of confessional ties on voting. In Catholic areas there is a permanently strong allegiance to Christian democracy. In Protestant areas, "core voting support" of the CDU is smaller and electors with a propensity to vote CDU are more likely to be affected by short-term factors, for example, the unpopular Strauss candidacy. There are particular explanations for the apparent exceptions. In Bremen there had long been conflict in the ruling SPD, and Bremen had been the scene of an anti-Bundeswehr demonstration by young leftists which, while not associated officially with the SPD, had been associated in many people's minds (possibly wrongly) with the Young Socialists, and by extension with the SPD itself. In Baden-Württemberg the CDU lost to the FDP rather than to the SPD.

In general, in 1980, the Christian Democrats did well in areas where there was a higher-than-average proportion of Catholics and where educational standards were relatively low. Conversely, they did badly in Protestant areas with a higher-than-average standard of education (see Table 4.2).

The poor overall performance by the Christian Democrats was likely to undermine those in the CDU/CSU who had suggested following a conservative anti-FDP policy, attuned to the susceptibilities of southern Catholics. Conversely, it was likely to strengthen those who stressed the necessity for a "northern strategy."

TABLE 4.2. Swing Away from the CDU/CSU by Land in 1980 (in percentage)

Lower Saxony	5.9	Hesse	4.2
Schleswig-Holstein	5.2	North Rhine–Westphalia	3.9
Baden-Württemberg	4.8	Saar	3.9
Hamburg	4.7	Bremen	3.7
Rhineland-Palatinate	4.3	Bavaria	2.4

Source: Compiled by author.

THE 1983 ELECTION

The CDU/CSU fought an extremely well thought out campaign. Their major slogan, *den Aufschwung wählen,* was a straight lift from the successful SPD campaign in the North Rhine–Westphalian Landtag (state parliament) election of 1975. It succeeded in throwing the SPD on to the defensive. The SPD were also unsuccessful in their attempt to transform the election into a *Raketenwahlkampf,* since opinion-poll evidence indicated that members of the public, although worried by the prospect of missile stationing, found the issues too complex to grasp. In the event, only 14 percent named foreign and security policy as the most important issues. On all the major issues, with the exception of protection of the environment, the voters rated the CDU/CSU's competence higher than that of the SPD (see Table 4.3).[4]

THE RESULT

After the election of March 1983 there was general agreement that there had been three winners and one loser (see Table 4.4). The clearest winner was the CDU/CSU, with 48.8 percent of the vote as compared with 44.5 percent in 1980. This was its second-best result ever. The 6.8 percent

TABLE 4.3. Confidence in the CDU/CSU's and SPD's Ability to Solve Problems (in percentage)

	CDU/CSU Jan. 83	SPD Jan. 83
Stimulating private investment	64	26
Limiting the total of foreign workers	58	18
Measures to economize	61	21
Improvement of economic situation	56	31
Protection against crime	57	37
Military security	61	40
Reducing government spending	56	22
Safeguarding energy supplies	62	47
Price stability	48	30
Safeguarding jobs	56	43
Safeguarding retirement pensions	41	41
Environment protection	36	42
Social security	36	47
"Good relations with young people"	38	50
Safeguarding peace	56	67
Employee accumulation of prosperity	25	53
"Good relations with the USSR"	34	71

Source: Survey by the Social Science Research of the Konrad Adenauer Foundation.

won by the FDP, though appreciably less than in 1980 (10.6 percent), must be accounted a success in view of the widely held expectation between September 1982 and January 1983 that the FDP would fail to clear the 5.0 percent hurdle for entry into the Bundestag. With 5.6 percent of the vote, the Greens scored a remarkable triumph for a new party. The clear loser in the election was the SPD, whose poll plummeted to 38.8 percent (from 42.9 percent in 1980), its lowest level of support since 1961.

TABLE 4.4. Federal Election of 1983 (1980 in parentheses)

	Votes (M)	Votes %	Gain/Loss	Seats[a]
Electorate		44.1	(43.2)	
Turnout		89.1	(88.7)	
CDU/CSU	18.9 (16.9)	48.8 (44.5)	+ 4.3	244 (226)
SPD	14.8 (16.3)	38.2 (42.9)	- 4.7	193 (218)
FDP	2.7 (4.0)	6.9 (10.6)	- 3.7	34 (53)
Greens	1.6 (0.6)	5.6 (1.5)	+ 4.1	27 (0)

Source: West German Press Office.

[a]There are 498 seats in the 1983 Bundestag rather than the usual 496. In both Bremen and Hamburg the SPD won one more direct seat than its share of the second vote entitled it to. The rule is that a party is always allowed to retain all direct seats; hence the two extra seats.

The 1983 election was essentially an election in which issues were decisive. Unlike the 1980 election, it was not a plebiscitary contest between two outstanding personalities. On that occasion "the concentration on Schmidt's and Strauss's personalities by default or design was symptomatic of the illusory paucity of real issues. It is not that there were no issues. Rather, that none seemed to hold the 'public interest.'"[5] Certainly in 1980 the personality of Chancellor Helmut Schmidt had proved to be a massive advantage to the governing coalition, and the personality of Franz-Josef Strauss had been an equally grave handicap for the CDU/CSU.

The concentration on issues was a great advantage to the CDU/CSU and enabled them to win a very convincing victory. The CDU/CSU won 180 direct (constituency) seats (121 in 1980) as against the SPD's 68 (127 in 1980). Another feature in the CDU/CSU victory was the leveling of the north-south cleavage. Indeed, the CDU made its greatest gains in Schleswig-Holstein. This leveling reflected the fact that in 1980, lacking a northern strategy, the CDU/CSU had been able to mobilize its potential in the south but not in the north. In 1983, in contrast, the centrist Kohl did not repel northern CDU voters as Strauss had done in 1980, and the SPD no longer had the attractive, quintessentially northern German Helmut Schmidt as chancellor-candidate.

MEMBERSHIP

As we have seen in the historical survey, the CDU/CSU basically developed in the 1950s as a *Kanzlerwahlverein*. This meant that although it was able to mobilize, albeit with increasing difficulty, considerable electoral support, it had a small and largely quiescent membership. The CDU had 303,300 members in 1969. This represented approximately 31 percent of all party members in the Federal Republic. A major priority for the CDU leadership was to secure an expansion of CDU membership in order to adjust to the new situation where the CDU/CSU, far from being able to count on the FDP as a coalition partner, had to reckon with a medium to long-term alliance between the SPD and FDP. These efforts were largely successful, and by 1982 the CDU had 720,000 members.

The CSU, out of power in the mid-fifties, started to expand its membership earlier. By the late sixties the CSU had around 73,000 members. In 1982 CSU membership had risen to about 175,000 members. Together, the parties now have 895,000 members, or about 48 percent of all party members in the Federal Republic.

SOCIAL COMPOSITION

Both the CDU and CSU are overwhelmingly middle class in composition. Only 10.43 percent of the membership of the CDU is working class. The figure for the CSU is slightly higher at 18.4 percent (see Table 4.5).

TABLE 4.5. Social Composition of the CDU and CSU (in percentage)

	CDU Membership Oct. 10, 1982	CSU Membership Dec. 31, 1981
Self-employed	24.75	20.7
Working class	10.43	18.4
Angestellte	27.96	27.8
Civil servant	12.43	15.7
Pensioner	4.88	4.9
Housewife	10.97	5.1

Source: Politisches Jahrbuch der CDU, Recklinghausen. Arranged by author.

THE CONFESSIONAL BALANCE

The membership growth of the CDU in the 1970s has somewhat modified the CDU's predominantly Catholic character. In 1971 three out of four members were Catholics. By 1982 the proportion of Catholics had declined to 59.31 percent. The CSU remains overwhelmingly Catholic. In 1981 82.2 percent of members were Catholics while only 17.2 percent were Protestant.

Thus, despite the expansion of the 1970s the social composition of the CDU/CSU has remained astonishingly stable. It is still the party of the old middle class and the self-employed. It remains also a predominantly Catholic party.

LEADERSHIP AND ORGANIZATION

In the Adenauer era the central organization of the CDU was kept deliberately weak. Its offices were distributed around Bonn rather than being centralized in one building, and the number of personnel was extremely limited. Adenauer rarely if ever visited the party's central offices during his period as chancellor.

As Christian Hacke observes, "Under Adenauer the CDU could hardly be called a party: it was, rather, a dependent branch of the parliamentary group in the Bundestag, which in its turn was only a body dependent on the chancellor. The party had no effective party headquarters but was at most an organization for fighting elections."[6]

The passing of CDU/CSU dominance signaled by the establishment of the Grand Coalition necessitated a strengthening of the party apparatus. The most important long-term reform was the creation of the post of secretary-general of the CDU in order to maintain the profile of the CDU in its new position of coalition partner of the SPD, a party traditionally blessed with a massive and reputedly efficient party apparatus. The establishment of the post of secretary-general meant that for the first time the Bonn head office had a full-time administrator whose job was to establish links with the party organizations in all regions and at all levels throughout the Federal Republic. Until then the Bonn office had contact only with the regional CDU organizations, who had deprived the Bonn headquarters of all contacts with district and local branches. The party thus ceased to be in the hands of the *Landesfürsten* (local notables) and regional offices in the way that it had been hitherto. This change was reinforced by a decision of the 1975 CDU Congress in Mannheim, which established the district (*Bezirk*) as the lowest organizational unit of the CDU. Local branches were to be centered on and communicate with the district level. This led to a further strengthening of the position of the CDU headquarters, since there was a great deal of interaction which bypassed the regional level.

The organizational history of the CDU in the 1970s is demonstrated by these two parallel developments, that is, the expansion in the powers of the party headquarters and the consequent reduction of the dominant influence of the Länder parties and the domination of the political activities of the local branches by the district offices. The key triangle of power in the CDU throughout the seventies was the Bundestagsfraktion, party headquarters (Konrad Adenauer Haus), and the districts which on the one hand are controlled organizationally by the Konrad Adenauer Haus but on the other provide the political backing for the Bundestagsfraktion.

THE RELATIONSHIP BETWEEN THE CDU AND CSU

The modernization and improvement of the CDU organization was a reaction to both the loss of the commanding governmental position it had enjoyed until 1966 and the steady rise in influence of the Bavarian sister party, the CSU. In the immediate postwar period the CSU had initially been very successful in its dual role of an autonomous state party in Bavaria and a semifederal party in alliance with the CDU. The CSU was, however, badly hit by the licensing of the Bayernpartei in 1948. This led to a loss of half its membership and the reinstatement of a more particularistic and backward-looking appeal in order to counter the attraction of the Bayernpartei. At this time the CSU was a *Honorationen* (selectively honored) party which relied on a network of local notables. This made the generation of new initiatives from within the party exceedingly unlikely.

The unexpected loss of power by the CSU in 1954 when a four-party coalition was formed against it, led to important changes which have been exhaustively documented by Alf Mintzel.[7] The post of secretary-general of the CSU was created, and the Munich headquarters was reequipped both in terms of personnel and technology. These changes stimulated a very steep rise in party membership. Between 1955 and the late sixties the CSU membership had expanded from 35,000 to 73,000 members. This had risen further to 175,000 by 1982.

This increase in membership was accompanied by very striking electoral advance. As the governing party in Bavaria and thus through the German system of "cooperative federalism" possessed of a great deal of influence in Bonn, the CSU has been able to reconcile rural backward-looking agricultural elites and modern industrial elites. It has succeeded through its decidedly nationalistic foreign policy position also in appealing to Protestant Franconia. This achievement is well summed up by Alf Mintzel:

> For the first time since 1806 a Bavarian party has united the forces of political Catholicism and secondly the CSU has also succeeded in integrating the divergent regional traditions of Old Bavaria, Franconia and Swabia. The CSU is no longer merely the Bavarian "party of order and the state" in the sense of being a Bavarian Christian Conservative voting bloc; it has become a party of all Bavaria representative of the modernising industrial state of Bavaria which the CSU has played a major part in creating.[8]

Since 1949 the CDU/CSU have had a joint parliamentary party though the CSU *Landesgruppe* has understood this parliamentary party as a permanent alliance whose terms have to be renegotiated at the start of every legislative period. The most serious threat to this cooperation occurred in 1976. The election results of 1976 had a contradictory effect on the balance of power in the CDU/CSU. Helmut Kohl's position was initially strengthened by the CDU performance in the election. However, the even greater success of Franz-Josef Strauss and the CSU led the CSU to expect even greater influence for the CSU Landesgruppe in the joint Bundestagsfraktion.

The failure of the CDU/CSU to obtain an absolute majority in a situation in which the FDP was pledged to continue in coalition with the SPD meant that although the CDU/CSU constituted the largest parliamentary party after the election, it was unable to dislodge the ruling governmental coalition. On November 18, 1976, the CSU Landesgruppe meeting in Wildbad Kreuth, Bavaria, doubtless disappointed by their succès manqué—after all if the CDU had done as well as the CSU, the Christian Democrats would have won the election—voted to end their joint parliamentary arrangement with the CDU. But in the following three weeks the costs of this step became increasingly apparent to the CSU. In the first place, Kohl took on an uncompromising stand: Either the alliance would continue or the CDU would extend its organization into Bavaria, and public opinion polls indicated that such an extension would hit the CSU badly, particularly in Franconia. In the second place, there was considerable resistance in some sections of the CSU to the decision of Strauss and the CSU Landesgruppe. As a result, the two Christian Democratic parties decided to patch up their differences and to vote together for Karl Carstens as Bundestag president and reestablish the joint Bundestagsfraktion.

1980 TRIUMPH OF THE CSU?

This victory of Helmut Kohl in November 1976 was relatively short lived. Kohl was a relatively ineffective leader of the CDU/CSU Bundestagsfraktion. He had been unable to make much impression on Schmidt, and this disappointed not only the CSU but also former supporters of Kohl such as Kurt Biedenkopf (CDU secretary-general from 1973 to 1977). In January 1979 Biedenkopf maintained—in what became known as the Biedenkopf Memorandum—that in the present "crisis-free" situation, it was going to be almost impossible for the Christian Democrats to win the 1980 general election. Nevertheless, he claimed, a change in leadership might help. As a first step Biedenkopf proposed that the joint parliamentary party should have two chairmen (one for the CDU and one for the CSU) together with a new "overall chairman." In effect, this was a proposal that Kohl should be demoted to chair the CDU alone. In addition, Biedenkopf proposed that the chancellor-candidate should not necessarily be the "overall chairman" of the parliamentary party. Already Biedenkopf seemed to be hinting at the possibility of a Strauss candidature—and within a few months he came out openly in favor of Strauss. Although his proposals were rejected by the CDU/CSU parliamentary party in January 1979, he had helped undermine Kohl's position.

That position had already been undermined by the Schleyer murder in late 1977 and by the Landtag election results in 1978. The murder of the West German industrialists' leader strengthened the coalition because the FDP stood firmly behind Schmidt throughout the kidnapping and murder of Schleyer and the Mogadishu hijacking incident. Strauss's candidature was helped by the election of Karl Carstens as president. In the first place, it removed another right-wing candidate who might have succeeded in rallying both Christian Democratic parties behind him. In the second place, Strauss's friends in the CDU and CSU were able to sound out opinion at the meeting of the presidential electoral college. Encouraged by these soundings, Zimmermann, the CSU chairman, announced on May 24, 1979, (one day after the presidential election) that Strauss would stand for the chancellorship. Strauss, of course, had the full support of the CSU; and some members of the CDU, notably Biedenkopf and Dregger, argued that he was the only man who could measure up to Schmidt. Moreover, he had been very successful in Bavaria, and he had had considerable experience in Bonn as a federal minister. However, many CDU members had their doubts about Strauss: His candidature would polarize politics and rule out any possibility of a coalition with the FDP; he would put off moderate voters; he was a member of the junior party, the CSU; the public, it was also suggested, would not have forgotten about the Spiegel affair, or, if they had, they would no doubt soon be reminded of it; finally, Strauss had not always been very loyal to the CDU—to some extent he had undermined both Barzel and Kohl in the 1970s. Nevertheless, in the end—after a month of indecision—the CDU/CSU parliamentary party, after seven hours of reputedly acrimonious discussion, opted for Strauss by 135 votes against 102 for Albrecht, with 15 abstentions. It was hardly a convincing victory. Indeed, to some extent Strauss stepped into a leadership vacuum: Kohl had proved rather ineffectual, and leading moderates like Stoltenberg and Albrecht had no particular desire to ruin their long-term leadership prospects by engaging in a (probably) losing battle against Schmidt in 1980.

Even if the Christian Democrats had opted for a centrist candidate in 1979, it is by no means certain that he would have done any better against Schmidt in 1980. The mood of the country was too much against change. The selection of Strauss may even have been a clever "sacrifice bid" on the part of the Christian Democrats: There can be little doubt that some of them saw his candidature (and almost certain failure) as the best way to remove Strauss finally from Bonn politics.

Certainly, it soon became apparent that Strauss was unlikely to be a winner. An opinion poll taken immediately after his selection as chancellor-candidate in July 1979 showed that a majority of Christian Democrats in the northern Länder would have preferred Albrecht to Strauss: Indeed, with Strauss as chancellor-candidate 13 percent of northern Christian Democrats said they would not vote for the CDU; and even in Bavaria 5 percent were opposed to his candidature. In addition, opinion polls from July 1979 to September 1980 were unanimous, and remarkably consistent, in putting Strauss far behind Schmidt—about 60 percent of those questioned regularly considered the latter as a suitable chancellor, whilst only 30 percent saw Strauss as such. Moreover, the Christian Democrats fell back at all four Landtag elections which took place between Strauss's selection and the federal elections—by 1.9 percent in Bremen, 3.3 percent in Baden-Württemberg, 5.1 percent in Saarland, and 3.9 percent in North Rhine–Westphalia.

1980–83

The SPD-FDP coalition victory was to a large extent a hollow one. Schmidt's policy of fighting the election more or less exclusively as a coalition chancellor had worked greatly to the benefit of the FDP and contributed to a sense of alienation in the SPD. The stage was thus set for increasing conflict between the newly strengthened FDP and the SPD at governmental level and further conflict between Helmut Schmidt and the governmental wing of the SPD and the party in the country. Relations between the SPD and FDP worsened sharply as the recession deepened and the FDP shared in the SPD's electoral unpopularity in a series of Land elections.

The CDU/CSU's reaction was to adopt the Kohl strategy of cultivating the FDP with a view to detaching them from the coalition. A series of meetings took place between Hans-Dietrich Genscher and Helmut Kohl, and the CDU expected the FDP to leave the coalition sometime after the Hesse election at the end of September 1982. Helmut Schmidt's short circuiting of the liberal leadership's strategy and the collapse of the SPD/FDP government on September 17, 1982, exposed differences between the CDU and CSU.

Franz-Josef Strauss wanted immediate elections, which in the climate of the time would almost certainly have catapulted the FDP out of the Bundestag. Kohl fought for a six-month gap between assumption of power and new elections. Kohl was intent on preserving the FDP as a coalition partner in order to preserve a balance between the CDU and CSU. He and his advisors were also convinced that a CDU/CSU government without FDP participation would be very unwise, given the unpopularity of some of "the cuts" they would have to make. The FDP's role in this scenario would be to take as much of the blame as possible for these cuts—a role they had already filled for the SPD.

Kohl's electoral strategy was successful in both its aims. The CDU/CSU victory was just short of an absolute majority. This gave Kohl a very strong mandate and ensured the continuance of the FDP in the coalition. An attempt by Strauss to secure either the foreign or economics ministries for himself was repulsed by Kohl, who had worked very closely with the leadership of the CDU Landesgruppe after October 1982.

In the months after March 1983 Strauss attempted to reassert control of the CSU Landesgruppe and to make the position of the FDP in the coalition as uncomfortable as possible. His position was seriously undermined by the revelation early in July that he was behind a substantial scheme of credits for East Germany. The revelation led first to the resignation of Franz Handlos, a CSU Bundestag deputy. Worse was to follow for Strauss. At the CSU Party Conference on July 16, 1983, in Munich he received only 662 of 949 valid votes, his worst result in 22 years.[9] Further, his position had to be defended by Kohl at the conference. And perhaps most significantly, CSU ministers in Bonn like Friedrich Zimmermann did very well in the votes for the party executive, while figures like Stoiber, the former secretary-general of the CSU and a man very closely identified with Strauss, did very badly. The impression left by the party conference was that the party membership did not support what they saw as Strauss's overaggressive rivalry with the CDU leadership and his own hostility to the CDU.

CONCLUSION

The victory of the CDU/CSU in the elections of March 6, 1983, was not an isolated phenomenon. What it did was to crown a decade of steady advance by the Christian Union parties. At the Land level the CDU/CSU is now poised to gain a two-thirds majority, and their dominance in local government is even more striking. With the exception of the Hanseatic cities of Hamburg and Bremen, the major cities of West Germany are firmly under Christian Union control. This position is further buttressed by the dominance of Christian Union sympathizers in key institutions like the Federal Constitutional Court, the broadcasting stations and, of course, the press. The trade unions, which are the last major stronghold of the adversaries of the Christian Union, are in a very much weakened condition, reflecting the worsening situation on the labor market in the last years.

At first sight, then, the position of the CDU/CSU is an enviable one— yet difficulties abound. The optimistic talk of *Aufschwung* and *Wende* has raised expectations among the voters. This places the government under an *Erfolgszwang*.[10] They have to appear to be making some gains, especially in the field of economics. Yet this has proved very difficult to achieve and there has been very little evidence of substantial economic recovery. Furthermore, any success in improving the position of its basically export dependent industries is unlikely to be accompanied by a recovery in employment. This is a very serious problem, since the baby boom of the fifties and sixties lasted longer in West Germany than the United States or the United Kingdom. This means that there will be an unusually high proportion of new entrants to the labor market for at least the rest of this decade, with all the attendant problems.

The CDU/CSU also labor under difficulties in choosing an economic strategy. Their earlier enthusiastic identification with Thatcherite policies has been tempered in recent years. The Catholic Social wing of the CDU, although weaker than in the past, has not lost all influence. Its most prominent exponent, Norbert Blüm, is minister of labor and will act to restrain full-blown attacks on welfare spending. Unlike Ronald Reagan or Margaret Thatcher, the CDU/CSU has still an interest in good relations with organized labor. This can only be achieved if the welfare cuts do not go too deep. In preserving relations with organized labor the CDU/CSU will, however, be unable to make the level of fiscal savings so avidly desired by their supporters.

One way of improving the situation on the labor market is fraught with difficulties. The very large numbers of foreign workers in West Germany present a very tempting target. The major problem is that very large numbers of them show no inclination to respond to financial inducements encouraging them to return home. Any measures which relied too openly on legal manipulation or the threat of force would be extraordinarily difficult, since international opinion sensitized by the excesses of the Third Reich would react very badly. In default of these, however, the problem is likely to remain a very large one.

External and security policy is the last main area of difficulty for the CDU/CSU. Although the result of the election represented a mandate for their policies, major difficulties remain. The failure of the Geneva talks led to the Pershing II missiles being installed as promised. This was accompanied by massive civil disruption and a damaging polarization of German society—a polarization which is very evident in the Christian churches, particularly among Protestants. Anxiety about the missiles is high even among those who generally support a pro-West and pro-NATO policy.

In government, the CDU/CSU have found it difficult to live up to the rhetoric of complete identification with the United States. The 1980s are, after all, not the 1950s. The rhetoric has to some extent been contained, but in a whole series of actions, including the response to the shooting down of the Korean jumbo jet, German response has been constrained by the importance of the trading relationships with the USSR. It was this contrast between rhetoric and action which created problems for Franz-Josef Strauss in the GDR credits case.

More serious problems are created for the CDU/CSU by the repercussions of the Lambsdorff affair. The question as to his successor will be likely both to create strains with the FDP and to inflame Franz-Josef Strauss's ambition to play a role in Bonn politics.

These difficulties notwithstanding, the general position of the CSU/CSU is an incredibly strong one and they do look like being the political grouping which will steer the Federal Republic through the very difficult choices ahead.

NOTES

1. Werner Kaltefleiter, "Eine Kritische Wahl: Ammerkungen zur Bundestagswahl 1983." Beilage zur Wochenzeitung das Parlament, April 9, 1983.

2. Peter Merkl, "Allied Strategies of Effecting Political Change and Their Reception in Occupied Germany," *Public Policy* 17: 75.

3. Werner Kaltefleiter, "Winning without Victory: The 1976 CDU Cam-

paign," in K. Cerny, ed., *Germany at the Polls, The Bundestag Election of 1976* (Washington, D.C.: AEI, 1978), p. 143.

4. Survey by the Social Science Research Institute of the Konrad Adenauer Foundation.

5. Juliet Lodge, "The West German Federal Election of 1980. Security for the 80's versus With Optimism Against Socialism," *Hull Papers in Politics*, no. 21 (1981): 31.

6. Christian Hacke in R. Morgan and S. Silvestri, eds., *Moderates and Conservatives in Western Europe* (London: Heinemann Educational Books), p. 25.

7. See Alf Mintzel, *Die CSU-Anatomie einer konservativen Partei 1945– 1972*, Cologne: West Deutscher Verlag, 1975).

8. Alf Mintzel, "Conservatism and Christian Democracy in the Federal Republic of Germany," in Z. Layton-Henry, ed., *Conservative Politics in Western Europe* (Macmillan), pp. 145–147.

9. *Die Zeit*, July 22, 1983.

10. The poor performance of the CDU in the state elections of September 1983 in Hesse and Bremen indicates this is a very real factor.

5

THE SOCIAL DEMOCRATIC PARTY

Gerard Braunthal

When a political party governs a democratic country for a long time, it can expect sooner or later to be replaced by the opposition. Regardless of whether the governing party lies on the left or right of the political spectrum, the bulk of the voters hold it responsible for their welfare. If an economic recession generates mass unemployment or spiraling inflation, the party in power knows that voter dissatisfaction will mount and that its period of governance will be threatened at the next election.

The Social Democratic party of West Germany (SPD), having been at the helm of government from 1969 to 1982, could not escape this fate. Yet, exceptionally, its ouster from power in October 1982 was not because of the West German voters but because of squabbles with its junior coalition partner, the Free Democratic party (FDP), over economic and fiscal policies to meet the recession, which led to the breakup of the coalition. A new conservative coalition cabinet, headed by the Christian Democrats, assumed power and received a stamp of approval from the voters in March 1983. Thus, the SPD once again became the major opposition party in Parliament. While criticism of the party in power is essential in a democratic state, the opposition party does not relish being Number Two rather than One, especially when the SPD had been in this inferior position for many decades since its inception in the nineteenth century.

In order to understand the recent events that catapulted the SPD from a position of power to opposition, we must first examine its history and the changes in its organization, membership, leadership, and ideology. We must ask whether these changes were inevitable, given the international and domestic environment, or whether the party could have avoided some crises through its own actions. Only then can we make some predictions about the party's future.

HISTORY

The SPD was founded in 1875 as an amalgamation of two rival socialist parties.[1] Although its program was Marxist, it envisioned evolutionary rather than revolutionary changes leading to socialism in Germany. Chancellor Bismarck, heading a conservative government for two decades during the Empire era, viewed the SPD as a threat and in 1878 outlawed it as a national organization. However, he allowed its candidates to run for election to the Reichstag (the lower house of Parliament). When Bismarck's antisocialist legislation expired in 1890, the party, which had maintained an underground organization, captured 20 percent of the vote for Reichstag deputies.

Around the turn of the century, the SPD had to contend with three rival wings vying for power. A radical left wing, led by Karl Liebknecht and Rosa Luxemburg, was pitted against a centrist wing, led by August Bebel and Karl Kautsky, and a reformist wing, led by Eduard Bernstein. The wings, none gaining supremacy before World War I, engaged in bitter fratricidal disputes over Marxist theory and practice. Yet, despite a failure to agree on how to achieve socialism in a country with a firmly entrenched capitalist system, the party grew by leaps and bounds because there was enough popular dissatisfaction with the system. As a consequence, the SPD numbered over 1 million members and received more than 4.2 million votes in the 1912 Reichstag election (constituting nearly 35 percent of the total) to make its bloc of deputies the largest in the Reichstag.

With the eruption of World War I, SPD leaders suddenly abandoned their pledge to promote international peace. Afraid that government officials would crush their organization built up laboriously over the decades, they provided support for the war instead. Less than three years later (in April 1917), radical SPD leaders who opposed the war effort were responsible for an intraparty split. They formed an Independent Social Democratic party (USPD) and called on war-weary and hungry workers to stage strikes against the government. One year later, the combination of strikes and military defeats made a continuation of the Imperial regime untenable. In November 1918, it resigned and the war came to an end.

In the initial period of postwar turmoil, the SPD and USPD assumed joint control of a provisional government, but soon the wartime split reemerged as the USPD pressed for radical reforms and the SPD opted for mild system changes. The SPD's call for a parliamentary regime to succeed the provisional government was acceptable to other political parties but not to the USPD left wing and to the newly formed German Communist party (KPD). In 1920, these two antisystem parties merged, and two years later the USPD right wing rejoined the SPD.

In the meantime, a parliamentary system was established at Weimar (1919–33). The SPD, shedding its continuous opposition role in the Empire era, gained legitimacy when its capacity to govern was demonstrated. One of its leaders, Friedrich Ebert, became the first president of the Republic, while others became chancellors and formed coalition cabinets (1919–20; 1928–30). Nonsocialist chancellors governed at other times, although with occasional SPD representation. Even though the first SPD-led cabinets could have produced some major socialist economic reforms, the SPD leaders were too timid and worried about the negative reaction of Allied governments and other German parties to initiate them. While they undertook moderate steps to expand the welfare state, economic crises, foreign intervention, and political assassinations led to extreme instability.

When the Great Depression caused unemployment, frustration, and alienation from the republican system among workers and the middle class, many turned to the extremist parties, especially to the Nazis. By January 1933 Adolf Hitler became chancellor. He lost no time in crushing the democratic order, including all parties other than the Nazis. In June, the SPD was banned and thousands of its leaders were arrested while others went into exile and encouraged resistance to the Nazis within Germany. Many in the resistance movement, including Social Democrats, perished in concentration camps. Those who survived often became party leaders in postwar Germany.

THE POSTWAR ERA

With Hitler's defeat in 1945, the Allied powers divided the country into four occupation zones. In East Germany, under Soviet occupation, the SPD was merged into the Socialist Unity party (SED), which had been created under Soviet auspices. For the SPD this was a bitter blow because during the Weimar era it had had its greatest strength in that area. In the West German zones and West Berlin, the party was reconstituted on the foundations set before 1933. Kurt Schumacher, a veteran leader whom the Nazis had imprisoned for years, became party chairman and was greatly responsible for the direction of policy.[2] Once again the party adopted a mixture of Marxist doctrine and reformist practice that had marked its position during the Empire and Weimar eras.

In 1949, the three Western zones of occupation were merged into a new state—the Federal Republic of Germany. In the first national election in August the SPD received almost 30 percent of the vote, but the Christian Democratic Union/Christian Social Union (CDU/CSU), led by Konrad Adenauer, outpolled it by less than 2 percent and formed a conservative coalition government without the SPD. The SPD did not gain too much additional support in the next four elections (1953, 1957, 1961, 1965) and thus had to remain on the opposition benches in the Bundestag (the lower house of Parliament). Its continuous electoral defeats were caused primarily by the successful economic revival sparked by the CDU/CSU-led government, Adenauer's strong anticommunist and pro-West position, the SPD's loss of its East German bastion, and the voters' lack of responsiveness to its neo-Marxist campaign rhetoric. The SPD lacked appealing alternatives to Adenauer's foreign policy, but in a spirit of cooperative rather than competitive interparty opposition supported much of the domestic legislation.

To stem the electoral defeats, a number of pragmatic and reform-oriented SPD mayors in several large cities called on the more tradition-oriented party leaders to change policies. At the 1959 Godesberg Conference such changes were made in the basic program of the party. The neo-Marxist ballast was thrown overboard and a moderate reform program, such as a minimum of planning and nationalization, was accepted. The SPD leaders knew that only a policy of deideologization and pragmatism would bring the party more votes, not just from the workers, its traditional base, but from an expanding middle class that was willing to support a moderately left but non-Marxist party.

Within the SPD, some top leaders, such as the strategist Herbert Wehner, urged the party high command to think of entering into a governing coalition with the CDU/CSU as a means of gaining legitimacy and political power; but such a policy was rejected until 1966 by other top leaders who were not keen on an "embracement" policy with the party's chief political opponent. In 1966, however, an economic recession precipitated a government crisis: The CDU/CSU could not maintain the continued coalition support of the small, liberal Free Democratic party (FPD) and was seeking another partner in order to have a parliamentary majority. The SPD agreed to enter a coalition cabinet as a junior partner, serving under CDU/CSU Chancellor Kurt-Georg Kiesinger.

From 1966 to 1969, the SPD shared in the formulation of foreign and domestic policies. Its contingent of cabinet members was led by Vice-

Chancellor and Foreign Minister Willy Brandt, party chairman since 1964 and mayor of West Berlin from 1957 until 1966.[3] While there was much accord between the coalition partners in the initial governing period, they disagreed increasingly on a number of policies and waged the 1969 election campaign as foes rather than allies. Although the CDU/CSU captured a plurality of votes in the election, it could not obtain the support of either the SPD or the FDP to assure it of a parliamentary majority. Therefore the SPD became the senior governing party in a coalition cabinet with the FDP, which concurred with the SPD on most domestic and foreign policies. The CDU/CSU moved to the opposition benches in the Bundestag, which it occupied until 1982.

Brandt, as chancellor, launched a modest set of labor, social, and economic reforms and speeded up a reconciliation policy with Communist states in the East (*Ostpolitik*). But when he lost his parliamentary majority in 1972 as a result of several deputies defecting to the CDU/CSU, he called for a new (and premature) election. The results were most encouraging to the SPD. For the first time the party outpolled the CDU/CSU (although by less than 1 percent) and with the FDP had a comfortable majority of 46 deputies in the Bundestag. The Brandt government viewed the results as a clear mandate to continue its domestic reform and Ostpolitik policies.

From 1972 to 1974 it moved ahead on its successful Ostpolitik but had to slow down on costly domestic reforms as a result of a new recession caused by the international oil crisis. Brandt faced other difficulties that eventually caused his resignation as chancellor in May 1974: Dissatisfied public service workers went out on strike; the radical Young Socialists (Jusos) in the SPD clashed with older members on pragmatic and ideological issues; Wehner, head of the SPD parliamentary group Fraktion (Bundestagfraktion) while on a visit to Moscow openly criticized Brandt's stand on Berlin; and a spy scandal broke in the Chancellor's Office that led in turn to revelations about Brandt's personal life.

Helmut Schmidt, who had held a number of ministerial posts (defense, economics, finance) and had been an SPD vice-chairman since 1968, succeeded Brandt as chancellor.[4] He formed a new SPD-FDP cabinet, appointing some ministers who were pragmatists and technocrats rather than intellectuals. Because Brandt remained party chairman, a collective leadership emerged that is unusual in German politics, where normally the chancellor is also party chief. The two SPD leaders apportioned their respective spheres of activities, but their personal relationship was cool, partly because of ideological differences between them (Schmidt was on the right in the SPD and Brandt on the left-center).

Schmidt formed a new SPD/FDP government following the 1976 election in which the two parties won only a narrow majority in the Bundestag. High unemployment, mounting welfare costs, and SPD intraparty squabbles and corruption scandals had not gone unnoticed among the electorate that again gave the CDU/CSU the highest percentage of votes. But once more the Christian Democrats could not find a coalition partner and remained in opposition.

The Schmidt government made no significant economic and social reforms in the 1976–80 legislative period because of continued financial constraints. Instead, it tried to restore full employment, reduce public borrowing, and put the old-age pension and health systems on a more sound financial footing. Yet by 1977 Schmidt was forced to begin some pump-priming public works construction programs when unemployment remained a critical problem. Within the SPD, criticisms kept surfacing about Schmidt's authoritarian and technocratic leadership style, his failure to accept many party recommendations for policy initiatives, and his willingness to make too many concessions to the FDP coalition partner, which was less sympathetic than the SPD to union aspirations and state intervention in the economy.

In 1977 the SPD's problems did not fade away. Factional disputes between young left activists and the party's municipal politicians flared in many cities, especially Munich and Frankfurt; new financial scandals erupted in some states (*Länder*) and cities; the feud between Brandt, Schmidt, and Wehner continued; and left-wing dissidents in the Fraktion broke party discipline by voting against or abstaining from some controversial government bills. But from 1978 to 1980 the party's standing in Land elections improved with the rise of Schmidt's popularity in the nation (in the wake of his cool response to terrorist acts) and decreasing ideological schism within the SPD.

The 1980 election confirmed Schmidt's popularity and his pragmatic domestic and foreign policies. Because the SPD had not fared as well in the election as its supporters had hoped, many were frustrated over its inability to emerge from the shadow of the chancellor, who kept some distance from a party lacking his own appeal in the nation. Once again Schmidt formed an SPD-FDP cabinet and expected to remain in power for another four years. But, as we shall see, his expectation was dashed by 1982 when interparty policy disputes led to the withdrawal of FDP ministers from the cabinet, which in turn led to the collapse of the cabinet and Schmidt's ouster as chancellor on October 1.

ORGANIZATION

The makeup of a party can have a significant effect on its political power either when it is in opposition trying to become the majority party or when it is the governing party trying to maintain itself in power. A unified party free of deep ideological schisms or leadership struggles will enjoy greater confidence among the electorate than a party whose leaders are feuding or jockeying for power and whose factions are deeply split along ideological lines.

In the historical survey, indications abounded that the party almost since its inception in the nineteenth century was rent by factionalism, leadership struggles, and pragmatic and ideological schisms. To see whether these are still present in the SPD of the 1980s we must first examine the party's organization in order to ask who sets policy, how much unity exists, and whether ideology plays a role in policy formulation.

Party policy is determined in the presidium, an "inner cabinet" of the eleven top leaders, consisting of the party chairman, the two deputy chairmen, the Fraktion chairman, the secretary, the treasurer, and five members at-large chosen by the party executive.[5] When the SPD was the government party, the chancellor and several SPD cabinet ministers held seats in the presidium, thus in theory facilitating joint policymaking on key domestic or foreign issues. More often in practice, however, the SPD chancellor would first make policy decisions in the cabinet and then inform the presidium, which meets weekly. If the presidium did not concur with a decision, it could do little about it because the chancellor, even though he was a top party official, felt that the national interest transcended party interest whenever the two did not coincide. Often there was an identity of interests because the more radical left wing of the party failed to obtain representation in the presidium.

The party executive (Vorstand) is the second most important body consisting of 39 members, again including the party chairman elected by the party convention. The rival party wings select slates of candidates for the highly coveted posts in the executive and normally win a share of seats proportionate to their strength. Thus, the left wing has captured about one-third of the seats, giving it a chance to participate in making decisions. Meeting once a month, the executive receives reports from the presidium and deals with basic party policies, organizational questions, and personnel matters.

The convention, usually meeting biennially, is in theory the highest organ determining policy, but in practice its role in policy making is limited. Its 400 delegates, elected at regional conventions, are primarily party functionaries and deputies who normally approve the party line. However, since 1968 a bloc of left-wing delegates, consisting of about one-third of the total, has challenged the leadership on a number of controversial issues ranging from nuclear energy and defense to state control of private investments.

In addition to these top three groups, the SPD structure consists of a party council, control and arbitration commissions, numerous other commissions, committees, ad hoc working groups, a trade union council (to coordinate activities with the trade union federations), a senior council (retired leaders), and a host of party associations. The latter, comprising workers, women, youth, the self-employed, health workers, teachers, lawyers, and others, were created to gain support from diverse social groups within the party and the population. Of the many associations, the Jusos (Young Socialists) were from 1968 on the most outspoken in their criticism of the leaders' reformist and pragmatic policies and the oligarchical rule prevailing within the party. The Jusos wanted the party to accentuate its socialist goals rather than make piecemeal reforms and thereby strengthen the existing capitalist system. They accused the party of lacking a political perspective and the government of being only a better technocratic alternative to the CDU/CSU. They urged more participation of citizens in politics and a democratization of the economy. The Juso challenge to the party peaked in the early 1970s but declined thereafter when it could score few successes as a minority pitted against a powerful right wing headed by Chancellor Schmidt.

The blue-collar workers in the party were worried about the Juso attempt to "march through the institutions" of the party and the state is an effort to capture them. To meet the offensive they formed the Association of Workers (AfA) within the party, although publicly the AfA was created to bring more workers into the party and ensure that their interests were met by party leaders. The AfA also maintained close ties to the German Trade Union Federation (DGB), the leading labor organization with 17 national industrial unions having in 1980 a total membership of 8 million. Although the majority of DGB leaders and members are Social Democrats, when the SPD was in power, labor interests did not necessarily prevail if they clashed with other interests or if the SPD's coalition partner, the FDP, vetoed a DGB request for government action.

In addition to youth and workers' associations, the SPD contains the Association of Social Democratic Women (ASF). Formed in 1972, it demands a greater role for women in the male-dominated party and seeks through political action to make legislative gains (for instance, abortion reform, a controversial issue even within the party). It also attempts to attract more women into the SPD in order to increase the female membership proportion of 20 percent. Such a task is not easy because many nonparty women or feminist-group members are not interested in becoming involved in partisan activities.

A brief description of the party's organization would not be complete without citing the party secretary, who provides support for the chairman and is in charge of operational activities; the regional associations in the Länder, districts, and subdistricts; and the 10,000 local branches situated in cities and small communities throughout the country. In the local branches, members have a chance to discuss party policies, assist in local, state, and national election campaigns, and help recruit new members.

MEMBERSHIP

The SPD has undergone an important social shift in membership that in turn has an effect on the party's electoral chances and its programmatic goals. After World War II the core group—the blue-collar workers—began to decline in percentage of the total labor force and by 1980 constituted only 28 percent of the SPD membership (compared to 45 percent in 1952). This group, whose members have a low level of education and low-to-middle income, hold traditional values in social, religious, sexual, and ideological questions, mostly are in the party's right wing, and demand that the party put priority on bread-and-butter issues.

The shrinking percentage of workers in the party made it imperative that the party tap new members from other social groups. It found them among salaried employees and civil servants (especially teachers) who make up the "new middle class" and the left-center bloc in the party. These groups, whose members are mostly more educated and have relatively high incomes, hold modern, secular, and progressive rather than traditional views. They put emphasis on quality-of-life issues, such as ecology and decentralization and democratization of institutions. When they joined the SPD en masse after 1969, it became less working class and more middle class. With this change, a confrontation between the two groups holding different values and having different priorities was almost inevitable. The confrontation was accentuated by the party's successful mobilization of left-wing students who formed the core of the Jusos and who made inroads into the party's power structure, especially at the local level.

The changed character of the membership in a people's party with over 950,000 members in 1981 meant that 1 out of 4 members was under 35 and that as secularization in society proceeded, an increasing number of less devout Catholics joined the SPD. By 1977, 53 percent of members were Protestant, 28 percent Catholic, and the rest mostly unaffiliated.[6] Even though these shifts took place in the membership, the party still could not expect automatic support from a similar proportion of young or Catholic voters.

LEADERSHIP

The party's quality of leadership has a direct effect on its ability to mobilize and retain new members and voters. Brandt, Schmidt, and Wehner formed the reigning troika until 1982. Each had his strengths and weaknesses as a leader, but as a team their frequent public feuds did not enhance the party's fortunes. Yet their remarkably long time in office showed that most members had confidence in them. Other leaders, many of whom were unpaid functionaries, served the party at national Länder, and local levels. Once again, intraparty tension arose because blue-collar workers and women were underrepresented in leadership posts as compared to their proportion in the membership. As a consequence of the social shift in leadership from proletarian to middle class—indicating the party had become catchall by encompassing most groups in society—there could be dividends in membership and voting support for the SPD.

Yet this potential for growth and political success was often negated by the already-cited factional disputes that erupted in many SPD local branches between the new young left and the older workers on the right. Party leaders warned the members about the formation of factions and cliques, but the warnings were in vain, given the generation gap and strong ideological differences. However, Brandt especially was able to defuse differences among the warring factions in order to mobilize the party against the CDU/CSU at election time.

In most organizations, a degree of oligarchy, in which the leaders set the direction of policy, prevails. In the SPD, this has been the norm, as noted already in 1911 by Robert Michels in his well-known treatise on political parties. Michels contended that "who says organization, says oligarchy."[7] When the troika of Brandt, Schmidt, and Wehner ruled the SPD from 1969 to 1982, the situation had not changed significantly, although the challenges from the Jusos, the workers, and the women associations introduced a measure of intraparty democracy that the SPD had not seen since its rebirth after World War II. The challenges questioned not only policies emanating from the top SPD organs but those from the SPD-led government as well. In most instances, the leadership prevailed, although it had to make compromises on occasion.

IDEOLOGY

The underlying reason for the challenges to the leadership concerned the failure of members to agree on ideological principles. The neo-Marxist Jusos were dissatisfied with the pragmatic tone set by Schmidt as chancellor and by most party leaders. The Jusos wanted the party to accept a policy that included socialist planks, such as limited nationalization of industry and state control over investment of industry. Their attempt to "reideologize" the party succeeded because the leaders realized that youth would not be attracted to the SPD banner if the SPD became merely another mass party leaning to the political center and hardly distinguishable from the CDU/CSU. On the other hand, the Jusos' attempt to put the party on a "system-transcending" course, in which the party would abandon its espousal of a mixed economic system—with strong backing for the free enterprise system—and instead support more socialist measures, failed. The left-center group, led by Brandt, was not ideologically averse but viewed it as impractical, while the right wing viewed it negatively for both ideological and pragmatic reasons. Consequently, the SPD pursued a slightly left-of-center course whose ideological foundation was set at Godesberg in 1959.

This brief survey of the party organization, membership, leadership, and ideology was intended to provide answers to the questions of who sets policy, how much unity prevails in the party, and what role ideology plays in its formulation of policy. Clearly, as we shall see presently in examining the party's more recent record from 1980 to 1982, the leadership ran into obstacles within and outside the SPD, intraparty factional disputes flared, and international events constrained its freedom of action.

1980–82: CRISIS ON THE HORIZON

Before we deal with the period of crisis of 1982, let us first assess the more auspicious beginning of Schmidt's last term of office starting in 1980. His SPD-FDP coalition won an expected victory in the October 1980 election against the CDU/CSU candidate for chancellor, Franz-Josef Strauss. The SPD received 42.9 percent and the FDP 10.6 percent of the total vote against the CDU/CSU's 44.5 percent. Despite the SPD-FDP victory, there was gloom in the SPD for not gaining more votes than the CDU/CSU, for being in the shadow of the chancellor who wanted to appear as a "better CDU chancellor," for its defensive posture during the campaign, and for its tactical campaign mistakes, such as not courting anti-Strauss CDU voters.

Shortly after the election, SPD and FDP negotiators began coalition negotiations to form a new cabinet and concur on a government program for the next four-year legislative period. They had little difficulty agreeing on the cabinet's composition, which consisted once again of thirteen SPD and four FDP ministers (with only a few changes in posts), but they had some difficulty agreeing on the government program. Bundestag SPD Fraktion leaders objected to their colleagues in the executive branch negotiating primarily for the SPD and wanted a share in policy making. They met with success when Schmidt yielded to their pressure. However, left-wing leaders complained that the government's coalition program lacked enough social democratic content and trade union leaders complained that the program did not contain new social reforms and made too many concessions to the FDP. In the next two years, these complaints surfaced time and again as the government's problems mounted.

ECONOMIC PROBLEMS

One of the major problems was the deteriorating economic and financial situation caused primarily by the international recession. In 1981 and 1982, SPD and FDP ministers clashed repeatedly on the best ways to cope with the national recession, as manifested in an increasing unemployment, a zero economic growth, a weakening in the domestic demand for goods, a decline in export orders, and a sharp rise in business failures. In early 1981, the debate over the budget started in Parliament. All parties concurred on the need for the country's finances to be consolidated and for the national debt to be curbed through sacrifice by the population. But disagreement broke out over the projected 1982 budget not only between the opposition CDU/CSU and the coalition parties—a normal occurrence in a democratic system—but between and within the coalition partners, mirroring an ideological schism over the allocation of wealth.

The more conservative FDP ministers insisted on major cuts in the social security budget, such as in direct payments of subsidies to parents of children regardless of the parents' income or relative need. SPD ministers, rejecting the FDP position, warned against the wholesale "disemboweling" of social security programs and demanded instead higher taxes and less tax loopholes for upper-income groups (unacceptable to the FDP) and the elimination of waste and abuse. Brandt assailed the FDP by telling SPD members: "We've been leaned on. It's gone to the limit of what Social Democratic self-respect allows! When it's necessary, it will be clear for everybody who is responsible [for] this!"[8] The continuation of the coalition was at stake. But after lengthy deliberations in the cabinet and Parliament, SPD and FDP deputies in September approved compromises in the 1982 budget, with only a few cuts made in the social security programs (as a concession to the SPD) and no new public employment programs scheduled (as a concession to the FDP). Both parties agreed that the mounting costs for welfare and unemployment must be curbed.

The worsening economic situation in late 1981 and 1982 produced even higher budget deficits than were forecast, which meant that the government had to contemplate new cuts in expenditures or more public borrowing. By early 1982 unemployment had risen to 1.7 million (8.2 percent), the highest in 27 years. The SPD left wing and labor urged the fiscally conservative Schmidt to swiftly initiate a job-creation program to bring down the high unemployment rate, while SPD Finance Minister Hans Matthöfer urged a higher tax on oil. When the FDP leaders opposed any tax increases, Schmidt, in order to engender coalition unity, threatened for the third time in 15 months to resign as chancellor—another indication that his coalition was unraveling. His threat to resign led on February 5 to an uneasy accord between SPD and FDP deputies who, supporting Schmidt on a vote of confidence, approved a $5.3 billion job-creation program, $2.6 billion in cheap loans to medium-sized industries, and a 10 percent bonus to certain firms for making investments.

Two months later, SPD convention delegates overwhelmingly approved a resolution intended to combat the continuing high joblessness through increased government borrowing and taxes, proposals that the FDP had rejected on previous occasions. The delegates also approved resolutions calling for a centralized direction of industrial investments and a government master plan for economic revival. These resolutions were not binding on the government, a fact underlined by Schmidt, who told the delegates that "the Chancellor cannot relinquish the power to set policy."[9] Moreover, his disagreement with some of the resolutions and his obvious desire not to alienate the FDP produced further strains with the other top SPD leaders and with the unions, who were worried about the continuing disappearance of jobs.

In June 1982, the coalition partners arrived at an accord on the basic outlines of the 1983 budget after another round of difficult negotiations. Once again each party put forward the position it had taken in the negotiations on the 1982 budget but finally accepted a compromise on the extent of public borrowing to meet the federal debt and on the size of the overall cuts. Yet this compromise could not prevent another disagreement on economic policy in early September, which proved fatal to the continuation of the SPD-FDP cabinet. The discord was sparked by Minister of Economics Otto von Lambsdorff (FDP) who, espousing the probusiness philosophy of his party (and the views of President Reagan and Prime Minister Thatcher), urged the cabinet to vote for drastic cuts in social programs and tax concessions for industry to stimulate investments. Schmidt, who in the past had made concessions to the FDP to prevent the fall of the coalition, was under intensive pressure from SPD and labor leaders to reject Lambsdorff's proposals. In this instance, Schmidt bowed to the entreaties from his party colleagues, thereby contributing to the breakup of the cabinet (to be discussed below).

INTRAPARTY DISCORD

Undoubtedly the budgetary problems faced by the government were the chief reasons for its troubles, but there were others contributing to the chancellor's downfall. Among these was a deep schism within the SPD on energy and defense issues that showed the voters how divided the major governing party was on two key aspects of the administration's policies. The schism, salutary as it may have been in promoting intraparty democracy by sparking a dialogue among SPD members, weakened the authority of Schmidt, who could not rely on the full support of his party for all of his domestic and foreign policies.

Since 1976 an intraparty dialogue had taken place on nuclear energy in which the Jusos and ecologists within the party insisted that less environmentally damaging energy alternatives be developed and that the government declare a moratorium on the construction of new nuclear plants. They were pitted against right-wing members, union leaders, and cabinet ministers who insisted that nuclear energy was needed to complement coal and other existing energy sources and that the elimination of the nuclear industry would mean increased unemployment. At the 1979 party convention, the majority of delegates supported a report which stated that existing nuclear power plants should continue operating, plants under construction should be finished, and some new plants should be constructed if waste disposal and safety requirements have been met. A minority of left delegates maintained its opposition to any new construction.

The Jusos, who lost the fight on a moratorium, continued the battle in 1980. Joined by the regional SPD in Land Hesse, they bitterly opposed the plan by Hesse's minister-president, Holger Börner, (SPD) to construct still another nuclear plant or enlarge an existing one in that state. In 1981, the intraparty dispute shifted to Hamburg. Mayor Hans-Ulrich Klose (SPD) resigned when a majority of party leaders in his city did not support him in his opposition to the further construction of a nuclear power plant in nearby Brokdorf. This feud cost the party many votes at the next election. In 1982, Schmidt maintained his commitment to nuclear energy at the party convention. Once again a two-to-one majority of delegates supported him, although with varying degrees of enthusiasm.

Another issue of intraparty discord centered on defense policy and especially on NATO's 1979 plan to deploy United States intermediate-range nuclear missiles in Western Europe, including 108 Pershing II and 96 Cruise missiles in the Federal Republic. Wehner and a few other SPD leaders opposed the plan because it would undermine détente with the East and accelerate the arms race. The chancellor and Defense Minister Hans Apel (SPD) supported the plan, primarily because of their concern about the growing Soviet arsenal of SS-20 missiles. At the 1979 party convention, left-wing speakers reiterated their opposition to the projected Western buildup, but Schmidt insisted that the West must have a bargaining counter in negotiations with the Soviets. He warned the delegates that if the resolution supporting the Western plan did not pass, the government might resign. His threat to resign, as well as Wehner and Brandt's belated support of the resolution, caused some left delegates to switch their vote in favor, but about 20 percent of the delegates maintained their opposition.

In June 1980, the Juso chairman voiced his mistrust of U.S. domination over NATO and of the FDP foreign minister's "vassal loyalty" to the United States. Brandt defended NATO as an element of stability and Schmidt contended that the Jusos' views on defense could not be taken seriously if they assailed those responsible for the country's defense. Earlier, Apel had warned the Jusos to refrain from criticizing the United States in order not to give the CDU/CSU a chance to talk in the 1980 election campaign about a "Moscow faction" within the SPD.

After 1980 the Jusos', as well as churches' and pacifist groups', criticism of the NATO decision gained more support within the SPD. The critics were worried not only about the spiraling arms race but the danger that West Germany would become a pawn in a superpower nuclear confrontation. In October 1981, the antinuclear groups staged the biggest demonstration in Bonn's history to protest the government's backing of the NATO plan. The Jusos and about one-fourth of the SPD Bundestag deputies supported the demonstration, and a number of SPD left-wing leaders spoke publicly against the nuclear arms buildup.

In early 1982, Schmidt once again warned his opponents in the party, who called for a moratorium on missile deployment until U.S.-Soviet talks at Geneva had concluded, that he would resign as chancellor if the party did not support him on the nuclear arms issue. In June, at the Munich party convention, the delegates, after lengthy and heated debates, backed him about two to one, but the party decided to convene a special convention in November 1983 to review the issue in the light of progress of U.S.-Soviet negotiations at Geneva. When the negotiations deadlocked, the sentiment in the party turned increasingly against the deployment of U.S. missiles. After Brandt and Bahr joined the opponents of deployment within the SPD, the die was cast at the special convention; an overwhelming number of delegates voted against deployment while Schmidt and a small band of diehards supported it. Soon thereafter, the party deputies voted in the Bundestag against a CDU/CSU-FDP resolution approving deployment, thereby ending a foreign policy consensus on a major security issue.

LAND ELECTIONS

The economic difficulties, SPD-FDP interparty schisms, and discords on nuclear energy and nuclear missiles within the SPD made governance difficult for Chancellor Schmidt from 1980 to 1982. They also contributed to the decline of the SPD vote in several elections held for Land parliaments (scheduled sequentially every four years). The first reversal for the SPD after the 1980 national election came in Land Berlin (West) where the SPD had either governed alone or in coalition with the FDP since 1946. In January 1981, the SPD-FDP coalition government suddenly resigned when it was implicated in an unsavory financial scandal. (It had underwritten credits to a city construction firm that had gone bankrupt.) The SPD selected Hans-Jochen Vogel, former mayor of Munich and then federal minister of justice, to head an interim SPD-FDP government until a special election was held in May. The election result was devastating to the SPD. Unlike its earlier high plurality or majority votes, it gained only 38.4 percent of the vote. The CDU received 47.9 percent, the FDP 5.6 percent, and the Alternative List (an amalgam of left-wing groups interested in environmental protection and disarmament) 7.3 percent. For the SPD the loss of power in one of their chief strongholds was a hard blow, especially when it realized that many young voters, dissatisfied with the SPD as an establishment party, had defected its ranks and switched to the Alternatives. A CDU minority government, which has received the tacit support of a number of FDP deputies, has governed the city since June 1981.

In March 1982, the CDU retained power in Lower Saxony but made significant gains at the expense of the SPD, whose electoral showing was the worst in 27 years. The CDU won many additional votes in urban working-class areas, normally SPD strongholds. Schmidt admitted to one newspaper that "the external image of social democracy played an important role in my party's poor showing."[10] The Greens, the counterpart of the Alternatives in Berlin, again drained votes away from the SPD (and FDP) to gain seats in the legislature.

Three months later, in June 1982, the SPD and the FDP suffered heavy electoral losses to the CDU and the Greens in Land Hamburg, another SPD working-class stronghold. The SPD acknowledged that national economic problems and the already-cited dissension within the Hamburg SPD over the local nuclear power plant (which caused Mayor Klose's resignation in 1981) were responsible for its poor showing. Although the SPD was able to retain power as a minority government under an SPD mayor (Klaus von Dohnanyi, who had succeeded Klose), it could do so only with the parliamentary support of the Greens. This constituted the first informal alliance between two parties which heretofore had remained cool to each other because of their disagreement on nuclear power and nuclear weapons. Although the SPD left wing and Greens concurred on these issues, the SPD majority, as noted earlier, took a contrary position to that of the Greens. As a result, the political situation in Hamburg did not stabilize after the election and the SPD could not gain support for a budget.

In December 1982, a special city-state election was held in which the SPD surprisingly regained an absolute majority, with much of the vote coming from blue-collar workers and middle-class individuals who had strayed to other parties in the previous election. But this time they wanted political stability and a chance to express their displeasure at some policies of the new CDU/CSU-FDP government in Bonn. Since the election the Hamburg SPD no longer has to depend on the backing of the Greens and governs alone.

In the meantime, in the September election in Hesse, another SPD stronghold, the CDU gained a plurality but could not form a new govern-

ment to replace the SPD-FDP coalition because the FDP, which had announced its intention to switch to a CDU-led government, received so few
votes that it lost all of its seats. Its poor showing was caused by voters who
blamed it for the recent breakup of the Bonn coalition. As a result, the SPD,
gaining sympathy votes for Schmidt's problems in Bonn, was able to remain in power, but only with the tacit support of the Greens, a situation
closely resembling that of Hamburg. As in that city, the SPD government
had difficulty concurring with the Greens on a number of legislative proposals. Consequently, it held a special election in September 1983 in the
hope of gaining a working majority. But this goal was not achieved, even
though it scored significant gains against the CDU. In January 1984 the
Greens decided to support the SPD minority government.

The last Land election scheduled prior to the March 1983 national
election occurred in October 1983 in Bavaria. Not unexpectedly the CSU
(Christian Social Union), the Bavarian counterpart to the CDU, again received an absolute majority of votes and the SPD nearly one-third. The
Free Democrats lost their representation and the Greens could not gain any.

This survey of Land elections from 1980 to 1982 shows that with few
exceptions the SPD fared poorly, especially in areas in which it held power.
Voters were blaming it for many of the ills facing the nation as well as for its
own disunity. For Schmidt, holding precarious power in Bonn, the election
results were discouraging and contributed to the finale of the coalition.

THE END OF THE SPD-FDP COALITION

In September 1982, signs of a governmental crisis in Bonn were multiplying over the already-cited SPD-FDP discord over economic policy.
SPD leaders knew that many FDP leaders wanted to end the coalition and
join the CDU/CSU in a new bourgeois coalition government. Led by
Foreign Minister Hans-Dietrich Genscher, these FDP ministers saw a coalition with the strife-torn SPD as a liability for their party and preferred a
tie to their erstwhile coalition partner in order to remain a viable political
force and achieve their economic goals.

Most SPD chiefs viewed the projected FDP torpedoing of the coalition
as a treacherous act designed to put the SPD into the opposition. In the hope
that the coalition might still survive, they counseled Schmidt and other
SPD ministers not to make any further concessions on the economic package to the FDP. Their anger at the FDP was fueled by the decision of the
Hesse FDP not to remain in an SPD-led coalition government after the 1982
Land election.

On August 30, Schmidt assured SPD presidium members that the Bonn SPD ministers would make no further concessions to the probusiness economic proposals put forward by the FDP minister of economics. On September 15, Schmidt met with his SPD cabinet colleagues to inform them of the backing he had from the party and the Fraktion for a possible end to the coalition—an end precipitated by Genscher's plan. On the same day, while the coalition cabinet met for its last session, Brandt and three top SPD leaders renewed their pledge to support Schmidt's intention to dissolve the Bundestag and call new elections. They also told Schmidt of their readiness to immediately schedule a special convention charged with issuing an electoral platform and assured him that the party would support his nomination as chancellor-candidate. In this moment of crisis, the strains between Schmidt and party leaders were momentarily forgotten.

On September 17, the four FDP ministers resigned from the cabinet after Schmidt insisted that they either adhere to the 1980 coalition program or quit. They had not planned to resign so soon, but Schmidt had forced their hands. Angry that they had not abided by the 1980 electoral mandate to govern jointly for the four-year legislative session, he, in an address to the Bundestag, charged them with having sown the seeds of dissension, wrecking the standing of the government, and being responsible for the breakup of the 13-year-old coalition. With a sure political touch, Schmidt asserted, "For us Social Democrats, the reputation and solidity of democracy is more important than tactical party advantages."[11]

But to blame only the Free Democrats for the coalition's end is to simplify history. What Schmidt could not say publicly but what opposition leaders did say was that the SPD's internal feuds and the left wing's criticism of some of his key policies has also weakened his authority as chancellor. Genscher, in a speech to the Bundestag, attributed the end to the SPD's abandonment of the coalition program and its adoption of left-leaning policies. These mutual recriminations were designed to put the blame for the crisis on the other party and gain electoral dividends whenever an election was scheduled.

Once the coalition fell apart, Schmidt's plan was to remain head of a temporary SPD minority government and then, knowing that such a government could not remain in power until 1984, call for an early national election, preferably in November or early December. The Basic Law (constitution) stipulates that the president of the Federal Republic can dissolve the Bundestag within 21 days and call for new elections 60 days later. Schmidt and the SPD, aware of the poor showing of the SPD in public opinion polls, were hoping that they could capitalize on the voters' sympathy for the FDP abandoning them in midstream. Their official argument was that an election would give the chancellor democratic legitimacy for a new government and new policies.

But CDU leader Helmut Kohl was in no hurry to have an early election. He wanted time to consolidate his own power in the party and to give the FDP an opportunity to rebuild its shattered image. Thus, he rejected Schmidt's plan for an early election and called on Schmidt to stop playing tactical games and resign. Because Schmidt had no such intention, Kohl decided, with the support of the FDP, to hold a "constructive" vote of no confidence, in which the Bundestag must have a majority for a new chancellor before ousting the incumbent—a constitutional provision to provide political stability.

THE SPD IN OPPOSITION

On October 1, 1982, Kohl, by a seven-vote margin, narrowly won the constructive vote of no confidence—the first successful one in West German history in which a change of government occurred in midterm. (A previous one initiated by the CDU/CSU in 1972 against Brandt had failed.) Kohl replaced Schmidt as chancellor, ending the SPD's 16-year participation in governments since 1966—their first three years, ironically, in coalition with the CDU/CSU. But as this crisis showed, West German parties switch partners with relative ease, though ideological distances may be far on some issues, even if as in this instance the SPD chiefs denounced their former FDP cabinet colleagues as having committed treason.

To buoy the dispirited SPD members, Schmidt, on the eve of the Bundestag vote, told 5,000 supporters marching by torchlight through the streets of Bonn, "Never fear, we social liberals and social democrats will be back again."[12] In the Bundestag, he reminded the deputies that a majority of voters in 1980 had not wanted a CDU/CSU chancellor to govern and that the switch of the FDP, while legal, had no moral justification.

On October 4, Schmidt, who had been in office for over eight years, and his cabinet were officially replaced by Kohl and a new CDU/CSU-FDP cabinet. In the ceremony marking the change of government, both leaders emphasized the importance of continuity in foreign policy. The new conservative administration, however, was expected to make changes in domestic policies.

Brandt, aware of pending changes, acknowledged that the SPD in opposition was not planning any frontal assaults against the new government.

However, the party attempted to win over public opinion by introducing a bill in the Bundestag which reflected its Keynesian approach to economic problems—an approach markedly different from that of the Kohl government. As part of a three-year program, the SPD called for more public investment to promote employment and economic growth. To finance the program estimated to cost nearly 10 billion deutsche marks, it suggested a supplementary tax of 5 percent on incomes of over 50,000 deutsche marks, to be limited to three years.[13] Needless to say, the SPD did not expect passage of a bill that would adversely affect the wealthy contributors donating funds to the conservative governing parties.

SPD leaders denounced the new government for its attempt to curb unemployment through deflationary measures and assailed the semiautonomous Federal Bank for contributing to unemployment through its tight money policies. They urged the bank to reduce key interest rates by 1-to-2 percent.

In the meantime, Kohl promised to hold a new election in March 1983 after having earlier rejected Schmidt's demand for an immediate election. Kohl presumed that by postponing the election until the later date, Schmidt's popularity would wane and the stature of the coalition ally, the FDP, would have increased again. Franz-Josef Strauss—Kohl's rival—hoped that the CDU/CSU might gain an absolute majority, thereby increasing his own power and shutting out the FDP.

A CHANGE OF THE GUARD

In late October, Schmidt withdrew his name as candidate for chancellor in the March 1983 election, citing his health as the primary reason. But political factors also played a role: He did not want to become a losing candidate after having made a name for himself as chancellor; nor could he expect to enter into possible coalition negotiations with the Greens, whose views were so antithetical to his. Many SPD colleagues, who had made last-minute pleas to Schmidt to run again, were disappointed, knowing that the only possibility for the SPD to regain power in March, slim as it was, rested on his coattails. But they also knew that Schmidt was angry about the continuing intraparty feuds concerning his former government policies and the lack of loyalty to him on the part of a minority in the party. Schmidt also resented the fact that the left wing had not been averse to have the party move to the 'opposition, where no further concessions would have to be made to a more conservative coalition party and where the party could assume a greater socialist profile. In short, Schmidt sensed that his time to lead the party into another election was over.

SPD leaders swiftly chose Hans-Jochen Vogel as the party's candidate for chancellor. The 56-year-old former housing and justice minister and former mayor of Munich and West Berlin, who had become head of the SPD Fraktion in Berlin, was a well-liked politician within the party. A pragmatist with a streak of idealism, he was sympathetic to the Brandt line: continue to reconcile the warring SPD factions and not to alienate the Greens, whose support might be needed in the Bundestag if they were able to gain seats. On the other hand, in any negotiations with the Greens Vogel would insist that they follow a pro-NATO line. Initially a right-winger in the party, he had gradually moved to the center, showing since 1981 a tolerance of the left-wing protest movements in West Berlin (where he had been sent to rescue the ailing SPD). With his nomination, he had become one of the senior leaders in the party.

At a conference of top SPD organs in Kiel on November 18 and 19, 1982, the delegates approved a declaration on the basic principles of the party in opposition. It declared that as a result of the SPD's policies when it was in power, millions of women, youth, and workers developed a new democratic self-consciousness that must not be infringed upon. It called for the equality of women, an expansion of codetermination (sharing in policy making) for workers at all levels, the creation and maintenance of jobs leading eventually to full employment, a maintenance of local fiscal autonomy, environmental protection, the promotion of legal guarantees to individuals, the preservation of social and domestic peace, an end to the arms race, and continued détente.[14]

The delegates also endorsed Vogel as the candidate for chancellor. By then he had become more explicit about the political possibilities after the March election. He was not in favor of a grand coalition with the CDU/CSU (on the 1966–69 model) or formal alliance with the Greens, but rather of wooing potential voters away from the Greens by emphasizing his party's commitment to the environment. He hoped to freeze out the Greens—and the FDP—from Bundestag representation in order to ensure an eventual absolute majority for the SPD. He knew that such a possibility was remote in 1983 because a government is seldom reelected during severe economic crises.

While the SPD was jockeying for position, on December 17, 1982, Chancellor Kohl deliberately lost in the Bundestag a vote of confidence by having CDU/CSU and FDP deputies abstain from voting—in order to give the federal president an opportunity to dissolve the Bundestag and clear the way for the promised March 1983 election.[15] On the eve of the no-confidence vote the campaign themes emerged. During the heated debate on the 1983 budget, SPD spokesmen assailed projected cuts in social spending and inadequate plans to combat unemployment as evidence of the government's intent to favor the wealthy over the poor. In reply, the government spokesmen contended that the massive unemployment (it stood at 2.2 million) could be cut back only through greater investment in industry to promote growth and competitiveness of German goods on the world market.

The SPD also assailed the government parties on their nuclear arms position. The party, however, still divided on this issue, had a difficult time convincing the public that its position fundamentally differed from that of the government. After all, Schmidt as chancellor had supported the missile plan. Thus the party hedged on taking an antimissile position, emphasizing instead that it was responding to new U.S. and Soviet positions. For instance, in order to defuse Kohl's charge that Vogel was "Moscow's candidate" in the election, the SPD only cautiously condemned President Reagan's zero option proposal (no new Western missiles if the Soviets dismantle theirs) and his refusal to seriously examine new Soviet proposals, which included the counting of British and French nuclear weapons as part of the Western arsenal. But the SPD did contend that all measures, such as extending the Geneva talks past the December 1983 deadline or basing cruise missiles on submarines rather than on land, must be taken to obviate the stationing of new U.S. missiles in Western Europe and to dismantle some or all Soviet missiles.

As part of the pending campaign, Vogel journeyed to Washington and Moscow to meet the top leaders and to set forth the SPD position on the arms issue. He reminded Reagan and Andropov that should the SPD form the new government in March, its position on the missiles would be determined by his party's assessment of the seriousness and progress of the Geneva negotiations. The SPD would support NATO deployment if the Soviets made no conciliatory moves and the Americans showed flexibility at Geneva.[16] Thus, the chief difference between the SPD and CDU/CSU-FDP on the missile issue at that time (but not after November 1983 when it opposed deployment) was the SPD's ambiguous support for the Western position while the government parties gave unconditional support. The CDU/CSU exploited this difference and accused the SPD of following a neutralist course.

THE ELECTORAL CAMPAIGN

Although nuclear arms became the central foreign policy campaign issue, for the average German voter the state of the West German economy was at least of equal if not of more importance as the electoral campaign got under way. On January 21, the SPD held its electoral convention in Dortmund to discuss and accept a party platform. Paralleling the Kiel Declaration of November 1982, the platform calls on nations to adopt an international employment pact and pledges that an SPD-led government would fight unemployment through a 35-hour week and early retirement, start a massive investment program, improve environmental protection and vocational training for youth, add more housing, emphasize energy saving and the use of local coal rather than nuclear energy. (If the latter has to be used, it must include full safety provisions and a solution to the nuclear waste problem.) In its foreign affairs section, it reaffirms the party's allegiance to NATO and its position on the missiles issue.[17]

As the campaign got into high gear, it assumed an international dimension that previous elections had not received. In this instance, the missile issue led to outside interference in the country's affairs. U.S. Vice-President Bush and French President Mitterrand paid visits to Bonn to underscore support for the governing coalition—while Foreign Minister Gromyko of the Soviet Union came to Bonn to defend the Soviet position—and thereby put the SPD into an awkward position for its more ambiguous stand.

In the meantime, Vogel and top SPD leaders appeared on television and radio, and crisscrossed the country to make numerous speeches designed to drum up support for the party among the faithful and less faithful. The party issued a boulevard paper for distribution to millions of households and plastered billboards with posters of Vogel and the local candidates. In the last few weeks—the "hot" segment—of the campaign, the SPD ran its propaganda under the slogan, "Germany must not tilt toward the right." It emphasized Kohl's intention to hike rents in subsidized flats, his possible intent to turn back abortion reform, his lethargy in the fight against unemployment that had reached 2.5 million (10.4 percent, the highest level since World War II), and his weakness in disarmament policy.[18]

Foreign interference continued during the campaign. To the discomfort of the SPD, the Soviet radio's German-language service broadcast predicted social unrest over rising unemployment if Kohl won the election and to the dismay of the SPD, President Reagan, who favored a CDU/CSU victory, told a news conference that it would be a "terrible setback" if the West Germans elected a government (read SPD) unwilling to deploy the NATO missiles should the Geneva talks remain stalemated. To soften the effect of foreign interference in the election, Vogel introduced the nationalist theme "in the German interest" into his speeches.

He had difficulty counteracting another interference in the election—the West German businessmen who, believing that an SPD-led government would not generate an economic recovery to justify investment and would provoke a flight of capital from Germany, were inserting clauses into orders for equipment voiding them if the SPD won the election. SPD leaders accused the CDU/CSU of intimidating the voters by provoking this "investment strike" to give the impression that an SPD victory would create an unfavorable environment.[19]

THE 1983 ELECTION

Although the campaign produced many fireworks and aroused the interest of foreign powers, it showed once again that the discord among parties on most domestic and foreign policy issues was not as great as their rhetorical bombast. Thus, the voters cast their ballots less on issues and more on their perception of which party was more competent to deal with economic problems. The verdict was clear: the CDU/CSU rather than the SPD. For the latter, the election results on March 6, 1983, were a major setback. The SPD won only 38.2 percent of the vote, a drop of 4.7 percent from 1980. The governing CDU/CSU received 48.8 percent and its coalition ally, the FDP, 6.9 percent, while the Greens got 5.6 percent. The CDU/CSU and FDP thus received a mandate to continue governing, and the SPD and the Greens, who had not been in the Bundestag previously, occupied the opposition benches. According to one survey, 1.6 million voters, especially in Protestant, small-town, or industrial areas, who had voted for the SPD in 1980 switched this time to the CDU/CSU. Most of these floaters were low- and middle-level civil servants and salaried employees, as well as workers, who were convinced by the CDU/CSU scare propaganda that under an SPD government, unemployment would rise. They were hopeful that a probusiness Kohl government would be more competent to deal with economic affairs and pull the country out of the recession. According to SPD Secretary Peter Glotz, many businessmen also had put pressure on their employees to vote for the coalition.

Among other voters who switched parties were 750,000 former SPD voters who cast their ballots for the Greens, primarily because they concurred with the Greens' unequivocal opposition to nuclear energy and nuclear missiles. This sizable loss of former SPD voters to the CDU/CSU and the Greens was only partly offset by 700,000 erstwhile FDP voters who, disillusioned about their party's coalition with the CDU/CSU, switched to the SPD. Although in every election voters float from party to party, in this one the SPD's loss of over 2 million—it had received a total of nearly 15 million—contributed to its debacle.

If the party could have at least capitalized on the widespread disapproval of the deployment of missiles and on a majority of respondents' views (according to survey data) that it was the most competent party to deal with security affairs, then perhaps the gap between the SPD and CDU/CSU vote might not have been as wide. But because economic issues were more salient, the SPD's loss was heavy in all Länder, although less so in its two city-state strongholds of Hamburg and Bremen. As a result, the SPD had only 193 seats in the Bundestag, compared to 218 in 1980. (The CDU/CSU had 244 in 1983, the FDP 34, and the Greens 27.) While the SPD Bundestag representation was the lowest since 1961, the party had one consolation: A slim majority of youth voting for the first time cast their ballots for it. (The Greens also benefited, as 25 percent of this group voted for them.)[20]

During the CDU/CSU and FDP postelection negotiations to form a new cabinet and to agree on a government program, a new SPD leadership team emerged, which was confirmed at the May 1984 party convention. Herbert Wehner, the elderly party statesman and Fraktion chief, had announced that he would retire and not run for the Bundestag again in March 1983. Schmidt had announced that he would resign as party vice-chairman in 1984 but would be a candidate again for the Bundestag. (He won.) Vogel was chosen to fill both the post of Fraktion chief and one of the two party vice-chairman posts. Brandt remained party chairman while Johannes Rau, minister-president of North Rhine–Westphalia, remained a vice-chairman.[21]

THE PARTY'S FUTURE

As the new SPD leadership examined the past in order to learn lessons for the future, it realized that many of the problems which the party confronted were unavoidable, given the international and domestic environment—for instance, the oil crisis of 1973 or the worldwide recession of the early 1980s that led to unemployment in West Germany. On the other hand, some of the problems—for instance, intraparty factionalism—could have been avoided if the leadership had been more firm in its integration moves. It also realized that building and maintaining governing coalitions are difficult in periods of economic crises, especially when the potential coalition partner will not concur with it on all domestic and foreign policies. Because the coalition partner normally is a minor party, it has assumed an importance in sharing power far above its small representation in the Bundestag. Thus, when the SPD was in power as the senior governing party from 1969 to 1982, it was dependent on the FDP for legislative support. The conservative position of the FDP on some domestic legislation (for example, extension of codetermination, redistributive taxes) meant that groups within the SPD became increasingly frustrated with their own party and deserted it in crucial elections.

Furthermore, the SPD leadership realized that any governing coalition is constrained by international developments, such as a worldwide recession, over which it has little control. When it was in power, the problems it faced increased measurably after the 1980 election and often reflected those confronting governments, regardless of ideological coloration, in other advanced industrial states. The problems included a persistent high unemployment, low economic growth, sectoral and structural weaknesses in industry, high costs of social security and health systems, and worry about the future of détente between East and West. Whether the new Kohl government can solve some of these problems remains to be seen.

In the meantime, the SPD must become accustomed to being once again out of power and in opposition. It must decide on how to challenge the conservative government, what alternatives to put forward, and how to increase its own strength in order to regain national power at some future election. Brandt and Vogel contend that the party must pursue a policy of constructive opposition in which it criticizes and presents alternatives. The task will be difficult, given the CDU/CSU's control of Parliament and the posts of chancellor, federal president, many Land minister-presidents, and mayors in numerous major cities. But, as Vogel asserted, in his inaugural speech as Fraktion chief, the SPD must not put its 1983 electoral program, which deals with short- and long-range legislative proposals, to rest.[22]

Vogel also called on the party to end the factional strife that had prevailed so often before the election campaign generated more unity in ranks. His call for integration and harmony in the SPD Fraktion has already produced favorable results and has almost ended the 14 years of sharp ideolog-

ical and social cleavages. True, the once powerful right wing in the Fraktion, led by the former defense minister Hans Apel, has not been happy
with Vogel's conciliatory line toward the left wing and the Greens, which
reminds them of Brandt's similar tactic in previous years. They do not like
Vogel's shift in position from the right (he had once been one of their leaders) toward the left-center because it will alienate further the crucial group
of blue-collar workers. The right-wing members contend that a new influx
of youth will radicalize the party, which in turn will lead to continued erosion of the workers' vote in coming elections. They criticize the party's left
intellectuals in Bonn for having attempted during the 1983 election to bring
about a new majority of counterculture youths, pacifists, and workers.
Such an attempt was bound to fail because these groups hold such disparate
views. In short, the right-wing members contend that the SPD can regain
power only if it follows a middle-of-the-road policy designed to win back
blue-collar workers who have deserted it.

On the other hand, Brandt and other left-center—and left-wing—
leaders assert that if the party relied only on the support of workers, it
would be doomed again to a maximum vote of 33 percent.[23] It needs the
backing of youth to maintain a minimum of 40 percent voting strength.
Given the social shift in membership in recent decades in which the new
middle class of salaried employees, civil servants, and intellectuals has
risen in proportion to the decline of blue-collar workers, it seems unlikely
that the party will shift back to the right in the immediate future.[24] The new
groups have captured leadership posts at all levels of the party; few workers
remain in such posts.

Among the new, young, left-oriented leaders whose rise to the top is
likely, as a result of the backing of Brandt, is Gerhard Schröder, a former
head of the Jusos; Oskar Lafontaine, mayor of Saarbrücken; and Björn
Engholm, party leader in Kiel. Once Brandt retires as party chairman,
probably in 1986 when his latest two-year term will expire, then these leaders are expected to move higher in the party hierarchy, although none of
them will receive the top post. For the chairmanship, Hans-Jochen Vogel
or Johannes Rau most likely will succeed Willy Brandt.

Rau, who belongs to the moderate right wing, is popular with SPD
members and voters in North Rhine–Westphalia where he serves as minister-president. Although he was a book dealer before entering politics, he
relates well to blue-collar workers, which is an important asset at election
time. Vogel, on the other hand, is viewed as an intellectual who, while enjoying some popularity in the party, maintains a greater distance to the rank
and file. Yet because Vogel was the chancellor-candidate in 1983, he has a

better chance to become a candidate again in the 1987 national election. Because some party leaders favor the earlier practice of having one person be both chancellor-candidate and party chairman, Vogel might also succeed Brandt as party chairman.

Despite his rise to top posts in the party, Vogel remains in the shadow of Brandt, who is once again providing strong leadership and taking policy initiatives that the party's left and right wings are supporting. For instance, Brandt's belated opposition to the missile deployment program proved popular among the SPD rank and file, especially among the young and the left. On the other hand, his negative position on missiles, paralleling that of the British and Swedish Socialists, has produced a strain within the Socialist International because the French and Italian Socialist leaders have come out in support of the missile program.

Strains have also surfaced between SPD and U.S. leaders. Brandt's call for European states to serve as a third force between the two superpowers, his endorsement of a nuclear-free zone in central Europe, his proposal to reform NATO, and his denunciation of Kohl's policy of closely supporting the United States in its European policies have not endeared him in the eyes of U.S. officials. They see Brandt moving closer to a neutralist, anti-American position, although he has denied the charge and reaffirmed his commitment to the West. But there can be no denial that the SPD has become more nationalist within the context of the East-West struggle and more critical of U.S. policies, especially under the Reagan administration. Should a liberal Democrat win the 1984 election in the United States, then the strained atmosphere may clear, although some discords on defense, NATO, and trade are bound to continue.

The new troika of Brandt, Vogel, and Rau also has to take positions on domestic issues that will not alienate the occasionally conflicting interests of the workers and the environmentalists and that will provide a convincing alternative to those presented by the government. The party sees the reduction of unemployment, the maintenance of the welfare system, the protection of the environment, the humanization of work, the integration of foreign workers and families into German society, and the protection of individuals against state surveillance as some of the important tasks ahead. It plans to introduce legislation in Parliament, such as the 35-hour week to create more jobs, which would attract new voters and retain its loyal supporters. But such bills will have little chance of enactment as long as the SPD remains in opposition at the national level. The party has greater opportunities to enact parts of its domestic program in those cities and the few states that it still controls, especially in northern Germany. The recapture of the Munich mayor's post in 1984 provided it with a much-needed symbolic victory. If it can regain other cities it lost in recent years (Berlin, Frankfurt, and so on), if it can gain a measure of support from new, young, or uncommitted voters based on its performance at these subnational levels, or if the Kohl government prematurely resigns as a result of a coalition crisis, then its chance for a return to power in Bonn, probably in a coalition with the Greens should they concur, will be enhanced. Municipal and state elections prior to 1987 will provide some clues as to the chances for the SPD to gain its objective.[25]

As part of its electoral strategy, the SPD plans in the 1980s to prepare and agree upon a new basic program to supplant the 1959 Godesberg Program. The updated version will provide an overview of existing problems and offer solutions, such as the ecological dimension lacking in the earlier document. This new program is expected to appeal to the bulk of the younger generation who must be won over, especially from the Greens or from their apolitical stance, if the party is to regain power. The task will not be easy; the challenges are many. Can the party meet them?

NOTES

1. For accounts of the SPD up to 1933, see W.L. Guttsman, *The German Social Democratic Party, 1875–1933: From Ghetto to Government* (Winchester, Mass.: Allen and Unwin, 1981); Richard N. Hunt, *German Social Democracy, 1918–1933* (New Haven: Yale University Press, 1964); Richard Breitman, *German Socialism and Weimar Democracy* (Chapel Hill, N.C.: University of North Carolina Press, 1981).

2. For accounts of the SPD after World War II, see Douglas A. Chalmers, *The Social Democratic Party of Germany* (New Haven: Yale University Press, 1964); Gerard Braunthal, *The West German Social Democrats, 1969–1982: Profile of a Party in Power* (Boulder, Colo.: Westview Press, 1983).

3. For a political biography of Brandt, see David Binder, *The Other German: Willy Brandt's Life and Times* (Washington, D.C.: New Republic Book, 1975); Terence Prittie, *Willy Brandt: Portrait of a Statesman* (New York: Schocken Books, 1974); Gerard Braunthal, "Willy Brandt: Politician and Statesman," *Governments and Leaders: An Approach to Comparative Politics*, ed. Edward Feit (Boston: Houghton Mifflin, 1978).

4. For a political biography of Schmidt, see Helmut Wolfgang Kahn, *Helmut Schmidt: Fallstudie über einen Populären* (Hamburg: Holsten, 1974). See also Wolfram F. Hanrieder, ed., *Helmut Schmidt: Perspectives on Politics* (Boulder, Colo.: Westview Press, 1982).

5. For details, see Gerard Braunthal, "The Policy Function of the German Social Democratic Party," *Comparative Politics* 19, no. 2 (Jan. 1977): 127–145.

6. SPD, organization division (Bonn), Mitgliederstand per 31. Dezember 1980 (unpublished); INFAS-Report, *Parteisoziologische Untersuchungen 1977 – Zusammenfassung der Ergebnisse* (Bonn–Bad Godesberg, 1978, hectographed), p. 7.

7. Robert Michels, *Political Parties: A Sociological Study of the Oligarchical Tendencies of Modern Democracy* (New York: Collier Books, 1962), p. 365.

8. *New York Times,* Sept. 8, 1981.

9. Ibid., Apr. 25, 1982.

10. Ibid., Mar. 23, 1982.

11. Ibid., Sept. 19, 1982.

12. *Newsweek,* Oct. 11, 1982. See also *Bulletin* (Bonn), no. 90 (Oct. 5, 1982): 823.

13. *The Week in Germany* (New York) 13/35, Oct. 8, 1982.

14. *Vorwärts,* Nov. 25, 1982.

15. Article 68 of the Basic Law provides the details. Article 67 deals with the already-cited constructive vote of no confidence used to topple Schmidt on October 1, 1982.

16. *Stuttgarter Zeitung,* Jan. 8, 1983; *Washington Post,* Jan. 8, 1983; *Der Spiegel,* Jan. 10, 1983.

17. SPD, executive, *Das Regierungsprogramm der SPD, 1983–1987* (Bonn, 1983).

18. SPD, *Intern,* no. 3, Feb. 18, 1983.

19. *The Week in Germany,* 14/6, Feb. 11, 1983; *New York Times,* Feb. 22, 1983.

20. *SM, Sozialdemokrat Magazin,* no. 4 (April 1983): 12–13; INFAS, "Politogramm, INFAS-report, Bundestagswahl 1983" (hectographed); *Vorwärts,* Mar. 10 and 17, 1983.

21. *Süddeutsche Zeitung,* Mar. 9, 1983.

22. Speech of March 8, 1983, reprinted in release (dated Mar. 10, 1983) by Jürgen Linde, SPD Fraktion official, to Fraktion members.

23. See Richard Löwenthal, "Identität und Zukunft der SPD," *Neue Gesellschaft* 28, no. 12 (Dec. 1981): 1085–1089; replies by a number of leaders in *Neue Gesellschaft,* 29, no. 1 (Jan. 1982): 4–5, 21–31.

24. Wolfgang Wagner, "The Change of Government in Bonn," *Political Affairs Review,* supplement to *The German Tribune,* no. 43, May 8, 1983.

25. *Vorwärts,* Mar. 10, 1983; *Die Zeit,* Apr. 1, 1983; DDP Wahlanalyse, Mar. 7, 1983.

6

THE FREE DEMOCRATIC PARTY

Christian Søe

In a representative system of government, a small party may occupy a strategic position that gives it a much larger political role than its modest size would suggest. West Germany's Liberal party, the Free Democratic party (FDP), is a classic example of such a phenomenon. Although its base among voters is very narrow and highly unstable, the FDP has played a crucial part in the electoral and governmental politics of the Federal Republic of Germany since the formation of the new state in 1949. Today this vulnerable yet influential party is burdened by greater problems than ever before in its history. It is a good time to take stock of the FDP's past and present role in West German politics before assessing its prospects for the near future. Apart from giving us a better understanding of the party's political behavior, such a study may better prepare us to reflect upon an important question: What difference would it make to West German politics if this traditional third party should not survive?[1]

OVERVIEW: THE FDP IN THE WEST GERMAN PARTY SYSTEM

The importance of the Free Democrats in Bonn was most apparent during the period of three-party politics that emerged after the first decade of political consolidation in West Germany. Until the Greens entered the Bundestag as fourth party in March 1983, the FDP had been the only parliamentary alternative to the large Christian and Social Democratic catchall parties for more than 20 years. Even before 1961, when the FDP became the last of several small postwar parties to survive in the Bundestag, the

Liberals had stood head and shoulders above these minor rivals.[2] In the first years of the Federal Republic, the FDP was an essential member of the bourgeois coalition that elected Konrad Adenauer, the CDU leader, to head the West German government and supported his direction-setting policies for the new state.

Throughout the sixties and seventies, the FDP remained an exception to the common generalization about an "inexorable trend" toward two-party politics in West Germany. At the same time, its chronic electoral weakness led observers to speak of the country's "two-and-a-half" or even "two-and-a-quarter" party system.[3] The FDP normally received less than 10 percent of the crucial second (or party) vote, which determines the parliamentary strength of the parties in federal politics. By contrast, the two major parties together gathered well over 80 and sometimes topped 90 percent (see Table 6.1). At the end of the sixties, the FDP's core of loyal supporters had dwindled to less than 5 percent, which is the minimum electoral strength required for parliamentary representation under West German law. On the other hand, opinion polls regularly indicated that many more voters wanted the small party to stay in the Bundestag. For the FDP, elections had become struggles for political survival, but it always managed to attract enough floating voters to keep its place in the Bonn legislature. The rate of turnover among its voters was much higher than for the big parties, however, with sometimes one-half or more of its electoral support coming from political itinerants.

The FDP would be of political interest, even if it were only a residual party that offered voters a quaint alternative or substitute to the large *Volksparteien*. By providing an additional parliamentary outlet, it contributes to the important function of political integration. It has even been suggested that the small party serves primarily as a "safety valve" for changing groups of voters who have become disenchanted with one of the major parties without wanting to support the other one.[4] From this perspective, the FDP will always have a high volatility in its transient electorate as well as a tendency or need to shift course to accommodate changing political moods among such situational voters. As we shall see, the political function and behavior of the FDP can be understood partly, but not fully, in such terms.

From a power politics perspective, however, the FDP's importance in the three-party system has derived from holding the numerical balance of power in the Bundestag. As long as the Christian Democratic Union/Christian Social Union (CDU/CSU) and the Social Democratic party (SPD) did not join forces in a great coalition (as they did from 1966 to 1969) or neither

Table 6.1. The Bundestag Elections from 1949 to 1983: Distribution of Second Votes and Bundestag Seats (without West Berlin delegation)

Election Year	CDU/CSU Vote	CDU/CSU Seats	SPD Vote	SPD Seats	FDP Vote	FDP Seats	Greens Vote	Greens Seats	Others Vote	Others Seats
1949	31.0	139	29.2	131	11.9	52	—*	—	27.9	80
1953	45.2	243	28.8	151	9.5	48	—	—	16.5	45
1957	50.2	270	31.8	169	7.7	41	—	—	10.3	17
1961	45.3	242	36.2	190	12.8	67	—	—	5.7	0
1965	47.6	245	39.3	202	9.5	49	—	—	3.6	0
1969	46.1	242	42.7	227	5.8	30	—	—	5.4	0
1972	44.9	225	45.8	230	8.4	41	—	—	0.9	0
1976	48.6	243	42.6	214	7.9	39	—	—	0.9	0
1980	44.5	226	42.9	218	10.6	53	1.5	0	0.5	0
1983	48.8	244	38.2	193	7.0	34	5.6	27	0.4	0

*Not applicable.

Note: Votes are given in percentages.

Sources: Peter Schindler, *Datenhandbuch zur Geschichte des Deutschen Bundestages 1949 bis 1982* (Bonn: Presse- und Informationszentrum des Deutschen Bundestages, 1983), pp. 34–39; Statistisches Bundesamt, *Wahl zum 10. Deutschen Bundestag am 6. März 1983, Heft 3, Endgültige Ergebnisse nach Wahlkreisen* (Stuttgart: Kohlhammer, 1983), Table 1.2, p. 7.

received a secure parliamentary majority on its own (as the CDU/CSU had from 1957 to 1961), the FDP provided the margin necessary to build a governing majority.

The balancing position in the three-party system gave the FDP what on first sight appears to be a superb bargaining leverage when it came to forming governments, filling political appointments, and deciding upon public policy. In political reality, however, the Liberals were never completely free to change partners or raise the price of their support at will. The nature of their political constraints will become evident later in the chapter. Despite such limitations, the majority-making role has been a profitable one. As junior member of all but two cabinets in Bonn since 1949, the FDP has filled a number of political posts and received other benefits of office quite out of proportion to its small share of seats in the Bundestag (see Table 6.2).

In some ways the FDP has functioned not only as a numerical but also as a kind of ideological balancer or flywheel, contributing to the moderate centrism of West German policy making. The small party has not always occupied a place somewhere between the Christian and Social Democrats. On economic issues it has often stood to the right of the former, while its civil liberties position has sometimes been to the left of the latter. Nevertheless, its inclusion in so many cabinets, headed by leaders of either of the two major parties, has provided an element of continuity and moderation, especially when chancellors have used the small coalition partner to curb the right or left wings of their own parties. In line with this, the FDP has tried to project itself as the "reasonable" alternative of "the center" in West German politics. Its middle-of-the-road emphasis, as will be shown later, became most important after the emergence of the three-party system and the competitive bidding for electoral support among members of the new middle class of salaried professionals.

This aspect of the FDP's self-image was promoted already in the late fifties by the party's chief theoretician, the legendary Karl-Hermann Flach. He developed the argument that German politics required a special corrective against both the excessive power-concentration and the lopsided right- or left-wing orientation of single-party governments by Christian or Social Democrats, with their respective clerical-conservative and socialist proclivities. From this perspective, the Westminster model of single-party government, which appeared to work so well in Britain, was not really appropriate for the Federal Republic, where more political checks and balances were necessary: Here, the FDP provided a moderating and balancing element through the device of coalition government. The small party has

Table 6.2. FDP Representation in West German Cabinets since 1949

Month of Cabinet Formation	Chancellor (Party)	FDP Share of Bundestag Seats[a]	Total Number of Cabinet Seats[b]	Number of FDP Cabinet Posts[c]	Ministries Held by the FDP
Sept. 1949	Adenauer (CDU)	12.9	14	3	Justice; Housing & Urban Aff.; Economic Co-operation
Oct. 1953[d]	Adenauer (CDU)	9.9	20	4	Justice; Housing & Urban Aff.; Economic Co-operation; Special Assignment[e]
Oct. 1957	Adenauer (CDU)	8.2	18	0	
Nov. 1961	Adenauer (CDU)	13.4	21	5	Justice; Finance; Economic Cooperation; Expellees; Federal Property
Dec. 1962[f]	Adenauer (CDU)	(13.4)	21	5	Justice; Finance; Economic Cooperation; Expellees; Research & Technology
Oct. 1963	Erhard (CDU)	(13.4)	21	5[g]	Justice; Finance; Economic Cooperation; Intra-German Aff.; Research & Technology
Oct. 1965	Erhard (CDU)	9.9	22	4	Finance; Housing & Urban Aff.; Intra-German Aff.; Research & Technology
Dec. 1966	Kiesinger (CDU)	(9.9)	20	0	
Oct. 1969	Brandt (SPD)	6.0	16	3	Foreign Aff.; Interior; Food & Agriculture
Dec. 1972	Brandt (SPD)	8.3	18	5	Foreign Aff.; Economics; Interior; Food & Agriculture; Special Assignment
May 1974	Schmidt (SPD)	(8.3)	16	4	Foreign Aff.; Economics; Interior; Food & Agriculture
Dec. 1976	Schmidt (SPD)	7.9	16	4	Foreign Aff.; Economics; Interior; Food & Agriculture
Nov. 1980	Schmidt (SPD)	10.7	17	4	Foreign Aff.; Economics; Interior; Food & Agriculture

| Oct. 1982 | Kohl (CDU) | (10.7)[h] | 17 | 4 | Foreign Aff.; Economics; Justice; Food & Agriculture |
| Mar. 1983 | Kohl (CDU) | 6.8 | 17 | 3 | Foreign Aff.; Economics; Justice |

[a]In percentages. In each case, the share of Bundestag seats held by the FDP and the other parties deviates slightly from their respective share of the second vote. There are four possible sources of such distortions in the electoral law: (1) The d'Hondt system of proportional representation is slightly biased in favor of large as against small parties; (2) the 5 percent "threshold" leads to a distribution of parliamentary seats only among those parties which receive more than the minimum share of second votes; (3) a party may win more direct mandates on the first (district candidate) vote than it would be entitled to under proportional representation, as based on the second (party list) vote, in which case it will retain these "additional" seats; (4) although a party falls below the 5 percent mark, it may gain parliamentary representation on a proportional basis (second vote) *if* it wins three or more district seats on the first vote (this has not happened since 1957).

[b]This total includes the chancellor. It records the number of seats at the time of cabinet formation.

[c]Some cabinet posts are far more important than others. The most desirable combination ever held by the FDP is the one from 1972 to 1982, which included three of the most important ministries in the cabinet (foreign affairs, economics, and interior) as well as the ministry of food and agriculture.

[d]The FDP left Adenauer's government coalition in February 1956. One-third of its parliamentary members, including all four of its ministers, stayed behind and formed a new party, the FVP, that was eliminated in the Bundestag election of 1957. Two of the former FDP ministers held their cabinet seats until then, while the other two were kept on until October 1956 only.

[e]No ministries held.

[f]During the Spiegel affair of 1962, the FDP ministers left the cabinet to force the resignation of Defense Minister Strauss (CSU). Adenauer used the opportunity to reshuffle the cabinet. Two FDP ministers with whom he had difficulties (Stammberger and Starke) were replaced by two other Free Democrats (Bucher and Dahlgrün). Another (Lenz) was shifted from the ministry of federal property to that of research and technology.

[g]The FDP lost the ministry of justice in March 1965, when Ewald Bucher resigned from the post after the passage of a law to extend the statute of limitations. He was replaced by a Christian Democrat.

[h]The resignation of several FDP parliamentarians from their party after the coalition changeover has not been taken into account. The four who left the FDP were Friedrich Hölscher, Helga Schuchardt, Ingrid Matthäus-Maier, and Andreas von Schoeler.

Sources: Peter Schindler, *Datenhandbuch zur Geschichte des Deutschen Bundestages 1949 bis 1982* (Bonn: Presse- und Informationszentrum des Deutschen Bundestages, 1983); Helmut Norpoth, "The German Federal Republic: Coalition Government at the Brink of Majority Rule," in E.C. Browne and J. Dreijmanis, *Government Coalitions in Western Democracies* (New York: Longman, 1982), Table 1.3, p. 25.

returned to this "functional argument" repeatedly when it has sought to justify the three-party system and its own role as majority maker.[5] It appears to
strike a responsive chord among many voters, at least in federal politics, although few end up supporting the FDP.

Many Free Democrats have wanted to establish a more substantive
identity for their party than that of a junior coalition partner with centrist,
balancing tendencies. The FDP has wrestled with this problem again and
again, without lasting success. Here too, Flach played a key role in seeking
to make the party's liberal self-image more meaningful by giving it a distinctly reformist orientation. He argued that Liberals must act as a force of
enlightenment and progress, guided by their central value of human freedom. They must constantly check against the danger of powerholders who
tended to depreciate or ignore the importance of human liberties. Such a
liberal vanguard was needed against both "the reactionaries," who celebrated the stagnation of the social order with its often-hidden power relationships, and "the socialists," who were caught up in a commitment to
egalitarianism that in practice had been a failure as well as a threat to freedom.[6] Flach, who finally became the party's first secretary-general from
1971 until his early death in 1973, is closely linked to the party's social-liberal development in the Freiburg Theses, which will be examined later in
the chapter.

Such attempts to define more clearly the FDP's political liberalism
have run into several obstacles. Within the general liberal-democratic am-
bience of West German politics, it has been difficult to establish a claim to a
distinctively liberal position that would clearly set the FDP apart from its
large catchall rivals. The latter are simply not as conservative or socialist as
Flach's juxtaposition suggests. The problem has been compounded by the
fact that the FDP's own right and left wings have disagreed, sometimes
profoundly, about the nature of their party's liberal commitment. Their factional differences can go far beyond policy priorities and touch upon the
proper role of politics and the state in the shaping of societal life. Finally,
the FDP's political behavior has often been guided by tactical and pragmatic considerations, derived from its unusually vulnerable yet influential
position within the political system. In fact, some observers have concluded that the small party—with one eye fixed anxiously on electoral survival and another eagerly upon the considerable benefits of office—has
been irrevocably caught up in a condition of "structural opportunism."[7]
Even from this perspective, however, the intraparty differences among
Free Democrats about political orientation and strategy can be important,
since they may condition or at least reflect the FDP's more practical calculations and moves in the competitive political arena.

The FDP's most decisive impact upon West German politics has come from its pivotal role in the transfer of power between the two major parties. Having made possible the election of Adenauer as chancellor in 1949, the FDP played a crucial part in the governmental turnover which terminated two decades of CDU-led cabinets in 1969. In that year, the Liberals joined the Social Democrats in electing Willy Brandt as chancellor and relegating the CDU/CSU to the parliamentary opposition. Thirteen years later, in the fall of 1982, the FDP finally abandoned this center-left alliance, led since 1974 by Helmut Schmidt. The Liberals returned to a cabinet coalition with the CDU/CSU by providing enough parliamentary support to carry a "constructive vote of no confidence." In this way, Chancellor Schmidt was toppled and replaced with the Christian Democratic leader, Helmut Kohl, on October 1, 1982.

In the short term, at least, such changeovers by the majority maker can be very costly. After each of the major transfers of power in Bonn, the FDP has been reminded of its political mortality by heavy defections of members and voters. Free Democrats had reason to fear the tenth Bundestag election, called for March 6, 1983—one-and-a-half years earlier than regularly scheduled—to give popular legitimation to Helmut Kohl's new center-right government. The manner of their midterm switch of partners had caused widespread dismay and seriously divided the small party. It was not forgotten that the FDP had fought the previous Bundestag campaign of 1980 with a pledge to continue in government with Chancellor Schmidt or that it had supported him in a vote of confidence as late as February 1982. The party's standing in public opinion polls dropped sharply, and there was reason to doubt its ability to survive. Within the larger context of a widely discussed West German governing crisis, the plight of the FDP contributed to the prospects of a considerable voter realignment and a possible revamping of the established party system.[8]

Although the Greens attracted enough votes in 1983 to become a fourth parliamentary party, the FDP finished the contest in much better shape than many had thought possible. It recovered strength before election day and received 7 percent of the vote on the second ballot. This was one-third less than its unusually good performance in 1980, but it still gave the FDP an apparently comfortable margin above the 5 percent threshold. Moreover, the Free Democrats continued to be needed as majority makers by their new coalition partners.

Insofar, the Liberals must be counted among the winners of the 1983 Bundestag election. But that is only half the story. The small party is burdened by serious problems. Its electoral base continues to be weak and unreliable, raising doubts about the FDP's political future—at least at the state and local levels of government. The membership structure, always very frail, has been further weakened by the many defections that accompanied the most recent change of course. At all levels the party suffers from a paucity of effective leadership personnel. Although the coalition shift is no longer an intraparty issue, there is still uncertainty and disagreement within the FDP over political orientation and strategy. Finally, the political constraints on the party's role as balancer between Christian and Social Democrats, underscored by the agonies of the coalition change in 1982, have become more severe since the Greens broke down the three-party system.

Before returning to the FDP's most recent change of coalition and its political survival in the mid-1980s, this chapter examines the small party's role in West German politics with special reference to (1) the dualist legacy of German liberalism; (2) the heterogeneous and residual character of the postwar Liberal parties in West Germany; (3) the FDP's special contributions to a redefinition of the national question and a corresponding change in *Ostpolitik* (relations with the East) in the late sixties and early seventies; (4) the special relationship of the Free Democrats to private enterprise and middle-class economic interests; and (5) the small party's own left-right divisions on policy and strategy as well as its corresponding changes of political course, first in the late sixties and then in the early eighties. The FDP's two traversals of the political spectrum, first in a leftward and then in a rightward direction, are in themselves remarkable undertakings. They will be studied in connection with the two major transfers of power that the Liberals have engineered. At the end, the chapter discusses some structural problems that beset the FDP as a coalition, voter, and member party.

The FDP's behavior will be interpreted largely in terms of efforts designed to defend and enhance its position in the political system—a position that is at once so fragile and so advantageous. However, even its most pragmatic calculations of competitive advantage will be affected by assumptions, perceptions, and evaluations of the larger environment within and upon which the party acts. Here, the disagreements between the FDP's left and right wings become an important factor in understanding its political behavior. The lines of division are not at all clearcut or permanent. Nor are the intraparty differences normally articulated in general, theoretical terms. However, it will be argued that the FDP's peculiar ambivalence in recent years about strategy and goals can also be understood, at least in part, as reflecting some fundamental tensions within modern liberalism. These differences concern the place of economic and noneconomic values in the social realm, as well as the proper role and limits of politics. They find contemporary societal expression in the "material" and "postmaterial" orientations discussed at greater length elsewhere in this book.[9]

THE DUALIST TRADITION OF GERMAN LIBERALISM

Modern German politics before Hitler encompassed four major traditions that spawned their own parties: liberalism, conservatism, socialism, and political catholicism. In reality, the boundaries that separated these political "camps" were not as clear or rigid as the reference to *isms* would suggest. The *Weltanschauungsparteien*, as these ideologically self-conscious parties came to be known, were never motivated by political doctrine alone. Practical considerations of partisan advantage and the special interests of their political clienteles had an important place in their lives as well.

After the Second World War, the ideological and social leveling of both citizenry and parties in West Germany, as in many other affluent industrial societies, tended to blur the traditional distinctions. Yet the *isms* have been fairly resilient as part of the vocabulary and symbolism of competitive politics. Even though agendas and strategies have been changed, the old references still serve as a rough means of distinguishing among rival parties and claiming historical legitimation for one's own. To be sure, a party's self-identification with a particular tradition will often be tentative and selective. This is especially so in the case of West Germany's Christian Democrats, whose postwar party reaches far beyond political catholicism to straddle several traditions.

As another new party, the FDP also lacks the strong sense of historical identity that, despite all reforms, still imbues the SPD. Moreover, the Free Democrats like to portray themselves as more pragmatic than their political rivals. But that does not deter the FDP from regarding itself as the rightful heir to the German liberal tradition. While it acknowledges that the CDU and SPD share with it a basic commitment to liberal-democratic values, the FDP follows Karl-Hermann Flach in referring to these parties as representatives of the conservative (or clerical-conservative) and socialist traditions respectively. Such a categorization has the additional advantage of suggesting that the three-party system, with the FDP as an integral element, has a kind of historical validity for Germany.

The liberal tradition in Germany encompasses much with which the FDP can proudly identify—such as the many legal protections against arbitrary power built into the Rechtsstaat. But the history of Germany's Liberal parties is also one of narrow interest promotion as well as factionalism, opportunism, and decline. Their development shows enough parallels with the FDP's contemporary plight to suggest that the small party may suffer from an identity problem that is more fundamental than the disadvantage of being squeezed in between the two large Volksparteien of postwar Germany.

Liberals in Germany, as in some other West European countries, have historically been split between a more progressive and a more conservative orientation. The German division originated in different priorities given to the issues of national unification and constitutional reform during the liberal upsurge that culminated in the 1848 revolution. The differences later took the form of divergent responses to Bismarck's effective but strongly conservative policy for a united German Reich. From 1866, there were separate liberal-democratic and national-liberal party organizations. The National Liberals in time became closely linked to the conservative economic and social interests of large industry, while the Progressives took up moderate reformist and emancipatory causes. The initial left-right division was thus overladen with other conflicts and complicated by later regroupings, but the basic dualism remained a characteristic of German liberalism before and after the First World War.

Apart from their lack of unity, Liberals in Germany appear to have been weakened by such factors as a paucity of effective leaders and a disinclination or inability to build strong political organizations. More fundamental, perhaps, was the fact that their ideological individualism—heavily compromised as it was by special interest promotion and other pragmatic considerations—had less appeal in an increasingly organized industrial society, where citizens were being politicized by new conservative, confessional, and socialist parties. Thus a part of the traditional liberal clientele in the Protestant middle classes, who felt threatened by the growing working-class movement, groped for more authoritarian promises of social order and national prestige than even conservative Liberals could offer. The workers, in turn, largely failed to respond when progressive Liberals, such as Friedrich Naumann, propounded a "social liberalism" that was intended to alleviate their material plight and raise them from "subjects" to full-scale "citizens" of industrial society. Finally, both the national and secular elements in liberalism estranged it from German Catholics, who had become politicized on behalf of their special educational and other cultural interests as a result of Bismarck's repressive *Kulturkampf*.[10]

Electoral history gives a graphic measure of the long-term erosion and final collapse of institutionalized liberalism in German politics. Once the largest parliamentary force, with a combined total of nearly one-half the popular vote in the first Reichstag election of 1871, the Liberal parties saw their share of the vote decline as the active electorate expanded rapidly in the following decade. They were still able to gather just over one-quarter of the vote in 1912 and after the First World War more than one-fifth in 1920. Thereafter the Democratic party (DDP) and the People's party (DVP), which represented the left and right wings of liberalism in the Weimar Republic, lost voters at nearly every election. Common problems of survival did not bring them together. The two parties were colleagues in most of the Weimar coalition governments until 1930 but could not create even a loose organizational union. In the last years of the Republic, they made some futile attempts to adjust to the rising nationalism and authoritarianism of Germany's middle-class Protestants. The Great Depression reduced both parties to political insignificance. They received a combined total of less than 3 percent of the popular vote in each of the 1932 elections.

In spite of considerable misgivings, the remaining handful of Liberal deputies in the Reichstag voted in March 1933 for the Enabling Act that facilitated Hitler's consolidation of power. Their parties dissolved themselves a few months later, as the National Socialists set about to establish a one-party state. Unlike the outlawed Social Democrats and Communists, the Liberals did not attempt to establish organizational continuity underground or abroad. With some individual exceptions, their record of political resistance to the Third Reich was meager when compared to that of German socialists or conservatives.[11]

UNITY AND DIVERSITY IN A RESIDUAL BOURGEOIS PARTY: THE FDP IN THE EARLY POSTWAR YEARS

The FDP was founded at Heppenheim in December 1948 by delegates from several Liberal parties that had been organized first at the local and then at higher levels in the western parts of Germany after the collapse of the Third Reich. There were considerable variations in the licensing practices of the Allied occupying powers. In some cases, the Liberals received permission to organize a little later than the Communists, Social Democrats, and Christian Democrats, but they were among the four party groups that enjoyed the advantages of an organizational headstart.[12] Almost everywhere these forerunners of the FDP ran considerably behind their Christian and Social Democratic rivals, but they gained representation in all but one of the state parliaments (Schleswig-Holstein from 1947 to

1950). In the Bizonal Economic Council of the British and American zones of occupation, a handful of Liberals could exercise pivotal influence in a manner that foreshadowed their later role in West German politics.

In the Soviet zone of occupation, parties had been licensed even earlier and at the zonal rather than local level from the beginning. From here, a relatively vigorous Liberal Democratic party (LDP) made considerable efforts to establish interzonal contacts among the Liberal organizations of postwar Germany. There were reciprocal moves from the Western zones. However, the growing East-West differences complicated and eventually blocked such all-German feelers, even before the East German Liberal Democrats completely lost their autonomy in the increasingly monolithic multiparty system of the German Democratic Republic. Contacts between them and their Western counterparts had already been disrupted before the latter called the founding congress at Heppenheim in anticipation of the formation of the new West German state.

Thus, the FDP overcame the longstanding organizational split of German liberalism but reflected the postwar division of Germany from the outset. In later years, however, the common claim to a liberal heritage would serve as reason for sporadic contacts between the FDP and LDP. And a considerable number of prominent Free Democrats, including the present party leader, Hans-Dietrich Genscher, began their political careers as members of the East German LDP in the early postwar years.[13]

The skeletal Liberal organizations in the Western zones represented a considerable variety of interests and ideas. Their outreach was offset from the beginning by the rapid emergence of the CDU as an effective catchall party for nonsocialists. With its broad centrist position and biconfessional appeal, the CDU offered many Germans of the middle classes as well as Catholic workers a welcome contrast to the divisive *Parteienpolitik* before 1933. Even Theodor Heuss, who became the first leader of the FDP, had been attracted by the idea of forming a single bourgeois party, and many potential Liberal voters and activists were lost to the CDU. Consequently, the postwar Liberal parties had a residual character from the outset. It has been well said that they were stocked in large part by people who found the CDU too close to the churches and the SPD too close to the trade unions, with their respective corporate interests.[14] But in the early years, even the Christian Democrats were far too "social" in their outlook for many Liberals.

The FDP's distinctive rejection of socialist and clericalist orientations found expression in its strong neoliberal commitment to a private enterprise economy, on the one hand, and its secular views on matters pertaining to education or publicly enforced morality, on the other. Otherwise, the basis of commonality within the party was rather thin. Some members of the founding generation, including Heuss, had been active Liberals in the Weimar Republic and retained a strong, conscious commitment to liberal ideas and values; but many others had no such political experience or clarity of convictions.

Party unity was therefore bought at the price of programmatic vagueness and organizational looseness. In its decentralized structure, the FDP appeared to some observers as resembling a cartel of state party organizations during the fifties. For many years it refrained from adopting a basic party program, as distinct from election platforms and special policy statements. This facilitated the coexistence of some very different outlooks and strategies within the small party, and early analysts were struck by its heterogeneity. Thus a 1949 report by U.S. military authorities characteristically emphasized the difficulty of locating the FDP on the political spectrum. While it was to the right of the Christian Democrats on economic questions, it was to the left and much closer to the Social Democrats on issues of cultural policy and the structure of the federal system. The report also stressed that there were ideological differences between the small party's own left and right wings that complicated the picture even more.[15]

Such differences could be explained in part as a legacy of the century-long split within German liberalism. But the FDP's ambivalence had also been conditioned by postwar circumstances and the influence of some early political entrepreneurs. In the southwest, for example, such founders as Theodor Heuss and Reinhold Maier reinforced a strong liberal-democratic tradition of that region. Here the party stressed its progressive commitment to cultural freedom and civil liberties, often in considerable disagreement with the more conservative orientation of the Christian Democrats. Similar patterns could be found in the city-states of Hamburg and West Berlin. In the central and western industrial areas of Hesse and North Rhine–Westphalia, on the other hand, the dominant wing of the FDP could be defined primarily by its strong support of industrial and business interests. Franz Blücher, who became party leader after Heuss was elected federal president in 1949, maintained close links to the region's industrial circles. Here and in some areas of Lower Saxony, the party also became a stopover for politically homeless voters and activists with ultraright orientations who had little or no connection to the individualist tradition of liberalism.

The FDP was not the only party to attract rightist elements in the early postwar period, and it probably contributed to their eventual assimilation into the new political order. However, some regional FDP leaders sought to cater to this constituency by adopting nationalist symbols and appeals. In turn, some nationalist activists tried to infiltrate the small party. Such activities resulted in a number of intraparty conflicts and public embarrassments in the early fifties. The FDP's ambivalence came on display in 1952. That year the progressives led in the defeat of a proposed *German Program,* that had nationalist-authoritarian overtones, but failed to get adopted its own *Liberal Manifesto.* The latter not only extolled the values of economic dispersion (through private enterprise) and cultural freedom. It also warned pointedly against extreme nationalism as a form of "illiberal collectivism."[16]

REDEFINING THE NATIONAL QUESTION AND OPENING UP TO THE LEFT: A NEW OSTPOLITIK

By 1969, when the Liberals entered a cabinet coalition with the SPD in Bonn, the FDP had undergone a remarkable change in its position on the national question, or *Deutschlandpolitik.* The SPD had moved in a similar direction, and their common policy toward Eastern Europe (Ostpolitik) provided the foundation for the first social-liberal cabinet under Willy Brandt. More hesitantly, the FDP had also begun to redefine much of its domestic policy orientation in terms of what came to be called social liberalism, as reformers sought to find historical legitimacy in the earlier progressive tradition of Friedrich Naumann. It is worthwhile to explore both these shifts that opened the federal party to the left and gave it a clearer and more progressive image than it had previously commanded.

There was never a wholesale purge of the nationalist elements in the party. Some were discredited by scandals or attracted to other political arenas. The most common fate was probably a gradual assimilation into the postwar order during the prolonged economic boom of the fifties and early sixties. Although the FDP continued to have a relatively strong national outlook, it found expression in misgivings about the neglect of "the German question" under Adenauer's determined policy of cultural, economic, military, and political integration with Western Europe. As members of his coalition government, the Free Democrats had endorsed this *Westpolitik,* but their national concerns gave rise to some differences of emphasis and sometimes even of substance.

The differences became more evident after Thomas Dehler replaced Blücher as FDP leader in 1954. Fiery in his patriotism as in his liberalism, Dehler was in some ways an antipode to the conservative old chancellor.

The coalition bonds also grew strained because the Liberals sought to emphasize their political autonomy, while the Christian Democrats strove to subdue the small and somewhat unruly partner. As the Free Democrats were not cohesive, Adenauer could sometimes bypass their leadership and play one group against another. But in their desire for control, the Christian Democrats went too far, and the Liberals bolted from the coalition. The CDU delivered the immediate cause for the breakaway when it pressed for an electoral law change that would have drastically reduced the parliamentary representation of the FDP and other small parties.

When it went into the parliamentary opposition, the FDP lost a third of its parliamentary deputies, including every one of its cabinet members and the former leader, Franz Blücher. The defectors formed a new party that stayed with Adenauer until its demise in the Bundestag election of 1957. Here, the CDU/CSU triumphed with an absolute majority of the popular vote, while the Free Democrats—who had begun with 11.9 percent in 1949 and declined to 9.5 percent in 1953—sank further to 7.7 percent. They had run the campaign as an independent "third force" in West German politics and made no formal coalition commitment. In addition to its losses of members and voters, the FDP saw important financial supporters turn away in disapproval.

The first coalition rupture in Bonn, like the later course changes, was costly to the FDP, but it permitted the Liberals to assert their political independence. Their act of defiance helped spare them from the fate that befell other small nonsocialist parties in those years of consolidation in West German politics: reduction to dependency status and/or eventual absorption by the Christian Democrats.

Under the stabilizing leadership of Reinhold Maier, the FDP recuperated as a political organization in the late fifties. Freed from the restraints of coalition discipline, it became more openly critical of Bonn's neglect of the East European dimension. In all this, however, the FDP did not question the fundamental assumptions of German reunification. It stressed the need for better relations with the East as a prerequisite for the restoration of a united German state in its old national boundaries. Any remaining hopes of this kind were shattered by the building of the Berlin Wall in 1961. Thereafter, the FDP's ideas on Ostpolitik took on a new realism.

The Bundestag election of 1961 marked the beginning of the end of the Adenauer era in West German politics. The Free Democrats received an unprecedented 12.8 percent of the popular vote and broke the absolute parliamentary majority of the CDU/CSU. As campaign manager, Flach had promoted the idea that the FDP would provide a check on the Chancellor party and bring new energy to the government. The Liberals appealed to a growing disenchantment with the aging chancellor by promising that they would go "with the CDU" but "without Adenauer." Their electoral success lost its sweetness when the FDP failed to deliver on the second part of this promise. Adenauer, backed by his loyal party, made it a condition of working with the FDP that he remain as chancellor until midterm. To make the Free Democrats more amenable, he even made some first gestures in the direction of the Social Democrats as alternative coalition partners.[17]

Adenauer postponed his retirement by only two years, but his initiative caught the FDP unprepared. The small party was simply not in a position to raise the stakes, although a majority coalition of SPD and FDP had become arithmetically possible for the first time in Bonn. Some progressive Liberals, like Flach, came to favor such an alliance, but it would have lacked a solid foundation at that time. Not only would its parliamentary margin have been razor-thin, but these two parties still saw each other as antipodes in the social and economic policy matters that lie in the hands of the federal government. Such differences were of much less significance in state politics, and there had been several SPD-FDP alliances at that level since the early postwar years. But in Bonn the FDP was not yet open to both sides. Adenauer's move, therefore, forced the small party into a corner, where it swallowed its pride and accepted his essential condition.

In response to a storm of intraparty and public criticism for having "toppled over" on the chancellor question, the FDP now became unusually eager to assert its independence within the coalition. Its new leader, Erich Mende, refused to serve in a cabinet under Adenauer. The Free Democrats also insisted on at least being served "the head" of Adenauer's loyal foreign minister, Heinrich von Brentano, who had come to symbolize a rigid policy toward the Soviet Union and Eastern Europe. Thereafter the FDP supported his more pragmatic successor, Gerhard Schröder (CDU), against some of the less flexible Christian Democrats in the government. In the Spiegel affair of 1962, the FDP even forced the resignation of the powerful CSU leader, Franz-Josef Strauss, from the cabinet by temporarily leaving the government. Defense Minister Strauss had misused his authority and then misled the Bundestag about his actions in connection with a massive investigation of *Der Spiegel,* a news magazine that had published alleged military secrets in an article critical of the minister.[18] This celebrated test of both freedom of the press and political accountability in the Federal Republic provided the occasion for the FDP's most famous performance as a liberal watchdog within the government.

When Ludwig Erhard replaced Adenauer as chancellor in 1963, Erich Mende entered the cabinet and used his position as minister of all-German affairs for some practical initiatives to strengthen the ties between the two Germanies. Some Free Democrats went further in their reexamination of the national issue and began to question the utility of keeping up legal claims to former German territories in Eastern Europe. The revisionists eventually came to the conclusion that Bonn should take an active role in promoting a détente between the states of Western and Eastern Europe, on the basis of a recognition of the territorial status quo created by the Second World War.

Such once-heretical thoughts became part of the intraparty discussion after 1966, when the FDP again broke out of a coalition with the CDU/CSU. The Liberals had differed with the Chancellor party over fiscal policy during the country's first recession, but they were also motivated by a desire to overcome the "topple over" image as well as by fears that the sinking ship of Erhard's government would drag down their own party. The Christian Democrats, for their part, had warmed to the idea of replacing their difficult partner by entering into a great coalition with the Social Democrats. At one time this unusually broad government formation had served the CDU/CSU as a threat to tame the FDP during the coalition negotiations in 1961 and again in the Spiegel affair of 1962. Now it finally became a reality when Erhard stepped down in favor of Kurt-Georg Kiesinger (also CDU) on December 1, 1966, less than five weeks after the small party's departure from his cabinet. The Liberals were taken aback by this development, which deprived them of the kingmaker function and relegated them to the unaccustomed role, as only member of the parliamentary opposition, of having to prepare and present solo commentaries and alternatives to the policies of the government.

In the following three years, the new revisionism took hold of the FDP, so that by 1969 it had abandoned the traditional insistence that Germany be reunified as a national state. The symbolic significance of this development can be understood by remembering that the idea of a unitary Reich had been a cornerstone of German liberalism for over a century.

There were a number of reasons for the FDP's adoption of a new Ostpolitik. The first somewhat cautious airings of these ideas had met with some positive public responses that encouraged the reformers and the party to go further. The relatively loose structure of the FDP probably made it easier to promote a change of course. The new policy could, in any case, be defended as stemming from legitimate national concerns that had been tempered by political realism. The fact that the early revisionists included such solid people as the party's long-time treasurer, Hans-Wolfgang Rubin, helped reduce worries about how the FDP's traditional supporters would react. In fact, some business and industrial circles showed considerable interest in building bridges to the East European states, where they correctly anticipated opportunities for increased trade. The reorientation also suited a general FDP strategy of projecting a more modern and dynamic image, as the small party cautiously shifted its electoral appeal toward the new middle class of salaried functionaries and professionals, while trying to hold on to its more conservative supporters in the old middle class. Nor can it be overlooked that the position to the right of the Grand Coalition, which some erstwhile Liberals might have desired, was now filled by a new party formed in 1964: Here, the National Democrats (NPD) had attracted some regional support by giving voice to nationalist and authoritarian grievances that had been awakened by the economic setbacks.

Finally, after the Christian Democrats had set an example for an "opening to the left," the Liberals decided that it was in their interest to follow suit. The constant dependence on the CDU/CSU as coalition partner in Bonn had greatly reduced the small party's freedom and political leverage. It is remarkable how long perceptual barriers hindered a serious consideration of the SPD as an eligible coalition partner in federal politics. Here, the FDP was long dominated by a *Bürgerblockdenken*—its self-perception as member of a bourgeois bloc that took nonsocialist positions in economic and social policy matters. By the mid-sixties, the small party had become hamstrung by its continued adherence to this "socialist-bourgeois" dichotomy, which had long been eroding for both the electorate and the leadership of the two large parties. In the Spiegel affair of 1962 and again after leaving Erhard's sinking government in 1966, the FDP made some hesitant gestures to reach an understanding with the SPD. But the Liberals were far too slow and uncertain. Perhaps only the great coalition, where Willy Brandt's party gained middle-class respectability by its demonstrated moderation and ability to govern (*Regierungsfähigkeit*), could have fully removed their political inhibitions.

The FDP's "opening to the left" was also promoted by a direct threat to its own political existence, for the Chancellor party had responded to the FDP's breakaway by pushing once again for an electoral-law change that would have reduced the small party to political insignificance, if not obliterated it altogether.[19] As part of the great coalition program under Chancellor Kurt-Georg Kiesinger (CDU), the SPD had agreed to support a major reform of the electoral law to ensure that future Bundestag elections would result in one party holding a clear parliamentary majority. The acknowledged goal, justified in terms of political stabilization, was to eliminate the need to build coalition governments in Bonn. However, the SPD became fearful that such electoral engineering might injure its own parliamentary position, and it finally backed away from the plan. In a very real sense, therefore, the CDU helped to drive the FDP into the arms of the Social Democrats.

Even then, the FDP moved cautiously in the coalition question for fear of losing old supporters. Significantly, the small party's decisive support of the SPD's candidate for the presidency, Georg Heinemann, in the spring of 1969 was *not* followed by any clear announcement about a similar coalition preference during the later campaign for the Bundestag. It was by this time obvious that the reform-oriented FDP and the SPD shared a foreign policy basis for cooperation, but the Liberals abstained from making a clear commitment until the end phase of the campaign. Their ambivalence was costly. Although the FDP attracted some new voters, it lost many more old supporters and received only 5.8 percent on the second ballot—its lowest poll in any Bundestag election until today. This was just enough to form a parliamentary majority with the Social Democrats, and the transfer of power took place. But the small party had almost destroyed itself in the process.

In Willy Brandt's SPD-FDP government, the Liberals took over the foreign ministry for the first time. With Walter Scheel's appointment to the post and Chancellor Brandt's active interest in Ostpolitik, the new government almost immediately seized the initiative for reform. By the fall of 1972, it could look back upon a dizzying record of change in this policy area, including agreements with Moscow and Warsaw that confirmed the existing frontiers in Eastern Europe as well as a basic treaty with the German Democratic Republic, in which the two German states recognized each other's sovereignty.

Although it had some antecedents, the Ostpolitik took less than three years to abandon positions which West German governments had defended for two decades. The Brandt-Scheel foreign policy ran into considerable resistance, including some within the ranks of the Social-Liberal coalition itself. Erich Mende, who had opposed Brandt's election to the chancellorship in 1969, tried to redirect his party toward a more "moderate" reform course for another year, before he and other dissidents left the FDP. They received considerable publicity but could not sustain a viable *National-Liberale Aktion*, organized to propagate their antirevisionist outlook. Some were absorbed by the CDU/CSU, where Mende himself became a backbencher. In their new role as parliamentary opposition, the Christian Democrats at first rejected the Brandt-Scheel Ostpolitik as a sellout of vital German interests. The Bundestag election of 1972, called a year early because defections had whittled away the government's slim majority, gave a resounding public endorsement of the Eastern policy and secured the coalition's parliamentary base. In the following years, the Christian Democrats grew to accept the basic transformation in Bonn's relations with its Eastern neighbors—much as the Social Democrats had earlier come to terms with the new reality shaped by Adenauer's Westpolitik.

Free Democrats look back upon this policy change as a major achievement. They had not been alone in pushing for the new course, but they had been among its early and most articulate proponents. Having helped to originate and legitimate a revisionist outlook upon Eastern Europe, they made the new Ostpolitik possible by triggering the first complete transfer of power between the two major parties in Bonn.[20]

FROM ECONOMIC CONSERVATISM TO SOCIAL LIBERALISM: THE ROAD TO FREIBURG

The reorientation of the FDP also included domestic policy matters. Speaking to the 1971 party conference in Freiburg, two years after the formation of the SPD-FDP coalition, Walter Scheel took a parting shot at the recent defectors from his own party: They "call themselves National Liberals because they are social reactionaries who cannot learn to distinguish between nationalism and patriotism." He went on to cast the FDP in the role of a progressive innovator in domestic affairs, where overdue reforms could now be undertaken because the détente of Bonn's Ostpolitik had cleared away obstacles rooted in cold war attitudes. "Those who do not yet know it," he announced, "should finally learn: In Germany, and not only in Germany, it is nationalism that is the most engrained enemy of all societal reform."[21]

Scheel's public enthusiasm for "inner reform" must be understood in context. His party had just barely survived a heavy loss of supporters who identified with a more conservative orientation in the FDP. As part of its attempt to project a more progressive image and offset the electoral losses by gains among less conservative voters, especially young people and members of the new middle class, the small party was now defining itself in the reformist tradition of Friedrich Naumann's social liberalism. Its Freiburg Theses of 1971, calling for a "democratization of society" and even for a "reform of capitalism," seemed to constitute an enormous programmatic step away from a position that had been correctly described a few years earlier as "very much to the right of the Christian Democrats in social and economic affairs."[22] How did this transformation come about, and what did it mean for the FDP and its role in West German politics?

The FDP had planted itself squarely in the right-of-center position from the beginning, when it was the only party in the Western zones to take an unequivocal stand for a private enterprise system and against the socialization of industry. In the Bizonal Economic Council, before the formation of the Federal Republic, the Liberal representatives had pushed such conservative (or neoliberal) views at a time when important economic and financial directions were being set for postwar Germany. Although few in number, they could be influential by cooperating with the Christian Democrats, who were evenly balanced with the Social Democrats on the Council.

In one decision that had a far-reaching impact on the domestic future of West Germany, the Liberals successfully promoted Ludwig Erhard for the key post of director of economic administration. Erhard was a professor of business economics who did not then belong to any political party. He came to personify the remarkable economic recovery that grateful Germans dubbed a miracle, or *Wirtschaftswunder.* His "social market economy" stood for a private enterprise system buffered by Germany's traditional social network of welfare legislation. It operated within the context of governmental regulations, of course, but departed radically from the extensive administrative controls and directives of the previous years. Both then and later, when he became minister of economics in Bonn under Chancellor Adenauer, Erhard received strong support from the Free Democrats. Erhard eventually joined the CDU, where he said that his neoliberal voice was more needed, but for a long time the Free Democrats had reason to regard him as really one of their own.[23]

In view of its well-known economic orientation, the FDP's support for Adenauer and its entry into his first coalition government were a foregone conclusion in 1949. In the Bundestag, the Free Democrats took up the seats to the right of the CDU/CSU, where they certainly belonged in economic and social policy matters. An early major policy disagreement with the CDU characteristically broke out over the codetermination law, which gave workers in the coal and iron industries representation on their company supervisory boards in equal strength to that of capital. Free Democrats regarded such representation, especially in a form that gave parity to labor through the trade unions, as an infringement on the rights of private owners and their managers to make decisions for the firm. On this question, the FDP was even more distant from the SPD, of course.

The FDP continued to be a stout defender of business interests. Its policy statements regularly stressed the need to adhere to a free market economy, oppose government meddling, and aid the middle class. These objectives were not always compatible in practice, for the FDP understood aid to the middle class to include special-interest promotion, such as tax concessions to business and protectionist measures for the farmers. Moreover, the party tried to reach out beyond business and agriculture to the self-employed, that is, the other elements of the so-called old middle class. Increasingly, it also sought to make electoral inroads among members of the growing new middle class of salaried professional people, middle-to-higher civil servants, and other salary-dependent middle-class employees, whose social and economic position generated a need for protection not provided by the market economy. This helps explain the FDP's considerable effort to emphasize that it supported the social—as opposed to socialist—buffers built into postwar order.

Despite such an incongruous mix of neoliberal market theory and special-interest promotion, there could never be any doubt that the FDP followed a generally conservative line in social and economic matters. Here, an early observer detected an unusually tense and almost diametrical contrast between the FDP and SPD as well as the interest groups most closely linked to each of them.[24] In a policy area where the larger and more inclusive parties sought to avoid sharp confrontations, the FDP did not hesitate to react antagonistically to economic and social reform proposals pushed by the SPD and the trade unions with potential support from the Catholic workers' wing of the CDU.

From early on, there were close ties between the FDP and the interest groups of business and industry as well as agriculture, rooted in similarities of ideology, social class, and material interest. The ties were strengthened by some overlapping of leadership personnel and, very importantly, substantial financial support for the small party from capital interests. Realistically, business and industry had early shifted most of their attention to the CDU/CSU as the major—and quite amenable—decision maker in economic policy. Nevertheless, the FDP continued to be regarded and treated as a useful adjunct or even, for some, as the party of preference. All this provided fuel for the frequently bandied charge that in Bonn, where economic, financial, and social policies were largely determined, the FDP amounted to a *Wirtschafts-* or *Unternehmerpartei,* a party of business whose chief functions were (1) to prevent the SPD from becoming a majority party by providing disaffected CDU voters with a nonsocialist alternative, (2) to keep the CDU in power by joining it in majority government coalitions, and (3) to offset the influence of the workers' faction (or social wing) of the CDU within such bourgeois cabinets.

It is fair to surmise that such factors contributed to the FDP's limited agility in coalition politics, especially at the federal level. On the other hand, the small party could develop views and interests that sometimes clashed with those of capital. This can best be seen in some decisions taken by the FDP to defend or enhance its own organizational position. An outstanding example was the transfer of power in North Rhine–Westphalia in early 1956: Here, the FDP overthrew a CDU-led government at midterm by changing to a cabinet coalition with the SPD, shortly before it also left the Adenauer coalition in Bonn. In any case, the party's dependence on financial aid from major private sources, and its consequent vulnerability to pressures from the same, were partly offset by the public financing of parties. This form of funding, which began in the late fifties, soon became a major source of revenue and probably helped free the FDP to consider seriously a coalition with the SPD in Bonn.[25] In the end, as we have seen, the opening to the left was delayed by perceptual barriers and electoral considerations.

The FDP's orientation in the late sixties was not limited to the Ostpolitik discussed earlier. The party also established its progressive credentials by opposing some far-reaching provisions of the 1968 Emergency Law, pushing for modern educational reforms, and proposing to liberalize the criminal and civil codes. Under Scheel's leadership, the Liberals projected a general spirit of innovation and reform, as in their election slogans of 1969, "We can change Germany" and "We're going to cut off those old pigtails." Yet this image obscured the fact that there had been far less change in the FDP's social and economic policy positions. This was evident in the shibboleth of codetermination policy, where the party's election platform announced support for a "sharing of power and responsibility" by employees but coupled it with a criticism of the "new concentrations of power" (read trade union power) that had emerged in the labor representation of the coal and iron industries.[26]

The Liberals finally revised their social and economic policy position in the Freiburg Theses of 1971, two years after the birth of the SPD-FDP coalition in Bonn. The theses located the party's general standpoint on four questions: (1) the rights and obligations of private property, (2) the spreading of opportunities for capital ownership and capital sharing, (3) the expansion of codetermination for employees in large companies, and (4) the protection of the natural environment in industrial society. Here and in a general introduction to the program, the FDP gave a far more "social" interpretation of liberalism than ever before.[27]

As in the past, the FDP stressed the political importance of defending and expanding individual freedom and choice, but these concepts were now more closely tied to ideas of social interdependence and responsibility. The new emphasis was reflected in the repeated usage of the formula "democratic and social liberalism." It showed up in demands for reforms that would promote equality of opportunity and democratize the authority relationships within social institutions. As a whole, the document was remarkable for its emancipatory and participatory commitment. It exuded a spirit of optimism about social reform and progress.

The most striking innovation lay in the approach to the capitalist economy. While the Freiburg program defended private enterprise, it expressed some reservations about the social consequences of unfettered capitalism: "The confidence of classical liberalism, that the goals of a liberal society could be reached from the automatism of a private economy, has been justified only to a point. There is no natural harmony between personal advantage and the public good." Indeed, "Capitalism, based on competition and individual performance, has led to great economic accomplishments but also to social injustices. Accordingly, the four Freiburg Theses dealt with the need for the "reform of capitalism" along with a "democratization of society," "progress through reason" and "human dignity through self-realization."[28]

The Freiburg statement did not constitute a complete party program, but it provided an eloquent expression of a political standpoint with unmistakenly "progressive" contours. Conservative critics, including defectors from the FDP, dismissed it as an opportunistic and short-sighted concession to the then still-modish demands of the student movement for societal reform. Such critics appeared to be vexed by the Freiburg call for a "democratization of society" at least as much as by the accompanying concern for a "reform of capitalism."

It is remarkable that the FDP reformers in 1971, while careful to emphasize the need for prudence and rationality in changing society, should not have shied away from trying to establish a link between their own efforts and what the program called the "world-wide youth rebellion" with its accompanying "profound and lasting changes in consciousness." Professor Maihofer, who headed the drafting commission, even sought to establish a grand historical legitimation by postulating two major phases of liberalism as a reform movement. The first phase had encompassed the classical bourgeois efforts to liberalize and democratize the political sphere, whereas the second was now presented as leading to similar changes in social and economic institutions.[29]

Most remarkable of all, if one remembers the party's older ideological location, is that the FDP could unite behind the Freiburg Theses. Here it is possible only to sketch some conditions which facilitated such a programmatic revision. The Freiburg program was adopted at a time when the FDP had reached its low electoral point within the West German party system, and the theses were clearly a late offspring of the activist drive for a reorientation and an opening to the left during the time of the great coalition. The low membership and comparatively loose structure of the party organization had made the task of determined reformers, many of whom had only recently joined the FDP, easier than would have been the case in a bureaucratically more rigid and inert mass-membership party. In addition, the loss of many stalwart National Liberals and old-middle-class supporters had removed the most serious obstacles to a programmatic rejuvenation.

At the time of the Freiburg conference, moreover, it could still be assumed that members of the new middle class—the increasingly important electoral target group of the FDP—would be receptive to the spirit of societal reform. There had not yet been a shattering of the comfortable outlook that took continued economic growth and prosperity for granted. Instead, Erhard's neoliberal market model had lost some ground to interventionist ideas since the mid-sixties, partly as a result of the great coalition's successful use of Keynesian anticyclical techniques to combat the recent economic recession. Apart from their possible appeal to middle-class predilections for some kind of steering toward long-term basic social goals, the Freiburg Theses also evoked older claims of progressive liberalism to represent qualitative reforms that do not emerge automatically from the clash of interests in the marketplace. More important, probably, the call for a humanized environment, democratized authority structures, and increased opportunities for self-realization echoed some of the "postmaterial" values and desires for "new" politics that were just then being discovered among younger people and members of the new middle class.[30]

Finally, however, it must not be overlooked that the Freiburg program could be adopted because it skirted the difficult business of establishing a well-defined policy consensus. Instead, it mixed attractive rhetoric and laudable concerns to arrive at some general recommendations. The declaration performed an important symbolic function for the FDP by giving the party a progressive image that would be attractive to supporters of the reform coalition. This may help explain the unusual degree of ticket splitting in the Bundestag election of 1972, when many citizens who cast their first vote for the SPD used the second and crucial vote to support the FDP. By attracting so many coalition supporters, the FDP ended up with 8.4 percent of the second vote, or almost half as much again as in 1969, although its share of first votes (4.8 percent) remained constant.

In the aftermath of the electoral triumph of 1972, it was easy to overlook that the SPD and the FDP had been drawn together less by domestic policy agreement than by the commonality of their Ostpolitik. The Freiburg Theses contributed to the illusion. And they obscured for a time that while some Free Democrats, like Maihofer, viewed the FDP-SPD coalition as an "historic alliance of the forces of progress" in Germany, many other Liberals regarded the political arrangement in far less ideological, far more pragmatic terms of temporary utility and convenience.

AFTER FREIBURG: THE RETURN
TO ECONOMIC CONSERVATISM

In retrospect, the Freiburg Theses almost appear to be a concluding act in the FDP's "opening to the left" rather than a signal for a new progressive advance. Rooted in tacit assumptions about continued prosperity, they were silent about the problems of unemployment and reduced growth rates that followed the 1973 oil embargo. Under Chancellor Schmidt, who replaced Brandt in 1974, West Germany was able to contain such economic problems with relative success until the end of the seventies, but the long period of crisis management left little room for the kind of reforms envisaged, however vaguely, in the Freiburg Theses. Instead, a mood of self-proclaimed "economic realism" began to reassert itself within the FDP. Its adherents now had to coexist with unregenerate "Freiburg Liberals," however, and so the traditional left-right division within German liberalism reemerged in a new form.

The tensions could eventually be felt throughout the party, despite busy efforts to paper over the differences with a flood of position statements during the seventies.[31] At the cabinet level, the successive ministers of economics, Hans Friedrichs and Count Otto von Lambsdorff, represented what came to be known as the economic, conservative, or right wing of the FDP. The successive ministers of the interior, Hans Maihofer and Gerhart Baum, became identified with the progressive "social-liberal," or left, faction. The position of the economic Liberals was strengthened by the fact that German business and industry had adjusted to the SPD-FDP coalition by renewing their links to the small party. In Freiburg, Walter Scheel had promised that the FDP would keep the SPD from enacting "socialist" policies just as it had earlier kept the CDU from straying onto a "clericalist" path.[32] It was just this function of braking the SPD that made the FDP useful to capital interests. But the new socioeconomic prudence and "realism" within the FDP also reflected a waning of the country's reform mood. By the middle of the seventies, some observers saw evidence for a socially conservative countertrend, or *Tendenzwende,* in West Germany.[33]

The new sobriety did not affect every policy area. For example, the Free Democrats remained supportive of a further liberalization of the legal system, while Christian Democrats adhered to more traditional views on such matters as criminal procedure or the enforcement of conventional morality. In the area of social and economic policy, however, the FDP did not become the reform agent that a cursory reading of the Freiburg Theses might lead one to expect. On such indicative issues as taxation, investment, and property policy, the FDP generally disagreed with positions favored by the left wing of the SPD and the trade unions. Chancellor Schmidt, who belonged to the conservative wing of the SPD, often found the little coalition partner useful as a restraint on his own Social Democrats. Inevitably, the alliance of the two parties began to show strains as the left wing became more impatient within the SPD.

Once again the issue of codetermination can serve as a political barometer. Against serious misgivings in the trade union movement and the SPD, the Free Democrats insisted on the adoption of a fundamentally new formula for employee representation, when codetermination was expanded for large companies outside the coal and iron industries. As a result, the Codetermination Act of 1976 does not threaten the ultimate authority of capital interests in the firm. It guarantees that the labor representatives shall not be exclusively composed of trade union officials and, further, that they can be outvoted on the company boards by the representatives of owners and management. With its electoral connection to the new middle class and its revived financial ties to business supporters, the FDP showed an understandable eagerness to take credit for ensuring that the salaried white-collar employees would be represented on the company boards by a member of the firm's top management.

During the seventies, it became evident that the Freiburg Theses could not paper over the growing left-right division within the FDP. The specific issues varied, but many of them can be linked to the tension between the traditional concern of economic liberalism for defending interests tied up with private enterprise and productive efficiency, on the one hand, and the concern of reform liberalism for promoting changes that are regarded as progressive, qualitative, and emancipatory, on the other. This goes far beyond a divergent set of priorities. The two "liberalisms" are divided by a very different understanding of the role of politics and government—as a rather passive agent of order in the former case, and as a much more active agent of reform in the latter.[34]

In some ways, these ideological differences within liberalism, which can be traced back to the nineteenth century in Germany and elsewhere, have taken on contemporary features similar to those that distinguish material and postmaterial values and the corresponding "old" and "new" politics. Such differences could remain submerged as long as economic growth and affluence appeared to be automatic, but they led to conflict when the scarcity dimension reasserted itself in the midst of prosperity. Seen in this light, the intraparty differences of the Free Democrats reflected value conflicts in the larger society and in the industrial world as a whole.

One can detect similar differences within the CDU and, especially, the SPD, but they could be a mortal threat to a small party with a schismatic history. Within the FDP, the basic tension between the reform and productivity concerns usually found expression in clashes on specific issues, such as atomic energy policy. It became articulated in a more general form during the major programmatic debate which preceded the annual party conference of 1977, held in Kiel. A party commission, headed by Economics Minister Friedrichs, had prepared a fundamental report on economic policy for the party. It emphasized the continuing importance of maintaining efficiency, extolled the market process as a means of stimulating economic growth, and censured the impact of much government intervention. In effect, the Friedrichs commission gave an updated statement of the neoliberal position.

A very different report came from another party commission, headed first by Interior Minister Maihofer and later by Gerhart Baum. It sought to carry forward the basic reform values of the Freiburg Theses and give them some contemporary applications. Although this second report dealt primarily with legal and social policy questions, it also addressed the economic dimension by calling attention to "the social costs of industrial production."[35] Here, the Baum commission spoke of the need for "qualitative structural change" and came out in favor of a vaguely envisaged "socially responsible economic policy" in contrast to what it condemned as "short-sighted and technocratic" approaches. Traditional economic policy was presented as being lopsidedly oriented toward "quantitative GNP-growth and a purely material understanding of prosperity." It was time, the Baum report argued, to measure economic policy more in terms of social indicators as well, including the spread of contentment and opportunities for self-development to as many citizens as possible. Basically, the Baum commission urged an adherence to the values of the Freiburg Theses in spite of economic setbacks that had not been foreseen in 1971.

The two party reports thus reflected the basic differences between the market and interventionist approaches to the economy as well as between material and postmaterial value orientations. The media gave unusual attention to the ensuing debate within the FDP, in which the left-right division had received sharper contours than normally. The party conference finally resolved the controversy in favor of a compromise policy statement that tilted heavily in the direction of the Friedrichs report.[36] Although the reform wing won occasional victories later, the economic policy of the party followed the general direction advocated by Count Lambsdorff, who had served as state secretary to Friedrichs and succeeded him as minister in 1977. Both men had close professional and political ties to business and industrial circles.

The left-right conflicts gave the FDP an ambivalent appearance at a time when it was seeking to establish an identity as a "programmatic party," in distinction to the amorphous and inert "mass parties." Clearly, the Liberals were not in agreement about the kind of "third force" they wanted to be. Throughout the seventies, they continued to hammer out policy statements for public consumption, but it became increasingly difficult to present a united front. There were obvious credibility problems. But there were times when the party could draw temporary advantage from its left-right dualism by appealing to two very different constituencies—in a "catch-both" manner, as it were.

THE BUNDESTAG ELECTION OF 1980

The FDP used such a double-track strategy effectively in the 1980 campaign for the Bundestag, when it appealed to center-right and center-left voters with positions of both its wings, as personified by Count Lambsdorff and Gerhart Baum respectively.[37] Two factors helped to push the intraparty differences into the background and make room for an unusual degree of political solidarity in that year: (1) the Liberal aversion to the chancellor-candidate of the CDU/CSU and (2) a major electoral defeat of the FDP in North Rhine–Westphalia only five months before the Bundestag contest.

In a widely distributed election pledge, known as the three-pointer, the FDP declared itself to be "*for* the government Schmidt/Genscher," "*against* single-party government," and "*against* Strauss." The last point referred to the controversial chancellor-candidate of the CDU/CSU, Franz-Josef Strauss, whom the FDP had forced to resign as defense minister 18 years earlier in the Spiegel affair. As leader of the CSU, the Bavarian sister party of the CDU, Strauss had remained an important figure in West German politics. If he was anathema to many Free Democrats, Strauss in turn made no secret of either his contempt for what he regarded as their political opportunism or his preference for their elimination from the Bundestag. His all-or-nothing strategy for returning the CDU/CSU to power, that many Christian Democrats themselves recognized as unrealistic in 1980, reflected his longtime political alienation from the perennial majority maker in West German politics. By choosing him for their candidate that year, the Christian Democrats had not only ensured a highly personalized election campaign but also removed any possibility that the increasingly conservative FDP might have reconsidered its coalition commitment to the SPD. Keeping Strauss out of the chancellery became an important plank in the FDP's platform of 1980, just as keeping him out of the cabinet had played a major part in its campaign of 1965.

The political defeat in North Rhine–Westphalia had a shock effect upon the small party. Here, where almost one-third of West Germany's population resides, the FDP had entered the state parliamentary election somewhat lethargically and stumbled against the 5 percent threshold. Coming so close to the national campaign, the elimination from the Landtag rallied the FDP to an unusually active effort under a quickly formulated new slogan, "This time everything's at stake!" Although polls consistently indicated that the FDP would stay in the Bundestag, the Liberals thus raised the issue of political survival, however indirectly, in their appeal for votes. In effect, they suggested that only their own continued presence in parliament and government could guarantee political stability and moderation in West Germany. Their three-pointer was really just another version of the party's traditional "functional argument."

For voters who backed the Social-Liberal government, the FDP provided reminders that it played a crucial part in keeping Schmidt's administration in office. Such coalition supporters still made up the bulk of the small party's voters. The more progressive ones could be attracted by the Liberal party's positions on civil rights and liberties, where the FDP sometimes stood left of the SPD. Gerhart Baum had gained respect among social libertarians for his public initiatives on behalf of "practiced humanity and tolerance" toward alternative lifestyles. They must have been appalled when Strauss or his conservative followers derided the interior minister for such gestures or charged him with being a "security risk" for allegedly failing to crack down on political extremists. Baum could also be identified with the FDP's claim to having an ecological commitment, although the minister was too much of an establishment politician to attract many countercultural voters. The same can be said of the party's young secretary-general and campaign manager, Günter Verheugen, who insisted that "social liberal" themes must occupy a prominent place in the FDP's self-presentation. In the preceding years, Verheugen had sought to invigorate the party organization by providing incentives for a larger and more active membership. He now tried, with some success, to mobilize Liberals for a more participatory campaign ("the campaign of 80,000") than in the past.

Count Lambsdorff played first violin among the promoters of the FDP's "economic realism." In this part of its strategy, the FDP also took special efforts to attract CDU-oriented voters who were disaffected by Strauss or fearful of a strong SPD in Bonn. Hans-Dietrich Genscher, who had become foreign minister and party leader when Scheel was elected federal president in 1974, canonized Lambsdorff as the "Erhard of the Eighties" at the beginning of the campaign. The economics minister understood how to generate publicity on his own by making observations that pleased the business sector and sometimes outraged trade union leaders. Once again, the codetermination issue figured prominently in the FDP's defense of what it called individual self-determination against organizational power—that is, its disagreement with the trade unions on how labor should be represented on company boards.

Foreign Minister Genscher personified the centrist image that campaign strategists wanted to project. He presented a calm, dependable contrast to the ebullient Bavarian chancellor-candidate, whose adversary rhetoric and political record stirred anxiety in many West Germans. But Genscher also managed discretely to raise middle-class fears of socialism by suggesting that Chancellor Schmidt needed "help" against the left wing of the SPD. The strong pitch to the middle classes, both old and new, figured prominently in the commercial part of the campaign. It included a large number of special interest messages published in homeowners' journals as well as trade and professional magazines for the following *Mittelstand* (upper-middle-class) groups: builders, architects, tax specialists, independent business people, self-employed artisans, medical doctors, pharmacists, business administrators, and farmers. Some members of the business community issued special recommendations to vote for the FDP. Typically, they used the pragmatic argument that while the Christian Democrats and their chancellor-candidate could not possibly win a parliamentary majority, a strong FDP could keep the reins on the Social Democrats. One such widely noticed recommendation came from a former CDU member of the Bundestag, Dietrich Rollmann, who sent it to all members of his Association of Independent Professions.

The FDP had been expected to increase its share of the vote in 1980, but its capture of 10.6 percent of the second ballot went beyond what most observers had thought possible when the campaign began. It was the party's third-best result in nine Bundestag elections and had been topped only in the distant election years of 1949 and 1961. The small party had benefited from ticket splitting, as in all recent elections. Its district vote was only 7.2 percent, but even this was better than it had polled on the first vote since 1965. Considerably more of the FDP's second-vote supporters had given their first vote to the SPD (36.5 percent) than to the CDU or CSU candidate (13.5 percent). Yet this was the highest first vote for the CDU/CSU found among second-vote FDP supporters since 1965, when the two non-socialist parties had been together in a coalition under Erhard (see Table 6.3). Presumably, a considerable share of these votes came from CDU supporters who were unhappy with their party's chancellor-candidate. The FDP made its greatest electoral advances among members of the new middle class—who total more than one-half of the party's voters—and among people in the independent professions and the self-employed (except farmers). These were the Mittelstand voters whom the party had courted so assiduously.[38]

The SPD improved its position only slightly over 1976, with 42.9 percent of the second vote, and it failed in the goal of again becoming the largest parliamentary party. It was almost wholly due to the FDP that the government parties could increase their share of the vote to 53.5 percent. That was not far below the peak reached by the Brandt-Scheel administration in the Ostpolitik election of 1972.

CHANGING PARTNERS AT MIDTERM: THE END OF THE SOCIAL-LIBERAL ERA

The election victory of October 1980 would have given the Bonn coalition another four-year lease on life, if the political will had been there to sustain it. Halfway through that period, however, the partnership broke up.[39] The FDP leadership engineered the change of government which brought the CDU/CSU back into power and returned the SPD to the opposition. While this outcome illustrated once again the disproportionate power the Free Democrats can exercise as balancing party, the events before and after the collapse of the Social-Liberal government also underscored the political uncertainties and risks that normally serve to constrain or inhibit such drastic uses of the pivotal position.

Table 6.3. Ticket Splitting among Second-Vote FDP Supporters, 1957–83 (in percentages)

Party Supported on the First Vote	Second Votes for the FDP							
	1957	1961	1965	1969	1972	1976	1980	1983
FDP	85.0	86.5	70.3	62.0	38.2	60.7	48.5	29.1
SPD	3.8	3.1	6.7	24.8	52.9	29.9	35.5	10.1
CDU/CSU	7.5	8.1	20.8	10.6	7.9	8.0	13.3	58.3
Greens	—*	—	—	—	—	—	2.0	1.7
Others or not valid	3.7	2.3	2.2	2.6	1.0	1.4	0.8	0.9

*Not applicable.

Sources: Statistisches Bundesamt, *Wahl zum 9. Deutschen Bundestag am 5. Oktober 1980, Heft 8,* and *Wahl zum 10. Deutschen Bundestag am 6. März 1983, Heft 4* (Stuttgart: Kohlhammer, 1980 and 1983), Table 2.13, p. 34.

145

At least from the summer of 1981, the West German public received a series of indications that some leading Free Democrats had wearied of the coalition and wanted to change partners. One important motivation was the deepening of their policy disagreements with the Social Democrats (much less with the chancellor than with his party), especially on economic strategy but later also in defense questions. More fundamentally, the restive Liberals had concluded that the FDP's best hope for political survival and influence lay in abandoning an ailing partnership that was rapidly losing popular support. Their fears of being dragged down in a forthcoming electoral realignment were not unrealistic, but the very act of getting ready for a breakaway increased the precarious situation of the FDP. That was because both public and party had to be prepared for the changeover, while the FDP remained a working member of the government team under Chancellor Schmidt, who still enjoyed great personal popularity.

There was a strong interest among Christian Democrats in renewing their ties to the Liberals. They had long since digested the basic settlement of the Ostpolitik that had once divided the parties so bitterly. On economic and fiscal questions, the FDP stood closer to the CDU/CSU than the SPD. Helmut Kohl, who had been the chancellor-candidate of the Christian Democrats in 1976, had long favored a coalition strategy for the return to power. He had good personal and political ties to Genscher. If Franz-Josef Strauss had not been chosen chancellor-candidate in 1980, there is at least a possibility that the FDP would have tried to complete its "opening to the right" of the late seventies by reconsidering the coalition issue at that time. Strauss and his conservative CSU were also a political problem for a middle-of-the-road CDU politician like Kohl, who saw the FDP as a potential check on both. After the electoral disaster of the all-or-nothing strategy pursued by Strauss in 1980, Kohl had little difficulty in promoting his alternative road to the chancellery.

Matters were more difficult for the FDP because of its existing alliance with the SPD. There could clearly be no parting of the ways without causing some, indeed considerable, offense. But could the move be prepared and implemented effectively, so that the losses were kept to a minimum and largely offset by the time of a new election? The small party had faced somewhat similar difficulties in opening itself to a center-left coalition in the late sixties. Its electoral support had plummeted to 5.8 percent in 1969, its lowest national result ever and dangerously close to the minimum for parliamentary representation. Yet the leftward shift had in some ways been easier to justify and explain than what was now being contemplated. In the first place, it had been undertaken from a position outside the government, as sole opposition party in the Bundestag. In the second place, the change of course had been the outcome of intraparty discussions and resolutions over several years. In effect, the coalition decision of 1969 had been legitimated in advance.

It can be argued that Genscher had tried to prepare his party and the public for another possible coalition shift since the late seventies and even that the move, when it finally came, only reflected changes in the sociopolitical trends of the past decade (the so-called *Tendenzwende*).[40] Certainly the FDP had become much more conservative in both substance and posture, as we have seen. The programmatic signal had been given in 1977, when the right wing had won the debate on economic strategy and goals at the party conference in Kiel. After the Bundestag election of 1976, Genscher had supported a "loosening-up" strategy toward the CDU in several states. Center-right coalitions had emerged at both the state and local levels of government, and a greater share of the FDP's national support in 1980 had come from center-right oriented voters than in any Bundestag election since 1965. Nevertheless, the FDP had fought and won the last general election as member of the Schmidt-Genscher coalition, and it was estimated that three-fourths of its voters preferred that alliance.[41] The Liberals could not possibly remain in the cabinet while preparing the displacement of their long-time partners without incurring charges of disloyalty.

The policy differences in the Social-Liberal coalition were real enough. Other chapters in this book explore the controversy between the SPD and FDP on how to deal with the mounting economic problems that beset the Bonn government after the 1980 election. In previous years it had resorted largely to borrowing to make up for the revenue shortages brought on by the troubled economy. Public indebtedness had consequently grown significantly already in the late 1970s. When the world recession hit West Germany with full force in 1981, bringing a drastic rise in unemployment and business failures as well as the country's first decline in domestic production, the deficit issue could no longer be sidestepped.

Confronted with the twin problems of consolidating the public household and stimulating an ailing economy, the government partners took divergent approaches that reflected their different ideological orientations and political constituencies. Basically, the SPD showed a preference for Keynesian techniques of pump priming, to be financed by public borrowing and some higher taxes. It projected itself as defender of West Germany's extensive social security programs with arguments that appealed to "fairness" and "social justice." The Free Democrats, on the other hand, were led by their economic wing (strengthened as a result of the 1980 election) in pushing for cuts in the social budget. Extolling the role of private enterprise in promoting economic growth, they opposed SPD proposals for publicly financed employment programs as well as higher income taxes and a special levy on high incomes. The Liberals presented their German version of supply-side arguments in terms of the need for more incentives to spur "individual initiative and responsibility." It took unusually long and difficult negotiations in the summer of 1981 before the two government parties could agree on the following year's budget. Soon thereafter, the worsening economy brought higher revenue deficits than had been projected, so that another battle ensued over the supplementary budget adjustments.

These differences over how to deal with the fiscal problems served as the background for a whole series of public gestures designed to prepare the opening of the coalition question. In the spring of 1981, Walter Scheel warned that the mounting problems would "seek out a new majority" in Bonn, if the Social-Liberal government failed to master them. In August, Genscher gave a widely observed signal in a public letter to leading party members. He wrote that the Federal Republic had arrived at a crossroad similar to the one facing it at the time of economic recovery after the Second World War: Now as then, the FDP was holding responsibility for taking the right direction. None of Genscher's readers could have failed to understand his analogy to the postwar debate over socialism versus private enterprise. He underscored the point by warning against the debilitating effects of runaway social programs and adding, "A fundamental change [Wende] is necessary." Although Genscher left room for interpretation, it was impossible to overlook his veiled reference to the coalition issue here and in some later public utterances.[42]

In April 1982, the SPD provided an opportunity for ideological sparring when delegates to its annual conference passed resolutions that would have required a much larger role for the government in stimulating and coordinating an economic recovery. While these measures reflected the disillusionment of many Social Democrats with the coalition's policy of fiscal conservatism, they could in no way bind the chancellor, as Helmut Schmidt himself made clear. Free Democrats nevertheless seized this occasion to come out in defense of a free market economy against the "radicals" in the SPD. Economics Minister Lambsdorff, who had been speculating publicly about an early termination of the alliance, dismissed the proposals as "socialistic instruments of torture."[43]

The problem was that the coalition switch could end up destroying the FDP rather than saving it. This was really a two-part dilemma. Firstly, the change could trigger a party split, similar to the breakaways that had followed the coalition rupture of 1956 or the reorientation of the late sixties. Progressive Liberals had already begun to turn their backs on the FDP, but it still harbored many pragmatic supporters of the Social-Liberal government as well as some idealists committed to the "historic alliance." The left and right wings were fairly evenly balanced on the party's executive, while the right wing greatly outnumbered the left within the parliamentary party after 1980. At the lower levels of the party organization, the picture was a mixed one. Center-left Liberals had long been more active in party work, but their enthusiasm began to lag noticeably after the 1980 Bundestag election. In some parts of the country, they lost control of a series of local organizations to newly participatory or recently recruited conservative Liberals. These events were a reversal of the social liberal takeover in the late sixties, but now as then the weaker faction held on to many positions. Genscher and Lambsdorff still received reminders that they did not enjoy undisputed authority. At the annual party conference in 1981, only about two-thirds of the delegates backed Genscher in supporting the NATO "two-track" decision, although he had turned the controversial issue of missile deployment into a question of confidence in his leadership. Lambsdorff normally carried majorities in favor of his economic arguments, but he often ran into strong verbal opposition from fellow Liberals. Some prominent members of the left wing, including Baum and Verheugen, regularly defended the alliance with the SPD. Although both men appear to have underestimated Genscher's determination, there were others who read the signs correctly.

The fatal weakness of the center-left wing turned out to be its inability to organize an intraparty opposition that went beyond occasional flights into publicity. In February 1982, for example, social liberals held a congress in Cologne to protest against the rightward drift of the FDP. They engaged in sharp reproaches of both leadership and the course of the party. While the participants probably reinforced their own ideological commitment in this public exercise, a major political effect appears to have been an alienation of many members in the parliamentary party, whose stand on the coalition issue would be crucial.

In addition to straining party unity, a coalition switch would court electoral disapproval, at least in the short run. Public reaction to a possible future event is a political question that can be explored but not settled by opinion polls. In the summer of 1981, the FDP commissioned a confidential, detailed survey intended to enlighten the leadership on this matter. If the ordering of such a study was indicative of restiveness less than a year after the Bundestag election, the polling results turned out to be Delphian. They could be used to support or oppose a change of coalition, as became clear when they were leaked to the press. While 77 percent of the FDP supporters polled in July 1981 spoke in favor of staying in Helmut Schmidt's government until the next scheduled election of 1984, only 56 percent described this as their "ideal coalition." Could it therefore be concluded that FDP voters attached great practical importance to the coalition commitment given a year earlier? Or was it safe to assume that unhappiness with the coalition had grown to such an extent that a switch, "properly" presented, would be widely accepted? The survey indicated that an election following such a change would result in losses of about one-third of the party's supporters (mostly to the SPD). However, this electoral exodus would be largely offset by gains of about one-fourth through new supporters (mostly from the CDU). In reporting on the already-leaked results, the party headquarters drew the wishful conclusion that the FDP now had a core of loyal supporters equal to about 6 percent of the electorate. To this should be added the many additional "coalition voters" who would support the FDP in alliance with one or the other Volkspartei.[44]

In reality, the FDP's solid core of voters was about half as large, or only around 3 percent of the electorate. That was the heart of the small party's chronic problem of political mortality. In terms of electoral arithmetic, it was possible that the FDP's losses of center-left coalition voters would not be offset in time by sufficient gains among center-right ones—in other words, an exact reversal of the process that had almost eliminated the party from the Bundestag in 1969.

In this connection, the timing of the election became a question of considerable tactical importance. A later survey, in March 1982, indicated that while almost three-fourths of the polled FDP supporters still favored a continuation of the alliance with the SPD until 1984, almost one-half (45 percent) now believed it would collapse before then. But an overwhelming majority (four-fifths) took the position that in such a case, an early election should *precede* the FDP's entry into a coalition with the CDU/CSU.[45] Clearly, the question of electoral legitimation would play a role in the public reaction to a government changeover, at least initially. Later, when the FDP made its "flying change" of partner, without a popular mandate, the small party had an obvious interest in delaying the follow-up election as long as possible.

Yet the political prospects appeared to be no less bleak from within the Social-Liberal coalition. Its victory in 1980 could be attributed largely to the Strauss effect. Thereafter, the governing problems in Bonn first took a heavy toll among SPD supporters. By the spring of 1982, Schmidt's party had sunk to its lowest point (hovering around 30 percent) since the early fifties. Support for the FDP had also begun to slip badly at that time. According to one poll in the summer of 1982, it had dropped to 5.3 percent, or only one-half of the small party's share of the vote less than two years earlier.[46] In state electoral politics, the decline appeared to be a negative trend which had been interrupted only temporarily by the special circumstances of the 1980 election. Here, the FDP had been eliminated from the parliaments of Hamburg and Lower Saxony in 1978, and from North Rhine–Westphalia in 1980. It managed to return to the Landtag in Lower Saxony in March 1982, but elections were to take place later that year in Hamburg, Hesse, and Bavaria. Further state elections were scheduled for 1983 in the Rhineland Palatinate, Schleswig-Holstein, and Bremen. In several of these upcoming contests, the FDP's prospects looked dismal.

The electoral problems of the Liberals had been intensified by the emergence of the Greens as an alternative for voters who were unhappy with the established parties. FDP strategists had recognized the "Green danger" early, but they downplayed its significance in public statements. Before the 1980 Bundestag election, polls and state elections had shown that the Greens had the potential of breaking down the three-party system or, worse yet, displacing the FDP as third party. The first prospect was fulfilled in the state elections of Bremen (1979), Baden-Württemberg (1980), West Berlin (1981), and Lower Saxony (1982), with the Greens outpolling the Liberals in the last two of these contests. The second and much grimmer prospect finally became reality in Hamburg on June 6, 1982. Here, the FDP failed to pass the 5 percent threshold for the second time in a row (it had barely missed in 1978), while the Greens not only became the new third party with 7.7 percent of the vote but also captured the balance of power between the Social and Christian Democrats.

The Liberals kept reminding whoever would listen that they had been the first party to have an environmental program (as part of the Freiburg Theses). Interior Minister Baum and the left wing could certainly be linked to ecological concerns, and these had held a prominent place in the 1980 election platform. But with the dominant economic wing's commitment to material values and the party's practical backing of industrial development strategies, the FDP was no match for the Greens among postmaterial, pacifist, and environmentally concerned voters. Instead, the occupation by the Greens of the far-left position on the political spectrum probably served indirectly to reinforce the rightward movement of the FDP—much as the presence of the nationalist NPD on the far right had affected the leftward shift of the Liberals in the mid-sixties and later.

After the June disaster in Hamburg, the election in Hesse on September 24, 1982, took on special significance. The state had been governed for the past 12 years by an SPD-FDP coalition, the last of its kind at the state level. Polls indicated that the CDU, which had captured a plurality already in 1978, had a good chance of winning a parliamentary majority this time. In the spring of 1982, the FDP in Hesse had pointedly declared its "equidistance" to the two big parties, and in mid-June it finally served notice that it would seek a coalition with the CDU in the new legislative period. The decision to renounce the Social-Liberal alliance was made by the state organization, based on fairly close votes in the executive committee (13 to 10 in favor) and a similar division at the party conference (169 to 129 in favor). With a few exceptions on the left wing, the FDP national leadership publicly endorsed the coalition move as a "decision for Hesse," emphasizing that this was the only way in which an absolute majority for the CDU might be prevented. In reality, Hesse was widely recognized as a dress rehearsal for Bonn.[47]

In the course of long and difficult negotiations in the summer of 1982, the Bonn coalition partners had reached agreement on yet another year's federal budget. Once again, however, the economic package was held together by overestimated government revenues that soon required adjustments in the form of more spending cuts or additional deficits. It was widely speculated that the FDP would use the attending conflicts as a reason for leaving the Schmidt government soon after the election in Hesse. Apart from the publicly displayed policy disagreements, a general justification for the shift could be provided by the argument that "governability" must be restored in Bonn. If the Christian Democrats won in Hesse, as anticipated, they would have a blocking two-thirds majority in the federal upper house (Bundesrat), where the members are appointed as representatives of the state governments. It could then be argued with some credibility that only a change of coalition in Bonn would resolve the potential deadlock of differently oriented majorities in the Bundestag and Bundesrat. The annual party conference in November would provide an appropriate forum for the Liberals to discuss and approve the breakaway.

While such a scenario provides a plausible explanation for Genscher's tactics, it is also clear that he played by ear and hesitated considerably in his various moves. In April-May 1982, two or three party strategists developed a game plan for the coalition change, but their specific proposals for minimizing the political costs within the electorate and the party were not followed.[48] In the end, Genscher was overtaken by events or, more precisely, by loss of the initiative to Chancellor Schmidt. Half a year earlier, in

February 1982, Helmut Schmidt had called for a vote of confidence in an attempt to tie wavering elements in both FDP and SPD closer to his government. It had been a stopgap measure at best. Now he decided to thwart Genscher's presumed time plan by forcing the FDP out of the coalition before the state election in Hesse. By casting the FDP as a disloyal partner, the chancellor could hope to rally his own party and mobilize support in the form of sympathy votes. Schmidt directly addressed the political ambivalence of the FDP during the parliamentary debate of September 9. Genscher, in turn, spoke darkly of the need for policy corrections. A few days later, Lambsdorff submitted an economic report to the chancellor in which he proposed drastic fiscal adjustments in the form of investment-oriented tax reforms and reductions of social spending. Although these proposals went considerably beyond anything the coalition partners had agreed upon, the document could have been treated as a "discussion paper." Instead, it served as a convenient casus belli to Schmidt, who had no interest in postponing the inevitable rupture. On September 17 he informed Genscher that the coalition had come to an end, whereupon the four FDP ministers turned in their resignations immediately.

On the same day, Genscher reported to his parliamentary party on the developments. He received an almost-two-thirds majority approval (33 votes to 18, with one abstention) for an immediate opening of coalition negotiations with the Christian Democrats. The national executive committee showed greater opposition (18 to 15 votes in favor of negotiations). Here, the call for a special party convention to make the final decision on the coalition issue was rejected by only one vote.[49]

In explaining the termination of the SDP-FDP alliance to the Bundestag on September 17, Chancellor Schmidt laid the responsibility squarely at the door of the small coalition partner. He urged the parties to make possible a dissolution of the Bundestag, through a simple vote of no confidence, so that an early general election could be held. There were obvious reasons why Christian Democrats and Liberals preferred to first replace Chancellor Schmidt with Helmut Kohl, through a constructive vote of no confidence, and then let the new government ask for popular legitimation at a later date. Schmidt's strategy would have benefited his own party by rallying its supporters and adding sympathy votes, while retaining for the SPD the so-called chancellor bonus or incumbency factor, with which a popular head of government can help his own party. Although many were upset, no one should therefore have been surprised when the Christian and Free Democrats moved quickly to negotiate a coalition agreement and install a government without an intervening election. Accordingly, Chancellor Schmidt was defeated in the Bundestag on October 1, 1982, by seven votes and replaced by Helmut Kohl.

Kohl's margin of victory was relatively thin. It is estimated that about two-thirds of the Liberals supported him in the secret vote, while one-third did not. From the intraparty discussions and public statements, it would appear that the division on the whole was a right-left one, with some individual exceptions. One of these was Hildegard Hamm-Brücher, who could not be counted to the "social liberal" wing in economic and fiscal questions. She gave a vigorous defense before the Bundestag of her decision to remain loyal to Chancellor Schmidt and the FDP's coalition commitment of 1980. (It is noteworthy that all but one of the eight women in the parliamentary party had opposed the coalition shift.) The only Liberal statement of the case for realignment came from Wolfgang Mischnick, the parliamentary leader of the FDP, who had served for years as conciliator between the divergent wings of the party. He reminded his listeners of the political achievements of the SPD-FDP coalition and acknowledged that he had only reluctantly come to the conclusion that a parting of the ways had been made necessary by unresolvable policy differences.

There followed a bitter feud within the FDP over the policy implications of the coalition switch, as well as the manner in which it had been carried out. It was possible to favor the more conservative course of a center-right government and yet be critical of what some called the leadership's *Putsch* from above. In its endorsement of the *fait accompli,* the party conference in Berlin from November 5 to 7 made some symbolic concessions to the latter criticism. While the resolution approved the majority decisions of the parliamentary party and executive committee to join the CDU/CSU in a new government, it disapproved of the "art and manner" in which the coalition agreement had been reached, without sufficient information or involvement of the party membership. It also censured both the refusal of the CDU/CSU to accept Gerhart Baum as a member of the FDP's negotiation team and the FDP's concession on this point. Finally, it stressed the importance of regaining the interior ministry for the FDP in any future cabinet reshuffle.[50] This last point referred to the replacement of Interior Minister Baum by Friedrich Zimmermann, a CSU politician renowned for his ultraconservative outlook. As compensation, the Liberals were given the politically less attractive ministry of justice, to which they appointed a member of the party's conservative faction, Hans Engelhard.

On personnel matters, the conference also made some conciliatory gestures, but the center-right wing clearly dominated the elections to various high party offices. A few outspoken adherents of the "social liberal" orientation were returned to the executive committee, and Baum received just one vote more than necessary to squeeze into one of the three deputy leaderships. The decisive contest resulted from the left wing's attempt to unseat Genscher. His rival for the party leadership was the moderate and integrative party leader from Schleswig-Holstein, Uwe Ronneburger. Genscher was reelected, but he gathered only 56 percent of the votes (against Ronneburger's 43 percent).

The atmosphere in Berlin was charged with bitterness and recriminations. Liberal party conferences normally produce vigorous debates, but here delegates indulged in taunts and other illiberal forms of acrimony— much of which did not enter the official record of the meeting.[51] Some of the dissidents resorted to dramatic gestures of powerlessness, including the presentation and withdrawal of critical motions (one example: "that the old pigtails must again be worn conspicuously . . .") and individual or group walkouts. The party's financial expert in the Bundestag, Ingrid Mattäus-Maier, delivered one of several political farewells to a mixed response of sympathy and scorn.

Günter Verheugen had resigned as secretary-general in protest over the coalition change. In Berlin he made a last futile attempt to win the conference for a set of "social-liberal" positions, drafted by him and others (including Baum) in the form of a Liberal Manifesto. A few weeks later he joined Matthäus-Maier in the SPD. Andreas von Schoeler, a prominent member of the parliamentary party who had been elected to the executive committee in Berlin, followed them. All three received SPD candidatures for the Bundestag election of 1983, and the first two were elected. About 2,000 dissidents took another route by forming a new party, the Liberal Democrats, at the end of November. It did not run candidates in the general election and has largely slipped from the public eye.[52]

THE BUNDESTAG ELECTION OF 1983

In the parliamentary debate about the impending change of government, Helmut Kohl had promised that his government would deal with only the most immediate problems facing the country, whereafter a new general election would be held in the spring of 1983.[53] His response to the widespread demand that the electorate be consulted represented a compromise between the wish of Strauss and the CSU to have an early election and the Liberal interest in a delay. Kohl thereupon arranged to lose a simple vote of confidence on December 17. Such a loss was a prerequisite for the early dissolution of the Bundestag, but here a clear majority in effect arranged to have itself voted out of office. Despite some reservations about this procedure, President Carstens decided to accept the outcome and dissolved the Bundestag on January 7, 1983. Some weeks later, the Federal Constitutional Court established the legality of these steps in a majority decision, clearing the way for the general election set for March 6, 1983. The parties had anticipated the decision and started their campaigns several weeks earlier.

There were a number of other unique aspects to the 1983 contest. It was the first "winter campaign" in federal politics, resulting in a cutback on outdoor political activities. Consequently, the media campaign played an even greater role than is already common in modern elections. There was relatively little time to plan and organize the contest, in contrast to the election of 1980, for which the FDP had begun preparing a year and a half in advance. The fact that this was the first Bundestag campaign to take place in the midst of a major recession explains why the overwhelming issue was economic strategy and competence rather than, as some had expected, the stationing of nuclear missiles in accordance with the "double-track" decision of NATO. Other differences resulted from the changed leaders, roles, or identities of the major competitors: Chancellor Kohl as leader of the governing CDU/CSU, Hans-Jochen Vogel as chancellor-candidate of the SPD opposition, a decimated and controversial FDP as pivotal force behind the political realignment, and the Greens as serious challenge to the three-party establishment.

The FDP had lost much blood in the political ruckus accompanying the transfer of power, and it began the campaign with the greatest handicap in its history. Even supporters of the center-right alliance had reservations about the manner in which the FDP had changed sides. Some media organs did not suppress their *Schadenfreude* in reporting on the miserable condition of the small party. Such erstwhile supporters as the weekly magazines *Stern* and *Der Spiegel* were particularly scornful toward Genscher. This was partly offset by a new appreciation of the FDP's constructive political and economic role, shown by such conservative newspapers as *Die Welt* and the *Frankfurter Allgemeine Zeitung;* but overall the Liberals had a poor press.[54] A standard joke translated the party's official abbreviation, FDP, to *"Fast Drei Prozent,"* or "almost 3 percent." Public opinion surveys and state elections confirmed that the party's support had plummeted. A poll taken right after the coalition collapse on September 17 registered only 2.3 percent for the FDP, and the Liberals received 3.1 percent in Hesse on September 26 (against 6 percent in 1978). Here, the Greens (with 8 percent) replaced them as third party and balancer between the CDU and SPD. In October, the FDP was also eliminated from the Landtag in Bavaria (with 3.5 percent). And in December, the Liberals failed for the third consecutive time to reenter the parliament in the city-state of Hamburg (2.6 percent), from which it had been absent since 1978. Here, the Greens, newly elected in June, had held the balance of power but had refused to play the role of coalition partner, so that new elections were called to break a parliamentary deadlock. While the FDP received uniformly disastrous results in these state elections, Schmidt's strategy of blaming the Liberals appeared to help the SPD, at least in the short run. It was returned as minority government party in Hesse and received an absolute majority in Hamburg.

The political scene abounded with reminders of the FDP's electoral mortality. A number of pundits wrote early obituaries on the small party, raising the important question of how the disappearance of the Liberals would affect West German politics. One realistic possibility was the emergence of a clear parliamentary majority of the CDU/CSU, as between 1957 and 1961. Yet polls indicated that most Christian Democratic voters agreed with Helmut Kohl in preferring a coalition of their party with the FDP to the prospect of single-party rule.[55] There was less reason to anticipate an SPD majority, even though the party recovered much lost ground in the first polls after the fall of Schmidt's government. It seemed possible, however, that the Greens might capture the balance of power in the Bundestag. The result could be either a stalemate similar to the one in Hamburg between June and December 1982 or, if the Greens should modify their abhorrence of coalition politics, a "red-green" alliance in Bonn. Some Free Democrats with long memories considered still another scenario, remote though it seemed: Should it become impossible to build a working majority in any other way, the Christian and Social Democrats might eventually come together in another great coalition. Liberals were not alone in finding all of these prospects unattractive, and this made it simple for the FDP to resort to its functional argument: German government must continue to operate with the FDP as a moderating, balancing third force between the two mass parties, ensuring both governability and controllability in Bonn. The small party's main slogan, "Germany needs the liberals," vaguely suggested this theme. It was made more explicit in longer electoral messages.

In terms of electoral arithmetic, the political fate of the FDP depended upon whether it could convince enough supporters of a center-right coalition that a vote for the Liberals would not be wasted. Polls showed that about two-thirds of the CDU/CSU supporters preferred a coalition with the

FDP to a government by their party alone.[56] The small party's electoral strategy concentrated on this factor from beginning to end. In all recent elections, the FDP has made a special pitch for the crucial second vote (the party vote which determines parliamentary strength). This time, however, it relied on such appeals even more than in 1972, when "borrowed" votes from SPD supporters had revived the FDP. In verbal and pictorial messages, the Liberals now directed themselves primarily to CDU/CSU supporters with appeals for the second vote of a "split ticket."

There was some initial disagreement among the small group of Liberal campaign planners in Bonn over whether their party should attempt to counter the SPD's charges of betrayal. In effect, some wanted to reverse the argument and show that the Social Democrats had strayed from the common ground of the coalition and thus brought the end on themselves. Others found this theme too defensive, and a somewhat different emphasis prevailed in which the FDP took credit for having put a stop to the governing crisis in Bonn. The campaign propaganda underscored that the small party had shown courage in pursuing a difficult but necessary political course. This theme was echoed in the FDP's second major slogan, "Freiheit braucht Mut" (Freedom requires Courage).

In order to gain publicity in a relatively economical way, FDP strategists hit upon the idea of having the party's leading politicians (including all members of the presidium) travel together on a "campaign train" between 27 cities and towns from January 10 to 18, 1983. Many journalists came aboard at one time or another, and the local and regional press reported widely on the activities of the traveling Liberals. During the week, individual members of the leadership group took prominent parts in 270 campaign meetings organized along the way by federal and local party workers. In later interviews, participants agreed that the overall political impact had been very positive for the FDP. The extended train journey had caught media attention and given a semblance of party unity. It had also motivated the local organizations to at least some political activity.

Another *novum* was the adoption of the American technique of direct mailing. It differed from the older practice (still used in 1983) of encouraging party activists to order and mail a standard letter directed either to young or older voters. The new campaign took the form of two messages drafted especially for propertied middle-class voters such as lawyers, doctors, taxi owners, and other small entrepreneurs. Using occupation lists acquired for this purpose, the party sent such individually addressed target letters to 500,000 persons. The first mailing, sent to arrive in the first part of February, emphasized the FDP's crucial role in guaranteeing that "the train keeps running in the right direction." The follow-up letter, sent 14 days later, asked directly for the second vote and emphasized that only a coalition of FDP and CDU/CSU could protect "the interests of the middle class" (Mittelstand). Both letters were signed by Dr. Irmgard Adam-Schwaetzer, the party's new secretary-general, who played a prominent media role in the campaign.

To an even greater extent than in 1980, the FDP also carried its middle-class appeal into homeowners' magazines as well as special trade and professional journals. The uniformly drafted advertisements all consisted of two glib messages, designed by the federal campaign planners. First came a short statement identifying the FDP with a sound and solid policy stand, usually on economic matters but sometimes on other issues, including defense, civil liberties, or social security. There were more than 30 versions of this part of the commercial, geared to slightly different readerships. It led directly into a more general political message introduced and interlaced with the main campaign slogan. Here, the FDP warned that "the CDU cannot make it alone" and pointed to the danger of a single-party government by the SPD or a "red-green" alliance. (However, one version also mentioned the FDP's opposition to single-party government by the Christian Unionists.) The short statement closely resembled those carried in the party's electronic media messages. Readers and viewers were urged to "take heart" and use "common sense" by casting their second vote for the FDP, "so that the new federal government can continue its work after March 6." The FDP always ended this version of the functional argument with a reminder of its special role in the party system: "Germany needs the Liberals so that the two sluggish power blocs of the Left and Right will continue to have the Liberal force of the center between them."

While the FDP thus promoted itself as both watchdog and pacemaker, it reflected the course change by giving special emphasis to the alliance with the CDU/CSU and its own special defense of middle-class interests. In some ways, the new alignment resembled the "bourgeois bloc" of the early postwar years. With Lambsdorff, the "Erhard of the Eighties," the FDP extolled the virtues of private enterprise and economic realism. It warned against socialist experiments and appeared less hesitant than the Christian Democrats to suggest the need for prudent cuts in the social budget. Characteristically, the one issue on which the CDU and FDP clashed most visibly concerned the future repayment of a compulsory loan, imposed by the government on high earnings to help reduce the fiscal deficit. In taking the position that the loan, though compulsory, was not a surcharge tax and must be paid back later, the Liberals represented the special interest of high-income voters, among whom the FDP draws a disproportionate share of its support. As in 1980, the Free Democrats organized a special Mittelstand convention a few weeks before the election, at which they drew attention to their own proposals for reducing the tax and regulatory burdens placed upon the business sector.

At the end of January, the FDP held its election convention in Freiburg. Compared to the Berlin conference in November, this was a harmonious event with most delegates eager to display party unity. More than 90 percent approved a resolution to continue the coalition with the CDU/CSU after the election in March. Yet a two-thirds majority also gave expression to the lingering unease over the manner in which the changeover had taken place: It changed the bylaws to require that a party conference must give prior endorsement to future coalition agreements. The Free Democrats also sought to reclaim their liberal image by adopting or renewing their commitment to several positions on civil liberties that went against the grain of many stalwart Christian Democrats. These included demands to give constitutional protection against the abuse of data collections on citizens, to abolish the conscience test for persons who object to military service, to extend social recognition to "new forms of cohabitation," to oppose further limits on the right to political demonstration, to reduce no further the age at which foreign workers' children may join their parents and obtain residence rights in Germany, and to eliminate a minor vestige of the criminal code's prohibition of homosexual activity.[57]

In the new law-and-order emphasis represented in the cabinet by Interior Minister Zimmermann, such liberal positions had little chance of being adopted, even if Free Democratic ministers had been willing to press for them. The demands served to salve the Liberal conscience and symbolize the small party's claim to curb the clerical- or statist-conservative elements on the right. One of the motions at the conference would have had a similar function: It was directed against Franz-Josef Strauss, whose inclusion in the cabinet after the election was feared by many liberally oriented voters. The FDP leadership managed to have the motion withdrawn without discussion by pointing out that it would serve only as a political provocation to the new coalition partner. At most, the Strauss factor played a tacit role in the FDP's self-promotions of 1983, as when the party stressed that Genscher would guarantee continuity in foreign policy and Lambsdorff would do the same for economic matters. The CSU leader was widely thought to desire either of these cabinet posts.

Campaign planners and activists later remembered an improvement in party spirit and public sympathy toward the Liberals a few weeks after the turn of the year. While it is necessary to allow for the foibles of memory and perception, such a shift does indeed appear to have taken place. It was reflected in the party convention at Freiburg and in the polls of late January and early February. By the second half of February, the positive trend appeared to have stabilized, and political insiders seemed fairly certain that the FDP would be returned to the Bundestag. News stories to this effect probably reinforced some "soft" or tentative support for the small party. On March 6, the FDP received 7 percent of the second vote. This was one-third less than in 1980 but far more than many had believed possible only a few weeks earlier. Moreover, the election guaranteed the continuation of coalition politics, when the CDU/CSU received 48.8 percent of the vote and 244 of the 498 seats, or six short of a majority.

There were few changes in Helmut Kohl's government, but one of them reduced further the FDP's weight in the cabinet. It retained the ministries of foreign affairs, economics, and justice but lost the ministry of food and agriculture, held since 1969 by Josef Ertl. The interior ministry continued to be headed by Zimmermann, but Franz-Josef Strauss did not join the cabinet as minister of foreign affairs or economics. Here, the FDP once again functioned as a buffer, for Kohl would have had a difficult time keeping his Bavarian rival at arm's length without the Liberal claim to these key ministries. It had been generally known before the election that Kohl preferred to receive less than a parliamentary majority for the Christian Unionists, making a coalition with the Free Democrats necessary. Both he and Genscher got what they wanted.

CONCLUSION

The victory against heavy odds in the Bundestag election of 1983 has given the small party another lease on life in federal politics. It provides no long-term guarantee of political survival and influence. At best, the FDP appears to be headed for some more lean years, in which it will be plagued by electoral vulnerability and membership weakness, loss of pivotal status and reduced influence as kingmaker, absence from many state legislatures and even more state governments, shortages of effective leadership at all levels, chronic scarcity of organizational (including financial) resources, and confusion about its identity and role in a more unstable, changing party system. The FDP will be dependent, to a considerable degree, on developments in the larger polity that are beyond its control. Its energies will be largely consumed by the exigencies of daily politics, including the tasks of cogoverning in Bonn and preparing for the never ending electoral bouts at the state and local level, staggered between the Bundestag contents. Under these difficult circumstances, the party motor will probably be kept running through "patch-up" repairs rather than a major overhaul. It will be a major accomplishment if the FDP can perform somewhere between its minimum organizational goal of political survival—or resurrection, in many places—and its maximum goal of political stabilization and increased influence at all levels of local, state, and federal government.

Even a cursory examination of the Bundestag election results indicates that the party is in difficult straits. The FDP's own analysis, presented to its executive committee, acknowledged that the relative success of March 1983 had depended more than ever on capturing supporters among the volatile situational voters, this time, primarily among CDU- and CSU-oriented ones. The report estimated that only about one-third of the FDP's voters from 1980 remained with the party two-and-a-half years later.[58] Furthermore, its supporters of 1983 showed a markedly weaker identification with the Liberal party than had their counterparts in 1980. One very rough measure of this development would be the first vote, where the FDP sank to its lowest point ever (2.8 percent), resulting in the greatest discrepancy between the first and second votes cast for the party in the history of the Federal Republic. Of the FDP's supporters on the second vote, 58.3 percent had cast their first vote for a CDU or CSU candidate, 10.1 percent for a Social Democrat, and only 29.1 percent for a Free Democrat. The other Bundestag parties, including the Greens, had much lower rates of ticket splitting among their supporters (see Tables 6.3 and 6.4).

If any reminder of political mortality had been needed, it was provided by the results of the Landtag contest in the Rhinland-Palatinate on the same day as the Bundestag election. (Such a coincidence of federal and state elections was itself another *novum* in West German politics). Here, 3.5 percent had voted for the FDP on the Landtag ballot—or only slightly more than the 3.2 percent who had cast their first vote for the Liberal candidates on the Bundestag ballot. Sharp on the heels of this defeat came another disaster, this time in Schleswig-Holstein. In the northernmost state only 2.1 percent had supported FDP candidates with their first vote on March 6, and the Liberals received almost the same result in the Landtag election two weeks later (2.2 percent as against 5.7 percent in 1979). Political observers had looked upon this contest as something of a test case for the "social liberal" wing of the FDP, as personified by Uwe Ronneburger, the state's party leader. In the end, Schleswig-Holstein's FDP appears to have had the worst of both worlds: Its commitment to seek a coalition gov-

Table 6.4. First and Second-Ballot Results for the Parties, 1953–83 (in percentages)

	1953	1957	1961	1965	1969	1972	1976	1980	1983
CDU/CSU									
First ballot	43.7	50.3	46.0	48.8	46.6	45.4	48.9	46.0	52.6
Second ballot	45.2	50.2	45.3	47.6	46.1	44.9	48.6	44.5	48.8
Difference	-1.5	+0.1	+0.7	+1.2	+0.5	+0.5	+0.3	+1.5	+3.8
SPD									
First ballot	29.5	32.0	36.5	40.1	44.0	48.9	43.7	44.5	40.4
Second ballot	28.8	31.8	36.2	39.3	42.7	45.8	42.6	42.9	38.2
Difference	+0.7	+0.2	+0.3	+0.8	+1.3	+3.1	+1.1	+1.6	+2.2
FDP									
First ballot	10.8	7.5	12.1	7.9	4.8	4.8	6.4	7.2	2.8
Second ballot	9.5	7.7	12.8	9.5	5.8	8.4	7.9	10.6	7.0
Difference	+1.3	-0.2	-0.7	-1.6	-1.0	-3.6	-1.5	-3.4	-4.2
Greens									
First ballot	—*	—	—	—	—	—	—	1.9	4.1
Second ballot	—	—	—	—	—	—	—	1.5	5.6
Difference								+0.4	-1.5

*Not applicable.

Sources: Statistisches Bundesamt, *Wahl zum 9. Deutschen Bundestag am 5. Oktober 1980, Heft 1, Ergebnisse früherer Bundestags- und Landtagswahlen* (Stuttgart: Kohlhammer, 1980), Tables 1.9 to 1.14, pp. 14–19; *Wahl zum 10. Deutschen Bundestag am 6. März 1983, Heft 3, Endgültige Ergebnisse nach Wahlkreisen* (Stuttgart: Kohlhammer, 1983), Tables 1.1, 1.2, pp. 6, 7.

ernment with the SPD in Kiel could not keep voters with a center-left orientation from leaving Genscher's party in droves, but it was more than enough to scare away potential CDU-leaning coalition voters.

After having been eliminated from these two parliaments, the FDP was no longer represented in six of the eleven state legislatures. In September of 1983, it also fell victim to the 5 percent clause in Bremen, where the left wing had maintained another outpost. The SPD managed to win an absolute majority on its own in this city-state, while the FDP plummeted from 10.7 percent in 1979 to 4.7 percent. On the same day, however, the FDP gained reentry to the Landtag in Hesse by winning 7.6 percent of the popular vote there, against its disastrous result of 3.1 percent a year earlier right after the collapse of the Schmidt-Genscher coalition in Bonn. The Hesse Landtag had been dissolved and an early election called in an attempt to break a parliamentary deadlock. The situation was similar to the one that had developed in 1982, when the Greens in Hamburg balked at giving coalition support to an SPD-minority government.

Instead of resolving the stalemate by creating a parliamentary majority, as a new election in Hamburg had done, the results in Hesse served to underscore further some of the hazards of majority building peculiar to the new three-to-four-party system that has been emerging in West Germany. In the hope of making a center-right majority in Wiesbaden possible, the CDU leadership in Hesse had openly encouraged some Liberal poaching of Christian Democratic supporters. The strategy backfired when the FDP's dramatic resurgence was more than offset by losses for the CDU. With only 39.4 percent of the state's popular vote, the CDU had to yield the position of largest party in the Landtag to the SPD (46.2 percent). If there had been no constraints on its role as balancer, the FDP could now have formed a new majority coalition with the SPD in Hesse, as it had from 1970 to 1982. But the Liberal commitment to an alliance with the CDU in state government could not be shrugged off after the election, given the dramatic circumstances of the realignment a year earlier and its reaffirmation in the recent campaign. In view of the Green abhorrence of coalition politics, the SPD continued in office as minority government. Before the end of the year, there were indications that the CDU had become interested in forming a great coalition with the SPD in Wiesbaden, but the Greens stole the initiative by finally agreeing to a working arrangement with the Social Democrats. The result was a "red-green" parliamentary coalition in support of key legislation. Even this limited concession to conventional politics has aroused the ire of such leading Greens as Petra Kelly, who oppose coalition politics on principle. At stake is a central element in the new party's anti-establishment character: Should it make political alliances with other parties and thereby risk becoming something of a left-wing functional rival or substitute for the FDP as majority maker? The issue is of crucial importance not only to the Greens and Liberals; it has ramifications for the large parties and the governmental process in West Germany as well.

At the beginning of 1984, the FDP was present in only five of the eleven state legislatures: The Saar, West Berlin, Baden-Württemberg, Lower Saxony, and Hesse. It was still junior government partner of the CDU in the first two (and least populous) of these states, while it occupied a handful of opposition seats in the last three. This means that about two of every five West Germans now lived in states that have some Liberals in the Landtag, but only one in twenty had a state government in which the FDP occupied any ministries. Twenty years earlier, it had been a member of cabinet coalitions in nine of the eleven states and was represented in all the parliaments. At the local government level, the picture is varied but rarely encouraging.[59]

This is a dismal situation for a party that in the past drew much of its political importance from membership in cabinet coalitions, including those at the state level of government. In each of the six states where it no longer has parliamentary representation, the FDP tried to remain politically visible through the public pronouncements and other activities of a "parliamentary work group" in the state capital. Absence from the Landtag is a major handicap. Media coverage of the small party becomes spotty, political recruitment suffers, and organizational resources dry up. The federal party must consequently step in to assist with many promotional burdens that the state organizations can no longer carry by themselves, especially at election time. That, in turn, is a heavy drain on the federal organization's resources, as its latest business report discretely complains.[60] Heavy federal campaign debts from 1983 have already enfeebled the party and led to a considerable pruning among its headquarter staff in Bonn. The resource problem is compounded by the fact that private contributions to the FDP have slowed down in the wake of judicial investigations of some dubious financing practices, highlighted by the so-called Flick affair. Near the end of 1983, after many months of investigation and numerous press leaks, federal prosecutors finally indicted several leading Free Democrats, including Minister Lambsdorff.

The electoral debility of the Liberals in state politics is far more serious than in the early seventies, when the FDP also suffered heavy setbacks after a major change of course. At that time it was eliminated from three parliaments (Lower Saxony, Schleswig-Holstein, and the Saar), but in each case it managed to rebound in the following election. Now the FDP is excluded from twice as many state parliaments (see Tables 6.5 and 6.6).

Table 6.5. The FDP's Record as Government and Opposition Party (until August 1984)

Land	In Government Coalition with Large Parties			In Opposition	Without Representation
	With CDU and/or CSU	With SPD	With CDU & SPD		
(Baden)	—a	—	Dec. 46/June 47	June 47/Apr. 52	—
(Württemberg-Baden)	—	Jan. 51/Apr. 52	Sept. 45/Jan. 51	—	—
(Württemberg-Hohenzollern)	—	—	July 47/Apr. 52	—	—
Baden-Württemberg	June 60/Dec. 66	Apr. 52/Oct. 53	Oct. 53/June 60	Dec. 66/today	
Bavaria	Oct. 57/Dec. 62	Dec. 54/Oct. 57	—	Oct. 45/Dec. 54 Dec. 62/Nov. 66 Nov. 70/Oct. 82	Nov. 66/Nov. 70 Oct. 82/today
Bremen	—	June 45/Nov. 51 Dec. 59/June 71	Nov. 51/Dec. 59	June 71/Sept. 83	Sept. 83/today
Hamburg	Dec. 53/Dec. 57	Nov. 46/Feb. 50 Dec. 57/Apr. 66 Apr. 70/June 78	Aug. 45/Nov. 46	Feb. 50/Dec. 53 Apr. 66/Apr. 70	June 78/today
Hesse	—	Dec. 70/Sept. 82	Oct. 45/Jan. 47	Jan. 47/Dec. 70 Sept. 83/today	Sept. 82/Sept. 83
Lower Saxony	May 55/Nov. 57 Jan. 77/June 78	May 59/May 65 June 74/Jan. 76	Nov. 46/Jan. 48	Jan. 48/May 55 Nov. 57/May 59 May 65/June 70 Jan. 76/Dec. 76 Mar. 82/today	June 70/June 74 June 78/Mar. 82

166

North Rhine–Westphalia	July 54/Feb. 56 July 62/Dec. 66	Aug. 46/Dec. 46 Feb. 56/July 58 Dec. 66/May 80	Dec. 47/June 47	June 47/July 54 July 58/July 62	May 80/today
Rhineland–Palatinate	June 51/May 71	—	July 47/Apr. 48	Dec. 46/July 47 Apr. 48/June 51 May 71/Mar. 83	Mar. 83/today
The Saar	Jan. 61/June 70 Mar. 77/today	—	Jan. 56/Dec. 56 June 57/Feb. 59	Dec. 56/June 57 Feb. 59/Jan. 61 May 75/Mar. 77	June 70/May 75
Schleswig-Holstein	Sept. 50/Jan. 52 Oct. 54/Feb. 71	—	—	Aug. 46/Apr. 47 Jan. 52/Oct. 54 Feb. 71/Apr. 71 Apr. 75/Mar. 83	Apr. 47/Sept. 50 Apr. 71/Apr. 75 Mar. 83/today
West Berlin	Oct. 53/Jan. 55 Mar. 83/today[b]	Mar. 63/Apr. 71 Apr. 75/June 81	Jan. 49/Oct. 53	Jan. 55/Dec. 58 Apr. 71/Apr. 75 June 81/Mar. 83	Dec. 58/Mar. 63
Federal Republic	Sept. 49/Feb. 56 Nov. 61/Oct. 66 Oct. 82/today	Oct. 69/Sept. 82	—	Feb. 56/Nov. 61 Oct. 66/Oct. 69	—

[a]Not applicable.

[b]The SPD-FDP government coalition in West Berlin left office in June 1981, after its defeat in the election of May. Members of the FDP in West Berlin's House of Representatives gave the new CDU-minority government parliamentary support from its inception in June 1981 (the so-called *Tolerierungspolitik*). In March 1983, soon after the Bundestag election, the FDP finally entered a cabinet coalition with the CDU in West Berlin.

Sources: Heino Kaack, *Die F.D.P.*, third edition (Meisenheim am Glan: Anton Hain Verlag, 1979), Table 3, p. 32: *Zeitschrift für Parlamentsfragen*, 1979–1984; *Die neue Bonner Depesche*, 1979–1984; Information from the Thomas Dehler House (the federal headquarters of the FDP), 1983 and 1984.

Table 6.6. The FDP as Government and Opposition Party in Bonn and the Länder since September 1949

| Date | Federal Government | Number of Länder or States | Länder with FDP in Cabinet Coalitions with Large Parties | | | | Länder with FDP in Parliamentary Opposition | Länder with No Parliamentary Representation of FDP |
			Total	With CDU or CSU	With CDU and SPD	With SPD		
Sept. 1949	Coal. with CDU/CSU	12	5	—*	3	2	6	1
31 Dec. 50	Coal. with CDU/CSU	12	5	1	3	1	7	—
31 Dec. 51	Coal. with CDU/CSU	12	6	2	3	1	6	—
31 Dec. 52	Coal. with CDU/CSU	10	4	1	2	1	6	—
31 Dec. 53	Coal. with CDU/CSU	10	5	3	2	—	5	—
31 Dec. 54	Coal. with CDU/CSU	10	8	5	2	1	2	—
31 Dec. 55	Coal. with CDU/CSU	10	8	5	2	1	2	—
31 Dec. 56	In parl. opposition	11	8	4	2	2	3	—
31 Dec. 57	In parl. opposition	11	8	3	3	2	3	—
31 Dec. 58	In parl. opposition	11	7	3	3	1	3	1
31 Dec. 59	In parl. opposition	11	7	3	1	3	3	1
31 Dec. 60	In parl. opposition	11	7	4	—	3	3	1

Date	Status							
31 Dec. 61	Coal. with CDU/CSU	11	8	5	—	3	2	1
31 Dec. 62	Coal. with CDU/CSU	11	8	5	—	3	2	1
31 Dec. 63	Coal. with CDU/CSU	11	9	5	—	4	2	—
31 Dec. 64	Coal. with CDU/CSU	11	9	5	—	4	2	—
31 Dec. 65	Coal. with CDU/CSU	11	8	5	—	3	3	1
31 Dec. 66	In parl. opposition	11	6	3	—	3	4	1
31 Dec. 67	In parl. opposition	11	6	3	—	3	4	1
31 Dec. 68	In parl. opposition	11	6	3	—	3	4	1
31 Dec. 69	Coal. with SPD	11	6	3	—	3	4	1
31 Dec. 70	Coal. with SPD	11	7	2	—	5	2	2
31 Dec. 71	Coal. with SPD	11	3	—	—	3	5	3
31 Dec. 72	Coal. with SPD	11	3	—	—	3	5	3
31 Dec. 73	Coal. with SPD	11	3	—	—	3	5	3
31 Dec. 74	Coal. with SPD	11	4	—	—	4	5	2
31 Dec. 75	Coal. with SPD	11	5	—	—	5	6	—
31 Dec. 76	Coal. with SPD	11	4	—	—	4	7	—
31 Dec. 77	Coal. with SPD	11	6	2	—	4	5	—
31 Dec. 78	Coal. with SPD	11	4	1	—	3	5	2
31 Dec. 79	Coal. with SPD	11	4	1	—	3	5	2
31 Dec. 80	Coal. with SPD	11	3	1	—	2	5	3
31 Dec. 81	Coal. with SPD	11	2	1	—	1	6	3
31 Dec. 82	Coal. with CDU/CSU	11	1	1	—	—	6	4
31 Dec. 83	Coal. with CDU/CSU	11	2	2	—	—	3	6

*Not applicable.

Sources: The table has been adapted from one developed by Heino Kaack, "Der Juniorpartner," in *Probleme von Koalitionsregierungen in Westeuropa* (Bonn: Liberal-Verlag GmbH, 1978), p. 69. For more recent data: Heino Kaack, *Die F.D.P.*, 3rd ed. (Meisenheim am Glan: Verlag Anton Hain, 1979); *Die neue Bonner Depesche*, 1979–1984; *Zeitschrift für Parlamentsfragen*, 1979–1984; information from the Thomas Dehler House FDP (federal headquarters), 1983 and 1984.

For reasons of political credibility and recruitment, among others, the FDP must keep searching for ways to restore its presence in state politics. Here, its attempt to add floating voters to its slim core of loyal supporters runs into three major problems. In line with its new alignment, the FDP has sought to attract CDU-oriented backers of a center-right coalition, except in the few cases where the "social liberal" faction remained dominant until recently. But the weak starting position of the FDP, underscored by low standings in the polls and loss of parliamentary representation in many states, makes it difficult to attract such potential supporters. They are likely to be moved by pragmatic considerations and know that a vote for the small party may be "wasted." The law of self-fulfilling expectations goes into effect.

In addition, the functional argument for coalition government, used so effectively by the FDP in federal politics, appears to carry much less weight at the state level. Here, government by a single party has become the norm and cabinet coalitions are now an exception (see Tables 6.5 and 6.6). In early 1984, nine of the eleven states were headed by single-party governments, and all but one of these (Hesse) were backed by one-party majorities in Parliament. Only two had coalition cabinets, as mentioned earlier. Voters appear to accept the new dispensation without serious misgivings. The conclusion that the *horror majoritatis* may be weaker in state politics than at the federal level seems to be supported by the special form of ticket splitting that took place in the Rhineland-Palatinate on March 6, 1983: Here, the voters gave the FDP 7.0 percent of the second vote for the Bundestag but only 3.5 percent of the vote for the Landtag, where the CDU has held a governing majority since 1971.

The last example also points to the third problem that confronts the FDP in Landtag elections: the impossibility of waging a campaign for the second vote. With only one vote for the state parliament, there is no way to distribute one's support between two parties. The Liberals have long benefited from this possibility in federal politics, and in 1983 they were dependent upon it for survival: Without a second-vote strategy, they would probably have been eliminated from the Bundestag. Conversely, the small party would do better in state elections if it could appeal for second votes there. This conclusion is supported by the results of the Bundestag and Landtag elections in both the Rhineland-Palatinate and Schleswig-Holstein in March 1983. The small party's supporters at the two levels of government were not completely identical, of course, but it is not a coincidence that its Landtag vote in each case was very close to its first vote for the Bundestag, while its second vote was twice as high in the Rhineland-Palatinate and three times as high in Schleswig-Holstein.

The weakness of the FDP's membership organization has often been linked to its feeble electoral condition. At the 1977 party conference in Kiel, Günter Verheugen described the relationship as a vicious circle: "We have bad election results because we have no organization, and we have no organization because we have bad election results."[61] As secretary-general, he attempted to invigorate the FDP by promoting the political schooling and participation of its members and strengthening the local network (the party base) in a major membership drive. On the whole, his ambitious plans for party reform were predestined for failure because they presupposed a political thrust of which the FDP was simply not capable: The vicious circle operated at this level as well. In any case, daily administrative tasks and the pressures of crisis management soon took precedence over party reform.

There were some exceptions. The schooling of Liberal activists in party work improved markedly under Verheugen's stewardship. And the membership figures, which had risen sharply after the consolidation of the Social-Liberal coalition in the early seventies, continued to improve, although at a markedly slower pace. They rose from a low point of 53,000 in 1971 to more than 87,000 in November 1981. Thereafter a reversal set in, and membership declined slowly at first, but continuously. The number of defections grew rapidly after the spring of 1982 when the change of coalition became imminent. By November 1982, the official count showed 81,000. This total reflected gains and losses until the late summer, when the Social-Liberal partners had clashed over the budget and the FDP in Hesse had announced its shift to the right. However, there is a time lag of several weeks in the recording of membership changes. Therefore the November 1982 tally did not take into account the waves of defections that followed the collapse of the Schmidt-Genscher coalition, the building of the Kohl-Genscher cabinet, and the victory of the center-right forces at the Berlin party conference. Before the March election, the total membership had dipped below 73,000, but the party was now referring to the losses in only very general terms that understated them by about one-half. Moreover, the net figures obscured the total in-and-out movement of party members: The total loss between November 1981 and March 1983 came close to 20,000 members, offset by a gain of some 6,000 new ones. In early 1984, when the situation appeared to have stabilized, party headquarters finally acknowledged that membership was "barely 70,000."[62]

The party's recent self-study report emphasizes that there are a number of reasons for the high membership losses, including some nonpolitical ones. Although it attempts to put its best foot forward in public, party headquarters recognizes that many valuable members have left as a result of the change of course, or the manner in which the realignment took place. A situational analysis prepared for the 1983 campaign strategists candidly described the recent defectors as "preponderantly active members—ones who have often been schooled as party workers and who have a long experience in the party organization." The newcomers, on the other hand, were "people who, on the basis of their occupational background are probably more preoccupied with their professions and less inclined to have time for party work."[63] It is not surprising that the 1983 campaign required little membership involvement, in contrast to Verheugen's participatory emphasis in 1980. Over one-half of the membership (54.7 percent) was classified as altogether "inactive" in the recent self-study, while another fifth (20.3 percent) showed up as "rarely active" (*wenig aktive*). Thus the "very active" (10.5 percent) and "active" (14.5 percent) members constituted one-quarter of a greatly diminished membership.[64]

Members and supporters of the FDP have always had a higher overall social, economic, and educational status than their counterparts in the CDU/CSU and SPD. The new self-study report gingerly suggests that there is a growing structural homogenization of the FDP as electoral and membership party: "Somewhat exaggerated [*Überpointiert*], it is possible to say that the FDP is in the process of developing a clearly recognizable socio-demographic center." The new members are predominantly drawn from the Mittelstand, both old and new, with the self-employed and independent professions (old middle class) increasing their share more rapidly than leading members of the administrative (new middle) class, while the percentage of students (and young people generally) has fallen markedly. Similarly, the party's supporters in the 1983 Bundestag election were drawn even more heavily than in recent years from these occupational groups. The report concludes that there are both risks and opportunities for the FDP in its growing identification with the upper middle class, whose members show a "readiness and ability to consider their own group-specific interests" when voting.[65]

The rightward shift has left its marks throughout the party. It is reflected in many leadership changes at the state and local level in 1982 and 1983. Even where the new leaders may not themselves be particularly conservative in their understanding of political liberalism, they and other members have accepted the coalition change and work within the new political setting. The party's 34 Bundestag members include only 8 of the 20 who opposed the coalition change in 1982.[66] The old youth organization, the Young Democrats (*Judos*), which had long exasperated the mother party with its radical postures, left the FDP in disgust after the Berlin conference, before being officially disowned. Its place was quickly taken by a better-groomed, well-behaved youth group, the Young Liberals (*Julis*), who had been waiting in the wings. They are still few in number, with a membership of almost 2,300 by the end of 1983. At the electoral level, three-quarters of the party's supporters in 1983 indicated a preference for the alliance of FDP and CDU/CSU, just as three-quarters had preferred a coalition with the SPD three years earlier.[67] Most of these were newcomers, of course, so that the change in orientation really reflects a turnover among the party's supporters.

These trends in leadership, membership, and electorate have conservative policy implications for the FDP, especially in economic and fiscal matters. Yet it would be a mistake to assume that the reform and civil libertarian elements in the party have been lost completely. Throughout the FDP one still encounters members who have been attracted to the party as a progressive force in West German politics. Close to a third (31.4 percent) of the party's more than 300 county leaders classified themselves as left-of-center on a general left-right scale in late 1983, while about one-quarter (25.4 percent) took a position right-of-center—with the left-oriented group tending further away from the center than the right one.[68] Considerable caution is necessary in interpreting these results, however, for it is likely that a scale for economic issues and another one for cultural matters would produce very different weightings. It is fair to surmise that the self-perceived left-of-center placement often reflects a secular, civil libertarian orientation which sees Christian Democratic positions as decidedly conservative. This outlook can easily coexist with laissez-faire views on economic matters, compared to which the CDU is relatively "social."

Many left Liberals participate in informal discussion rounds, so that something of a supportive network has been maintained. They are well represented in the theoretical organ *Liberal*. Among the prominent Free Democrats, they include Gerhart Baum, Hildegard Hamm-Brücher, Uwe Ronneburger, Liselotte Funcke, and Burkhard Hirsch.[69] One of their main concerns today is that the FDP take a stronger role in curbing the cultural conservatism of the CDU and, especially, the CSU. In particular, they are critical of the statist law-and-order positions represented by Interior Minister Zimmermann.

The party is no longer condescending toward left-wingers, including the remaining "social liberal" elements, as it had been in some cases after the coalition change. It is now generally recognized that the FDP needs to have a broader and more appealing image than that of a kind of political action committee on behalf of the material interests of the Mittelstand. At the 1983 party conference, held in November in Karlsruhe, the delegates polished up the FDP's liberal credentials in lively discussions about the laws on demonstrations, political asylum, and other civil rights matters. Here, some postmaterial concerns were well represented, in areas where they do not conflict with the investment- and productivity-oriented emphasis of the economic wing. A special party commission, headed first by Adam-Schwetzer and now by Baum, is attempting to define a new basic Liberal program with contributions from members of the center-left faction. While the new program will hardly echo the social liberalism of the Freiburg Theses, it can be expected to include a strong civil libertarian theme.

If supporters of a progressive reform role for the FDP have their way, the new program will include more. In the first year after the coalition change the most prominent and articulated advocate of this position was Ralf Dahrendorf, director of the London School of Economics. He had played a major part in the FDP's reorientation during the late sixties when he provided intellectual legitimation for the small party's modernization as well as its role as political gadfly under the great coalition. After serving in Scheel's foreign ministry and at the European Community, Dahrendorf withdrew from active politics for a long period. Since his recent return to active party service, he has reminded the FDP that its liberal commitment must go beyond the productivity policies that are so dear to the economic wing. He acknowledges the importance of backing investment-stimulating efforts that will revive economic growth, rather than taking prosperity for granted as the Freiburg Theses had done. Yet he calls upon fellow Liberals and the FDP to recognize and take advantage of some important opportunities for enlarging the realm of individual choice or "life chances" that are present even in this period of economic and social dislocations. Dahrendorf urges the FDP to show more concern for social indicators that measure "quality" as well as "quantity" in life improvement. He declares that "the social democratic century" has expired but speaks on behalf of replacing its historic assumptions of a social security state with a "new social contract" that will redefine the parameters of social responsibility and individual performance. As Dahrendorf sees it, Liberals should be a factor of "creative unrest" in a changing society. They should promote administrative and societal decentralization as something that has value apart from its possible importance for economic flexibility and efficiency. And he reminds the party of its traditional commitment to the protection of civil rights and liberties. In other words, Dahrendorf appears to be translating some postmaterial concerns into positions that the FDP can include in its political liberalism. He readily admits that he is devoid of the tactical and integrative skills that are demanded by day-to-day politics, but he appears to reach for the role of educator on behalf of such a dynamic understanding of liberal ideas.[70]

Some of these views, and others like them, may crop up in the new program, but that does not mean they must have much relevance for the political behavior of the party. Having traversed the spectrum of politics from center-right to center-left and back again in less than two decades, the FDP is now inclined toward a more sedentary existence than Dahrendorf appears to have in mind. His suggestion that a period in the opposition or even outside the Bundestag might serve to revive the FDP was made before the victory in March 1983, but the idea would be unlikely to find converts among the party's career politicians and functionaries at any time. They are mostly pragmatic beings, concerned with the immediate problems of political survival and influence. From this perspective, Dahrendorf's views are primarily of interest if they can improve upon the small party's "marketability" so as to strengthen its position in parliament and government.

It is to be expected that there will be other initiatives to establish a distinctive image for the FDP. Recently Genscher and Jürgen Morlok, the young state party leader in Baden-Württemberg, have been among the Free Democrats who advance elitist ideas for the reform of higher education in West Germany. They advocate institutional reforms designed to identify and give advanced technical or scientific training to outstanding students in order to fill the country's growing needs in this area, where some perceive a creeping technological gap. The new emphasis differs considerably from the more democratic reforms in education with which the FDP became identified in the late sixties. Some members of the party are in turn responding with a defense of the party's social liberal commitment to the spreading of educational opportunity. The debate can be understood in terms of the party's search for political market gaps, but it also dovetails with the stronger entrepreneurial orientation and the emphasis on *Leistung* (achievement) by the center-right.

In the summer of 1984, the FDP finally began to face up to its leadership problems at the federal level. The issue was forced by developments that almost simultaneously created the need to consider replacements for the posts of secretary-general, minister of economics, and national party leader. After having deflected many controversies in the past, Genscher retreated before heavy intraparty criticism of two major decisions and shortly before the annual party conference in June 1984 announced his plan to serve only one more two-year term. Even then he was reelected with only 62 percent of the votes cast on a ballot that contained no rival candidate.

The first question on which Genscher had capitulated concerned his planned parliamentary support for a bill designed to give amnesty to campaign donors who had violated tax laws with contributions channeled indirectly to the political parties. The scandal involved many donors and had also blighted the CDU/CSU and SPD. However, the FDP appeared to have been tainted to an unusual degree. In particular, the party was hurt by the charges that large financial contributions by the Flick concern may have been linked to some special tax concessions granted the firm on the recommendation of the minister of economics. The sharp public criticism of the proposed amnesty reawakened the FDP's claim to possess a special sensitivity for upholding legality. In the face of a brewing party revolt, the FDP leadership drew back from the controversial amnesty proposal shortly before its consideration by the Bundestag. Chancellor Kohl and his CDU/CSU, who had committed themselves to the bill's support, were chagrined when it had to be withdrawn quickly.

The second retreat by Genscher followed on the heels of the first. He had intended to replace the parting secretary-general, Irmgard Adam-Schwaetzer, with a politically unknown choice of his own. His plan ran into another party protest shortly before the annual conference. The result was the nomination and election of a more political figure, Helmut Haussmann, a member of the party's center-left wing in the Bundestag. In contrast to Adam-Schwaetzer, who had been the only woman in the parliamentary party to support the coalition change in 1982, Haussmann had favored a continuation of the alliance with the SPD. Like other critics who remained in the FDP, however, Haussmann had accepted the party's decision. His election is one of many indications that the end of the Social-Liberal era is no longer an issue that deeply divides the party.

Haussmann was widely expected to drive for a more distinctively progressive image for the FDP than its three cabinet members provided. It appeared increasingly doubtful that Justice Minister Engelhard could long survive intraparty dissatisfaction with his weak leadership and conservative legal positions. He had supported the amnesty proposal and appeared to offer little resistance to the law-and-order emphasis of some of his cabinet colleagues. Economics Minister Lambsdorff finally abandoned his post in June 1984, when his indictment in the Flick affair led to a court decision to open proceedings against him. Genscher indicated that he would like to remain foreign minister, but he came under pressure to step down as party leader.

New electoral disappointments help explain the party's restiveness. In the spring of 1984, the FDP won reelection to the Landtag in Baden-Württemberg, but its result in this traditional stronghold of the party dipped from 8.3 to 7.2 percent. Morlok had hoped to improve his party's situation and possibly gain entry into a cabinet alliance with the ruling Christian Democrats. Instead, the CDU could retain its parliamentary majority, and the Greens (with 8.0 percent) passed the FDP as third party in yet another state legislature. In June 1984, the FDP failed to meet the 5 percent requirement, for the first time at the national level, in the election to the European Parliament. Thus, the Free Democrats will be absent from the Strassbourg assembly until at least 1989. Here too the Greens, who received 8.2 percent of the vote compared to the FDP's 4.8 percent, have replaced the Liberals as third West German party. It appeared possible that the Free Democratic position would deteriorate even further in 1985, when elections were planned in North Rhine–Westphalia as well as two of the five states in which the party still had Landtag representation: the Saar and West Berlin. Early polls gave no reason for optimism.

In these dismal circumstances, it was hardly surprising that many Free Democrats hoped to reinvigorate their party with a new leadership. A major problem, however, was the depletion of its scarce resources in this area. It is presently too early to tell whether the widespread turnover at the top of the state and local party organizations after the realignment in 1982 has really produced a new generation of vigorous and able leaders, as Genscher and others like to suggest. But there is reason for remaining skeptical about the party's ability to overcome its leadership shortage soon. First, with the decline of the FDP's presence as parliamentary party and cabinet member in state politics, it is no longer a readily available short route to public office for pragmatic and ambitious young politicians. Second, the small party's image has become too undistinctive or uncertain to attract the more conviction oriented kind of political personality. The result is an embarrassing lack of qualified personnel when party or government posts do open up. An example is the series of frustrations encountered by the FDP in its attempts to fill the ministry of economics in the Saar, one of a mere handful of cabinet posts still held by the party in state government. It will take a mixture of political success and credibility to make the small party attractive to able leadership personalities.

At the federal level, the party also had painfully little to choose from when it became necessary to find major candidates to fill Lambsdorff's and Genscher's shoes. When Lambsdorff left the cabinet in June 1984, the FDP fell back on Martin Bangemann, who had just lost his seat in the European

Parliament. Bangemann also became the prospective successor to Genscher when the latter announced his decision to step down as party leader at the time of the annual conference in 1985. As secretary-general of the party after Flach's death, Bangemann had caused a rumpus when he recommended a "loosening up" of the coalition question in 1975. He had resigned from the party post and later entered the European Parliament, where he gained in political stature as leader of the Liberal group. As his party's top candidate in the European election, he had fought a vigorous campaign in a rather hopeless situation. In contrast to Genscher, Bangemann made a relatively forthright and dynamic appearance, but some critics feared that he might be a little impulsive and lack tactical prudence.

There is no reason to believe that Bangemann and Haussmann can exorcise the structural problems that haunt their small party, but they may help to improve its battered image. Voters still appear to identify the FDP primarily in terms of its coalition alignment and secondarily in terms of its leadership and policy differences from the major partner. In Bonn, the party's civil libertarian tradition should continue to distinguish it from the CDU/CSU, as long as the Christian Unionists are represented by such politicians as Strauss and Zimmermann. Special-interest promotion on behalf of the middle classes and a tougher commitment to "economic realism" also set the FDP apart from its more populist partner. In 1980 and 1983, the FDP attracted voters not only as a *Mittelstandspartei* but also as a check on Schmidt's left and Kohl's right wing, respectively. In other words, the party is perceived as more than a promoter of special material values alone. Its political future may well depend upon whether it can keep its credibility as the moderating-balancing party that periodically arouses electoral fears or dislike of single-party government in Bonn. Such a role is not incompatible with some distinctive elements of political liberalism. And it is here that the right-left differences can again become important in the party's struggle for existence and influence.

There is a paradox in the FDP's perennial role as junior cabinet member in Bonn: While West German political culture appears to encourage and legitimate the sharing and curbing of governmental power through the process of coalition politics, it does not fully endorse the pivotal function that accrues to the majority-making party. This was already evident in state politics in the fifties, and it was reaffirmed in the late sixties when the FDP made possible a transfer of power between the major parties in Bonn. The few leading Free Democrats who initiated the breakaway from the Social Democrats in the early eighties could therefore anticipate the sub-

sequent charges of willfulness and disloyalty. This helps explain their un-
edifying tactical maneuvers as they sought to minimize the political costs of
a realignment held to be necessary for reasons of both governmental policy
and party survival. The accompanying agonies would be likely to discour-
age the Liberals from another pivotal shift in the near future, even if such a
possibility had not been foreclosed by the emergence of the Greens as
fourth party in the Bundestag.

With its peculiar combination of ideological ambivalence, electoral
vulnerability, and positional influence, the FDP has played a crucial role in
West German party politics since the late forties. Since the late seventies, it
has been threatened by the electoral dealignment that led to the emergence
of the Greens as a political factor. The election victory of 1980 resulted
from a transient situation that was favorable to the Social-Liberal coalition
and the FDP in particular. To be sure, the Liberals can take credit for having skillfully exploited the opportunity to improve their competitive position in that year. However, they did not reverse the negative structural
trend, and the circumstances of the coalition changeover largely destroyed
Genscher's hope of restoring his party by completing its political "reopen-
ing to the right." It is not certain that the small party can regain stability and
recover its political leverage. Much will depend upon circumstances that
lie beyond its influence at this point.

Yet it should not be overlooked that the Greens, who have so far been
able to profit from the generational value change and displace the FDP as
third party in many state parliaments, could develop their own problems of
political cohesion and survival. Even if their principled aversion to bargaining and compromise should fail to split the environmentalists into factions, it makes them unattractive or unavailable coalition partners for other
parties. Here, the recent establishment of a parliamentary red-green alliance in Hesse bears watching. Should it turn out to be even moderately
successful and followed by others, West German party politics may turn
out to become dominated by a left and right bloc. Should the FDP manage
to survive as a member of the latter, it would have even more difficulties
projecting itself as a moderate third force of the center than it has at present.
If it disappears, the CDU/CSU may finally govern alone again, with considerably more influence accruing to the Bavarian Christian Democrats
than when the Liberals were in the cabinet. Another possibility, of course,
is a grand coalition of the major parties, legitimated by a new version of the
"governability" argument.

There is really no indication that the Greens will ever become as pragmatic in their coalition politics as the FDP has been over more than three

and a half decades. In the coming years, therefore, the balance of power in West German party politics is likely to be significantly affected by the behavior of the Greens' leadership (rotating or otherwise) and the reactions of the other parties and the voters thereto. It would be ironic if the parliamentary presence of the Greens should lead to a reappraisal of the functional contributions to stability, moderation, and flexibility in the West German governmental process made by the Free Democratic party—however much of this party's behavior may be rooted in a "structural opportunism" rather than a clear or consistent sense of what its political liberalism should connote.

NOTES

1. It is still true that "very little of substance has appeared in English on the Free Democrats," as Gordon Smith wrote in 1979. See Gordon Smith, *Democracy in Western Germany* (New York: Holmes and Meier, 1979), p. 166, footnote 6. Over the years, however, a few good articles have appeared. The following five are among the best: Gerard Braunthal, "The Free Democratic Party in West German Politics," *The Western Political Quarterly* 13, no. 2 (June 1960): 332–348; R.E.M. Irving, "The German Liberals: Changing Image of the Free Democratic Party," *Parliamentary Affairs* 23 (Winter 1969–70): 46–54; Heino Kaack, "The FDP in the German Party System," in Karl H. Cerny (ed.), *Germany at the Polls: The Bundestag Election of 1976* (Washington, D.C.: American Enterprise Institute, 1978), pp. 77–110; Helmut Norpoth, "The German Federal Republic: Coalition Government at the Brink of Majority Rule," in Eric C. Browne and John Dreijmanis (eds.), *Government Coalitions in Western Democracies* (New York: Longman, 1982), pp. 7–32; and the most recent article, David Broughton and Emil Kirchner, "Germany: The FDP in Transition—Again?" *Parliamentary Affairs* 37, no. 2 (Spring 1984): 183–198.

2. That is the reason for the exclusion of the FDP in the standard study of "minor" parties in West Germany. See Stephen L. Fisher, *The Minor Parties of the Federal Republic of Germany: Toward a Comparative Theory of Minor Parties* (The Hague: Nijhoff, 1974).

3. Irving, *The German Liberals*, pp. 47 and 54.

4. Elisabeth Noelle-Neumann, "Ventil zwischen den beiden Grossen. Die Aufgabe der FDP," in *Frankfurter Allgemeine Zeitung*, 12 August 1982. The thesis is further developed and illustrated with recent polling data in the same author's study, *Die FDP in der Zerreissprobe. Capitalumfrage Sommer 1982* (Allensbach: Institut für Demoskopie, n.d., 1982). It is Noelle-Neumann's argument that the FDP has in fact functioned as a useful, stabilizing element (a *Ventil*, or

"safety valve") by permitting dissatisfied voters of one or the other major party to "blow off steam," as she also explained at the Pacific Workshop on German Affairs on April 9, 1983 (see the forthcoming proceedings of that conference, to be published by the California State University at Long Beach). Noelle-Neumann believes the FDP should recognize and accept this important function, which requires the party to move leftward or rightward in search of the kind of dissatisfied voters it must attract to survive. By the early 1980s, she recommended that the FDP should shift toward CDU/CSU-oriented voters, since it had lost the ability to attract the critical younger people, who now supported the Greens as a political alternative to the established parties. Understandably, Free Democrats would like to define their party in more substantial terms. For one FDP reaction to Noelle-Neumann's argument, see Ralf Dahrendorf, *Die Chancen der Krise* (Stuttgart: Deutsche-Verlagsanstalt, 1983), p. 45.

5. The most succinct official statement is probably the one contained in *Liberale Standpunkte 1978*, pt. 2, "Die Rolle der Liberalen," reprinted in Günter Verheugen (ed.), *Das Programm der Liberalen. Zehn Jahre Programmarbeit der F.D.P.* (Baden-Baden: Nomos, 1979). For Flach's main argument, as summarized in this paragraph, see Karl-Hermann Flach, *Dritte Kraft. Der Kampf gegen Machtmissbrauch in der Demokratie* (Bonn: FDP, n.d., 1957), pp. 5–21.

6. Karl-Hermann Flach, "Mehr Freiheit für mehr Menschen," in Karl-Hermann Flach, Werner Maihöfer, and Walter Scheel, *Die Freiburger Thesen der Liberalen* (Reinbek bei Hamburg: Rowohlt, 1972), p. 21.

7. The term has appeared in several places. It was used by Rudolf Wildenmann, a well-known German political scientist, in a discussion of the Bundestag election of 1980. Bonn, October 6, 1980. General references to the FDP's political opportunism are plentiful. For one example, see Otto Kirchheimer, "Germany: The Vanishing Opposition," in Robert Dahl (ed.), *Political Oppositions in Western Democracies* (New Haven: Yale University Press, 1966), p. 243, footnote 2.

8. See William M. Chandler, "West Germany's Governing Crisis and the 1983 Bundestag Election," paper presented at the annual meeting of the Canadian Political Science Association, Vancouver, June 6–8, 1983.

9. See Russell J. Dalton and Kendall L. Baker, "The Contours of West German Opinion," in this volume.

10. In 1871 Bismarck instigated a political attempt to transfer the educational and some other cultural institutions of the Roman Catholic Church in Germany upon the state. The Catholics mobilized in self-defense through such political means as the Center party. Bismarck later abandoned his repressive policy and concluded a concordat with Pope Leo XIII, but the cultural cleavage remained an important feature of German electoral and party politics before 1933 and, to a lesser extent, after 1945.

11. Two recent articles by prominent Free Democrats discuss the subject: Hildegard Hamm-Brücher, "Anmerkungen zum Versagen des politischen Liberalismus vor und nach 1933 und zu seinen Folgewirkungen nach 1945," *Lib-*

eral, 25, no. 3 (March 1983): 171–180; and Ralf Dahrendorf, "Deutschland und die Liberalen 1933 und 1983," *Liberal* 25, no.3 (March 1983): 227–231.

12. See Gerhard Loewenberg, "The Remaking of the German Party System," *Polity* 1, no. 1 (Fall 1968): 86–113.

13. Others include Karl-Hermann Flach, the former secretary-general and chief theorist of social liberalism; Wolfgang Mischnick, the leader of the FDP's parliamentary group in the Bundestag since 1968; and Wolfgang Schollwer, the party's former press secretary, who made significant contributions to the party's rethinking of Ostpolitik in the 1960s.

14. Similar formulations have been used by many authors. For a recent example, see Karl Moersch, *Kurs-Revision: Deutsche Aussenpolitik nach Adenauer* (Frankfurt: Societäts-Verlag, 1978), p. 90.

15. *Political Parties in Western Germany*, prepared by the Political Activities Branch, Civil Administration Division, Office of Military Government for Germany (U.S.), 1 August 1949, Edward H. Litchfield (Director), pp. 24–28. A similar evaluation is given by *Elections and Political Parties in Germany, 1945–1952* (Office of the U.S. High Commissioner for Germany, 1952), pp. 4–5.

16. The two programs are reprinted in Peter Juling, *Programmatische Entwicklung der FDP 1946 bis 1969. Einführung und Dokumente* (Meisenheim am Glan: Verlag Anton Hain, 1977), pp. 120–128.

17. See Herbert Knorr, "Die Grosse Koalition in der parlamentarischen Diskussion der Bundesrepublik 1949 bis 1965," in *Aus Politik und Zeitgeschichte*, no. 33/74 (August 17, 1974).

18. For a dramatic and insightful presentation of the Spiegel affair in English, see David Schoenbaum, *The Spiegel Affair* (Garden City: Doubleday, 1968).

19. See David Conradt, "Electoral Law Politics in West Germany," *Political Studies* 18, no. 3 (September 1970): 341–356.

20. For an account of the new Ostpolitik's genesis, written by a Free Democrat, see Karl Moersch, *Kurs-Revision: Deutsche Aussenpolitik nach Adenauer* (Frankfurt: Societäts-Verlag, 1978). Moersch, a former press secretary and parliamentary state secretary of his party, left the FDP at the time of the coalition change in 1982. He did not belong to the left wing of the party but became critical of what he regarded as the leadership's opportunism and lack of liberal principles.

21. Walter Scheel, "Für eine Gesellschafts und Aussenpolitik der Toleranz und der Vernunft," in *Die Freiburger Thesen der Liberalen*, p. 13.

22. Alfred Grosser, *The Federal Republic of Germany* (New York: Praeger, 1964), p. 68.

23. See, for example, Karl-Hermann Flach, *Erhards schwerer Weg* (Stuttgart: Seewald, 1963).

24. Rudolf Wildenmann, *Partei und Fraktion*, 2nd ed. (Meisenheim am Glan: Verlag Anton Hain, 1954), pp. 91–93. See also Gerard Braunthal, *The Federation of German Industry in Politics* (Ithaca, N.Y.: Cornell University Press,

1965), especially pp. 103–106, where the FDP's ideology and close ties to business are discussed.

25. See Rüdiger Zülch, *Von der FDP zur F.D.P.* (Bonn: Eichholz Verlag, 1972), pp. 27–28.

26. The 1969 election platform is reprinted in Juling, *Programmatische Entwicklung* pp. 200–208.

27. Walter Scheel, *Die Freiburger Thesen der Liberalen,* pp. 57–123.

28. Ibid., p. 64.

29. Ibid., pp. 57–58.

30. Ronald Inglehart, "The Silent Revolution in Europe: Intergenerational Change in Post-Industrial Societies," *American Political Science Review* 65, no. 4 (December 1971): 991–1017.

31. See Verheugen (ed.), *Das Programm der Liberalen,* for a collection of the decade's programmatic statements.

32. As quoted by Heino Kaack, "Die Liberalen," in Richard Löwenthal and Hans-Peter Schwarz, *Die zweite Republik* (Stuttgart: Seewald Verlag, 1974), p. 425.

33. The widely perceived decline of interest and confidence in social reform was a major subject of cultural and political debate by the mid-seventies. For a somewhat later example, see Ralf Dahrendorf, "Die Leitsterne unserer Politik erlöschen," *Die Zeit,* August 26, 1977 (North American ed.,), p. 3. Dahrendorf's interpretative commentary makes the point that the new middle class, which a few years earlier had made possible the "leftward" shift of the Federal Republic (and, one might add, the FDP), was now moving in the other direction: "Its self-confidence is gone and has been replaced by a growing fear of the future." The conservative policy trend was assessed by Rolf Zundel, a keen political observer who has written extensively on the FDP, in his article, "Bilan d'une politique intérieure conservatrice," in *Documents. Revue des questions allemandes,* September 1976, pp. 38–46.

34. See Ralf Dahrendorf, *Die Chancen der Krise,* pp. 37–40.

35. The quotations are translated from the section on "socially responsible economic policy" in the Baum commission's report, *Aktuelle Perspektiven des sozialen Liberalismus* (Bonn: Perspektivkommission der Freien Demokratischen Partei, July 25, 1977), pp. 19ff. The report of the Friedrichs commission appeared as *Grundzüge liberaler Wirtschaftspolitik* (Bonn: F.D.P.-Wirtschaftskommission, July 13, 1977).

36. *Kieler Thesen 1977—Wirtschaft in sozialen Rechtsstaat,* reprinted in Verheugen, *Das Programm der Liberalen,* pp. 288–327.

37. This section draws upon an extensive description and analysis of the 1980 campaign, completed by me in June 1981: "The Free Democrats in 1980: The Electoral Resurgence of the Pivotal Third Party." A copy of the manuscript has been deposited in the archives of the Friedrich Naumann Foundation at the Theodor Heuss Akademie, Gummersbach. A revised and shortened version of that

study is included as part of my chapter on the FDP in a forthcoming book on the Bundestag elections of 1980 and 1983, edited by Karl H. Cerny.

38. The term *Mittelstand* is notoriously difficult to translate or explain. There is no English equivalent, but the traditional usage of "middle classes" (still found in England) comes close. In German, the social category Mittelstand is defined by objective (socioeconomic) characteristics and subjective status assignments or aspirations. In using the elusive term to define its political position, especially in economic policy, the FDP is identifying itself with the achievement orientation of both old and new middle classes. For a discussion of social status and class in the Federal Republic, in which the problem of defining the Mittelstand is included, see Dieter Claessens, Arno Klönne, and Armin Tschoepe, *Sozialkunde der Bundesrepublik,* 8th ed. (Düsseldorf: Eugen Diederichs Verlag, 1980), pp. 295–308.

39. This section contains a presentation similar to that of a section in my forthcoming chapter on the ninth and tenth Bundestag elections (see footnote 37).

40. Such an argument is well presented in R.E.M. Irving and W.E. Paterson, "The *Machtwechsel* of 1982–83: A Significant Landmark in the Political and Constitutional History of West Germany," *Parliamentary Affairs* 36, no. 4 (Autumn 1983), especially page 427.

41. *Analyse der Bundestagswahl 1980* (Bonn: FDP, 1980), p. 18. A poll taken before the election found that 78 percent of the FDP supporters preferred a coalition with the SPD. Only 11 percent expressed a preference for an alliance with the CDU/CSU. 83 percent of the SPD supporters preferred a coalition of SPD and FDP. See the study *Bundestagswahl 1980* (Mannheim: Forschungsgruppe Wahlen e.V., 1980), p. 29.

42. The statement by Scheel is included in the documentation of the coalition crisis and change of government presented by Klaus Bohnsack, "Die Koalitionskrise 1981/82 und der Regierungswechsel 1982," *Zeitschrift für Parlamentsfragen,* February 1983, pp. 5–33. See p. 7, footnote 10. The full text of Genscher's letter is contained in *Informationsbrief Nr. 9/81* (Bonn: FDP, August 20, 1981), pp. 2–7. This information letter, for which the secretary-general is normally responsible, has become an important part of the regular communication between the party leadership and the ranking party members at the federal, state, and local levels of politics.

43. As quoted by Bohnsack, "Die Koalitionskrise 1981/82," p. 12.

44. "Umfrage über Wahlverhalten und Koalitionspräferenz," *Informationsbrief Nr. 9/81,* (Bonn: FDP, August 20, 1981), pp. 7–12.

45. "Wählerstrukturen im Frühjahr '82," *Informationsbrief Nr. 2/82* (Bonn: FDP, April 29, 1982), pp. 11–14.

46. The polls of the Allensbach Institute show that the FDP's electoral support began to drop markedly in the spring of 1982, from 9.6 percent to 6.8 percent between February and June of that year. In the same period, the SPD's rating sank from an already low point of 33.9 percent (compared with 42.9 percent in the elec-

tion of October 1980) to 31.1 percent. See "Dokumentation," in Elisabeth Noelle-Neumann, *Die FDP in der Zerreissprobe,* table headed "Sonntagsfrage," p. 1 of the documentation. Bohnsack, "Die Koalitionskrise 1981/82," p. 15, reports that the FDP had sunk to 5.1 percent by the end of July.

47. "Landesparteitag Hessen," *Informationsbrief Nr. 5/82* (Bonn: FDP, June 18, 1982), pp. 2–3.

48. This information comes from interviews with FDP campaign planners in March 1983.

49. See Bohnsack, "Die Koalitionskrise 1981/82," p. 26. On 28 September, when presented with the draft of the coalition agreement worked out between the negotiators of the CDU/CSU and FDP, 32 members of the Liberal parliamentary group voted to approve the agreement, 20 opposed it, and 2 abstained. In a second vote, 34 members approved of a constructive vote of no confidence on behalf of Helmut Kohl, while 18 disapproved and 2 abstained. See *Informationsbrief* (FDP: Bonn, September 29, 1982), pp. 1–2. The 20 critics of the coalition change in the parliamentary party, 18 of whom were staunch in their opposition, comprised the following: Gerhart Baum, Wolfram Bergerowski, Carola von Braun-Stützer, Günther Bredehorn, Sibylle Engel, Olaf Feldmann, Rita Fromm, Klaus Gärtner, Hildegard Hamm-Brücher, Helmut Haussmann, Burkhard Hirsch, Friedrich Hölscher, Ingrid Matthäus-Maier, Erke Noth, Hansheinrich Schmidt, Uwe Ronneburger, Helmut Schäfer, Andreas von Schoeler, Helga Schuchardt, and Manfred Vohrer.

50. The text of the party resolution on the coalition change is found in *Die neue Bonner Depesche. Die Liberale Zeitung,* November 1982, p. 8.

51. The protocol of the Berlin conference is nevertheless a goldmine for the study of the intraparty conflict. It records the full speeches as well as many of the more clearly articulated reactions. Additional information on the proceedings has been gathered in interviews and from press reports.

52. The Liberal Democrats delayed their entry into the electoral arena until the state contests in Hesse and Bremen in October 1983, where they received 0.2 and 0.1 percent of the vote respectively. Already in the fall of 1982, a poll had indicated that a new Liberal party would have little chance of passing the 5 percent hurdle, even if it included all the Free Democrats who had been critical of the coalition change. This may help explain the inability of the new party to attract defectors who held elected positions. The two other Free Democrats in the Bundestag who left their party, Helga Schuchardt and Friedrich Hölscher, also ended up supporting the SPD.

53. This section draws from a more extensive discussion of the 1983 Bundestag election in my forthcoming chapter, mentioned in footnote 37.

54. See Elisabeth Noelle-Neumann, "Schweigespirale gegen die FDP," *Die politische Meinung,* January-February 1983, pp. 5–7. For a different perception, see Günter Verheugen, *Der Ausverkauf. Macht und Verfall der FDP* (Hamburg: Rowohlt, 1984), p. 167.

55. Werner Kaltefleiter, "Die FDP muss von der Union Wähler holen," *Die Welt,* November 5, 1982.

56. Ibid.

57. *Die neue Bonner Depesche,* February 1983, contains 64 pages of documentary material on the electoral convention. The change in the bylaws is recorded on page 7 of the party journal. Further information on the convention has been drawn from the protocol, interviews, and press reports.

58. *Bundestagswahl 1983. Analyse des Ergebnisses der F.D.P.* (Bonn: FDP, 1983). This 16-page analysis was submitted to the party's national executive on 3 May 1983. It is necessary to regard any estimate of the "flow" of voters between the parties, from one election to another, with great caution. The FDP's estimate of its own turnover of voters is unusually high, but this is in itself of potential political importance. For a much lower estimate of the electoral turnover see INFAS-Report, *Politogramm Bundestagswahl 1983* (Bonn–Bad Godesberg: INFAS, 1983), pp. 39–40.

59. For some fairly recent data on party representation in local government, see the report by Hans Clemens Weiss, *Im Dienste der Demokratie. Parteien in der Bundesrepublik Deutschland* (Bonn: Inter Nationes, n.d., 1984), pp. 22–23.

60. F.D.P. Die Liberalen, *Geschäftsbericht 1981/82* (Bonn: FDP, 1982), pp. 1–4.

61. Verheugen's remarks at the Kiel conference are located on pages 118–129 of the protocol. His reform proposals were outlined in *Freie Demokratische Korrespondenz,* Nr. 195 (Bonn: FDP, August 25, 1977).

62. "Ergebnisse der Befragung der Kreisvorsitzenden der F.D.P.," *Informationsbrief Nr. 1/84* (Bonn: FDP, February 7, 1984), p. 2.

63. *Fakten zur Planung des Bundestagswahlkampfes 1983,* "Interne Struktur," (Bonn: FDP, November 9, 1982), p. 2. The situational analysis, prepared by section 3 of the party headquarters, discussed the party's problems briefly but frankly.

64. "Ergebnisse der Befragung," *Informationsbrief Nr. 1/84,* p. 14.

65. Ibid., p. 22.

66. The 20 are listed in footnote 49. The eight who have returned to the Bundestag are Baum, Bredehorn, Feldmann, Hamm-Brücher, Haussmann, Hirsch, Ronneburger, and Schäfer.

67. *Bundestagswahl 1983. Analyse des Ergebnisses der F.D.P.,* p. 11. A more recent tally for the Young Liberals (Julis) shows a total membership of 3,500. See "Die Julis in Aufwind," *Informationsbrief Nr. 2/84* (Bonn: March 15, 1984), p. 3.

68. "Ergebnisse der Befragung," p. 20.

69. These are the best-known discussants only. Several of them, like Hamm-Brücher and Ronneburger, are really more centrist than leftist in their liberalism, but they share important concerns with the left wing of the party.

70. Ralf Dahrendorf has advanced his ideas in the journal *Liberal,* of which he is now chief editor, as well as in his book *Die Chancen der Krise.*

7

THE GREENS:
ECOLOGY AND THE NEW LEFT

Wilhelm P. Bürklin

The new political party, the Greens, is one of the most notable facets of recent West German politics. With balloons in front of its headquarters, posters of brightly painted environmental scenes, and flowers on the desks of its delegates, the Greens has become the first new party to enter the West German Parliament since the early postwar elections. The party has benefited from the decline, since 1972, in voter support for the three major parties, as shown in Figure 7.1.

Formed from a series of regionally limited, single-issue electoral organizations and public-action interest groups, the Green Party is now supported by ecologists, and nuclear energy opponents, and more and more by the radical political left. Increasingly, it has managed to capture from the Social Democrats the role of public spokesman for progressive, civil liberties political positions—the new politics.

The party platform as laid down in the Saarbrüker Program characterizes the Greens as a grass-roots democratic, ecological, social, and non-violent (*basis-demokratisch, oekologisch, sozial und gewaltfrei*) alternative to the established parties. It can be described as roughly following programmatic positions of

Ecology	over	Economy
Collective responsibility	over	Individual performance (*Leistungsprinzip*)
Decentralized	over	Centralized societal organization
Neutralism	over	NATO[1]

The autonomous and often regionally limited electoral groupings that were to form the Greens began, in 1978, to bring a breath of fresh air into a series of local and regional legislative bodies. They formed a loosely organized unit for the first direct election to the European Parliament in 1979 and then obtained a permanent organizational structure on the national level with the foundation of the Greens in early 1980.[2] Today the party has some 30,000 members, who despite the formation of this "new" political party represent electoral groupings which exist within a broader context of historical and contemporary protest movements.

THE DEVELOPMENT OF WEST GERMAN
PROTEST MOVEMENTS

It is no exaggeration to maintain that the contemporary peace and ecology movements in West Germany have their roots in the Enlightenment and particularly in Kant's *Zum Ewigen Frieden* (1775). The progress of this stream can be followed through the entire nineteenth century down to today—for instance, the youth movement of Imperial Germany and the disarmament movement prior to World War I.

In post–World War II West Germany, the peace movement responded to the nation's integration into the Western alliance and its rearmament. And since the early 1950s it has come to include a wide spectrum of organizations. In 1956, protest was largely directed against the rebuilding of the military, the acquisition of nuclear weapons, and the newly reintroduced conscription. In 1957 a central body, Kampf dem Atomtod (Struggle against Atomic Death), was formed by several Lutheran organizations, the German Labor Federation (DGB), and the Social Democratic party (SPD), so that a peak of strength was reached in 1958 when some 150,000 persons took part in demonstrations. Thereafter the DGB and the SPD distanced themselves from the movement and it quickly lost importance. Later, in 1960, an Eastern March Movement was founded, which would ultimately give way to the broader Extraparliamentary Opposition (APO).

SPD support for extraparliamentary protest reaches back to the late 1950s, but its accommodation with other parliamentary parties in the mid-1960s channeled further support to the formalized APO. Antiauthoritarian protest then culminated in the student movement of 1967–68—chiefly supported by those who had no direct experience of war and who had grown up during the era of the "economic miracle." For these young people the advent of the first postwar economic recession (1966–67) and of "emergency legislation" signaled a turn toward authoritarianism.

Figure 7.1 Electoral participation, and party percentage for SPD, CDU, CSU and FDP (second vote, Zweitstimme) in the national elections 1949–1983)

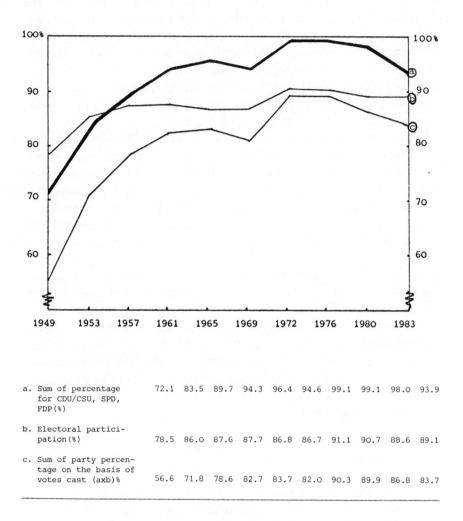

	1949	1953	1957	1961	1965	1969	1972	1976	1980	1983
a. Sum of percentage for CDU/CSU, SPD, FDP(%)	72.1	83.5	89.7	94.3	96.4	94.6	99.1	99.1	98.0	93.9
b. Electoral participation(%)	78.5	86.0	87.6	87.7	86.8	86.7	91.1	90.7	88.6	89.1
c. Sum of party percentage on the basis of votes cast (axb)%	56.6	71.8	78.6	82.7	83.7	82.0	90.3	89.9	86.8	83.7

189

Thereafter international developments redirected the focus of the protest to the civil rights movement and the Vietnam War, shattering for many the image of the United States as a model of democracy.

As awareness grew and new issues became recognizable, "actionist" protest became directed against single-issue ills, such as urban renewal and expressway projects, and in support of self-help groups among youth and the underprivileged. The self-consciousness this brought forth in the early 1970s resulted in *Bürgerinitiativen* (public-interest action groups), out of which increasing cooperation and coordination grew. In 1972 the National Association for Environmental Protection (BBU) was created, which experienced great growth through the politization of nuclear energy: Mammoth demonstrations and illegal occupations of nuclear sites brought the ecology movement to the attention of the public.

The protest movement today, however, extends beyond the *ecology* movement: Of particular topical significance is the new *peace* movement, which has grown rapidly since 1981, bringing 300,000 demonstrators to Bonn in June 1982. Other demonstrations—both large and small—were conducted in opposition to the stationing of new nuclear weapons in Europe. The women's movement, which developed in the early 1970s around the abortion issue, has since developed into something of a feminist subculture.

The building of a genuine "counterculture" is a major goal of additional groups, such as communes, co-ops, self-help bodies, and other service cooperatives.[3]

For these protest groups the Greens are increasingly becoming the political and parliamentary representatives. In the view of many political commentators, such protest could, at least in the *short* run, become an important force in the West German political system.[4] This chapter explains that view by emphasizing the following characteristics of contemporary West German political culture:

1. changes in *social structure:* the trends toward a postindustrial society and the declining importance of older class cleavage structures;
2. changes in basic *value orientations:* the long-term rise of the "participatory citizen" role, which can be clearly observed in West Germany; and
3. change in *behavior of the political elites:* particularly the altered political stance of Social Democratic politicians no longer representing groups on the left of their party.

On the basis of these changes the following explains the development, in the late 1970s, of the Greens into a competing political party. The discussion begins with an examination of recent election statistics. The hypothesized relationship between changes in political culture and the party's development is then tested using data from a 1980 preelection survey and the 1982 General Survey ("Allgemeine Bevölkerungsumfrage in den Sozialwissenschaften").

THE GREENS IN RECENT ELECTIONS

Analysis of the electoral figures of the Greens at the constituency level does not lead to a satisfactory explanation of the party's electoral support: The correlation between the share of the vote for the Greens and those factors which traditionally provide an explanation for the vote of the established parties (for example, religion and class) are low and differ very greatly from region to region; nor do other former cleavages of the German political system explain the success of this new party.[5] Case-by-case inspection of each constituency indicates the Greens mobilize along "new" political conflict lines:

1. The Greens obtain their best results in those districts where their radical ecological-policy position meets actual or potential *ecological problems.* Regionally, their best results correspond almost identically with politicized environmental conflicts. The immediacy of extending the runways of the Frankfurt Airport or building a nuclear power plant in southwest Germany was translated by the Greens into votes.

   This relationship was first hypothesized for results of the 1980 Bundestag election[6] but appears to hold for the 1983 election.[7] It also explains the regional differences in the electoral figures of the various Landtag elections since 1978; as indicated in Table 7.1, the Greens obtained their best results in the states of Hesse, Lower Saxony, Baden–Württemberg and in the autonomous cities of Hamburg and Bremen, where the governments took a decidedly pronuclear position at a relatively early point. These governments facilitated the development of nuclear installations and utilized the repressive means at their disposal to combat the growing resistance to these installations.

2. While this explanation strongly supports the thesis of *interest-bound protest* as a main determinant of the vote, certain other electoral regularities appear to support the *value-change* thesis. This view sees the rise of the Greens as a consequence of long-range value shifts which accompany the movement toward a "postindustrial society." First of all, according to this interpretation, electoral patterns become especially clear in larger cities and those with universities— in the latter, independently of politicized, environment-oriented conflicts. Support for the Greens is particularly strong in the larger cities, and above all

Table 7.1. Electoral Figures of the GRÜNEN in the Elections to the Landtag, Bundestag and European Parliament, 1978–1983

Landtag elections:

4.06.1978	Hamburg	RL[1]	3,5%
		GLU[2]	1,0%
4.06.1978	Niedersachsen	GLU	3,9%
8.10.1978	Hessen	GAZ[3]	0,9%
		GLH[4]	1,1%
		GLU	0,01%
18.03.1979	Berlin	AL[5]	3,7%
18.03.1979	Rheinland–Pfalz	——	——
29.04.1979	Schleswig–Holstein	GL[6]	3,4%
7.10.1979	Bremen	BGL[7]	5,1%
16.03.1980	Baden–Württemberg	GRÜNE	5,3%
27.04.1980	Saarland	GRÜNE	2,9%
11.05.1980	Nordrhein–Westfalen	GRÜNE	3,0%
10.05.1981	Berlin	AL	7,2%
21.03.1982	Niedersachsen	GRÜNE	6,5%
6.06.1982	Hamburg	GAL[8]	7,7%
26.09.1982	Hessen	GRÜNE	8,0%
10.10.1982	Bayern	GRÜNE	4,6%
19.12.1982	Hamburg	GAL	6,8%
6.03.1983	Rheinland–Pfalz	GRÜNE	4,5%
13.03.1983	Schleswig–Holstein	GRÜNE	3,6%
25.09.1983	Bremen	RGL[7]	2,4%
		GRÜNE	5,4%
25.09.1983	Hessen	GRÜNE	5,9%

European Parliament:

10.06.1979	GRÜNE	3,2%

Bundestag elections:

5.10.1980	GRÜNE	1,5%
6.03.1983	GRÜNE	5,6%

---

[1]Rote Liste-Wehrt Euch   [2]Grüne Liste Umweltschutz

[3]Grüne Aktion Zukunft   [4]Grüne Liste Hessen

[5]Alternative Liste   [6]Grüne Liste

[7]Bremer Grüne Liste   [8]Grüne-Alternative Liste

Source: Statistisches Bundesamt

in the precincts of the "new middle class" of white-collar employees. In some of these precincts the Greens gained 20 percent of the vote in 1983.

3. Aside from these geographical and social-structural factors, which primarily explain the *mobilization success* of the Greens, there is another "new" cleavage which explains another aspect of the electoral figures: The main characteristic which divides the voters of the Greens from those of the established parties is their *generation,* especially the difference between those age cohorts belonging to the prewar as opposed to the postwar generation. In the 1980 election only 22 percent of CDU voters were under 35 years of age (SPD 32 percent, FDP 34 percent), while the corresponding figure for the Greens is 71 percent. And while half of the electorate of the established parties is more than 45 years old, this figure for the Greens is 18 percent. As can be seen from Table 7.2, this age distribution changed slightly in the Bundestag election of 1983. But while the bulk of voters was still below 35 years of age, the relative balance between those under 25 and those over 25 has shifted: The Greens have succeeded in becoming a credible alternative for the latter age group.

Table 7.2. Age Distribution of Voters between Parties. Bundestag Election, 1980, 1983

| Age Group | Bundestagsvote 1980 | | | | Grüne 1983 |
	SPD	CDU	FDP	Grüne	
18-25	14.3%	9.4%	13.6%	43.3%	33.1%
25-35	17.5	12.8	20.3	27.2	34.3
35-45	18.3	20.4	24.3	12.1	14.6
45-60	25.1	27.7	24.0	11.0	11.9
60 +	24.8	29.7	17.8	6.5	6.1
Sum	100.0	100.0	100.0	100.0	100.0

Source: Statistisches Bundesamt (1982:59; 1983a:25)

This trend indicates that the electoral support for the Greens has become older and therefore more stable. This is further supported by a comparison of cohort-specific vote gains between the 1980 and 1983 elections:
The Greens, although largely backed by the youngest voters, increased
their share of the vote less in this age group than among those in the 25-to-
35 cohort and—most surprisingly—in the 35-to-45 age group. Nevertheless, in 1983 still two-thirds of their electorate is under 35 years of age.

Table 7.3. Bundestag-Vote for the Grünen 1980, 1983

Age Group	Relative share for the Grünen		Relative Gain %
	October 1980	March 1983	
18-25	4.8%	13.9%	190
25-35	2.4	9.2	280
35-45	.9	4.4	390
45-60	.6	2.4	300
60 +	.4	1.2	200
All groups	1.4	5.3	280

Source: Statistisches Bundesamt (1982:56; 1983a:23) own calculations

The generational cleavage is paralleled in the age structure of the respective party candidates. Out of the 302 candidates of the Greens for the
1980 Bundestag election, 110 candidates, or 36 percent, were below 30
years of age; half were below 33. The distribution was slightly older in
1983. Meanwhile, the candidates of the established parties were generally
ten years older. The Greens are characterized by the figures in Table 7.4 as
the party of the postwar generation in West Germany. This leads us to look
for the patterns of voter alignments in the West German political system.

While at first glance the electoral success of the Greens can be
explained by unsatisfactory environmental policies, one must not ignore
that such a one-issue party seems most attractive when ecological concerns

Table 7.4. Bundestag-Candidates 1980 by age and party

Age	SPD	CDU	CSU	FDP	Grüne	Grüne 1983
18-30	4%	10%	7%	8%	36%	21%
31-40	32	26	34	36	33	50
41-50	39	37	38	29	18	17
51 and older	25	27	21	27	13	22
Sum %	100	100	100	100	100	100
N	(483)	(493)	(89)	(368)	(302)	(318)
Median	43.3	43.8	43.5	42.1	32.9	34.0

Source: Statistisches Bundesamt (1982:97; 1983b:12ff) own calculations

are insufficiently recognized in the regular political demand structures. Further examination of the linkages between social structures and political attitudes, and—more importantly—the linkage between party identification and the representation of various social interests by the established parties, it is pointed out here, is necessary to understand the current and future support of the Greens.

The following pages demonstrate that as postindustrial change occurred in West Germany, with an associated decomposition of established social structures and resulting value shifts, the SPD leadership was incapable of sufficiently meeting demands. So the Greens gained the advantage of demographic shifts and divisions between the *old and new left*—the industrial working class and the postindustrial protest groups—providing a new outlet for seemingly deprived political interests. Traditional party elites, unable to meet the demands of new social interests, provided the arena for a Green coalition.

POSTINDUSTRIAL MODERNIZATION AND THE MALAISE OF THE LEFT

Established relationships between social structure and party system have (not only in the German case) recently been altered by urbanization, industrialization, democratization, the educational boom, increased geographical and social mobility, and other forces of modernization. Among the features of this development of the modern industrial state into the post-industrial welfare state[8] are the emergence of new forms of political participation,[9] and the creation of channels for the expression of the new politics in, for instance, the formation of new political parties.

In this process of change a decisive role is commonly attributed to the comparative level of development in the social organization of production.[10] This results in a society based on a progressive division of labor, an increasingly differentiated social structure, and an elaborate system of expressing specialized political demands. Class antagonisms no longer present themselves in such stark terms due to social legislation and increased prosperity, while increasing geographical and social mobility facilitate the formation of a heterogeneous social climate.[11] Thus, the cultural relevance of homogeneous social groups, such as labor unions, are sharply reduced as crosscutting social identities replace the familiar patchwork social map of the past. This means there is less party loyalty and a less socially structured electoral behavior.[12]

Furthermore, the shift of blue-collar employment from a secondary to a tertiary economic status, behind white-collar employees, increased the pressure on left-oriented parties to redefine themselves from the labor union versus employer relationship to a value-based solidarity (*Wertgemeinschaft*) on such issues as the emancipation of the individual from social forces.[13] Contemporary leftism does not now face clearly defined capitalism so much as a system of public and private bureaucracies diffusely restrictive of individual freedom.

Thus, leftist political parties must adapt to this shift in such a way as to maintain their support base in the old left while appealing to those with the new values. The intraparty conflict which results becomes particularly acute when the party approaches the role of *government responsibility,* for then all supporters must face the immediate and concrete question of who the political opponents are. While the old, union-organized left is willing to make use of the public bureaucracy and the state repressive mechanisms in order to pursue its particular interests, the new left rejects this use, the new left sometimes even finding its "own" party establishment reprehensible when in power.

The "educational revolution"[14] exaggerates the problem, since the rising informational level has led to less differentiation between the intellectual abilities and political sophistication by many youth, on the one hand, and the dominant political and social elite, on the other. But this has not meant increased access to power for these youth, for the added complexity of political decisions has led to a greater difference between their respective chances to exercise influence over the decisions. The contrast leads to a greater focus on social problems and further influences the stance youth take toward political authority.[15]

Against this background the prospect for a party of the new left to become a relevant factor is further influenced by two additional socioeconomic factors: the level of social welfare and the *costs of this welfare* for the general community. For in an economy based on growth such costs—from environmental pollution to fear of a nuclear accident—are taken increasingly seriously by many citizens. And as the level of these costs rises in relation to the individual's own welfare, demands for cost reductions increase.

In a competitive democracy such demands might be expected to be aggregated in the existing party system. However, this is possible only if the cleavages run *between* rather than *within* the parties. As long as parties of the left as well as of the right take the "establishment" view favoring economic growth, both remain political opponents of nonmaterially oriented social groups, which means the nonmaterially oriented, opposed by the well-organized interests in society, stand little chance of reaching their goals and are more frustrated by the effective barring of their participation in political decision making.

The "new" conflict-dimension this adds to old cleavage lines involves groups defined on the basis of material interests—employer organizations as well as labor unions—though competing with each other, facing those holding nonmaterial interests in the environment, peace, and so forth. This new conflict-dimension shares with the "old politics" left-right conflict the opposition between forces of reform and forces of conservatism. Whereas the old dimension divides "haves" from "have-nots" over the level of governmental intervention in socioeconomic development, the new divides conventionally mediated interests ("establishment") from groups pursuing unconventional strategies for acquiring political power. The two axes of political conflict are thus:[16] the *value dimension* dividing those with conservative-traditional goals from those with social reformist-egalitarian goals; and the *normative dimension* dividing the old and the new politics,[17] those with high or low levels of commitment to social institutions and to

conventions of political participation. This last dimension can be interpreted as a conflict between *realism* (pragmatism) and *idealism*.[18]

How these cleavages affect West German politics, especially between
the SPD and the Greens, is the subject of the empirical analysis which follows.

THE NEW CONFLICT DIMENSION

A factor analysis of the attitudes held by supporters of the major parties indicates how the perspectives of these individuals differentiate them in
the dimensions just described. The factors used to identify the differences
are related to those defined by Miller and Levitin (1976), who define *new
politics groups* on the basis of attitudes toward protest, law-and-order,
counterculture, and the state repressive mechanisms; to Hildebrandt and
Dalton (1977), who develop a *new politics dimension* in terms of Inglehart's postmaterialist index ranking the personal importance of various
political problems; and to Kaase and Klingemann (1979) and Barnes and
colleagues (1979), who measure the establishment-antiestablishment dimension via perceived closeness to various social groups and political parties.[19]

The two-factor scales which result demonstrate the relation of the
Greens to the three other parties on the Old–New Politics dimension. Thus,
the second dimension measures the realignment of the party system.
Within the major dimensions it also demonstrates the still-high importance
of the old politics (*Eigenvalue* 1.90, or 50 percent variance explained) and
the growing weight of the new politics factor (1.33, 33 percent). These factors differentiate between traditionally defined interest groups, on the one
hand, and the alternative orientation of the Greens, on the other.[20]

Figure 7.2 presents the results in terms of responses for the election of
1980. It is noteworthy that at that time, in spite of the seeming indifference
of the Greens on the matter of class conflict, they were considered, on the
old politics dimension, as conservative. By 1983 this had changed, so the
party was perceived as more left.[21]

Thus, this research indicates, since the distance of the Greens, left or
right, on the old cleavage between traditionally defined interests does not
distinguish the party, this dimension is irrelevant for support of the new
politics. In terms of the present analysis, the variable "occupation," while
explaining a respondents location in the *old politics* dimension, has no
explanatory power for the *new politics* factor. This is demonstrated, when
considering both the respondents' class and the occupation of the head of

Figure 7.2 Old and New Conflict Dimensions in Advanced Indus-trial Societies: The German Party System of 1980

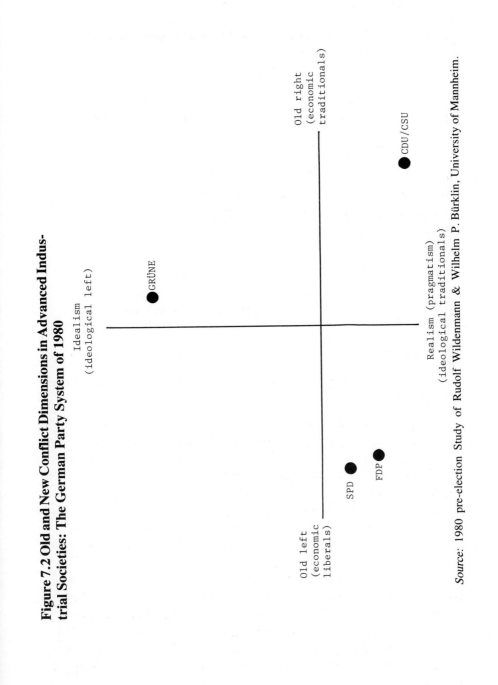

Source: 1980 pre-election Study of Rudolf Wildenmann & Wilhelm P. Bürklin, University of Mannheim.

household, in Table 7.5. The new conflict dimension cuts across the established partisan alignments.

Table 7.5. The Placement of Social Class on the Old and New Conflict Dimension, 1980*

"Class" by Head of Household	New Dim.	Old Dim.	n	"Class" by Self-Placement	New Dim.	Old Dim.	n
Working class	-.02	.15	621	Working class	.01	.13	543
New Middle Class	-.01	-.01	817	Middle Class	-.07	-.03	960
Old Middle Class	.00	-.44	144	Upper Middle	.08	.08	152
Farmers	-.31	-.35	37	Upper Class	-**	-**	9

*Numerical entries are the mean index score for each social group. Positive values on the New Dimension denote a "New-Politics"-orientation. Positive values on the Old, the Partisan Dimension denote old left, negative values old right orientation (see Figure 2)

**Insufficient numbers

Source: 1980 Pre-election study, Rudolf Wildenmann & Wilhelm P. Bürklin, University of Mannheim.

There are difficulties in determining how different age groups are affected by social change, and how they are thus aligned politically.[22] So in this analysis a division into three broad generations is used: (1) the generation which experienced the Nazi dictatorship and World War II and which contributed substantially to postwar reconstruction—the generation which holds the current societal elite positions; (2) the generation which matured just after the war; and (3) the generation which experienced primary socialization only during reconstruction and has matured during the period of economic and political stability.

Since, as we have seen, educational differences affect the new conflict dimension of postindustrial society, educational groups are also differentiated here. The categories used correspond to the three-tier structure of the German education system: low (*Volksschule*—elementary education); medium (*Realschule*—commercially oriented high school); high (*Gymnasium*—completion of an academic high school, including those who attended college).

Figure 7.3 Generational Groups in the Party Space: 1980

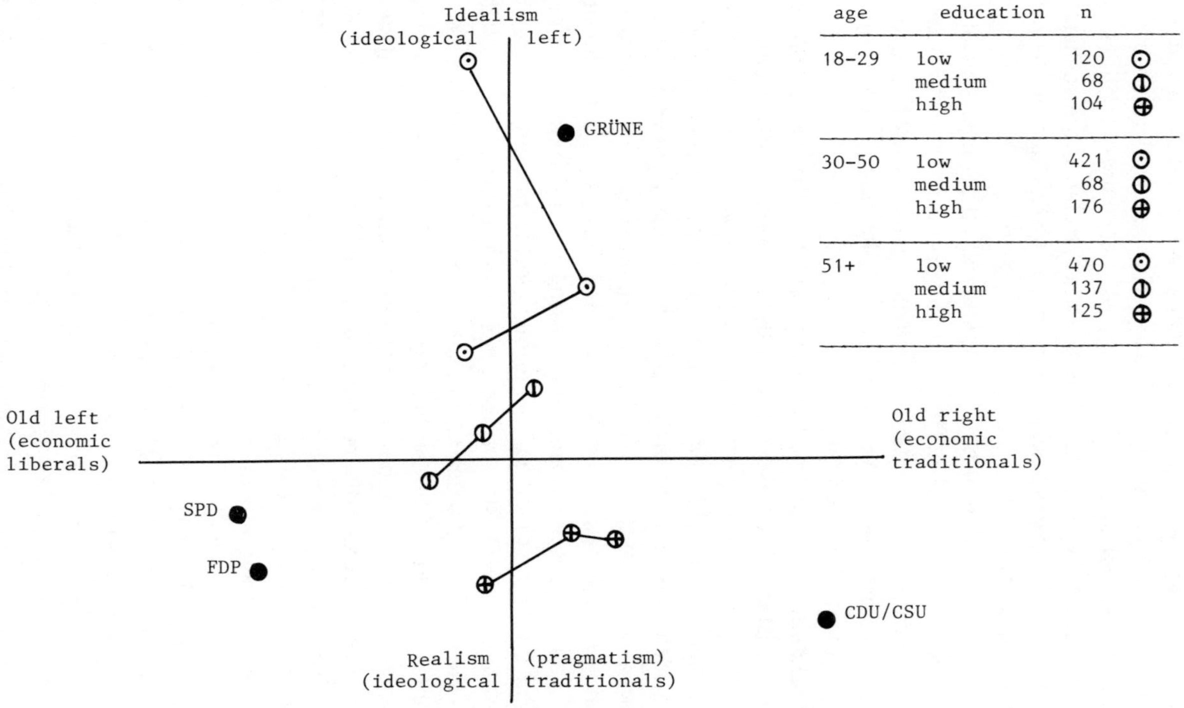

age	education	n	
18-29	low	120	⊙
	medium	68	⊖
	high	104	⊕
30-50	low	421	⊙
	medium	68	⊖
	high	176	⊕
51+	low	470	⊙
	medium	137	⊖
	high	125	⊕

Source: 1980 pre-election Study of Rudolf Wildenmann & Wilhelm P. Bürklin, University of Mannheim.

Figure 7.3 shows the interrelationships among these variables; both education and age have a significant effect upon the new, or new politics, political orientation, with age being a major factor in locating the position of an individual on our attitudinal axis. The better educated in all age groups tend toward the new political outlook, but on the old politics dimension, in the oldest age group higher education correlates with an increase of conservative-traditional values, while in the lowest age group it tends toward the leftist positions.

The new dimension of political conflict has the greatest meaning for the young and well educated. These individuals have the intellectual qualifications for substantive political participation but have not begun to rise to positions of social power. As "unattached intellectuals"[23] they constitute the core of the new politics group.

In relation to political parties it appears to be the *young leftists* who have most distanced themselves from the traditional party establishment (see Figure 7.4). Those whose primary socialization took place before 1945 are placed in the old politics dimension. For those socialized after the end of strident class conflict in the party system (that is, after the SPD 1959 Godesberg Program), left attitudes are progressively less related to the terms of traditional class conflict. And for those socialized during the Grand Coalition (1966–69) and the following Social-Liberal coalition, the traditional definition of left has increasingly lost its meaning. Among these persons one finds the best representatives of a truly "new" left, a left that is close to the ideological space occupied by supporters of the Greens.

Tables 7.6 and 7.7 further break down the elements of the dimension regarding support for established authority. The variables analyzed include: (a) two that refer to the perceived trust (or "distrust") of authorities—one on a specific- and one on a diffuse-support level (based on Easton's 1965, 1975 distinction); (b) one variable referring to the belief in the responsiveness of the political system—the belief in the ability to influence decisions of political authorities; (c) the scales "liberal-democratic rights," "conflict openness," and "new politics" which measure dimensions of the basic liberal orientation; (d) a last scale consisting solely of one item, that dealing with nuclear energy. This item was not the only single-issue position in the 1980 West German political debates, but it was the key issue of a no-growth, antitechnological dimension. The opposition of the politics of quantitative growth was made concrete in the opposition to nuclear energy and in the more recent political debates, the opposition to nuclear weapons.[24]

Figure 7.4 Old and New Left Groups in the Party Space: 1980

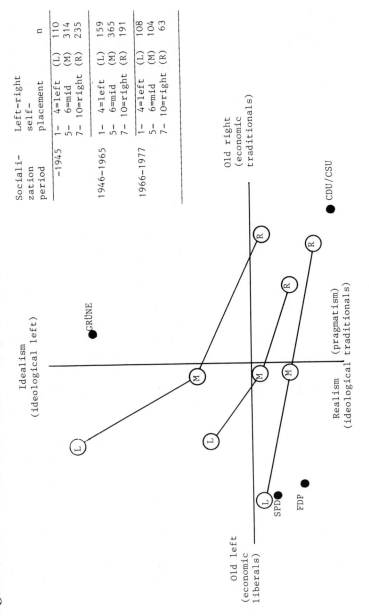

Sociali-zation period	Left-right self-placement		n
–1945	1–	4=left (L)	110
	5–	6=mid (M)	314
	7–	10=right (R)	235
1946–1965	1–	4=left (L)	159
	5–	6=mid (M)	365
	7–	10=right (R)	191
1966–1977	1–	4=left (L)	108
	5–	6=mid (M)	104
	7–	10=right (R)	63

Source: 1980 pre-election Study of Rudolf Wildenmann & Wilhelm P. Bürklin, University of Mannheim.

203

The following are scale items:

Scale   Scale Items

I. Liberal-democratic Rights   1. Everyone should have the right to
                                            express his or her opinion, even
                                            when the majority is of another
                                            opinion.
                                        2. A functioning democracy is not
                                            possible without a political opposi-
                                            tion.
                                        3. Every democratic party should
                                            have the basic right to participate
                                            in government.

II. Conflict openness   1. Conflicts between the various in-
                                            terest groups in our society and
                                            their demands on the government
                                            are detrimental to the general
                                            mood.
                                        2. The citizen does not have the right
                                            to strike and demonstrate when it
                                            disturbs public order.

III. System responsiveness   1. I don't think that public officials
                                            care much about what people like
                                            me think.
                                        2. Generally speaking, those we elect
                                            to (Parliament) lose touch with
                                            the people pretty quickly.
                                        3. Voting is the only way that people
                                            like me can have any say about
                                            how government runs things.

IV. Political Distrust   1. Our democratic constitution cer-
                                            tainly has its weaknesses but is
                                            nevertheless the best imaginable
                                            form of government.
                                        2. If the Parliament and the govern-
                                            ment did anything not in ac-
                                            cordance with the Federal Con-

	stitution, the Supreme Court would be able to stop it.
V. Government Distrust	1. Generally speaking, would you say that this country is run by a few big interests looking out for themselves or that it is run for the benefit of all the people.
	2. How much do you trust the government to do what is right?
VI. New Politics Orientation	(Salience rating on four core issues: old age social security; prices, education, and good relations with the United States)
VII. Antinuclear Orientation	Nuclear energy resources should be developed further in order to meet our future energy needs.

The correlation of these scales, presented in Table 7.6, in terms of age groups, supports the suppositions drawn from Figure 7.2 and 7.4: Leftism among youth is not related to class loyalties but to basic orientations on "liberty" and to opposition to nuclear energy, economic growth, and technological progress. Young leftists also tend to question the legitimacy of political institutions; their criticism is radical democratic and conflict oriented in nature and, due to the high level of abstraction, appears to be directed against the system of established conflict mediation which is felt to hinder the attainment of new left goals. The indication that the low correlation on the "system responsiveness" scale might override this explanation can be rejected when it is realized it is criticism of the old left that is system internal and is directed against the bureaucracy in general. An antinuclear, antitechnology attitude does not coincide with left orientations in older persons, however, and must thus be explained by other variables.

The maintenance of political attitudes unsupportive of social structures, which was already clear in Figure 7.4, is further supported here. This realignment is especially strong among the young left. How this value structure supports a new party alignment is indicated by Table 7.7, where the relative effect of each variable is indicated when the weight of each of the others is controlled.

Table 7.6. Covariates of Left-Right Self-placement in the age cohorts

| | Correlation-Coeff. (R) Generation (Cohort) | | |
	18-29	30-50	51 +
Working Class	.02	.03	.15
Distrust Political System	.24	.02	.05
Distrust Government	.06	.06	.24
New Politics Attitude	.13	.06	.04
Antinuclear Attitude	.38	.19	.05
Liberal Democratic Rights	.11	.09	.03
Conflict Openness	.28	.14	.10
System Responsiveness	.12	.14	.01

Source: Compiled by author.

This further explains differences between the generations. In the youngest group "distrust of government" helps explain realignment, while realignment in the oldest generation requires more serious challenges to attitudes of political trust. Leftist attitudes together with liberal orientations most clearly lead to realignment among youth but play a minor role for the elderly. For all value orientations and for all age groups the factor of opposition to economic growth and to nuclear energy has the clearest effect.[25]

Party realignment in favor of the Greens, then, among older age groups appears related to social interests and to a lack of fundamental political trust, while among younger citizens it is related to liberal orientations.

WHAT HAS CHANGED: THE ROLE OF POLICY PROGRAMS AND POLITICAL LEADERSHIP

Since the rejection of party affiliation and established institutions is not explained by left-liberal attitudes, one must assume that the holders of

Table 7.7. Determinants of Party Realignment by Generation

| | Stand. Beta-Weights Generation (Cohorts) | | | |
	18-29	30-50	50+	
Distrust Political System	—	.14	.22	
Distrust Government	.20	.11	—	
Left Orientation	.31	.13	.13	
New Politics Attitude	.10	.09	.09	Party Realignment
Anti-nuclear Attitude	.24	.21	.26	
Liberal Democratic Rights	.16	.07	—	
Conflict Openness	—	.10	—	
System Responsiveness	—	—	—	

Source: Compiled by author.

these attitudes no longer feel themselves represented by the programs and leaders of the old parties. The members of this "value community" are forced to look for new leaders. As Sundquist has observed,[26] new voters are less likely to develop strong party ties when they cannot find the parties solving the problems that concern them deeply. This is particularly true when leadership seems to fail on moral issues.

Under these circumstances realignment occurs from a lack of capacity of political parties to respond to popular demands, rather than from a change of attitudes on the part of the population.

With the problem of response evident in the Social Democratic party since the mid-1970s, the unity identified by Inglehart has dissipated. No longer do the German Social Democratics illustrate the fact that the two forces can be held together in one party even in a society undergoing very rapid change. The strains between the traditional base and a New Left wing of this party have been acute, but a judicious mixture of idealism, compromise, and firmness among its leadership have maintained the party's cohesion, making possible some significant accomplishments.[27]

The idealistic reformist public policy has been hindered by a variety of undesired side effects as well as by the economic slowdown. The frustration of the new left rose with the chancellorship of Helmut Schmidt. His image was that of a *pragmatist*, not an *idealist*, and he clearly lacked the personal charisma of his predecessor, Willy Brandt—at least in the left wing of the SPD. Schmidt's policies were defined in terms of old politics conflicts, while his popularity was based on his success in economic and fiscal matters, not on his dedication to reformist social policy. To youth and intellectuals he appeared to be a typical member of the establishment.

Among those with solidly anchored party identification, the effects of such factors may be minimal. But for those just entering politics and political participation, the development of allegiance to an established party can thus be weakened. The chances for success by new parties are correspondingly augmented due to these uncommitted youth. This can be demonstrated with empirical research: The new politics groups that increasingly supported the SPD into the 1970s[28] changed the trend in 1980 when 21 percent of the postmaterialist "protest generation" voted for the Greens. In 1982 the trend was reversed when every second voter in the group cast a ballot for the Greens while the SPD share dropped to a bare 24 percent (see Table 7.8).

The leadership of the Greens actively strove to augment the trend. With rock concerts, innovative posters produced by an artists' cooperative, a modern war-crimes trial in Nuremberg, and constant debates that seemed to be media happenings, such telegenic former SPD members as Petra Kelly and Otto Schily attracted youth to the party message.

The trend and the efforts were helped by the economic circumstances of the early eighties. The uncommitted and the frustrated found little future with established forces in the receding labor market.

Table 7.8. Vote Intention of Different Value Types and Generations 1980-1982

Age-cohort 1980 (1982)	Value type	1980 Vote intention				1982 Vote intention			
		SPD %	CDU %	FDP %	Grüne %	SPD %	CDU %	FDP %	Grüne %
18-29	Postmaterialist	55*	13	11	21	24	16	13	48
(18-31)	Materialist	51	41	7	2	30	50	9	10
30-39	Postmaterialist	65	13	18	2	35	21	20	24
(32-41)	Materialist	58	33	6	3	25	56	13	5
40-50	Postmaterialist	71	10	10	10	32	34	28	6
(42-52)	Materialist	49	42	8	1	26	56	13	4
51 +	Postmaterialist	58	17	17	8	19	44	22	15
(53 +)	Materialist	43	51	5	1	31	59	3	1

*Entries are relative (%) share of votes for the two pure Inglehart value types. For simplicity of reading the mixed type is omitted here. These figures may not add to 100% caused to rounding.

Source: 1980 Pre-election study of Rudolf Wildenmann & Wilhem P. Bürklin; 1982 Allgemeine Bevölkerungsumfragen in den Sozialwissenschaften (ALLBUS).

THE WEST GERMAN LABOR MARKET IN THE 1980s

Since the beginning of the 1980s, West Germany has been affected by rapidly rising unemployment. In the winter of 1981–82 the number of unemployed reached the two-million threshold, and by the next winter unemployment stood at the highest level since World War II. In February 1983 over 2.5 million were registered as employment seeking; these accounted for 10.4 percent of the total labor force.

Those with few resources were increasingly affected, especially the youth. Although in comparison to such nations as Britain and Italy youth unemployment is still low in West Germany, its level has been rising since 1980 (one-third of all unemployed were under 25 at the beginning of 1983).

The number of chronically unemployed has also grown. Most affected are those for whom such disadvantages as age, health, and the lack of special skills overlap. Whereas this condition was once concentrated in socially marginal groups, more and more in the mainstream of German society are now affected. Part of the reason is the elimination of jobs due to greater efficiency; another part is the new technologies that are even affecting the service sector. This sector, especially in the area of government employment, accounted for most of the growth from the fifties through the seventies: As long as the economy and private consumption were rising, the growth in public expenditures created few problems. But stagflation, along with technological change, has continued to have a strong affect. Some analysts are predicting that in the mid-1980s, unemployment could reach over four million, with effect even being felt by such professions as teachers, doctors, and social workers.

This increases the potential for protest: The public has already been shocked by a number of strikes. And the growth of unemployment is contributing to anomie and to certain processes of sociopolitical disenchantment. The Greens gain some advantages from this, and with their emphasis on a no-growth economy and antimaterialism intend to gain more. But whether they, as an organized party, can satisfy the demands of those in this situation is still open to question.

THE GREENS AS AN ORGANIZED PARTY

Founded as the representative of environmental and antinuclear interest groups, but supported by individuals who reject many established values, the Green party has tried to forge new means of governance but has faced a variety of internal difficulties. As the party won representation in one state parliament after another in the post-1979 period, it played a very reticent role in governance. Maintaining its opposition to established power, and fearing cooptation, it refused to take part in coalitions. When it was strong enough to hold the swing votes that could make or break a coalition, it provided voting support to an SPD government but did not take part in exercising responsibility. In Hesse not even this kind of agreement could be maintained, and new elections ultimately had to be called. As the 1983 national election approached, there was only one state where the Greens were even considering playing more than a passive role in government responsibility.

So, early 1983 involved a great deal of conjecture on what the role of the Greens would be if the party was admitted to the national Parliament, especially if it had the votes to make or break a coalition. Within the party there was general support for giving passive backing to an SPD government, but there were those who looked forward to actually playing a role in the various ministries. Both possibilities became such a campaign issue that CSU leader Franz-Josef Strauss warned that an agreement of the "red" Socialists and the Greens could result in a "Carrot coalition."

In the campaign the Greens tried to ignore this problem and placed their emphasis on educating the voters to their political stand. Their innovative television broadcasts pictured technological decimation of trees and families, while their famous poster of all the military and missile sites in West Germany made voters aware of how vulnerable they were as targets for a war from the East.

The election to the Bundestag negated the question of what the Green role would be in a new coalition: Though they gained 26 seats with 5.6 percent of the vote, they were not strong enough to be coalition makers. But it did not immediately change their mode of operation. After midnight, on the night of the election, Petra Kelly, now a member of the Bundestag, led other Greens to the front door of the Bundestag building and burned a papier-mâché rocket that had the bumper stickers of the other parties pasted on it. In the interest of openness the parliamentary delegation of the party also strove to further participatory democracy by holding policy and strategy sessions on the lawns near the national legislature.

The established parties had hoped that the election would force the Greens to recognize the responsibilities of power. Insofar as inclusion meant dealing with real problems, they expected increasing cooptation to their own way of thinking and operating.

But the determination of the Greens was underestimated. Though the weaknesses of the party were often evident in the open meetings, and though such leaders as Petra Kelly suffered physically from the stress of responding to broad democratic pressures, the party maintained its practices and its principles.

However, one organizational principle threatened to tear it apart. Prior to the election it had been agreed that no one in a leadership post or an elected position would maintain that official function for more than two consecutive years: By the time of the election, for instance, Petra Kelly was no longer on the executive committee. This meant that by March of 1985 every Green delegate to the Bundestag would have to resign in favor of another member of the party. Though this maintained the antiestablishment inclination of Green supporters, it created potential problems of power for the party; and it conflicted with the ambitions of party politicians. So a conflict raged. After Otto Schily indicated opposition to this rotation principle in a Luxembourg radio broadcast, he found himself under increasing attack within the party. And in early 1984 General Bastian, a former military leader who had helped to gain the party legitimacy with older voters, kept his parliamentary seat but resigned from the party over the rotation issue, proclaiming that radical leftist forces were gaining too much authority over such decisions.

Though the party in late 1983 lost seats in two state elections and gained admission to the European Parliament in 1984, there is some question whether the attitudinal groups from which it gains power will continue to be tolerant of the internal problems.

CONCLUSION I: THE QUESTION OF PARTY REALIGNMENT

The attitudinal foundation for the Greens will remain. As this chapter has indicated, the post-1978 electoral success of the party is not merely a consequence of a *newly emerging* "generational cleavage." It is the growth of new values. Since the early 1960s a dramatic age-specific differentiation of political attitudes has been taking place in West Germany and elsewhere.[29] Though it is the youngest group that is decidedly critical toward established authority, one must note that the young have always been more favorable toward political change, and one must explain the increased degree of observed age differences in attitudes in recent years. In other words, one must explain why the age difference emerges and why it leads to partisan realignment.

There is a powerful explanation for these processes in general, and the German situation in particular, in the concept of the "third generation" of a political system.[30] What is meant here is the effect of the declining importance of political socialization within party subcultures in an *era of pragmatic politics*. In other words, we can observe over generations a pattern of declining importance of industrialization-era conflicts. The third generation to experience these conflicts did so as the children of the second, or "realignment," generation—and their experience of these conflicts, between labor and management for instance, is less immediate. The "children of normal politics" today are therefore open to both new ideologies and new parties, if these support new answers to the questions of political and individual destiny. If in the political situations where the ties between the youngest groups and the established parties is weakest, the present economic situation and/or the future expectations of these groups are frustrated by the policy programs of the parties, the probabilities of realignment to parties which will better represent these interests increase.

This has been the case in West Germany since the late seventies. Youth unemployment has increased, and particularly for the better educated, job prospects have declined drastically with the developing economic crisis. This crisis has forced the public service, for instance, to reduce its personnel expenditures by freezing most new job openings. Given the fact that in the late 1970s 80 percent of all university graduates in West Germany entered public service,[31] these events take a dramatic meaning, especially through the additional difficulty that the private sector is neither able nor willing to compensate with new job opportunities. The future expectation of the new potential political elites has thus been seriously frustrated and their ideological protest against the established elites has found substantial electoral support.

CONCLUSION II: THE FUTURE

Provided the continuance of today's basic value orientations and that of present economic difficulties, the Greens appear somewhat justified in viewing their electoral prospects in coming years with a degree of optimism. But, the 1983 parliamentary elections can be expected to have altered somewhat each of these preconditions for the party's optimism. On the one hand, with the change of government from SPD to CDU, the former no longer will be the party to bear the blame for the economic difficulties which deprive the young of employment. And, insofar as the visible opponent of the new left will have changed from the "establishment" as represented by the SPD to that as represented by the CDU, former loyalties to the old left may once again emerge. Thus, not only is the SPD no longer in the position of formulating often-unpopular economic policies but may, as well, find it easier in the future to bridge the gap between old left and new left interests. If the SPD can maintain a relative openness to the new left (and the new politics), it may win back Green voters.

Such a conscious strategy on the part of the SPD, nevertheless, is hindered by a number of factors. Since the new left has developed in terms of a dynamic, independent working class, the split in the left has become very deep. A clearly positive stance of the SPD toward the new politics would now be necessary; only rather fundamental ideological changes in the party's course would carry the importance that rather minimal concessions on the part of the party leadership may thus far have had. And such changes have met resistance from the working class, still a traditional power base for the SPD. However, a return to old, class-based politics—although it may reunite many on the left—could be expected to appeal to a now clearly declining proportion of the electorate.

The dilemma which Social Democrats therefore face lies in the need for a convincing revitalization of their traditional ideological position, one which could align young voters of the third generation with those who have never experienced the immediacy of class conflict. In the important concerns of their individual and collective destiny, many today find convincing answers provided by the Greens—not by the SPD. The future prospects of the Greens thus depend upon the sources of ideological leadership which the younger generation perceives.

NOTES

1. For detailed discussion of these programmatic positions see Rudolf Brun, ed., *Der Grüne Protest* (Frankfurt: 1978); Hans-Werner Lüdke and Olaf Dinné, eds., *Die Rünen, Personen—Projekte—Programme* (Stuttgart: 1980); Lutz Metz and Ulf Wolter, eds., *Die Qual der Wahl* (Berlin: 1980); Jörg Mettke, ed., *Die Grünen. Regierungspartner von morgen?* (Berlin: 1980); Wolf Schäfer, ed., *Neue Soziale Bewegungen: Konservativer Aufbruch in buntem Gewand?* (Frankfurt: 1983); Christian Graf von Krockow, ed., *Brauchen wir ein neues Parteiensystem?* (Frankfurt: 1983); the programmatic book of Maren Manon-Griesbach, *Philosophie der Grünen* (Munich & Vienna: 1982); and the critical comments of Ulrich Rödel, "Die Grünen und das Prinzip der Basisdemokratie," and Peter Dudek, "Nationalromatischer Populismus als Zivilisationskritik," in Schäfer, *Neue Soziale Bewegungen*.

2. For a description and documentation of these processes, see Karl-Werner Brand et al., *Aufbruch in eine andere Gesellschaft. Neue soziale Bewegungen in der Bundesrepublik* (Frankfurt & New York: 1983); Dieter Rucht, "Institutionalisierungstendenzen der neuen sozialen Bewegungen," in Herrmann Hartwich, ed., *Gesellschaftliche Probleme als Anstoss und Folge von Politik* (Opladen: 1983); Mettke, *Die Grünen*; and the detailed analysis of Anna Hallensleben, "Die Entwicklung der Grünen Liste Umweltschutz in Niedersachsen von ihrer Entstehung 1977 bis zur Gründung der Partei DIE GRÜNEN 1980," Dissertation, University of Gottingen.

3. See Brand et al., *Aufbruch in eine andere Gesellschaft.*

4. Rudolf Wildenmann, "Protestpartei gefragt," *Capital,* no. 9 (1977), and "Protestpotential," *Capital,* no. 8 (1978); Rainer-Olaf Schultze, "Nur Parteiverdrossenheit und diffuser Protest? Systemfunktionale Fehlinterpretation der Grünen Wahlerfolge," *Zeitschrift zur Parliament* 11 (1980): 292–313, and "Wählerverhalten und Parteiensystem in der Bundesrepublik Deutschland," in Hans-Georg Wehling, ed., *Westeuropas Parteiensysteme im Wandel* (Stuttgart: 1983); Werner Harenberg, "Sicherer Platz links von der SPD? Die Wähler der Grünen in den Daten der Demoskopie," in Mettke, *Die Grünen,* pp. 38–50. Ferdinand Müller-Rommel, "Die Grünen—künftig ein fester Bestandteil unseres Parteiensystems?" in Wehling, *Westeuropas Parteiensysteme,* pp. 83–94; Ralf Dahrendorf, "Es ist nicht alles Weimar, was bunt ist. Warum nicht fünf statt drei?" in Krockow, *Brauchen wir ein neues Parteiensystem?*; Bernd Guggenberger, "Umweltschutz und neue Parteibewegung. Wieviel Zukunft hat die Volksparteiendemokratie?" in Krockow *Brauchen wir ein neues Parteiensystem?* Heidrun Abromeit, "Parteiverdrossenheit und Alternativebewegung. Thesen zur Weiterentwicklung des Parteiensystems der Bundesrepublik," *Politische Vierteljahreschrift* 23 (1982): 179–195.

5. For an aggregate analysis of the vote for the Greens, see the regular "Berichte der Forschungsgruppe Wahlen," Mannheim, the reports of INFAS, Bonn, and Troitzch (198). For analysis of survey data, see Max Kaase and Hans D. Klingemann," Sozialstruktur, Wertorientierung und Parteiensystem: Zum Problem der Interessenvermittlung in westlichen Demokratien," in Joachim Matthes, ed., *Sozialer Wandel in Westeuropa* (Frankfurt: 1979), pp. 543–573; Ferdinand Müller-Rommel and Helmut Wilke, "Sozialstruktur und 'postmaterialistische' Wertorientierungen von Ökologisten," *PVS* 22 (1981): 383–397; Ferdinand Müller-Rommel, "Parteien neuen Tyups in Westeuropa: Eine vergleichende Analyse," *Zeitschrift für Parliamentsfragen* 13 (1982): 369–390; Wilhelm P. Bürklin, "Die Grünen und die 'Neue Politik,' Abscheid vom Dreiparteinensystem?" *PVS* 22 (1981): 359–382, and "Die Wähler der Grünen im Zyklus neuer Werte und politischer Deprivation," Dissertation, University of Mannheim (1983); also, the contributions of Manfred Berger et al., "Stabilität und Wechsel: Eine Analyse der Bundestags wahl 1980," in Max Kaase and Hans-Dieter Klingemann, eds., *Wahlen und politisches system. Analysen aus Anlass der Bundestagswahl* (Opladen: 1983), 12–57; Ursula Feist and Klaus Liepelt, "Neue Eliten in alten Parteien," in Kaase and Klingemann, *Wahlen und politisches system,* pp. 81–100; and Dieter Fuchs, "Politischer Protest und Stabilität des politischen Systems," in Kaase and Klingemann, *Wahlen und politisches System,* pp. 121–143. For discussion of these data, see Horst-Dieter Rönsch, "Die Magister wandern weiter," *Kritik* (1979): 19–31, and "Die Wählerbasis der Grünen—Sozialstruktur und Einstellungen," in Metz and Wolter, *Die Qual der Wahl,* pp. 32–53; Werner Harenberg, "Sicherer Platz links von der SPD?"; Müller-Rommel, Die Grünen; and Schultze, "Nur Parteiverdrossenheit und diffuser Protest" and "Wählerverhalten und Parteiensystem."

6. Wilhelm P. Bürklin, "The Grünen in West Germany: An Answer to Post-industrial Change?" Paper prepared for the Annual Meeting of the Midwest Political Science Association, Milwaukee 1982.

7. Lutz Hildebrandt and Lutz Metz, "Akute Umweltkonflikte und die Wahlentscheidung für die Grünen." To appear in *WZB-Mitteilungen,* no. 25 (Berlin).

8. Daniel Bell, *The Coming of Post-Industrial Society* (London: 1973); Samuel Huntington, "Post Industrial Politics: How Benign Will It Be?" *Comparative Politics* 6 (1974): 163–191.

9. Barnes et al., *Political Action: Mass Participation in Five Western Democracies* (Beverly Hills, Calif.: 1979).

10. William Kornhauser, *The Politics of Mass Society* (London: 1959); Morris Janowitz, *Political Conflict* (Chicago: 1970) and *Social Control of the Welfare State* (New York: 1976).

11. Ralf Dahrendorf, "Recent Changes in the Class Structure of European Societies," in S. Graubard, ed., *A New Europe* (Boston: 1967).

12. Franz Urban Pappi, "Parteiensystem und Sozialstruktur in der Bundesrepublik," *PVS* 14 (1973): 191–213; Seymour Martin Lipset, "Whatever Happened to the Proletariat? A Historic Mission Unfulfilled," *Encounter* 56 (1981): 18–34; Kendall L. Baker, Russell J. Dalton, and Kai Hildebrandt, *Germany Transformed: Political Culture and the New Politics* (Cambridge, Mass.: 1981).

13. For a discussion of the left-right problem, see Seymour M. Lipset et al., "Psychology of Voting: An Analysis of Political Behaviour," in Lindzey, ed., *Handbook of Social Psychology,* vol. 2 (Reading, Mass.: 1954), pp. 1124–1175; Detlef Murphy et al., "Haben 'links' und 'rechts' noch Zukunft; Zur aktuellen Diskussion über die politischen Richtungsbegriffe," *PVS* 22 (1981): 398–414; Bürklin, "Die Grünen und die 'Neue Politik'"; Wilhelm P. Bürklin, "Konzept und Fakten: Zur Notwendigkeit der konzeptionellen Fundierung der Diskussion der politischen Richtungsbegriffe, "Links" und "Rechts," *PVS* 23 (1982): 339–345; Lipset, "Proletariat."

14. Eric Allardt, "Past and Emerging Political Cleavages," in Otto Stammer, ed., *Party Systems, Party Organizations and the Politics of New Masses* (Institut für Politische Wissenschaft and der Freie Universitat Berlin: 1968), pp. 66–74.

15. For more detail, see David Easton, *A System Analysis of Political Life* (New York, London, Sidney: 1965), and "A Reassessment of the Concept of Political Support," *British Journal of Political Science* 5 (1975): 435–457.

16. Hans D. Klingemann and Franz Urban Pappi, *Politischer Radikalismus* (Munich & Vienna: 1972).

17. Kai Hildebrandt and Russell J. Dalton, "Die Neuer Politik," in M. Kaase, ed., *Wahlsoziologie Heute* (PVS Sonderheft: 1977), pp. 230–256.

18. Edward Hallett Carr, *The Twenty Year's Crisis. An Introduction to the Study of International Relations* (London: 1974); Bürklin, "Die Wähler der Grü-

nen." A discussion of how different generations label these dimensions can be discerned in Murphy et al., "Haben 'links' und 'rechts' noch Zukunft," and "Programmatik oder analytisches Konzept? Eine Antwort auf die Kritiken von Klingemann und Bürklin," *PVS* 23 (1982): 460–465; Hans-Dieter Klingemann, "Fakten oder Programmatik? Die Thesen vom Murphy et al. "uber den Bedeutungswandel von 'links' und 'rechts'" *PVS* 23 (1982): 214–224. Bürklin, "Die Grünen und die 'Neue Politik.'"

19. Further discussion of spatial models of party systems are in Philip E. Converse, "The Problem of Party Distances in Models of Voting Change," in M. Kent Jennings and L. Harmon Zeigler, eds., *The Electoral Process* (Englewood Cliffs: 1966), pp. 105–207; Donald Stokes, "Spatial Models of Party Competition," in Campbell et al., eds., *Elections and the Political Order* (New York, London, Sydney: 1966). Pappi, "Parteiensystem und Sozialstruktur." Kaase et al., "Sozialstruktur, Wertorientierung und Parteiensystem." Baker, Dalton, and Hildebrandt, *Germany Transformed,* and Bürklin, "Die Grünen und die 'Neue Politik.'"

20. Bürklin, "Die Grünen und die 'Neue Politik'," pp. 363ff.

21. Forschungsgruppe Wahlen, "Bundestagswahl 1983," pp. 40ff.

22. For an elaborate analysis of generational effects on political attitudes, see Converse, *Problem of Party Distance.* For the German system, see Rainer M. Lepsius, "Wahlverhalten, Parteien und politische Spannungen. Vermutungen zu Tendenzen und Hypothesen der Untersuchung der Bundestagswahl 1972," *PVS* 14 (1973): 295–313.

23. Kornhauser, William, *The Politics of Mass Society* (London: 1959).

24. The items for Scales I, II, and IV are drawn from the "democracy scale" of Kaase and Wildenmann: See Max Kaase, "Demokratische Einstellungen in der Bundesrepublik Deutschland," in Rudolf Wildenmann, ed., *Sozialwissenschaftliches* Jahrbuch für Politik (1971), pp. 119–326; and see Wilhelm P. Bürklin, "Links und/oder demokratisch? Dimensionen studentischen Demokratieverständnisses," *PVS* 21 (1980): 220–247. Those for Scale V have been analyzed elsewhere as "political trust" (Barnes et al., *Political Action*). And those for Scale VI are those of the "new politics" core index used by Baker, Dalton, and Hildebrandt, *Germany Transformed.* The items were analyzed by multidimensional scaling methods. Unidimensional solutions for Scales I to V resulted.

25. For more detail, see Bürklin, "Die Wähler der Grünen."

26. 1973, pp. 28ff.

27. 1977, p. 243.

28. Baker, Dalton, and Hildebrandt, *Germany Transformed.*

29. M. Jennings and Richard G. Niemi *Generations and Politics. A Panel Study of Young Adults and Their Parents* (Princeton, N.J.: 1981); Barnes et al., *Political Action.*

30. Beck, Paul Allen, "A Socialization Theory of Partisan Realignment," in Richard G. Niemi et al., eds., *The Politics of Future Citizens* (San Francisco: 1974), pp. 199–219.

31. Blossfeld, Peter, "Bildungsreform und Beschäftigung der jungen Generation im öffentlichen und privaten Sektor. Eine empirische vergleichende Analyse," *VASMA-Arbeitspapiere* 31 (Mannheim: 1983).

8

INTERNATIONAL POLITICS AND THE 1983 ELECTION

Arthur M. Hanhardt, Jr.

INTRODUCTION

A national election in the Federal Republic of Germany (FRG) is more than a purely domestic event. The Federal Republic is deeply involved in international politics and trade, and is located at the front of the East-West confrontation. Also, the citizenry of the Federal Republic is acutely aware of politics and the international environment. This stems partly from Nazi Germany's defeat in World War II and from "serving as the pressure point testing the resolve and might of the two superpowers."[1] Foreign policy issues are factors in nearly all FRG national elections.

Despite the importance of foreign policy issues, domestic problems (including unemployment, inflation, and welfare) remain the major concerns of the German electorate. Contrary to the beliefs of U.S. officials, newspaper editors, and columnists, the 1983 election campaign was decided on bread-and-butter issues rather than on peace, the stationing of U.S. missiles, or other foreign policy issues.

This chapter examines the role of the Federal Republic in world politics following the 1980 federal election, international politics and outcome of the 1983 election campaign, and the impact of international issues on the 1983 election. In addition, other countries' views of the FRG are examined in light of the 1983 election outcome.

This study is based on an analysis of German periodicals and newspapers, the INFAS-Report *Politogramm Bundestagswahl 1983,* and publications issued by the major political parties.

THE FEDERAL REPUBLIC OF GERMANY IN WORLD POLITICS: 1980–1982

The period between the 1980 election and the installation of the Kohl government in October 1982 was marked by West German involvement in a wide range of foreign policy problems. Three issue areas are stressed here: U.S.-FRG relations, FRG relations with the German Democratic Republic (GDR) and the Soviet Union, and the NATO two-track decision on the stationing of new intermediate-range U.S. missiles in the Federal Republic.

U.S.-FRG relations were the subject of much debate in the Federal Republic after the coalition of the Social Democratic party (SPD) and the Free Democratic party (FDP) was reelected in October 1980. German reaction to the Soviet invasion of Afghanistan, the resulting Olympic boycott, the hostage crisis in Iran, and U.S. nuclear weapons policies had all complicated relations between Chancellor Helmut Schmidt and President Jimmy Carter. Neither had much liking for the other, and Schmidt had made clear his hope that Ronald Reagan would succeed Carter following the November 1980 U.S. elections. After Reagan had been elected, Schmidt used all his influence to be the first head of government to meet with the president-elect in order to symbolize a new era in U.S.-FRG relations.

Schmidt's hopes were for more predictable and consistent policies from the forthcoming Reagan administration, thus establishing a more stable basis for U.S.-FRG relations. Schmidt's expectations faded with the continued U.S. opposition to the Soviet gas pipeline contract and the lifting of President Carter's grain embargo, imposed in the wake of the Soviet invasion of Afghanistan.

U.S.-FRG relations were complicated by the rise of the "successor generation." A new generation of elites was coming to the fore in the Federal Republic, a generation without direct involvement in World War II. For many younger Germans, the U.S. was no longer a model to be followed uncritically, as memories of wartime destruction, the Marshall Plan, and the cold war were replaced with critical attitudes relating to U.S. policies in Vietnam, international economics, and Central America. The successor generation was asserting West German interests as it interpreted them. This assertiveness included questioning U.S. troop-stationing costs and bemoaning the high U.S. interest rates, which were widely felt to have a negative impact on the FRG economy. Some West Germans in 1982 were criticizing the U.S. for not providing the "locomotive" to pull the market economies out of the worldwide recession. Finally, U.S. Central American policy was mobilizing increasing condemnation from the West German center-left.

In spite of ensuing tensions, the FRG government remained firmly committed to the U.S.-FRG alliance. Much of the attention given to the problems of the North Atlantic was devoted to how they could be solved.

Equally important in the 1980–82 period were FRG relations with the German Democratic Republic and the Soviet Union. Immediately after the 1980 election, the German Democratic Republic announced a virtual doubling of the mandatory exchange of deutsche marks into East German currency required of Western travelers. This was a shock to the Federal Republic, and the timing showed the extent to which the German Democratic Republic wished to see a safe return of Chancellor Schmidt. The FRG response was mild, without strong countermeasures. The government felt the reprisals would not be in the interests of the East German people and would play into the hands of the government, which clearly sought to reduce West German influence by any means.

The chill in FRG-GDR relations continued in the interelection period under discussion. The German Democratic Republic insisted on demands that the Federal Republic adamantly refused to accept: recognition of a GDR citizenship and the exchange of ambassadors between East and West Germany. Amid this standoff, Chancellor Schmidt and Secretary General Erich Honecker met in the German Democratic Republic in December 1981, just at the time that the Polish government announced the imposition of marshall law. An essential element in German-German relations affecting the climate for the runup to the 1983 election was the contradictory preference the East Germans had for the SPD-FDP government, while being unable to gain the concessions it wanted.

An element of the SPD-FDP *Ostpolitik* was the notion that improved relations with the German Democratic Republic could only be achieved via the Soviet Union. In dealing with the Soviets, Chancellor Schmidt viewed his role as an intermediary or "interpreter" between East and West, while seeking better commercial and economic relations with Moscow. The agreement on the Soviet gas pipeline was an important element in assuring sound business relations with the Soviet Union, and the meeting between Helmut Schmidt and Leonid Brezhnev in 1981 highlighted Schmidt's intermediary role. U.S. opposition to the pipeline agreement tended to undermine Schmidt and probably helped to frustrate his efforts to improve relations with East Germany.

The Federal Republic's role in promoting the two-track missile plan also frustrated Schmidt's efforts to improve ties with the Soviet Union. Chancellor Schmidt "invented" the two-track policy in 1977 to maintain a strategic balance in Central Europe in response to the Soviet deployment of SS-20 intermediate-range missiles. On one track NATO forces would deploy Pershing II and Cruise missiles, while on the second track negotiations with the Soviets would be aimed at reducing theater nuclear forces. During 1980–82 Western deployment became imminent as Soviet SS-20s were coming on-line in increasing numbers. Meanwhile, the Reagan administration was showing little enthusiasm for the Intermediate-Range Nuclear Force (INF) talks at Geneva. "Interpreter" Schmidt, unable to exert significant influence on the INF talks, was forced to continue public support for NATO deployment in the face of rising public protest as evidenced in the massive October 1981 antinuclear demonstration in Bonn. Throughout 1982 Schmidt was caught in an increasingly uncomfortable squeeze between the deep FRG commitment to NATO and growing domestic opposition to deployment, especially within the ranks of his own SPD.

INTERNATIONAL POLITICS AND THE
1983 ELECTION CAMPAIGN

Party Platforms and Programs

The Christian Democratic Union (CDU) and its Bavarian sister party, the Christian Social Union (CSU), defined their foreign policy objectives in light of postwar West German foreign policy. The coalition stood for close alignment with the United States and support for the North Atlantic Alliance. The Christian Democrats' chancellor-candidate, Helmut Kohl, said during the 1983 election campaign that "without the protection and commitment of the United States of America, the Federal Republic of Germany would not exist in its present form." The CDU/CSU desired to pursue friendship and cooperation with the United States and the rest of the Western nations.

Just as they strived for good relations with the U.S., the CDU/CSU wished to maintain continuity in their relations with the Soviet Union. This meant improved trade with the Soviets on the economic side. Politically, peaceful coexistence and a forthright give-and-take relationship with the USSR was sought.

The CDU and CSU are unwavering in their support for NATO. They believe that the free European states must work together militarily to defend Western Europe. Furthermore, the CDU/CSU believes that Western European freedom depends on NATO. To the CDU/CSU, the North Atlantic Alliance is not simply a community of arms but also a community of ideas and ideals bringing together nations with similar constitutions and comparable conceptions of human and civil rights, and peace and freedom.

During the 1983 campaign, the Social Democratic party based its foreign policy platform on two principles: freedom and human rights. They believed that all people have the right to freedom and humane treatment. From this standpoint, the Social Democrats demonstrated that they opposed marshall law in Poland, economic exploitation of the third world, and U.S. involvement in Central America.

Like the CDU/CSU, the SPD affirmed its dedication to the North Atlantic Alliance, although not as stridently as the CDU/CSU. On the issue of security policy, the SPD's main emphasis was on promoting disarmament, particularly regarding medium-range nuclear missiles in both the East and the West. Hans-Jochen Vogel, the SPD's chancellor-candidate, called on the United States and the Soviet Union to move from their respective positions toward a compromise at the Geneva talks. Vogel and the SPD felt that the best solution would be the zero-option plan or total removal of European-based medium-range nuclear missiles. In view of this policy, the SPD opposed the "automatic" stationing of Pershing II and cruise missiles in the FRG.

The Free Democratic party (FDP), now the coalition partner of the CDU/CSU, also believed in "security" politics and close cooperation with other European nations. The FDP enthusiastically supported the European Communities (EC). This position reflected the European policies of Hans-Dietrich Genscher, West German foreign minister and FDP chairman. On the issue of deploying new nuclear missiles in Europe, the Free Democrats supported an elimination of U.S. and Soviet medium-range nuclear missiles in Europe.

The Green party, a new political force in the Federal Republic, was mainly concerned with the nuclear arms race, environmental and population problems, and north-south relations. The Greens campaigned for multilateral disarmament and supported the Strategic Arms Reduction Talks (START) and the INF talks in Geneva. Furthermore, the Greens staunchly opposed the stationing of American nuclear missiles in the Federal Republic.

The Greens initiated intensive debates concerning these issues within the Federal Republic. They organized large demonstrations to protest against nuclear weapons and energy, U.S. and Soviet military policies, and Western exploitation of the third world. The Greens claim that they support an "ecologically minded" foreign policy.

The International Factor

Generally, the West German electorate seemed to be more concerned about bread-and-butter problems (unemployment and job security, inflation, law and order, and a clean environment) and less concerned about foreign policy issues. At the same time foreign travel played a role in election campaign strategies for all parties. Clearly, there is a certain discrepancy between public concern and campaign activities.

Table 8.1 shows issue saliency as ranked in the 1980 election. The ranking is determined by stating that a particular issue area was personally "very important." If 70 percent or more of the sample felt the issue was very important, then its salience was coded as high, 50–59 percent as medium, and below 49 percent as low.

Table 8.1. Rank of Major Campaign Issues, 1980

Salience to Electorate	Issue
Very important (above 70 percent)	Inflation
	Unemployment and Job Security
	Security of Pensions
	Energy Policy
Moderately important (50–69 percent)	Law and Order
	Environmental Policy
Less important (below 49 percent)	Good Relations with the United States and the Eastern Bloc

Source: Forschungsgruppe Wahlen, "Wahlstudie 1980, 1.Welle" (Mannheim: Institute für Wahlanalysen und Gesellschaftsbeobachtung, 1980), pp. 112–113.

The results indicate that the average German voter tended to be more concerned about domestic rather than foreign policy issues in 1980.

If domestic issues are the primary determinants of an election outcome in the Federal Republic of Germany, then what do party officials and chancellor-candidates expect to gain from the foreign travel that is a prominent feature of electoral campaigning? There are four potential benefits: (1) Politicians wish to convey to the electorate that they have the ability to communicate with world leaders; (2) candidates want to increase their international exposure and improve their reputations as international, as well as national, personalities; (3) travelers seek expanded media coverage and to be portrayed as potential world leaders; and (4) party leaders hope to gain first-hand information and direct impressions of foreign leaders and their policies.

Compared to the 1980 election campaign, there was a significant increase in the frequency of international travel by party officials ande chancellor-candidates prior to the 1983 election. This is, in part, illustrated by Chancellor Kohl's visits to United States and the Soviet Union, Genscher's appointments in the United States and elsewhere, Hans-Jochen Vogel's travels to Moscow and Washington, and Green party leader Petra Kelly's stop in Washington.

Three factors in 1983 help to explain why there was an increase in the number of international visits by party officials and chancellor-candidates between 1980 and 1983. One, the emergence of the Greens on the Federal Republic's political landscape contributed to the increase. Two, the 1983 federal election was perceived as more significant than that of 1980 by Americans. The U.S. government considered the election a test of the Federal Republic's loyalty to the North Atlantic Alliance and a referendum on the deployment of the U.S. Pershing II and Cruise missiles. This perception encouraged West German visits to Washington. Three, aside from Hans-Dietrich Genscher, the chancellor-candidates had little experience in international affairs. Vogel's career was highlighted by terms as mayor of Munich and as interior minister and an unsuccessful mayoral candidature in West Berlin. Kohl, too, was mainly identified with domestic politics. Both used preelection foreign travel to enhance their bona fides through consultations with world leaders in both the East and the West.

With the sudden ascension of the Kohl government in October 1982, other countries began to consider their position toward the composition of the new West German government. The primary countries examined in this section of the chapter are the United States, the Soviet Union, the German Democratic Republic, and France. Each of these countries had special interests in the outcome of the election and took steps to influence the outcome while, of course, proclaiming that it would be unthinkable to interfere with or affect West German internal affairs.

The U.S. and all the other countries discussed here viewed the election mainly within the context of the confrontation between East and West. The Reagan administration clearly favored a continuation of the Kohl government, even if an absolute CDU/CSU majority meant a prominent place for Franz-Josef Strauss after the election. Washington saw much uncertainty in the possible return of an SPD government under Vogel. As Jan Reifenberg pointed out in a series of reports from Washington for the *Frankfurter Allgemeine Zeitung,* official Washington was never enthusiastic about the SPD Ostpolitik and Reagan saw in Helmut Kohl a kindred soul. With Kohl, the Federal Republic commitment to the two-track decision would be assured and the NATO alliance strengthened in its resolve to face the Eastern threat as perceived by Reagan and his foreign policy advisors. President Reagan expressed this view in a national press conference in January. Subsequent efforts by Reagan to express a more balanced view did not detract from what amounted to the most serious U.S. intervention in a West German election since 1957, when John Foster Dulles suggested that a socialist government in the Federal Republic would be a catastrophe.

In January 1983 Vice-President Bush traveled to Western Europe to explain the U.S. position on the INF and START talks in Geneva. Painfully aware that his mission would doubtlessly be interpreted as an attempt to influence FRG voters, bush nonetheless made Bonn his first stop. Bush's visit to Bonn and Reagan's comments were part of a pattern that included the differential treatment accorded Kohl and Vogel on their visits to Washington: Kohl was granted two and one-half hours of President Reagan's time, while Vogel had to make do with just 30 minutes.

The Soviet Union was as interested in influencing the FRG election as was the U.S. Moscow saw its interests best served by supporting the Social Democrats and the Greens in the Federal Republic. The news releases of TASS and Novosti were a principal means of broadcasting the Soviet position. The Soviet news agencies held that the CDU/CSU were parties willing to accept U.S. intermediate-range nuclear missiles in the Federal Republic, therefore increasing the risk that West Germany would become a nuclear battlefield. The Soviets emphasized that the NATO missile policy was designed to limit nuclear war to the European theater, while sparing the U.S. The identification of the NATO missile policy with purely U.S. interests was meant to drive a wedge between West Germany and the U.S. in accord with the overall Soviet aim of breaking up the North Atlantic Alliance.

Meanwhile, the Soviets made it clear that the policies of the SPD, while not totally in accord with Soviet views, were at least moving in a direction consistent with Soviet aims. To emphasize their preference, the Soviets gave particular attention to SPD foreign policy expert Egon Bahr during Vogel's visit to Moscow in January 1983. Bahr, a harsh critic of the U.S. policy and former architect of SPD Ostpolitik was singled out as a potential spokesman for achieving desired Soviet goals, that is, no NATO missile deployment, inclusion of French and British missiles in the negotiations, and acceptance of a nuclear-free zone in Central Europe.

In an attempt to counter Vice-President Bush's visit to Bonn, Soviet Foreign Minister Andrei Gromyko also spent three days in Bonn in January. Andrei Gromyko comported himself with his routinized toughness leavened by occasional humor. Gromyko emphasized the Soviet position and riveted the attention of the West German press on Soviet goals and desires vis-à-vis the forthcoming election. Gromyko and the Soviet press harshly critized Bush's "cynical" effort to massively interfere in West German internal affairs.

During the final days of the election campaign, the Soviets launched an intensive print medium and radio effort to influence West German voters. The Soviets finally made clear that a SPD government was the only possibility to deflect the Federal Republic from stationing the provocative new missiles. Vogel was falsely proclaimed as opposed to the two-track policy. Massive anti-NATO demonstrations were staged in Leningrad and Minsk. At these rallies, factory workers adopted resolutions on the "rocket" issue in the Federal Republic and endorsed statements supportive of the West German peace movement. Foreign correspondents in Moscow were offered free flights to attend these rallies, and TASS and Novosti gave these events priority treatment on its international wire services on the first of March, five days prior to the FRG election.

Along with the U.S. and the Soviet Union, the German Democratic Republic had a strong interest in the outcome of the March election. The German Democratic Republic was interested in continuity in West German Ostpolitik and opposed the two-track decision. German Democratic Republic aims were articulated primarily through speeches and letters by Erich Honecker, secretary-general of the East German Socialist Unity party (SED).

While Honecker attempted to keep the door open to possible continuation of a Kohl government, he gave support to the West German peace movement. This came in a letter dated the fourth of February suggesting that Kohl accept Swedish Prime Minister Olaf Palme's suggestion for a nuclear weapons free zone in Central Europe. Kohl predictably rejected Honecker's suggestion. Yet the point had been made and was given wide attention: The GDR preferred the SPD and the aims of the peace movement to a continuation of the Conservative-Liberal coalition.

France assumed an important place in the international standing of the Kohl government immediately after the first of October, when Kohl and his principal advisors visited Paris. The mild tensions between Paris and the new Bonn government stemmed from Socialist Mitterrand's previous sympathies for the SPD. Mitterrand's preference for CDU arms policies, however, prevented overt support for the SPD during the 1983 campaign. Indeed, French policy makers were wary of the peace movement and the SPD, both of which were suspected of harboring neutralist tendencies.

The twentieth anniversary of the German-French Friendship Treaty brought President Mitterrand to Bonn in January. The treaty had been the work of Adenauer and de Gaulle, and, since Kohl considers himself the political grandson of Adenauer, the event could only enhance Kohl's image as a statesman.

The chairman of the French Socialist party, Lionel Jospin, visited Cologne at the end of February to express solidarity with the SPD. This effort to counterbalance Kohl's use of French support for CDU defense and national security policies was half-hearted and ineffective.

Other countries also had views and interests regarding the FRG election. The British government of Margaret Thatcher aided Kohl by dampening demands for EC reforms. The Italians expressed official alarm lest a "red-green" coalition come into power in Bonn. Finally, the Chinese government made clear its support for Helmut Kohl's tough policies toward the Soviet Union.

The 1983 FRG election was an international event attracting both attention and involvement. How did foreign influences affect the outcome?

INTERNATIONAL ISSUES AND THE ELECTION OUTCOME

The foregoing has documented the principal foreign efforts to influence the outcome of the FRG election. Analyzing the relationship between the efforts and the outcome is fraught with risk. For example, there is little in the attitudinal data that allows for direct conclusions concerning the impact of, say, the Gromyko visit to Bonn on voting behavior.

An indirect method for assessing the impact of international politics on the election is to look at the relative saliency of international and domestic issues. Analysis of salient issues suggests that while the SPD was viewed as competent in the foreign policy area, the CDU-CSU was viewed as competent in the domestic bread-and-butter issues most salient to the voting public. INFAS data comparing the most important substantive is-sues affecting electoral decisions in 1980 and 1983 found the following:

Table 8.2. Issue Salience Change: 1980–1983 (in percentage)

	1980	1983	Change
International issues:			
Peace policy	33	37	+4
National security	26	15	-11
German-German relations	12	6	-6
Bread-and-butter issues:			
Unemployment	30	62	+32
National debt	33	33	0
Pensions policy	39	33	-6

Source: INFAS-Report, *Politogramm Bundestagswahl 1983* (Bonn–Bad Godesberg: INFAS, March 1983), p. 71.

In dealing with the most important issues of the election, it turned out that "with the exception of two policy areas, peace and Ostpolitik, the [CDU/CSU] was able to convince the electorate more strongly of their competence [than the SPD]."[2] Thus, the CDU/CSU was seen as more com-petent than the SPD in those issue areas most salient to the voting public.

The conclusion to be drawn from a combination of attitudinal data and voting results is that the views, interests, and actions of other countries had little impact on the FRG voter. In fact, the polling data in the weeks before the election showed clear decline in the perceived importance of national security issues.[3]

More detailed analysis of attitudinal and electoral data may turn up subtle relations among international issues, foreign influences, and voting behavior in the March election. However, it seems unlikely that these analyses will deviate far from the preliminary judgments of Max Kaase, Klaus Liepelt, and Elizabeth Noelle-Neumann on the day after the election. None of these eminent figures in West German opinion and election research accorded much significance to national security and peace issues in determining the outcome because of the predominance of domestic economic issues.

OTHER COUNTRIES' PERSPECTIVES

International politics following the election results indicated adjustments had to be made, especially among those countries whose efforts had been directed toward returning the SPD to power: the Soviet Union and the German Democratic Republic.

The Soviet Union adjusted quickly to the "reality" of a continuing CDU/CSU-FDP government. Official statements stressed that Chancellor Kohl had vowed continuity in policies toward the East. And although the Soviets had stated loudly and often that the election would be a plebiscite on the stationing of U.S. missiles, the line quickly reversed and held that the "result of the Federal Election was in no way a vote for the stationing of new American atomic weapons."[4] This shift in the Soviet position prepared the way for continued Soviet efforts to encourage the FRG anti-nuclear missile movement.

The German Democratic Republic had also made the missile issue the central feature of its efforts to influence the election outcome. The German Democratic Republic reacted cautiously to the reelected Kohl government, with no official public statement until March 13, when Honecker spoke of common areas of interest between the Federal Republic and the German Democratic Republic. Unofficially, the German Democratic Republic and Soviet leaderships considered the coalition with the FDP the "lesser evil" compared to an absolute CDU/CSU majority with Strauss as foreign minister.[5]

Official Washington was pleased with the election outcome and saw its policies confirmed by the West German public. This, it was maintained, would ease disarmament discussions in Geneva by assuring that the Federal Republic would not balk at the stationing before the missiles should be bargained away. Others warned that Kohl, in spite of his victory, should not be pushed too far, since opposition to missile stationing was still strong in the Federal Republic of Germany.

In other quarters, the French were relieved to see an end to what was interpreted as a move toward neutralism in the Federal Republic of Germany prior to the election. The results were consistent with French interests by assuring a stable partner. The People's Republic of China, through its official news agency Xinhua, stated that the Federal Republic had strengthened its commitment to NATO in a way consistent with West German security interests. And, finally, Prime Minister Margaret Thatcher phoned Chancellor Kohl to personally congratulate him on a victory that helped stabilize the alliance.

The postelection perspectives tend toward either gratification at a realization of expectations or an acceptance of new state of affairs. In either case, the result was widely anticipated and presented nothing shocking to the international community.

SOME POSTELECTION FOREIGN POLICY ISSUES

Although foreign policy issues did not have a major impact on the outcome of the 1983 West German election, the election did play a role in shaping West German foreign policy on the Euromissile issue, relations wioth the German Democratic Republic and the domestic debate on foreign policy issues.

The decisiveness of the CDU/CSU-FDP virtually assured the deployment of the Pershing II and Cruise missiles as planned in the fall of 1983, barring an unlikely agreement by the U.S. and the USSR at the Geneva INF talks. To be sure, the confrontation between the government and the Greens and the peace movement promised a "hot autumn" (*heisser Herbst*) to oppose missile deployment. Indeed massive and peaceful demonstrations took place throughout West Germany, notably at Mutlangen and, in October, in Bonn. The demonstrations were impressive, but a basic truth of parliamentary democracy came into play: The opposition SPD and Greens lacked the votes to implement their policy alternatives in the Bundestag.

The Kohl government did all it could to influence the INF talks in the hope of achieving a negotiated settlement that obviated the need for missile deployment. There was some frustration in West German government circles at the inability to influence some kind of accord between the superpowers. Yet there was no question of Bonn's jumping the deployment track. The missiles began arriving at the U.S. base at Mutlangen at the end of November.

The deployment could have been expected to have complicated West German relations with the German Democratic Republic. Dire, but unspecific, warnings of the consequences of new NATO missiles in the Federal Republic emanated from East Berlin. In spite of the rhetoric, Kohl and Honecker went to great lengths to assure each other of continuity in FRG-GDR relations. In practical terms this meant seeking stable German-German relations even as the Soviets moved their short- and medium-range missiles into East Germany and Czechoslovakia to counter NATO deployment.

The first indication of "business as usual" with the German Democratic Republic came with Franz-Josef Strauss's surprise negotiation, in June 1983 of a one billion deutsche mark loan to the German Democratic Republic from a consortium of mainly Munich banks. This deal was announced without the specific concessions that Strauss and the CSU had customarily demanded from the German Democratic Republic. This defect led to the resignation of several CSU stalwarts who felt themselves betrayed by an opportunistic Franz-Josef Strauss. Ultimately the German Democratic Republic did ease conditions along the border by dismantling some obsolete security devices and, in the spring of 1984, dramatically increasing the approvals of exit visa applications.

Relations between East and West Germany since March 1983 illustrate the paradoxical ease with which communist regimes can deal with conservative governments. The Kohl-Honecker meeting at Yuri Andropov's funeral underlined the facility with which the two governments can deal with each other despite the spectacular efforts of East Germans to depart illegally for the West. While the Honecker regime continued to clamp down on independent peace groups, exit visas were being approved at record rates (100 per day in 1984 compared to 25 per day in 1983). Kohl government loans to buttress the GDR economy have eased domestic pressures on the East German leadership. Neither side has made any substantial concessions on fundamental foreign policy issues.

The March 1983 election changed the foreign policy debate in the Federal Republic. The national emergence of the Greens as a new factor was noted above. The Greens' vision of a deindustrialized, demilitarized, and reunified Germany as a paragon of international peace and understanding appealed to many of the young voters. How effective the Greens will be in articulating their foreign policy alternatives depends on their ability to remain a viable force in West German politics. This visibility is being tested by organizational problems exemplified by the resignation of the Greens' peace and defense policy expert, General Gert Bastian, over the inability of the "nonparty party" to agree on consistent policy objectives. Rotation in office at midterm is another issue that will test the Greens' ability to function as an effective alternative to the established parties.

A further shift in the West German foreign policy debate was signaled by the SPD's rejection of NATO deployment in the autumn of 1983. Chancellor Helmut Schmidt could cajole the SPD to accept his view of political realism within the framework of a governing coalition. Out of office, Schmidt was powerless to resist effectively a long-term SPD swing to the left. This will mean more radical SPD stands on West German arms and NATO, as well as such matters as U.S. policy in Central America, Europe, and the Middle East. A new party program to replace the 1959 Godesberg declaration seems certain.

The Conservative-Liberal coalition will meanwhile defend the status quo. With the missile deployment issue "managed" for the time being and with German-German relations in relatively good form, the Kohl government will be expected to come forward with foreign policies that match the potential leadership role of the Federal Republic of Germany in international councils.

CONCLUSION

In 1983 there was great international interest in the FRG national election. Compared to the 1980 election, which was widely regarded as a contest between the chancellor-candidates Schmidt and Strauss, the 1983 election involved the controversial issue of NATO missile deployment. This engaged those countries with a stake in NATO policies.

Missile deployment, as an issue, was overwhelmed in January and February by the salience to the electorate of bread-and-butter economic issues. Undaunted by this development, foreign political figures—U.S. Vice-President Bush and Soviet Foreign Minister Gromyko, among others—traveled to Bonn, while chancellor-candidates Vogel and Kohl went abroad to polish their international images as world statesmen.

Was this merely "sound and fury" or did the international aspects of the 1983 election really signify something? Although the national security and peace issues had low saliency in the minds of the electorate in the period immediately before ballots were cast, concern with international issues had two long-term impacts that will affect policies in the Federal Republic for some time. First, hopes and fears about the West German international situation contributed to the success of the Greens in clearing the 5 percent hurdle. The Greens in the Bundestag may do as much for political consciousness raising as many more formal efforts at citizen political education. The Greens' concern with war and peace issues will have an impact well beyond the elections.

Second, although the West German voter turned to pocketbook issues in returning Chancellor Kohl, it is clear from both attitudinal data and behavior in such forms as demonstrations, that peace issues will remain near the center of the political stage. Elected on the basis of hopes and fears, those confirmed in power on March 6, 1983, will face a critical audience whose concerns will perhaps, be conditioned by new saliencies.

NOTES

1. Kendall L. Baker, Russell J. Dalton, and Kai Hildebrandt, *Germany Transformed* (Cambridge, Mass.: Harvard University Press, 1981), p. 105.

2. INFAS-Report, *Politogramm Bundestagswahl 1983* (Bonn–Bad Godesberg: INFAS, 1983), p. 107.

3. Ibid., table following p. 69.

4. *Frankfurter Allgemeine Zeitung,* 9 March 1983.

5. Ilse Spittmann, "Nach der Wahl" in *Deutschland Archiv* 16, no. 4 (March 1983): 337–339.

9

POLITICAL ECONOMICS

H.G. Peter Wallach

If "good economics is good politics," the West German success of the fifties, sixties, and seventies seems obvious: The "economic miracle" of postwar production turned into a series of consumer waves, such as the *Fresswelle* (eating wave), and ultimately provided the world with *Modell Deutschland.* German solidity, perseverance, care, and organization, it seems, gained rewards in the counting house as well as in the parliamentary house. The success of capitalism and stable government apparently went hand in hand. Bipartisanship and economic adjustments resolved minor problems, such as the 1965 inflation; and even the public, which in other countries might have maintained demands for increasing shares of the pie, was willing to show restraint when asked. The Federal Republic had institutions, citizen attitudes, and leaders that made it economically sound and globally competitive.

But the globe changed in those 30 years. So the question of today is how well can government and economics work in tandem in the future.

In the financial area there are now banks that are international, corporations that are multinational, and technologies that demand new, sometimes transnational, industrial organizations. Thus, when focused on economic problems, domestic policies are no longer as easily isolated as they once were.

National politicians, even when they are called world leaders, now have only limited influence beyond their jurisdictions. Urged to respond to local pressures, they find there are demands that cannot easily be met with good economics. There is not even a cliché which reads, Good politics is good economics.

In September of 1982 this became obvious when economist-turned-politician Helmut Schmidt was forced to resign. During the campaign that followed Helmut Kohl, his successor, used the slogan "now for an upswing" while West Germans, like citizens of other Western nations, discussed structural weaknesses, a more mechanized world, new lifestyles, and the potential of economic self-sufficiency for underdeveloped nations. Germans were most worried about the future of their nation in a world that had experienced a prolonged recession.

In this chapter all these topics will be discussed. To cover them we first turn to the economic structure of West Germany and the economic memory of West German citizens. Then we present the economic issues of the late seventies and early eighties, as they became political issues. Which brings forth the last section, an analysis of future problems and prospects for the political economic health of the Federal Republic of Germany.

ECONOMIC EXPERIENCE AND POLITICAL PERSPECTIVE

For Germans economics and politics have always been intimately entwined. Though international issues, bureaucratic authority, and the power of Prussia or Bavaria have long been on the political agenda of Germany, questions of economic growth and economic power have generally been considered more important than those of individualism, federalism, or civil rights. Financial perspectives have separated the German political parties since national unification, while the establishment of the nation in 1870 was based on an earlier customs union joining principalities in the area.

As the formation of such a union suggests, there has been a general acceptance of the role of government in economic affairs. Adam Smith's "invisible hand" and the support for the ultimate "laissez-faire" idea that government should not be involved in economic affairs has hardly had strong support in Germany, for early artisans felt they were protected by the government, and later corporations found government backing advantageous. Even before the rise of industrialization and modern politics the structure and growth of local economies was often shaped by the responsible bishop, the authority of the day. Thus, at the beginning of the nineteenth century, while British economists were promoting economic growth unhampered by government, German economists such as Friedrich List were pointing out that economic progress can be promoted with a united central government rather than the localism of numerous minor governments. So throughout a unification that meant increased Prussian power to other European nations, industrial development under a single authority was the topic for those inside Germany.

Astute politics prevented the new investment possibilities from turning into the most extreme kind of class warfare. Although the revolutionism of Karl Marx and the more moderate socialism of Ferdinand Lassalle had, by 1870, found fertile support in the plight of those who felt exploited by factory work and urban living conditions, it did not take root during the chancellorship of Otto von Bismarck. The "Iron Chancellor" instituted policies of economic security and paternalism to appease the demands of the working class and to associate them with conservative concerns. Social security, health insurance, and old-age assistance, administered by corporations and labor unions, under governmental supervision, provided for the major concerns of employees. The government, through the civil service, also became the major employer of the "middle class."

This led to a kind of economic development that differentiates Germany from other capitalistic nations: a development of large corporations. Neither the ideology nor the governmental structure of the day encouraged small entrepreneurs, of the kind so common in the United States and Great Britain. The large corporations worked well with centralized government, and they grew readily in a climate where organization was highly admired.[1] Thus, by the beginning of the First World War German industry was not based on small machine shops, innovative invention, or high-risk investment. It was based on the capital-intensive fields of energy, machinery, and steel. Even the chemical and drug industries, which could have been more decentralized, were organized with the help of government regulation into such firms as I.G. Farben and Bayer.

In this atmosphere it is not surprising that Germans, when economic difficulties arose, were unlikely to just blame themselves. After all, their place of work was not owned, created, or changed by their own efforts. Distant bosses and distant governments had to be depended upon.

Therefore, when the 1922 inflation struck, Germans who were taking wheelbarrows of money to the store to buy a few loaves of bread were especially conscious of their susceptibility to economic forces. Having become dependent on the security their government had provided them they now became hyperconscious of the threats to that security. So when the other side of the economic whipsaw, depression, occurred in the early thirties, they turned to a leader who promised to take severe action. The blame Hitler placed on a seemingly wealthy minority and the solutions he proposed in terms of strict organization, they found appealing.

By building streets and rearming soldiers the Nazi regime increased the subservience of the citizens. It imbued a sense of responsibility in its citizens, which made loyalty and responsibility equal.

This raised questions in the minds of Germans when World War II was lost and the division of the nation into East and West disabused them of the dream of dominance over Europe.

Meanwhile the victor powers considered the future of Germany. In the United States the desires of those who wanted to dismember German industry and return the area to a semirural state were represented in the Morgenthau Plan. At the same time, there were suggestions elsewhere that German firms be controlled by firms in England, Russia, France, and the United States, or that the economy be centralized within each of the four occupation zones by the authorities in that zone. But none of these plans would be implemented.

Germans strove to counteract any idea of economic dismemberment. Faced with the destruction of one-third of the productive capacity, they first turned to rebuilding what had been. But they also considered means for improving the economic output and the social organization of the society. A free market economy, some realized, was one of the possibilities: It would counteract the negative results experienced during strong centralization, and it would encourage new initiatives to fill the extensive demands of postwar deprivation. The personal initiative and responsibility encouraged by a free market system would also help individuals adjust to scarcity, the diversity of controls in the four zones of occupation, and the lack of a genuinely German government.

These arguments seemed to gain validity as the "iron curtain" became an increasing threat. By 1948 Western statesmen saw them as a necessary means toward building a stronger Europe and a stronger defense.

New measures found support. First there was a currency reform and a quasi-German government was created in the British and U.S. occupation zones, known as Bizonia, to administer it. Then the U.S. Marshall Plan program of financial aid helped reconstruct and modernize German industry. Finally, West Germany formed its own government. All of which had the purpose of combating the threat of communism with the means of economic security and political unity—a means which seemed justified with the advent of the Berlin airlift and the Korean War.

But international affairs are not solely responsible for the "economic miracle" of the fifties. Economist Henry Wallich gives other reasons: (1) that the division of Germany made the Federal Republic increasingly dependent on foreign trade, (2) that most of the industrial capacity of Germany was in the West, (3) that skilled refugees escaped from East Germany to West Germany, (4) that women became part of the productive labor force, and (5) that the hard-working labor force volunteered effort in rebuilding the infrastructure as well as fulfilling employment responsibilities.[2]

Through the policies of the post-1948 Christian Democratic governments these factors contributed to the growth of what came to be known as the *social market economy*. As articulated by Economics Minister Ludwig Erhard and Finance Minister Fritz Schäffer, these policies relied on free market forces while accepting the influence of government. They thus rejected the strong centralization of the Hitler era; the attempts at price control and rationing exercised during occupation; and the central planning, large government expenditures, and inflation then being experienced in Great Britain and the Scandinavian nations. They provided a *mixed economy*.

Support for such a program did not just result from the recent experiences of the German people. It also reflected their fear of inflation: For the 1922 difficulties, perhaps more than the depression that followed, indicated instability to citizens who had long placed large parts of their earnings into savings.

So the policy of tight money, a balanced budget, and antiinflationary pressure was aided by the economic ideology of the population. It was thus possible, when expenditures were increasing rapidly, for Erhard to make effective television speeches asking citizens to restrain their demand and show a willingness not to drink so much "expensive wine."

This meant the government could overcome the most consumer oriented demands of democratic society and could concentrate on the balance of payments and the increase of capital. In this last effort the government was aided by a successful decontrol effort that was not approved by the occupation powers; but increased profit margins maintained the value of money and ultimately reinstated the German tendency to save and invest. Concurrently the decontrol furthered adjustment to market pressures and thus helped Germany establish the industry that was most beneficial to the international marketplace.

In the first years this social market economy was hardly social nor beneficial to everyone. It favored the strong and only helped the weak insofar as a limited social safety net provided funds. But as the economic miracle took effect, the strong were able to help the weak, unemployment was reduced, investment increased productivity, and the social security system was refurbished. Perhaps Germans had the patience to take the hard times in preparation for the good because there was no other outlet for their energy in light of the controls of the occupation powers. Whatever the reason, Germans became confident that their own efforts in a free market, with appropriate government incentives, could succeed. If military power had been the mark of the original unification of Germany, economic power was the pride of the new Federal Republic.

The establishment of that pride directly involved labor. Codetermination (*Mitbestimmung*) was developed after the war to involve labor in the governance of industry: It guaranteed labor representation on boards of directors and on local "work councils" in the coal and steel industries, thus involving workers in responsibility for the profit and progress of their employer and furthering cooperation rather than challenge in the effort to improve conditions. In addition, labor efforts were not complicated by competition among unions; for after the war Hans Böckler and others re-structured the Nazi-developed German Labor Front to form the German Trade Union Federation (*Deutscher Gewerkschaftsbund,* or DGB), an um-brella association that promoted the unity, rather than the differences, among the unions. Thus, from the forties to the early eighties there were fewer strikes in the Federal Republic than in any other industrialized Euro-pean or North American nation. In the first part of this period wage de-mands were also relatively modest.

Such calm progress had its effect on the political front. The Christian Democrats, usually in tandem with the Free Democrats dominated every coalition into the middle of the sixties; and the major opposition party, the Social Democratic, reduced its economic demands. In the 1959 Godesberg Program the Socialist party moderated its commitment to centralized plan-ning and articulated strong support for private enterprise. In effect, the competition of German politics would no longer be based on sharply differ-ent goals and methods but instead would be marked by degrees of variance between the major parties.

However, this greater economic consensus did not limit progress. When the recession of 1966 created nervousness among voters, at a time that saw the revival of a neo-Nazi party, the Christian Democrats and So-cial Democrats joined to form the Grand Coalition. This provided the So-cial Democrats with the opportunity to demonstrate responsibility and, with the help of Economics Minister Schiller, their ability to manage the social market economy. They supported the Keynesian solutions of deficit financing, increased expenditures by government, lower taxes, and re-duced interest rates. To facilitate this program Schiller developed means for greater integration between the national governments, state govern-ments, and the Bundesbank (the central bank).

The resultant rebound and demonstrated success in financial management further promoted German confidence. Added to the reputation of the Volkswagen "Beetle," German machine tools, and the technical advisors who were working on hydraulic projects in Egypt and steel mills in India, was the strength of the German currency. As a result, Finance Minister Franz-Josef Strauss was able to make nationalistic statements about the superior management practiced in his nation and London newspapers were able to comment on the new respectability of Germany. More importantly, the German government and the Bundesbank were able to make demands of nations that desired special economic consideration or loans. Meanwhile, private and public policy in the Federal Republic furthered unique antiinflationary programs: For instance, excess profits were exported to third world nations as capital and investment. This continued to increase the influence of West Germany.

The domestic results of this success were more complicated. The demands of the workers increased and the long-restrained threat of strikes was reflecting a change. The guest workers (*Gasterbeiter*) who had entered Germany from other Common Market nations and from Yugoslavia since the 1950s now included a veritable tide of individuals from Turkey, Morocco, and a variety of cultures that had not traditionally been part of the German street panorama. And student activists, along with a very few blue-collar voters, were demonstrating for reform in the social structure.

Like residents of other Western nations, Germans who had achieved economic well-being were reevaluating the national purpose and personal ethics. Discussions about the rigidity of the economic structure and the bureaucracy arose in the Federal Republic at a time when Americans questioned the Vietnam War, the French were challenging centralized controls, and the British voters were requesting a greater distribution of privilege. In the Federal Republic this period led to a new political constellation; the first government in which the Christian Democrats did not take part, the Social Democratic party–Free Democratic party (SPD-FDP) coalition elected in 1969.

Economics helped the SPD gain this victory. Polls indicate voters trusted the Party with economic affairs more than they had in the past,[3] and the election returns demonstrate the Social Democrats increased their support among urban laborers, service workers, and public employees.[4] It seems the promises of educational reform, continued economic growth, more adaptive management of the bureaucracy, and expansion of codetermination had borne fruit. It was expected that Brandt and Schiller, the Social Democrats who had been most evident in the Grand Coalition, would make the promises work.

But rising expectations can produce mixed results: Over the next five years the government would begin the reform effort, would develop some severe schisms, would lose both Brandt and Schiller from the cabinet, and would win the most definitive election of its history. That the 1972 election would give the Social Democrats five more seats than the Christian Union parties won was to Brandt's credit, but that a larger than usual proportion of that vote came from the young indicated a cleavage that would last. The pace of reform was to become an issue of ideological and generational division in the SPD. It was already recognized as an issue when the Young Socialists Organization (Jusos) protested the formation of the Grand Coalition, and it had divided the party in the 1970 and 1971 conventions when that advocate of economic fine tuning, Schiller, rejected proposals for a sharply graduated income tax. But with the international stagflation of 1972 and the oil crisis of 1973, the cleavage became more evident. To lessen it and to aid all sides the Social Democrats increased benefits to the poor and to workers, and supported business investments.

This hardly resolved the difficulties. Before the 1972 election Schiller resigned over a bill to control currency speculation, and after the election government efforts to be fiscally responsible by cutting expenses resulted in sporadic civil service strikes and slowdowns. The internal party differences on these and other issues weakened Chancellor Brandt to the point where, when he was caught in a spy scandal, he also resigned.

In the SPD-FDP government that then took office, headed by Helmut Schmidt, Brandt played a major role as communicator between the left and the leadership, for Schmidt's personality and perspective contributed to the incipient divisions. He was more critical and less patient than Brandt. With great self-confidence and a doctorate in economics, he said he was more able. Thus there were constant difficulties as Schmidt promoted the tax reform package but opposed programs to reform property law, reduce government encouragement of investment, and expand social services for the young. Schmidt strove to teach his detractors some economic lessons, to rely on the desire for security and reward of older workers, and to appeal to the needs of coalition politics in the promotion of a moderately reformist economic program. He was not helped by the fact that in some Social Democratic state governments reform had a much higher profile, especially in the area of education.

That his economic politics were acceptable to the general public, and grudgingly continenced by the left wing of the party was partly the result of the coalition with the economically conservative Free Democrats. This small party was especially successful after the 1976 election in demanding limited expansion of pension rights, only a minor extension of codetermination, continued government oversight of wage rates, and promotion of investment opportunity. As the seventies drew to a close and as the worldwide increase in bankruptcies, unemployment, and inflation affected West Germany (though more moderately than elsewhere), such conservative pressures seemed to gain support in the population. Voters were looking for leaders who would conserve what had been gained. They reelected, in 1980, the Schmidt government, but by increasing the vote for the Free Democrats rather than that for the Social Democrats.

In the meantime, other forces were impressing themselves on all Western economies, and especially on that of West Germany. The comparative power of various economic institutions was changing, and while some voters saw inflation as the major threat, others feared unemployment. In the Federal Republic of Germany this would ultimately mean the demise of the Schmidt government. In every nation it would mean reduced discussion about the economic future.

It is these issues which are important to the eighties and the real purpose of this chapter. To be able to consider them in depth, it is first necessary that we examine the West German economic structure.

THE POLITICAL ECONOMIC STRUCTURE
OF THE FEDERAL REPUBLIC

One of the problems of any analysis of this sort is that while politics is sometimes emphasized and economics is underscored in other paragraphs, it is difficult to deal with the two separately. Quite possibly the intertwining is best understood by examining how major elements of each are structured. With the assumption that in this work of political science some structures are already evident, this short section concentrates on economics. But it starts with the governmental institutions of economics.

Of course, the first of these institutions is the administration, the cabinet; in West Germany this usually includes a minister of economics and a minister of finance, as well as a minister of economic cooperation. Of these the minister of economics has the broadest responsibilities and the least specific powers. He is expected to deal with the general well-being of the nation. The minister of economics meets with foreign officials, makes pronouncements on future initiatives, and is expected to further a positive direction. The minister of finance operates in a more limited, though not less difficult, arena: he is responsible for the financing of government; his office coordinates the collection of taxes and the accounting of funds. The minister of economic cooperation deals with third world problems: Unlike the minister of economics, he primarily discusses issues with representatives of industrialized nations when the problems concerning less industrialized nations are involved.

Other ministers with major economic responsibilities are those for agriculture; labor, family, and health; transportation and communication; housing and urban development; education and research; and inner German affairs (dealing with East Germany). But unlike the situation in the United States, even when these ministries supervise national policy, the administration of their responsibilities, even in the area of tax collection, is often undertaken at the state level.

In their official roles these ministers affect taxation and the distribution of services and resources. They can adjust the antiinflationary value-added tax, the redistributive income tax, and a variety of enterprise taxes that affect the behavior of business.

They can also set the tone for less official decisions.

In their ultimate role of maintaining the economic future of the nation, the cabinet members are helped by the quasi-independent central bank, the German Bundesbank: In fact, some ministers have the nonvoting right to sit in on Bundesbank board meetings, and the president of the Bundesbank may sit with the cabinet. But the apparent political integration of the bank does not add to its power or reduce its contradictory obligations under the Bank Act of 1957 "to support the economic policy of the federal government" (Article 12) and to "secure the exchange rate" (Article 3).[5] What the integration does is provide a linkage for economic planning, a restraint on possible conflict, and a united voice in mobilizing individuals to make beneficial financial decisions, for one of the most important effects of economic leadership is not in the laws passed or financial actions taken, but in the ability of government policy and Bundesbank information to propituously affect the day-to-day decisions made in every home and business. For this reason the Bundesbank issues monthly reports on the economic status of every aspect of the economy and regularly provides interpretations of these reports.

In other regards the Bundesbank is somewhat limited in power. Though it has the usual authority to buy and sell foreign currency, set interest rates, establish a discount policy, and enforce reserve requirements, it is always susceptible to unique international and domestic forces. For instance, since the relative float of currencies was established in the early seventies, the bank has only had a short-term effect on dollar exchange rates when buying or selling currency; its effect on Common Market currencies has been greater because of the Common Market agreements on maintaining firm relationships between European currencies.

On the other hand, in dealing with interest rates the Bundesbank is limited by domestic banking traditions but strengthened when it can cooperate with domestic banks. The reason for the limit is that neither industries nor banks in West Germany find it totally honorable to operate on credit; thus, the major banks strive to maintain deposits sufficient to cover their investments and are less susceptible to the rates on borrowed money than are United States banks. However, when too much money is deposited in German banks in order to take advantage of a currency revaluation or high interest rates, the Bundesbank and the private banks act in concert in lowering interest rates to limit the inflationary effect of the cash inflow. They also act together when setting interest arrangements that will partly ensure isolation from foreign economic decisions.

This means that the major independent banks can exert power of their own. They are the repositories of deposits, the agents of international exchange, the sources of financing, and the major vehicles of investment. In fact, their role in investment is so great that in West Germany the major banks act as the stockbrokers and thus, as the holders of trust accounts, make most of the major investment decisions.

Since four (now three) major banks have dominated the investment field, money has largely been available to large and established businesses.

These businesses are often the same corporations that dominated the German scene before the Second World War: the iron and steel corporations of the Ruhr, the machine builders of the Rhineland, the shipping concerns in Hamburg, and so on. They are centralized and act unitarily through interest organizations. In addition,

> the political foundations of the business community and of the Bonn Republic are inextricably merged. Like the military in Latin America or the state bureaucracy in Japan, the credit that business [rather than government or fortuitous circumstances] has been given for the "economic miracle" of the 1950s has provided it with a pervasive legitimizing myth. As a result, it still enjoys . . . a preeminent place in West Germany's political life.[6]

The problem is that since the business community provided basic needs for a world that rebuilt after the war and materially expanded in the next 20 years, it has established stability in markets that have had short-term rather than long-term variations. Now it is threatened by international competition and the possible need for fundamental restructuring. But business is also now more independent because of its multinational character.

More obvious has been the role of organized labor, largely through the DGB. It has restrained wage demands, negotiated for job security, involved workers in industry governance, and maintained consciousness of the needs of investment as well as personal income. The effectiveness of labor is the result of strong linkages with political figures in both political parties and constant education programs for the membership.

But the individual family may be the uniquely important institution in German economic planning, for it is this unit that adjusts to requests for restraint and that tends to save 16 percent of earnings.

GERMAN ECONOMIC AFFAIRS IN THE EARLY EIGHTIES

The extraordinary cooperation of these institutions was especially notable from the oil crisis of 1973 to the strikes of 1984. Called conjuncture, when applied to the interaction of government, labor, and employers, it is directed toward stability more than rapid growth, security rather than equality. Thus, the unions acquiesced when there was an obvious need for investment, while banks did not conflict with corporations because they held the capital. In addition, government often has a major stake in corporations (until the sixties it had the major interest in Volkswagen), and even the most socialist of recent chancellors, Brandt, had close ties with business. But from the late seventies until his demise there was no one who represented the cooperation of "conjuncture" more than Helmut Schmidt.

Social Democratic Chancellor Schmidt weathered the 1976 election, amidst the highest unemployment rate in nearly a quarter of a century, by promising jobs through a growth of investment and reminding workers of the social safety net his party had implemented. That he would not back much extension of that net, and that he trusted in corporate growth, gave him the reputation of being the "best chancellor the Christian Democrats have ever had." And he was not prone to shrug off the judgment. As the inflation of the seventies became manageable in Germany, and as the unemployment rate declined, before rising again, he established a regular policy of meeting with officials of the major economic interests. This effort helped alleviate some of the problems, so his 1980 opponent could not ask at the last preelection debate, "Was your economic situation better four years ago?"

But the West German economy was under great pressure before 1980 even began. High interest rates in the United States were furthering worldwide inflation while putting pressure on the West Germans to charge equally high rates in order to prevent a flight of currency. This in turn restrained investment, increased unemployment, and ultimately put pressure on the social service funds of the government. Only by maintaining an inflation rate lower than that of neighboring nations could West Germany stay competitive in the West. It is not clear if a slower inflation rate in the United States would have helped the Federal Republic in the long run, but Schmidt was known for "lecturing President Carter" on good economics, thus assuring his reputation as an expert economist while blame for domestic judgments was placed elsewhere. This was necessary, for as election day approached, the unemployment rate began to increase again and the government had to resort to deficit financing.

Such borrowing would become an issue in the campaign, but it was an issue in the hands of Franz-Josef Strauss, who did not have the Schmidt reputation for finesse. As finance minister in the late sixties Strauss had often seemed belligerent, and his campaign was combative toward communist nations, which meant that those looking for economic cooperation feared he would jeopardize the patience the unions had shown, would become demanding of allies, and would hurt business with Eastern Europe.

Schmidt won the election of 1980. But the increased share of the vote for the government coalition was only an increase for the Free Democratic Party, an increase that added to the power of Vice-Chancellor Hans-Dietrich Genscher and Economics Minister Otto von Lambsdorff. Schmidt's efforts to maintain cooperation in the interest of the security of the workers would thus soon be jeopardized.

The Iranian oil-price boom, sharply higher interest rates in the United States, and the Reagan model of supply-side economics were all felt in West Germany in 1981; but they did not cause immediate pressure on the government because of a short-lived upsurge in exports. Yet they made evident threats to the economy, giving employers the opportunity to force labor unions to accept modest pay settlements. When profits came under pressure, the corporations also strove to reduce their comparatively large contributions to unemployment and health insurance funds, and to pensions. They demanded cuts in the social safety net.

In Count von Lambsdorff, corporations found a willing ally. The Free Democratic Economics Minister had once been an insurance executive. He proposed strong cuts in health and unemployment insurance programs.

Schmidt's dilemma was now set. Bankers, corporation chiefs, and his own coalition partners were all proposing solutions already being practiced in the United States: the reduction of regulation, sharp limitations on social services, a curtailment of expensive government programs, and more pro-business tax arrangements. While some of those around Schmidt desired moderate Keynesian pump priming and a guarantee of basic security to all residents of West Germany, the left wing of the Social Democratic party continued to blame industry for the crisis and recommended greater inter-ventionism by the government.

In good times the formula for answering such demands is to provide something for everyone. But the Social Democrats felt they could only guarantee the most important services, while increasing unemployment benefits with government funds financed by a temporary tax surcharge on those with a high income.

The answer to this was a threat of resignation from the Free Demo-crats.

Then, when midsummer unemployment passed the 6 percent mark and it became evident that West Germany, for the first time in 30 years, would have a second year of negative growth in the gross national product figures, fundamental questions about the nation's economy filled the media. Were economic programs too security oriented? Had enough atten-tion been paid to research? Was money properly invested? Were workers properly trained? Was German "solidity" a victim of a spoiled generation? Where could new markets be found? How could competition from Japan be matched?

In this atmosphere of doubt Schmidt gained the unified support his party had long deprived him of. He was encouraged not to make any more concessions to the Free Democrats and, if necessary, to resign and call for new elections. On September 17 he demanded Free Democratic allegiance to his economic program and was rejected: Four FDP Ministers resigned, and on October 1, 1982, Chancellor Schmidt was deprived of the opportu-nity to call for new elections.

It was not immediately clear if the new Kohl government would call any elections, but by embracing Economics Minister Lambsdorff, it guaranteed that the political discussions of the next six months would be centered on the economy as well as personalities, foreign affairs, environ-mental issues, and the role of government. The question of personalities became less important when Schmidt resigned from the race for reelection.

Meanwhile, the new coalition did not immediately demonstrate strong support of the Lambsdorff program; after all, the Christian Union parties also had a strong labor contingent. So social programs were capped in re-gard to cost-of-living increases, the expansion of pension benefits was limited, promises to reduce certain social programs in the future were made, and a tax surcharge which would be considered a "loan" was instituted. In a few areas, for instance, health insurance, minor charges were established as a disincentive to demand. And investment in housing and durable goods was promoted through tax breaks and direct subvention.

By Christmas of 1982 there were rumors that Lambsdorff was unhappy with the new coalition, as the Christian Union parties discussed a broad range of new taxes. On January 17 the Christian Union leadership even announced it would turn the tax surcharge "loan" into a tax if it had a clear majority after the new elections.

It was in the area of government administration that the coalition partners agreed. Efficiency studies were begun, agreement was reached on where the most important services of certain ministries were, and cuts of as much as 20 percent were made in the services considered less immediate, while civil service salary increases were reexamined.

The fight for voter opinion was on. Everyone could agree that the economy was ill, but the Bundesbank Reports had been mildly optimistic since mid-1982,[7] and blame or credit for a downswing or an upswing had not been established. Each side strove for position and each side watched the developing statistics. Unfortunately for the nation those statistics were not good. On the Friday before the March 6, 1983, election the unemployment rate was announced as over 10 percent. Already in January a *Spiegel-Emnid* poll had shown that 17 percent of the population felt they were in dire economic circumstances, and 48 percent felt the nation was in dire circumstances.[8] When asked which party could best solve the economic problems, respondents generally favored the Christian Union-Free Democratic coalition: Approximately double as many expected the incumbent coalition to improve the unemployment picture, reduce the deficit, and provide for more home building than the Social Democrats. Even in guaranteeing the social safety net and providing for a fair tax system, the Social Democrats were only slightly more trusted than the coalition.[9]

After the election, leading pollsters would use these poll results to explain that economics had been the issue throughout.[10] But what is not so easily explained is how voter opinion about economic programs was formed. According to Professor Elizabeth Noelle-Neumann, director of the Christian Union–oriented Allensbach Polling Institute, the upsurge for these two parties, noted by most pollsters after mid-January,[11] was a result of the January 17 announcement of tough economic decisions by the party executive committee. By turning the surcharge loan into a tax, cutting back on government programs, and suggesting further reductions in social programs, Dr. Noelle-Neumann suggests, Chancellor Kohl looked more like a leader and the party program seemed more definitive.[12] What is not clear from her data and that of the other institutes is to what degree the upsurge was really a result of this economic program or of the reaction to SPD candidate Vogel's visit to Moscow which took place at the same time.

There is no doubt pressure was put on voters to consider the Kohl government advantageous for the German economy. Interviews began to appear suggesting the Social Democrats would only produce a depression.[13] This seemed to be self-fulfilling when it also became known that some businesses had included clauses in major contracts that made the fulfillment of terms dependent on the outcome of the election: The suggestion was that business would be unwilling to invest if a coalition of the Social Democrats and Greens was formed.

The fear of the Greens was justified from the point of view of investors, for that party had come out for a zero-growth economy and regularly announced that economic growth was harmful to the environment. As an Allensbach Institute poll published in the magazine *Capital* had pointed out, 60 percent of those who intended to vote Green did not feel investors should receive a profit.[14] In light of this it is interesting to note that the Greens did especially poorly in those working-class districts where unemployment was high.

The party that stood at the opposite end of the economic spectrum from the Greens was that of the Free Democratics. In the *Capital* poll its adherents were most likely, of the four parties, to support profit;[15] and on the campaign trail Lambsdorff regularly made the most proinvestment pronouncements. Even *Der Spiegel,* in an article that reminded readers that the FDP had long called itself liberal, used the headline, "FDP: 'Definitely Right of the Union.'"[16] The small-business advocates who had originally joined the Free Democrats to maintain free competition now joined with supporters of big business who wanted to protect what had already been gained. This represented the wishes of the FDP voters of March 6 and of many of the new delegates the party seated in the Parliament.[17]

But as the election approached, and for a time thereafter, the FDP voice was lowered: Lambsdorff and other leaders of the party had been "charged" in the Flick affair. This meant they were accused of taking bribes from an industrialist who was looking for favorable tax policies. It may be that the affair had no effect on the election, and in 1984 it is not clear the trial will prove great wrongdoing; but the journalistic discussion affected the willingness of the subjects to speak in public.

What is fact is that on March 6 the Free Democrats were returned to the Bundestag and the Christian Union parties did not get quite enough votes to rule alone. The new coalition, like the one that had just preceded it and the one that had occupied the stage in the previous 13 years, would have the Free Democrats in the role of economic counterweight on the right.

The election was held amidst the highest unemployment rate since the establishment of the nation and amidst reminders of the bankruptcy of AEG, the major electronics firm, and the difficulties of some banks. But it was also held at a time when Bundesbank predictions were improving, the oil crisis had turned into an oil glut, reports of high exports in 1982 were being substantiated, and settlement on the loans to Poland were being reached. The dire conditions of the present were moderated by the expectations of the future and by the new coalition's campaign slogan, "now for an upswing" ("Jetzt mit Aufschwung"). Because the social safety net had held, and was expected to continue with the CDU/CSU in power, trust in that upswing was possible.

But, of course the election did not make an immediate difference; it just legitimized the coalition and brought forth a slightly more Bavarian-CSU-oriented cabinet.

The following months were also not good for the Federal Republic: President Mitterand blamed his own nation's problems on the German-dominated European exchange rates; Volkswagen, which had declining sales at home also reported difficulties in its Brazilian, Mexican, and United States operations; Banks that had been hurt by the Polish difficulties now found themselves involved in the threatened defaults throughout Latin America; and West German industry, which has nearly one-fourth of its foreign investment in Brazil, was caught in the dilemmas of that potentially prosperous nation. By June it seemed as though the government might be apologetic at the economic summit conference at Williamsburg, Virginia; but Chancellor Kohl simply raised the old issue of American interest rates and otherwise expressed trust in the ultimate success of Reaganomics, for he knew that some progress was being managed in Germany: The high value of the U.S. dollar was helping exports, and the Bundesbank promotion of special interest rates was helping the housing and machinery industries, while unemployment had receded since the February high point announced just before the election contracts were fulfilled. With a decline in American interest rates there was also hope for German rates. In the meantime the government was carefully considering means for more efficiently delivering social services. With nearly 50 percent of the budget in such services, and with over half of that directed toward pensions, careful thought was going into possible cuts.

Some of the cuts could, by the end of 1983, be postponed. The export of machinery and management consulting was helping the Federal Republic; and with the dollar an increasingly strong currency, nations throughout the world were finding West Germany a reliable trading partner from among the technologically advanced nations. The question was, could the progress last?

By late spring of 1984 the inequalities in the progress already gained cast major doubts on further success in the much-lauded "model" nation. For the belt tightening of recession, which had taken place in most industrialized nations, was met during the West German upsurge by increased profits for industry but not by increased employment for displaced workers. So steel, which was especially hard hit with layoffs, faced contract demands for a 35-hour week and a continuation of previous salary levels. Since the employers found immediate support from the center-right government,[18] labor reacted strongly with associated strikes in printing and banking. The breakdown in cooperation was exacerbated when the important, export-oriented, automobile industry found it necessary to close and other employers began a series of lockouts.

The possibility for radicalization was evident. Government refused unemployment benefits for many affected, laborers felt the security of their jobs was no longer guaranteed, and there were associated actions against the increased use of such new technologies as computers because they would eliminate the need for workers in this manufacturing society.

All this furthered the discussion on the general direction of the West German economy.

THE FUTURE

Prediction is rarely the forte of scholars, and in an arena such as political economics it is further complicated by the relative interdependence of economic and political systems in the multifaceted, modern, capitalistic, democratic states of today.

Furthermore, the West German situation, as demonstrated in the last pages, is especially susceptible to international pressures. With 25 percent of its production export related, as opposed to 9 percent for the United States, West Germans are sensitive to buying decisions in the United States, product developments from Japan, and the increasing self-sufficiency of the third world. In addition, as coal becomes less usable as an energy resource, this often sunless country must look to neighbors for fossil fuels and to nuclear development for self-sufficiency. In partial response to these factors and in part as a result of the relative strength of the nation's currency, the banking community has become tied to international decisions,[19] and the transnational efforts of the European Economic Community have added to the potentialities and tensions.

But the most important questions in recent discussions about the West German economy have centered around the ability of the domestic economy, especially domestic production, to meet the demands of the future. During 1982, 1983, and 1984, this discussion has been especially pointed as exports have increased but unemployment and uncertainty have lowered consumer confidence.

What has focused the discussion is that so-called high technology has not reached West Germany in the way it has reached Great Britain, Japan, and the United States. There is no robot industry in West Germany, the major computer makers have not brought out personal-sized units, and most of the electronic machine-tool facilities in the Federal Republic are imported. With a few notable exceptions, such as the Siemens research into industrial x-ray applications and Mannesmann's investment in personal computer peripherals, the investment of West German industry has not been in the newer electronic fields. The most consumer-oriented of the traditional electronics firms, such as AEG and Grundig, were weakened significantly by the recent difficulties.

The future direction that seems to have received the most attention in West Germany is that of bioengineering. When Hoechst made an investment in research at Massachusetts General Hospital, in Boston, Americans became aware that they were not paying enough attention to this field. But it must be noted that the investment was made in the United States, and thus far the recognition of the need for research by West Germans has not met with many patentable applications.

The reason these fields are not growing rapidly in West Germany is that they require specialized research facilities, training that is only now being developed there, and venture capital. The last item on this list is especially difficult to acquire in a land where security is more important than risk and where large banks allied with large businesses control most capital.

The psychological and social structure that may result from high technology is also not predicated on the conditions in the Federal Republic—for a world of personal computers, creative individuality, individualized demands, the development of crafts, and self-initiative is not a world of security through bureaucracy and large corporations. Without the entrepreneurial tradition that has been so important in the United States, it will be harder to make the transition from big corporations to cottage industries that recently saved the northeastern part of the United States: While much of the worst damage of the economic crisis in the United States has been to smokestack industries, in the Federal Republic it has been in bankruptcies of small businesses. The question for Germany is whether the decline of large industries and the robotization of others can be met by new economic and social structures that occupy individuals and support financial well-being.

West Germany does not have a service economy or a tradition of rapid adaptiveness. In a period of crisis it has citizens that primarily desire security and confidence. So the possibility of long-range adjustments will be difficult.

What may help the economy is that, although there will be additional losses on investments in Latin America during the short term, if domestic productivity goes into a permanent decline, it may be at a time when the return from the South American continent of promise is beginning.

West Germany also has high regard for research and is known to be effective in adapting "pure" results to practical applications. It may be helped by the fact that while the proportions of the health budget committed to research is lower in West Germany than in the United States, the private and public budgets for mechanical and chemical research are more than equal.

How all this is affected by the political situation and how it will affect politics is a question subject to broad conjecture.

Quite possibly, if there must now be a transition to the creation of venture capitalism and the development of cottage industries, the current coalition is more appropriate than that including the Social Democratic party. For the "class-mass" base of the party of Brandt and Schmidt has meant concern with organized unions, the relationship of individuals to large economic institutions, and bureaucratic planning. The Free Democrats, who have never gained the support of even 13 percent of the electorate, are closest to some of the entrepreneurs and shopkeepers of Germany. But the Christian Union parties have, with an organization based on the integrations of a wide variety of interest groups, provided for adaptation to the independent efforts of pluralistic demands. The big question for them is how well they can provide for the disruptions adaptation will produce in the lives of individual citizens and communities.

In the long run there are some bigger political issues to be considered. The most important may concern the ability of national governments in Europe to maintain authority when economic issues are largely international. This may mean the Economic Community will regain power once there is a united upturn again. If such an upturn does not occur dissatisfaction will grow; atomization may result, and all the usual problems of division will make governability a problem.

The more immediate indications are that as long as trust and productivity can be maintained, with the help of social services, the sensitivity of the government to potential political instability will provide appropriate support for the established economic system. It is quite possible that the pension program will lose as adjustments are made in services; but one suspects that where the adjustments have to be in the economic power of established institutions, they will be made without direct government urging.

The economic model of the last two decades is unlikely to be the economic model of tomorrow, nor is there likely to be a West German economic disaster. For it is possible that the model of cooperation, between the economic and political sectors, will continue. The single-minded goals of that cooperation and of the national will, barring foreign threat, indicate government will play the light-handed nudger and intermediary as investment forces make extensive adjustments and laborers, pensioners, and everyday citizens must be considered.

NOTES

1. Jürgen Koecka, "The Modern Industrial Enterprise in German," in *Managerial Hierarchies,* ed. Alfred D. Chandler, Jr., and Herman Daems (Cambridge, Mass.: Harvard University Press, 1980), pp. 77–116.

2. Henry Wallich, *Mainsprings of the German Revival* (New Haven: Yale University Press, 1955), pp. 15–21.

3. Polls on deposit at the Zentralarchiv für empirische Sozialforschung: Baumert, Scheuch, and Wildenmann, Study 055 (1961); Kaase and Wildenmann, Study 556 (1965); Klingemann and Pappi, Study 426 (1969); Berger et al., Study 635 (1972).

4. Max Kaase, "Determinanten des Wahlverhaltens bei der Bundestagswahl 1969," *Politische Vierteljahresschrift* 11, no. 1 (1971).

5. Frederick G. Reuss, *Fiscal Policy for Growth without Inflation, The German Experiment* (Baltimore: The Johns Hopkins Press, 1963), p. 53.

6. Peter Katzenstein, "West Germany as Number Two: Reflections on the German Model," in *The Political Economy of West Germany,* ed. Andrei S. Markovits (New York: Praeger, 1982), p. 202.

7. *West German Bundesbank Monthly Reports,* 1982–1983.

8. "Zweifeln zu Viele SPD-Wahler on der SPD?" *Der Spiegel,* no. 7, Feb. 1983.

9. Ibid., p. 36.

10. Press conference in the Wissenschaftszentrum, Godesberg, by Max Kaase, Klaus Liepelt, and Elizabeth Noelle-Neumann on March 7, 1983.

11. "Halbe Wahrheiten," *Der Spiegel,* no. 8, Feb. 1983, pp. 56–57.

12. Professor Elizabeth Noelle-Neumann at the March 7, 1983, press conference.

13. "Speigel Gespraech." *Der Spiegel,* no. 11, March 1983, pp. 61–64.

14. *Capital,* March, 1983, pp. 15–16.

15. Ibid.

16. No. 9, March, 1983, p. 42.

17. Douglas Webber, "A Relationship of 'Critical Partnership?' Capital and the Social-Liberal Coalition in West Germany," *West European Politics* 6, no. 2 (April, 1983): 61–86.

18. For a discussion of the corporate philosophies of the various governments, see Kenneth Dyson, "The Politics of Corporate Crisis in West Germany," *West European Politics* 7, no. 1 (January 1984): 24–46.

19. Gerd Junne, "Multinational Banks, the State and International Integration" in *German Political Systems*, ed. Klaus von Beyme (Beverly Hills: Sage, 1976), pp. 117–137.

10

CONCLUSION

George K. Romoser
H.G. Peter Wallach

In the subtitle to this volume "crisis" refers to the central events of the eighties—the crisis over energy and economy, the concern with missiles, and the 1982–83 resignation and election which expressed them—as well as the long-term difficulties of postindustrialization and great-power competition. The "continuity" is evident from a reading of these chapters—in the ability of West Germans to cope with these crises, and in the attitudes with which they respond to problems. The political institutions, each article demonstrates, seem to adapt even though concerns continue, while the people, Dalton and Baker point out, make practical choices that are sometimes in ironic conflict with personal ideologies.

This West German experience contains lessons for other Western democratic nations. Directly on the borders of the iron curtain, with a democratic identity partly built on economic success, the Federal Republic of Germany is the arena where international competition and the linked accomplishments of society, economics, and politics are often most focused.

It is the doubts and criticisms in the nation, explained here in the chapter by Romoser, that blur this focus. Yet the fact that most of the authors give only minor attention to the fears, resentments, and perspectives which tend to make headlines suggests that the problems regularly pondered by West German intellectuals and non-German observers alike are subordinate to current concerns. Though some doubts remain, West Germany seems to have overcome the worst burdens of history and culture. Today it lives with borders determined by that history as well as a continuation of suspicions about its power, achievements, and attitudes, while it concentrates on the challenges of the future. Quite possibly the worries the Americans, French, and Russians have about West Germany are only secondary worries for West Germans.

But if there are lessons in this experience, and if the particularities of West Germany do not render them exceptional, special attention must be given to the comments by Bürklin and Romoser: Frustration with the nature of established political opposition may lead to new outlets that splinter parties and could even affect governmental forms.

The technology and human adjustment that faces the Federal Republic has an effect throughout Europe. In France it brought about a government that tried to change economic institutions, and in Sweden it returned a government of the left after the ideals of conservatism failed to become a united political force. Elsewhere there is talk of the decline of political parties, the atomization of communities, and the possibilities of control by centralized machines. While citizens and politicians worry about such long-term pressures, they strive to plan and adjust with short-term structures.

The Federal Republic, with the election of 1983, recovered a coalition that had established its nationhood and prompted its "economic miracle." But the Christian Union parties (CDU/CSU) and the Free Democratic party (FDP), which constitute that coalition, face elements of rigidity. Søe explains that the smaller partner will not soon have an opportunity to change again: It has lost numerous liberal voters, is committed to a conservative economic platform, has created cynicism among former partners, and houses the major political scandal of contemporary West Germany. Now locked into a CDU/CSU marriage, the policy maneuverability most open to the Free Democrats is in the areas of civil liberties and international relations. But it has not provided new initiatives on foreign affairs; and on such technology-related civil liberties issues as privacy, it has failed to provide firm leadership. Nor has the party heeded those who want it to promote a more scientifically oriented education system and a more unified elite. In a pragmatic sense the little brother of every recent government has fallen into the undistinguished role of checking the more extreme wings of the Social Democratic party (SPD) or the Christian Social Union: But if Franz-Josef Strauss should now fade from the scene, even this role may become superfluous. That would leave the Christian Union parties with a politics that the voters accept, Dalton and Baker tell us, but with which they are not in full agreement. Moreover, the chapter by Paterson points out, the party of conservative inclinations and governmental responsibility is marked by internal differences and a lack of leadership strength: Even though an economics of restraint may be necessary during the current crisis, the Christian Democrats must deal with trade union members. Even though the nation wishes to support the North Atlantic Alliance, it finds party members have increasing doubts about the location of major nuclear weapons.

Trade with the Eastern bloc is desirable even if party rhetoric seems to oppose it. So this pair of parties, the CDU/CSU, dominating most of the elite institutions in the Federal Republic, finds it difficult to maneuver just as the demands of the future require this capability.

The SPD, a party that has traditionally been the bastion of antielitism, and that lost the most votes in 1983, is in weakened condition. Braunthal writes that the Social Democrats lacked an image of strength on economic affairs in the coalition with the Free Democrats, and now have lost grassroots support, while they face the appeals of the Greens on the left. The party, under Brandt and Vogel, in pursuit of the young generation that could give it renewed strength, is positioning itself further left with opposition to missile deployment, a rethinking of social programs, and attention to environmental affairs. But this is at the expense of traditional support; blue-collar workers look at the approach with skepticism. With the stalwartness of Helmut Schmidt gone, Willy Brandt having become too old, or at least too controversial, to hold high governmental office, and Hans-Jochen Vogel less than secure as a long-term leader of the party, the SPD faces substantial leadership problems which are compounded by discrepancies between the trade union components of the party and the activists of the professional classes who were recruited to the SPD in the last two decades.

Thus, one might think, the Greens have an outstanding opportunity. The frustrations of becoming an organized party, however, tend to weaken their effectiveness. The alternatives they represent, described by Bürklin, will have increasing appeal when the frustrations of a stagnated economy, a deteriorating environment, and a lack of relief from the threats of war are felt strongly. At a time when established institutions seem not to provide clear solutions to problems, and when highly trained young people find too little access to decision making, the original participatory emphasis of the Greens appears inviting. But the fact that participation in organizational affairs is not only hard work, and often frustrating, but also potentially disorienting, is now facing the Greens.

They are not lacking in evidence of the divisions and jealousies they had first promised to supplant. They are facing organizational problems in at least two respects: How much effort is to be devoted to national issues, or to what degree will they return to their roots by concentrating on decentralized economic and social issues? And, what will be the future strength of tightly disciplined and organized left cadres in the Greens as distinguished from the "spontaneous" participatory elements (so close to the "flower power" of the sixties) which have thus far received the most attention?

In the West the example of the Greens would be strong if the organization could demonstrate cohesive effectiveness, for every country has strong interest groups concerned with disarmament, the environment, a steady state economy, and more involvement with government. For the moment, however, there is some question whether the Greens can be the vehicle for coalescing such concerns. It is more likely that if technological improvement results in decentralized economic and social activity, the Greens will serve as a model of decision formation.

Of more immediate concern to the allies of West Germany are economic and foreign policies. Some think that almost every day provides reasons to ask if this bulwark of NATO support will melt into neutralism or even move toward some form of nationalism. Though such views certainly exaggerate the real situation, Hanhardt points out that arms issues will affect future relations with Germany and the international effectiveness of future German governments. Chancellor Helmut Kohl, aware of this, occasionally travels between Moscow and Washington trying to defuse the reasons for threat and fear. So in light of the reactions within the Republic, actions outside it may be highly important.

The economic arena is not as dependent on great-power dominance. But numerous doubts about West Germany's economic future are raised by Wallach. While some of the crises of the recent past were internationally generated, the nation of steel and machinery did comparatively well during them. And at the beginning of the recovery it seems to be doing even better. But guest workers (*Gastarbeiter*) are now a burden from the more secure economic past, and expectations of an affluent life are being reduced as industry and entrepreneurs search for a route to the high technology future. Might the newest German citizens, the children of the guest workers, eventually provide that innovativeness and drive which so often seems to be a necessary leaven for progress? The answer cannot yet be given; it is reasonably certain, however, that the industriousness and solid financial investment of the Germans will also have to play a role.

It is the people of the country who will ultimately affect its continued transformation. They are described by Dalton and Baker as willing to make the necessary decisions for stability but as uneasy about the social and international directions of current government policy. With the recent economic crisis in mind, they are ready to support the necessity for tough and conservative measures. But they may create difficulties for governments if their interests and their international ideals are not sufficiently respected. Moreover, divided Europe remains, with divided Germany in the middle. There are few indications of change in that situation, but one would be foolhardy to assert that there will never be tensions between the status quo and pressures for some sort of change.

We thus return to a central theme of this book's opening chapter. Romoser stressed the twin aspects of stability and innovation in the German political culture. It is clear that there is little support in the Federal Republic for political extremism from any direction. Less clear is the particular mix between security and change that will emerge in the next years. A measured and cautious conclusion might be that the forces of innovation and change will be more powerful in rhetoric than in actual effects on institutions and policies. Such a phenomenon is hardly novel in political life, but actions may ultimately speak louder than words, with words playing a highly important symbolic role, defusing conflict and institutional or policy change.

Readers of these chapters will have gained an enhanced appreciation of the particularities of the German situation. Anxieties about the "successor generation" of political leaders or about "value changes" in the Federal Republic, they will understand, must be considered in terms of the strength of the West German political system and the value changes occurring elsewhere. One can expect neither a reincarnation of the immediate postwar years nor much further "overcoming of the past" than has already taken place on a practical level. West Germany now faces a future based on confidence in past success, concern for Central Europe in current conflicts, and attention to the development of economic and social values that satisfy individual aspirations of pragmatism and idealism.

The answers that citizens of the Federal Republic develop for themselves will not always satisfy observers in other nations, for West Germans are not likely to be selfless. Their needs include their own security and progress, and they desire some of the same psychological confidence that can bring ambitious people into conflict. Whether it is pipelines or great-power negotiation, political cabarets or campaign bluster, they will use the usual routes of democracy to achieve solutions that satisfy domestic interests.

No matter how this future is achieved, as every chapter here indicates, the most extreme expressions of the past are not likely to be relived, for the stability of institutions has become established and the citizens find there are appropriate outlets to process their differences. Simultaneously the constraints of international pressures are in the consciousness of most West Germans, and the constraints of domestic conventions prevent radicalism from making too rapid an advance.

In this volume, written as a contribution to a better understanding of West Germany, the future is inferred from educated conjecture. We rely on that better understanding and upon a recognition that every form of change is not threatening, to suggest that there is now much worth watching. In coming years, which may evidence increasing signs of "inward turning" among Western countries, it will be vital to respond to provincialism with a cosmopolitan judgment of one's own.

INDEX

ABOUT THE EDITORS
AND CONTRIBUTORS

Kendall L. Baker: Dean of Arts and Sciences at Bowling Green State University, is the senior author of *Germany Transformed: Political Culture and the New Politics*. Earlier he wrote on partisanship, political socialization, and political communications in West Germany.

Gerard Braunthal: Professor of Political Science at the University of Massachusetts–Amherst, is known for the books entitled, *West German Social Democrats, 1969–1982: Profile of a Party in Power, Socialist Labor and Politics in Weimar Germany: The General Federation of German Trade Unions,* and *The Federation of German Industry in Politics,* among others.

Wilhelm P. Bürklin: A member of the political science department at the University of Mannheim, recently published *Grüne Politik. Politische Zyklen, Wähler, und Partiensystem* in West Germany. His articles and papers on the Greens have appeared in the United States as well as West Germany.

Russell J. Dalton: Associate Professor of Political Science at Florida State University, is adding *Public Opinion and Political Parties in Western Democracies* to *Electoral Change in Advanced Industrial Democracies* (written with Scott Flanagan and Paul Allan Beck) and *Germany Transformed* (written with Kendall L. Baker and Kai Hildebrandt).

Arthur M. Hanhardt, Jr.: Professor of Political Science at the University of Oregon, wrote *The German Democratic Republic*. His articles about both Germanies include political socialization, nuclear policy, legislative representation, and international relations as topics.

William E. Paterson: Reader in Politics at Warwick University, is known to Britons for his articles on West German Politics. His books include *The SPD and European Integration, Social Democratic Politics in Western Europe,* and *The West German Model* (edited with G. Smith).

George K. Romoser: Professor of Political Science at the University of New Hampshire and Fellow at the Harvard University Center for European Studies, cofounded the Conference Group on German Politics. A specialist on political ideas, he has held visiting chairs at the Universities of Mainz, Munich and Mannheim. His writings on German politics include a 1969 study on the establishment of the Grand Coalition.

Christian Søe: Professor of Political Science at California State University–Long Beach, is the author of a forthcoming book on the Free Democratic party. He is editor of the annual series *Comparative Politics* and has published a book subtitled *Eine Analyse der SPIEGEL-Affaere.*

H.G. Peter Wallach: Associate Professor of Political Science at Central Connecticut State University, writes about political leadership, public law, and economic policy in comparative terms. His most recent article relates economic trends and election returns in all the nations of Western Europe.

THE BIG FLATLINE

THE BIG FLATLINE

OIL AND THE NO-GROWTH ECONOMY

Jeff Rubin

palgrave
macmillan

THE BIG FLATLINE
Copyright © Jeff Rubin, 2012.

First published 2012 by Random House Canada

First Published in the United States in 2012 by PALGRAVE MACMILLAN® in the United States—a division of St. Martin's Press LLC, 175 Fifth Avenue, New York, NY 10010.

Where this book is distributed in the UK, Europe and the rest of the world, this is by Palgrave Macmillan, a division of Macmillan Publishers Limited, registered in England, company number 785998, of Houndmills, Basingstoke, Hampshire RG21 6XS.

Palgrave Macmillan is the global academic imprint of the above companies and has companies and representatives throughout the world.

Palgrave® and Macmillan® are registered trademarks in the United States, the United Kingdom, Europe and other countries.

ISBN: 978–0–230–34218–7

Library of Congress Cataloging-in-Publication Data

Rubin, Jeff, 1954–
       The big flatline : oil and the no-growth economy / Jeff Rubin.
          p. cm.
       Includes bibliographical references and index.
          1. Petroleum products—Prices. 2. Energy consumption. 3. Economic development. 4. Petroleum industry and trade. I. Title.

HD9560.4.R82 2012
338.2'3282—dc23   2012018338

A catalogue record of the book is available from the British Library.

Design by Newgen Imaging Systems (P) Ltd., Chennai, India.

First Palgrave Macmillan edition: October 2012

10 9 8 7 6 5 4 3 2 1

Printed in the United States of America.

In memory of my parents,
Shirley Rose Rubin and Dr. Leon Julius Rubin

CONTENTS

INTRODUCTION

THE LAST MAJOR BARE-KNUCKLE prizefight in America happened in 1889. Shortly after midnight on July 8, John L. Sullivan knocked out Jake Kilrain in the seventy-fifth round, and with that an era was over.

And rightly so. Illegal in thirty-eight states at the time, bare-knuckle matches were barbaric. Gloves became mandatory when boxing adopted the Marquess of Queensberry rules, a civilized turn that set the stage for the advent of great heavyweights like Jack Dempsey and Joe Louis. Although gloves helped usher in boxing's golden age, tossing out the London Prize Ring Rules that had governed bare-knuckle matches came at a cost. In the bare-knuckle days, fighters were so worried about breaking a hand that most of their punches were body shots. Today's fight crowds may love seeing heavyweights land knock-out punches to the head, but what's less thrilling is the number of brain-related injuries suffered by boxers. Repeated blows to the head can lead to something doctors call Dementia Pugilistica, a condition every bit as bad as it sounds.

Even changes made with the best intentions can have unintended consequences. More than a century ago, the powers that be intervened to do what they thought was best. They never dreamed that gloves could create any problems beyond putting a few bare-knuckle fighters out of work. And today, the folks pulling the levers of the global economy are making choices that are already costing us much more than you might think. When it comes to setting economic policy, trying to cushion the blow can sometimes be a whole lot worse than taking a few punches with the gloves off.

The economic recovery since the world officially crawled out of the last recession in 2009 has been wobbly at best. If you read the business section or listen to financial market pundits, you'll know that majority opinion suggests the roots of the financial crisis of 2008–9 lay in the debt-ridden wreckage of the US housing market. The prescription resulting from that diagnosis involved taxpayers around the world opening up their wallets to bail out insolvent banks. The sums of money required were enormous, but we were told the ramifications of doing nothing would be even greater. Finance ministers and central bankers warned that government intervention was desperately required to save the global financial system from collapse and spare us from an economic fate worse than the Great Depression.

And so taxpayers underwrote the biggest bailout in the history of the financial industry.

If flaws in the global financial system were serious enough to jeopardize our economic future, then common sense dictates that deep reforms would unfold once the crisis passed. Since banks barely escaped insolvency as a result of carrying too much debt and exposure to poorly understood financial derivatives, it was fair to assume that regulators would soon put global banks on a much tighter leash. After shelling out trillions to prop them up, taxpayers reasonably expected to see new safeguards put in place to keep us from tumbling into the same mess ever again.

Well, guess again, because little has changed.

The global financial system is still as interconnected and full of risk as ever. A few familiar players are missing, such as Bear Stearns and Lehman Brothers, but the cast of characters is otherwise intact. And once again we're hearing ominous sounds from the financial markets. Only this time around, instead of the US housing sector being shaky, the deepest rumblings are emanating from across the Atlantic.

Europe is in the grip of a financial crisis. Greece is close to defaulting on its debt, and Portugal, Italy, Ireland and Spain aren't in much better shape. The European Central Bank is writing checks to keep these governments afloat and hold the euro-zone together. Meanwhile, German taxpayers, who are footing much of the bill to keep their neighbors solvent, are wondering what they're getting for their money and if they'll ever see any of it again.

In the world of modern finance, you don't have to live in Europe to be touched by what happens in Athens or Madrid, any more than you needed to own a home in Cleveland to feel the collapse of the subprime mortgage market. Thanks to our integrated global banking system, a financial market accident in one corner of the world now puts everyone at risk. An investment arm of your local bank could be exposed to a French bank, which in turn holds a big position in Greek bonds that are about to go horribly offside. When that happens, the pain ripples from Greece's bond market, to the French bank, to your regional investment dealer, and eventually to your doorstep. Half a world away, you and millions of other depositors have a direct interest in Greek debt, even though none of you personally has invested a penny in Greece.

In this era of electronic trading, money travels at the speed of light across national borders with little regulation. The global financial system is an interconnected web that links our economic fates together as closely as our Facebook pages. When Greece or Italy can't pay their bills, there are few places to hide. We learned that lesson a few years ago when homeowners in Florida, Nevada and Arizona began missing their monthly mortgage payments.

There certainly wasn't any cover to be found inside the walls of a Canadian investment bank. Why do you think I'm an author now?

I spent nearly twenty years as chief economist of CIBC World Markets, a major Canadian investment bank with clients and operations around the world. It was certainly a good way to earn a living. Global investors are constantly grappling with changing financial conditions, which puts the services of a chief economist in high demand. One week you're advising sovereign wealth funds in exotic locales such as Kuwait or Singapore, and the next you're back in North America telling heavyweight pension funds how economic events will impact stocks, bonds and currencies. On other days, you're visiting global financial capitals and eating at nice restaurants with powerful portfolio managers and high-ranking government officials.

The press frequently chases you for comments, which opens up an entirely different aspect of the job. A chief economist is a de facto spokesperson for a bank's position, whether or not that's something either party really wants. Ultimately, it was that part of the job that forced me to rethink my two-decade-long career.

I remember the moment it dawned on me that big life changes could be on the way. It was a cold November night, and I was flying back to Toronto on the bank's corporate plane with Gerry McCaughey, CIBC's chief executive, and other senior bank officials. We had just left Montreal after hosting a dinner for the CEOs of some big Quebec corporate customers. A dozen or so top executives from prominent companies had come to a posh club in old Montreal to hear what we had to say. I led off with some opening thoughts about the economy. Then we went around the table to hear each CEO talk about what was happening with their firm and in their industry. After an elaborate meal (washed down with a memorable vintage Bordeaux), McCaughey concluded the evening with remarks on the bank's strategy and objectives. And then we headed for the airport.

Over the years, I'd crisscrossed the country on the corporate jet to speak at dozens of similar dinners. This time, though, I had a lot more on the line.

Earlier in the year, I had written an essay on the shifting pattern of global oil demand for an anthology about the future of energy consumption, and the publisher had asked me if I would be interested in turning it into a book. I figured I should take a crack at it, so for months leading up to that night in Montreal, most of my free time had been spent plugging away at a manuscript for a book on the global economy. I didn't know how it would turn out, but by the time I finished the manuscript, publishers in Canada, the United States and the

United Kingdom were on board, and I was excited about becoming a first-time author. But there was a hitch: I hadn't yet told anybody at CIBC what I was doing.

I had been thinking that CIBC might embrace my book, *Why Your World Is About to Get a Whole Lot Smaller.* I even thought the bank's brokerage arm, Wood Gundy, would be a natural marketing outlet. Prior to talking to McCaughey on the airplane, I had negotiated a bulk discount from my publisher in case any Wood Gundy brokers or other CIBC staff wanted to give a copy to clients. In retrospect, it was a naive expectation. I could tell from McCaughey's initial reaction as we flew through the night sky toward Toronto that I might have to seriously rethink my future.

I learned several things on the plane that night—among them, that you don't get to be CEO of a major Canadian bank without knowing how to turn a withering stare on an employee. After hearing my pitch, McCaughey replied curtly that I would need to get permission from the legal department. His icy look alone was enough to get me second-guessing my future at the bank.

I can't say I was surprised when the bank's lawyers sent down word four months later that permission would be denied. Economists at big banks do publish books, but most often the subject matter is along the lines of how your retirement savings can outperform the stock market. Mine was about how triple-digit oil prices were going to reverse globalization. CIBC doesn't sell oil, and it sure doesn't sell de-globalization.

Looking back, I realize that McCaughey was only doing his job, which was to protect the bank's interests. But I didn't write the book so that it wouldn't get read. I'd been preaching its themes to whoever would listen at CIBC for years. It was time to take the message to a broader audience.

By the time I stepped away from the job, CIBC had much bigger things to worry about than my literary ambitions. At the time, the bank, like many financial institutions, was knee-deep in fancy financial market derivatives called collateralized debt obligations (CDOs).

Prior to the housing market crash, CDOs, which are backed by assets such as homeowner subprime mortgages, were making investors a ton of money. They also seemed to be relatively safe investments, at least according to rating agencies that granted many of these debt instruments gold-plated Triple-A status. But when mortgage holders who took on too much debt stopped making payments, the market imploded in a hurry. CIBC, for one, had to write down billions due to its CDO exposure.

How could so many smart bankers have stumbled down this path? One critical factor was losing sight of how rating agencies make money. They don't get paid by investors who base decisions on their ratings, but by the issuers of the securities that are being rated. Big agencies such as Standard & Poor's, Moody's and Fitch have a vested interest in keeping the folks who pay the bills happy. In economics we use the term *moral hazard* to describe a situation in which the interests of two parties entering into an agreement aren't aligned. The way debt rating agencies are compensated, they have an incentive to hand out generous ratings while at the same time they're insulated from the negative consequences of being wrong. That's a dangerous combination.

Investment bankers will tell you that steering clear of moral hazard requires keeping your head up and your eyes open. When the housing market crashed, CIBC and other financial institutions were caught skating across the ice with their heads down. They paid dearly for it on the bottom line. I must confess that CIBC's dwindling stock price, which shrank the value of the unvested bank shares and annual bonus I left behind, made my transition from long-serving Bay Street economist to fledgling author much easier to handle.

The experience also left me with a more jaded perspective on Canadian financial institutions than the one the country's politicians sell to the rest of the world. Canada's finance minister, Jim Flaherty, often holds up the nation's banks, and their regulatory supervision, as shining examples of why we don't need a radical reform of the global financial system. To be fair to Flaherty, other banks around the world had a more disastrous ride than Canadian institutions. My former bank may have sunk shareholders, but at least it didn't sink taxpayers. Nor did any of Canada's other big banks. Elsewhere, financial institutions such as the Anglo Irish Bank, based in Dublin, took part in blowing up entire national economies while leaving taxpayers to pick up the bill.

Discovering the nature of a disease is the first step to finding a cure. What's true for medicine also applies to the economy. Understanding the reasons for the last recession is critically important if we want to avoid another financial crisis.

I CAN STILL SEE Scott Stevens hitting Eric Lindros in game seven of the National Hockey League's (NHL's) Eastern Conference finals. Lindros carried the puck across the blue line with his head down, and Stevens, maybe the hardest hitter of his generation, lowered his shoulder and delivered a check that's still talked about by hockey fans more than a decade later.

Lindros had been anointed as the next Wayne Gretzky while he was still playing minor hockey as a teenager. Even watching Lindros at fourteen, scouts knew his package of size, speed and skill made him a can't-miss prospect. And they were right. Lindros won a Memorial Cup with the Oshawa Generals, a pair of gold medals at the World Junior Hockey Championships and an Olympic medal, all before lacing up his skates in the NHL. Selected first overall in the 1991 NHL entry draft, by the time Lindros landed with the Philadelphia Flyers, he was on track to go down among the best ever to play the game.

But even before he lay crumpled on the ice after the Stevens hit, Lindros's career was already off the rails. He had just returned to the ice after missing thirty games with a concussion sustained in the regular season. Game seven was his second game back in uniform. His career lasted for several years after that hit, but many hockey fans believe he was never the same.

Pittsburgh Penguins captain Sidney Crosby was the next prodigious hockey talent to be ordained the new Gretzky. As they did with Lindros, fans have followed Crosby since he was a child. Like Lindros, he was also the first overall pick in the draft, and he became a national treasure after scoring the overtime goal against the United States that won the gold medal for Canada in the 2010 Vancouver Olympics. And like Lindros's career, Crosby's could be derailed by concussions. He has struggled to get back on the ice since suffering a concussion in early 2011, and some say he should stay away from the game altogether for the good of his long-term health.

A rash of concussion-related misfortune has turned head trauma into a major issue for both the NHL and the National Football League (NFL). The summer of 2011 saw the deaths of three former or current NHL enforcers, each of whom battled problems stemming from concussions. Meanwhile, the NFL is being sued by seventy-five former players who allege that the league has been concealing the harmful effects of concussions since the 1920s.

Head injuries are now an unavoidable issue for both leagues. But concussions are only part of a much larger picture. The NHL and the NFL need to understand the true nature of the problem and take steps to change it. Players are bigger and faster than ever before. These days, kids are barely out of the womb before they're on sport-specific regimens that include weight training, protein-rich diets and missing school for far-flung road trips with their teams. A modern-day NFL safety hits like a human missile, often making helmet-to-helmet contact with a defenseless receiver. Likewise, a body check from a 230-pound NHL defenseman is like getting run over by a pickup truck.

Modern equipment that is lightweight and ultra-strong only amplifies the problem. Designed to offer protection from injury, today's shoulder pads, elbow pads and football helmets have actually turned players into weapons. As with the introduction of boxing gloves at the turn of the century, the evolution of professional sports has come with unforeseen consequences. Bigger, armor-padded combatants playing at faster speeds have made traumatic brain injuries systemic to sport. A season in a professional league is now a war of attrition; the question isn't if players will get hurt, but when.

So-called purists argue that big hits are part of the game. I've split a pair of season tickets to the Toronto Maple Leafs for years and enjoy a good hit as much as anyone, but when hardly a week passes without a professional athlete suffering a major head injury, it becomes clear that something is wrong. The leagues are reluctant to overhaul the rules for fear of alienating fans. But not recognizing that the world has changed is just sticking your head in the sand. Lindros played 813 games in the NHL, but most were sadly short of his full potential. Crosby's career may be abbreviated in his mid-twenties. How many more transcendent talents does the game need to lose before it wakes up?

The changes needed aren't just cosmetic. Over the years, players have lost a fundamental respect for their opponents. Does every off-balance skater have to be crushed into the boards? Do linebackers need to deliver kill shots to every helpless receiver who's going to the ground anyway? The Darwinian ethos of today's sports culture won't be easy to change. Professional leagues need to lead by example, and coaches must teach kids from an early age that winning is one thing, but winning at all costs is another. Concussions are a problem, but the real issues run much deeper.

What's true for professional sports applies equally to the world of international finance. To fully understand the precarious state of the global economy, the financial world needs to wake up to the idea that the last recession was much like a concussion: it hurt a lot, but it's not the real issue.

In *Why Your World Is About to Get a Whole Lot Smaller*, I argued that the US housing market wasn't responsible for blowing up the global economy. It was a symptom, not the cause. Federal Reserve chairman Alan Greenspan was spurred to hike interest rates by soaring oil prices, which were stirring inflation. Higher interest rates pricked the housing bubble, and the rest of the world was dragged down when the bubble burst.

The Fed's new chairman, Ben Bernanke, appears to be undeterred by the policy failures of his predecessor. His efforts to stimulate economic growth with rock-bottom interest rates and trillion-dollar quantitative easing programs will prove just as unsuccessful as Greenspan's attempts to keep the economy afloat. Bernanke believes that holding interest rates near zero will encourage Americans to spend money, particularly on new homes. But what's holding back the housing market isn't the cost of taking out a mortgage, but a lack of jobs and economic growth. And that has little to do with the Fed's monetary policy. The real culprit lies somewhere else.

The same factor that caused the last recession is ready to deep-six the global economy once again. And this time the economic shock will be greater than we saw last time around. Oil prices are again on the march. And make no mistake, higher energy prices aren't a symptom of our economic problems—they're the cause. The price of Brent crude, the de facto oil benchmark used in pricing almost three-quarters of the oil traded in the world, crossed the triple-digit threshold in early 2011, and it hasn't looked back since. Even West Texas Intermediate, the US-based price, is trading around $100 a barrel. And these oil prices won't fall until they trigger another global recession—one that will last much longer than just a few quarters.

Of course, there is at least one group that's content to see triple-digit prices, and that's Big Oil. High prices are inspiring oilmen to scour the earth like never before. They're drilling miles beneath the ocean floor, leveling boreal forests to dig up tar sands and learning how to get at oil that's trapped in shale rock. Meanwhile, Western governments are swarming around the Middle East, even launching a couple of military invasions, in a bid to get their hands on every last drop of the region's treasure trove of oil before it too is sucked dry.

The cost of tapping the extra energy we need to fuel our economies is mounting for both our wallets and the environment. Catastrophic environmental events, such as BP's Macondo well leak in the Gulf of Mexico or the nuclear accident at Fukushima, are happening with alarming frequency. Each one illustrates just how far we're pushing the limits of our energy consumption.

Even more unnerving, neither BP nor the Tokyo Electric Power Company (TEPCO) had any idea what to do when disaster struck. At one point, BP engineers tried to plug the gushing Macondo well with golf balls. The multinational oil giant, regarded as one of the industry's best deepwater drillers, has yet to explain the advanced engineering theory behind that failed procedure. When the Fukushima reactors were flooded by a tsunami, TEPCO's nuclear technicians scrambled into nearby neighborhoods to borrow flashlights so they could read control panels. Such jerry-rigged operational responses hardly instill confidence in the failsafe nature of our global energy system.

How many once-in-a-century accidents have to happen before we recognize that they've become the norm and not the exception? And if we accept them as the norm, what does that say about our relentless quest for more energy?

We can't continue to increase our energy consumption exponentially without expecting to pay ever-greater costs. Even as our attempts become more desperate, it's easy to understand why we keep trying. When we stop finding new sources of energy, our economies stop growing.

Growth is the Holy Grail of modern societies. It's the common denominator underlying nearly every action taken by corporations and governments. Whether it's the sales manager at your local electronics store, the developer of a new housing project or a finance minister trying to close a huge budget deficit, each one prays at the altar of growth. Economic expansion comes in all shapes and sizes. It can be spotted in the building cranes above your city's skyline, in the bustle of shoppers at the mall on a busy Saturday and in the freshly turned sod of a new subdivision. All of this activity feeds into Gross Domestic Product (GDP), the total measure of what a country's economy produces each year.

Of course, growth also comes with a lot of costs. Without growth, we could stop building new highways for the burgeoning number of new vehicles that hit the road every year. We wouldn't have to build more nuclear energy facilities or coal-fired power plants to meet our expanding electricity needs. We could stop our cities from sprawling into the countryside to make room for new suburbanites. And we could cut back on the amount of greenhouse gases we emit into the atmosphere.

For the economics profession, the notion of a world without growth is pure science fiction. While most economists now acknowledge that expensive energy curtails GDP, the majority also believe that technological innovations will allow us to leap over the hurdles presented by resource scarcity.

Historians take a different view. The decline of the Roman Empire has captured the world's imagination for centuries, as has the collapse of Mayan society and the disappearance of people from Easter Island. Indeed, history is the story of the rise and fall of civilizations large and small. The exact reasons for social collapse are rarely known, but many theories cite resource scarcity as a contributing factor. Whether constraints on resources, such as food and water, are the driving reason behind societal failures will remain lost in the mists of time, but one thing is indisputable: civilizations that once flourished have eventually floundered. But most economists these days seem to have short memories. Viewed from the limited perspective of the postwar era, resource constraints, and a scarcity of fossil fuels in particular, appear to them to be no match for human ingenuity, which keeps finding ways to supply the world with more energy. However, rising resource prices are telling us that technological advancements are now coming up short.

We could hardly pick a worse time for higher energy costs to start squeezing the growth out of the global economy. The modern world counts on economic growth to support population expansion, as well as satisfy the desire for higher incomes and all the extra things that money can buy. Since the last recession, the need for GDP growth has become even more urgent. Economic growth will provide the financial wherewithal that allows governments to service the debts accumulated during that downturn. Right now, though, the global economy is discovering that chasing growth is a catch-22. Our countries need GDP growth to repay the debt acquired during the last oil price-induced recession, but achieving that growth will bring back the same high prices that killed growth in the first place.

Finding the energy to fuel our economies is no longer enough; we need that energy to be affordable. That's why the oil industry is going to such lengths to tap the world's resources. That's why we're changing dictatorial regimes in Libya, propping up an absolutist monarchy in Saudi Arabia, digging up pristine forests in northern Alberta and drilling beneath the icy waters of the Arctic Ocean.

In the United States, the Obama administration, which just fined BP billions for the Macondo fiasco, is back issuing permits for deepwater exploration in the Gulf of Mexico. I guess the White House is betting other offshore drillers will have better luck contending with the ultrahigh pressures at the bottom of the ocean. On the other side of the world, China is building new nuclear plants in coastal areas that are prone to the same magnitude of earthquake that caused the Fukushima disaster. Beijing is undoubtedly hoping for a luckier roll of the dice when the next seismic event occurs.

The choice currently being made by most politicians simply to cross their fingers and hope for the best is hardly a sound way to deal with mounting energy costs. And in any event, the solution to higher energy prices won't come from finding larger oil reserves or building more nuclear plants. Nor will it come from a technological breakthrough in renewable energy. We aren't going to suddenly discover that solar panels or wind turbines hold a magic key that will power our economies. Instead, the solution to higher energy costs is quite simple: learn to use less energy. That doesn't mean returning to the Stone Age. As you'll see in this book, people in some countries, such as Denmark, live quite happily while also using a lot less energy. And you may be surprised to find out what's at the heart of that country's success.

The sooner more nations learn how to curb energy demand, the better it will be for everyone. In a world of energy scarcity, consuming more fuel comes at someone else's expense. One country's gain is another's loss. It's a pending reality that will affect how much oil everyone gets to burn from now on. And if you live in North America or western Europe, you can expect your fuel allotment to be much more modest than it has been for the last few decades.

The prospect of burning less oil may sound benign, but it carries profound economic consequences. Oil powers economic growth. That means if we cut back on oil, we cut back on growth. In a post-carbon world, our economies may run on a different fuel, but for now they're still critically dependent on oil and will continue to be so for the foreseeable future.

Over time, our economies will become greener and more efficient. That's the hope, anyway. In the last forty years, we've made massive gains in fuel efficiency in places such as North America, western Europe and Japan. But at the same time, economic growth and a rising global population have meant that our total energy consumption has become greater than ever before. And now emerging economic giants such as China and India are looking to claim a larger share of the global energy supply. Hundreds of millions of Chinese and Indians are moving from rural lives, where they consumed sparse amounts of fuel, to energy-intensive urban lifestyles. As these folks fill up the gas tanks of their brand-new cars and flip on light switches in their new apartments, how will the world keep pace with the fresh demand for energy?

One day, we may come up with a fuel alternative that will allow our energy consumption to increase by leaps and bounds. Renewable energy certainly has room to become a larger part of our power mix, and thanks to technological advances, that's exactly what's happening right now. But renewable energy won't come close to supplying the power we need to shelter us from the consequences of ever-higher oil prices. In the here and now, our economic fates are still unavoidably tied to fossil fuels.

No matter how much crude we're able to pull out of the ground, oil prices keep marching higher. Every year, the world notches more economic growth, which means each year the global economy needs more barrels of oil to keep running smoothly. As oil continues to get more expensive, the question is how much longer we can count on economic expansion to continue. And if growth grinds to a halt, what will that mean for the world? Will a static global economy cause our standard of living to regress? Or does this lurking new reality have other dimensions that might soften the blow?

Many folks are already questioning whether the boundless pursuit of personal consumption is really the key to a sense of well-being, particularly when we see the toll our ravenous lifestyles take on the planet. Countries that rank the highest on the United Nations' Index of Human Development don't have the largest or fastest-growing economies. Could there be a lesson there?

Maybe we can live with less GDP growth and not feel the poorer for it. The Germans have been learning to job-share, and it seems to be working fine for them. But that's in the developed world. In the developing world, millions of people struggle to put food on the table and keep a roof over their heads. These countries aren't working with much of a buffer. If GDP growth stagnates, what happens to the burgeoning populations inside the borders of poor nations?

What will China's and India's increasing consumption of the world's natural resources mean for them? Is their appetite for energy sustainable? And if it's not, what are the consequences for the amount of fuel left over for the rest of us? China and India are the locomotives of global economic growth. If they stall, how will that affect economies that have spent a decade riding on their coattails?

However uncertain the future appears, we know one thing for sure: a world of energy scarcity will be dramatically different from the world we have known. Yet when we look ahead, it's difficult to envision a future that offers such a stark contrast to our energy-abundant past. Ready or not, though, we'll soon have no choice.

The standard of living in the Western world has leapt far beyond what our parents and grandparents knew. In the coming years, it will be much more challenging for our children to achieve similar gains. Tomorrow's kids won't live in as many square feet of space, own as many flat-screen televisions or have as many cars in the driveway. But for all the material things they give up, they may be compensated in other ways.

Energy scarcity could become the environment's best friend. In the last few years, the world has been hit with record droughts that have pushed food prices sky-high. Could a permanent slowdown in economic growth be exactly what the climate change doctor ordered?

Of course, we'll still need to figure out how to feed the 10 billion people the UN forecasts will be sharing the planet by the end of the century. Will this projected human population meet a Malthusian fate, or can we navigate our way to a brighter future?

The shape of the world to come is still very much up for grabs. Living in a static economy will be much different than living in the world we've come to know. Even those of us in affluent countries in North America and Europe will have to start making real changes before long—and many Europeans are getting a taste of that future right now.

We'll undoubtedly encounter more than a few surprises along the way. I'm betting some of them will be big enough to change the way we judge this new world. The stakes are high, and we can't afford to lose, but we also have much to gain.

Part One

Chapter 1

CHANGING THE ECONOMIC SPEED LIMIT

THOSE WHO WERE AROUND in the 1970s will remember when speed limits were lowered in an attempt to stop drivers from burning so much gasoline. In the United States, the first Organization of Petroleum Exporting Countries (OPEC) oil shock spooked the president so much that he established a national speed limit of fifty-five miles per hour through the Emergency Energy Conservation Act. A slower speed limit didn't win Richard Nixon any fans among car-loving voters, but his hand was forced by oil prices that were punishing the US economy.

Well, speed limits aren't the only thing that can change when crude prices go up. Today's oil prices are changing the speed at which economies can grow. Just as people require food, economies require energy. The relationship is straightforward: economic growth is a function of energy consumption, full stop. And without question, the most important source of energy for the global economy is oil.

For most of the last century that worked out just fine. Cheap oil allowed global economic growth to keep marching higher. But in the last decade, that has all changed. Triple-digit oil prices are now forcing economies to downshift into a much lower gear. For some of the world's biggest economies, expensive oil means shifting all the way into park.

That's not a message most of us want to hear. Instead of making hard choices, we tinker around the edges. We order a new transmission, when it's the whole engine that's cooked. Making the wrong call on your car is bad enough; it's a whole lot worse when governments get the entire economic picture wrong. And right now that's exactly what's happening: governments around the world are being led astray by the belief that their economies are operating well short of their potential.

Sounds innocent enough, doesn't it? It's not. An economy's potential growth rate may be the single most important thing policymakers need to gauge. If they don't get it right, a lot of other things will go terribly wrong.

Central banks and finance ministries measure an economy's potential growth rate to help keep a country running smoothly. Economists look at two basic factors to gauge an economy's potential. The first is productivity growth, most often defined as the change in output per person. The second is labor force growth. Add the two together and you get an economy's potential growth rate.

It works like this. If productivity is growing at 2 percent a year and the labor force is growing at 1 percent a year, then the sum of the two numbers gives a sense of your country's potential rate of GDP growth. In this case, 1 percent plus 2 percent equals 3 percent. That means your economy can happily grow by 3 percent a year. Any higher and inflation will kick in; any lower and it's a good bet that more people will soon find themselves unemployed. The Federal Reserve Board pegs the US economy's potential growth rate at around 3 percent. Similarly, the Bank of Canada believes the Canadian economy can notch annual growth of 3 percent without running into problems.

When you hear Fed chairman Ben Bernanke or Bank of Canada governor Mark Carney talk about sustainability, they're not referring to an environmental initiative; they're discussing potential growth. These central bankers believe that an economy growing at less than its ideal rate means there's slack in the system. What do I mean by slack? Well, on the productivity side of the equation, it could mean that factories are working at less than full capacity. A weak order book, for example, could mean a plant runs one shift a day instead of two. Slack can also show up in the form of a company shelving plans for a new factory until sales improve. In terms of the labor force, slack means that more companies are laying off workers and fewer companies are hiring new ones. In an economy not working up to its potential, the unemployment rate will climb, while the jobs-wanted index shrinks.

If an economy is expanding above its potential growth rate, a whole other set of issues is created. Strong growth probably means the unemployment rate is falling, which is generally considered a good thing. But a fully employed population has a lot of cash to spend. That results in a lot of money chasing a limited supply of goods and services. In an economy cranking beyond its growth potential, factories are already working overtime, meaning the option to simply make more stuff to meet that demand isn't available.

Under these conditions, workers have the bargaining power to command top dollar from desperate employers, which only fuels inflation. Consider, for example, what happened in northern Alberta in the middle of the last decade. In a bid to take advantage of soaring oil prices, energy companies accelerated plans for billions of dollars' worth of construction projects in the province's tar sands. All that spending drew thousands of workers from around Canada and the world to the city of Fort McMurray. Even with the influx of people, a limited pool of workers chasing an abundance of jobs sent wages through the roof. And it wasn't just oil-patch jobs proper; even kids pouring coffee at the local Tim Hortons were getting retention bonuses for staying more than three months. Fort McMurray's economy boomed past its potential growth rate, which pushed the cost of living beyond that of cities ten times its size. A zero percent vacancy rate in the city's rental market meant that transplanted workers, if they could find a room, were forced to pay triple what they would in Calgary, Vancouver or Toronto.

Some new arrivals were even desperate enough to pay top dollar to rent out garage space from locals. Despite high wages, the numbers of the city's working poor swelled, as did the number of squatters living in the surrounding woods. In Fort McMurray, the insidious effects of inflation meant that some workers who relocated to take advantage of a seemingly can't-lose opportunity actually wound up in a situation that was economically untenable. Regardless of where you are in the world, when prices start rising faster than incomes, all those people working hard to get ahead are actually getting poorer.

For the economists who preside over a country's financial well-being, understanding where an economy is positioned in relation to its potential level of output is critical to determining how it should be managed. If there's slack, policymakers see a green light to add stimulus, which they believe will lead to growth without an undue risk of inflation. If an economy is already operating close to its potential, then stimulus measures will only bring about inflation rather than additional growth.

Here's where things get really interesting.

The difference between an economy's potential growth rate and what the economy is actually producing is known as an output gap. The bigger the gap, the more policymakers believe they need to step on the gas to try to close it. This is part of the economic theory behind the regular interest rate pronouncements you hear from such bankers as Bernanke and Carney. The Fed, for instance, estimates the US economy, in the wake of the 2008 recession, is operating as much as 6 percent below its potential level of GDP. Armed with a belief that the economy is underperforming, the Fed, at a meeting in August 2011, vowed to leave interest rates at "exceptionally low levels." Since then, Bernanke has said that the benchmark rate will likely stay near zero until at least late 2014. The Fed is rarely so precise, typically preferring to use language that leaves more wiggle room to adapt to the ever-fluid conditions of the national economy. By assuring the market that rates will stay at zero percent, the Fed is trying to instill borrowers with enough long-term confidence to take out loans that will be used to spur economic activity.

Conventional economic wisdom suggests that rock-bottom interest rates are the proper remedy for a struggling economy. And the Fed isn't alone in its prognosis. Judging by potential economic growth, many countries in Europe and North America appear to be struggling to close output gaps that are wide enough to drive a truck through. The culprit seems obvious: rising unemployment. Considering that jobless rates in some of the world's wealthiest nations, such as the thirty-four countries that belong to the Organisation for Economic Co-operation and Development (OECD), are almost double what they were a decade ago, it's easy to understand why so many government number crunchers believe there must be a tremendous amount of idle capacity in their economies.

But that thinking misses a crucial piece of the economic puzzle. A decade ago, oil cost $20 a barrel, a fraction of what it does today. Remember the equation for an economy's potential growth rate? The two components were productivity and labor. The price of oil doesn't enter into the calculations governments use to determine how much stimulus is needed to help stir a flagging economy. If it did, central bankers from Bernanke and Carney to Mario Draghi of the European Central Bank would be far less eager to use monetary policy to increase the amount of money circulating through the system. Politicians, meanwhile, would also be more hesitant to approve fiscal measures, such as stimulus packages and deficit spending, that are designed to boost employment and spur economic growth. All told, the economists pulling the levers on the global economy are unleashing a massive amount of stimulus into the world. But what if the game has changed? What if they're using the wrong tools for the task at hand?

Could the best-educated economic minds in the world really be so far off course? In a word—yes.

But it's not without good reason. Yardsticks such as potential economic output have helped OECD economies achieve an impressive track record of growth throughout the postwar era. A half century of success certainly helps to breed confidence. Throwing out what has been a winning formula is tough to do under the best of circumstances, let alone when the harsh new reality of world oil markets I'm about to describe may seem far from certain.

What we do know with certainty is that oil prices have quadrupled over the last ten years. You don't need to look any further than the nearest gas station for evidence of this sharp step change in the cost of energy. It's a shift that will permanently shackle the growth potential of the world's oil-burning economies.

Finance ministers and central bankers have already spent billions of your tax dollars to try to boost flagging economic growth. But the problem they're attempting to fix has been misdiagnosed using the wrong tools. When you change the price of oil, you change the economy's speed limit. Until we realize the implications of slower economic growth, we won't be able to make choices that will help us deal with this new reality.

THE CAUTION FLAG IS WAVING, BUT IS ANYONE PAYING ATTENTION?

So what do we know about this new world of higher energy costs?

To begin with, the countries guzzling the most oil are taking the biggest hits to potential economic growth. That's sobering news for the United States, which consumes almost a fifth of the oil used in the world every day. Not long ago, when oil was $20 a barrel, the United States was the locomotive of global economic growth. Washington was running budget surpluses. The jobless rate at the beginning of the last decade was at a forty-year low. Around the country, people slept soundly knowing that dreams of early retirement were almost in reach, as the value of their savings increased with each record high notched by the Dow.

That seems like a lifetime ago, not just ten years. Economic growth in the United States is now struggling to get off the mat. Its budget deficit is more than a trillion dollars, and almost 13 million Americans are now unemployed. At the same time as America's economy was deteriorating, world oil prices were quadrupling. This is not a coincidence.

And the United States isn't the only country getting squeezed by higher energy costs. From Europe to Japan, governments are scrambling to get GDP growth back on its feet. But the economic remedies being used are actually doing more harm than good, based as they are on a fundamental belief that economic growth can return to its former glory. During those salad days, it stands to be repeated, oil was around $20 a barrel. Leading central bankers and policymakers have failed to fully recognize the suffocating impact of $100-a-barrel oil on economic growth. Running huge budget deficits and keeping borrowing costs at record lows are only compounding current problems. It's throwing good money after bad.

Maybe it's hope or maybe it's denial, but world governments are still clinging to the idea that the good times of renewed and steady growth are right around the corner. And no country is hungrier for economic growth to resume than the United States. That desire is spurring Washington into running a trillion-dollar budget deficit, while leading the Fed to peg interest rates at zero in an attempt to induce an economic turnaround. By any historical benchmark, these actions are extreme. The US budget deficit, as a percentage of GDP, hasn't been this high since the country went into hock to fight the Second World War. There isn't much more the American public could ask the Treasury Department or the Fed to do that isn't already being done.

But neither huge budget deficits nor zero interest rates are long-term substitutes for cheap oil. In the end, an economy can't grow if it can no longer afford to burn the fuel it runs on. Of course, throw enough money at any situation and it will make a splash. When the water settles, though, nothing has really changed. The reality is that the price of oil has lowered the economy's speed limit. The Fed can continue printing American dollars at a dizzying clip, but no amount of monetary or fiscal pump-priming will change that basic economic reality. The sooner central bankers and finance ministers realize that, the better off we'll be.

Massive budget deficits and rock-bottom interest rates are the wrong prescription for the realities of the energy-constrained world we now live in. The US stimulus package in 2009 approved more than $700 billion in spending that was designed to kick-start a recovery. That money has put people to work and will help improve the country's infrastructure, but eventually it must be repaid. In the final analysis, the spending amounts to a very expensive short-term patch. Even worse, these policy measures, which are being enacted in the eurozone as well as the United States, are not only burdening national economies with a crushing amount of debt, they're also awakening the nasty specter of inflation. If policymakers don't start making the right calls soon, an already bad economic situation will become that much worse.

ECONOMISTS ARE HOOKED ON GROWTH

I suppose it's only natural for central banks and finance departments to hold on tight to the idea of economic growth. For starters, growth is a top priority for politicians who, by definition, are constantly chasing reelection. A sick economy is a surefire way to lose voters.

But the bias toward chasing growth runs even deeper. Central banks and treasury departments are, after all, chock full of economists who are taught from the first day of class to treat growth as gospel. It's stamped into an economist's DNA. As an undergraduate student at the University of Toronto, nearly every economics exam I wrote dealt with the idea of maximizing economic growth. The tune stayed the same at McGill University, where I went to graduate school. It wasn't until I had years of real-world experience under my belt as chief economist of an investment bank that I began to understand what the textbooks were missing. The task of investing my own money is one thing, but the responsibility of guiding other people's investment decisions spurred me to challenge even my most basic economic assumptions.

After watching GDP growth shrink in the face of steadily rising oil prices, I couldn't escape the notion that growth might someday become finite. During my formal training, steeped in conventional economic theory, the idea of static growth was never even considered. It doesn't matter which school of economic thought you subscribe to or where you belong on the ideological spectrum, the notion of growth is an unquestioned tenet of the discipline.

If you're from the University of Chicago, once home to the high priest of laissez-faire economics, Milton Friedman, you believe that a pause in economic growth, such as a recession, is a temporary event. Leave the market alone to do its work and the economy will get back on track. This was the line of thinking behind the economic policies of Ronald Reagan and Margaret Thatcher in the 1980s that drastically reduced the role of government. To free-market acolytes, an issue like rising joblessness isn't a problem so much as a hiccup. High unemployment rates force workers to lower wage demands until it becomes profitable for someone to hire them. It's the market (and certainly not tax-and-spend liberals in government) that will get an economy growing again, the thinking goes.

If you're from the Keynesian school of thought made famous at Cambridge University, you believe that recessions are remedied through government intervention. Modern-day Keynesians such as *New York Times* columnist and Princeton University professor Paul Krugman are outspoken proponents of stimulus spending. Krugman, for example, believes Obama's stimulus efforts are far too small to get the job done. He advocates even more government spending on new public works projects, such as bridges, highways and tunnels. Another path favored by Keynesians is slashing interest rates to encourage borrowing, which will lead to spending that will revive the national economy. Without such interventionist steps, Keynesian economists believe a recession can deepen into a long period of painful contraction, like the Great Depression of the 1930s.

Whether you're a free-market type or you believe in government intervention, your common ground with most economists is an

sector. It also favors products made in the United States over imported goods. When US goods become cheaper at home and abroad, factories start to hum, which gives rise to more manufacturing jobs.

The Fed believes that implementing such expansionary monetary policy will keep the United States from falling into an even deeper recession than the one faced in 2008. But quantitative easing is based on the conventional economic thinking that a return to growth is just around the corner. What's really standing in the way of growth is the cost of oil. And oil prices aren't coming down regardless of how much money is put into circulation. Fiscal and monetary policies need to be recalibrated to account for the economy's slower potential growth rate. But neither politicians nor average citizens want to hear that slower growth is here to stay. A booming economy makes for wonderful times. Jobs are plentiful. Property values rise. The stock market clocks double-digit gains. Wages go up. The world feels like your oyster. Why would we want to get off that ride if we don't have to?

OIL IS THE FUEL OF GROWTH

Why exactly is oil so special? For starters, it provides more than a third of the energy we use on the planet every day. That's more than any other energy source. But even that statistic doesn't come close to capturing oil's importance to the world. Where oil is truly indispensable to the global economy is as a transit fuel.

More than two-thirds of every barrel of oil produced goes toward transportation, whether it's in the form of gasoline, diesel, jet or bunker fuel. Planes, trains, cars, trucks, ships and even motorbikes all run on oil. Take away oil and we'll need to come up with another 6 billion ten-speeds and a whole lot of kayaks to help folks get around.

Just how unique is oil? Oil can be stored. It doesn't spoil. It can be easily moved through pipelines, trucks or tankers. It's found all over the world. It's used to make pop bottles and to power fighter jets. Most critically, it packs an unparalleled amount of energy into a tiny package. Given the same volume, oil contains twice as much energy as coal and four times as much energy as natural gas. That is why no matter how much shale gas is drilled in North America it can't substitute for oil as a transit fuel. Neither can the natural gas liquids that typically accompany shale gas. Less than 1 precent of all the vehicles in North America run on propane, the natural gas liquid most widely used as a transit fuel. Indeed, the record price gap between oil and its supposed substitutes, shale gas and natural gas liquids, is testament to what poor substitutes they really are.

We're making strides at developing alternative energy sources, but we still don't have anything close to a viable substitute that captures all of oil's magical properties.

The price of oil is the single most important ingredient in the outlook for the global economy. Feed the world cheap oil and it will run like a charm. Send prices to unaffordable levels and the engine of growth will immediately seize up.

You can draw a straight line between oil consumption and GDP growth. The more oil we burn, the faster the global economy grows. On average over the last four decades, a 1 percent bump in world oil consumption has led to a 2 percent increase in global GDP. That means if GDP increased by 4 percent a year—as it often did before the 2008 recession—oil consumption was increasing by 2 percent a year.

At $20 a barrel, boosting annual oil consumption by 2 percent seems reasonable enough. At $100 a barrel, it becomes easier to see how a 2 percent increase in fuel consumption is enough to make an economy keel over and collapse.

Fortunately, the reverse is also true. When our economies stop growing, less oil is needed. Shrink a country's economic activity enough and its oil intake suddenly becomes manageable again. For example, following the big downturn in 2008, global oil demand actually fell for the first time since 1983.

The relationship between oil and economic growth is a two-way street. Buying oil stocks, for example, is always a great idea when crude prices are going up. But when high oil prices trigger a recession that clobbers demand, crude prices come tumbling back down to earth, bringing those same oil stocks along for the ride.

That's why the best cure for high oil prices is high oil prices. When prices rise to a level that causes an economic crash, lower prices inevitably follow. Over the last four decades, each time oil prices have spiked, the global economy has rolled over into a recession. The problems may take different guises, such as stagflation in the 1970s or the financial market meltdown in 2008. Regardless of what story made the most headlines at the time, oil prices were lurking at the root of the problem.

Consider the first oil shock, created by OPEC following the Yom Kippur War in 1973. Set off by this Arab–Israeli conflict, OPEC's Arab members turned off the taps on roughly 8 percent of the world's oil supply by cutting shipments to the United States and other Israeli allies. Crude prices spiked, and by 1974, real GDP in the United States had shrunk by 2.5 percent.

The second OPEC oil shock happened during Iran's revolution and the subsequent war with Iraq. Disruptions to Iranian production during the revolution sent crude prices higher, pushing the North American economy into a recession for the first half of 1980. At the same time, higher energy prices also spurred on the inflation that compelled Volcker to keep pushing interest rates higher. The economy notched a brief recovery, but a few months later, Iran's war with Iraq shut off 6 percent of world oil production, sending North America into a double-dip recession that began in the spring of 1981.

When Saddam Hussein invaded Kuwait a decade later, oil prices doubled to $40 a barrel, an unheard-of level at the time. The First Gulf War disrupted nearly 10 percent of the world's oil supply, sending major oil-consuming countries into a recession in the fall of 1990.

Guess what oil prices were doing in 2008 when the world fell into the deepest recession since the 1930s? From trading around $30 a barrel in 2004, oil prices marched steadily higher before hitting a peak of

$147 a barrel in the summer of 2008. Unlike past oil price shocks, this time there wasn't even a supply disruption to blame. The spigot was wide open. The problem was, we could no longer afford to buy what was flowing through it.

There are many ways an oil shock can deep-six an economy. When prices spike, most of us have little choice but to open our wallets and shell out more for what we burn. Unless we want to stop driving our cars or burning heating oil, what else can we do? Something has to give. Paying more for oil means we have less cash to spend on food, shelter, furniture, clothes, travel and pretty much anything else you can think of. A poll by the American Automobile Association in 2011 found that motorists still planned to hit the road for summer vacations, despite pump prices close to $4 a gallon. Americans, it seems, will always keep on truckin'. What changes is how much cash is left over to spend on hotels, restaurants and other holiday expenses. Soft consumer-demand numbers across the American economy confirm this same trend. Expensive oil, coupled with the average American's refusal to drive less, leaves a lot less money for the rest of the economy.

The International Energy Agency (IEA) is already warning that households are spending as much on energy as they have during past oil-induced recessions. There's only so much money to go around. When oil prices go north, consumer spending has no choice but to head south.

Expensive oil doesn't just curtail domestic spending; it also fosters a massive shift in wealth and power from countries that import oil to those that produce it. As oil prices ran higher between 2005 and 2007, OECD countries shipped nearly a trillion petrodollars to OPEC nations.

Think about the last story you heard about the extravagances of Middle Eastern oil sheikhs. An extra trillion dollars pays for a whole lot of indulgence. Consider Prince Alwaleed's plans for Kingdom City in Saudi Arabia. The prince recently commissioned a $1.2-billion construction project to erect the world's tallest building. His new tower will surpass the 160-floor Burj Khalifa (also built with oil money) in neighboring Dubai. What else but the price of oil could allow the world's tallest buildings to rise up from the desert sands?

The same petrowealth allows billionaire Sheikh Hamad, a member of Abu Dhabi's ruling family, to emboss his name on an island he owns off the coast of the United Arab Emirates. The name HAMAD rises above the landscape in letters half a mile high and two miles across. It's immodest, certainly, but I suppose humility isn't a priority for someone whose name is now visible from space.

Fatih Birol, the chief economist at the IEA, the energy think tank of the OECD, estimates that annual revenues for OPEC's twelve members reached a trillion dollars for the first time in 2011. America, meanwhile, is running a trillion-dollar budget deficit to feed its oil-sucking economy. It might save everyone some time if the United States just shipped its stimulus spending straight to OPEC or directly into the pockets of oil-exporting dictators.

But the transfer of massive amounts of wealth isn't even the biggest issue. When oil prices go up, so does inflation. And when inflation goes up, central banks respond by raising interest rates to keep prices in check. Between 2004 and 2006, US energy inflation ran at 35 percent, according to the country's Consumer Price Index (CPI). In turn, overall inflation, as measured by the CPI, vaulted from 1 percent to nearly 6 percent. You'll remember what happened next. A fivefold bump in interest rates was the last straw for the massively leveraged US housing market. Higher rates popped the speculative housing bubble, which brought down not only several prominent Wall Street investment banks but also the entire global economy.

Unfortunately, history seems to be repeating itself right now. The same pattern of oil-driven inflation is with us again. And to rub more salt in the wound, world food prices are coming along for the ride. According to the food price index tracked by the United Nations Food and Agriculture Organization (FAO), the cost of food rose nearly 40 percent between 2009 and the beginning of 2012. Looking back even further, since 2002, the FAO's food price index, which measures a basket of five commodity groups (meat, dairy, cereals, oils and fats and sugar), is up by roughly 150 percent.

A double whammy of rising oil and food prices means inflation will be here sooner than anyone would like to think. In India, the whole-sale price index, the country's key inflation gauge, was at near-record levels, above 9 percent, for most of 2011. In response, India's central bank embarked on a program of interest rate hikes, boosting rates at least thirteen times since the spring of 2010. The situation is also bad in China, where inflation hit a three-year high of 6.5 percent in July 2011, well above the government's stated goal of 4 percent. China is charting a difficult course, attempting to keep economic growth run-ning at more than 8 percent while holding inflation in check at the same time.

Rising inflation rates in China and India are a clear signal that those economies are growing at an unsustainable pace. China has made GDP growth of more than 8 percent a priority, but it needs to realize that higher energy prices have lowered the economic speed limit. The country will have to recalibrate its thinking on potential economic growth to recognize the dampening effects of high oil prices. Growth might not stall entirely, as it has in some countries in North America and Europe, but clocking double-digit gains is no longer feasible, at least without triggering a calamitous increase in inflation. If China and India, the new engines of global economic growth, are forced to adopt anti-inflationary monetary policies, the ripple effects for resource-based economies such as Canada, Australia and Brazil will be felt in a hurry.

China and India are painfully aware that Brent crude traded in triple digits for nearly all of 2011. Its recent high of $126 a barrel is only $20 off the 2008 oil price spike that brought eight years of global economic expansion to a screeching halt. Triple-digit prices will drive a stake through China's and India's lofty economic hopes, which hinge on burning more and more barrels of oil.

China and India are looking to achieve the same sort of sustained economic growth that North America and Europe enjoyed in the post-war era. That's entirely understandable, but there's an unavoidable obstacle that puts such ambitions out of reach: today's oil isn't flowing from the same places it did yesterday. More importantly, it's not flowing at the same cost.

Conventional oil production, the easy-to-get-at stuff from the Middle East or west Texas, hasn't increased in more than five years. And that's with record crude prices giving explorers all the incentive in the world to drill. According to the IEA, conventional production has already peaked and is set to decline steadily over the next few decades.

That doesn't mean there won't be any more oil. New reserves are being found all the time in brand-new places. What the decline in conventional production does mean, though, is that future economic growth will be fueled by expensive oil from nonconventional sources such as the tar sands, offshore wells in the deep waters of the world's oceans and even oil shales, which come with a long list of environmental costs that range from carbon dioxide emissions to potential groundwater contamination.

The arrival of these new sources of oil points to the same thing: oil will be getting more expensive. Where will that leave the global economy? Well, we know that when oil prices rise, economies eventually contract and roll over into a recession. The downturn then causes oil demand to drop and prices to plunge back down. But the minute the economy recovers, so too does demand, giving rise to the very same price hikes that trigger another recession. How does this ride end?

PEAK OIL IS REALLY ABOUT PRICES, NOT SUPPLY

When oil prices start to climb, the peak-oil debate inevitably moves back into the spotlight. In brief, the idea of peak oil holds that geological limits to the amount of oil that can be tapped means global oil production will eventually top out and then embark on an irreversible decline. It's a contentious topic. The message that oil's days are numbered is clearly not something the energy industry wants to hear. At the same time, the shrill tone taken by some peak-oil proponents, who see a coming oil crisis unleashing a doomsday scenario on us all, doesn't do their position any favors with the rest of the energy world.

I'll leave the geological argument to the geologists and petroleum engineers, where it belongs. What's important here is the link between oil prices and economic growth. Focusing on this relationship casts the debate in a very different light.

Like Mayan predictions for the end of days, predictions for peak oil come and go with some regularity. To the great consternation of peak-oil proponents, the oil industry continues to confound projections by getting better at pulling oil out of the ground. Better technology has kept the oil industry a step ahead of the best estimates of the peak-oil geologists.

That's a familiar story for the peak-oil movement, which got its start after an American geophysicist, M. King Hubbert, predicted in 1956 that conventional oil production in the lower forty-eight states would peak by the early 1970s. Hubbert was right, but subsequent projections have been derailed by the development of new sources of supply in Alaska and under the Gulf of Mexico. More recently, crude from Canada's tar sands and shale deposits has kept the oil supply from following the same bell-shaped curve Hubbert used to describe the trajectory of conventional US production.

As new sources of oil are discovered, and the definition of what counts as oil has expanded to include new sources of supply such as bitumen from the tar sands, the peak crowd has been forced to roll back predictions for the dreaded peak to points further in the future. A popular view now held by many peak-oil advocates sees oil production reaching an undulating plateau, sparing the world from the sharp drop-off in production foreseen in earlier predictions.

It's easy to get caught up in the semantics of the peak-oil debate. Just what is oil? Are new sources of supply really producing effective substitutes for the conventional oil we're losing to depletion? But the issue that should be at the forefront of peak-oil discussions isn't physical supply but economic cost. World supply may continue to defy peak-oil predictions, but that's just a geological sideshow. What matters to the economy is the price it takes to get the new supply flowing. It's not enough for the global energy industry simply to find new caches of oil; the crude they find must be affordable. Triple-digit prices make it profitable to tap ever more expensive sources of oil, but the prices needed to pull this crude out of the ground will throw our economies right back into recession.

What geologists don't get is that peak oil isn't about supply: higher prices will always fetch more oil supply. It may not be exactly what purists think of as oil, but hey, if it burns, it'll do. Peak oil is really a demand phenomenon rooted in economics, not geology. It doesn't matter if billions of barrels are waiting to be tapped in unconventional plays such as the tar sands or oil shales if the cost of extraction is beyond our capacity to pay. In other words, the only peak that matters is the one determined by what we can afford, not by how much we can drill. Potential oil resources are only meaningful if we have the money to actually pay for the fuel. Otherwise, who really cares if we can pump it out of the ground?

The energy industry's task is not simply to find oil, but to find stuff we can afford to burn. And that's where the industry is failing the global economy. Prices have more than quadrupled over the last ten years. Each new barrel we pull out of the ground is costing us more than the last. The resources may be there for the taking, but our economies are already telling us we can't afford the cost.

Today, the world burns about 90 million barrels of oil a day. What if that's enough? If our economies are no longer growing, maybe we won't need any more than that. We might even need less. Maybe the oil trapped in the tar sands or under the Arctic Ocean can stay where nature put it.

Some people might call that an oil peak. Others might just call it the end of growth.

Chapter 2

DEBT IS ENERGY INTENSIVE

THOSE LUCKY ENOUGH TO travel down the Italian coast will tell you that the ruins at Pompeii are not to be missed. Uncovered in the 1700s, Pompeii is a snapshot of what Roman life was like circa AD 79. It's also a plucky little set of ruins. In the last two thousand years, Pompeii has survived the eruption of Mount Vesuvius, the fall of the Roman Empire, the Dark Ages and a pair of world wars.

And right now, the ruins are falling apart.

Exhibit A is the House of the Gladiators, a stone building on Pompeii's main street thought to have been a training ground for fighters. The Gladiator House made it through volcanoes and Allied bombers, but in the end, Italy's debt problems turned out to be too much for it to withstand. It unceremoniously collapsed into a pile of rubble in late 2010.

And it's not just Pompeii. Archeologists are sounding alarm bells about other national treasures, including the Grand Canal in Venice and Florence's Duomo. The deteriorating state of historical sites has worried Italians for years. But only now are austerity measures forcing such deep cuts to the country's culture budget that there's no government money for ancient monuments. Italy is now pinning its hopes on wealthy philanthropists stepping in with cash to help preserve cultural treasures, including the Colosseum.

Italy's crumbling landmarks are only the tip of the iceberg.

Take a look around Europe. Whether you're Italian, Greek, Irish, Spanish, Portuguese or even British, it must be painfully clear that your economic future is full of IOUs. Look no farther than Greece. Each one of its 11 million citizens owes the equivalent of 30,000 euros. It doesn't matter that Greek citizens didn't personally sign loan papers, their government borrowed the money on their behalf. But no one gets a free ride. Greece's problems are exacerbated by a culture of tax evasion that forced the government to rack up massive budget deficits to fund public services. Now, one way or another, the Greek people will end up paying for that debt.

In the aftermath of the financial crisis of 2008, Greece was not alone. Governments around the world piled up debt in a double-barreled attempt to fight the recession and save a global banking system on the edge of collapse. And now countries are left with huge budget shortfalls that dwarf anything we've seen in the postwar era.

At its worst, Ireland's annual budget deficit accounted for nearly a third of its GDP. Portugal's deficit in 2010 was 8.6 percent of GDP, down from 10 percent a year earlier. Severe austerity measures will help cut that figure into the range of 4.5 percent in 2011. Similar measures, though, aren't working as well in Greece, where a shrinking economy means the country's annual budgetary shortfall remains stuck in the double-digit range, where it has been for the last several years. To put those numbers in perspective, the European Monetary Union (EMU) sets a ceiling on budget deficits of 3 percent of GDP as part of its criteria for inclusion in the eurozone.

Annual deficits, of course, don't simply go away when the calendar turns the page. Budget deficits pile up on each other, compounding into mountains of national debt that can become bigger than the economies they're financing every year. Japan's national debt, for instance, is now more than twice as large as its annual GDP. Greece's total debt is running at more than 150 percent of GDP. Italy's debt is roughly 120 percent of GDP. That's twice as much as the threshold set out for inclusion in the EMU, which requires that a country's debt-to-GDP ratio doesn't exceed 60 percent. In the United States, the Obama administration is running a budget deficit of more than a trillion dollars. That's caused the country's debt-to-GDP ratio to nearly double in the last three years to more than 70 percent, as Washington has strung together a series of record deficits to help fight the effects of the recession.

Nearly every OECD country is drowning in red ink these days. Governments are counting on an economic recovery to act as a life preserver. But bringing economies to life, as we saw in the last chapter, requires burning more oil. Economic growth and oil consumption are joined at the hip, a relationship that casts government debt in a brand-new light—one with a decidedly oily sheen.

We know that servicing debt is very energy intensive. We also know there's an ocean of debt out there. What's not clear, from Athens to Washington, is exactly how governments will pay back an already crushing debt load that's only getting bigger. Whether it's the taxes you pay or the public services you depend on, it doesn't take long before your government's financial problems are knocking on your door. In the United States, that could mean cuts to Medicare. It certainly means the federal government can transfer less money to each state, which is bad news for education, among other things. Older schools get closed, new schools don't get built, class sizes go up and kids are sent to schools that are farther away from home. The burden of servicing the national debt means everything else gets the short end of the stick, as costs are passed from Washington to the state level and on down to municipalities. Streets are patrolled by fewer police officers. Snow is plowed less often in the winter. Cities can run fewer buses, and the ones that do roll by cost more to hop on.

In Europe, the consequences of the fiscal problems are even more severe. In the UK, record budget deficits, and the accompanying

austerity measures that include crippling increases in university tui-
tion, contributed to a widespread dissatisfaction among young people
that fueled some of the worst rioting in years. The images of violence,
looting and arson that broke out in cities across England in 2011 left
an indelible impression. In Athens and Madrid, general strikes are now
routine, as are the ensuing clashes between police and protesters, many
of whom are now packing everything from stones to petrol bombs.

Saddling a worried electorate with debt and budget cutbacks is a
time-tested way for a government to find itself out of work when the
polls close. Ireland is a case in point. In February 2011, the incumbent party, Fianna Fáil, suffered the worst election defeat for a sitting
Irish government since 1918. In Greece, President George Papandreou
found his country caught between meeting the ever more draconian
fiscal demands of its foreign creditors and a rising resistance to austerity measures among its citizens. His government collapsed, forcing
Papandreou's resignation. In Italy, Prime Minister Silvio Berlusconi,
who had managed to survive corruption charges and salacious sex
scandals, couldn't outlast his country's debt crisis. He resigned in
November 2011, after seventeen years as the dominant force in Italian
politics. Even Germany's Angela Merkel, whose country remains the
economic stalwart of the EU, is looking over her shoulder as opponents
make political hay criticizing the country's outsized role in backstopping the monetary union.

Europe is stuck in a quagmire of austerity measures, budget deficits and financial bailouts. As its political leaders are finding out, it's
a situation fraught with the likelihood of debt default, social upheaval
and political change. The economic hopes of an entire continent are
wrapped up in a single magic bullet: growth. Were a strong-enough
economic rebound to take hold, it could slay the deficit and spare
the EU. A sharp rebound in economic growth would fill government
coffers with tax revenues that could be used to pay back the huge
amounts owed to creditors. At the same time, a turnaround in the EU's
financial fortunes would spare citizens from suffering through more

income-sucking tax increases and bone-deep cuts to social spending. The debt-strapped countries borrowing the money, the bondholders on the hook for billions and the EU taxpayers footing the rest of the bill could all come out okay if Europe's economy recovers.

But pulling off such a recovery will take copious amounts of energy. The question that needs to be asked is whether the global economy can afford the fuel bill.

The pace of economic growth needed to allow a heavily indebted country such as Greece to service its debt means burning an incredible amount of oil. German taxpayers and the bondholders funding EU bailouts may not realize it yet, but the debt being accumulated in countries such as Greece and Portugal might as well be denominated in barrels of oil. If the eurozone needs economic expansion to pay back debt and that growth can only happen by burning more fuel, the price of oil starts to loom pretty large.

Global oil consumption in 2000 was roughly 76 million barrels a day, with Brent crude averaging $28.50 a barrel; the world's annual oil bill was $791 billion. Skip ahead to 2010. World consumption was up to 87 million barrels a day, with Brent averaging $79.50 a barrel. The combination of higher prices and more demand had quadrupled the annual fuel bill to $2.5 trillion. Only a year later, Brent crude was averaging more than $100 a barrel. That price increase alone added more than $500 billion to what the world spends each year to keep the wheels turning.

The extra money didn't fall from the sky. The cost is footed by the world's major oil-consuming economies, and the cash is shipped into the outstretched arms of oil-exporting nations like Saudi Arabia, Russia and Canada.

When the world's annual fuel bill was less than $800 billion, oil-importing nations like the United States clocked healthy economic growth year after year. Now that the world is spending more than $3 trillion a year on oil, those same economies are floundering.

This isn't a coincidence.

Triple-digit oil prices turn the sovereign debt market into something resembling a giant Ponzi scheme. The investors who are buying the bonds that allow governments to roll over the debt amassing in the financial system are essentially making larger and larger bets on future economic growth. But as oil prices climb higher, the prospects for that growth become ever more tenuous. It's like doubling down just as the odds are turning against you.

Think about buying a 30-year government bond today. In effect, you're betting a country's tax base will expand for the next three decades. Remember, though, that the economy's speed limit changes along with the price of oil. What happens if an economy, denied the cheap energy it needs, can only grow at a fraction of its previous pace, if at all? How would tax revenues increase enough for a government to make debt payments? And if a country can't make those payments, what happens to the value of your 30-year bond? In order to avoid default, will governments try to reschedule much longer repayment terms than were initially agreed to by the bondholder? And if so, how receptive do you imagine the bond market would be to the next government debt issue?

The relationship between growth and debt suddenly shows up in very stark terms. If investors can no longer count on growth, what happens to the appetite for government bonds? The nasty kicker in all this for a government is the timing: just when a stagnant economy makes a government's borrowing needs the most urgent, the doors to new money start to close.

If you're wondering why governments are continuously borrowing money, it's a good question. Governments don't pay off debt the way you pay down your mortgage. Although they make constant debt payments to creditors that have lent them money in the past, governments are continually writing more IOUs to finance current deficits. Government debt is really a revolving door.

The bigger a country's economy, the more debt it can carry. The idea is similar to a bank calculating the size of your mortgage by looking at your income. In addition, the credit ratings handed out by agencies such as Standard & Poor's and Moody's play a role in determining how much it costs governments to borrow money. These agencies closely monitor national balance sheets and then advise investors about a country's fiscal health. The amount of debt a country already has on the books in relation to the size of its economy is key in judging a country's creditworthiness. The massive accumulation of US debt since the 2008 recession, for instance, didn't do the country any favors with ratings agencies. Standard & Poor's—troubled by the increasing size of the national debt, the pace of government spending and a rocky outlook for the US economy—downgraded the country's credit rating in August 2011. The United States had maintained S&P's coveted Triple-A rating since 1941.

Governments that sport a low debt-to-GDP ratio have the luxury of borrowing at a cheap interest rate. The lower the interest rate, the fewer tax dollars need to be devoted to servicing the national debt. That leaves more money for things such as education, health care and the other social services we all hope governments can provide. In contrast, a high debt-to-GDP ratio leads to a low credit rating. By some estimates, S&P's downgrade of US debt will cost the country tens of billions of dollars a year. The higher borrowing costs leave Washington with that much less money to spend on everything else.

Consider what happens if your country's economic growth flatlines. In a static economy, only one half of the debt-to-GDP ratio is going up—the wrong half. If debt continues to increase and GDP stays the same, one of the key ratios used to determine borrowing costs starts to look pretty shaky. That means your government will have to start paying a higher interest rate if it wants to continue financing its debt. But that's not all. What it costs you to borrow money from your bank is pegged to your government's borrowing costs. If your government has a sterling Triple-A credit rating, it's able to borrow money from the bond market at the cheapest possible rates. Those low borrowing costs trickle down to your country's banks and on to you. Conversely, when

a country's debt-to-GDP ratio goes in the wrong direction, governments are forced to dangle higher interest rates to entice bond investors
to assume a greater degree of risk. When your government pays more
to the bond market, it eventually means that you and everyone you
know will pay more to take out a loan. This cycle of higher borrowing
costs only makes it that much harder for your economy to grow.

Start piling on debt without economic growth and pretty soon a
government's borrowing rate will go through the roof. Greece, for one,
is now paying over 20 percent interest to borrow from the bond market. That's why it's so desperate for bailout funds from the EU. Without
those emergency funds, Greece is at the mercy of the bond market and
its usurious interest rates. In the event that growth comes to a complete
standstill, persuading creditors to keep financing government deficits
becomes a hard sell.

Static growth means the revolving door of government debt could
stop revolving. If your government can't keep rolling over its debt in
the financial markets, that's bad news for everyone. The national debt
will quickly start to feel like your personal debt, since governments will
have few choices but to raise taxes to service the debt. You can figure
out what that means for your after-tax income—if you still have an
income. The inevitable budget cuts will put a lot of workers, particularly those in government, on the breadlines. In the United States, for
instance, the public sector is taking a beating. Cash-strapped state and
local governments cut more than 140,000 jobs in 2011, according to
the Labor Department. That's on top of the 200,000 jobs eliminated
in 2010. All told, more than 500,000 public-sector jobs have been shed
in the States since the recession began in 2008.

Digging out from under this situation is a tall order that requires
governments to raise a lot of cash. Of course, the more a government
flirts with a debt default, the more compensation investors require to
entice them into the bond market. Not that investors in government
bonds aren't used to facing risk. Over the course of a 30-year bond, it's
only natural for an economy to stumble through a few rough patches.

After all, which country hasn't had a recession in the last three decades? Historically, bond investors have been willing to ride out the cyclical bumps, secure in the belief that recessions are temporary events and eventually an economy will get back to growing. Even during the downtimes, they'll keep financing government debt, knowing the payoff will come when the economy perks up.

But what happens if a bond investor loses faith in a country's economy? The prospect of static growth puts a chill on investors that have bought bonds expecting to receive a steady stream of interest payments for the next thirty years. Again, take Greece as a test case. Its economy is suffocating beneath the weight of the draconian budget measures demanded by its creditors. Its economy is shrinking, and a turnaround is nowhere in sight. All of that means the country's debt-to-GDP ratio will keep deteriorating, which will lead to even higher borrowing costs. Meanwhile, austerity measures and budget restraints will become even harsher in an attempt to appease the European taxpayers funding its bailout. A partial list of these measures, which are designed to drastically reduce the size and role of the Greek government, includes: tax increases, public-sector wage cuts, reduced health care spending, school closures, cuts to social security for seniors and the privatization of state-run enterprises such as airports and electrical utilities.

Greece is trapped in a brutal downward spiral. That's why the bond market doesn't want any part of financing Greece's deficit. Any confidence that its economy will recover has all but vanished.

And soon it won't just be Greece's economy that isn't growing. The cheap energy that allowed for economic growth in the past is gone, and it's not coming back. It's a relic of a different time. The world's bond markets have yet to fully absorb the financial risks of slower growth, but they will soon. As economic growth slows to a crawl, it will become more expensive for governments to issue bonds. If a government is looking to assign blame for the higher costs, it won't need to look any further than the price of oil.

The European countries in the worst financial shape all share the expensive distinction of having little or no domestic oil production. It should come as no surprise that Portugal, Ireland, Italy, Greece and Spain are at the bottom of the EU's fiscal totem pole. Known by the unflattering acronym PIIGS, these countries are most at risk of economic collapse due at least in part to the misfortune of missing out on the geological lottery. Unlucky as that may be, the reality of triple-digit oil prices leaves these countries little room for fiscal optimism.

When a debt-laden country finds its economy choking on the punitive cost of oil, it has two choices. The first is to squeeze a teetering economy even harder in the hope of cutting a path back to prosperity. The second choice is to default on its debt.

The first option, as Greece makes abundantly clear, isn't working. In a vacuum, tax hikes and spending cuts can allow a country to reduce its budget deficit. But in the real world, those tactics can easily become self-defeating. The more brutal the fiscal austerity measures, the greater their economic impact, which only deepens the recession. Any deficit reduction achieved through spending cuts is more than offset by the negative fiscal consequences of a deeper economic slowdown.

The amount of money collected from taxes is a function of economic activity. Less activity shrinks tax revenues. It seems straightforward enough, but it's not a tune EU creditor nations want to hear. Before they open the purse strings and offer emergency funding, they want to know that politicians won't spend it like drunken sailors. It's an understandable position. If I lend you $100 until tomorrow, I want some assurance you don't plan to spend $500 today.

Greece is bending over backward to meet the EU demands. As a result, the only sure thing is that the bailout money won't be repaid. Right now, Greece's economy is contracting by roughly 5 percent a year. The EU can demand all the austerity measures it wants, but at that rate Greece's debt is only going to get bigger.

That leaves the second option. Default.

CAN THE EUROPEAN MONETARY UNION SURVIVE?

Greece will do what Greece has always done, which is default. It's nothing new for the country. Over the last two hundred years, Greece has been in a state of default more than half the time. With such a storied track record of delinquent borrowing, it shouldn't come as a shock to its partners in the EMU that Greece will once again look to wipe the slate clean with a default.

And this time Greece has company. Ireland and Portugal are facing massive fiscal problems, as are the major eurozone economies of Spain and Italy. Chunks of stone aren't falling from the Colosseum because Rome wants it to happen. Italy's economy is on the ropes, the country is crumbling, and Italians can do little but watch.

It wasn't always like this. In the past, European countries had an escape hatch that could save a bankrupt government from officially entering into default. But membership in the EMU took that option away. The seventeen countries in the EMU traded the freedom of autonomous currencies for the combined economic strength of the euro. And for much of the last decade, a strong euro made that look like a good bargain. Now that tough times are here again, though, a drowning country like Greece is nostalgic for the bygone days of the drachma. Prior to adopting the euro, if Greece found itself in a fiscal mess, it would invariably devalue its exchange rate. For Greece, in particular, this was an especially effective tactic. A plunging drachma would breathe new life into tourism, Greece's most important industry. Over time, a pickup in tourism spending would send more tax dollars to Greece's government, helping the country back onto its feet.

But now Greece has no choice but to look to its European partners for a bailout. In practice, that means German taxpayers end up sending welfare checks to Athens. In the old days of a plunging drachma, Germans would pay less money and get a holiday in Santorini for the trouble of helping Greece out.

So why would Germany saddle itself with the problems of a southern neighbor? It turns out Germans get much more for their money than a holiday in the Greek islands. The weak economies of the PIIGS help to hold down the value of the euro. For Germany, the world's second-largest exporter, a weaker euro translates into jobs and profits for domestic industries, as German companies do booming business around the world. If you're wondering about the advantages of holding the euro down against competing currencies such as the US greenback or the Japanese yen, just ask Volkswagen, Adidas, Mercedes-Benz, Siemens, Henckels or Audi. Better yet, just walk down a city street and see how long it takes before a Volkswagen rolls by or someone with three stripes on their shoes walks past. Easier still, check your kitchen. I'm betting you have at least one Henckels knife in a drawer, if not a whole block on the counter.

The question Germany must now ask itself is whether the substantial benefits of a weaker euro are worth the costs of backstopping such bailouts. As the economic woes spread from Greece to other struggling eurozone economies, the folks in the Bundestag are staying up at night trying to figure out an answer.

The longer creditor countries such as Germany try to save the PIIGS, the closer the European debt crisis comes to washing up on the home front. Standard & Poor's now considers only four members of the EMU—Germany, Finland, Luxembourg and the Netherlands—worthy of its top credit rating. And the agency recently put even those economies on credit watch, a step that's often a prelude to a downgrade. If that happens, those countries will have to spend more money financing their own debt, leaving less to contribute to emergency funds for their neighbors.

IT REALLY ISN'T ABOUT GREECE

When Germans finally tire of sending welfare checks to Greece and force the country to bolt from the euro, it won't be leaving on its own.

Its expulsion from the EMU will trigger a domino effect among its fellow PIIGS. Economists call this contagion—just like a virus spreading from one person to another. Contagion is the real reason the EU is so worried about Greece.

Much like Greece, Portugal depends heavily on tourism to make its economy go. And also like its Hellenic neighbor, Portugal is getting billions of euros from bailout packages funded by its EU partners. But if Greece dumps the euro and brings back the drachma, Portugal's tourism industry will be at a huge disadvantage. If the price of a holiday in Santorini is cut in half due to a devalued drachma, can the beaches of the Algarve compete when tourists are still being charged prices in expensive euros? Politicians in Lisbon will quickly realize they can't.

Portugal's most sensible option will be to follow Greece's lead and leave the monetary union. A return to the escudo will allow Portugal to say hello to tourism dollars and goodbye to the austerity measures being demanded by Angela Merkel, the International Monetary Fund and the European Central Bank. It will lose bailout funding, but given its current situation, Portugal must ask how much it will really lose in the long run.

If Greece and Portugal leave the EMU, can Spain and Italy be far behind? Before you know it, a road trip through western Europe will once again fill your pockets with the bright colors and confusing denominations of stand-alone currencies. The political dreams of pan-Europeanism will soon give way to the imperatives of economic reality. The euro will survive, but by shedding the weaker southern economies, its value will strengthen. German automakers, to name one group, won't welcome this news. A stronger euro will boost the sticker price of German-made cars around the world, making Fords or Subarus that much more attractive in comparison. The currency union will continue, but it will shrink to a handful of northern European countries, including France, the Netherlands and Germany.

Many will argue that the EMU should have taken that shape from the start—that throwing the PIIGS into a currency union with Germany and France was an unnatural configuration similar to putting Mexico into a currency union with the United States and Canada. When economic times are good, Mexico would be fine. But when the business cycle turned down, it would be an entirely different story. Without the ability to devalue the peso and juice its economy, Mexico's situation would soon turn just as desperate as Greece's is today.

What will the EU look like once the monetary divorce is finalized? The currency sphere is only part of the picture. If the EMU unwinds, can the EU's free-trade zone be far behind?

One of the core arguments in establishing the euro was to prevent countries from devaluing currencies to gain a competitive edge over neighboring states. Being in a monetary union stopped a country like Spain from weakening the peseta and shifting its economic problems elsewhere. All other things being equal, a weak peseta makes Spain's exports look more attractive than goods coming from places such as Germany and France. The currency gap allows Spain to effectively ship its unemployment to surrounding countries. That's great if you're a Spanish worker. Not so much if you're looking for a job in Marseille or Hamburg.

The lure of currency depreciation has seldom been more attractive for countries such as Spain and Greece than it is today. National unemployment rates are trending as high as 20 percent. With one out of every five workers on the street, politicians in Athens and Madrid have plenty of incentive to walk away from the euro. If the weak sisters do indeed leave the EMU, it remains an open question whether they would be allowed to stay in the free-trade zone.

Once out of the EMU, Greece's drachma is forecast to drop as much as 40 percent against the euro. That's hardly a level playing field for a free-trade zone. Factories in Athens would start taking business from plants in Munich and Amsterdam. Tolerance for such beggar-thy-neighbor currency depreciation wears thin in a hurry, particularly when unemployment is already a problem in most countries in Europe. That's one of the reasons that tariffs are erected in the first place: to protect domestic economies from cheaper goods supported by devalued currencies.

In the light of such a competitive imbalance, can European free trade survive? And if the free-trade zone is altered, what will that mean for labor markets? Will workers from fiscally wayward countries that abandon the euro retain the right to work throughout the EU? While mobility has benefited an expanding European economy, allowing workers to find jobs and employers to find staff, it won't look nearly as attractive when the continent's economy contracts.

But even broader implications exist for Europe.

Any sovereign debt default by an existing EU member will surely raise the bar for future entrants into the EMU. How will applications from places such as Albania, Serbia and Turkey be viewed in light of a defection by countries in southern Europe? Former Eastern bloc nations such as Romania, Poland and Hungary have long hoped that membership in the EMU will help stabilize their shaky economies. With the experience of Greece and Portugal still fresh, do you think existing members of the EMU will be excited to throw open the door to new applicants? Such questions are easy to muse about in the abstract. But if you're an unemployed worker in Kraków, your day-to-day life hinges on the answers, as do your family's prospects.

These questions also affect the balance of power throughout the region. Rejecting the applications of former Eastern bloc nations will be considered a bad move by those in the EU who believe a unified Europe will give the region the clout needed to compete in the global economy in the coming decades. In other places, though, the move would be welcomed. Russia would be happy to see EU expansion grind to a halt. Moscow's traditional sphere of influence in eastern Europe has already been eroded by the pull of the EU and NATO. The Cold War may be over, but that doesn't mean Russia has stopped being a major player on the world stage. If Europe's influence shrinks, it leaves room for Russia's to expand.

The stakes at play in sovereign debt defaults go well beyond the euro. A breakup of the EMU opens the door for all kinds of economic and political shifts. You can bet the Europe of tomorrow will look very different from the Europe of today.

ARE WE BAILING OUT COUNTRIES OR ARE WE BAILING OUT BANKS?

America's mortgage crisis didn't stay American for long. Because of the deep interconnectedness of the global financial system, the United States' problems quickly became the world's problems. And that's what worries the powers that be in Europe today. When the subprime crisis unfolded in 2008, the US government quickly stepped into the fray. Ostensibly, Washington was looking out for homeowners. The real impetus for the government bailout money was saving the banks. Saving a few voters' houses was just an ancillary benefit.

Exposure to Greece's economic problems has already cut the market value of French banks in half. Two of the country's banking giants, Société Générale and Crédit Agricole, own Greek bank subsidiaries. By comparison, German banks have less direct exposure to Greece. That would seem to make the situation less serious for Germany than for France. But it doesn't. What matters to Germany is the fate of French banks. Germany's financial sector is inextricably bound to France's, and as a result, bankers in both countries are terrified of a Greek default. So while it appears that Berlin is trying to prop up a failing Greek economy to help save the eurozone, what's really at stake is the solvency of Europe's biggest banks.

A sovereign debt default would send shock waves throughout Europe's banking system. Massive write-downs at banks would be followed by even bigger bailout checks to help save those same financial institutions. And the fallout won't be limited to Europe. That was the great lesson of the US subprime crisis: no one is safe. A Greek default might start in Athens, but it would quickly spread to Paris, Berlin, New York and Tokyo. Today's interconnected financial market gives everyone exposure to everyone else.

Will taxpayers be asked to finance another massive bank bailout? Will protest movements such as Occupy Wall Street morph into a broader-based political opposition that will demand far more in return for the next round of bailouts than the free ride the banks got the last time around? The Occupy movement has been dismissed by the conservative establishment as mere fringe groups of young people camping in city parks. But what if they're simply the most vocal representation of a deeper current of dissatisfaction among citizens? Could other changes be on the way?

The financial industry is overdue for a deep structural overhaul that will help to eliminate some of the conflicts of interest that led to the 2008 financial crisis. During the Great Depression, for instance, US lawmakers adopted the Glass-Steagall Act, legislation that separated the different parts of a bank's business. Under the act, a bank's traditional deposit-taking business was walled off from the proprietary trading desks that make huge leveraged bets in stock, bond and currency markets. Separating bankers lending money from traders investing money, the thinking went, would help to mitigate the type of rampant speculation that led to the stock market crash of 1929. Wall Street, of course, chafed at having its wings clipped. The financial industry argued that too many rules limited its global competitiveness. Buoyed by a culture of deregulation that took hold in the 1980s, Wall Street was able to get Glass-Steagall repealed in 1999. The recent carnage in the banking industry has led to calls for a return to tighter regulations. Of course, in the United States, which takes pride in its freewheeling business culture, regulation is almost a dirty word. So far, a push back toward the days of Glass-Steagall has been rebuffed.

Until changes are made, however, don't expect to see taxpayer-funded bank bailouts end anytime soon. Consider what recently happened at Swiss-based UBS, one of the world's largest and most reputable banks. In September 2011, a mid-level employee on the bank's proprietary trading desk racked up a $2.3-billion loss. That was a hard hit to UBS's bottom line. But it's even worse for the Swiss taxpayers who will end up bailing out the banking giant in the event of another credit crisis. But can any of us really expect anything different in a system that rewards risk takers with annual bonus checks in the seven figures and leaves taxpayers to backstop the losses when big bets go horribly wrong?

Simply resurrecting old barriers between deposit-taking institutions and investment banking may not go far enough to fix our banks. In countries where another round of bailouts would mean taxpayers become the de facto owners of banks, outright nationalization could be the end result. The hue and cry that would go up from the corridors of financial power would be deafening. But putting investment bankers on civil service salaries might actually bring about the types of reforms needed in the financial services industry without the bother of passing new legislation to rewrite the rules for financial markets. That's not in the cards for Wall Street or Bay Street, but it is a possibility in smaller countries where rounds of taxpayer-funded bank bailouts have destroyed the financial industry's political capital.

Without the giant bonuses that motivate bankers to take big gambles with other people's money, maybe the world's banks would go back to doing what they used to do, which was to prudently lend out depositors' money to customers. Whatever shape it takes, the coming European banking crisis, following so closely on the heels of the subprime mortgage crisis, is about to push the pendulum back to ever greater government regulation of financial markets.

WILL AMERICA DEFAULT?

The financially strapped PIIGS aren't the only countries at risk of default.

America's annual budget deficit is seemingly treading water at more than a trillion dollars. That's a big gap between what America spends and what it takes in from tax revenues every year. At nearly 10 percent of GDP, America's budget deficit actually puts it in the same league as Greece. While Greece can look to its friends in the EU for cash, America's biggest lender also happens to be its biggest political adversary.

It's no small irony that in a post–Cold War global economy, the last bastion of Communism has become the banker to capitalism's fallen angel. Economics makes for strange bedfellows. Irony aside, though, the People's Bank of China is the institution that keeps funding America's monstrous budget deficits. And it has been doing so for some time. Nearly every month, China's central bank allows Uncle Sam to pay his bills by showing up and buying bonds at the US treasuries auction. These regular public auctions are held by the US Treasury Department, which sells a range of securities to raise money for the country. For example, a Treasury bill, or T-bill, is a short-term debt obligation backed by the US government that carries a maturity of less than a year. Throughout the year, the Treasury holds different auctions for 3-month, 6-month and 52-week T-bills. Similarly, the Treasury also sells T-bonds, which are long-term securities with maturities of ten years or more, and T-notes, an intermediate security with a maturity between one and ten years. China is the single largest holder of US treasuries. All told, Communist China holds more than $3 trillion in foreign reserves, more than half of which are in US assets.

If China wakes up one day and decides to stop lending to the United States, the world's largest economy could soon join the PIIGS.

Of course, China's willingness to fund America's huge budget deficit isn't an act of charity. The People's Bank of China buys US Treasury bonds to help keep its currency from rising against the US dollar. China's demand for treasuries is tantamount to a demand for US currency. In foreign exchange markets, such demand is what allows a currency to hold its value. For the last decade, the relationship between a cheap yuan and a strong US greenback has been a fundamental component of the global economy.

Globalization allowed for a mutual dependence to develop between America and China. Poles apart on an ideological level, economically the pair has made sweet music together. A rapacious American consumer has dined on cheap labor from China for years. Meanwhile, China's central bank has cycled the savings of these same workers into US treasuries, an investment that allows Americans to keep buying Chinese goods. This self-reinforcing cycle of trade and capital flows defined the apex of the global economic model. Americans were able to purchase more for every dollar of income, since just about everything they consumed came from a sweatshop halfway around the world. With a nation of eager buyers across the Pacific ready for its goods, China became the world's factory.

But China achieved that position in a different world from the one we live in today. In order to staff its factories, China uprooted millions of peasants from traditional lives of rural farming and put them to work. The sheer size of China's massive labor force, combined with rock-bottom wages, gave China an economic advantage over all comers. China could make things cheaper and faster than any other country, a capacity that led to a line of customers out the door. A world that still seemed to enjoy an abundance of natural resources also helped. China's plants could run all day on cheap power from coal-fired plants, while affordable oil made the cost of shipping goods to faraway markets an incidental expense.

But a new landscape of energy scarcity means distance now costs money. Shipping a crate of dollar-store bobbles across an ocean doesn't make as much financial sense when oil is at $100 a barrel. Rising salaries are also cutting into China's wage advantage, one of the growing pains, party leaders are finding, of its turn toward capitalism. Workers are now agitating for higher salaries and better working conditions. So far, Beijing is supporting the push for higher wages. Better pay not only helps to allay worker concerns, it also boosts activity in the domestic economy. An increase in domestic spending reduces China's reliance on foreign exports as a means to expand the country's economy. Still, higher wages also mitigate China's competitive advantage over its Asian neighbors and countries in the developing world that are vying for the same customers. In short, new dynamics are in play, which are loosening the glue that holds China and the United States together.

Changes to the economic landscape will soon demand different policy responses from Beijing. China's economic priorities are shifting away from supplying the American market with cheap goods and toward battling the inflation that's taking hold inside its own borders. Chinese inflation, as we saw in the last chapter, is verging on getting away from the country, running higher than 6 percent at times in 2011. One way for China to tame this inflation is to let the value of its currency rise.

Faced with the menace of inflation, the prospect of spending billions on US treasuries in order to hold down the value of the yuan may start to seem like the wrong move. If China allows the yuan to strengthen against the US dollar, that would effectively reduce the prices China pays on imported goods such as oil and corn. Along with collaring inflation on imports, a stronger yuan would also give Chinese consumers more purchasing power. Replacing foreign customers with domestic ones is already part of China's long-term economic plans, so it's easy to envision the country hastening the process. And putting the Chinese consumer in the driver's seat of the country's economic growth could seem like a good idea to Beijing right about now, given the economic plight of Europe and North America.

The time isn't far away when selling goods to the rest of the world will simply be gravy for China, which has 1.3 billion consumers inside its own borders. Look no further than its booming auto sector for an indication of how superfluous the rest of the world could soon become. The Chinese car market is now the biggest in the world, nearly 50 percent larger than the market for vehicles in the United States. The global auto industry knows which way the wind is blowing, and it's digging in for the long haul. Recently, German automakers BMW and Audi became the latest companies to announce big spending plans for new Chinese factories. And China isn't even an auto-exporting nation. Someday that may change, but right now these new plants are being built to service domestic demand. Auto ownership in the country is still less than a tenth of what it is in the United States, meaning the Chinese market has plenty of room to run.

Allowing the yuan to rise would give prospective Chinese drivers more buying power to purchase vehicles made in domestic factories. So far, the People's Bank of China has resisted the idea of letting the yuan strengthen as a means of battling inflation. Instead, the bank has chosen to fight inflation using a combination of interest rate hikes and tighter lending requirements for its banks. These moves are designed to put the brakes on economic activity, which helps keep prices from rising. But it also forces China's economy to bear the full brunt of the country's inflation. If China wants to share some of that economic pain, it could decide to export part of the burden to the United States.

If China wants to strengthen its currency, all it needs to do is stop buying US treasuries. Cutting its participation in Treasury auctions would decrease the demand for US dollars in global currency markets, causing the US greenback to weaken against other currencies. If China wanted to further accelerate the yuan's rise against the US dollar, it could also start selling down its massive holdings of US treasuries. Flooding the market with treasuries would shrink the universal appetite for buying US bonds at future Treasury auctions, depressing the dollar even further.

That's an uncomfortable amount of power for one country to hold over another.

If the People's Bank of China decides to skip the next US Treasury auction, it wouldn't take long for Americans to notice. The huge pool of savings that China's central bank invests in the United States helps to hold down America's borrowing costs. Without China's backing, the United States would have to pay higher interest rates on every bond it sells. What would this mean for the average American? Well, everything from the price a bank charges for a car loan to mortgage rates are benchmarked to the Treasury's borrowing rate. If China decides it's better off with a stronger yuan, that rate will inevitably rise—and the consequences will touch every American who holds any debt.

Of course, the Fed could try to counteract the loss of Chinese demand for treasuries by cranking up the printing presses even further.

That's essentially what Fed chairman Bernanke has done with the rounds of quantitative easing he has employed since 2008. By stepping into the market and buying treasuries on its own, the Fed has infused the US economy with cash. Buying its own bonds offers a reasonable facsimile of Chinese demand that helps hold down borrowing costs. At least for a while.

But when a government starts printing money to finance its own debt, isn't that just another form of default?

I bet the Greek government wishes it could do that right about now. But unfortunately, Greece doesn't have a currency of its own. (And even if the drachma were around, who would want to hold a Greek bond?) But the United States isn't Greece. Not only does America have its own currency, but the US dollar is also the world's reserve currency. That means the United States can borrow money from all over the world and then repay foreign lenders with US dollars. Nothing too tricky about that. But consider what happens to the value of that debt if the United States decides to devalue its currency by printing money to buy its own bonds. Sure, the United States still repays its loans, but the actual value of the payments isn't worth as much. That's a good spot to be in if you're the United States. Not so much for lenders.

When the concept of a default comes to mind, you may be picturing a deadbeat who won't repay his creditors. Maybe he refuses to make interest payments or perhaps even tries to skip out on the full value of a loan. But those are only some of the ways a default can occur. In the old days of metallic money, a sneaky form of default could come about when a country attempted to debase its currency by putting less gold or silver into each coin. More recently, a country that runs into hard economic times might decide to change the promise of value made by its currency. The US government used this tactic on two occasions. In the days of the gold standard, paper currency could be physically exchanged for gold bullion. During the American Civil War, the government suspended the convertibility of the American dollar into gold. And during the Great Depression, in 1933, Washington once again stepped into the currency market, reducing the amount of gold that backed each US dollar.

In the modern world of fiat currency (the term for the paper money we all know and use), old-time currency debasement has been replaced by exchange rate depreciation. Instead of a sovereign ruler instructing the royal mint to use less gold in each coin, governments now tell central bankers to print more money. A surplus of a currency in the market lowers its value in relation to the currencies of other countries. It's supply and demand in action.

Printing more money to lower the value of your currency may not technically be called a default. But if something walks like a duck and quacks like a duck, does it really matter what it's called?

If China stops attending US Treasury auctions, forcing the Fed to print more money to make up the shortfall, then the increase in the amount of US currency in circulation will lead to a devaluation of the dollar. While the United States will be able to keep making loan payments, those payments will be much less valuable to creditors.

Japanese investors found this out the hard way. In the 1970s, the Japanese, who helped fund the deficits created by US involvement in the Vietnam War by buying US bonds, were taken to the cleaners by a plunging greenback. Between 1971 and 1981, the US dollar dropped 40 percent against the yen. That meant that for every dollar Japan invested in US treasuries, it only received 60 cents in return.

So what would happen if the US dollar fell by 40 percent against the yuan? An argument could be made that a weak US dollar would boost exports. But exports carry a relatively small overall weight in the US economy. As a share of GDP, exports from the United States account for about a quarter of what they represent for countries such as Germany and Canada, which rely much more heavily on selling goods to the rest of the world. What's more, any gains from boosting exports would be more than offset by the rising price of imports.

Which brings me back to oil. No import is more important to America's economy than oil. And the more it costs the United States to import oil, the harder it becomes for the country's economy to grow. The United States accounts for about a fifth of the oil consumed in the world every day. That's an expensive tab at the best of times, let alone when the dollar is weak.

As I've just said, a shift in China's monetary policy toward a strong yuan would force the United States to fund more of its debt at home. Part of that responsibility would be borne by the Fed's printing presses. No doubt Bernanke has many more tranches of quantitative easing up his sleeve for the days ahead. The rest of the adjustment would come from cutting government spending and raising taxes to reduce the size of the deficits that must be funded.

The pending battle to pare down America's huge budget deficits won't be limited to showdowns in Congress, like the one over the debt ceiling that rocked markets during the summer of 2011. It's likely to spill over into the streets, just as it has in Europe. In Wisconsin, that has already happened, after the Republican governor rescinded the collective bargaining rights of state employees, claiming the state's fiscal crisis was so severe that taxpayers could no longer afford to give state workers the right to strike. Demonstrations by disenfranchised workers on the steps of the Capitol building in Madison looked eerily similar to protests on the other side of the Atlantic. North of the border, Canada's federal government, which has yet to face a debt crisis, has nevertheless already attempted to short-circuit the right to strike for federal civil servants, as well as airline and postal workers.

Ideology guides different politicians to take different approaches to managing debt. For Tea Party Republicans, busting public-sector unions is a fitting response to a state fiscal crisis. If you're a Democrat, you're more inclined to go after special tax breaks given to the oil industry or look to raise the amount millionaires pay in personal income tax. Left wing or right wing, politicians and governments are now living in a radically different financial reality than they've known in the past. Triple-digit oil prices mean there's simply less money to go around. Sacred cows are about to get slaughtered on both sides of the political divide as financial austerity replaces fiscal largesse.

STIMULUS NO LONGER ON THE TABLE

Say what you will about stimulus packages, governments were able to marshal a massive amount of cash to battle the financial crisis in 2008. Governments threw so much money into getting us out of the last mess, there's hardly any ammunition left to fight another recession. The massive coordinated fiscal stimulus deployed by countries such as the United States, Great Britain and Japan last time around has left those nations far too broke to pull the same thing off again.

While it may look as if a lack of political will is standing in the way of international action to resolve the eurozone's financial problems, it's actually a lack of available cash. Neither governments nor taxpayers have the wherewithal to bail out any more troubled banks. Even worse, the IOUs written to pull us out of the last recession need to be repaid. That's a tall order for any government. Instead of riding a new wave of economic growth, countries are struggling under the twin burdens of massive debt and triple-digit oil prices.

The actions taken to stave off the last recession will make it that much harder to stay afloat during the next downturn. National balance sheets are drowning in red ink. Governments can only hope the next recession is far enough away to give the world time to get its fiscal house back in order. A decade or so of economic growth would do nicely. But triple-digit oil prices combined with the trillions of dollars of debt that have just been racked up make a return to the days of robust growth a nonstarter.

Even worse, the situation in the Middle East, home to the world's cheapest oil, is becoming ever more volatile. Instability in the region threatens to disrupt oil supplies and send energy prices even higher. If that happens, then the next recession may be just around the corner.

Chapter 3

THE ARAB REVOLT

THE I-405 IS THE busiest road in America. Every day, some 400,000 vehicles crawl along the freeway's twelve lanes before spreading out across Los Angeles and the rest of southern California.

Doing the math, that's nearly 3 million cars a week, or 145 million a year. And that's just one highway. America's 2.7 million miles of paved roads is the largest network in the world. Consider the endless gallons of gasoline burned by the cars that fill up those roads, and it's easy to understand how America guzzles more oil than any other country.

I'd like to say that America's huge appetite for oil is why you should care about the supply still buried under the Saudi Arabia desert. But it's not only American appetites we need to worry about here. In the last five years, China has spent more than $700 billion on transportation infrastructure, more than twice as much as the United States. Construction of twelve national highways there was recently completed, roughly thirteen years ahead of schedule. China's expressways, most of them less than ten years old, now cover the same distance as the US Interstate system, which took three decades to build.

All those new roads will soon be carrying a whole country full of new drivers. You can guess what the added demand will do to oil prices. If you've ever wondered why you should worry about the future of the Middle Eastern oil supply, all those roads in China are your answer.

REGIME CHANGE NEVER HELPS OIL PRODUCTION

The world's oil-consuming powers have long coveted the treasure trove of petroleum wealth in the Middle East. And those powers aren't shy about safeguarding the region's oil production, even if it means direct military intervention or staging a coup d'état.

The British began angling for political control of the region and its vast crude reserves in 1908, when the Anglo-Persian Oil Company made the first discovery there. In the lead-up to the First World War, Persian supplies became vital to Winston Churchill's plan to replace coal with oil as the fuel of the British Empire's navy. In 1914, Churchill moved to secure the Royal Navy's oil supply, gaining a 51 percent stake in Anglo-Persian through a £2.2-million investment that effectively nationalized the company. During the Second World War, Churchill then engineered the replacement of Persia's pro-German ruler, Reza Shah Pahlavi, by his more British-friendly 21-year-old son, Muhammad Reza Pahlavi.

A decade later, Western powers once again intervened to protect oil interests in the region after Mohammed Mossadegh, the new prime minister, nationalized the Anglo-Iranian Oil Company, bringing the country's oil reserves under Iranian control for the first time. Mossadegh's political grip on the country effectively marginalized the Shah's power. In 1953, the Shah, with the help of the CIA, attempted a countercoup. Mossadegh caught wind of the plot, and the Shah was forced to flee the country, eventually landing in Rome. The Shah didn't know that the apparently failed coup had actually rallied key factions of the military to his cause. Faced with an upsurge of support for the

Shah, Mossadegh fled, and the younger Pahlavi returned from his brief exile to regain his throne.

The Shah protected British and American oil interests in Iran until 1979, when he was overthrown by a popular revolution and replaced by an Islamic fundamentalist regime led by Ayatollah Khomeini. Until his downfall, the Shah's decades-long rule of Iran was marked by the same brutality that defined Moammar Gadhafi's regime in Libya and Hosni Mubarak's years in Egypt. Now deposed, these three rulers also shared another trait: each made sure the oil kept flowing into world markets. For years, these regimes counted on steady oil production to bring cash into the country and keep Western powers so happy that they would tolerate what these men were doing to their own citizens.

And for years, they were successful. Before the Iranian revolution of the late 1970s, the country was pumping almost 6 million barrels a day. Some forty years later, Iran's production is still below 4 million barrels a day. Under Gadhafi, Libya maintained oil production of about 1.6 million barrels a day. The country's postrevolution oil industry is back on its feet, but it's still struggling to return production to prewar levels.

Regime change has never been good for local oil production in the Middle East, no matter which leader gets ousted or who enters the picture after he's gone. Even when Western powers go so far as to occupy a Middle Eastern country, oil production still doesn't respond the way invaders would presumably hope. Take the most recent American invasion of Iraq, for instance. When Iraqi dictator Saddam Hussein ran the show in Baghdad, during its peak years in the 1980s, the state-owned Iraq Petroleum Company cranked out more than 3.5 million barrels a day. Almost a decade after the United States invaded the country and toppled Hussein's regime, Iraq's production is still less than it was twenty-five years ago by roughly 500,000 barrels a day. Of course, the Bush administrations never acknowledged that their motive for going to war against Iraq, not once but twice, was oil, just as the Eisenhower administration didn't own up to the CIA's involvement in the overthrown Iranian government in the 1950s. But it hardly seems like a coincidence that the first site American troops secured when they reached Baghdad in the Second Gulf War was the Oil Industry building. Were they expecting to find weapons of mass destruction there?

Likewise, the Brits still aren't confessing to their real reasons for joining the US-led invasion, nor to harboring their own ambitious plans for the country's oil sector. Despite then prime minister Tony Blair's denials that access to Iraq's oil fields motivated British involvement, minutes of meetings between government officials and domestic energy firms show that oil was indeed considered in pre-invasion deliberations.

With Saddam removed from power, Iraq's oil resources were thrown open to the world's biggest energy companies. It didn't take long to divvy up the spoils. In one of the largest land grabs in the history of the oil industry, the new Iraqi government handed out twenty-year production contracts to multinational energy giants including BP, Exxon and Shell. Foreign corporations now control half of Iraq's 112 billion barrels of oil reserves.

Iraq's massive oil reserves stoke endless optimism about the country's potential output. After the invasion, the US Department of Energy predicted Iraqi production would reach 3.5 million barrels a day by 2005 and as much as 4 million barrels a day by 2010. Instead, the Sunni insurgency broke out. Pipelines and oil facilities were sabotaged, oil workers were captured and suicide bombers targeted foreign engineers. Before a period of relative calm descended in 2009, Iraq's output was often below 2 million barrels a day. By the end of 2011, the country's daily production had ramped up to a twenty-year high of around 3 million barrels. Still, that's a long way off the Iraqi government's forecast that the country will produce a world-leading 12 million barrels a day by 2017.

Iraq undoubtedly does contain vast unexploited oil reserves, but fearless predictions for spectacular production gains overlook both the region's history and its present reality. The country's oil industry is an obvious target for sectarian violence, which has roots that long predate the formation of modern Iraq. For centuries, the portion of the Ottoman Empire that we now call Iraq comprised three separate and distinct provinces, Mosul, Baghdad and Basra. Following the First World War, the victors combined these provinces into a single country. Removing the borders, though, didn't alter deep divisions among Kurds, Sunnis and Shiites. In 1920, Britain imposed a foreigner who had never seen the country, Faisal I, of the Hashemite Monarchy that today rules Jordan, as king of Iraq.

Nearly a dozen coups later, one of which included the beheading of King Faisal II in 1958, Saddam Hussein rose to power in 1979. His brutal methods worked to keep Iraq together in name, but the people remained no more unified than the ethnically diverse comrades forced together by Joseph Stalin under the banner of the USSR.

Undeterred by their failure to pump more oil out of Iraq, Western powers were still game to enter Libya in 2011. The coalition of NATO forces that intervened in Libya's civil war did help put an end to a brutal forty-year dictatorial regime. But it's also hard to ignore that Libya is home to the largest oil production and reserves in North Africa.

Once again, Western nations claim oil had nothing to do with intervening in Libya, just as oil had nothing to do with deposing Saddam Hussein. Instead, NATO described its involvement as a humanitarian mission. But if protecting a defenseless population from a ruthless dictator was the reason for going into Libya, why isn't NATO knocking on other doors as well? Syria and Yemen, to name just two countries, are home to dictators just as brutal as Gadhafi. Is it a coincidence that oil production in those countries is insignificant compared with Libya's?

Oil-consuming countries in the West remain optimistic that Libyan oil production will buck the established trend and surpass prerevolutionary levels. Prior to the civil war, most of Libya's 1.6 million barrels a day went to European markets. How much oil Libya will pump in the future is anyone's guess. Like Iraq, modern Libya is a postcolonial concoction, created when Italy amalgamated the three historically

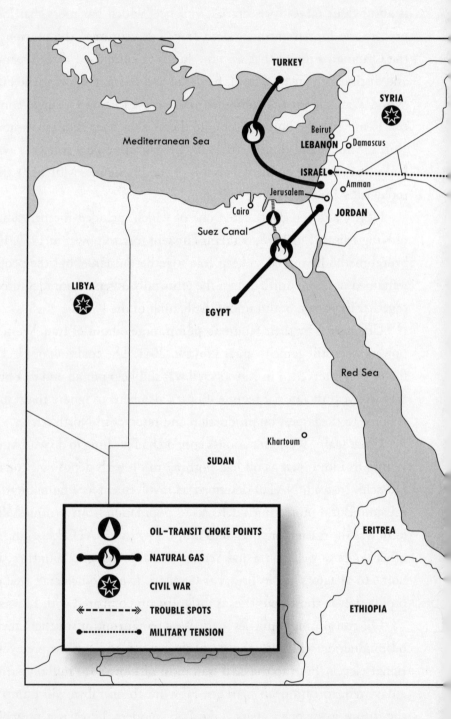

TURKEY

SYRIA

Mediterranean Sea

Beirut

LEBANON · Damascus

ISRAEL

Jerusalem · · Amman

Cairo

Suez Canal

JORDAN

LIBYA

EGYPT

Red Sea

Khartoum

SUDAN

ERITREA

ETHIOPIA

OIL-TRANSIT CHOKE POINTS

NATURAL GAS

CIVIL WAR

TROUBLE SPOTS

MILITARY TENSION

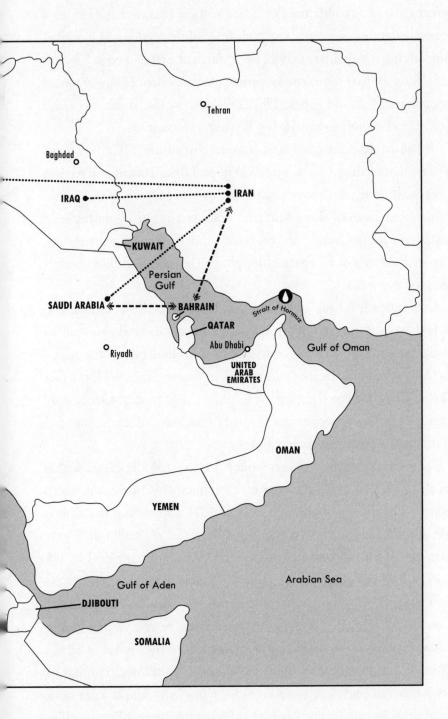

Tehran

Baghdad

IRAQ

IRAN

KUWAIT

Persian
Gulf

SAUDI ARABIA

BAHRAIN

QATAR

Strait of Hormuz

Abu Dhabi

Riyadh

UNITED
ARAB
EMIRATES

Gulf of Oman

OMAN

YEMEN

Gulf of Aden

Arabian Sea

DJIBOUTI

SOMALIA

distinct areas of Tripolitania, Cyrenaica and the Fezzan. Establishing a cohesive federal state from those divisions, while negotiating a myriad of underlying tribal alliances, will be as much of a challenge in Libya as it is in Iraq. In that light, the lessons of past experience suggest global energy markets should expect Libya's oil output, like Iran's and Iraq's before it, to be another casualty of Western intervention.

In the Middle East, oil and totalitarianism are a familiar pair. Military dictatorships have controlled Egypt, Libya, Tunisia and Algeria for years, while absolutist monarchic rule exists in Oman, Bahrain and Saudi Arabia. Each of those countries is either a major oil producer or has strategic control over a vital oil-transit choke point such as the Suez Canal or the Strait of Hormuz, through which some 16 million barrels of oil pass every day.

An implicit quid pro quo has existed between Western democracies and Arab dictatorships: in exchange for a steady flow of oil to global markets, Western governments turn a blind eye to the measures Middle Eastern regimes take to stay in power. Since 9/11, the fact that the West has been fighting the terrorist threat from al-Qaeda only makes it easier for governments to justify increased military, financial and political support for such regimes.

Consider American foreign policy in the Middle East, which runs the gamut from inconsistent to contradictory. On the one hand, President Obama spent the first half of 2011 applauding the democratic impulse behind the Arab Spring. On the other hand, only a year earlier, the White House announced the largest military deal in US history, a $60-billion arms sale to Saudi Arabia. The infusion of new weaponry will no doubt buttress the military capacity of a strategic ally in the Middle East. Still, before approving the sale, White House decision makers clearly had to come to terms with the House of Saud's long track record of human rights violations. It's a tradeoff familiar to every American president since Franklin Roosevelt. And if a constant flow of arms to those countries isn't sufficient, America offers its allies in the region further protection, mostly from a possible Iranian attack, by maintaining military bases in Qatar, Bahrain and the UAE.

Even the best efforts of the United States, which include Operation Desert Storm and Operation Iraqi Freedom, may not be enough to hold together the old order in the Middle East. The shaky patchwork of dynastic absolute monarchies and military dictatorships, funded by petrodollars and armed by oil-consuming powers, is crumbling from within. Despite fears in the West about the disruptive potential of al-Qaeda and Islamic fundamentalism, neither the terrorist organization nor hard-line Muslims were behind the revolts against repressive regimes in Tunisia, Egypt and Libya. The real catalyst turned out to be hunger.

The Middle East is fortunate that it can export more oil than any other place, because desert sands are ill suited to raising crops. For years, a steady stream of petrodollars has made it possible to swap hydrocarbons for carbohydrates. That's a workable trade when oil prices are rising faster than food prices. But when food prices take off, the system breaks down. Throw in a global recession that sends oil prices tumbling and the oil-for-food arrangement becomes even more strained. Nothing sends a person into the street quite like an empty stomach.

Food supply isn't the only thing struggling to keep pace with a burgeoning population in the Middle East. So is employment. Double-digit youth unemployment is systemic in the region. A hungry population full of young people unable to find enough work to put food on the table only promises to keep stoking unrest throughout the Arab world.

As more regimes topple in North Africa and across the Middle East, the West will be sincere in its efforts to help new democracies take root. Ending decades of oppression, though, doesn't change the cold truth that regime change isn't good for oil production. That awareness is uppermost in the minds of Saudi Arabia's oil customers in the West. Oil markets get jittery about uprisings in countries such as Libya, Egypt or Syria, but the prospect of a revolt in Saudi Arabia is the energy world's worst-case scenario. The kingdom not only produces more than 9 million barrels of oil a day, it also keeps enough spare capacity in reserve to make up for shortfalls when production falters elsewhere in the region.

It's no coincidence that the forthright President Obama will call for dictators elsewhere in the Middle East to stand down but remains silent about the need for political reform in the Kingdom of Saudi Arabia. The deep and tangled ties between America and Saudi Arabia are laden with decades of hypocrisy. Still, the long-standing economic relationship ranks among the most important between any two countries in the world today. A disruption to production in Saudi Arabia, the world's second-largest oil producer after Russia, would make the loss of Libyan output, or that of any other OPEC producer for that matter, look minor by comparison.

Concerns about Saudi Arabia aren't just theoretical. In neighboring Bahrain, an absolutist monarchy sits tenuously atop a country divided by fundamental religious and economic differences. A Sunni elite minority lives in glass towers in the capital city of Manama, while a politically disenfranchised Shiite working class is ghettoized in suburban slums, shut out from high-paying jobs in government, the military and the private sector.

A former British colony, the island kingdom of Bahrain was supposed to be a constitutional monarchy run by an elected parliament. At least, that was the plan when Britain turned over the island to home rule. Instead, in 1975 the monarch, Isa bin Salman Al Khalifa, suspended parliament and imposed an autocratic rule that remains in full force today.

The Arab Spring has created a crisis for Bahrain's ruling class. Inspired by the success of popular revolts in surrounding countries, the Shiite majority—held in check for decades—is calling for the abolition of the Sunni monarchy. Protesters numbering in the hundreds of thousands have taken to the streets in a bid to replace the king with a democratically elected government and have been brutally put down.

Only a short causeway separates Bahrain from Saudi Arabia. The proximity to the Saudi kingdom, coupled with Bahrain's historic ties to Iran, make Bahrain a key pawn in the ongoing cold war between the Saudi and Iranian regimes. Much of Bahrain's Shiite population has

Iranian roots, a cultural heritage that troubles Saudi rulers. Bahrain's political importance and strategic location in the Persian Gulf also aren't lost on America, which keeps the US Fifth Fleet parked offshore from its naval base on the desert island kingdom.

Recent events have done little to calm Saudi concerns about Bahrain. If social and political upheaval jumps across the border, it wouldn't be the first time. In the mid-1990s, rioting in Bahrain stirred the sympathies of Shiite activists who oppose the Saudi regime. Any renewed calls for democracy in Bahrain are sure to echo in the kingdom once again, forcing the House of Saud to quell any opposition to its authority. Although Saudi Arabia's Shiite population remains a disenfranchised minority, several million do live in the oil-rich eastern provinces, a region critical to the petrowealth that keeps the House of Saud in power.

That's why the Saudis were quick to dispatch troops to Bahrain to help the Sunni ruler contain the local ripples of the Arab Spring. It's also why King Abdullah, Saudi Arabia's octogenarian monarch, is loosening the purse strings like never before. Some $100 billion in additional spending has already been dished out to shore up support among the Sunni majority. The largesse includes the creation of tens of thousands of new public-sector jobs, one-time bonus payments for existing civil servants and the construction of some 500,000 new houses.

If the royal patronage works to head off potential unrest inside the kingdom, it will be money well spent for King Abdullah. However, any apparent kindness shouldn't be confused with a softening of the House of Saud. Following the death of Prince Sultan, a relatively progressive voice and next in line for the throne, Prince Nayef was appointed Crown Prince. Nayef, a former chief of the country's massive internal security force, was a hard-line conservative closely aligned to the country's Wahhabi clerics. Outside Saudi Arabia, the prince gained notoriety in the last decade for expressing his view that 9/11 was a Zionist plot. The country will be spared a Nayef regime, as the newly appointed crown prince also has recently died. As crown princes drop like flies, a geriatric regime headed by an ailing octogenarian clings to power over an exploding population of young people—60 percent of the country is now under 30 years of age.

Are the billions of dollars in fresh handouts from the Saudi government a sign of a regime on its last legs? Could Abdullah's death and the conservative Nayef's succession be the catalyst for another Arab revolt? Is the House of Saud about to become next in the list of deposed Middle Eastern despots? Perhaps, but if so, it bears asking: what might take its place?

A long history of autocratic rule in Saudi Arabia has left a social and political vacuum. Saudi Arabia, like other countries in the region, has limited exposure to democracy. Only recently have women been given the right to vote in municipal elections, the only kind that exist in the country. A step toward universal suffrage is positive, no doubt, but it should be noted that Saudi women still need a male escort to drive them to the polling station.

If the House of Saud does fall, it's hardly certain that a Western-style democracy will rise in its place. A country such as the United States has had more than two hundred years to develop its democratic system of checks and balances and organized political parties. In the wake of a revolution, Saudi Arabia would be lucky to have twenty days in which to do the same thing. What's more, the established institutions best equipped to fill the political void are hardly synonymous with the notion of civil liberties. One option is Islamic fundamentalism, which has deep roots across the Middle East. In Saudi Arabia, Wahhabi clerics are already a well-organized political entity with the wherewithal to rule the country. And while secular government is considered the most progressive option by Western political standards, in the Middle East, secular hasn't meant a separation of Church and State; it has meant military dictatorships. Whether it was the Baath party's dictatorial rule in Iraq or Syria, or strongman dictatorships in Egypt, Libya, Tunisia and Algeria, the region has known little else. Israel and Turkey are the only countries in the area where a government can be voted out of power. Suffice to say, it's unlikely the Arab world will look to the Jewish state as a role model.

I'm not saying that democracy can't work in the Middle East, only pointing out that a popular uprising won't necessarily result in the best-case scenario dreamed up by a liberal-thinking West. A post-Gadhafi Libya, for example, is already taking a fundamentalist turn, as evidenced by the calls now being heard for the imposition of Sharia law.

But what if democracy does take hold? That would certainly advance the cause of freedom in the Middle East, but, speaking solely from an economics perspective, new governance wouldn't necessarily translate into more oil exports. And I suspect that without the promise of increased oil flow, Western nations really won't stay that concerned about what form of government evolves in the region.

In fact, the pursuit of democratic forms of government could lead to less oil, not more. Democracy would give ordinary people who have never had a say in resource management a vote on what should be done with their hydrocarbon reserves. When the polls open, the newly enfranchised masses might elect leaders who want to sell fewer barrels to Western oil consumers.

In Egypt, the voices of the Arab Spring have already closed one important energy supply line. The fall of Mubarak's regime meant an end to Egyptian natural gas flowing to Israel and Jordan, since, not surprisingly, that supply arrangement was unpopular among the Egyptian people. The pipeline that runs from the Sinai Peninsula into Israel, and on to Jordan, has now been repeatedly bombed, an act that would have been unthinkable when the country was under Mubarak's iron grip.

That's bad news for Israel, which relies on the pipeline for about 40 percent of its natural gas. The news is even worse for Jordan, which counts on the same pipeline to supply the gas used to generate roughly 80 percent of its power. Ironically, losing the pipeline may force Jordan, a longtime Egyptian ally, into the arms of Iran, which has offered to replace the lost gas supply.

More importantly, the loss of Egyptian gas has put Israel and Turkey on a collision course. It will certainly expedite Israel's efforts to tap large gas fields under the eastern Mediterranean, which Turkey has its own plans to develop—plans that include military escorts for drilling ships.

For oil consumers in the West, the takeaway from the Arab Spring is that regime change can lead to dramatic shifts in energy policy. In the Middle East, you can never tell exactly how the dominoes will fall. In one instant, Mubarak's reign is ending to applause from all, and in the next, Israel and Turkey are bumping into each other in the Mediterranean. And of course there's also the international showdown brewing over Iran's nuclear program, which promises to open up another frightening can of worms.

At the very least, we know that energy supply in the region is politically fickle. Will new leaders feel compelled to listen to the voices on the street that swept them to power? The answer feels like yes. And if the answer is yes, what will that mean for supply contracts inked by deposed rulers? New regimes born in the aftermath of the Arab Spring may be less inclined to supply oil to customers in Europe or North America. Production contracts could instead be granted to energy-hungry countries such as China and India, both of which have massive sovereign wealth funds looking for opportunities to invest in energy.

No matter what form political change may take, the region's history makes it abundantly clear that, for world energy markets, social upheaval invariably leads to less supply.

OPEC CAPACITY IS TAPPED OUT

Events taking place above the ground aren't the only thing you should worry about in the Middle East. Apart from the inherent political instability, the global economy has other reasons to expect less oil from the region in the future. Beneath the ground, the Middle East's legendary oil reserves are showing signs of mortality.

The twelve members of OPEC supply roughly a third of the world's oil needs. That's about 30 million barrels a day, of which OPEC's Middle Eastern members, including Saudi Arabia, Iran and Iraq, account for approximately two-thirds. After decades of the region pumping countless barrels, geologists and economists are wondering how much longer Middle Eastern oil reserves will be able to continue to support such a heavy drain.

It's a contentious point. As the big dog of OPEC oil supply, Saudi Arabia's reserves have drawn the most scrutiny. The kingdom currently pumps more than 9 million barrels of oil a day, a figure it claims it could ramp up to 13 million barrels if the global economy needed the production. The Saudi energy minister and Saudi Aramco, the country's state-run oil company, routinely dismiss concerns that the country's actual production capacity would fall short of those levels if put to the test.

Saudi Arabia's argument is essentially threefold. When it comes to current production, Saudi Aramco argues the giant fields that have served the country for decades still have considerable headroom to pump out more barrels. What's more, the Saudis say they've yet to turn to new extraction methods developed in the last decade, which have helped extend the life of older fields around the world. When output does waver, the kingdom says it has proven reserves it is waiting to tap. When pressed, the Saudis also point out that the country remains underexplored. The seemingly limitless production from existing finds like Ghawar, a prolific field unmatched by any other in the world, has made spending on further exploration largely unnecessary.

But should these Saudi claims be trusted? The Saudis keep industry data behind the curtain of a totalitarian regime. Outside engineers and geologists haven't been granted an opportunity to verify Saudi assertions about future capacity. That leaves us reading the tea leaves to get a sense of what's unfolding behind the walls of the world's most important oil producer.

As an economist, I put more weight on what a country actually produces than on what it says it can produce. Saudi Aramco claims daily production can be quickly lifted if the world needs it to turn up the volume. But the country hasn't sustained output of 10 million barrels since the early 1970s. When oil prices marched to triple digits in the last decade, the Saudis knew full well the devastating effect such a rise in cost would have on the global economy. The offices of Saudi Aramco are full of people with advanced degrees from top business schools such as Oxford and Wharton. So why didn't the Saudis ramp up production to bring oil prices down to more affordable levels? It has been suggested the Saudis withheld production to boost revenues from high prices. But the well-trained economists at Saudi Aramco know that thinking is shortsighted.

The immediate effect of triple-digit oil prices is to put a damper on economic growth. Plunging the world into a recession sends oil prices tumbling and keeps petrodollars out of Saudi coffers. No country in the world is more invested in keeping the global oil market healthy. The House of Saud has literally thousands of members who depend on a steady diet of oil revenues to feed their lifestyle. More importantly, oil money allows the royal family to buy off an increasingly rebellious populace with billions in handouts. Without wads of cash available to mollify an alienated and largely unemployed population of Arab youth, the House of Saud is just as vulnerable to the internal revolts of the disaffected who brought down Mubarak and Gadhafi.

If Saudi Arabia could prevent oil prices from rising to levels that induce a recession, the regime's survival instincts alone would seem to demand that its national oil company try to pump every possible drop. But that's not what has happened. When President George W. Bush came to his ally King Abdullah with hat in hand in 2008, he knew that more Saudi production could help stave off a dire economic decline. And what did King Abdullah do for his friend? Saudi Arabia boosted production by a scant 300,000 barrels a day, most of which was of a heavy sour variety that most refineries can't process. Why didn't King Abdullah ride to the rescue in a white hat with guns blazing?

The recession that followed destroyed demand for millions of barrels of oil. That was just as bad for Saudi Arabia as it was for the United States. Meanwhile, the global economy continues to shudder from the aftershocks of that recession. Europe's postrecession struggles, for one, might have been softened if the Saudis had increased production at the time. Instead, Europe's debt crisis seems likely to send the world into another recession, which, in turn, will take a heavy toll on oil demand and prices.

Of course, American motorists don't want to hear about the intricacies of the oil markets when they shell out four dollars a gallon at the pump. And so US politicians take the easy route and blame foreign suppliers for high gas prices. That scores more points with voters, particularly when the bad guys are in the Middle East, rather than actually facing the unpleasant realities of global supply and demand.

None of which means Saudi Arabia isn't still critical to global oil markets. That's why President Obama continues to support the House of Saud, while turning his back on other dictatorial regimes. Saudi production is critical to keeping prices from soaring higher. If the Arab Spring sweeps the House of Saud from power, the world will face a supply disruption that will send prices rocketing to unheard-of heights.

When it comes to lowering oil prices from current levels, however, the Saudis are now much less influential than in the past. All evidence suggests the Saudis lack the capacity to ramp up production to keep prices from moving higher. Whether it's a supply disruption from another country or simply an increase in world demand, Saudi Arabia doesn't have a trump card left to play. That's troubling news for the rest of us, who have not only counted on Saudi production for years but still need it to be there for decades to come.

Unfortunately, there is an even bigger threat to Saudi crude exports: the country's own insatiable thirst for oil.

RUNAWAY FUEL CONSUMPTION CANNIBALIZING
EXPORT CAPACITY

Go outside Riyadh into the desert and you'll hear the sound of roaring engines. Young Saudis spend entire nights drag racing under the desert stars. When gasoline costs 12 cents a liter, less even than bottled water, it's a relatively cheap pastime. Egregiously subsidized fuel prices are the most tangible way Saudi Arabia's average citizens benefit from the country's petrowealth. And what better way to take advantage of cheap gas than by turning loose 400-horsepower engines on desert drag strips?

With the Arab Spring sweeping across the region, you can bet fuel subsidies will be the last thing cut by a Saudi regime already nervously looking over its shoulder. Add up all that fuel consumption, though, and pretty soon it's a bigger threat to global oil supply than the depletion of Saudi's aging oil fields.

Oil-consuming countries need to appreciate the ramifications of the quickening pace of oil consumption in the Middle East. In the final analysis, the world doesn't care how much oil is produced by Saudi Arabia or any other OPEC nation; what matters is how much of it gets exported. And every year that number is becoming a smaller portion of the region's output.

Saudi Arabia's daily oil exports, around 7.5 million barrels in 2005, fell to less than 6 million barrels in 2010. Whenever OPEC announces a production increase, oil-importing countries assume that the higher output will translate into more exports. In reality, the exact opposite has occurred for most of the last decade. When Saudi Arabia ramped up production in 2011, it used more than half the increase to meet its own surging power demands.

Domestic oil consumption is increasing more than 5 percent a year in Saudi Arabia and elsewhere in the Middle East to meet domestic demand that stems from subsidized gasoline that costs roughly a tenth of what drivers pay in North America. It's a sweet deal for Saudi motorists, but the discounts don't stop there: Saudi citizens enjoy the cheapest power rates in the world.

As with any good deal, there's a catch. How do you suppose Middle Eastern countries generate electricity? There's no coal in the region to speak of. Hydroelectric dams aren't exactly abundant in the desert. Western governments, meanwhile, frown upon Middle Eastern states building nuclear power plants (although Iran doesn't seem to be asking permission). So power in the Middle East comes from oil and natural gas, the same hydrocarbons the West wants to see exported to global markets.

It shouldn't come as a surprise that rock-bottom power prices mean electricity demand is increasing by leaps and bounds throughout the Middle East. In Saudi Arabia, power-generation capacity is increasing 10 percent a year. At that rate, the size of the country's electrical grid will double to 68,000 megawatts by 2018. Even the Saudis recognize the downside of feeding such an immense appetite for oil-fired power. Saudi Aramco's chief executive warned in 2010 that domestic oil consumption, if left unchecked, would hit a staggering 8.3 million barrels a day by 2028. That's an untenable amount, nearly matching current Saudi production.

Of course, several practical constraints make that type of linear growth in domestic demand unlikely to occur. Saudi Arabia will continue to use a tremendous amount of oil for power generation, but the country's rulers know that export revenues are the alpha and omega of their wealth. Whether it's the thousands of members of the House of Saud who need stipends or the generous spending required to keep citizens from pouring into the streets, the royal family is beholden to export dollars to retain authority. Dwindling exports would also reduce the country's importance to the United States, an uncomfortable outcome for the House of Saud, whose members know that American military support is the kingdom's best chance for survival. Saudi Arabia won't continue generating power at the expense of exports indefinitely.

Nevertheless, the trend of Saudi power demand clearly points upward. And the more oil Saudis burn to generate electricity, the more expensive it will be to fill your tank.

Cheap power rates and subsidized gas are only partially responsible for Saudi Arabia's growing domestic oil appetite. The rest is being driven by thirst. Whether or not you believe that Saudi Arabia is running out of oil, the country is most certainly running low on water. Rainfall in the desert kingdom averages about four inches a year, and water is consumed at a rate fifteen to twenty times greater than natural replenishment. The country's aquifers, the so-called "fossil water" composed of rainfall from thousands of years ago, are already about 80 percent depleted.

Saudi Arabia, like most countries, uses more water for agriculture than for any other activity. For more than twenty years, the country's aquifers have allowed the country to be a self-sufficient producer of wheat. But farming a desert isn't easy. Agriculture accounts for more than three-quarters of total water consumption, a burden now too much for Saudi aquifers to handle. Since 2008, the country's annual wheat harvests have collapsed from 3 million tons to about 1 million. Meanwhile, wheat consumption in the country continues to increase by about 5 percent a year.

To make up the shortfall, the Saudis have turned to imports. To avoid the vagaries of world food markets, the kingdom has put its petrowealth to work, snapping up agricultural land in places such as Ethiopia and Sudan, and now wheat grown in those countries is ending up on the tables of Saudi households. As the developing world grapples with food shortages, it remains to be seen how much longer Saudi Arabia can expect those countries to export wheat when local populations are staging food riots.

Drinking water is an even more acute issue for the region. To battle the problem, wealthy countries such as Saudi Arabia and the UAE are spending billions constructing giant desalination plants to turn seawater into fresh water. Saudi Arabia already gets nearly 70 percent of its drinking water from these plants. The Saline Water Conversion Corporation produces 3.36 million cubic meters of desalinated water a day, yet it's not keeping pace with a demand for fresh water that's tearing ahead at 7 percent a year. Water, like oil, is massively subsidized by the Saudi government. That allows the average Saudi to use 950 cubic meters of water a year, nearly twice the global average.

Running a desalination plant consumes a huge amount of energy. So much so that the Saudis are essentially trading oil for water. The country is reportedly burning more than a million barrels a day in its network of desalination facilities. To meet projected increases in water usage in the coming years, the kingdom will need to build more plants, which means burning even more oil.

So much energy is required by the desalination process that Saudi Arabia has been forced to invest billions in nuclear power plants and solar energy projects. By 2030, the kingdom plans to have sixteen nuclear reactors on line to help meet its energy needs. To witness Saudi Arabia, whose oil reserves have long been the envy of the world, embrace nuclear power is disconcerting. Yet that's exactly what's happening.

What are the ramifications for Saudi's oil customers in the West? Chances are that less of the world's oil supply will be coming from OPEC, which will only make every other barrel of global production that much more expensive.

Whether it's because of social unrest, a lack of spare production capacity or a swelling appetite for its own product, the Middle East's wherewithal to lift oil output in the coming years is looking ever more fragile. Yet the IEA is now counting on the Middle East and North Africa to supply as much as 90 percent of the additional oil the world will burn in the next decade. If that oil doesn't flow, it's far from obvious where we'll find the fuel to power tomorrow's economic growth.

Chapter 4

HITTING THE
ENERGY CEILING

THE COLDEST BOTTLE OF whisky in the world can be found on a desolate chunk of rock near the North Pole.

A few years ago, this frozen bottle of Canadian Club became the cocktail of choice on Hans Island, replacing a high-end bottle of Danish schnapps that had been there since 2004. The island is nestled in a remote strait between Greenland and Ellesmere Island, and dropping by isn't like taking a weekend breather to the Bahamas. Nevertheless, Danish icebreakers and Canadian helicopters periodically make the trek into the High Arctic for a visit. Once there, a handful of dutiful soldiers will disembark and spend a few hours stomping around the island's barren half a square mile before planting a fresh flag and going home—but not before leaving behind their national libation of choice.

This Arctic bottle swap is part of a low-key turf war between Canada and Denmark. While not exactly India versus Pakistan over the Kashmir, the territorial dispute, now four decades old, is more than just a frivolous patriotic flap between global lightweights. Both sides will tell you it's about Arctic sovereignty.

Really, it's about oil.

When pundits like me say the era of expensive oil is upon us, Arctic exploration is what we're talking about. It's hard to imagine a worse place to work than the Arctic Ocean. The cost, not to mention the logistics, of towing a massive drilling platform through iceberg-filled waters is staggering. And then a crew has to be flown in to drill several kilometers into the frozen seabed before any oil is even produced or shipped. It's not for the faint of heart. If oil companies had any other choice, they wouldn't be there. The Arctic is, quite literally, the end of the earth. And that's exactly where the energy industry is being forced to search for oil to keep the global economy humming.

Just last year, Exxon, the world's largest oil company, signed a deal with Russia to explore in the Arctic. According to President Vladimir Putin, Russia and Exxon could spend as much as $500 billion over the life of the deal. Granted, Putin is known to talk a big game, but even the suggestion that they are signed up to spend half a trillion dollars shows how much oil companies are now forced to shell out to find deposits big enough to supply the world's energy needs.

Here's the catch: for those oil resources to become tomorrow's fuel supply, oil prices have to keep climbing. The extraction economics—towing drilling platforms into the High Arctic, conducting environmental assessments, paying skilled workers, operating in subzero temperatures, maintaining icebreakers to bring tankers through frozen waters, not to mention actually drilling into the ocean floor—simply won't work otherwise. But higher prices, as we saw in chapter 1, also kill demand. As I wrote in that chapter, that's the dilemma we face with the world's remaining oil supply: we can't afford the prices needed to lift it out of the ground.

The difference between what the oil industry calls a resource and what it calls a reserve helps to shed light on this predicament. The first term is used to account for what's in the ground. The second refers to what can be economically extracted. Canada's tar sands, for example, contain more than 170 billion barrels of proven oil reserves, giving the country the third-largest reserves in the world, behind only Saudi Arabia and Venezuela. It's a big number, but it's dwarfed by estimates of the resource held in the deposit, which are in the ballpark of 1.6 trillion barrels. That's more than the current assessment of the total proven reserves held by every country in the world. Calculating the number is also a largely esoteric exercise, since prices won't ever climb high enough to make it worthwhile to extract the vast majority of the resource.

From a geological standpoint, you can always boost production by accessing increasingly costly or environmentally hazardous sources of new supply. Canada's tar sands are a case in point, as are the oil industry's expensive forays into the deep waters of the Gulf of Mexico, offshore from west Africa and into the High Arctic. The higher crude prices go, the more oil the industry will extract from the bowels of the earth.

Oil is a big-money game. As long as there are profits to be made, the energy industry will keep finding ways to pull more oil out of the ground. But make no mistake—technological breakthroughs you may have read about, like hydraulic fracturing, which are helping the industry increase production, aren't a magic bullet that will solve the world's energy needs. Fracking, for example, involves injecting an oil and gas formation with a high-pressure mixture of water, chemicals and sand to help increase the porosity of the subsurface rocks that hold the resource. The more space that can be created between the rocks, the more oil or gas is able to flow up through the wellbore. The technique has been around for decades, but it's only in the last ten years that rising commodity prices have provided enough incentive for the industry to get serious about its use. In some jurisdictions, concerns that fracking could contaminate water supplies have put the industry at odds with landowners and environmental groups. Controversy aside, from a strict supply perspective, fracking is not going to allow the global industry to boost production enough to prevent prices from climbing ever higher. Such technological advances offer nice additions to crude supply around the edges, but they're unable to do the heavy lifting that's needed to meet the world's future oil demands.

More significant production gains will come from sources such as the deposits of bitumen and heavy oil found in Canada and Venezuela. Higher oil prices and improvements in production efficiency recently allowed Venezuela to categorize more of the resources contained in its Orinoco heavy oil belt as proven reserves. The Orinoco belt, or Faja as it's known locally, is now credited with 297 billion barrels of reserves, up from 211 billion. That's more than the 265 billion barrels stored under the oil-rich deserts of Saudi Arabia and the 170 billion in Canada's tar sands.

No one is saying the size of these resources isn't impressive. But when it comes to the health of the global economy, size doesn't really matter; the issue is the price per barrel we'll need to pay to justify hauling that oil out of the ground.

The huge caches of oil found in Canada and Venezuela are what are known as unconventional resources. Compared to conventional oil, which is the stuff you might think of as flowing out of the ground Beverly Hillbillies style, unconventional oil is much harder to get at. How hard? you ask.

Take the Alberta tar sands as an example. Oil-soaked sand must first be dug up and trucked to giant industrial plants called upgraders. The sand is then blasted with intense heat to separate the oil from the sand; the oil is then mixed with other chemicals to produce what's called synthetic crude. This mixture is shipped to a refinery, where it's further processed into a product we can use, such as gasoline or diesel fuel. Since the tar sands are in northern Canada, this work is done in temperatures that in the long winters routinely dip to 40 degrees below freezing, and it uses the biggest trucks and heavy equipment ever built. The remoteness of the mines even spurs some companies, such as

Canadian Natural Resources, to build airstrips to ferry workers in and out on Boeing 737s.

Compare that effort and expense with Spindletop, the conventional discovery credited with kicking off the Texas oil boom in 1901. At its peak, easy-to-refine crude from Spindletop literally gushed out of the ground at the astounding rate of 75,000 barrels a day. To put that in perspective, in 2010 the average daily production of a Texas oil well was 6 barrels. In total, the state's 158,000 wells produce just shy of 1 million barrels a day. After a hundred years of exploration, there are no Spindletops left to find. Instead, the global energy industry is spending hundreds of billions pulling oil out of places such as Canada's tar sands and the Faja. That's just the cost of doing business these days.

Unfortunately, Big Oil's bottom line isn't the only place taking a hit—it's bad for you too. No one knows this better than the IEA. Every year, IEA economists issue a voluminous report called the *World Energy Outlook*, in which they attempt to reassure anxious energy consumers in the West that future energy supplies will be there when needed. Typically, the report offers an optimistic vision of future fuel consumption. As with any undertaking involving imperfect information, forecasting future energy supply and demand involves making an enormous number of assumptions about how events will unfold. Historically, the assumptions used by the IEA help to paint a picture that favors the oil-consuming countries that pay its bills. By contrast, the story told by OPEC, not surprisingly, is one that bodes well for oil-producing countries. In both cases, the forecasts need to be taken with a grain of salt.

It's striking that even the IEA is now having a hard time sounding confident about future energy abundance. Despite record prices, conventional oil production hasn't grown since 2005. A lack of new supply finally spurred the IEA to remove its rose-colored glasses and acknowledge the finite nature of the reserves the world will be able to practically exploit. According to the IEA's 2010 *World Energy Outlook*, 80 percent of all the oil fields operating today won't be producing in another twenty-five years. While the same thing could have been said twenty-five years ago, replacing today's fields is a much taller order than it ever was in the past. The nature of world oil production these days means you have to run much faster just to stand still. Every year, the world loses about 4 million barrels a day to flagging production in depleting fields. For world supply to increase, then, the energy industry must first replace the 4 million barrels that are being lost to depletion. In 2010, global production notched a net increase of 2 million barrels, but to achieve that increase, the oil industry actually had to add 6 million barrels of new production.

The good news is that the global oil industry is astoundingly good at finding new reserves and bringing on new production. The bad news is that the oil we're losing to depletion is the low-cost stuff we can afford to burn. Even if technology allows us to keep pace with the treadmill of depletion, continually replacing cheap conventional crude with more expensive unconventional oil is shifting the industry's cost curve to a place our economies simply can't afford.

To up the ante even further, the IEA forecasts that much of the new oil production will come from the very same OPEC countries that are currently bubbling over with social unrest. I'm all for populist rebellions against brutal government repression, but if the region's history has taught the economist in me one thing, it's that oil production, as we saw in the last chapter, doesn't increase during a revolution—or after.

Despite its more sober outlook, the IEA still maintains that OPEC has enough spare pumping capacity to keep the world economy running smoothly. But the IEA's forecast that future Saudi production will reach 14.5 million barrels per day is higher than even Saudi Aramco's best guess at its future capacity. To be sure, Saudi Arabia is still OPEC's kingpin, but that doesn't change the reality that Saudi oil production is below where it was in the 1970s. In fact, the kingdom surrendered its role as the world's largest oil producer to Russia in 2006.

If Saudi Arabia can no longer raise output, who can?

OLD KING COAL—AN EXPENSIVE OLD SOUL

Oil isn't the only vital resource that's getting uncomfortably pricey for the global economy. Cheap coal has been one of our energy staples, but assuming that we still have an abundant supply of coal may be no more valid than our earlier belief in the abundance of cheap oil.

Oil may be the world's transit fuel, but coal is the world's principal source of electric power, particularly in countries such as China, where power demand is growing at double-digit annual rates. Some 40 percent of all the electric power in the world is generated from burning coal. It's second only to oil in terms of its total contribution to global energy use.

And affordable coal may soon be running out just as fast as affordable oil is.

No matter how plentiful it once was, no resource can withstand the pressure of an exponential growth in demand. China burned 3.7 billion tons of coal in 2010, according to the US Energy Information Agency, compared with 1.2 billion tons in 2000. Most everyone knows that oil prices have quadrupled in the last decade. Given such a dramatic rise in China's coal consumption, it shouldn't come as a surprise that coal prices have increased just as quickly.

China may still consume only half as much oil as America, but the Chinese economy has long surpassed the United States in coal consumption. In fact, China burns nearly twice as much coal as the United States while only possessing half of its coal reserves. A burgeoning Chinese vehicle fleet is still powered by oil, but coal is behind China's world-leading economic growth, accounting for more than three-quarters of the country's power. An ever-increasing supply of coal is needed to keep China's factories humming, its lights on and, most of all, its GDP growing.

China is acutely aware that coal, like oil, is getting more expensive to burn all the time. Just as oil prices hit unprecedented highs a few years ago, so too did the price of its hydrocarbon cousin. Newcastle coal, named for the Australian port from which much of it is shipped, is the benchmark coal price for Asia. At the peak of the boom in global commodity demand in 2008, coal prices rose to almost $200 a metric ton, a price matching the lofty $147-per-barrel perch reached by oil prices at the time. Only record coal prices didn't get nearly as much public notoriety as record oil prices. (If drivers were forced to fill up at the local coal pump every week, the Newcastle price would draw much more attention.)

Oil prices tumbled a drastic 70 percent when the recession hit. Though coal didn't fall as dramatically, its price still dropped by more than half. And, like oil, coal prices perked up again along with the global economic recovery.

In today's economy, in order to expand their GDP, countries need to burn more hydrocarbons. That's why China is digging up its coal reserves at a pace never before seen. China's official growth plan calls for burning as much as 5 billion tons per year, more than a third higher than recent consumption. The country already accounts for almost half of global coal production, yet it holds less than 15 percent of the world's coal reserves. The country now uses more coal each year than the United States and Europe combined. Once a coal exporter, its massive consumption now forces China to be a net importer. Something has to give. At the current rate, China's coal reserves will be depleted sooner than anyone had previously imagined.

It's easy to see why most climate change scientists worry that China's ambitious coal consumption targets will throw off enough carbon emissions to cook the atmosphere and trigger cataclysmic climate change: it is already a world-leading carbon emitter. But as we'll explore later on, before global warming spells the end of the world, those same climate change scientists need to ask where China is going to get all the coal it's expecting to burn. To fulfill the carbon emission projections made by groups like the Intergovernmental Panel on Climate Change (IPCC), the Chinese economy may need to burn through the coal supplies of several planets.

A few doors west, India's fuel demands are also bolting higher. Overall, world coal consumption, according to the IPCC, is forecast to double over the next two decades. That covers the demand side of the equation. But we still need to ask where we'll get all this coal.

As growing power shortages across the country will attest, China is already struggling this year to come up with the 3.7 billion tons of coal it burned last year. That's why Chinese companies are scouring the world looking for new coal reserves. State-run Chinese firms shelled out more than $32 billion to acquire foreign mining companies between 2005 and 2010. The biggest splash came in 2008 when Aluminum Corporation of China, a state-run mining firm known as Chinalco, paid $14 billion for a 9 percent stake in Anglo-Australian mining giant Rio Tinto.

If you ask the world coal industry, experts will tell you that enough coal exists to fuel the generation of electricity for the next two hundred years. In one sense, the coal industry experts are probably right. The world will never geologically run out of coal, just as it will never run out of oil. But just as the world is rapidly running out of affordable oil, the same constraint is being felt in the world coal market.

As it turns out, our supply of economically viable coal is a lot smaller than we think. At least, that's true for the high-grade coal in demand around the world. Not all coal is created equal. Energy content is critical when it comes to what kind of coal is worth the trouble of shipping and what coal stays home. The highest grades, such as anthracite and bituminous coal, can have as much as five times the energy content of other "brown" varieties, such as sub-bituminous and lignite. If you have to ship five times as much low-grade coal to match the energy content of high-grade coal, it's evident why it makes little sense to transport low-grade coal to faraway power plants.

Unfortunately for the world's economy, the most abundant forms of coal are those so-called brown coals with a low energy density. The world has a lot of brown coal, but shipping it is another story. It's not worth loading brown coal onto a boat when the bunker fuel used to cross the ocean is worth more than the cargo. Not surprisingly, the type of coal with the highest energy density, anthracite, has been depleted far more rapidly than coal with lower energy content. Its percentage of total coal production has fallen steadily, while the percentage of lower-grade coal has risen.

Because of huge differences in energy content between coal grades, physical tonnage can offer a misleading picture of energy supply. For example, coal production in the United States, which boasts the world's largest reserves, has never been greater. But from the standpoint of how much energy is produced, coal peaked in 1998. While physical production has grown since then, the substitution of lower-grade coal for higher grades has resulted in a reduction in actual energy content. In fact, America's production of high-grade anthracite has been steadily declining for more than sixty years. Annual production is now less than a quarter of its 1950 level. Production of the next-highest grade of coal, bituminous, peaked in 1990 and has since been declining as well. But despite a drop-off in high-quality production, the total coal output from US mines has increased by roughly 20 million tons per year. All that coal, though, packs a smaller energy punch than less tonnage of better quality did years ago.

Less energy for more tons mined—just another example of the concept of diminishing returns that's now common in our energy landscape.

What makes the depletion of high-quality coal reserves even more troubling is that most coal doesn't leave home. The vast majority of coal production, some 85 percent, is burned in the country where it's mined. That leaves only 15 percent of global coal production available for export. The lion's share of coal is concentrated in only seven countries: China, America, Russia, South Africa, Australia, India and Indonesia. By and large, the coal these countries mine goes to a captive domestic audience. The exception is Australia, which exports three-quarters of its production. Because Australia's domestic power market is relatively small, only needing to serve 20 million people spread across a coal-rich continent, Australia can ship most of its coal to China and Japan, and on its own, it accounts for about 40 percent of global exports.

Imagine if 85 percent of the world's *oil* was burned where it was produced, and only 15 percent of global production was available for export. The global economic map would look a lot different than it does today. The US economy, for one, would be dramatically altered. The United States burns two to three times as much oil as it produces every day. If it couldn't secure daily oil imports of 8 to 10 million barrels, it wouldn't be the world's largest economy. If the United States had to rely on homegrown fuel, its GDP would shrink to a shadow of what it is right now.

Scary as it might sound to a US trucker on the I-90, that's precisely where the American economy would be if oil were more like coal. But the reality of the energy world is that oil is a good traveler. For coal, proximity is the name of the game.

When you consider that oil and coal are the two most important fuels in the world, accounting for almost two-thirds of all the energy consumed each day, it's hard not to recognize that oil and coal that cost more have sobering implications for global economic growth. Perhaps, in a postcarbon world, we'll discover new ways of harnessing energy that free us from the constraint of the planet's increasingly finite supply of economically usable hydrocarbons. But that day is still in the distance. In the meantime, we're staring at the depletion of the resources that power the global economy. And that can't help but have a huge impact on the pace at which our economies will be able to grow in the future.

TOMORROW'S POWER?

In some circles, there's one energy source that does offer a potentially viable alternative to oil and coal. But every time nuclear gets a foot in the door, the world gets an unpleasant reminder of why no one wants to see a reactor outside their living room window.

The meltdown of three reactors at a nuclear power station in Japan in early 2011 marked the latest setback to nuclear energy's chances of becoming the fuel of tomorrow. News of three damaged reactors at the TEPCO nuclear plant didn't take long to reverberate around the world. Before the accident at Fukushima, the nuclear industry was coming off a good run. Concerns about carbon emissions had translated into a new receptiveness toward the nuclear industry, which almost had its ducks in a row for an aggressive global expansion. That completely changed in the hours after the tsunami struck the Japanese coast in March 2011. Uranium prices plunged, as did the shares of uranium producers such as Saskatchewan-based Cameco. Firms that build reactors, such as France's Areva, and engineering companies that design nuclear power plants, such as Montreal's SNC-Lavalin, also took a hit. Investors quickly sold off everything that had anything to do with generating nuclear power.

Governments were also bailing out on the industry, even those who'd been counting on nuclear to play a bigger role in a carbon-constrained future energy mix. The dull thud of future business hitting the floor is a familiar sound to nuclear industry veterans. It was last heard after Chernobyl. Before that, it was Three Mile Island.

Global warming may pose far greater dangers down the road than a reactor meltdown, but nothing scares people more than radiation. And not just in Japan, which suffered nuclear horrors during the Second World War. Halfway around the world, people in Boston were measuring for trace fallout in rainwater. On the west coast of North America, folks from Los Angeles to Vancouver worried that radioactive discharge would wash ashore from thousands of miles away. Ships were diverted from Tokyo Bay to avoid possible radiation exposure. Even the US Navy ordered vessels to redeploy to the leeward side of the Japanese islands.

No matter how exaggerated the fear, Japan's nuclear accident became the world's nuclear accident. It was another kick in the teeth for the nuclear industry and the countries that depend on splitting the atom to power their electrical grids.

Of course, countries don't just randomly decide that they're going to invest in nuclear technology. Generally, the countries who are betting big either lack domestic hydrocarbon resources, like France, or have an enormous energy appetite that dwarfs domestic energy production, like the United States. The fact that Japan would rely so extensively on nuclear power is a compelling example of how basic economic imperatives are hard to ignore. A little more than half a century after Hiroshima and Nagasaki, Japan trails only the United States and France in nuclear power usage.

If you look at the country's bill for fuel imports, it's easy to see why nuclear plays such a big role in its energy grid. Japan's economy burns roughly 4.5 million barrels of oil every day, ranking it third in the world behind the United States and China. That's a pretty big appetite for a country that has less than 150,000 barrels a day of domestic oil production. The rest of those barrels have to come from somewhere, which leaves Japan at the mercy of import prices.

Its dependence on foreign oil bit Japan hard during the first OPEC oil shocks. Not even the United States suffered as much as Japan during the oil embargo of the 1970s. After seeing the economic damage that an oil price shock could unleash, Japan made a concerted national push toward nuclear energy, which now accounts for nearly a third of its power supply. Even so, Japan still relies on oil for nearly half of its energy needs. Japanese motorists, in particular, depend almost exclusively on imported oil, which makes buying even more oil on world markets to fuel power plants the last thing Japan wants to do.

Yet if history is any guide, Japan's hydrocarbon fuel bill will be significantly greater in a post-Fukushima economy than ever before. Like the accident at Three Mile Island in 1979, the impact of the Fukushima meltdown will be felt for decades. Overnight, the accident in Pennsylvania undermined American confidence in the safety of nuclear power. There wasn't a brand-new reactor built in the United States for decades. And judging from the public reaction to the accident in North America, Fukushima will put the kibosh on any budding hopes for a nuclear renaissance in Canada and the United States for years to come.

In Japan, the nuclear industry's very existence is now at stake. Its key player, TEPCO, is developing a public persona comparable to the one BP now enjoys in Louisiana following the Macondo well disaster in the Gulf of Mexico. As with BP, the aftermath has been nearly as upsetting as the actual event. It took months for TEPCO to admit its reactors experienced core meltdowns, when in fact those events occurred almost immediately after the plant was swamped by the tsunami. An international team sent by the World Atomic Energy Commission also found that the radiation released in the early stages of the disaster was double what TEPCO had previously admitted.

If you check TEPCO's track record, you won't be surprised by the lack of candor. Like BP, TEPCO is no angel. Between 1977 and 2002, TEPCO was found to have falsified nuclear safety data on at least two hundred separate occasions. In 2005, public disclosure of the firm's nuclear indiscretions forced the resignation of the company's president and several board members. Safety concerns were so rampant that the Japanese government forced TEPCO to shut down seventeen of its reactors for inspection. And TEPCO's problems didn't end there. In 2007, only two years after TEPCO was allowed to restart these reactors, an earthquake forced the company to admit that its reactor in the Chuetsu-oki region was not built to withstand such tremors. The government subsequently ordered TEPCO to shut down that plant.

More recently, yet another TEPCO president resigned after the firm posted the largest loss in Japanese corporate history. Since Fukushima, TEPCO's shares have fallen more than 80 percent. Future liabilities, meanwhile, are staggering. The Japanese government is considering injecting at least a trillion yen, almost $13 billion, into the crippled utility to stave off a potential bankruptcy. And that money won't even account for all the environmental damage that will stem from the radiation from the Fukushima plant.

So much for the Japanese nuclear industry's world-leading earthquake-resistant construction standards. Japanese firms have been selling that perception for years, at home and abroad. The industry's safety record, though, tells a different story. While it took the largest tsunami in more than a century to trigger the event, the Fukushima disaster occurred in an industry where decades of safety breaches and cover-ups pointed to a major accident just waiting to happen.

The policy fallout from Fukushima is reaching well beyond Japan. While the earlier meltdowns at Three Mile Island and Chernobyl put the brakes on most nuclear expansion, the few reactors that were built after those disasters were far more costly because of new mandatory safety features. Naturally, the mounting costs of new reactors only added to big power companies' growing aversion to the industry.

When you get right down to it, generating tremendous amounts of nuclear power from a very small amount of fissile material, like enriched uranium, isn't all that expensive. The real costs are found in the safety and containment systems needed to prevent deadly radiation from leaking into the atmosphere. More safety means higher costs, which only makes the power generated that much more expensive.

After each nuclear disaster, the bar is set that much higher for safety. Reactors built between Three Mile Island and Chernobyl cost 95 percent more than those built before 1979. Compared to existing nuclear facilities, the power generated in plants built after Three Mile Island was 40 percent more expensive. After Chernobyl, the cost curve went up again. Additional safety and containment measures sent construction costs up more than 85 percent, while prices for nuclear-generated power increased by another 40 percent.

For the nuclear industry, the biggest cost wasn't found in the reactors that were built, but in the ones that were scrapped after each accident. Plans for hundreds of reactors were shelved as communities around the world said *not in my backyard*. And it wasn't government regulators who provided the check on the industry, but the market. Wall Street, for one, couldn't find investors willing to finance nuclear expansion. With no access to capital and spiraling costs, the power industry turned to alternatives, including hydroelectric, natural gas and, of course, coal.

Fukushima is having the same impact right now. In Japan, it may take decades before people return to the area around Fukushima. And TEPCO's unwillingness to acknowledge the scale of the disaster is hardly helping win back the hearts and minds of the public. Japanese citizens have learned only too well that when something goes wrong inside a domed building down the road, the local utility operator doesn't have the answers.

Germany was one of the first nations to react to Fukushima. A big nuclear player, Germany has dragged its feet on the issue of new reactors. It has been reluctant to license new plants, but it is willing to extend the operating permits of existing facilities. That same practice is par for the course in North America, where plants with expired due dates remain in service to help hold down electricity costs. Fukushima struck a raw nerve with the German public. Faced with new polls showing that more than 70 percent of the population was against nuclear power, the government did an about-face on a decision to extend the lives of its aging fleet of seventeen nuclear power plants until 2036. Chancellor Angela Merkel, historically a strong proponent of nuclear power, immediately decided to close seven of the oldest reactors pending a safety review. Two have been permanently boarded up. Germany then made the bombshell announcement that it will shutter all of its nuclear power plants by 2022, some fourteen years ahead of its previous schedule.

The big issue Germany now faces is how to replace the lost power from these reactors. Nearly 30 percent of Germany's electricity comes from nuclear, roughly the same proportion as in Japan. While Germany will undoubtedly boost the contribution from renewable sources, an area in which it already leads the world by a wide margin, few believe solar and wind can make up the gap. The more likely substitute is natural gas.

But for Germany, going to natural gas means greater energy dependence on gas-rich Russia. Germany already gets almost a third of its gas supply from Russia, an amount that is increasing with the opening of the Nord Stream, a giant pipeline under the Baltic Sea. A reliance on Russian gas will extend Moscow's influence farther into Europe, a geopolitical leverage the EU can't be happy to see.

Other countries are also reconsidering nuclear power. Switzerland is now looking to phase it out altogether. In the United States, home to the most reactors in the world, the construction of a new plant in the state of Georgia was regarded as the first stage of a nuclear renaissance. Prior to Fukushima, fourteen more states were considering proposals for new nuclear power plants. But as Americans watch the environmental and economic fallout from the Japanese disaster, the country's nuclear revival looks as if it will be nipped in the bud.

In today's environment, public anxiety will make building new facilities nearly impossible. A recent Gallup poll found that seven out of ten Americans were fearful of a nuclear accident. A CBS poll found support for nuclear power had slipped to 43 percent, lower even than in the aftermath of Three Mile Island.

The nuclear industry is feeling the effects of Fukushima nearly everywhere except in China and India. That's where power needs are the greatest, and it's why both countries are, by and large, holding the line on ambitious nuclear plans that were announced prior to Fukushima.

As might be expected, China's nuclear energy plans are aggressive. Currently, twenty-five reactors are under construction, which will be added to the fourteen the country already has in service. The buildup will offer a fivefold increase in China's nuclear power generation capacity by 2020. The burgeoning fleet of nuclear facilities is a pillar of the country's objective to obtain a fifth of its energy from non-hydrocarbon sources within the next decade. Reaching that goal is a cornerstone of China's plan to lower the carbon intensity of its economy.

Will China meet its nuclear goals? Like Japan, China is no stranger to devastating earthquakes. A magnitude 7.3 quake in Tangshan killed a quarter of a million people in 1976, and at least 87,000 perished in a quake in Sichuan in 2008. Following Fukushima, China ordered a full review of its nuclear agenda, but whether it will make any changes to that agenda remains an open question.

India's plans are nearly as big. More than half of its 1.2 billion people still need to be connected to an electrical grid. The country will have to find the energy from somewhere. India's oil consumption is already roughly three times its domestic production. And thanks to demand spurred by record auto sales, the country's fuel bill is only heading higher.

Fukushima or no Fukushima, it appears that India's plans to order as many as twenty-one nuclear reactors will charge ahead. India's politicians are paying ample lip service to the idea of nuclear safety, but the proof will be in the pudding. Construction on two 700-megawatt atomic power plants in Rajasthan is expected to be completed by 2017.

While India's and China's nuclear plans could go ahead undeterred, public sentiment toward nuclear power in Japan is now overwhelmingly negative. Unsurprisingly, the Japanese people want even less to do with nuclear than the Germans. They want their government not only to scrap plans for any new reactors but to shut down facilities currently in operation.

In a stunning reversal of national energy policy, all of Japan's 54 nuclear reactors have been shut down following scheduled maintenance checks. Since their shutdown, no reactor has yet been granted permission to restart.

Local governments in Japan have the power to withhold permission for the nuclear power stations to restart. Sensitive to the huge shift in public sentiment against nuclear power, Tokyo is backing them up. In the course of roughly a year, Japan may go from a country drawing nearly a third of its power from reactors to a country that has effectively become nuclear free.

A permanent loss of 30 percent of the energy in the electrical grid means Japan will have to tap other sources, which means imports will need to rise. Whether it's oil, natural gas or coal, Japan is about to add to the demand for global resources. Barclays Capital estimates Japan may have to burn another 250,000 barrels of oil a day to make up for the lost nuclear power. Meanwhile, RBC Capital Markets estimates that Japan, already the world's largest coal importer, may have to increase coal-fired power generation by as much as 20 percent.

Japan's nuclear accident makes the world's reliance on hydrocarbons that much greater. At the same time, oil and coal prices are telling us those resources have never been scarcer. It took a once-in-a-century tsunami to trigger the Fukushima disaster. On the surface, that could seem like a singular occurrence unlikely to be repeated. Yet in the big picture of the energy world, these one-off events are happening with surprising regularity. It was only a few months before Fukushima that BP's Macondo well was gushing millions of gallons of oil into the Gulf of Mexico. Are Macondo and Fukushima just a tragic coincidence, or is nature trying to tell us something?

It's certainly not a message most of us want to hear. Fukushima and the Deepwater Horizon rig are both products of an insatiable demand for energy, which compels us to harness ever more costly and tricky sources of supply. The more our economies grow, the more energy and power they need, prompting the development of even riskier resources, from the deep waters of the Arctic to environmentally hazardous shale oil in America's heartland.

Will the prices needed to pull these new sources of supply out of the ground actually end up killing the world's appetite for it? In some places, that has already happened.

Chapter 5

THE KEYSTONE CONUNDRUM

I LOVE TO FISH. Over the years, I've been lucky enough to fish some pretty spectacular waters. Selwyn Lake, a remote glacial lake that straddles the 60th parallel on the Canadian Shield, is a spot that really stands out. Two-thirds of it is in the Northwest Territories; the rest, including the fishing lodge, is in northern Saskatchewan. That's where I flew last summer, along with my regular fishing buddies, Murray, Harvey and Maurice.

Fishermen from around the world are drawn to the Canadian north by the prospect of hooking a giant lake trout. These fish, which find enough food to grow in the short time each year when the water is ice free, need cold, clear, and deep lakes to survive. Left undisturbed, they can reach world-record sizes. Some of the fifty-pound monsters lurking in northern Canadian lakes have been swimming in those same icy waters for up to a hundred years. Landing a trout anywhere close to that size is the treat of a lifetime for a fisherman.

At Selwyn, like most northern lakes, the standard practice for sport fishing is catch and release, which fisheries experts figure is the best way to maintain fish stocks. Intuitively, it seems to make sense. Releasing fish for others to catch means more fish for everyone.

Or so I thought. While there is a strict limit at Selwyn Lake on how many fish you can keep, there are no restrictions on how many you can catch. In the space of one morning, for instance, Murray and Maurice landed no fewer than 101 lake trout. On another part of the lake that same morning, Harvey and I caught 40 more. The two fish we kept made for a delicious shore lunch. At the time, I didn't give much thought to the 139 we let go.

In the back of my mind, I suppose I liked to think they all swam happily away, feeling lucky to get a new lease on life. I figured that eventually those trout would grow to become the thirty-pound brutes that keep remote fishing lodges in business. But though we caught a lot of fish on our trip to Selwyn, we never saw any even close to that size. It wasn't until I got back to Toronto that I found out why.

Not long after we returned home, Harvey's wife, Hindy, sent an email about barotrauma. My previously clear conscience about the other 139 trout quickly clouded over. Barotrauma, I learned, is a condition that affects fish caught in depths greater than 60 feet. When these fish are hauled out of the water, nitrogen gas contained in their swim bladders begins to expand. The amount of swelling is proportional to the depth. Pulling up a fish from 100 feet can cause a swim bladder to triple in size. Under natural circumstances, the swim bladder controls buoyancy and gradually adjusts as a fish rises to the surface. But when a trout is yanked into a boat, there's no time for the bladder to adjust. The effect of the sudden ascent resembles the bends that hit a scuba diver who ascends too fast. Unlike divers, though, trout don't get to recover in hyperbaric chambers.

In extreme cases, the force of a swelling swim bladder can push it out of a fish's mouth. These fish are usually goners. But even those without visible signs of distress, such as those protruding swim bladders or bulging eyeballs, can succumb to pressure-related internal injuries within weeks of being caught and released.

Our fish finders showed that we hooked nearly all of the trout in at least 60 feet of water. Some were as deep as 100 feet. It's almost certain that every fish we hauled up was put through some degree of barotrauma. If the mortality rate was even 20 percent, that would mean in just one morning we needlessly killed almost thirty fish. Some research suggests the mortality rate due to barotrauma runs well north of that figure.

Over the course of a couple of days on the lake, the four of us released more than 300 fish. Our guides said a larger group had just caught over 600 fish. How many ultimately survived the ordeal is anyone's guess.

At Selwyn Lake, the vast majority of the fish we caught were around five pounds. The trip and the rugged landscape of northern Saskatchewan were outstanding, but I must admit to being a bit disappointed that we didn't see anything close to trophy size. After reading up on barotrauma, though, I couldn't help but think that this could be the explanation.

A month later, I had a chance to take my son Jack to another remote fishing lodge, this one located on an island off the coast of British Columbia. King Pacific Lodge is on Princess Royal Island, a 1,000-square-mile jewel in the heart of the Great Bear Rainforest. The island is framed by coastal mountains and blanketed by virgin woodland that contains some of the world's oldest trees. Some grow for up to 1,500 years and tower 300 feet above the ground. Peering at the forest through the primeval mist that often covers the island is like stepping out of a time machine into a prehistoric age.

Ecotourists come from around the world to see the wildlife, which ranges from bald eagles to rainforest wolves to the endangered marbled murrelet, a member of the auk family. The island is also a sanctuary for the spirit bear, a rare type of North American black bear endowed with white fur that is found nearly exclusively in the rainforests of British Columbia's Pacific coast. For centuries, members of the Gitga'at First Nation have safeguarded the spirit bear. When the fur trade came to British Columbia, the Gitga'at, who don't hunt the bear, never spoke about it to outsiders in order to shelter it from European trappers.

The Gitga'at aren't the only protectors of the delicate ecosystem on Princess Royal Island; distance is also a friend. More than 500 kilometers separates the island from Vancouver and the bustle of British Columbia's lower mainland. Unfortunately for rainforest conservationists, the island is also less than 100 kilometers from the town of Kitimat, which is the proposed terminus for a new pipeline that would carry crude from Alberta's tar sands. Dubbed Northern Gateway, the proposed pipeline will cost $5.5 billion and ship some 525,000 barrels of oil a day. I figured Jack and I had better do our salmon fishing before that pipeline ever gets built. The industry is quick to assure anyone who will listen that Northern Gateway will adhere to the highest standards of environmental safety. All ships that enter the port, for instance, will be pulled by tugboats and guided by land-based radar. Only double-hulled tankers will be allowed into the terminal. I don't doubt that the industry will fully deliver on these safety measures, but it only takes one *Exxon Valdez*, and Jack and I won't have a chance to fish those pristine waters ever again. And neither will anyone else.

Opponents of the proposed pipeline don't have to look far for a cautionary tale illustrating the likelihood that human error will some-day enter the equation. Even now, the *Queen of the North*, part of the BC Ferries fleet, is resting underneath 1,400 feet of water not far from the northern edge of Princess Royal Island. The ferry sank a few years ago when it scraped its hull against a small island in a channel on the way up to Prince Rupert. Locals from the nearby village of Hartley Bay scrambled into boats in the middle of the night and saved 99 of the 101 people on board. The wrecked ferry still holds thousands of gallons of diesel, and every day a bit more seeps out of its fuel tanks and

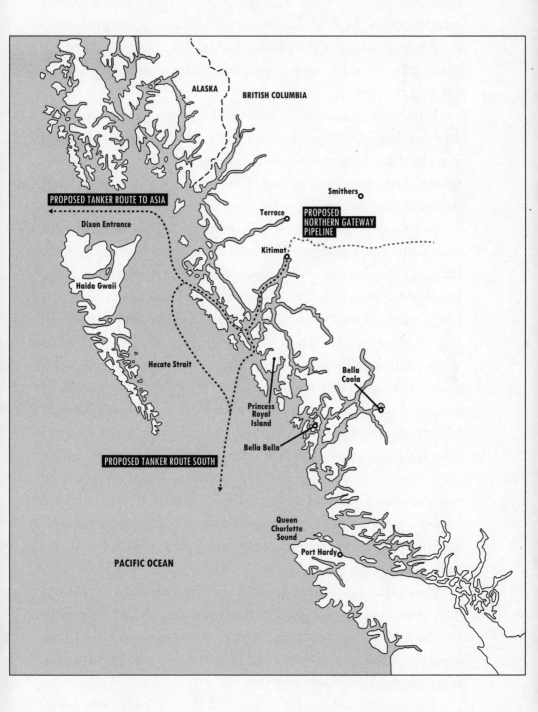

into the surrounding water. That spill is bad enough, but it's a pittance compared with the 2 million barrels of oil that a supertanker would carry from Kitimat. If the pipeline goes ahead, every year hundreds of tankers will need to safely negotiate the same passage that sank the *Queen of the North*.

Even though Northern Gateway has yet to receive regulatory approval, Jack and I are happy we made it to Princess Royal Island when we did. The salmon run was amazing. We also encountered pods of whales on nearly every outing. Watching a humpback whale lunge out of the water is a truly majestic sight.

Among the many differences between fishing for salmon on the West Coast and angling for lake trout in northern Saskatchewan are the rules governing the catch. Instead of catch and release, the standard for salmon fishing in British Columbia is catch and kill. King Pacific Lodge will even send your catch to a local fish processor, which will fillet and package your fish to your liking.

In contrast to the hundreds of fish we pulled out of Selwyn Lake, salmon fishing on Princess Royal Island is conducted within strictly prescribed limits. In a three-day trip, each person is limited to eight salmon, four coho and four chinook. And these rules aren't for show. Canada's Department of Fisheries patrols the waters to make sure no liberties are taken with the salmon run. We experienced that firsthand when we were intercepted in the middle of nowhere. Officers searched our boat to make sure our catch was within the legal limit and that we were using the proper barbless hooks, which do less harm to fish that are hooked but get away.

Over three days of unforgettable fishing, Jack and I caught our limit. And once we had each reached our maximum, we were done. Not only did we stop catching fish, but we stopped casting our lines altogether. Once you stop hooking fish, it naturally follows that you aren't risking killing them anymore.

The fish Jack and I took home from British Columbia were a fraction of the number my buddies and I inadvertently killed at Selwyn

Lake. We all want to live in sustainable ways, but sometimes what seems like the sustainable solution can actually have the exact opposite effect.

WHAT DIRECTION WILL OIL FLOW?

Catch and release or catch and kill? Which one is really better for the environment? It's a question lobbyists would have done well to ask before mobilizing against TransCanada's proposed Keystone pipeline. The $7.8-billion pipeline system would take crude from Alberta's tar sands down through the Midwest and on to Texas, where Gulf Coast refineries are eagerly awaiting the new feedstock.

The project could now be scuttled after concerns about the pipeline's potential impact on a major aquifer in Nebraska turned into a political hot potato. President Barack Obama put Keystone in limbo when he blocked the project application, citing the need for further review. TransCanada intends to reapply, but a decision won't be made until after the November 2012 election. The delay may well turn out to be a politically savvy move. Local politics carry a big stick in an election year. Politicians know that postponing a decision on Keystone is a much more palatable course to voters than giving Big Oil the green light to run bulldozers through America's heartland.

It's catch-and-release politics. And just like fishing in northern Saskatchewan, environmentalists could find that an apparent victory over Keystone will do more harm than good for the environment. The US economy, meanwhile, is set to learn a hard lesson.

If the aim of the anti-pipeline demonstrators was to keep TransCanada from building the 1,600-mile Keystone line, then mission accomplished. But if the agenda was to fight global carbon emissions by hindering the expansion of Alberta's tar sands production, then little has changed. What's more, a win for Nebraska's farmers has now dramatically increased the risk to the pristine rainforests along the BC coast. When supertankers are navigating the narrow inlet into Kitimat, I wonder if the environmental lobby will regret that Keystone didn't find an acceptable route through the network of highways and byways that already exists from Montana to Texas.

Output from Canada's tar sands, currently about 1.5 million barrels a day, is forecast to double by 2020. Until Keystone was tripped up by the Nebraska aquifer, the project looked like the best option for getting new production to world markets. In the long run, several new pipelines will be needed to handle the extra volume coming from the tar sands. But in the short term, you can think of the competition to build a new line as a horse race. Keystone had the inside track, but the political delay has now swung the door open for Enbridge's Northern Gateway to take the lead. Regardless of which pipeline gets the nod, once construction begins, the necessity for oil sands producers to build the other line will be alleviated.

Right now, Canadian oil companies have a huge incentive to fast-track another pipeline out of Alberta. The bulk of the province's tar sands output currently ends up in refineries clustered throughout the US Midwest. An increase in volume from the tar sands, combined with prolific production from so-called Bakken shales, a new oil play being exploited in North Dakota and Montana, has created a supply glut at those refineries. As it stands, Canadian oil only makes it as far south as Cushing, Oklahoma, the terminal point for the pipeline system. The plan for Keystone would extend the system another 435 miles to the Gulf Coast, effectively connecting landlocked Cushing to world oil markets. Gulf Coast refineries also hold more spare capacity than those of any other refining region in the United States. The proposed Keystone line would facilitate an ideal marriage between Texas refineries hungry for more supply and new Canadian oil in need of a home.

A surplus of oil backing up at Cushing has turned into a sweet deal for Midwest refiners, and it's why West Texas Intermediate (WTI) crude traded more than $20 a barrel lower than benchmark world oil prices for most of 2011. Without a new pipeline, Midwest refiners will get to keep paying a discounted price for Canadian oil.

Considering that Canada exports more than 2 million barrels of oil a day to the US market, getting shortchanged by $20 on every barrel sold is no trifling matter. It works out to some $40 million a day or roughly $1.25 billion a month in foregone petrodollars. And it's not just Canadian oil producers that take a hit to the bottom line. The royalties collected by Alberta's provincial government shrink right along with the price of WTI, as do the corporate taxes collected by Canada's federal government.

What exactly happens to that missing $20 a barrel? US motorists certainly don't get a break at the pumps. By and large, American drivers pay the same price no matter where in the country they live. No, the big winners are the oil companies that own the Midwest refineries; they've been pocketing huge profits on the back of abundant supplies from Canada.

In the refining business, the difference between the cost of feedstock, such as bitumen from Alberta's tar sands, and the price charged for end products, such as gasoline and diesel, is known as the crack spread. A wide crack spread means refiners are making a lot of cash. In Cushing, crack spreads have been as much as five times wider than margins for refineries in other parts of the United States. On the Gulf Coast, for example, refineries pay the going rate for Light Louisiana Sweet crude, which trades near the same price as Brent crude, the benchmark world oil price. The story is much the same for refineries on the Pacific and Atlantic coasts. Refineries in the Midwest, in contrast, get to fatten up at the expense of Canadian oil exporters. Keystone would have changed that game. Until a major new pipeline is constructed, crack spreads in the Midwest will remain wide open. But just as water doesn't flow uphill, it's unnatural for oil to keep flowing to places where it gets sold at a discount.

If President Obama finds the flow of oil from Canada's tar sands too hot to handle, the Chinese will certainly have no qualms about taking it off his hands. In the event that Enbridge gains approval from Canada's National Energy Board to build Northern Gateway, a zero-sum world

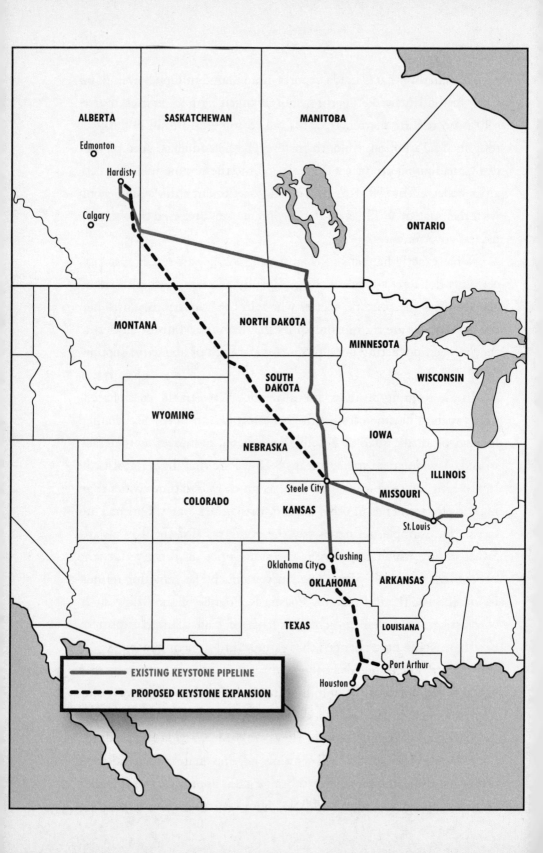

EXISTING KEYSTONE PIPELINE

PROPOSED KEYSTONE EXPANSION

will only tilt that much further in China's direction. Once oil tankers load up at Kitimat and hit the high seas, their cargoes will go to the highest bidder. In all likelihood that means China. Before building a new pipeline, companies like Enbridge secure commercial agreements, known as shipper commitments, to make sure the pipe will be filled with product. It's an open secret in Canada's oil patch that members of the Asian market are part of the group that has already secured space on a potential new line to the Pacific coast.

Turn back the clock only five or six years, and the thought of Alberta oil heading directly to China would have been unthinkable. Why ship oil across an ocean when the world's best customer lives next door? The historic ties between Canada's oil patch and the United States run deep. It's no accident that Calgary is often described as the most American city in Canada. The neighborhood of Mount Royal, where many of Calgary's oil patch millionaires now live, was originally dubbed American Hill due to the number of wealthy Yankee businessmen who settled there early in the last century. One of the city's most influential players, Imperial Oil, is nominally based in Calgary but is controlled by ExxonMobil, which owns 70 percent of the company. When it comes to the history of Canada's oil patch, the commercial compass in Calgary has always pointed south to Houston.

When I was still making regular stops in Calgary as chief economist of CIBC World Markets, the circuit often included visits with Alberta's ministers of energy and finance. During a number of these meetings, I remember being told in no uncertain terms that a direct investment in the province's tar sands by a state-owned company would be wholly unwelcome. State-owned companies, the ministers would suggest, don't play by the same commercial rules as the good old boys from Texas.

How times have changed. In 2010, China's state-owned refining company, Sinopec, paid $4.65 billion for a 9 percent stake in Syncrude, which runs the largest of Alberta's four tar sands mines. It was the first time a Chinese company took a direct position in a producing tar sands asset, but it won't be the last.

Before that deal, Chinese companies had already picked up stakes in a number of early-stage projects that have yet to reach commercial production. A year earlier, PetroChina, one of the country's state-owned exploration companies, spent $1.9 billion for a 60 percent share of a project being developed by Athabasca Oil Sands Corp, and it paid another $680 million for the remaining stake in early 2012. Prior to that, Sinopec and China National Offshore Oil Corp. (CNOOC), another state-run company, each picked up ownership positions in smaller players with big plans on the drawing board. And China's interest in Canada's oil patch isn't limited to the tar sands. Late last year, Sinopec paid $2.9 billion for Daylight Energy, a midsized exploration and production company with operations in Alberta and British Columbia. Suffice to say that Alberta's stance on China has changed since the province's cabinet ministers were telling me that national oil companies should stay home.

Money talks, and China has a lot to spend. Regardless of the rhetoric I was fed by its politicians, Alberta is now clearly open for business. Canadian tar sands players angling for a generous buyout would much rather think about what to do after the check is cashed than worry about who's writing it. Likewise, Calgary's investment bankers are never ones to turn down a potentially juicy commission. Local rainmakers are undoubtedly picking up some Mandarin to help grease the wheels for future transactions.

China's deep pockets have also obviously made an impression on the Alberta government. That's not hard to do when you're willing to pay world oil prices that are as much as $20 a barrel higher than Canada's one-time favorite customer to the south. The pull of the Chinese market is also being felt in Ottawa, where politicians are taking a long look at the merits of giving the go-ahead to Northern Gateway. Shortly after Obama's pronouncement on Keystone, Canada's minister of natural resources, Joe Oliver, said he wants a regulatory decision on Northern Gateway by 2013, a full year ahead of the previous schedule.

It's tough to refute the benefits of opening up new markets for Canadian oil, which is currently being held hostage by US refiners. If Washington continues to drag its feet on Keystone, expect to see Canadian politicians shift their focus from winning US congressional support to fast-tracking a pipeline to the Pacific.

Of course, even a rock-solid business case for building Northern Gateway still doesn't mean it will see the light of day. The pipeline already faces fierce opposition from conservationists who are worried about what the project will mean to the ecosystems on the Pacific coast. And that's only part of the battle. The project faces an even stiffer test in persuading members of the First Nations that a new pipeline is in their best interests. The pipe will cut across lands that are traditionally claimed by First Nations groups, and these unresolved land claims are a potential quagmire that could derail Enbridge's hopes for the line.

Native land claims clashing with grand plans for pipeline projects are a familiar story in Canada. The Mackenzie Valley Pipeline project, intended to bring natural gas from the Arctic to southern markets, was held back by land claims for decades. When natural gas prices were flying high a few years ago, the line looked like it might finally go ahead. By the time years of hearings brought an agreement to hand, natural gas prices were in the process of cratering, which killed the financial incentive for the pipe. Northern Gateway is dealing with different land claims in different economic times, but it's still an open question whether Enbridge will be able to successfully negotiate its way through the tangled issue.

That said, oil is Canada's number one export. At current prices, pipeline economics make for a powerful political force. Northern Gateway would move more than half a million barrels a day of very precious oil. The new line would also end the supply glut in the Midwest, which would help boost the price of WTI at Cushing. All told, a new pipeline would lift the revenues of Canadian oil companies by billions of dollars. More cash flow means more profits, which means more revenue in government coffers and eventually back to Canadians. The stakes are high enough that Enbridge and Ottawa won't hesitate to cut some big checks to gain the support of local interest groups.

Ottawa has the incentive to do everything it can to make one of the proposed pipelines a reality as soon as possible. If Northern Gateway goes ahead, the big loser will be the US economy. President Obama knows full well that the United States needs as much Canadian oil as it can get. If the political winds don't shift soon, America's loss could turn into China's gain. Maybe Obama should have joined Jack and me on our fishing trip to Princess Royal Island. He might have learned that catch and kill, despite how it looks, is a better option in the long term than catch and release.

Right now, the odds are stacked against Keystone. And what's bad for Keystone will turn out to be even worse for Princess Royal Island and the rest of Canada's pristine North Pacific coast. There is, however, one ray of hope: the end of growth. The same triple-digit oil prices that will bring Chinese tankers halfway around the world to fill up on oil extracted from tar could soon deep-six the global economy. If China's economy stops growing at its current clip, maybe it won't need to import oil from the tar sands. The twists and turns of the Inside Passage will be left for salmon to navigate, not supertankers.

That's one of the silver linings of a static economy. A new world of slower growth will certainly usher in some painful changes, but it also might save one of the largest remaining temperate rainforests in the northern hemisphere. That's good news for the spirit bear—and the salmon run. As for the rest of us?

We all might find ourselves in that world of no growth much sooner than we ever could have thought.

Chapter 6

THE DANISH RESPONSE

THE FIRST THING I noticed on a flight into Copenhagen a few summers ago was a ring of wind turbines surrounding the city. Not far from the city's harbor, the sweeping arc of offshore windmills is a hard sight to miss. I found out later that this is exactly what the Danes have in mind. The gleaming white windmills, which rise more than 100 meters above the deep blue waters of the Øresund strait, are intended to be an unmistakable symbol of Denmark's commitment to renewable energy.

The rest of Denmark's bona fides when it comes to green living are also tough to ignore. In the last two decades, Denmark has cut its carbon dioxide emissions by 13 percent. That makes for a remarkable contrast with North American emissions, which have increased by 30 percent since 1990, the baseline year for the Kyoto accord. The credit for reversing greenhouse gas emissions is often given to eco-friendly initiatives like the wind turbines I saw dotting the Copenhagen seascape. It's a success story the Danes are literally selling to the rest of the world. Denmark, which in 1991 became the first country to set up an offshore wind farm, now garners 11 percent of its exports from sales of energy technology. At home, wind power accounts for an impressive 20 percent of domestic electricity generation.

Denmark clearly has plenty of good reasons to be proud of its environmental track record. From the moment I glimpsed the wind turbines from my plane seat, though, I couldn't get away from a niggling curiosity about how the country generates the rest of its power. At the conference I was attending, a speaker from a local power company presented on Denmark's world-leading green technology. I tracked him down after my own talk, figuring he was just the person to ask. He hemmed and hawed, but when I pressed him, he reluctantly told me how his country generates the other 80 percent of its power.

Coal.

I was floored. The first thought that crossed my mind was "Something is rotten in the state of Denmark!" For a country striving to be completely independent of fossil fuels, Denmark couldn't have picked a worse way to generate electricity. Coal is 20 percent dirtier than oil and twice as dirty as natural gas. With big dollars at stake selling green energy technology around the world, I can understand why Denmark wants to showcase its offshore wind farms instead of its coal-fired power plants. But the cold hard truth is that it is smokestacks, not wind turbines, that allow most Danes to turn on the lights.

Coal's share of power generation, I found out, is the same in Denmark as it is in China. Where China's carbon footprint now dwarfs every other country in the world, though, Denmark's is actually shrinking. How can this be?

To answer this energy riddle, you need to look past how power is generated in Denmark and into the prices Danish citizens pay for electricity. Households in Copenhagen pay roughly 30 cents per kilowatt-hour for power. That's two to three times the average price in North America. In Denmark, government-regulated power prices are laden with carbon taxes, which means electricity isn't cheap, whether it's wind powered or coal fired. Not surprisingly, Danes use a fraction of the power that North Americans consume.

All those world-famous windmills, it turns out, aren't behind Denmark's falling emissions. The real reason for its smaller carbon footprint is its high electricity prices, which put a huge damper on power demand. The coal that *doesn't* get burned because power is so expensive is more important to the level of Denmark's carbon emissions than the coal that does get burned.

That's good news for the planet's future. Despite its offshore wind farms, Denmark shows that carbon abatement isn't limited to places with ideal conditions for wind power—or solar or hydroelectric, for that matter. Higher energy prices are a tactic that can be applied anywhere. The market is oblivious to whether the wind blows or the sun shines. Charge enough for power in any country in the world and people will use less electricity. It's basic economics.

If capping carbon emissions is the goal, the solution isn't to rush out and build wind turbines; simply raising prices will do the job. Consider, for instance, the state of Montana or the province of Alberta, both of which have huge coal reserves. What's more, citizens there consider energy abundance a veritable birthright, so few think twice about burning as much of it as possible. Even in those places, though, I bet charging 30 cents per kilowatt-hour would cut the demand on the local power grid in a hurry.

To lower carbon emissions, you don't need to build a single wind turbine or invest even a dollar in so-called clean coal technology. Just charge more for power and emissions will come down as a result.

WHY ARE SO MANY DANES RIDING BIKES?

Denmark's track record of environmental success also has a lot to do with cars. Or I suppose I should really say a lack of cars. Cyclists are everywhere in Copenhagen, which boasts some of the best bicycle lanes in the world. They even have their own traffic signals. And it has paid off. No matter where you go in Copenhagen, nearly everyone seems to get there on a bike.

When you see so many physically fit, rosy-cheeked, good-looking Danes peddling around the city, the first thing you think about is renewing your gym membership. After that you can't help but appreciate how an entire population seems to be so environmentally conscious. It's admirable, no doubt, and Danes should certainly be proud. But once again, the economist in me, ever on the lookout for price signals that explain human behavior, felt compelled to ask more questions.

It turns out that driving a car in Denmark, much like turning on the lights, is a very expensive proposition. The biggest cost isn't even at the pumps. While fuel is more expensive in Denmark than it is in Canada or the United States, gasoline prices in Copenhagen are largely in line with the rest of Europe. Yet few other major European cities have the same volume of bike traffic as Copenhagen.

What differentiates Denmark from its neighbors is the cost of buying a car. Danish car buyers pay a tax ranging from 100 to 180 percent of the vehicle's sticker price; the exact amount depends on the size of the engine. For the cost of one vehicle with a gas-guzzling V-8 in Denmark, for instance, you could buy up to three cars in North America. If my fellow Torontonians had to pay those prices, the number of bikes on the road might start to rival Copenhagen.

Of course, ending a hundred-year-old love affair with the automobile won't come easy. A few years ago, for example, Toronto's city council passed a new annual vehicle registration tax that cost Toronto car owners the princely sum of $65 a year. That was too much for Torontonians to stomach. Facing disastrous pre-election polling numbers, the incumbent mayor headed for the exit. One of the first acts of the new mayor, Rob Ford, was to announce that the city's war against the car was over. He and his new council canceled the tax.

Defenders of North America's car culture will also argue that the sprawling landscapes of cities such as Los Angeles, Phoenix and Calgary make Copenhagen-style bike usage impractical. Getting to work every day certainly can't be like training for a triathlon. And frigid winter temperatures in some cities are also clearly unsuitable for year-round cycling. Those are fair points, but what the Danish model shows us is that prices influence demand. The Danes have crafted policies that encourage conservation. There's nothing stopping civic governments in North America from doing the same.

The world won't always look the way it does now. The sprawl that defines many North American cities is a result of cheap oil that makes it affordable for suburban homeowners to commute to work. Replace inexpensive oil with triple-digit prices and cities will eventually shrink back to their original bike-sized urban cores. When gasoline prices move high enough, you can also bet that suburbanites and city-dwellers will start agitating for better transit options. High fuel costs will force these types of changes on all of us before you know it. Denmark is meeting this pending reality on its own terms. The rest of us would be wise to consider how that country is doing it.

Copenhagen's trademark windmills act as a smokescreen that obscures a more important takeaway than the mere viability of green energy. The power the Danes use is not much greener than anywhere else. Denmark is green because the Danes have learned how to use less power.

I'm sure a good number of Danes would take issue with me. They'll point to their coal plants, which are among the most carbon efficient in the world. They'll rightly note that those same power stations do double duty, generating heat as well as electricity. While all of that is true, it misses the fundamental point. Prices are what have made the difference. Prices are what matter.

Of course, selling green technology around the world is far more lucrative for Denmark than simply showing the rest of us how to use less energy. That's why the offshore wind turbines are in full view of the capital city and why Denmark has put its environmental branding front and center. But the real lesson we need to take from Denmark is how to curb our energy appetite. If we don't, we'll be at the mercy of fuel prices that are only marching higher. Wind and solar are welcome additions to the power grid, but the world still runs on hydrocarbons.

What's more, a focus on new sources of energy supply only considers half of the equation; the other half is demand. And here, conservation is a practical solution that's available right now.

Someday, economically viable fuel alternatives will unseat hydrocarbons from the top of the energy pyramid, freeing our electrical grids and our gas tanks from the clutches of high prices. But that day isn't today. In the here and now, our economic success in the face of triple-digit energy prices will hinge on burning fewer hydrocarbons. That means we all have to learn how to use less energy.

That's exactly what the Danes have done. In Copenhagen, households use nearly a third less energy than in North America. Expensive power is all the motivation Danes need to switch off lights when they leave a room. Or don a sweater in the winter instead of cranking up the thermostat. In the summer, Danes spend more time in the fresh air and less time straining the electrical grid by cooling their houses with air-conditioning. Compare Copenhagen with a city like Houston. To escape the summer heat, Houstonians move from air-conditioned houses to air-conditioned cars to air-conditioned offices and back again. Copenhagen doesn't face the same oppressive summer heat as Houston, but the stark differences in energy usage between the two cities are worth considering. Are Danes worse off for living in smaller houses and cutting back on air-conditioning? Is Copenhagen turning into an abandoned wasteland, strangled by punitive energy costs?

Far from it. Copenhagen is one of the most attractive cities in Europe to visit. Tourists come from around the world to enjoy its charms. And it's not like Danes are flooding foreign embassies in a desperate attempt to emigrate to places with cheaper power. Surveys show Danes, who enjoy one of the highest standards of living in the world, are among the happiest people on earth. As could be expected, the amount of out-migration in Denmark is negligible.

As much as Denmark is a living, breathing example of environmental success, it's only fair to note that the battle against carbon emissions is easier there than it is elsewhere. Denmark has no significant hydrocarbon reserves of its own, which means its politicians don't need to worry about appeasing a carbon-intensive energy industry. In the same spirit, the country also doesn't have an auto sector to speak of. In Denmark, no one needs to worry about currying favor with autoworkers to get reelected.

Getting ahead of the curve on the environment is a whole lot easier when you don't need to undermine key parts of your economy to do it. When Denmark slaps a sky-high tax on new cars, it only hurts some other country's auto exports. And it's not like German autoworkers get to vote in Danish elections. Contrast Denmark's situation with the pressures faced by the government of my home province of Ontario. While this may surprise people south of the 49th parallel, Ontario actually produces more cars than any state in the union. When the global recession sent automakers reeling toward bankruptcy, Ontario, along with Canada's federal government, spent billions of taxpayer dollars to help keep General Motors and Chrysler solvent. Across the border, politicians in Washington doled out even more money to those same companies in order to safeguard high-paying manufacturing jobs.

Likewise, the oil industry also gets billions in subsidies from governments in the United States and Canada. In the United States, government tax breaks for Big Oil are wrapped in the rhetoric of promoting energy self-sufficiency and reducing the country's dependence on imported oil from faraway lands that could become unfriendly at any moment. In Canada, subsidies are granted under the guise of protecting one of the country's leading exports.

Danish politicians don't have to contend with the powerful lobbying efforts of Big Auto or Big Oil. Nor does Denmark have to worry about penalizing hard-working coal miners or assembly-line workers. The country is politically free to impose what are, in effect, huge carbon taxes that encourage energy conservation. While admirable from an environmental standpoint, for a country that's forced to buy oil and coal from foreign producers, slashing energy consumption also makes a tremendous amount of economic sense.

Half a world away, the Japanese are coming to the same conclusion.

WILL THEY BE RIDING MORE BICYCLES IN TOKYO?

Like Denmark, Japan is largely devoid of domestic hydrocarbon reserves. That forces the country to import nearly every last drop of the 4.5 million barrels of oil its economy burns every day. As we saw in the last chapter, in an effort to reduce its oil imports, Japan turned to nuclear energy, which before the Fukushima meltdown accounted for nearly a third of the country's power generation.

Japan has no obvious substitute for its lost nuclear power. Practically and economically, that makes for a country highly motivated to adopt Danish-style energy conservation. Finding ways to save oil is nothing new for Japan, which became a pioneer in energy efficiency after the OPEC oil shocks of the 1970s and 1980s. Without hydrocarbon reserves, Japan had few choices at the time. Today, the Fukushima disaster is forcing the country to draw on that experience.

The new catchword in Japan is *setsuden*, or electricity conservation. These days, the concept is evident almost everywhere. Office dwellers are going without air-conditioning, while factory workers are switching off lights and machinery when they're not needed. In stores, escalators are becoming staircases. And households across the country are being encouraged to scale back power usage by as much as 20 percent. Even Japanese businessmen, renowned for their conservative attire, are being asked to wear casual clothes to work rather than dark suits, the idea being that dressing in breathable material will reduce the strain on office air-conditioning.

Are Tokyo's streets soon to be filled with businesspeople in cream-colored open-neck shirts riding bicycles?

In another sign of the times, Toshiba is about to launch a new flat-screen television designed specifically for countries, like Japan, that are experiencing frequent electricity blackouts. The TV can run for three hours on a rechargeable battery, so no one has to miss a favorite program due to a power outage. Nissan and Mitsubishi are advertising that electric cars aren't just for making routine trips to work or the grocery store. The manufacturers are now considering boosting the capacity of electric car batteries to enable motorists to power hot plates with their vehicles. No power in the kitchen? No problem. Dinner can be cooked using the family sedan.

Other firms across the country are even changing the hours of the workday. The Tokyo Stock Exchange, for one, is starting work earlier in the morning to cut down on air-conditioning needs. The Exchange has also turned off its electronic stock price ticker and closed the visitors' gallery to avoid having to light and cool the room.

Setsuden is defining the new contours of an energy-constrained Japanese economy. Similar changes may soon decide the shape of your economy as well.

A magical new power source isn't waiting in the wings to solve Japan's energy problems. Instead, the country is figuring out that the alternative to building more nuclear reactors is using less electricity and closing the energy gap in other ways. Here, the cost of fuel will actually turn out to be one of Japan's best friends. High prices enforce an economic discipline that will naturally curtail energy use.

Certainly other steps will help along the way. More electric vehicles are bound to be on roads in Japan, and around the world, before too long. Wind and solar power will continue to become more affordable and more efficient, which will add to the role they're able to play in supplying tomorrow's power needs. And more inventive measures are being found all the time. In Paris, an ambitious car-sharing service using electric vehicles has been launched. The French are hoping the new communal car plan will meet with the same success that a similar bicycle-sharing scheme did a few years ago. Other cities are bound to follow suit.

But the really big changes that will come in an energy-constrained future won't have to do with the type of vehicles we drive or how we generate electricity. Instead, what will matter most is the energy that's *not* used. The real energy savings, as Denmark knows, happen when fewer cars are on the road and less power is used at home.

Of course, that still leaves us with one very large concern. Higher energy prices will undoubtedly get us to use less energy. But if economic growth, as we found out in chapter 1, is a function of energy consumed, what kind of an economy is possible in a world of energy conservation? Can the global economy continue to expand without using more and more energy? And if not, what does a static economy look like?

Part Two

Chapter 7

ZERO-SUM WORLD

THE BLACK SEA SHIPYARD in the Ukrainian port city of Nikolayev was established by a Belgian-owned concern in the late 1890s as the Nikolayev Shipbuilding, Mechanical and Ironworks. Since then, it has gone by many names: the Andre Marti Shipyard, Nikolayev South Shipyard and Soviet Shipyard Number 444. Among other notable vessels, the yard launched the battleship *Potemkin*. A mutiny on board the *Potemkin*, made famous by an eponymous silent film, was a key event in the Russian uprising of 1905, a precursor to the 1917 revolution that overthrew Czar Nicholas II and ushered in the Soviet Union.

If you visited the Black Sea Shipyard in the mid-1990s, you would have come across the rusting remains of the *Varyag*. When shipbuilders laid down the keel for the *Varyag* in 1985, the massive steel hulk was to become the Soviet navy's second Kuznetsov-class aircraft carrier. But that was before the fall of the Berlin Wall. Construction of the *Varyag* halted in 1992, after the Soviet navy stopped making payments to the shipyard. Following the breakup of the Soviet Union, ownership of the *Varyag* was transferred to Ukraine. Instead of becoming the pride of the fleet, the *Varyag*, which was 70 percent complete, was stripped of her engines, electronics and rudder, and left to rust.

Originally projected to cost $2.4 billion, the ship was put up for auction in 1998 and sold for the bargain-basement price of $20 million. As part of the sale, Ukraine stipulated that the *Varyag* couldn't be used for military purposes. That was fine with the buyer, a small Chinese tourism company, Chong Lot, which said it planned to turn the boat into a floating casino off the coast of Macao.

The boat spent the next few years being towed around the Black Sea, as Chinese diplomats worked to get Turkey's permission to let the steel carcass through the narrow straits of the Bosporus. It took until 2001, but the *Varyag* eventually made it into the Mediterranean. Denied access to the Suez Canal for safety reasons, the *Varyag* set out on the long haul through the Strait of Gibraltar, around the Horn of Africa and back up through the Indian Ocean to China, a trek that cost millions in fuel and labor and took more than a year and a half to complete. But the ship's saga didn't end there.

Instead of docking at Macao, the tugboats made for Dalian, a naval port on China's northeast coast. Once there, the *Varyag* slipped off the radar. It reemerged in 2005, painted the distinctive gray of the People's Liberation Army Navy.

Only twenty aircraft carriers are currently in service around the world, according to *Jane's Fighting Ships*, the definitive guide to the world's warships. The United States operates eleven, Italy two, while Spain, Russia, France, Brazil, India, Thailand and the UK have one each. The *Varyag*, which needs years of sea trials and crew training before it is operational, will become China's first aircraft carrier and the flagship of its navy. Chinese officials, who sidestep questions about the floating casino cover story, are plainspoken about the carrier's future role in protecting the country's foreign interests—oil being at the top of the list.

BILL CLINTON ONCE SAID, "When word of a crisis breaks out in Washington, the first question that comes to everyone's lips is, 'Where's the nearest carrier?'" America's role as global superpower rests on the back of its aircraft carriers, the most powerful military assets in the world. China intends to join the club, a development that has the full attention of its neighbors. The Philippines, Singapore, Indonesia, Malaysia, Cambodia, Thailand and Vietnam are all running into problems with China and its territorial claims to most of the oil- and gas-rich South China Sea.

China's years of practicing a good-neighbor policy appear to be coming to an end. It's getting more aggressive in pressing its rights, recently sending an unmanned submarine to plant a flag on the ocean floor of the South China Sea to act as a symbol of its military capability and regional dominance. China is also reportedly calling the *Varyag* the *Shi Lang*, after a 17th-century admiral who conquered Taiwan—a not so subtle nod to its plans for the craft.

China's energy interests span the globe, meaning the *Shi Lang* could end up off the coast of Africa or in the Middle East. It could also sail to South America, where China is looking to get more and more of its future oil supply. A burgeoning relationship with Hugo Chávez's government in Venezuela could lead to more barrels being shipped from the Faja, the country's heavy oil belt, directly to Chinese refineries. That would be unwelcome news for the United States, the current destination for more than half of Venezuela's oil exports.

How many tanks of gas Chinese drivers burn never used to pose a threat to anyone in North America or anywhere else for that matter. In the early 1980s, China's oil consumption was a modest 2 million barrels a day. Now, its daily intake is a not so humble 9 million barrels. Fortunately for China's ever-increasing fuel needs, world oil production grew so robustly in the last three decades that the extra demand was easily handled.

But when global fuel demand is increasing faster than global supply, something has to give. China's appetite for more oil will come at the expense of someone else's oil diet. Economists use the concept of "zero sum" to describe this type of situation. In zero-sum conditions, one party's gains are offset by another party's losses. When it comes to energy, that means every time you fill up at the gas station, you take away a tank of fuel from someone else.

In a zero-sum world of global oil supply, China's demand for fuel will come at the expense of the United States. Americans consume more than 20 percent of global oil production while producing less than 10 percent. That's a big gap that the United States currently bridges by importing oil from foreign countries. If China's economic growth continues to outpace the United States', China will gain a comparative advantage in the global competition for more barrels.

Consider each country's relationship with Venezuela, home to the world's largest oil reserves, according to OPEC statistics. An oil tanker takes less than two days to travel from Venezuela to the US Gulf Coast, where refineries are set up to handle the country's supply of heavy crude. Proximity alone makes the United States the natural destination for Venezuelan oil. By comparison, a journey across the Pacific takes much longer and costs much more. Yet since 2005, Venezuela's exports to China have more than tripled, to 125,000 barrels a day. Over the same time frame, Venezuela's oil exports to the United States have steadily fallen, to less than a million barrels a day from more than 1.5 million. China also recently lent Venezuela $20 billion to ramp up petroleum production, and you can bet the intention behind the loan wasn't that Venezuela would send more oil to the United States.

China's relationship with Venezuela will become even more of a concern to the United States if a proposed pipeline is built to carry oil from the Faja across Colombia to the Pacific coast. Colombian president Juan Manuel Santos considers the new pipeline an economic priority for his country. If constructed, the new South American pipeline, a conceptual mirror of Enbridge's Northern Gateway proposal, would give China a direct connection to the world's largest oil reserves.

A pipeline to Colombia's Pacific coast wouldn't spell an end to the trading relationship between Venezuela and the United States, but it would certainly mean more barrels heading to China and fewer to the

Gulf Coast. In a zero-sum world of global oil supply, if the United States is forced to reduce its oil consumption, American drivers will bear the brunt of the decrease. More than two-thirds of the oil burned by the US economy is used as transit fuel, whether for gas-guzzling cars, diesel-burning trucks or jet-fueled airplanes.

To see zero-sum dynamics already at play, you need only look at the global auto industry. In the United States, automakers are now selling around 13 million vehicles annually, a sharp decline from nearly 18 million a few years ago. Over the same period, vehicle sales in China have soared, hitting 18 million last year. And China isn't the only country seeing explosive growth in its auto sector: in the last decade, annual sales in India have quadrupled, to 2.7 million vehicles.

Chinese motor vehicle sales, according to auto industry expert J.D. Power and Associates, are expected to double to 35 million units by 2020. Sales in India, meanwhile, are expected to more than triple to 11 million vehicles over the same time frame. Those may seem like gigantic increases, but the growth is only an extrapolation of what has already happened in those markets in recent years.

Soaring Chinese auto sales have sent worldwide auto registrations to unprecedented heights. Global vehicle ownership reached the one billion mark in 2010, according to *Ward's Auto World*, a key source for industry statistics. Globally, that equates to one vehicle for every seven people. A 30 percent increase in Chinese registrations in 2010 pushed the total past the billion-vehicle milestone. Vehicle registrations had already doubled between 2006 and 2010. At over 100 million, China is now home to the second-largest vehicle fleet in the world, surpassing Japan and trailing only the United States.

Yet even with the sharp increase in the number of drivers in recent years, only one out of seventeen people in China owns a car. In India, that ratio is one in fifty-five. By comparison, a total fleet of 240 million vehicles in the United States means more than one vehicle exists for every licensed driver in the country. As economic conditions in China and India continue to progress toward the standards enjoyed in

OECD countries, growth in their domestic auto markets is inevitable and seems relatively boundless. If you're a General Motors or an Audi, it's not too hard to figure out where you'll be breaking ground on your next factory. And of course, new car plants in China and India mean new jobs, which will keep a zero-sum world of GDP growth tilted toward Asia and away from North America.

Although vehicle sales in emerging markets will definitely be robust to say the least, they aren't likely to come even close to the heady forecasts from outfits like J.D. Power, since their projections leave out a crucial element: fuel. If predictions for vehicle usage in China and India come to pass, the extra fuel needed to power those vehicles will put even more strain on the global oil supply. The increase from today's consumption levels alone would be more than half the total amount of gasoline and diesel fuel currently burned in North America.

In theory, I suppose it's possible that in the next decade half of the North American auto fleet will be replaced by vehicles that run on electricity or natural gas. But considering that the latest numbers from the US Department of Energy show there are still fewer than a million alternative-fuel vehicles on American roadways, I wouldn't want to bet on it. Nevertheless, in the coming years, we know that more drivers in China and India will be on the road than ever before. When it comes to consuming oil, China and the United States will soon be trading places.

WHY CHINA CAN AFFORD TRIPLE-DIGIT OIL PRICES WHILE AMERICA CAN'T

Most fans of business television are familiar with *Squawk Box*, a daily morning show on CNBC that runs prior to the New York Stock Exchange's opening bell. The hosts talk fast and a bit too loudly, I suppose to mimic the energy of a trading floor. It's not a bad program, if you're into that kind of stuff. Back in 2007, I'd just released a research report at CIBC World Markets predicting that nearly all of the future growth in world oil consumption would occur outside the United

States and other OECD markets. A CNBC producer called wondering if I would talk about the report on his show. I was happy to oblige since I would already be in New York speaking to clients.

The producers set me up in a camera-crammed studio above the floor of the exchange. Right out of the gate, I could tell that the interviewer had already written off the report. Did I really believe, he asked, that starving peasants in China would be filling up their gas tanks while motorists in Manhattan wouldn't be able to afford to drive? I tried to manage the tone of my response, attempting to counter his sarcasm with what I hoped was a more thoughtful note (though a matching touch of derision may have snuck into my answer). The upshot was, yes, absolutely, the numbers show that's exactly what will happen, I said. I couldn't help but point out, moreover, that not everyone in China was starving, and certainly not the folks whom I expected to be buying cars. But the interviewer, and probably most of the audience, wasn't buying what I had to say.

Persuading North Americans that their oil-guzzling days are over while people with a fraction of their average national income will be filling up at the pumps was a hard sell back then. And despite recent demand numbers that tell the same story, it still is. But to close your eyes and hope the world stays the same is really just sticking your head in the sand. Change in world oil consumption isn't coming—it's already here.

Growth in oil demand is heavily skewed toward emerging-market economies and away from advanced industrialized countries. Consumption in China and India is increasing at roughly 10 percent a year. In 2010, China added almost a million barrels to its daily oil intake. And it doesn't seem to matter what's going on in the rest of the global economy; those countries are only getting thirstier for oil. During the last recession, for instance, nearly all of the demand destruction that occurred for oil happened in OECD countries, such as the United States and Europe. Just prior to the recession, in the winter of 2007, OECD oil demand reached 50 million barrels a day. At the bottom of the recession in the spring of 2009, that consumption had fallen to 45 million barrels. On a peak-to-trough basis, the OECD shed 5 million barrels a day in oil demand. In contrast, oil consumption in China and other emerging-market economies barely dipped over the same period. Since the economic recovery took hold, oil-demand growth in China has resumed at its prerecessionary pace of around 10 percent a year. OECD countries, meanwhile, continue to see consumption flatline or even decline.

The numbers show that oil demand in emerging markets is far less sensitive to triple-digit oil prices than demand in more traditional oil markets. When energy analysts, who are still in a US-centric mindset, attempt to explain why higher prices aren't affecting demand the way their theoretical models suggest they should, the first reason they reach for is state subsidies. In the big picture of global oil demand, however, that's a pat answer that falls well short of capturing what's actually going on. In India, for example, the state's total annual subsidies for gasoline and diesel amount to less than $10 billion a year. That's not much more than American taxpayers used to shell out to fund corn-based ethanol production. Indeed, when it comes to subsidies, the definition is very much in the eye of the beholder.

In some countries, determining the shape of a fuel subsidy is straightforward: governments step in and regulate prices at the refinery, a classic form of subsidy that directly cuts fuel costs for citizens. In the United States, refineries are free to sell their products at market prices, but that doesn't mean subsidies don't exist elsewhere in the system. The United States has some of the lowest fuel taxes in the world. While most Americans wouldn't consider low fuel taxes a hidden subsidy, low taxes mean cheaper fuel, which lets drivers burn more gasoline and diesel; the effect on consumption is the same. You don't have to look any further than our bike-riding Danish friends in the last chapter for evidence of the relationship between taxes and consumption. High fuel taxes mean Europeans have been paying the equivalent of triple-digit prices for years. And their declining fuel consumption bears witness to how tax-driven pump prices can change transportation habits.

The biggest reason that fuel consumption in places such as China and India is so resilient in the face of triple-digit oil prices has little to do with subsidies and much more to do with what's driving demand. Oil consumption in emerging-market economies is much more sensitive to income growth than to pump prices. Many auto purchasers are first-time drivers who have only recently made the jump from living off the land to earning a regular paycheck in a city like Beijing or Mumbai. Turn off the road from any of those new superhighways in China and you don't have to travel far before the familiar trappings of the developed world fall away. Instead of seeing an Audi whiz by on a paved road, you're more likely to pass an oxcart on a narrow dirt track leading to a village. That's the world from which China will recruit its future drivers. If you've never owned a car before, changes in the price of gasoline aren't going to determine how much fuel you will burn. If you can afford to trade in your bicycle for a new car, then it's a safe bet your income has just gone up by leaps and bounds.

In China and India, incomes are growing several times faster than in North America, western Europe or Japan. Static income growth in OECD countries means that higher gas prices have a meaningful impact on household budgets. Spending more money on fuel means there's less money to spend on everything else. When incomes are rising as quickly as they are in China and India, on a relative basis, everything is much more affordable. The faster your income grows, the cheaper cars become, and the more you have the wherewithal to fill up your tank at whatever the world oil price happens to be.

If incomes were still growing in OECD markets at the same pace they are in China and India, vehicles would be flying off car lots in those countries as well. But they're not, and they're not likely to anytime soon. Give North American households, which typically own several vehicles, the kind of income growth that's happening in emerging markets and the extra money would buy a yacht, not another car. In China and India, a brand-new car isn't replacing an older vehicle with too many miles on the odometer; it's taking the place of walking or riding a bicycle. For people who were living as peasants less than a generation ago, earning a regular wage is a transformative development in the way life is lived.

The use of oil-fired power generation also separates emerging economies from most developed nations. With the notable exception of post-Fukushima Japan, few OECD countries generate a significant amount of electricity using oil. In North America, coal, natural gas and hydroelectric do the heavy lifting for the electrical grid. In China and India, power generation can still consume a significant amount of oil. China's fleet of coal-fired power plants handles most of the country's electricity needs, but when coal supplies get interrupted, the country falls back on its network of diesel-fueled power stations to make up the shortfall. That's exactly what happened when floods hit Australia a few years ago, shutting down most of the country's coal exports to China.

Fundamental differences exist in oil consumption trends between the developing world and OECD countries. The OECD is becoming the junior market for oil, a situation that becomes more apparent with each passing year. Oil consumption in those countries peaked right around the time oil prices first hit $70 to $80 a barrel. In the United States, the quintessential car-loving nation, oil consumption has dropped more than 10 percent, about 2 million barrels a day, from its prerecession peak. The US economy is still the world's fuel hog, gobbling up around 19 million barrels a day, but consumption is clearly heading lower. After the next recession, the US economy's daily oil intake could drop as low as 15 million barrels a day. Over time, it will drop even more. Indeed, in a zero-sum world, such a decline is actually inevitable if economic growth in China and India is to continue. That's the picture I was trying to paint for CNBC's audience a few years ago. Today, that landscape is much easier to see.

OIL IS REDRAWING POLITICAL AND MILITARY ALLIANCES

A zero-sum relationship in global oil markets casts a long shadow over current international relations. Economic growth demands oil, which makes petroleum reserves a vital strategic asset for every country in the world. Access to oil, already a key driver behind political and military decision making, is also becoming essential to the new economic relationships currently being forged.

The *Shi Lang* (ex-*Varyag*) is the most visible symbol of China's efforts to develop a blue-water navy capable of navigating across the world's largest oceans. One day China may need to defend critical oil shipping lanes in the Middle East. When that happens, it wants the option of sending the *Shi Lang*, or another carrier, to safeguard its interests.

China's ties to Venezuela also bear watching. Ideologically speaking, shared socialist values make the pair natural trading partners. The relationship defines the changing face of world oil markets. China is emerging as the world's most important oil customer, while Venezuela's heavy oil reserves are the largest in the world. It's a logical fit that's now a growing concern for the United States.

The proposed pipeline to the Pacific coast represents a significant challenge to America's traditional sphere of influence in the western hemisphere. For nearly two hundred years, US foreign policy in South America has been guided by the Monroe Doctrine, which essentially means that America doesn't take kindly to foreign nations playing in its backyard. The United States boasts a long and often dubious track record of intervention, with a list of notable hits that include a CIA-sponsored coup in Guatemala in the 1950s, the attempted Bay of Pigs invasion in Cuba during the 1960s, the Iran-Contra affair in Nicaragua and the 1983 invasion of Grenada. If China starts siphoning off even more oil supply from Venezuela, history suggests the United States will try to take steps to maintain the status quo.

I'll save those scenarios for Tom Clancy to describe in his next thriller. What history shows us is that wars can be won or lost on the issue of oil supply. The Germans found that out in the Second World War when they lost access to oil and had to start manufacturing it out of coal. Without oil, the world's mightiest armies grind to a halt. Tanks don't run. Jet fighters don't scramble. And frigates stay in port instead of patrolling the high seas.

The world's militaries, which guzzle an astounding amount of oil, have good reason to be concerned about their reliance on fossil fuels. Few are more aware of fuel's cost than the Pentagon. The US military is the world's single largest industrial user of oil, burning around 350,000 barrels a day. If it were a country, the US Armed Forces would be the 38th-largest oil-consuming nation in the world, slotting in just below Sweden. That makes its operating budget especially sensitive to the price of oil. Every $10 increase in the price of a barrel costs the Pentagon about $1.3 billion. Washington would love to shave these operating costs as it grapples with its trillion-dollar budget deficit. Whether the Pentagon will be successful in decreasing its oil addiction is up in the air. The US Air Force, for instance, burns roughly 2.5 billion gallons of jet fuel a year. It knows it needs to safeguard itself against a disruption to foreign oil supplies and is attempting to wean its fighters and bombers off oil by switching to biofuels. Homegrown biofuels offer some certainty that future supply will be there when needed, but there's a catch: right now, the best available biofuel substitute costs about $35 a gallon, roughly ten times the price of conventional jet fuel.

As oil supplies become scarcer and fuel more expensive to burn, the impact on economies, markets and politics will be even more profound. In a world of triple-digit prices, economic and political power shifts from major oil-consuming countries to major oil-producing countries. That heightens the importance of net exporters such as Canada and Russia, but it's a scary prospect for the global stature of net importers such as the United States and Germany. For countries that depend even more heavily on imported energy, such as Japan, the likelihood of increased energy scarcity promises to put already vulnerable economies on an even shakier footing.

Conversely, nations with abundant energy resources become more powerful and affluent. Few countries are in better shape in this regard than Russia, which is using the clout of its massive oil and gas reserves to extend its influence across Europe. The security that comes from a steady stream of petrodollars also allows Venezuelan president Hugo Chávez to thumb his nose at the United States and stoke anti-American sentiment across Latin America.

The rise of sovereign wealth funds and state-owned oil companies can also be traced to the money that triple-digit oil prices have sent coursing into the global petro-economy. In the coming years, even more of the world's petroleum supply will be controlled by state-run actors. Companies such as Saudi Aramco, Rosneft, Indian Oil, Sinopec and PetroChina already rank among the heavyweights of the world oil industry.

As these companies get even bigger, more oil will be traded on a state-to-state basis, leaving fewer barrels for the open market. State-run companies in China and India already have long-term supply contracts with Saudi Aramco. Indeed, half of Saudi Arabia's crude exports now go to China, which has surpassed the United States as the kingdom's largest customer.

Over time, these types of state-to-state deals will spawn a new network of international relationships. Alliances between nation-states will increasingly revolve around the security of energy supply rather than shared political or economic values. We are already seeing that on today's world stage. The global balance of power is undergoing a seismic shift, and geopolitics are at the epicenter. Consider Germany's announcement that, in the wake of Japan's nuclear disaster, it would become nuclear free by 2022. That declaration brought a broad smile to the face of Russian leader Vladimir Putin. Whether or not most Germans realize it, their country just became a lot more dependent on Russian gas.

European natural gas production is rapidly depleting. It fell by about 6 percent between 2005 and 2010, and it's expected to decline at roughly the same rate for the next several decades. Russia, meanwhile, has massive stores of natural gas just waiting to be tapped. As European demand grows, Russia is ready to fill the void. Europe already imports about half of its natural gas supply, an amount that's expected to increase to more than two-thirds in the next few decades.

The opening of the Nord Stream, the world's longest subsea pipeline, is a flashpoint for concerns about Russia's growing influence in Europe. The Nord Stream, which began to flow in late 2011, runs for more than 1,200 kilometers under the Baltic Sea, connecting the Russian city of Vyborg, near the Finnish border, to Greifswald in northeastern Germany. Russia is already the source of about a third of German gas imports, a number that will only go up as nuclear plants come off line and the Nord Stream reaches full capacity. The more gas Russia sends to Germany and the rest of Europe, the more Russia can use its energy exports for political and economic leverage.

Ukraine knows full well how that story can play out, having had its gas supply from Russia cut off several times over the last decade. Roughly 80 percent of the natural gas that Russia sends to Europe gets there via Ukraine. In exchange for cut-rate prices on natural gas, Ukraine has long given Russia a sweet deal on shipping costs. But this relationship is hardly harmonious. When Russia periodically pushes to collect more money for its gas, Ukraine counters with a demand that Russia pay more for pipeline access. The situation last came to a head in 2009, when Russia turned off the gas supply just as Europe was facing a wave of freezing winter temperatures. The dispute was eventually settled with the help of loans from the International Monetary Fund and the World Bank. The larger disagreement, however, remains unresolved. Indeed, part of the motivation for building the Nord Stream is to circumvent Ukraine. The Baltic pipeline lessens Russia's dependence on the transit routes that run through eastern Europe and effectively increases its clout with wealthy European nations.

The United States is keenly aware of Russia's newfound importance to Germany, the largest economy in Europe. It hopes the emergence of shale gas plays in eastern Europe might mitigate Russia's growing influence. Poland, for example, is in negotiations with energy giants such as Exxon to develop its gas reserves. The same advances in directional drilling technology and fracking practices that have opened up shale reserves in Canada and the United States can be used to exploit Polish reserves, which are estimated to contain as much as 5.3 trillion cubic meters of gas. But just as shale drilling has inspired environmental opposition in North America, it's also stoking controversy in Europe. Poland has lobbied hard within the EU against the adoption of any European-wide rules that would ban fracking.

France is driving much of the opposition to shale gas. The stance isn't surprising, considering nuclear-powered France would love to step in to help Europe with its future power needs. The French government recently passed legislation banning both fracking and the production of shale gas. If France is successful in pressing its case in the rest of Europe, Paris-based Areva, one of the world's biggest nuclear energy companies, will be a prime beneficiary.

That economic self-interest drives government agendas isn't news. But as chess pieces are moved around the board, it's becoming ever more apparent that energy is dictating political, economic and military strategies.

HOW CURRENCY SHIFTS AFFECT OIL CONSUMPTION

When it comes to gaining a larger share of the world's oil diet, sometimes the checkbook can be mightier than the sword. In the competition for more oil barrels, China's central bank carries far more clout than the military threat posed by its nascent blue-water navy ever could.

If China wants to muscle away oil supply from the United States, an arms race is the last thing it needs to pursue. Oil, like most internationally traded commodities, is priced in US dollars. That means when the dollar falls against other currencies, it takes more greenbacks to buy every barrel of oil. That reality cuts two ways. For Americans, it means oil gets more expensive. If you live in a country with a currency that goes up against the greenback, then oil becomes cheaper. If the greenback were to plunge against the yuan, the decline would effectively transfer millions of barrels of oil consumption from the United States to China.

So what is the likelihood that the US dollar falls against other major currencies? With the euro sinking under the weight of the PIIGS, it's understandably hard to envision how the greenback might suffer a significant drop as well. After all, currency markets are also a zero-sum game. If one major currency is going down, another major currency must be going up. Right now, investors are bailing out of a PIIGS-riddled euro and piling into US dollars. But this situation is only temporary.

Once the PIIGS leave (or are expelled from) the EMU, the euro will rally against the US dollar. A currency backed by the strong northern European economies of Germany and France will quickly attract global capital flows. And when the reformulated euro goes up, the greenback will go down.

The US government, as we saw in chapter 2, is heavily dependent on the savings of other countries to pay its bills. China, of course, is at the top of this list. Oddly enough, few in Congress see it that way. The prevailing view is that the People's Bank of China has nowhere else to invest its massive foreign reserves but in US treasuries, arguably the safest and most liquid market in the world. That belief takes the urgency out of curbing America's borrowing habits. Why bother to cut spending or raise taxes if you know your banker has no choice but to continue to lend you more money?

Folks on Capitol Hill and Wall Street need to recognize that China's central bank isn't motivated by the same goals as other market participants. China isn't like a retail investor looking for a fund manager to deliver a few extra percentage points to juice a portfolio's return. China's state-owned foreign reserves don't go into US treasuries because they offer a better rate of return than other investment options. No, China pumps its billions into US treasuries because that's what it takes to hold down the value of the yuan against the US dollar. The amount of foreign reserves that need to be invested and the return they fetch is incidental to that task. To date, an undervalued yuan has supported China's economic growth by making its goods more affordable in the US market. But as we have already explored, that dynamic is changing with the economic awakening of 1.3 billion Chinese consumers.

If the People's Bank of China decides that holding down the yuan is still an economic priority, then so be it; China has the cash, and there is certainly no shortage of treasuries to buy. But what happens if China's central bank suddenly gets very different marching orders? Can a stagnant American economy continue to be a primary driver of China's economic growth? Triple-digit oil prices are already squeezing profits on merchandise that needs to make a long trip across the Pacific to get to customers. And when Chinese goods arrive, they're entering a market that isn't what it used to be. Debt-laden US buyers are still hungover from a decade-long spending binge. Consumers are pulling in their horns while there are some 5 million fewer jobs in the US economy than there were four years ago. Not exactly a promising combination for Chinese exporters.

If China saw fit to torpedo the greenback, it certainly wouldn't take much. One call from the politburo in Beijing to the People's Bank of China could trigger a long slide for the dollar. The ramifications of a weaker greenback would quickly ripple through to energy markets, allowing China to stand back and let its beefed-up purchasing power redistribute the world oil supply accordingly.

GROWTH IS ZERO SUM TOO

If I told you that one country quadrupled its oil consumption in the last decade while another was using fewer and fewer barrels, which do you think would be posting stronger economic growth? The first one, right? Welcome to the new world order. China's ability to consume a larger share of the world's oil supply translates into a bigger share of global economic growth. Looking ahead, the gap between the world's two economic heavyweights will only get wider.

In a zero-sum world, if Chinese oil consumption doubles over time, the number of barrels going to the United States could be chopped in half (or something close) since the energy pie is only so big. It's a simple notion that will soon become a stifling reality for the United States and other OECD countries.

If oil is the fuel that drives economic growth, and oil consumption is a zero-sum game, then so too is economic growth. Ultimately, that might be all the reason China needs to abandon its cheap yuan policy and turn its back on US treasuries. Instead of a cheap yuan facilitating export-led growth, China will let a rising yuan power domestic growth.

Only a decade ago, America was the engine of the global economy, a role that China has now assumed. With the notable exception of oil, China uses far more resources than the United States. Whether it's coal or copper, China now accounts for nearly half of global demand. That's why commodity markets these days are taking more cues from the People's Bank of China (and fewer from the Fed) than at any time in the past. A slowdown in China's economy, which until recently used to chug along at a 10 percent growth rate every year, is a lot more important to global commodity demand than whatever happens in a US economy that's hard-pressed to expand at a fraction of that pace.

Economic growth has always been competitive, but never to this point has it been zero sum. Triple-digit oil prices are an unmistakable sign that we're entering a very different world from the one we've known. In the past, an abundance of resources allowed for much more economic growth than is possible today. Even if China's economy expanded at twice the pace of the US economy, what really mattered was that both were getting bigger. Mutually occurring growth was feasible in the last decade because we were not yet in a zero-sum world.

Now, zero-sum conditions (or something closely resembling that state) are just around the corner. That means growth in certain regions of the global economy will dictate that other economies no longer grow—or, even worse, shrink.

Emerging economies such as China's and India's will still be affected by rising oil prices, but the effect will be much more muted than the impact of high prices on the mature economies of the OECD. Between them, China and India have 2.5 billion consumers just waiting to spend newly earned paychecks. Triple-digital fuel prices might cut China's annual economic growth to 5 percent from 10 percent, but the country's economy will still be expanding. This won't be the case for other countries. Whatever rate of economic expansion China and India are able to sustain will come at the expense of growth elsewhere in the world. If you live in an OECD country, chances are your economic growth is about to get squeezed.

WHERE WILL THAT LEAVE THE WORLD'S POOREST COUNTRIES?

Some people think a touch of comeuppance for the developed world wouldn't be such a bad thing. Organizations from the United Nations to Oxfam have long wanted to redress the imbalance between the world's haves and have-nots. Advocates for poor countries have called on richer nations to forgo economic growth in favor of greater global equity.

While a noble goal in principle, the promise of an economic slowdown is unlikely to win the hearts and minds of voters when polls open in the United States, Canada or the United Kingdom. Much to the contrary, deteriorating economic conditions in OECD nations will make wealthy countries even less eager to share resources with the rest of the world. At first blush, it may appear that under zero-sum conditions, an economic slowdown in OECD countries will free up vital resources for developing countries. A closer look, though, shows that not every emerging economy is created equal.

If karma had a vote, static growth in North America, western Europe and Japan would make more resources available for the poor countries of sub-Saharan Africa and south Asia. In practice, it's debatable how much oil, fertilizer or grain will be left for those countries after global giants such as China, India and Brazil take their share.

Unfortunately, a zero-sum world will be no more liberating for the world's poorest countries than economic conditions were in the last century. The closer Chinese and Indian households come to achieving first-world lifestyles, the higher their extra resource consumption will drive commodity prices, limiting the access to those resources for the rest of the developing world. As we will see later, those dynamics are already apparent in today's food prices. The cost of basic staples such as wheat, rice and corn is heading ever higher, increases that are creating shortages in places that need food the most.

In the developed world, the situation will be much less dire. We'll all still be fed and reasonably clothed. That said, we will feel the presence of the emerging economic giants keenly. More and more, foreign and economic policy will be tilted toward establishing stronger ties with new superpowers such as China and India. That's really what Canada's proposed Northern Gateway pipeline is all about. And that's just the tip of the iceberg. When stagnant growth becomes the norm across the OECD, the few economies that are still expanding will represent a lifeline that other countries will be desperate to catch. At the same time, triple-digit oil prices will make our economies feel ever more distant from those faraway centers of growth. As China and India march inexorably into the future, our own economies are about to take a hard turn back to the past.

Chapter 8

THE STATIC ECONOMY

AVIS RENT A CAR runs a depot out of the parking lot of my former office building in downtown Toronto. Unlike the acres of room that rental agencies have at airport locations, space is at a premium in the heart of a cramped city. A limited number of parking stalls forces Avis to perform a constant balancing act between cars ready to be rented out and the steady stream of vehicles being returned.

Over the years, I noticed a funny thing about the employees at Avis: many of them started to have gray hair. I doubt these pensioners figured they'd spend their golden years jockeying cars around an underground lot. Still, most of them seemed to have a pretty good time doing it, at least if the banter I caught on my way into work was anything to go by.

Whether it's as rental-car jockeys or Wal-Mart greeters, more and more seniors are staying in the workforce longer. And this trend, clear in the employment statistics, doesn't look as if it will change anytime soon. The number of seniors working past retirement age, according to the US Bureau of Labor Statistics, is forecast to increase 85 percent between 2006 and 2016.

The demographic challenge facing North America is well known. As baby boomers reach retirement age, government and corporate pension plans are straining to keep up with an unprecedented number of retirees. At the same time, increases in health care expenses and the cost of living mean retirement savings aren't going as far as they used to.

For many senior citizens, part-time work at places like Avis is the ticket to help close the gap between the money coming in and the cash going out. In the United States, a White House–appointed committee floated the notion of raising the retirement age from 65 to 68 as a way to help curb the federal deficit. The idea didn't gain political traction, but it does point toward the type of changes that are in store for North America's job market and its workforce.

In a static economy, it won't just be GDP growth that languishes; so will job creation. This is where the ramifications of a zero-growth economy really hit home. Unless you're an economist, the idea of GDP may just be an abstract number you see dutifully reported in the business pages. Jobs, on the other hand, are as real as it gets. When you don't have one, you don't need a statistician to tell you that you're unemployed.

In the United States, unemployment rates have nearly doubled in the last decade. Job creation has become a battle cry for politicians across the country. Everyone seems to have a plan to get more Americans back to work. Former Massachusetts governor and Republican presidential candidate Mitt Romney says fostering job creation through economic growth is his top priority. He has a 59-point plan to get America working again and, if elected, intends to submit a jobs package to Congress on Inauguration Day. President Barack Obama failed to get his American Jobs Act through Congress in the fall of 2011. Since then he has barnstormed the country trying to sell its merits ahead of the November 2012 election. Even former president Bill Clinton recently chipped in with his two cents in *Back to Work*, essentially a book-length policy memo advising Democrats on how to spur the economy and create more jobs.

Beneath the slogans and campaign rhetoric, plans to put America to work share a common denominator: the idea of growth. Get the economy growing again and jobs will follow. But those plans don't account for a new world of higher energy costs that will prevent the economy from growing at the pace achieved in the last decade, when it pumped out a steady stream of new jobs every month. Time will show that those were the good old days. What do you do about job creation now that the economy's potential growth rate has downshifted into a much lower gear?

Huge budget deficits aren't the answer, and neither is printing money. Rather than boost payrolls, those measures just increase the national debt and stoke inflation. At the same time, few voters are willing to back a government that stands by passively while more and more people find themselves out of work.

Regardless of political stripe, everyone understands that a sustained period of rising joblessness can cause a country to crumble. Tax revenues go down, public services are cut, infrastructure falls apart, crime rates increase and so does homelessness. It's a downward spiral. If we're to manage the slowdown in growth and avoid its worst consequences, the notion of what constitutes full employment needs to be recalibrated to account for the new economic reality. Just as oil trading at $20 a barrel is a thing of the past, so too are jobless rates in the low single digits.

Although jobs may become scarcer, at the same time we may also see fewer people looking for work.

CLOSING BORDERS

History suggests that rising unemployment in any country results in tighter border restrictions. A crackdown on immigration goes hand in hand with slower economic growth. All too often, such policies are shaded by xenophobia and even outright racism. In economic terms, though, the equation is straightforward: when the pie isn't growing, cutting fewer slices means everyone at the table gets a larger portion.

Since the recession of 2008–9, immigration quotas have shrunk in many of the world's richer nations. The lingering fallout from the economic slowdown for national jobless rates is making new immigrants less needed and, of course, less welcome. Whether they are fording the Rio Grande into the United States or crossing the Mediterranean into Europe, migrants will find it more difficult to gain access to places such as North America and western Europe. Countries in the OECD are slowing the flow of legal migrants by lowering immigration quotas. Meanwhile, other steps, such as the physical walls erected along the US border with Mexico, are attempting to curb illegal migration. In Arizona, police now have the authority to ask anyone they suspect of being an illegal immigrant for identity papers. The controversial legislation has echoes of France's recent deportation of groups of Roma (gypsies) to eastern Europe.

In Europe, borders are suddenly reappearing where they haven't been seen in nearly two decades. One of the consequences of the Arab Spring is a new wave of migration out of North Africa. In the past, Spain and Italy struck deals with Arab dictators such as Moammar Gadhafi to prevent migrants from crossing the Mediterranean and illegally entering continental Europe. But when those strongmen fell, so did the tacit agreements. Tens of thousands of people have reportedly fled North Africa for greener European pastures.

The exodus has spurred France and Italy to resurrect old borders and to staff crossings with passport-inspecting gendarmes. Such measures violate the Schengen agreement, which eliminates many border controls and allows EU-member countries to act as a single state when it comes to international travel. Other countries are following suit. Denmark, for example, recently reintroduced customs agents and gave them the power to stop and inspect vehicles coming into the country from Germany and Sweden. In Holland, the Dutch government plans to install a network of video cameras at major border crossings with Belgium and Germany.

As the formerly borderless contours of the EU are reshaped along old lines, how much longer will EU-member states support unrestricted worker mobility when countries are struggling to employ their own domestic labor force?

I saw the benefits of EU labor mobility firsthand when I had an opportunity to speak at an energy conference in Cork, Ireland, in 2006. At that time, the Irish economy was red-hot, an oddity that flipped the country's typical migration pattern on its head. Ever since the great potato famine some 150 years ago, migration has more or less been a one-way flow off the island, but in the middle of the last decade, people were actually moving to Ireland for jobs. I was staying at an upscale hotel where pretty much the whole staff seemed to be Polish. A few years later, Ireland's real estate market and its banking sector went bust, taking its economy along for the ride. I haven't been back to Ireland since, but I have a strong hunch that Cork's hotels are now staffed by more Irish workers and far fewer Poles.

In a zero-growth economy, the need to recruit labor from abroad evaporates. Instead, we're more likely to divvy up available jobs among people already at home.

WORK SHARING AND A GRAYING LABOR FORCE

A slowdown in growth can certainly bring out the ugly side of human behavior when it comes to immigration policy. On a much brighter note, lower rates of job creation also have the potential to foster a stronger sense of community as industries move toward employment models that promote job sharing.

In Germany, a job-sharing program known as Kurzarbeit helped the country weather the latest recession with resounding success. The thinking behind Kurzarbeit is that holding down part of a job is better than having no job at all. Instead of, for instance, three people working full time and one person being unemployed, under Kurzarbeit four people divide the work of three jobs and split the paychecks. The government then tops up the wages of all four workers. The program isn't perfect, but it is credited with saving more than half a million jobs during the last recession.

The program has helped put Germany on a much better footing compared with other countries. More people going to work every day allows Germany to keep tax money coming in, while reducing the number of unemployed workers who depend on the state. It also allowed German companies to retain skilled workers during the economic downturn. All told, Kurzarbeit has worked largely as hoped. Not only did job sharing keep unemployment in check during the recession, but maintaining continuity in the workforce has helped the jobless rate fall quickly during the recovery. Among OECD countries, Germany is the only nation that can boast a lower jobless rate today than in 2008.

Of course, Kurzarbeit does come with one very large caveat: state subsidies. In 2011, Germany budgeted 5.1 billion euros for the program to help cover the lost income of nearly 1.5 million workers. Germany's economic success in the years preceding the recession gave the country the ability to support such a program. Not every country that could benefit from a Kurzarbeit-style program would have the same financial wherewithal. Indeed, for job sharing to be viable under static economic conditions, the program would have to be tweaked to become less reliant on subsidies. Still, the principles that guide Kurzarbeit are robust and not necessarily contingent on government support.

Originally designed as a temporary measure, Kurzarbeit is becoming a more permanent feature of the German labor market. Ángel Gurría, the OECD's secretary-general, suggested that the widespread adoption of similar programs in other countries would have blunted the impact of unemployment on as many as 25 million workers in the OECD community since the last recession. Instead, jobless rates throughout most OECD countries remain persistently high. For Kurzarbeit to work elsewhere, the program would need to be tailored to suit the specifics of different labor markets. In general, though, it's easy to envision job sharing becoming a standard practice that helps countries around the world deal with the fallout of a static economy.

As an economist, I'm continually intrigued by people's instinctive capacity to adapt to changing economic circumstances. When the exchange rate between the Canadian and US dollars swings one way or the other, shoppers on both sides of the border quickly head to whichever spot holds the most value for their hard-earned dollars. When fruit is in season, grocery stores lower prices and customers fill up their baskets. Homeowners who may not even consider themselves financially savvy lock in mortgage rates in anticipation of a central bank rate hike. Over many years of watching the economy, I've come to appreciate that people respond to all manner of economic signals. In a zero-growth economy, changes in the demand for labor will no doubt induce a range of responses from the workforce.

Tomorrow's labor market will navigate more than a few twists and turns as it adapts to slower growth. Our workforce, for one, will get older. When the job market weakens, youth unemployment is quick to go up. Entry-level jobs held by young people are often less stable, meaning that when the economy dips, they're among the first to disappear. Fortunately, young people typically have fewer commitments and more flexibility than their older counterparts. An option currently being taken up by more young people is staying at home. Rather than venturing into the cold world of landlords, empty fridges and utility bills, the so-called boomerang generation is choosing to stay with Mom and Dad until well past their teen years. This trend points to a big potential increase in postsecondary-school enrollment. If young people don't need to hold down jobs to pay bills, they still need to be doing something with their time; heading to college is something many parents are eager to support. Delayed entry into the workforce is one response to the diminished job prospects that come with slower economic growth. If twenty-somethings can't find jobs, school becomes an attractive alternative. For a country as a whole, more schooling will not only keep youth unemployment from heading higher, but over time it will also result in a better-educated labor force.

As one tail of the labor force is about to get shorter, the other tail is about to get longer. At the same time as fewer young people are entering the workforce, more older workers will be staying in it. Just like the car jockeys at Avis, tomorrow's labor force will see more people working well past what we now consider retirement age. The underfunded state of many private- and public-sector pension plans may leave many people with little choice but to keep working.

As the number of retired workers continues to increase, pension benefits are becoming more dependent on the investment returns earned by pension fund managers. The future of many pension plans is already threatened by huge looming actuarial liabilities. What that term means is that pension plans expect to pay out more in the coming years than they expect to bring in. When the economy was growing and the stock market was booming, pension funds were able to mitigate the potential shortfall brought about by an aging workforce by making savvy investments. In a static economy, though, the opportunities to notch stellar investment gains shrink considerably. Even public-service pension plans, typically the Cadillacs of the pension world, will be affected, as has already happened in bankrupt countries such as Greece.

A squeeze on pension income will provide all sorts of incentives for retirees to find part-time jobs. This trend may cause society at large to reassess how we think about retirement. In North America, economists consider the working population as those between the ages of 15 and 65. But that definition hasn't changed for decades, despite increases in life expectancy. People are living longer and are healthier than ever before. Most pensioners these days are capable of participating in the labor force well beyond their formal age of retirement. So don't be surprised if you see a lot more gray hair in tomorrow's labor force. You can also expect that some of the part-time positions held down by seniors will be created through Kurzarbeit-style job-sharing plans. That might just be the right prescription for retirees looking to top up shrinking pension checks while managing rising health care costs at the same time.

MORE MANUFACTURING JOBS IN A LOCAL ECONOMY

In tomorrow's static economy, job sharing may well become commonplace, but the jobs being shared may not be the type you expect. High oil prices won't just usher in slower economic growth, they will also increase the importance of local economies. In my first book, *Why Your World Is About to Get a Whole Lot Smaller*, I detailed how soaring fuel prices will change the dynamics of international trade by dramatically increasing transoceanic transport costs. In a world of triple-digit oil prices, distance costs money, pure and simple.

Connecting cheap labor in Asia with rich consumers in North America makes all kinds of economic sense when oil is $20 a barrel. But when oil prices escalate, it's less profitable to ship most goods across the Pacific. Changes in transport costs are radically rerouting global supply chains, bringing many of them much closer to home. Hauling iron ore from Brazil to feed Chinese steel factories and then shipping the finished product back across the Pacific to North America isn't economically viable when oil prices are trading in the triple-digit range. Instead, we could see iron ore from Labrador loaded on trains and shipped to factories in Rust Belt cities such as Pittsburgh, Cleveland or Hamilton, Ontario. Old steelworks may reopen to supply nearby construction companies with finished steel. Likewise, as I also pointed out in my last book, sending billions of dollars' worth of refrigerated food across an ocean makes little economic sense. Rather than importing clementines from China or strawberries from Spain, high oil prices will encourage us to buy fruit from local orchards.

More and more, we're hearing stories about multinational firms moving production back to North America from China. One example is Global Sticks, a Canadian company that's among the world's largest manufacturers of sticks used for ice cream treats and Popsicles. Global Sticks recently moved its manufacturing plant from China to Thunder Bay, Ontario. When oil was $20 a barrel, it made sense for Global Sticks to manufacture its products using low-cost Chinese labor and then ship them back to North America. Now, the cost of moving billions of wooden sticks across the Pacific to your neighborhood ice cream shop trumps the amount saved in low Chinese wages. The mass production of Popsicle sticks is precisely the type of low-margin manufacturing that used to be tailor-made for China. Once those businesses moved offshore, North American business leaders and politicians thought it was a given that they were gone for good. But that assumption didn't account for a fivefold increase in the price of fuel.

Rising shipping costs act like a built-in tariff by adding to the price of imported goods. The farther away you get from the end market, the higher the tariff. And distance isn't the only trade barrier now facing Chinese exporters. Climbing unemployment in North America and Europe is making those markets less receptive to goods made by foreign workers who toil for much lower wages in a faraway land.

Trade protectionism is on the rise around the world, meaning manufacturing is getting less mobile and more insular. Consider President Barack Obama's liberal use of nontariff barriers such as the Buy American provisions now in place for federal procurement. Obama's job creation plan requires materials used in federally funded infrastructure projects to be sourced in the United States. That's not only a big blow to Canadian exporters that would love to get a slice of Washington's stimulus spending, it's also a potential breach of the North American Free Trade Agreement.

As I mentioned earlier, by flooding the system with cash, the Federal Reserve's quantitative easing program is also working to devalue the US dollar. A cheaper dollar is both good for US manufacturing, making goods cheaper at home and abroad, and punitive to foreign producers trying to crack the US market. In a job-hungry world, even free-market–loving America is becoming more protectionist.

Globalization's so-called race to the bottom to capitalize on the lowest wage rate anywhere in the world is about to hit some big roadblocks in the static economy just ahead.

The contours of our economy are already changing, at least in North America. The lost manufacturing jobs of yesteryear are coming home. Over the next decade, manufacturing will account for a larger share of employment and a larger percentage of GDP. That shift is already apparent in the strength of the recovery in US manufacturing since the recession. According to a closely watched survey from the Institute of Supply Management (ISM), nearly 70 percent of manufacturing companies expect revenues to continue to increase in 2012. The ISM's semiannual report from December 2011 shows the US manufacturing sector has grown for 28 consecutive months and counting. Those looking for factory jobs in the United States should keep tabs on the exchange rate between the dollar and the yuan. If China skips a few Treasury auctions, the greenback is primed to slide by 20 to 40 percent. That kind of sharp decline would cause North America's hollowed-out manufacturing sector to fill back up in a hurry.

Globalization ushered in a massive redistribution of income among countries. A huge pool of cheap labor brought companies, ranging from auto plants to call centers, to places such as China and India. The shift was a boon for those countries and the bottom line of multinational corporations, but someone always gets the short end of the stick. In this case, it was North American workers. Not only did they lose their jobs, but their bargaining power also took a hit each time another overseas factory opened.

The competition for jobs in a globalized world put governments in a tough spot. If a multinational company found that setting up shop in, say, South Korea was too expensive, it could always try Vietnam, India, Mexico or any other country willing to cut it a better deal. One country could always be played off against another. Attempts to better regulate companies or increase corporate taxes are easily thwarted when there's a looming threat of production being moved to a friendlier jurisdiction. When capital is mobile and labor is not, the playing field tilts toward footloose multinational firms at the expense of local wage earners.

But the reverse is also true. The less mobility exists in the system, the more bargaining power shifts back to the local economy. That's why labor unions push for trade barriers while corporations clamor for free trade. When products are protected, so are domestic factory workers.

For North American workers, trade protectionism doesn't have to come in the form of a tariff. High oil prices will make it more expensive to get to work every day, but they'll also bring offshore jobs back home. In a world where distance costs money, unemployed factory workers will see a return of long-lost jobs, and governments will regain the ability to increase corporate taxes. Just as cheap oil tipped the scales in favor of mobility, triple-digit oil prices will shift the balance of power back toward local labor and government.

WHITHER THE HEDGE FUND MANAGER AND INVESTMENT BANKER?

In a zero-sum world, as we saw in the last chapter, if something is growing, then something else must shrink. If you're looking for the most likely candidate to counterbalance a rejuvenated manufacturing sector, a contraction in the number of financial services jobs is a good bet. No part of the economy has grown as mightily as financial services in recent decades. Figuring out why isn't hard. Even looking at my own career makes the reasons for the investment banking industry's rapid expansion abundantly clear.

I started in the industry more than twenty years ago as a young economist at Wood Gundy, a venerable blue-blood Canadian brokerage firm. Before that, I'd spent six years at Ontario's Ministry of Treasury and Economics, which is now the Department of Finance. Back then, the investment world was much different than it is now. Rather than working with the balance sheet of a giant bank or a publicly traded company, the money that most brokerage firms invested came from a firm's partners. That meant risk and reward were judged very differently than they are by today's investment bankers.

Making the wrong call on the market could cost you everything. It almost did for Wood Gundy. The firm had a long-established presence in London, England, dating back to the turn of the 20th century. At that time, Canada was growing, and its cities and provinces needed money for infrastructure. Wood Gundy made a lot of money for itself and investors by selling provincial and municipal bonds out of its London branch. When Margaret Thatcher's privatization push arrived in the 1980s, Wood Gundy's established connections in London helped it win the right to be the Canadian distributor of the last tranche of the government's shares in British Petroleum. By rights, the deal really should have been a home run for Wood Gundy, but when the stock market crashed in 1987, BP's shares sank along with it. The firm almost failed, which would have been a financial catastrophe for the partners. (A former executive once confided to me that only a last-minute cash infusion from one of Canada's wealthiest families kept the sheriff from padlocking the company's doors.)

In the 1980s, the same tide of deregulation championed by Thatcher in Britain and Ronald Reagan in the United States swept across other OECD countries, including Canada. Until then, the financial services industry had been divided into four separate pillars: banks, trust companies, brokerage firms and insurance. Cross-ownership was prohibited. When the restrictions preventing banks from owning brokerage houses were lifted, the major Canadian banks jumped at the chance to get into the lucrative business of investment banking.

In 1988, the Canadian Imperial Bank of Commerce (CIBC) scooped up Wood Gundy and used it to build an investment banking platform. Like many in the brokerage industry, the Wood Gundy executives were a sharp and hungry bunch. It didn't take long for a sort of reverse takeover to unfold at CIBC. The bank's senior executive positions were soon filled with former Wood Gundy staff, who imported the same aggressive deal-making culture that worked in the brokerage business to the bank as a whole.

Even more important than the change in corporate culture was the transformation in the way deals were funded. Instead of relying on a limited pool of partners' capital, former Wood Gundy bankers could now cut deals using the comparatively limitless funds provided by the bank's balance sheet. That meant bigger deals and larger profits. The razor-thin margins earned by traditional deposit-taking and commercial banking operations paled in comparison with the spectacular returns notched by the investment banking arm, encouraging CIBC to give more of its balance sheet to the rainmakers from Wood Gundy.

By the late 1990s, the deal flow at CIBC shifted into overdrive. Backed by the capital of a major Canadian bank, the scale of deals soon dwarfed anything ever dreamed of at Wood Gundy. CIBC World Markets became the newly minted investment banking arm of CIBC. And for a while all seemed right with the bank's world. CIBC World Markets was in the top tier of Enron's banking group, a lucrative spot to be in at the time. The investment bank was hitting home runs on Wall Street, leading initial public offerings for sexy new technology plays such as fiber-optic cable provider Global Crossing. Everybody was cashing in (including me, by that point the investment bank's chief economist).

In this new world of investment banking, the rewards for chasing big deals far outweighed the consequences when something went sour. When CIBC paid $2 billion to settle a lawsuit stemming from its intimate involvement with Enron, it wasn't the partners' capital that was at risk, as in the days of Wood Gundy. Instead, CIBC shareholders absorbed the losses. Similarly, when CIBC wrote off billions as a result of its investment bank's exposure to the US subprime mortgage market, it was once again the bank's shareholders who took it on the chin.

The transformation of modest brokerage houses such as Wood Gundy into bulked-up investment banks was a story that played out across North America's financial services sector. Unlike in Canada, Wall Street brokerage firms didn't even need to be bought by large commercial banks in order to enlarge their capital base. Instead, they tapped the public market, turning private partnerships into publicly traded companies with huge valuations. After all, why use your own money to finance deals when you can use someone else's?

If access to public money wasn't enough to supersize Wall Street deals, American regulators also contributed to the trend, easing the rules limiting the amount of money investment banks could borrow, allowing banks to pile up debt that dwarfed their equity. At the same time, the Clinton administration made a quiet but profound decision to leave the financial derivatives market largely unregulated. This followed the repeal of the Glass-Steagall Act, which had maintained walls between the pillars of the financial services industry in the United States since the 1930s. At the same time, former executives from Goldman Sachs, such as Robert Rubin and Hank Paulson, were now running the Treasury Department. Not surprisingly, Wall Street got nearly anything it wanted in those days. What else would you expect when regulators are recruited from the ranks of the regulated?

By the time Lehman Brothers and Bear Stearns blew up, their leverage had climbed to more than thirty times equity. At that level of debt, even small adverse market moves could send an investment bank into insolvency. After years of deregulation, no one should have been surprised. Give investment bankers all the financial incentive in the world to borrow money, strip away most of the rules and consequences, and the real question is how these brokerage houses stayed afloat as long as they did. Wall Street's only salvation was that it had become too big to fail.

As brokerage houses expanded, so did the financial industry's importance to the economy. Since the Second World War, the finance, insurance and real estate sector (FIRE) has doubled in size, rising from 10 percent of US GDP to 20 percent. Similar growth occurred in Canada and other OECD countries. More capital led to bigger deals, which helped drive the stock market ever higher. A soaring market also generated a tremendous demand for all types of wealth management professionals, from brokers to financial planners to accountants.

The boom in the financial services industry, like all things, can't last forever. Government-sponsored bailouts of unregulated capital markets could be the final straw that leads to voters demanding change. The policy pendulum is already swinging from the self-regulatory extremes prescribed by free-market ideologues such as Alan Greenspan back toward a system of increased oversight that will rein in the reach and power of the financial sector. In Europe, regulators are considering new rules that will restrict the leverage allowed in the banking system, as well as the imposition of a tax on financial market transactions.

In the United States, changing the current system will not be as easy. Wall Street is in a seemingly unassailable political position, with deep ties to the Obama administration as well as to influential members of Congress. But Wall Street has held similar sway in Washington before only to see changing economic circumstances curb its influence. In the Roaring Twenties, Wall Street dined out on largely unregulated markets. Fraud and corruption were systemic. That all changed when the Depression struck. An epidemic of bank failures compelled Washington to pass the Glass-Steagall Act that I mentioned above, to erect barriers between deposit-taking institutions and investment banks. Under the act's regulatory yoke, the United States enjoyed a remarkably stable financial system for the better part of five decades. That era ended with the push toward deregulation advocated by Reaganomics in the 1980s.

The lack of oversight that led to the subprime mortgage crisis offers ample evidence that regulatory reform is long overdue. The last round of bailouts has also stoked pent-up public demand for change. If another round of bank failures leads to more public bailouts, no amount of campaign funding from investment banks will save politicians from the wrath of taxpayers who are still waiting to see any meaningful regulatory reforms for the industry. If financial institutions are now too big to fail, the solution seems simple: make them smaller. Returning to the divisions sanctioned under Glass-Steagall is a step in that direction. Regulating the derivatives market and reining in the industry's use of leverage are two more measures that will help shrink the size of the institutions and the financial sector's economic footprint.

REDEFINING THE ROLE OF GOVERNMENT

Governments will be compelled to wield a larger regulatory stick over financial markets, but their imprint on the rest of the economy will become fainter in tomorrow's static economy. Any way you slice it, most governments currently have a large presence in their national economies. In North America, government spending accounts for roughly a fifth of GDP. Whether that's too big or too small to suit your ideological preferences, governments in Europe and North America are facing a diminishing capacity to spend money.

A static economy will necessitate changes in the services governments can provide to citizens. Government will become less about ideology and politics and more about what taxpayers can and can't afford. Without economic growth and the tax revenue that comes with it, governments will be forced to turn to the private sector. When that happens, private-sector outsourcing shouldn't be interpreted as a vote of confidence in the corporate ethos—far from it. Too many Wall Street scandals, and betrayals of trust by companies such as BP and TEPCO, have taken the bloom off the corporate rose. It's just that when you park ideology at the door and start designing budgets, the numbers show the private sector can deliver many services more cheaply than government. And when incomes are being squeezed by slower economic growth, cost resonates pretty loudly.

Cheaper, by the way, doesn't necessarily mean more efficient. The average private-sector worker doesn't churn out three widgets an hour while lazy public-sector employees only turn out two. The rate of widget production isn't the point; what matters is wages. Private-sector companies pay workers less to do the same jobs as government employees. That's what allows the private sector to provide services cheaper than government. And that holds true for everything from office workers to garbage collectors.

When dollars need to be slashed from the budget every year, saving on wages can be the difference between offering a service and going without. While most of us don't want to fire civil servants per se, many folks would wield the ax themselves if the alternative was losing the service altogether. Take my hometown of Toronto as an example. A hot-button issue in the last municipal election was whether city garbage collectors should retain their union-negotiated right to eighteen paid sick days a year. Needless to say, when garbage collectors get paid to be sick eighteen days a year, they will be sick for exactly eighteen days each year. For a city facing a budget crisis, paying for workers to stay home eighteen days a year is a luxury that is hard to justify. The new mayor of Toronto hails from the suburbs, where trash collection has already been contracted out to the private sector. He's vowing to do the same for the city. The writing looks to be on the wall for Toronto's garbage workers, who could soon be replaced by lower-paid, and no doubt healthier, private-sector employees.

The substitution of cheaper private-sector workers for less flexible and more expensive public-sector labor won't be limited to garbage collection. I noticed that the last time I renewed my car's annual registration and picked up a new license plate sticker. For my entire driving life, I've made a once-a-year trek to a government office run by Ontario's Ministry of Transportation. But that annual ritual is a thing of the past. The service is now delivered at kiosks in places such as Canadian Tire, a national retail chain. They'll even collect money for unpaid parking tickets on the city's behalf. Instead of a civil servant making $50,000 a year plus benefits, a store clerk earning minimum wage processes my fees.

The private sector won't just take over garbage collection and issuing license plate stickers. Crumbling infrastructure is already a familiar sight in many North American cities. Whether it's a bridge collapsing over the Mississippi River in Minneapolis or concrete chunks falling from overpasses in Montreal, the public infrastructure that we all use is getting older. Unfortunately, infrastructure is expensive, and these days governments only have so much money to go around. It's only a matter of time before decaying bridges and pothole-strewn roads are hived off to a private-sector consortium willing to return them to proper working order. Of course, once infrastructure is recapitalized, the public will need to pay to use it.

Toronto motorists who take Highway 407 already know that model firsthand. Skirting the city's northern edge, the privately owned expressway would never have been built with purely public money. The government has too many other priorities and not enough money in the kitty to go around. Instead, the toll road was privately financed and is run by a Spanish consortium that turns a steady profit for the effort.

The prospect of more toll roads is probably unsettling to those concerned about the consequences for low- and middle-income citizens. Such worries could ease if oil prices continue to march higher. If we stand back and let the market find its own equilibrium, then rising pump prices will ration demand for roadways. Something of a return to the days of Henry Ford's Model T could unfold. Back then, only the rich could afford to drive and everyone else found another mode of transportation. Does it make sense for everyone to pay for roads and bridges they won't be using? As the number of people on the roads shrinks, public officials will feel less pressure to spend scarce tax dollars maintaining highways. Instead of funneling money to public roads used by privately owned cars, governments may decide to invest in subways and other mass transit rail systems.

The effects of smaller government budgets won't just be felt on the roads. Other traditional government services will also take a hit. Torontonians got a preview of what's to come when the city's budget-slashing mayor took a run at public libraries. Canadian author Margaret

Atwood, a national icon, quickly joined the battle over library closures, galvanizing readers across the country to come to the defense of Toronto's libraries. Her support helped stem the tide, but you can be certain the library budget won't be safe for the rest of the mayor's time in office.

As much as I love books myself, faced with the alternative of cutting essential workers such as firefighters, police or ambulance drivers, I may have to accept that a publicly funded library system is an expensive bricks-and-mortar institution that could become a thing of the past. Perhaps more people will download books from the Internet rather than visiting a public space. We'll lose the benefits of a communal gathering place, but other venues can emerge to fill the void. We may also see changes to the funding model. In the early 20th century, Andrew Carnegie's foundation built thousands of libraries across North America to the great benefit of generations of readers. Perhaps some other wealthy philanthropists are waiting to do the same.

Universities already rely heavily on private fundraising. I was recently invited to a gala at the University of Toronto to kick off a campaign to raise $2 billion for the school. It's the largest fundraising effort in the history of Canadian universities, but it certainly won't be the last. At a time when Ontario's provincial government is struggling with a record budget deficit, scooping up outside cash to bolster public funding will soon no longer be a luxury, but a necessity.

In the United States, Harvard, the world's richest school, boasts an endowment fund of more than $32 billion. Such a bounty highlights the gap that can develop between haves and have-nots. I'm sure most state-run colleges would give their eyeteeth for a fraction of Harvard's Ivy League largesse, just as small Canadian schools would love to tap the University of Toronto's alumni lists. In a perfect world, funding for schools would be more equitable, but under zero-growth conditions, that won't happen.

In tomorrow's static economy, more libraries could be named after local tycoons who like the idea of having their name engraved on the front of a sandstone building. Trash collectors won't be getting eighteen paid sick days a year, and you'll more often deal with minimum wage clerks rather than civil servants. Contributions from rich alumni will help fund the colleges your kids attend. And those same kids, incidentally, are more likely to live at home much longer before eventually finding apartments and getting jobs.

For governments to maintain the same number of services when the economy is stagnant, or shrinking, as they offered when the economy was expanding, they're going to have to find cheaper ways to deliver those services. In many instances, the private sector will be the lowest-cost alternative. In a static economy, the more jobs a government can outsource, the more services it can provide.

THE NEW CONSUMER

In Canada and the United States, consumer spending currently accounts for about two-thirds of GDP. In tomorrow's economy, you can bet that shoppers will be curbing the spendthrift ways that retailers have come to know and love. Most customers will have less money to spend, but that's only the beginning. Changes to attitudes and lifestyle may soon affect spending more than a lack of income growth.

In an expanding economy, spending money becomes habitual. When an economy stops growing, a natural repercussion is that people spend less. Big begets big and small begets small. In other words, downsizing in one area has a cascading effect across the board.

Take house sizes, for example. The bigger the house, the more stuff you need to fill it up. Kitchen appliances, furniture, clothes—the list goes on. I lived in a semidetached house for nearly twenty years in Riverdale, a downtown Toronto neighborhood. The house was 2,000 square feet, not a bad size, but probably smaller than you would expect for the chief economist of a major Canadian investment bank. Our kids grew up there, they never wanted to move, and it was close to the city's financial district where I worked for two decades. A consequence of four people living in a relatively modest house is that you don't have a whole lot of space. Buying something new means chucking out something else to make room.

We saw in the last chapter how consumption of scarce resources such as oil will become a zero-sum exercise between competing countries. That's a macro example, but the zero-sum principle applies just as well to tinier areas—like my old clothes closet. Small houses come with small closets. Mine was jam-packed. If I bought a ski jacket, a new suit or even a pair of jeans, I needed to say goodbye to an older piece of clothing. In the fall, I put all my summer shirts away in a dresser to make enough room for my winter clothes. This is hardly a burden, but I don't think it's something that most folks in oversized suburban homes ever need to consider. If people had to throw something out each time they bought a new shirt, I guarantee that people would buy fewer clothes.

What holds true for clothes closets is equally true for the rest of the house. My 2,000-square-foot inner-city home had less furniture than a 5,000-square-foot suburban house. When you downsize your home, you also automatically cut other expenditures at the same time. Smaller homes come with smaller utility bills and lower property taxes. They cost less to insure, and most importantly, they cost less to buy, which shrinks monthly mortgage payments. Sometimes small begets small in an effortless way.

I grew up in a modest postwar suburban bungalow that was bulldozed after my parents sold it to make room for a house twice the size. In a smaller world, these giant suburban homes will become as obsolete as the SUVs parked in their driveways. The suburban landscape is defined by energy-sucking McMansions. Before long, these storehouses of consumer goods will be demolished to clear the way for smaller homes better suited to the finite dimensions of tomorrow's economy.

A smaller home will be a blessing when income growth starts to slow. The need to buy less stuff will free up much-needed cash to pay for energy and food. Since the last recession, energy expenditures have spiked and now account for as large a percentage of OECD household budgets as in past economic slowdowns. Higher energy costs are flowing directly into food prices through the cost of the diesel fuel that runs tractors, the fertilizer that feeds crops and the gasoline needed to transport food to grocery stores. As food and energy prices push inflation higher, they also squeeze out other consumer spending. That's a drastically different world than the one we've come to know.

In a globalized world, the proportion of the household budget that was spent on food steadily declined as high-cost food grown locally was replaced by cheaper imports from around the world. Three decades ago, North Americans spent a quarter of the household budget on food. Today, that figure is down to about 10 percent. But food inflation is now running much faster than that of other goods. Food's share of household expenditures is heading higher, leaving less money for everything else.

Faltering income growth is inconsistent with the world most Western consumers have come to know. But having less disposable income may not be as painful as you think. A growing body of research shows that consumer satisfaction hasn't kept pace with increasing consumer expenditures. Similarly, other studies in OECD countries show that our sense of individual well-being lags behind increases in personal income growth.

In the United States, for example, real income per capita has more than doubled since the Second World War. Despite increased wealth, however, studies find that Americans are no more satisfied than they were sixty-five years ago. In polls that gauge well-being, citizens in countries with less personal consumption, such as Denmark, consistently score higher than Americans. An international study on life satisfaction conducted by Gallup ranked the United States 19th, a disproportionately low standing in relation to its per capita income and consumption. A similar trend is evident in Canada. According to the University of Waterloo's Canadian Index of Wellbeing, increases in

GDP haven't resulted in commensurate gains in life satisfaction. Since 1994, the sense of well-being among Canadians has only improved at about a third of the rate of the country's economic growth.

Part of the explanation for the discrepancy may be found in what Thorstein Veblen, a 19th-century economist, termed conspicuous consumption. This type of spending is driven by a need to demonstrate social status. Instead of buying stuff you really want, you buy to keep up with the Joneses. Veblen theorized that conspicuous consumption sparked by the need to bolster status doesn't necessarily lead to increased personal satisfaction or enjoyment.

In the postwar era, conspicuous consumption has meant buying bigger houses, faster cars and more expensive suits. But what happens if society's values change along with the economic speed limit? If conservation and sustainability become the watchwords for a new generation of eco-conscious adults, maybe keeping up with the Joneses will mean building a rooftop garden or installing solar panels in your backyard.

A Rolex watch, to pick another example, has long been a token of wealth and status, but there's no reason that can't change. Judging by the protesters in the Occupy movement, a significant segment of our society has lost faith in the merits of unregulated capitalism. To them, a Rolex isn't a sign that the wearer is an investment banker worthy of respect. Instead, it signals that the person who owns it may be about to break another securities law or make millions engineering a Ponzi scheme that will bilk suckers out of their life savings. As always, virtue is in the eye of the beholder. If values change, wearing a diamond-encrusted watch may someday send the wrong message.

Consumer spending doesn't necessarily have to be conspicuous to be unsatisfying. As per capita income increased in the postwar era, it stoked expectations of ever-larger increases in future consumption. Consider your situation if you've never owned a car before. Even if your first vehicle is an underpowered subcompact, you're likely to be over the moon to have it. Every time you slip behind the wheel, you're grateful that you're not waiting at a bus stop in the driving rain. Instead of being jostled by strangers with questionable personal hygiene, it's just you and your car. You settle into your seat, turn on your favorite radio station and get yourself home after a long day at work. Now *that* is consumer satisfaction.

After four or five years, you may want to trade in your subcompact for something a little better. If your income keeps rising, chances are that every few years you'll keep trading up for something more powerful, sportier or more luxurious. But compared with the joy of owning your first subcompact, the marginal benefit from each subsequent trade gets smaller and smaller over time. Economists describe this condition as one of diminishing returns. This principle suggests you won't be much happier in a fancier car than you initially were in your subcompact. And what's true for vehicles also applies to a slew of other things that we buy every day but don't necessarily need.

My own twelve-year-old Audi helped me recognize a long time ago that buying something newer doesn't always mean getting something better. I love driving a car with a stick, and Audi stopped selling standards in Canada many years ago. If I traded in my car for an automatic version of itself, I know my level of consumer satisfaction would actually go down.

As we adapt to a world of static economic growth, less consumption could begin to look like a virtue. Could tomorrow's society embrace conservation the way yesterday's consumers grasped materialism? The end of growth doesn't mean the end of consumer society as we know it, but it could mean that we develop a new sensitivity to an increasingly finite world. Fewer material purchases will also reduce our energy needs—a critical consideration in the years to come.

A new generation of consumers is already forming in OECD countries. Younger people are eschewing their parents' materialism in favor of simpler lifestyles. If this intergenerational shift in values continues to gain traction, it couldn't be better suited to our changing economic environment.

We could all do a lot worse than make the best out of having less. If our incomes stop growing and jobs become scarcer, then at least our leisure time will grow. It won't be money that makes our world go around, but time. And we may learn to spend our time in ways that are more satisfying than simply looking for opportunities to spend money. Embracing leisure time could be a key part of adjusting to a world in which our economies are no longer expanding. Maybe the concept of diminishing returns will aid the transition away from consumerism. If more stuff doesn't make us any happier, then why not try less stuff for a while? I'm betting that most of us who live in OECD countries can learn to live with less and not feel poorer for it.

For others, the task could be far more challenging.

Chapter 9

ALL BETS ARE OFF

THE MOST FAMOUS WAGER in the history of economics involves a biologist, the price of tungsten, and three of the four Horsemen of the Apocalypse.

Stanford professor Paul Ehrlich planted the seeds of the bet in 1968 when he published *The Population Bomb*, a controversial book in which he argued that rampant population growth would cause civilization as we know it to collapse. The earth, Ehrlich wrote, can only produce so much food and support so many people. If the global population expands beyond this capacity, it will trigger any number of horrific consequences—the war, pestilence and famine promised by the Horsemen—until balance is restored.

As you might guess, *The Population Bomb* is not a cheery read, but it sold more than 2 million copies, and its ideas are woven into the fabric of the modern environmental movement. The 1960s and 1970s were a time of much soul-searching about the harm inflicted on the planet by human activity. Anxiety about the environment inspired, among other things, a new wave of thinking about sustainability. The Club of Rome, for instance, was founded in 1968 by an international group of scientists, academics, industrialists and politicians who shared a belief that people must take action to keep the world from heading off a cliff. In 1972, the club released a report called *The Limits of Growth*, which argued that pending resource scarcity would make it impossible for the global economy to grow at rates achieved in the postwar era. In the last forty years, the Club has distributed more than 12 million copies of the report, which also asserts that global society is likely to overshoot the planet's carrying capacity. Once that happens, the club contends, society won't be able to avoid a large-scale environmental collapse.

Prophets of doom have sounded similar alarms before. Some two hundred years ago, Reverend Thomas Malthus warned that population growth was an inexorable force that would exhaust the land's capacity to provide sustenance. He foresaw starvation and pestilence arising as an inevitable result of overpopulation, bringing about a dying off that would cull the number of people in the world. Along with epidemics that would increase the death rate, Malthus also believed that moral restraint was necessary to keep the birthrate in check. He advocated celibacy, particularly for the poorer segments of society who couldn't afford to raise children (critics have since taken Malthus to task for his own three kids).

Ehrlich is arguably the most famous contemporary apostle of a Malthusian worldview, foreseeing the mass starvation of hundreds of millions of people just around the corner as humanity loses the battle to feed itself. He and the Club of Rome weren't alone in issuing warnings; a series of similar doomsday predictions also appeared in the popular press. The survivalist current at the time even inspired a miniboom in North American farm prices, as people took to the country to prepare to live off the land.

But an economist at the University of Maryland, Julian Simon, wasn't buying what Ehrlich was selling. Just as human ingenuity has thwarted Malthus's predictions for the past two centuries, Simon believed that innovation would continue to solve the problems posed by population growth. Economics taught him that when faced with a scarcity of resources, people get better at gathering raw materials, become more efficient and find viable substitutes to use instead. In short, humanity doesn't roll over when confronted by adversity; it adapts. Simon even argued that population growth will help to solve issues that arise from resource scarcity. Necessity being the mother of invention, he believed that increasing the sheer volume of people on the planet would inspire more innovation and spur technological progress. More human beings means more brainpower is available to tackle any problem, much like adding RAM to a computer.

Simon and Ehrlich came from completely different academic disciplines, which clearly shaped their attitudes toward the issue of population growth. Simon completed his doctoral degree in economics at the University of Chicago in 1961. In his research, he was drawn to exploring the economic effects of population change. His free-market upbringing at the Chicago School clashed with Ehrlich's stance on demographics. Ehrlich, now head of Stanford's Center for Conservation Biology, did his graduate work in entomology at the University of Kansas, studying with renowned bee researcher Charles Michener. Along the way, Ehrlich's ecological interests dovetailed with demographics and the study of population.

Here's where the bet comes in. Simon believed that Ehrlich's environmental approach to the consequences of population growth failed to account for the way prices motivate human behavior. In 1980, he challenged Ehrlich to a wager, the outcome of which continues to resonate more than three decades later. Simon bet that a basket of five basic commodities (tin, tungsten, copper, nickel and chromium) would decline in value over the next decade as people adapted to changes in supply and demand. Ehrlich believed that with more people bidding for the same finite resources, prices would spike. Each professor put $200 on each commodity, and the loser had to pay up at the end of ten years.

Simon won. As he predicted, new methods of resource extraction emerged, processing techniques improved and alternative raw materials were adopted. Prices for nickel and chromium fell as better mining and smelting methods were developed. Tungsten and tin became cheaper as the world began to use substitutes such as ceramics and aluminum. Similarly, the demand for copper wiring fell, as global telecommunications firms discovered the magic of fiber-optic cable.

When resource consumption put humanity to the test, ingenuity triumphed.

Economics was vindicated, a fact that was widely publicized, much to the glee of free-market economists who since then are quick to trot out the results of the Simon–Ehrlich wager whenever anyone calls future resource abundance into question.

Losing the bet made for a rough few decades for the Ehrlich camp. Nevertheless, finding answers to the challenges that come with an expanding global population is not as clear-cut as the wager's results might suggest. Ehrlich may have been wrong about commodity prices—and way off the mark on mass starvation—but he was right about population growth. With roughly 4.5 billion inhabitants in 1980, the world added nearly a billion people over the next ten years, the largest increase for any decade up to that time. Yet, instead of hundreds of millions of poor people dying in the developing world, as Ehrlich forecast, measures of human welfare have improved. People are living longer and healthier lives, overall child mortality rates are down and average life expectancy is up.

At the same time, the rate at which the population is growing has continued to increase. We recently topped 7 billion, and more people are coming into the world every day. Simon was right about falling commodity prices in the 1980s, but that doesn't necessarily mean the consequences of rampant population growth can be dismissed. The noted evolutionary biologist E.O. Wilson, for one, has memorably described the pace of human population growth in the last century as more bacterial than primate. Not only is the human biomass greater than that of any other large animal that has ever existed, but we've also altered the biomass of other species to suit our needs, causing a proliferation of cattle, pigs, chicken and sheep—the animals we eat. Meanwhile, the ranks of animals that eat us—lions, tigers and grizzly bears—have dwindled.

Our impact on the world's plant life has been even more profound. We've cleared and cultivated nearly 40 percent of the earth's ice-free land for agricultural purposes. More than half of the planet's flora is now tied to human activity. Moreover, plant life everywhere has become more homogenous at the expense of ecological diversity as the same crops are planted around the world to conform to current dietary tastes.

And we're transforming more than just the biological world; we're reshaping the physical landscape as well. In coal mining regions, we've reduced mountains to nubs to exploit the underlying ore. In the Appalachians, for instance, the mining industry has destroyed hundreds of mountaintops over the last century. We've drained inland seas for our irrigation purposes. The Aral Sea in Uzbekistan was once the fourth-largest lake in the world, but so much water has been diverted toward cotton farming that it is now essentially a desert. In northern Alberta, Syncrude's tar sands mining operation moves 30 billion tons of earth every year, twice the amount of sediment that flows down all of the world's rivers annually.

Humanity's presence is also altering the biosphere's natural cycles. The best-known consequence of our interference is global warming, which is melting glaciers and raising sea levels. But we're also aggravating other processes, such as the nitrogen cycle. Our agricultural needs prompt us to remove nitrogen from the air and apply it to the land through artificial fertilizers. Nitrogen is a game changer for farming and has allowed for a massive increase in the size of the human biomass. Artificial fertilizers boost farm yields and the size of livestock, allowing us to consume ever-greater amounts of food. In particular, protein—essential for growth and relatively scarce in nature—is now much more abundant thanks to fertilization. The results aren't as good for the world's oceans, though. The fertilizer-rich runoff that drains from farmland into rivers, lakes and eventually the sea creates perfect conditions for algae to flourish. The resulting algal blooms choke off other marine life and create coastal dead zones, which are now common around the world.

Our impact on the physical environment is leading some geologists to refer to the modern era as a new geological epoch. The preceding eleven thousand years are known as the Holocene, which roughly translates into "most recent era." Now they say we have entered the Anthropocene, or "age of man."

Geological nomenclature is of little concern to most economists, who don't pay attention to how we change the landscape or whether the human population increases at the same pace as bacterial reproduction. What matters is what markets tell economists through price signals. And for a long time, falling resource prices—from oil to food to the items in Simon's commodities basket—signaled that population growth wasn't hindering resource consumption.

But at the start of the last decade, things started to change. Commodity prices began to rise. Not just a single commodity or even a group of related materials, but prices for almost everything rose in unison. As the calendar changed to a new millennium, the world woke up to find economic revolutions under way in China and India. Demand for commodities spiked, and the price for everything from wheat to copper to oil suddenly became supercharged.

The industrial revolutions in China and India are a testament to Simon's optimism about human ingenuity. In the last decade, the world has achieved breakthroughs in resource extraction and found ways to use raw materials more efficiently. But economic growth is also pressuring global resource consumption as never before. Essentially overnight, hundreds of millions of people moved from leading quiet lives in rural villages to urban lifestyles that can increase resource consumption by a factor of ten. The resulting explosion in commodity demand is a greater test of our ability to stretch the world's resources than mere increases in global population. In other words, the planet can probably handle 7 billion people, but not 7 billion people adopting the consuming patterns of a Western lifestyle.

Commodity prices are telling us that the rapid rates of economic growth achieved by countries such as China, India and Brazil are unsustainable. Too much demand chasing a finite supply of resources will continue to send commodity prices higher. We saw earlier how rising resource prices are already choking off economic growth in the world's fastest-growing economies. High prices stoke inflation and trigger interest rate hikes, which stifle the amount of money that's available to feed growth. When Simon and Ehrlich made their bet, conditions were considerably different.

An across-the-board increase in commodity prices over the last decade makes it worth revisiting the Simon–Ehrlich wager. Taking a longer view, we see that the bet's outcome changes depending on its start date. Commodity prices rose steadily through the 1970s. By the time the two men placed their bets, prices were ready to drop as economic signals spurred industry to increase supplies and find cheaper substitutes. If we recalibrate the bet to start in 1990, Ehrlich would have won in six of the decade's ten years. If the betting starts in 2000, Ehrlich also reaps a resounding victory.

Market prices are telling economists something very different today than in 1980, when Simon and Ehrlich locked horns. Human ingenuity will still make breakthroughs, but rising commodity prices point to a world in which technological innovations can no longer keep pace with the rate at which our economies are consuming key resources.

REBEL, MIGRATE OR DIE

History shows that hungry people have three choices: rebel, migrate or die.

These options are even more alarming considering how much of the world's population is getting hungrier. Population in developing countries is swelling, which means the world needs to produce more food every day. At the same time as populations in developing countries are increasing, OECD countries are starting to close their borders. Opportunities for people to move to wealthy nations that can better support a larger population are becoming scarcer. Even places with immigration policies that still encourage new arrivals, such as Brazil, will become less welcoming as economies cool. If migration is less viable, hungry people are put into the dismal corner represented by options one and three.

When you combine a static economy with rapid population growth, it's not hard to figure out what happens to per capita income: it shrinks in a hurry. More people dividing the same amount of money equals less cash to go around. For the 1.5 billion people who subsist on less than $1.25 a day, how much can per capita income fall before the death tolls and rebellion predicted by Ehrlich come to pass?

In the last forty years, the world has gone in the other direction, making large gains in life expectancy while reducing infant mortality rates. In the 1950s, global life expectancy was 48 years, a figure that's now at 68. At the same time, the infant mortality rate has fallen from 130 for every thousand births to fewer than 50 per thousand. More people living past infancy coupled with longer life spans are key reasons that the global population has nearly doubled in the last four decades.

But such impressive improvements were achieved when economies were growing rapidly. What happens if growth falters? How will the world's poorest people fare? Population increases in the last few decades are bringing the planet's carrying capacity back into question. If we want to ensure that Ehrlich's apocalyptic predictions don't come true, we need to recognize that per capita resource consumption can't keep increasing indefinitely.

How much will living standards in parts of the developing world be squeezed by the hundreds of millions of people in Asia who are moving toward OECD levels of resource consumption? A burgeoning middle class in China and India has the purchasing power to buy everything from oil and coal to wheat and rice. In a zero-sum world, people who lack economic clout will be priced out of the market. Will that mean they don't get to eat? Will the ascendance of China and India into the upper echelons of the global economy be achieved at the expense of other developing nations? It's a story that should sound familiar in Britain and the United States, both of which built empires on the backs of other countries' people and resources.

China, of course, would like to cultivate a different perception. Chinese leaders are quick to remind others just how much its economic growth benefits the rest of the world. If China falls on tough times, countries that depend on it for their own economic well-being would certainly suffer. But it's worth wondering how much conflict and social unrest is created in other places, such as the Middle East and Africa, by the enormous appetite for resources in China and India.

Does China's success come at the expense of other countries whose economies aren't growing fast enough to keep pace with rising food and energy prices? The impulse behind the Arab Spring was a lack of food, a problem that hasn't gone away. In countries such as Somalia and Sudan, to name just two, far too many people go hungry every day. When civil unrest can be traced back to hunger, it casts economic growth in a much harsher light.

It takes seven pounds of grain to raise a pound of beef. That ratio tells you that the more cheeseburgers are eaten in sprawling urban centers in China and India, the fewer rice bowls are filled in the countryside. New city-dwellers with steady paychecks can afford higher-protein diets. Grain that would normally feed poorer people in rural areas is thus being used instead to fatten up livestock. In traditional Chinese cooking, a little bit of meat goes a long way: chop up a scrap of pork, mix it with vegetables and rice, and it can feed a whole family. However, the numbers show that more folks in China are trading in their stir-fries for cheeseburgers. In recent decades, global meat consumption has grown at twice the pace of population growth.

And it's not just cheeseburgers. When China and India burn more oil and coal, that translates into fewer resources and higher power costs for other developing countries. Consider, for example, Pakistan, which lives in the shadow of India's economic success. It's experiencing the worst electricity crisis in its history. In the summer of 2011, half of Pakistan's power-generating capacity was off line because utilities couldn't pay for fuel. Cities in Pakistan are routinely subjected to electricity outages that last upward of fourteen hours. In rural areas, the power rationing is even more extreme, and blackouts can last even longer.

Energy shortages have not only turned off the power for millions of Pakistanis, they've also shackled the country's economic growth. Pakistan's income per capita is increasing at its slowest rate since 1951 and now sits at a quarter of the pace enjoyed by neighboring India. Faced with mounting power outages, multinational firms are pulling out of the country and the economy is collapsing. And social and fiscal conditions will only get worse as Pakistan's population continues to grow.

People in Karachi may be able to live without air-conditioning and even cars, but they can't go without food. For the developing world, food shortages are the biggest challenge arising from growing populations. Projections for population growth see most of it occurring in countries such as Pakistan, Bangladesh, Uganda, Ethiopia and the Democratic Republic of the Congo. The UN predicts the global population will increase by 3 billion people this century, most of whom will be born in the developing world. Higher food and energy prices can mean the difference between life and death in many of these places. It's potentially devastating that the most explosive population gains will be concentrated in the countries that can least afford it.

FOOD PRICES ARE THE GATEKEEPER OF POPULATION GROWTH

When Malthus made his predictions two hundred years ago, he couldn't foresee how unlocking the power of hydrocarbons, first in coal and later in oil and natural gas, would boost the land's carrying capacity.

Energy abundance not only powered the Industrial Revolution and the economic growth achieved since then, but it has also allowed for huge increases in food production and, by extension, population.

Energy has never been in higher demand than it is in today's world of commercial farming. The quantum leaps made in agricultural productivity in the postwar era were achieved by channeling greater amounts of energy into food production. Farming is now extremely energy intensive, whether the power is diesel for tractors, fertilizer for crops or electricity to run irrigation systems.

The more hydrocarbons we burn, the more carbohydrates we can grow. But there are other consequences to that equation: higher energy prices flow directly into higher food prices. In fact, world food prices are rising even faster than energy costs. The UN's food price tracking index reached a new record in January 2011, eclipsing the previous high set in 2008. Back then, soaring food prices sparked riots in the developing world. Turn the clock forward to 2011, and it should come as no surprise that countries in the Middle East and North Africa were again convulsing with social and political unrest.

Rising food prices have different consequences depending on where you live. For people in OECD countries who spend no more than a tenth of their income on food, more expensive grocery bills are an annoyance. But for the planet's poorest 2 billion people, higher food prices are the difference between eating two meals a day and trying to survive on one.

Poor harvests in key grain-exporting countries such as Russia, Canada, Ukraine and Australia are pushing wheat prices toward the historic highs set during the food crisis of 2008. A drought in Russia in the summer of 2010 caused the country to cut wheat exports entirely. The ban remained in place for nearly a year, until yields improved and wheat supply once again exceeded the demands of the domestic market. Prior to the ban, Russia, the world's third-largest producer of wheat, barley and rye, exported a quarter of its 97-million-ton grain harvest every year.

For countries that rely on food imports, dwindling exports from major suppliers can have sweeping implications. Dictators throughout the Arab world have seen how hunger can quickly turn into revolution. Egypt's ousted dictator Hosni Mubarak found that out the hard way, as did Libya's Moammar Gadhafi and Tunisia's Zine El Abidine Ben Ali. By the look of things, Syrian president Bashar Assad will soon be joining this club.

Rulers in the Middle East and elsewhere in the developing world are learning there's a direct correlation between keeping people fed and staying in power. Algerian president Abdelaziz Bouteflika picked up that lesson by watching the fate of his dictatorial brethren. When food riots broke out in his own country, his government ordered 800,000 tons of wheat to help keep the peace. And Algeria isn't the only country in the region to resort to food to head off popular unrest: Saudi Arabia followed Algeria's lead, announcing plans to double its wheat inventories.

But ordering food is merely a stopgap. The underlying issues faced by the developing world don't have an easy fix. Take Egypt, the most populous country in the Arab world. In 1960, fewer than 28 million Egyptians lived inside the country's borders. By the time Hosni Mubarak took power in 1981, that number had swelled to 44 million. Today, Egypt is home to 80 million people. Given its current birthrate, the country's population will double to 160 million by the middle of the century. I'm sure if Malthus were around, he would wonder how a country that averages only two inches of annual rainfall could possibly sustain a population of 160 million when it's already struggling to provide for 80 million people today.

As much as Egyptians welcomed the overthrow of the Mubarak regime, it doesn't change the country's dilemma when it comes to food. Almost all of Egypt's arable land lies along the banks of the Nile River. An area that accounts for only 3 percent of the country's landmass now needs to support a population that has nearly tripled in the last fifty years. The plight of Egypt wasn't helped by nearly three decades under the yoke of a dictator whose family and military cronies bled the country's treasury dry. But even with a government that doesn't steal billions from its people, Egypt will still struggle to feed its population.

As its numbers continue to soar, Egypt will be forced to import more food. That's a particularly tall order given that roughly 40 percent of its national food bill is already spent on imports, including 60 percent of its grains. Moreover, the price of those imports is going through the roof. When 30 million Egyptians live on less than two dollars a day, it's easy to see why the consequences of food inflation are so dire.

Changes to autocratic regimes can happen overnight, but countries such as Egypt have problems that can't be solved even if the populace takes to the streets. As time goes on, it will only become harder for Egypt to feed its growing number of citizens. Egypt has all the markings of a country with a population that has outstripped the carrying capacity of the land.

When food prices peaked back in 2008, the increase came after eight solid years of global economic growth. Now, only a few years removed from the deepest recession of the postwar period, prices are again at record levels. Higher energy costs have ushered in a new era for food prices, which is ominous news for people in the developing world who are already struggling to put food on the table.

WILL GLOBAL FOOD MARKETS CONTINUE TO WORK?

Unprecedented demand for energy and resources may simply overwhelm our capacity to keep pace with a constant stream of solutions and innovations. Record food prices signal that feeding 7 billion people every day will become an ever-harder job for the global economy to manage. The task will be even more daunting as more people look to adopt the protein-rich diets enjoyed in wealthy countries.

The challenge of feeding a growing global population doesn't get any easier when major food-exporting countries decide to curtail shipments. That's not how markets are supposed to work. Higher food

prices should lead to more food production, not less. According to conventional economic theory, higher prices encourage producers to bring
on more supply. But that only happens in a free market. Governments
don't necessarily respond to price signals in the same way as corporations that are motivated by maximizing profits. Indeed, in some cases
governments may head in the opposite direction.

That's precisely what happened during the food crisis of 2008, and
it's something global food markets are likely to see again. Instead of
soaring food prices leading to more exports, governments diverted food
production to meet the demands of domestic markets. Food didn't go
to the highest bidder, but to the citizens of the countries in which it
was produced.

When prices for luxury consumer goods go through the roof, politicians aren't compelled to intervene in the market. But when the price
of basic foodstuffs soars, governments know they could face rioting in
the streets. At that point, you can toss out everything the textbooks say
about supply curves.

Economic theory insists that during the food crisis of 2008, record
grain prices should have pulled supplies out of world granaries as never
before. Instead, no fewer than twenty-nine food-exporting countries
banned exports and dedicated food grown at home to a hungry domestic populace. The increased scarcity sent global prices that much higher.
Countries that could still import food began hoarding supplies in case
the trend of exporting countries holding back crops became even more
widespread.

Economists who believe in the unfettered workings of the free market certainly wouldn't approve of blocking food exports. But they don't
have to win elections or stay in power. The experience of the last food
crisis shows that relying on the market mechanism of higher prices
can leave a country full of hungry people. If pushed, food-exporting
countries won't hesitate to sacrifice foreign markets in favor of holding
down domestic prices. That tendency is hardly reassuring to nations
who import large amounts of food. Even countries in the Middle East

that boast vast petrowealth can't buy food when foreign governments cut off supply. That's part of the reason oil-rich countries such as Saudi Arabia are taking matters into their own hands and snapping up agricultural land in other places. According to Oxfam, foreign interests have purchased more than 125 million acres of land in Africa in the last decade. That's more farmland than exists in Canada's prairies, one of the world's major breadbaskets.

It remains to be seen whether that accumulation of land will be an effective hedge against future bans on food exports. If push comes to shove, the food grown on those 125 million acres of African land could stay put. Governments are happy to take Middle Eastern petrodollars when times are good, but if food becomes scarce, those agreements may not be worth the paper they're printed on. A hungry population, as recent uprisings show, will not stand idly by as domestic crop production leaves to grace dinner tables in another country.

THE YANGS' NEW WORLD

North America is home to 5 percent of the world's population, yet its ecological footprint is larger than any other continent's. When you pit the standard of living and consumption habits of Canadians and Americans against those of people elsewhere, it's not hard to figure out why we leave such an outsized imprint on the environment.

In China, for example, car ownership stands at 20 cars for every thousand people, or 2 percent of the population. In North America, 435 out of every thousand people own a vehicle, or 43.5 percent. On a per capita basis, North American cellphone usage is double China's. Similarly, 60 percent of North Americans own a computer, compared with 4 percent of Chinese. Perhaps not surprisingly, North America's annual per capita carbon dioxide emissions stand at 13 metric tons, compared with 3 metric tons in China.

All of the stuff we own—computers, cars, cellphones, fridges—is built using an enormous amount of raw materials. Take copper as an example. It conducts electricity and heat better than almost any other material, which means it's used practically everywhere you look. From air-conditioners to flat-screen televisions to the wiring in your electrical appliances, copper is all around you. Of course, that only holds if you're reading this book in North America or Europe. If you're in rural China, copper is nearly absent from your home.

What happens when more of China's farmers make the jump from village life to modern cities? I recently picked up a story by *Bloomberg Businessweek* that did a good job painting the picture. It begins with 76-year-old Yang Caiguan and his wife, who have just moved from a traditional mud-brick house in the country to a four-bedroom apartment in Daojiang, a town in Hunan province. The Yangs' industrious son, who built a fortune as a factory owner, transplanted his parents to the city. He spent more than $50,000 buying and outfitting their new apartment, which is located in a gated community about five miles from their old home.

The transition to urban living is full of revelations for the Yangs, and also for the future of global resource consumption. The couple, who cooked over an open woodstove for decades, have traded that in for a new gas stove containing 10 pounds of copper. Their new refrigerator, which allows for the simple pleasure of eating ice cream whenever the mood strikes, is good for another 4 pounds of copper. The washing machine has almost 2 pounds and the hot water heater another pound. Each of the two air-conditioners in the Yangs' condominium unit contains 13 pounds of copper. Add in the rest of the appliances and the wiring in the apartment, and the Yangs' new home is using more than 85 pounds of copper, or about ten times the national average.

Needless to say, it's taking the couple some time to adjust to the amenities of modern living. They've never had a freezer before or an electric-ignition stove. They rarely draw on the hot water tank in the bathroom, since they prefer to bathe in the same plastic tub they've used for years. In their old home, ventilation was a few holes punched in the wall near the roof, not double air-conditioners. And they didn't need much copper for plumbing, since the toilet at the back of the house was open air.

The Yangs aren't alone in making the transition to an urban life-style. Millions of Chinese have made the same jump, and millions more are waiting to follow them. China already accounts for 40 percent of global copper consumption. Its annual domestic copper use has tripled in the last decade to nearly 7 million tons, a number that's only going up as per capita consumption increases. In twenty-five years, China's annual copper consumption is projected to reach as much as 20 million tons. But there's a major hitch that will keep those forecasts from coming true: that annual total is more than the current annual output of all the world's copper mines put together.

The finite nature of copper resources means China's consumption simply can't continue to grow exponentially. After all, China isn't the only nation that needs the world's resources. There are another 5.7 billion people outside China who want to consume the same copper, potash and oil being gobbled up by the Chinese.

The resource consumption of China's burgeoning ranks of Yangs is already rippling through the rest of the world. In London, for instance, thieves recently stole a life-size bronze statue of Dr. Alfred Salter, a social reformer who fought to improve the plight of the country's poor. The memorial figure sat on a bench in the Bermondsey district, the same neighborhood that had its former squalor immortalized in the pages of *Oliver Twist* (stealing the statue of a social crusader has a certain Fagin-like heartlessness befitting of Dickens). With copper prices at nearly four dollars a pound, the city will have to find a less costly way to commemorate Dr. Salter's good deeds.

High copper prices have British thieves breaking into everything from power stations to train yards in search of scrap metal. The UK scrap industry does billions of pounds' worth of business a year, much of it in cash, which makes it a magnet for criminals. Commuters have become used to transit delays due to the theft of copper cables from rail networks. Similarly, across the country thousands of households have experienced blackouts after metal thieves nicked power cables.

The theft of public statues and bits of railroad infrastructure underscore the finite nature of the global resource supply. Fresh demand for copper is pushing prices higher, and the end is nowhere in sight. North Americans consume more than five times the amount of base metals, fresh water and protein as people in the developing world. A direct relationship exists between global consumption per capita and the number of people who can achieve OECD lifestyles.

The more Yangs there are in the world, the fewer people the planet can support.

WRESTLING DOWN GLOBAL BIRTHRATES

The United Nations estimates that the world's 7 billionth person was born on October 31, 2011, most likely in Uttar Pradesh, the poorest and most populated state in India. According to the UN, the child is unlikely to have access to electricity or indoor plumbing and has only a 60 percent chance of attaining literacy. Overall, the UN estimates that 2.5 billion people in the world lack basic sanitation.

The UN's forecast for the global population to reach 10 billion this century leaves you wondering how the planet will support another 3 billion bodies. What will be left of the earth's remaining forests, jungles, oceans, rivers and wildlife? Even if we sacrifice the environment entirely, what kind of quality of life can the world's 10 billionth person expect?

Population growth is widely recognized as the key reason for economic underdevelopment in poor nations. When we look to the future, a stagnant global economy is a grim backdrop for rampant population growth. Faltering economies will put the brakes on population increases one way or another. Sadly, we could see a reversal in some of the gains we've made in human health and life expectancy.

The demographic implications of rapid population growth were the impetus behind China's infamous one-child policy. The country's Communist government adopted this drastic policy in 1979 to keep family size in check and hold down the country's population. On that score the policy has worked, reportedly leading to 400 million fewer people in China as a result. But the totalitarian family planning practices also come with horrific costs, including female infanticide and forced abortions.

China continues to reject overtures from international organizations to end the policy, although demographic shifts may encourage Beijing to give more serious consideration to changing its stance. Just as birthrates have nose-dived in OECD countries, the same demographic trends are emerging in cities such as Shanghai, which have bridged the gap to Western living standards.

In the big picture of global population growth, however, modern industrialized cities in China are no longer the main event. Most of the world's new babies will arrive in developing countries in south Asia and sub-Saharan Africa. Unlike China and India, globalization has left these countries behind. For them, a leap forward into Western living standards isn't waiting just around the corner. But a leap of sorts is exactly what's required. Birthrates in the developing world must come down if the planet hopes to avoid the Malthusian consequences of out-of-control population growth.

In the early 20th century, Dr. Kwegyir Aggrey, an American-educated missionary and intellectual born in Ghana, worked to raise the understanding of Africa among people in the West. A brilliant orator by all accounts, Dr. Aggrey spoke passionately about the role that education could play in improving social conditions. He once said, "The surest way to keep a people down is to educate the men and neglect the women. If you educate a man you simply educate an individual, but if you educate a woman, you educate a nation." What was true for Dr. Aggrey a hundred years ago is still true today.

The ramifications of gender equality and female education ripple into every corner of society. For evidence, you don't need to look any further than declining birthrates in OECD countries in the postwar period. In fact, you can take my own family as an example.

I met my wife, Deborah, when she was a national television reporter for the Canadian Broadcasting Corporation. Work and life kept us busy, and we didn't have our first child until Deborah was thirty-nine. We now have two children, Jack and Margot. In Canada, two-career couples are a common story. Like us, many people don't have children until much later than was the case for previous generations.

That's part of the reason Canada's fertility rate is only 1.58. If not for immigration, Canada's population would actually be shrinking, as would the populations of most other OECD countries. In Japan and South Korea, fertility rates are below 1.25. Compare those numbers with Niger, which has a world-leading fertility rate of 7.6. Let that sink in for a minute: the average woman in Niger has more than seven kids. In Uganda, the fertility rate is 6.69, and in Somalia it's 6.35.

The United Nations Population Fund has found that educated women are likely to marry later and have smaller and healthier families. As female education rises, studies show that infant mortality rates fall and family health improves. Children of educated mothers are themselves more likely to achieve higher levels of education, feeding into a virtuous cycle. An increase in female education also translates into more women in the workforce, which boosts household income and GDP. And none of that even begins to engage broader questions of morality, gender equality and social justice.

Consider the situation of a woman in Uganda working as a reporter for the Ugandan Broadcasting Corporation. She may decide, as Deborah did, to hold off on getting married until later in life. Along with being busy with work, she would also have the financial wherewithal to stay single. All of which adds up to a reduction in the number of years she is actively looking to have children.

Educated women are also more aware of reproductive choices, such as contraceptives. A study from Bangladesh shows that women with postsecondary degrees are three times as likely to use contraceptives as women with no formal education. These same women are also ten times more likely to stay single rather than marry. According to the World Watch Institute, two out of every five births result from unintended pregnancies. That figure seems high, but if it's even remotely close to the mark, its implications are staggering. If births dropped by 40 percent a year, the global population would stabilize, and much of the demographic challenge facing the world would disappear.

But we're a long way from that becoming a reality. Universal education and gender equality are two of the eight pillars laid out by the UN as part of a campaign to end global poverty by 2015. The UN won't meet its goal, but at least it's moving in the right direction. According to UN estimates, more than a billion women live in unacceptable states of poverty, most of them in the developing world. Organizations such as the UN, the World Bank and even the US military's Joint Chiefs of Staff recognize that education holds the key to pulling countries in the developing world out of their current quandary. It may not be possible to fast-forward economic development in many poor countries, but support for female education does seem to be gaining critical mass, at least among intergovernmental agencies, nongovernmental organizations (NGOs) and relief organizations.

In tomorrow's economy, global population growth, like everything else, will have to adjust. Just as birthrates have come down in the developed world, the same change must occur in places such as Bangladesh, Pakistan, Uganda and other population hot spots.

Could a static economy hold positive unexpected consequences for world population growth? A lower global economic speed limit just might, if it helps spark the empowerment of women in the developing world. Even brutal dictatorial regimes could soon recognize that explosive population growth and food scarcity is an untenable combination. The pragmatic instinct to head off popular unrest may lead to more progressive approaches to education and family planning than we have yet seen. A Chinese proverb says that women hold up half the sky. When high prices curtail access to raw materials, some countries may find that empowering the long-neglected female half of the population is the most practical way to negotiate the demographic challenges to come.

Stranger things can happen. Just consider what triple-digit oil prices have in store for the environment.

Chapter 10

WILL TRIPLE-DIGIT OIL PRICES SAVE THE PLANET?

BRITISH NOVELIST WILLIAM GOLDING published his first book, *Lord of the Flies*, in 1954. The story, as you may remember from high school, follows a group of schoolboys marooned on an island. Removed from civilization, the boys devolve into a primitive state of disarray as the forces of anarchy and brutishness clash with order and rationality. As countless English teachers have observed, the novel explores the duality of human nature, the fragility of society, and the relationship between morality and immorality. It may also be an allegory of the Second World War.

As it happens, in the 1960s, Golding became a fellow villager of James Lovelock, an independent scientist and a pioneer of the environmental movement. In the early days of the space race, Lovelock was invited to work at NASA's Jet Propulsion Laboratory outside Pasadena, California. His work on atmospheric gases fit with NASA's hopes to detect life on other planets. Lovelock's research for the Mars project, which led to the Viking mission, set his imagination spinning. He started to think of Earth not as a collection of disparate parts inhabiting the same planet but as a single entity—a superorganism.

Lovelock sees Earth as a complex web of interconnected systems. Everything on the planet is related: flora, fauna, air, water, rocks and all the stuff in between. He hypothesized that Earth is a self-regulating system that keeps its climate and chemical makeup at the levels needed to maintain life. This superorganism, among other things, regulates global air temperatures, the amount of oxygen in the atmosphere and the salinity of the oceans. When one organism, humans primarily, throws the biosphere's delicate balance out of whack, the entire system adjusts to return conditions to a state of equilibrium. In short, everything is connected and everything affects everything else.

After returning home from his stint at NASA, Lovelock, on a walk with Golding to the village post office, explained his grand theory of the planet to his neighbor. Golding was captivated and proposed that such a big idea needed a sweeping name to match it. A Nobel laureate steeped in myth and metaphor, Golding marshaled his literary faculties and suggested that Lovelock call it Gaia.

The Greek goddess of the earth, Gaia is sometimes considered to be Earth itself. Also known as Ge, she provides the root word for "geography" and "geology." Unlike nurturing images of Mother Nature, Lovelock's version isn't always tender. When Gaia is threatened by a rogue factor, such as carbon dioxide emissions, she defends herself by purging the offending agent and restoring balance to the system. Lovelock believes such a response is unfolding right now through climate change, or global heating as he prefers to call it. In a prediction that would make even Malthus shudder, Lovelock forecasts that an increase in global temperature will unleash a climate shift that will wipe out millions of people around the world.

Lovelock's most pessimistic visions could come straight from the pages of a postapocalyptic novel. As great swaths of the earth transform into deserts, the climate will become too hot for plants to grow. Food will be scarce, and millions will starve. The remaining bastions of humanity will gravitate to the polar regions and the few other remaining spots on Earth that can still sustain life. Lovelock is clearly not for the faint of heart.

To attempt to avoid this potential cataclysm, Lovelock has become an outspoken proponent of emissions-free nuclear energy (a stance that hardly endears him to parts of the environmental movement). He has also floated suggestions for ways humans could intervene in climate change through mass-scale planetary engineering efforts designed to lower global temperatures. Again, not measures typically embraced by most environmentalists.

Lovelock's ideas have polarized the scientific community for decades. He'd be easier to dismiss if he weren't so often right. He was way out in front of the pack on global warming, sounding alarms that other scientists scoffed at before they eventually had to capitulate to his views. His early work in atmospheric chemistry led to the discovery of the hole in the ozone layer. He was even right that planetary probes would fail to detect life on Mars, which flew in the face of NASA's hopes (and funding aspirations) at the time. And the mainstream scientific community is coming closer to Lovelock's view that global warming could unleash a climactic Armageddon if immediate steps aren't taken to reduce emissions.

The IPCC, established by the United Nations in 1988, comprises thousands of scientists and is the largest publisher of peer-reviewed climate change research in the world. In 2007, the organization shared the Nobel Peace Prize with Al Gore for increasing public knowledge about climate change and laying the groundwork to counteract such change. In its latest comprehensive assessment report from 2007, the IPCC warns that human-generated emissions are causing global temperatures to rise. An increase of 4 degrees Celsius in the next hundred years, they say, would create devastating consequences for humanity. Droughts will cause global food production to fall. Low-lying coastal areas will be flooded as glaciers melt and sea levels rise. Bangladesh and Vietnam will be in serious trouble, as will major metropolitan centers such as New York, London, Tokyo, Hong Kong, Karachi and Calcutta. Up to half of the land species on the planet will be threatened with extinction. Among other consequences, mosquitoes will thrive, exposing billions more people to diseases such as malaria and dengue fever.

But the IPCC also says this disastrous outcome is avoidable. If we curb our emissions by burning fewer hydrocarbons and switch to cleaner energy sources, we can cut the expected temperature increases in half, sparing the world from the worst consequences of climate change. Of course, cutting back on hydrocarbons is easier said than done. In the 21st century, burning hydrocarbons is a catch-22. Burning more oil, coal and natural gas is critical to achieving the economic expansion that's needed to support the billions of new people who are projected to inhabit the planet. But chasing that economic growth could throw so much carbon into the atmosphere that it may undermine humanity's very survival.

Thankfully, there is another way to look at this dilemma. If the abundance of hydrocarbons in an industrialized world has brought us to the brink of catastrophic climate change, then the scarcity of those same resources could be what saves us from environmental disaster. The future of our planet's climate may soon be out of our hands—and that may not be such a bad thing.

As the stakes of the climate change debate continue to rise, it's hardly surprising that the issue is becoming ever more politicized. The environmental movement is no longer a backwater group of underfunded hippies. Instead, it's a well-financed lobbying machine, with high-profile players from Al Gore to Leonardo DiCaprio. Environmentalists believe that critical changes to government and corporate policies are needed to put the world on a path to permanently reducing emissions. Green political parties around the world are mobilizing voter support for legislation that will change our carbon practices. If human decision making got us into this mess, the hope is it can also get us out.

On the other side, climate change skeptics, most of whom don't want costly new environmental policies to upset the financial status quo, are working to sway public opinion against the idea of global warming. Big Oil, for one, still isn't shy about casting doubt on the notion that humans are responsible for increases in global temperatures. Among other things, climate change deniers argue that global warming is a naturally occurring phenomenon, perhaps linked to an increase in solar flare activity from the sun. Skeptics also contend that naturally occurring emissions have an underappreciated influence on atmospheric carbon levels. When the Icelandic volcano Eyjafjallajökull erupted in the spring of 2010, global warming skeptics said it released more carbon into the atmosphere than all of the emissions savings mandated by world governments in the previous five years. Environmentalists countered that foregone emissions from grounded air travel more than offset the volcanic activity. (What I can say for certain is that Eyjafjallajökull cost me a trip to Portugal.)

The presence of large natural sources of carbon emissions hardly takes polluters off the hook. Just because nature can overwhelm us with a volcanic eruption at any moment doesn't mean our effect on the environment isn't just as profound. We can't excuse our contributions to the global carbon footprint because multiple sources of emissions exist. As the IPCC points out, our current rate of carbon emissions combined with the atmospheric buildup since the Industrial Revolution puts us on track to reach dangerous concentrations of greenhouse gases irrespective of random volcanic events.

The amount of carbon dioxide in the atmosphere is now greater than at any time in the last 640,000 years. The IPCC's 2007 report notes that eleven of the previous twelve years (1995–2006) were the hottest since instrumental readings of daily temperatures began in 1880. In the last century, the average world temperature increased by 0.7 degrees Celsius, with Arctic temperatures climbing at twice that rate over the same period. The evidence of global warming since the IPCC's last report is even more compelling. The US National Snow and Ice Data Center found that in 2011, the Arctic ice pack shrank to the second-smallest area ever recorded, only marginally bigger than levels in 2007.

With the exception of hardcore climate change deniers, most folks find it hard to ignore the mounting evidence that human activity is warming the planet. Personally, I'm willing to accept the link between rising global temperatures and human-made carbon emissions. Think of all the smoke that has been belched out by factories from Victorian-era London to modern-day Shanghai. Two hundred years of spewing filth into the atmosphere has to have had consequences for the biosphere.

At the same time, I'm not losing much sleep worrying about the worst-case scenarios from Lovelock or the IPCC. I find the IPCC's assumptions for economic growth—and, more to the point, fuel demand—hard to swallow. In its forecasts, the IPCC takes a business-as-usual approach to resource consumption. But projections that model the future by extrapolating from the quantity of hydrocarbons we currently burn are implausible.

The Achilles heel of the dire predictions for climate change is the computer modeling by IPCC scientists that assumes our hydrocarbon consumption will continue to increase at the same rate over the next few decades as it has in the past. Economic growth drives carbon emissions. When growth is shuffled to the back burner in a static economy, emissions will come down too, removing the need for stringent climate change policies. The pace at which our economies grow is far more important to the level of future emissions than any government-mandated carbon reduction schemes.

Like the central bankers and finance ministers we met in the opening chapters, staunch environmental advocates need to recognize that the global economy has downshifted into a much lower gear. And gearing down economic growth, as they'll see, is the most direct way to reduce carbon emissions.

The big question climate change scientists need to ask is where we'll get all the fuel needed to raise global temperatures to forecasted levels. The Exxons, BPs and Suncors of the world tell us they'll discover it, but as I've already pointed out, the real issue isn't locating resources, it's being able to afford to pull them out of the ground. Can we pay the cost of the new sources of supply that Big Oil is discovering? We only have to look at today's fuel prices for an answer. If supplies of oil and coal are abundant enough to fulfill climate change projections, then why are prices already so high? Soaring prices indicate scarcity. And if carbon-emitting fuels are getting scarce, how does that change the outlook for growth in carbon emissions and the nature of the climate change debate? Those are the questions policymakers need to ask before charging ahead with financially punitive plans for carbon abatement. If they don't, governments could squander billions implementing measures to help the environment that will ultimately prove unnecessary.

The specter of climate change takes on a very different shape in a world of fuel abundance and robust economic growth than it does when fuel is scarce and economies are faltering.

WHY EMISSIONS CONTROLS DON'T WORK

To date, attempts to regulate emissions have been driven by a belief that we need to decarbonize our economies. Therefore, governments try to reduce fossil fuel consumption by putting a price on carbon emissions. Some countries do this through carbon taxes, while others try to control pollution using elaborate cap-and-trade systems, which involve shuffling around carbon credits. The rationale behind these policies is straightforward: make emitters pay for emissions and they'll emit less.

The reasoning is sensible enough, but it hasn't worked in practice. So far, international climate change treaties have failed to gain universal acceptance or institute significant penalties around noncompliance. And without a globally agreed-upon price for emissions, carbon pricing schemes just won't work; emissions will simply migrate to jurisdictions where they cost less. That's the fundamental flaw in the Kyoto Protocol. By seeking to cap emissions in half the world, the international pact merely diverted emissions to the other half of the globe. Since there are no borders in the atmosphere, emissions from one country affect everybody's climate.

Hopes for the Kyoto accord were misplaced from the outset. Its design encouraged emissions growth to shift from rich nations to poor countries that are exempt from the protocol. And that's exactly what's happened. The developing world is responsible for 90 percent of the increase in global emissions since 2000. During that time span, China's emissions have doubled, pushing it past the United States as the world's largest emitter. Redistributing carbon emissions is not the same as actually reducing total global emissions, which are now 50 percent higher than in 1990, the benchmark year used by the Kyoto treaty.

To actually reduce global emissions, every country would need to agree to a global framework that included a universal price for carbon. That's why voluntary pacts, such as the post-Kyoto agreements negotiated at climate change summits in Copenhagen (2009), Cancún (2010) and Durban (2011), are meaningless. If emissions can simply move to another part of the world, then the difference made by voluntary commitments to reduce pollution is of little consequence.

So far, the rest of the world is showing little inclination to come on board for emissions controls. China and other developing countries argue that cumulative emissions are what counts when it comes to climate change. By that measure, they insist that countries such as the United States foot more of the bill. Since the Industrial Revolution, the United States has produced an estimated 27 percent of global carbon emissions, compared with only 9.5 percent for China. Although China's current emissions outpace America's, in cumulative terms the contribution from the United States is nearly three times as much. Neither China nor the United States currently puts a price on carbon, and neither appears likely to make a policy change anytime soon. As long as the world's two largest emitters won't pay for carbon, it's tough to persuade Canada, or any other country, to charge domestic industries and consumers for emissions.

One notable exception is the European Union. At least for the moment, the EU is taking the environmental high road and charging for emissions. But the system is far from perfect. It has put a low cost on emissions and offers a plethora of carbon credits, which gives the agreement little financial bite. And even the environmentally conscious EU is beginning to doubt whether its efforts are worthwhile if the rest of the world doesn't follow suit. In the absence of a global deal on carbon emissions, the EU's Energy Department is debating whether to continue with its transition to non-carbon energy sources. The continent's economic woes are undoubtedly throwing cold water on its environmental conscience. An attempt to show global leadership is commendable, but so too is looking out for a populace that's struggling under the weight of a financial crisis.

The prospects for establishing a global framework for carbon pricing are as remote today as ever. International summits in Copenhagen, Cancún and Durban failed to come up with any concrete measures that will help to meaningfully reduce carbon emissions. Meanwhile, plans by individual governments are also struggling to find traction. In the United States, the American Clean Energy and Security Act, also known as the Waxman-Markey bill, would have capped carbon emissions and established a trading scheme. But the bill died on the Senate floor in 2009.

The political fallout from the Fukushima nuclear disaster is also hurting the outlook for future reductions in carbon emissions. As plans to expand the capacity of nuclear power generation are canceled or delayed around the world, the prominence of hydrocarbons in tomorrow's economy only increases.

Japan has acknowledged that in 2012 its greenhouse gas emissions will rise to as much as 16 percent above 1990 levels, in sharp contrast to its commitment under the Kyoto Protocol to reduce emissions to 6 percent below the benchmark year. Japan has now shuttered all 54 of its nuclear reactors following the disaster at Fukushima. To replace the lost electricity generation, Japan is dusting off retired oil-fueled power plants. Reactivating the mothballed stations, including a mammoth facility south of Tokyo at Yokosuka, will help Japan meet its domestic energy needs, but it will also cause a sharp rise in its carbon emissions. The story is similar in Germany, which is also veering away from nuclear power after the accident in Japan. To make up for the decline in nuclear energy, Germany has announced that it will need to build more coal-fired plants, in addition to importing more natural gas from Russia.

A weak global economy makes marshaling the political will to tackle climate change even more difficult. Measures such as carbon pricing are a tough sell at the best of times, let alone when an electorate cares far more about job creation than melting glaciers in Greenland.

In the United States, President Obama recently directed the Environmental Protection Agency (EPA) to withdraw an air quality proposal that would have tightened pollution standards for US industries after Republicans complained the new federal regulations would kill thousands of future jobs and cost the economy billions. The timing of the decision, directly on the heels of yet another dismal employment report that showed zero job creation, left little question about the president's priorities. His opponents have been making hay with criticism that federal regulations are choking the economy. An inability to create jobs has left Obama with little political cover from which to launch environmental initiatives. As triple-digit oil prices continue to stifle American economic growth, you can bet the political clout of the environmental lobby, and the EPA, will keep taking a back seat to economic considerations, regardless of who is in the White House or which party controls Congress.

North of the border, too, economic imperatives are trumping environmental ambitions. Canada is backing out of the Kyoto Protocol just in time to avoid paying a huge bill for falling short of its commitments. Canadian carbon emissions are 30 percent higher than they were in

1990. Canada would have had to pay $14 billion to buy emissions credits from the rest of the world to comply with its obligations under the treaty. Instead, Prime Minister Stephen Harper decided to skip out on the deal and weather the heat from the global community. The South Pacific island nation of Tuvalu, for one, which is losing land to rising ocean waters, called the decision "an act of sabotage on our future." For Harper's Conservative government—never shy to remind Canadians it was the former Liberal regime that ratified Kyoto—the loss of international stature is outweighed by what else can be done with $14 billion.

HOW YOU REALLY STOP EMISSIONS

The simple unspoken truth is that a recession is the best possible way to tame runaway carbon emissions. An economic slowdown will stop the growth of emissions dead in its tracks. And the deeper the recession, the better it is for the atmosphere.

In fact, recessions do better than simply stop emissions growth: they actually reduce emissions levels. And, unlike the grand plans laid out at climate change summits, recessions don't take three or four decades to do the job; they do it nearly overnight. According to the IEA, in 2009, global carbon dioxide emissions fell for the first time since 1990.

The ripple effects from an economic slowdown elicit all sorts of environmentally friendly results. Consider, for example, the number of resource megaprojects that were canceled after commodity prices plunged during the last recession. In Alberta's tar sands alone, the oil industry canceled or delayed $50 billion of planned capital spending. The US environmental movement—backed by celebrity activists such as Robert Redford and Daryl Hannah—is deeply opposed to tar sands development. They can boycott the tar sands all they want, but on a practical level, falling oil prices carry far more consequences for the economic well-being of tar sands mines than any environmental protest.

Nevertheless, it's unlikely you'll ever hear politicians praising the environmental benefits of an economic recession. That message would be tantamount to political suicide. Instead, we hear political leaders babble about sustainable growth and commit to targets for reducing carbon emissions that are so far in the future most of them won't even be alive, let alone still in power. That makes for politically palatable greenwash, but it doesn't do anything about how much carbon dioxide the world is pumping into the atmosphere. Lower the economic speed limit, however, and emissions can't help but come down and lower the atmospheric thermostat at the same time.

Not surprisingly, it's tough to find any country in the world where voters are willing to forgo their own financial well-being in the interests of climate stability for people not yet born. No matter how compelling the scientific case for the adverse effects of climate change, or how much we profess concern for future generations, when the rubber hits the road, the vast majority of people are more concerned with the here and now. Curbing emissions will always take a backseat to the more tangible imperatives of job creation and personal financial stability. Just look at the Obama administration's decision to put the EPA's air quality proposal on the shelf. The White House undoubtedly believes the EPA's plan is good environmental policy, but that's a secondary concern when the economy is faltering.

Before we get too despondent about lax environmental standards, maybe we need to take another look at what environmental policies really accomplish in a world where oil costs more than $100 a barrel and coal more than $100 a ton. If the objective of climate change policy is to reduce carbon emissions, then that's exactly what's achieved by higher energy prices. And governments don't need to lift a finger. Throw a fossil-fuel wrench into economic growth and you also put the lid on carbon emissions. If energy costs are going to hammer the economy anyway, we may as well recognize the concurrent environmental benefits. Given the alternative of Lovelock's vengeful Gaia, perhaps we should even rejoice.

In a zero-growth world, governments don't need to step in with punitive carbon taxes or ineffectual cap-and-trade schemes, nor will we need to depend on the whims of environmentally conscious consumers or ecologically progressive companies. When our economies shrink, our carbon emissions will tumble without any legislative effort whatsoever.

Just look at what happened when the Soviet Union collapsed. The fall of Communism sent Russia's economy into a tailspin and lowered carbon emissions by a staggering 30 percent nearly overnight. And it's not like the Russian government made a policy objective out of carbon emissions; the Kremlin had more pressing concerns at the time than the environment. The latest recession had the same dampening effect on emissions. In the United States, energy-related carbon dioxide emissions fell 3 percent in 2008 and another 7 percent in 2009. That's more than was called for by the Waxman-Markey bill.

Of course, painful economic contractions don't come about by design—far from it. As we saw in chapter 1, governments threw the kitchen sink at the global economy in a bid to avoid a recession. That's why many countries now have so much debt that they're lurching toward bankruptcy. If persuading voters to put a price on carbon emissions is hard when economic times are good, try selling them on the benefits when the economy isn't growing.

That said, global warming is too large an issue to simply ignore. Governments know that voters want to see them do something about it—and that's where emissions intensity targets come in. Few countries will actually commit to reducing total emissions (Denmark being a notable exception), but many politicians around the world will sign up for emissions intensity targets. They demonstrate all the earmarks of environmental concern without hurting economic growth or, it should be noted, actually working to reduce emissions. In other words, adopting such targets is classic political greenwash.

Emissions intensity targets involve reducing carbon emissions per unit of GDP. When it comes to helping the environment, the emissions part of the equation is less of a problem than GDP. The way these targets are set up, economic growth leads to a higher emissions threshold as GDP (the denominator of the equation) gets bigger. That means an economy can pump out more carbon while still staying on the right side of its targets. Each unit of GDP may be emitting less carbon, but the total amount of carbon emissions is actually going up. The faster economies grow, the more carbon they are allowed to produce. These are the types of environmental policies that politicians can live with. They look good to the public, but come with no real economic cost.

Similar intensity targets for oil consumption have proven to be just as ineffectual at curbing fuel intake. But you wouldn't know it by listening to the political rhetoric. In the United States, politicians like to flaunt the idea that America has cut its oil intensity in half since the first OPEC oil shocks. That may be true, but the US economy is also much bigger than it was forty years ago, which means the country's total annual oil consumption has actually increased.

Intensity targets are even palatable for recalcitrant carbon emitters such as China. Over the next five years, China has committed to reducing carbon emissions per unit of GDP by 17 percent (a plan that depends on the massive nuclear expansion discussed in chapter 4). Of course, when China agreed to the targets, its annual economic growth was nearly 10 percent. At that rate, intensity targets are hardly the check on carbon emissions that Beijing would have you believe.

A plan with more bite would involve capping the total level of emissions. That's a path that China and India, among other countries, have steadfastly refused to take. They know that agreeing to hard targets for absolute emissions levels would result in an unacceptable reduction in economic growth. That would mean fewer citizens following in the Yangs' footsteps and making the transition to an urban lifestyle.

Furthermore, asking people in China and India to stop improving their standard of living in order to help save the world is more than a touch hypocritical when wealthy OECD countries won't reduce their own emissions to help do the same. It's a particularly tough request in light of China's position that cumulative pollution matters just as much as current emissions.

As it stands, agreeing to fruitless emissions intensity targets is a much more palatable option for governments than taking meaningful action to reduce global carbon output. But in a static economy, that could change. Slower GDP growth reduces the level of emissions allowed by such targets. In other words, in a zero-growth economy, emissions intensity targets can actually start to sting. Of course, governments may not let it come to that. As Canada has shown by reneging on Kyoto, once environmental agreements start to come with real economic costs, governments will pull the chute on voluntary international treaties with impunity.

Before that happens, however, higher energy prices are set to make emissions intensity targets even more superfluous than they are now. Indeed, triple-digit prices for oil and coal could relegate government emissions policies to the sidelines.

WHERE WILL WE GET ALL THAT COAL?

Higher energy prices will accomplish what politicians and environmentalists can't: a permanent reduction in carbon emissions.

Governments around the world have long thought that the path to a greener atmosphere begins with decarbonizing our energy systems—electricity generation in particular. Despite efforts to usher in more renewable power generation, however, the amount of carbon emitted per unit of electricity produced has actually increased by 6 percent globally in the last two decades. Even environmentally unfriendly coal still commands a 41 percent share of global power generation.

Regardless, when it comes to reducing emissions, altering the energy mix by adding more renewable sources is a red herring. What the world really needs to do is use less power. And that's exactly what is about to happen in tomorrow's economy.

Higher oil and coal prices are already putting the squeeze on economic growth and fuel consumption. In the last few years, power shortages have become commonplace in China, India and the rest of Asia. Price and availability are stopping these countries from burning more coal, not costly environmental regulations. As prices keep rising, it will only become more apparent how unnecessary international treaties and carbon taxes are for lowering emissions.

In China, power users aren't even paying full freight for the coal that's burned to keep the lights on. China's government has seen to it that coal-based power prices have only risen at a fraction of the actual increases in coal prices. That's a huge subsidy, and one that's unsustainable for a country burning more than 3 billion tons of coal a year. The Chinese Electricity Council warned that in the first four months of 2011 alone, the five largest power-generating groups in the country lost more than 10 billion yuan after they were forbidden from passing rising coal costs on to customers.

Chinese authorities can cap power prices for the time being, but that will only bankrupt the country's coal-fired utilities. At the same time, China's industries and consumers are living under a subsidized umbrella of false power costs. Eventually, resource scarcity will assert itself. Both China and India will have to ration power, which will put the brakes on economic activity. That process has already started with the rolling blackouts that are now a permanent feature of the economic landscape in those countries.

Few climate change experts take such economic considerations into account when making their big-picture forecasts. The IPCC, for example, released a series of models for the future of global carbon emissions in its benchmark 2007 report, presenting no fewer than 40 different scenarios. The bottom line of the exercise was to conclude that unless immediate action on carbon abatement is taken, emissions would soon exceed critical levels and induce catastrophic climate change. More than a thousand of the world's foremost climate change scientists took part in the multiyear modeling exercise. In terms of the science behind global warming, I buy the group's declaration that a causal relationship exists between higher levels of atmospheric carbon dioxide and increases in global temperature. They say that if we can stabilize carbon dioxide levels at around 450 parts per million, then we can hold a temperature increase to 2 degrees Celsius and avoid some of the worst-case scenarios for climate change. That sounds good to me. But when we work backward from the emissions projections contained in their models, we find something even better.

The amount of hydrocarbons that would need to be burned to fulfill the IPCC forecasts is staggering. The panel projects that oil consumption, for instance, will be greater in a hundred years than it is today. And that's not to say anything of coal, the largest source of human-generated carbon emissions. The majority of the IPCC scenarios see world coal consumption doubling over the next two decades. About 80 percent of the projected global increase is expected to come from China and India. But those forecasts are an extrapolation of current economic growth rates. The climate change experts who modeled the IPCC scenarios didn't ask where all that extra coal will come from—or, more importantly, what it will cost. And the projections are based on unrealistic expectations for hydrocarbon supply over the next several decades.

It's worth reemphasizing that the factor which most influences global consumption isn't the amount of resources contained in the ground but the affordability of those resources. As we discussed in chapter 4, there's a big difference between a resource and a reserve. How much oil and coal is left in the ground doesn't matter if our economies can't afford to burn it. For all intents and purposes, those hydrocarbons might as well not even exist. When we consider the price we'll need to pay to burn tomorrow's resources, humanity's chances of avoiding a climate catastrophe look a whole lot better than most IPCC models would suggest.

One outspoken critic of any model that assumes future resource abundance is Dr. David Rutledge, an engineering professor at Caltech.

He estimates the total amount of coal available to be mined (past, present and future) at 662 billion tons. That's well short of the World Energy Council's calculations, which put that same figure at 1,162 billion tons. The maximum cumulative coal production assumed by an IPCC scenario is 3,500 billion tons.

The discrepancy, according to Rutledge, arises from a lack of rigor around estimates for national coal reserves. Current estimates for US coal reserves, for example, are based on data that haven't been updated since the 1970s. Once countries start paying more attention to estimates, reserves figures are consistently marked down. That's what has happened in mature coal-producing regions such as Germany and England. Whether or not Rutledge's numbers are exact is not the point. If his basic assertion that world coal reserves are consistently overestimated is accurate, the IPCC scenarios become much less frightening.

In a report to the German parliament, the Energy Watch Group, a Munich-based think tank, predicts that world coal production will only be able to increase 30 percent from current levels. And that assumes coal can be delivered to the places that need it the most, which is hardly a given. The cost of shipping coal, as we saw in chapter 4, means that only 15 percent of global production is currently being exported.

China is expected to hit peak coal production much sooner than the rest of the world, given its torrid pace of extraction. That's why it has sent its national energy companies on a global shopping spree to snap up available sources of supply. A major problem with this strategy is the lack of mines close enough to China to make it economically viable to ship coal back to the country. Unexploited coal reserves in Montana aren't any use to a thermal power station in Zhejiang. That could leave China scrambling for other energy options.

In the United States, too, the outlook for coal consumption is cloudy. In the last decade, 90 percent of new applications for coal plants have been delayed or canceled, according to the Energy Department. Coal-fired power plants are still being built, but costs are increasing due to tighter emissions standards designed to reduce the negative effects of pollution on health and the environment. What's more, newly abundant supplies of natural gas from shale reserves make it a cheaper fuel than coal for power generation, signaling that more electricity will soon come from gas-fired plants.

A NEW HOPE

The world won't burn anywhere close to all the fossil fuels needed to realize the IPCC's dire climate change predictions. That's undoubtedly good news, yet environmentalists are unlikely to embrace the potential salvation offered by expensive energy. If higher commodity prices spare us from the worst consequences of global warming, the environmental movement could be marginalized.

If that happens, it would be an unfortunate step backward for the world. Most of what green parties advocate makes a lot of sense, even if only considered within the context of energy costs. In a world of triple-digit oil prices, conservation measures that reduce fuel consumption are precisely what we need.

Nevertheless, governments still need to understand what higher energy prices mean for climate change. Many environmental policies are based on an assumption that future resource supply will be abundant, and while they may be implemented with the best intentions, they won't make any sense in the coming world of fuel scarcity. Given today's grim fiscal realities, we can hardly afford to make the wrong choices, implementing expensive environmental programs designed for a different world than the one we will be living in.

Why spend billions developing carbon capture and storage technology to trap emissions from coal plants if we're not going to burn all the coal necessary to make dire climate change predictions a reality? For that matter, governments need to ask whether we should really be burdening our economies by putting a price on carbon at all. Similarly, does it make sense to mandate auto manufacturers to increase fuel efficiency standards when pump prices will already be spurring drivers to burn less gasoline? When fuel costs $7 a gallon, as it does in Europe, you won't need policymakers telling you to drive a more fuel-efficient vehicle; prices will already have dictated the change.

I'm sure that many energy industry executives will agree with me—for all the wrong reasons. If you run a coal-fired power plant or operate a tar sands mine, why wouldn't you want to hear someone suggest you don't have to worry about the atmosphere or, more importantly, pay anything for your carbon emissions? For large industrial carbon emitters, maintaining the status quo is an inviting option.

I also don't expect the environmental movement to simply roll over and accept that slower economic growth will resolve the issue of global climate change. I doubt you could find any environmentalists willing to sit on their hands for a few decades, trusting that high fuel prices will quash demand and save us from catastrophic global warming. No one who takes the threat of climate change seriously would bet our planet's future on the accuracy of a twenty-year forecast for hydrocarbon depletion and higher energy prices.

I'm not expecting anyone to make that leap of faith because I wouldn't either. Instead, just observe what triple-digit oil prices are doing to the global economy *right now*. The onset of high prices has already led to the deepest postwar recession on record, and their quick return is now threatening us with a double-dip slowdown from which there is no obvious path to recovery. Once we tip over that brink, just watch what happens to carbon emissions.

The reduction in emissions that's about to occur because of high costs is exactly the kind of adjustment environmentalists say we need. The green movement will get its wish, but it won't stem from forward-thinking government policies or altruistic voters worried about their grandchildren's future. Instead, it will result from a profound slowdown in economic growth, which we currently lack the tools to fix.

And we won't have to wait several decades for carbon emissions to fall; the wheels are already in motion. Economic growth is being hammered all around the world. The time frame for the next global recession isn't decades away—it could be mere quarters from now.

Of course, by definition recessions are temporary affairs. A slow-down could bring our atmosphere a brief respite, but won't emissions pick up again when the global economy comes back to life? It's fair to think that a recession-induced reduction in emissions would be a mere hiccup in the larger scheme of things. After all, during the economic recovery in 2010, global emissions rose by nearly 6 percent, one of the strongest increases on record. By historical standards, even the deepest downturns rarely last more than four or five quarters. But the next recession will be different from ones we've known in the past. This time around, we'll have to do without economic growth for much longer than a few quarters or even a year: we're about to face a permanent slowdown in growth.

As I've argued, the economic recovery since the last recession was predicated on an unsustainable level of fiscal and monetary stimulus. And worse yet, even the wobbly recovery we're now seeing has brought back the same triple-digit oil prices that sank us into a recession in the first place. Now that our petroleum-dependent economies are again under the yoke of high oil prices, what options do governments have left? As we saw in chapter 2, the last round of fiscal stimulus burdened world governments with debt levels that will take a generation to pay off. Borrowing rates are already at record lows, meaning little stimulus is left in the tank to spur growth. Indeed, rising inflation levels may force interest rates to go higher.

The environmental movement won't have to hold its breath very long to see what high fuel prices will mean for the atmosphere. Triple-digit oil prices are already here—and they herald the end of growth.

Like everything else, even our seemingly inexorable march toward environmental self-destruction is about to run out of fuel. If Gaia's vengeful climate change really is about to devour humanity, then triple-digit oil prices may just give us all a brand-new lease on life.

CONCLUSION

ON A HOT SUMMER night in 1965, California Highway Patrolman Lee Minikus stopped Marquette Frye on suspicion of drunk driving. It was a routine traffic stop, but what followed was anything but routine. Frye was arrested, along with his stepbrother, who was a passenger in the car, and his mother, who was in her house and came outside to see what was happening. Neighbors and passersby gathered to watch the ruckus, and more police soon arrived to disperse the crowd. Shortly after that, bottles and bricks began to fly.

It was the spark that set off the Watts Riots, among the most violent events of the civil rights era. More than a thousand people were injured, thirty-four died and at least six hundred buildings were damaged or destroyed in the six days of rioting following Frye's arrest. When the Los Angeles police couldn't bring the rioters under control, fourteen thousand National Guard troops were mobilized to help restore order. A section of south-central Los Angeles covering 45 square miles was cordoned off to stop the rioting from spilling into other neighborhoods.

The riots became a defining moment of the 1960s. Unbeknownst to the people out in the streets, the civil disturbance also quietly intersected with dire circumstances unfolding on the other side of the world. As the Watts Riots raged in southern California, India and Pakistan were falling into the grips of a famine. For thirty-five trucks that were stopped at the National Guard's cordon, the most pressing issue wasn't civil rights in the United States, but hunger in the developing world.

The convoy, prevented from getting to the LA harbor by the guards-men, was carrying seeds from an experimental agricultural facility out-side Mexico City.

These particular seeds had been developed at the International Maize and Wheat Improvement Center by Norman Borlaug, an American agronomist who had been working on agricultural research in Mexico since 1944. Borlaug was born on a farm in Iowa in 1914. By the time he reached college, the Midwest was turning into a dust bowl, and Borlaug, like so many others, could only watch as people around him went hun-gry. Graduating with a doctoral degree in plant pathology, the farmer's son dedicated himself to the art and science of growing food.

After arriving in Mexico to work on a hunger-fighting project funded by the Rockefeller Foundation, Borlaug made an agricultural breakthrough on the propagation of wheat that changed how the world feeds itself. Tall, majestic-looking stalks of wheat may have been inspir-ing, but he figured out that smaller plants actually produced better yields. The result was dwarf wheat.

Agricultural researchers at the time were using fertilizers to boost the amount of grain a plant produces, but the application led to top-heavy plants on long stalks that fell over due to their own weight. Dwarf wheat is a stubby, unimpressive-looking plant with a short stem that's strong enough to support much larger seed heads than its taller cousins. The simple insight that bigger isn't always better had a pro-found effect on crop yields, allowing wheat output on a given piece of land to quadruple on average.

Between the early 1940s and the early 1960s, Mexican wheat pro-duction increased sixfold. In 1963, Borlaug traveled to south Asia to try to persuade the governments of India and Pakistan that planting high-yield dwarf wheat could head off a famine. It took two years to win their support, but it was time well spent. What followed became known as the Green Revolution.

The thirty-five trucks stopped by the National Guard were car-rying 500 million high-yield seeds bound for the subcontinent. The seeds eventually made it past the riot police and onto the ship. Once planted, they helped to increase yields in Indian and Pakistani wheat fields by more than half. The next crop was even better, and by 1968, Borlaug's high-yield agricultural techniques had helped Pakistan become self-sufficient in wheat production. India achieved the same status a few years later. By the early 1990s, Pakistan's wheat output had risen fourfold from levels in the mid-1960s, while India's production had increased fivefold.

Borlaug was awarded the Nobel Peace Prize in 1970. In presenting the award, the Nobel committee said of Borlaug, "More than any other single person of this age, he has helped provide bread for a hungry world." Credited with keeping hundreds of millions of people from starvation, Borlaug may have saved more lives than any other person in history. By one calculation, every day, half of the world's population eats a grain descended from the high-yield plants developed by Borlaug and the other agricultural researchers of the Green Revolution.

More than forty years ago, Borlaug and his colleagues found a way to expand the limits of a finite world. Today, we need to draw on the same spirit of ingenuity, innovation and tenacity to help us negotiate demographic pressures that will mount with renewed urgency in the coming years.

WHERE HAVE YOU GONE, NORMAN BORLAUG?
A NATION TURNS ITS LONELY EYES TO YOU

The American journalist George Will is attributed with saying that the future has a way of arriving unannounced. Whether we're ready for it or not, a world of static economic growth is almost here. The biggest question now is how well we deal with it.

Hydrocarbons have powered the world for more than a century. Fossil fuels aren't going anywhere anytime soon, but neither are higher prices. If we want the future to be as good as the past, our approach to economic growth needs to change, and that change needs to happen now.

Recognizing the ramifications of a lower economic speed limit is a necessary first step. Triple-digit oil prices, record budget deficits and potentially catastrophic levels of carbon in the atmosphere are telling us the same thing: endless economic growth is unsustainable. We can either listen to these warnings and adapt to their message or cling to past practices that are putting us on a collision course with scarcity.

We saw in chapter 1 how governments are pulling out all the stops to shock the global economy back to life. Interest rates are at rock-bottom levels, central banks are pumping money into the economy through quantitative easing measures and governments are spending billions on stimulus packages. Add it all up, and it means future taxpayers are being hamstrung with mountains of debt that will need to be repaid.

And for what? These policies are chasing a vision of the world that's already in the rearview mirror. Running up huge deficits to spur economic growth is the wrong move when high oil prices are inexorably pushing the global economy closer to a static state. Instead of fighting against the tide, we need to swim with the current.

Practical experience tells us that racking up massive amounts of debt is rarely a prudent fiscal choice. Just look at how things turned out for homeowners who bit off more than they could chew when interest rates fell in the last decade. We're still reeling from the consequences of the resulting housing crash. But those folks could have made different choices, just as our governments can today.

Rather than go further into hock, other homeowners chose to pay down their mortgages. That may have meant scrimping on some luxuries, but such restraint pays off when the rough patches inevitably come. That's the wonderful virtue of being debt free. Right now, our governments are like homeowners who are choosing to pile on expensive credit card debt while still carrying big mortgages.

No matter what stimulus measures are put in place, we can't make our economies grow at the rates they used to because the energy that drives them now costs five times as much as it did only a decade ago. In economics, prices matter. Triple-digit fuel prices mean that our economies will slow down no matter how much stimulus we force-feed into the system.

Instead of trying to spur spending by keeping interest rates near zero, central banks need to ensure that inflation is held firmly in check. Rather than run huge budget deficits, governments need to get their fiscal houses in order, so we can pay for programs and services that will help us succeed in a new world of slower economic growth.

Governments must also stop trying to shelter their economies from higher energy costs. Prices are only a messenger; the real issue is the underlying scarcity they signal. If American motorists paid the same fuel taxes as drivers in Europe, the United States would care much less about geopolitical uncertainty in the Middle East or Venezuela. Similarly, if China forced power consumers to pay the full price for coal, the country would burn far less of it than it does now.

Other countries would do well to watch how Denmark and Japan are facing up to a world of higher energy prices. Denmark has demonstrated over the course of two decades that prices, not supply, are the key to energy conservation. Japan, in turn, is showing that *setsuden* is an economically practical and environmentally friendly alternative to burning more fossil fuels.

The steps being taken to blunt the pain of slower economic growth are only delaying troubles that will hit us eventually. Billions of dollars of stimulus spending may create a temporary upswing in employment, but it provides only a short-term Band-Aid for our deeper economic problems. What's even worse, the debt left behind, as Europe's fiscal crisis shows, can be crippling.

Slower economic growth means less job creation and higher unemployment. There will still be jobs, but many of us will need to adapt to changes in the type of work we do and how we do it. In chapter 8, we saw how the FIRE sector (finance, insurance and real estate) has doubled in size and now accounts for as much as 20 percent of economic activity in OECD countries. As the FIRE sector shrinks in a static economy, it will mean fewer job openings for stockbrokers, insurance salesmen and real estate agents. Folks currently in those jobs could face some tough times, but it's not as if they'll stay unemployed indefinitely.

As the contours of the new economy take shape, fresh opportunities will emerge. In a world where distance costs money, our hollowed-out manufacturing sector will fill up again. More of the products we buy will be made locally and sold regionally. If you're selling mutual funds now, you may soon be selling widgets from a local factory. You might even find yourself making them. Or perhaps you'll join a reemerging agriculture industry. Triple-digit oil prices will make importing apples from South Africa prohibitively expensive, but it doesn't mean we'll stop eating fruit. The small orchards and farms that disappeared due to the cost efficiencies of globalization could be set to reappear. As farmland is reclaimed, people will need to grow the produce, sell the food and run the business of agriculture. Peddling fruit to local grocery stores may be different than pushing insurance to young drivers, but it can still provide a decent living.

Overall, we'll need to become much more nimble in our approach to employment. Instead of drawing a salary from a single job, more people could find themselves cobbling together multiple income streams through several different gigs. What we lose in stability, we could make up in variety and shorter workweeks. Job sharing could also become a much more common practice than it is today. Germany's successful experience with its Kurzarbeit program shows it's a viable option.

To facilitate the transition to slower economic growth, governments need to be financially flexible. That's what's so alarming about our current deficit spending. Instead of bailing out banks, governments should be saving their fiscal ammunition to foster initiatives such as job sharing and training programs. Many of us will need to embrace the idea of retraining to adapt our skills to the shifting needs of our national economies.

Older workers may learn something on this front by watching the younger generation. My kids are certainly growing up differently than I did. If you're under thirty, multitasking is a way of life. The generation coming up is much better equipped to handle the variable nature of the pending work world than people my age.

But we will all need to be open to the idea of change. Most of all, getting us to use less energy will be critical going forward. Escalating resource prices are telling us that conservation has never been more important than it is right now.

There's one fact that should provide some comfort: the frightening predictions of doomsayers from the Reverend Malthus to Paul Ehrlich and James Lovelock haven't come to pass. When faced with big problems, we've always found ways to adapt, and there's no reason that we won't do so again. Human ingenuity shouldn't be underestimated. Even now, there are more Norman Borlaugs working tirelessly to help usher in a better future. Undoubtedly, some of these researchers will make breakthroughs in renewable energy that will help us transition away from our hydrocarbon economies. But that's still an eventuality. Right now, renewable sources are only a welcome part of the energy mix; they don't offer a panacea.

The demographic challenges we face can't be sold short. There are 7 billion people on the planet, and they all need to be fed—and the number goes up every day. In his 1970 Nobel lecture, Borlaug warned that even with more productive varieties of grain, rampant population growth was putting the world on a collision course with food shortages. What we need now is not a single Green Revolution, but a series of answers that will help us navigate a crushing demographic problem.

Recalibrating expectations for our future lifestyles is a place to start. In a static economy, we'll have less income growth, which will translate into us owning less stuff. Rather than fighting to retain our current degree of consumption, perhaps we can learn to appreciate what we gain on the other side of the ledger. We'll buy fewer things, but we'll also have more time to enjoy our lives. Does anyone really like the rat race? Maybe we all need to slow down and take a minute to breathe. Go for a walk instead of driving to the mall. Ride a bike rather than turning over an engine. Put on a sweater instead of cranking up the thermostat.

Sustainability isn't just an abstract notion; it's the governing idea behind the kinds of economies we need to foster. The world is full of helpful examples: bike lanes in Denmark, *setsuden* in Japan and Kurzarbeit in Germany. We need to embrace these tactics and make many other fundamental changes to the way we live.

We can still shape the future we want, but only if we're willing to relinquish the past we've known. As the boundaries of a finite world continue to close in on us, our challenge is to learn that making do with less is better than always wanting more.

SOURCE NOTES

INTRODUCTION

p. 6: A copious amount of ink has been spilled dissecting the US housing crisis and subsequent stock market crash in 2008. For a particularly lively account of the bubble that developed for collateralized debt obligations and the emergence of the credit default swap market, see *The Big Short* (2010) by Michael Lewis.

CHAPTER 1: CHANGING THE ECONOMIC SPEED LIMIT

p. 27: For a broader take on how Reaganomics fostered the culture of deregulation that still persists in the United States, see *The Price of Civilization: Economics and Ethics After the Fall* (2011) by Jeffrey Sachs, director of the Earth Institute at Columbia University.

pp. 30–31: Oil's usage has changed over the years. Today, it's primarily relied on as a transit fuel, while being replaced by natural gas in other areas. In the 1970s, for example, a quarter of global oil consumption went toward power generation, a figure that's now fallen to less than 5 percent. In places such as North America, natural gas has largely replaced oil as a home heating fuel. Natural gas is also a ready substitute for oil as a feedstock in the production of petrochemicals. Unfortunately, the substitution of natural gas for oil ends there. Natural gas has yet to make an appreciable dent in the demand for oil as a transit fuel. That's one reason for the huge price spread between the two commodities, especially in North America, where the emergence of shale resources has sent natural gas pricing tumbling. It took a big jump in oil prices (the OPEC oil shocks) to get North Americans to switch from burning oil in their furnaces to burning natural gas, and it will take an even bigger jump to get them to switch their gas tanks over.

p. 35: Those old enough to remember the 1970s know that waking the specter of inflation is a scary prospect for any economy. Against a backdrop of historically low interest rates and expansionary monetary policy, it bears noting that the mandate of many of the world's central banks is to keep inflation in check. The Bank of Canada (BoC), for instance, has an inflation control target of 2 percent, the midpoint of a control range of 1 to 3 percent. Recently, the BoC's target inflation range was extended for another five years, until the end of 2016.

CHAPTER 2: DEBT IS ENERGY INTENSIVE

p. 49: The euro was launched in 1999, with the introduction of banknotes and coins following in 2002. Eleven countries originally adopted the currency: Belgium, Germany, Ireland, Spain, France, Italy, Luxembourg, the Netherlands, Austria, Portugal and

Finland. Subsequently, Slovenia, Cyprus, Malta, Slovakia and Estonia joined the currency union. Collectively, these countries make up the euro area, also commonly known as the eurozone. Roughly 330 million EU citizens use the euro as their currency. The European Commission offers an extensive chronological account of the thirty-year process that led to the adoption of a single European currency at ec.europa.eu /economy_finance/emu_history/index_en.htm.

p. 51: Standard & Poor's (S&P) cut the debt ratings of nine eurozone governments in January 2012. Among the downgrades, S&P removed the AAA status of France and Austria, cutting their ratings a notch to AA+. France's first-ever downgrade from S&P is particularly worrisome for the ECB, which depends on the large economies of France and Germany to backstop efforts to pull the eurozone out of its fiscal crisis.

p. 55: What makes the $2.3-billion trading loss at UBS even more disturbing is that Swiss taxpayers already paid a huge sum to bail out the bank in 2008, after UBS wrote down $56 billion in credit losses. Given that the combined assets of UBS and Credit Suisse, Switzerland's other major bank, are four times the size of the country's GDP, Swiss taxpayers have considerable reason to worry if financial markets take another turn for the worse.

p. 57: According to the US Treasury Department, China holds roughly $1.5 trillion in American government debt. Japan is the second-largest buyer of US treasuries, holding about $885 billion.

CHAPTER 3: THE ARAB REVOLT

p. 66: For a detailed account of the countercoup that unseated Mohammed Mossadegh and reinstalled the Shah as Iran's ruler, see *All the Shah's Men: An American Coup and the Roots of Middle East Terror* (2003) by Stephen Kinzer.

p. 68: The size of Iraq's oil reserves are open to dispute. The US Geological Survey estimates only 78 billion barrels. The figure quoted in the text is from the US Department of Energy. The Iraqi government estimates Iraq's reserves at more than 300 billion barrels. That would make it the largest reserve in the world. But this claim, along with the Iraqi government's prediction that the country will ramp up current oil production of around 2.5 million barrels a day to a world-leading 12 million barrels a day, must be taken with a large grain of salt.

p. 68: Iraq's oil output is rising, but efforts to boost production face considerable hurdles, including widespread pipeline sabotage, such as an explosion of the Ceyhan pipeline in 2011. Other attacks on energy targets include a strike on the country's largest refinery, located in the northern city of Baiji. In addition, Iraqi crude exports are increasingly bouncing up against infrastructure constraints at key export terminals, such as the port at Basra.

p. 72: The US Energy Information Agency (EIA—not to be confused with the IEA, the International Energy Agency) identifies seven global oil transit choke points: the Strait of Hormuz, the Strait of Malacca, the Suez Canal, the Strait of Bab el Mandeb, the Turkish Straits (comprising the Bosporus and the Dardanelles), the Panama Canal and the Danish Straits. These narrow channels are part of shipping routes considered critical to global energy security. The Strait of Hormuz is the most important of these waterways. In 2011, roughly 35 percent of all seaborne-traded oil passed through the Strait, or nearly a fifth of the oil traded globally (www.eia.gov/cabs/world_oil_transit_choke points/full.html).

p. 79: OPEC's Middle Eastern members are Iran, Iraq, Kuwait, Libya, Qatar, Saudi Arabia and the United Arab Emirates. The twelve-member group is rounded out by Algeria,

Angola, Ecuador, Nigeria and Venezuela. The figures for the cartel's contribution to global oil supply can be found at www.opec.org/opec_web/en/.

p. 85: Saudi Arabia currently burns more than 3 million barrels of oil a day to meet domestic energy needs, which represents roughly a third of its production. According to *Arab News*, nearly half of that amount, some 1.5 million barrels a day, is used to power an extensive network of fuel-hungry desalination plants. In response to this growing drain on oil output, Saudi Arabia's national science agency announced a new initiative to begin building solar-powered desalination plants. Unfortunately, the scale of the efforts will be tiny. The first plant is expected to produce a mere 30,000 cubic meters of water, compared with the mammoth oil-fired Shoaiba plant (Stage 3) that produces 880,000 cubic meters of desalinated water every day.

CHAPTER 4: HITTING THE ENERGY CEILING

p. 89: Production of shale gas has more than its share of critics, many from the environmental movement. A 2010 documentary, *Gasland*, by filmmaker Josh Fox chronicled some of the environmental mishaps that have occurred as a result of drilling in the Marcellus formation in Pennsylvania, New York, Ohio and West Virginia. Hydraulic fracturing, the key process used to extract shale gas, was exempted in 2005 from the Safe Drinking Water Act (1974), a step that paved the way for a wave of drilling across the country and put a spark to much of the current controversy over fracking.

p. 93: The data on China's coal consumption is measured in short tons, a unit of weight equal to 2,000 pounds. The EIA calculates coal usage in short tons as opposed to long tons (2,240 pounds), the standard unit for measuring coal in the United Kingdom. Neither should be confused with a metric ton, also known as a tonne, which is 1,000 kilograms, or 2,204 pounds.

p. 95: If the IEA can be criticized for the size of some of its more recent downward revisions to expected world oil supply, those revisions pale in comparison with the haircuts that world coal reserve estimates have taken. Since 1980, world coal estimates have fallen by 50 percent. In some countries, reserve estimates have been literally wiped out. Coal reserves in Germany, one of the oldest coal-producing nations, were chopped from 183 billion tons in 1996 to 23 million tons in 2004—a 99 percent reduction in the span of eight years. Coal reserves in Poland, the EU's largest producer, have been halved since 1997.

p. 95: Another dramatic example of coal depletion is found in the UK. In the 19th century, there were more than three thousand coal mines in Britain. Today, there are six. At the turn of the last century, Britain exported almost a third of its total coal production. By 2010, the UK was importing almost 60 percent of its coal. Resource depletion in domestic coalfields was first documented in the 19th century by British economist Stanley Jevons. He's the namesake of the Jevons paradox, a concept that points out how an increase in the efficiency of resource extraction leads to an increase in resource consumption. For a discussion of the paradox, also known as the rebound effect, see pages 118–29 of my first book, *Why Your World Is About to Get a Whole Lot Smaller* (2009).

pp. 104–105: Japanese regulations require reactors to close every thirteen months for maintenance and inspections. Normally, the process involves taking nuclear plants off line for two or three months. However, in the wake of the Fukushima disaster, none of the reactors closed for inspection has been restarted. Given the regular scheduling of temporary maintenance shutdowns, all of Japan's fifty-four nuclear reactors are expected to be shuttered by the summer of 2012, making the country effectively nuclear free.

pp. 104–105: According to the Tokyo Institute for Energy Economics, even stepping up the amount of power generated from oil, coal and natural gas will leave Japan with a 10 percent shortfall in power supply if the country's nuclear reactors are permanently shut down. In that light, the energy conservation achieved through *setsuden* is set to loom even larger in Japan's future.

pp. 104–105: Growing power shortages may also threaten Japan's industrial base. Hiromasa Yonekura, chairman of Sumitomo Chemical and head of the Keidanren, Japan's powerful business lobby, recently warned that power shortages could cause a stampede of manufacturing plants out of the country. His comments followed a number of high-profile announcements by Japanese manufacturers that decided to move plants elsewhere. The list of firms taking business offshore includes heavyweights such as Mitsui Mining & Smelting and Renesas Electronics.

CHAPTER 5: THE KEYSTONE CONUNDRUM

pp. 109–110: The spirit bear, also known as the Kermode bear, is a contradiction in terms, a black bear with white fur. The reclusive bear, and the recessive gene responsible for its unusual coat, continues to fascinate and puzzle geneticists. For a deeper look at the ghostlike bears that inhabit Princess Royal Island, see Charles Russell's *Spirit Bear: Encounters with the White Bear of the Western Rainforest* (1994).

pp. 110–111: The story of the *Queen of the North* was recounted by Bruce Barcott in the August 2011 issue of *National Geographic* ("Pipeline Through Paradise," ngm.national-geographic.com/2011/08/canada-rainforest/barcott-text).

p. 119: Enbridge hopes to complete a public and government review process for Northern Gateway by mid-2013. Pending regulatory approval, ground will be broken in mid-2014, and oil will start flowing through the line in late 2017. However, as TransCanada's experience with Keystone shows, political, social and environmental forces can render corporate timelines for major infrastructure projects meaningless.

CHAPTER 6: THE DANISH RESPONSE

p. 121: Information about Denmark's environmental track record, including its level of carbon dioxide emissions since 1990, comes from figures available through the State of Green, a government-backed initiative to raise international awareness of the country's green credentials (www.stateofgreen.com).

pp. 124–125: The argument for the relationship between urban population density and vibrant cities is well documented. Jane Jacobs, for one, argued convincingly against urban sprawl in her seminal work *The Death and Life of Great American Cities*, which has influenced thoughts on urban planning since its publication in 1961.

CHAPTER 7: ZERO-SUM WORLD

pp. 135–136: The figures for Venezuela's oil exports to the United States come from the EIA. US oil imports from Venezuela reached a high of 1.77 million barrels a day in 1997 (www.eia.gov/dnav/pet/hist/LeafHandler.ashx?n=pet&s=mttimusve2&f=a).

pp. 137–138: The figure for the number of licensed American drivers comes from the US Federal Highway Administration, an agency within the Department of Transportation (www.fhwa.dot.gov/ohim/onh00/onh2p4.htm).

p. 138: The number of Alternative Fuel Vehicles calculated by the Department of
Transportation doesn't include hybrid electric vehicles or flexible fuel vehicles that
run on an ethanol blend of less than E85. According to data from *Wards*, the cumulative number of hybrids sold in the United States surpassed 2 million in 2011. The
Department of Energy says there are more than 8 million flex fuel vehicles on US roads,
although many owners are unaware their vehicles have this capability. Most of the 2,400
fueling stations that offer E85 are located in the corn belt in the Midwest.

p. 140: According to the IEA's discussion of subsidies in its *World Energy Outlook 2011*, Iran
and Saudi Arabia lead the world in fossil fuel subsidies. According to the IEA, fuel subsidies are most prevalent in the developing world. However, it should be noted that the
IEA uses a narrow (and arguably self-serving) definition of what constitutes a subsidy.
Tax breaks and incentives, loan guarantees, public money for research and development
and, most of all, very low fuel taxes are not considered subsidies by the IEA. If they were,
we would find the incidence of subsidies much more frequent among OECD members
such as the United States and countries in western Europe than current IEA numbers
indicate.

pp. 143–144: The figures for daily oil consumption of countries around the world come
from the CIA World Factbook (https://www.cia.gov/library/publications/the-world-
factbook). The United States is the world's largest oil consumer, guzzling more than 19
million barrels a day. Occupying the last spot on the list is the tiny island nation of Niue.
On average, its 1,311 residents burn a cumulative total of 40 barrels a day.

p. 147: While it has yet to surpass the United States in oil consumption, China leapfrogged
the United States in 2010 to become the world's largest energy-consuming nation,
according to BP's *Statistical Review of World Energy*. Yet on a per capita basis, the Chinese
consumer burns only a fraction of the energy consumed by the average American, pointing to a seemingly limitless potential for demand growth. Of course, triple-digit oil and
coal prices will rein in Chinese energy demand, just as higher prices have curbed energy
demand in OECD economies.

CHAPTER 8: THE STATIC ECONOMY

pp. 155–156: For an in-depth consideration of how physical barriers, such as the walls erected
along the US–Mexico border, divide our world, see Marcello DiCintio's *In the Shadow of
the Wall: Travels Along the Barricades* (forthcoming fall 2012).

p. 160: A study that explores the trend toward a graying workforce was released in 2010 by
Boston College's Sloan Center on Aging & Work. Among other findings, the research
study, *Working in Retirement: A 21st Century Phenomenon*, concluded that the linear progression of a traditional career path that begins at an entry-level job and ends in retirement no longer fits with current workplace realities. The emerging experience of workers
of all ages suggests that multiple exit and re-entry points out of and into the workforce
throughout one's working life are becoming more common (familiesandwork.org/site
/research/reports/workinginretirement.pdf).

pp. 161–162: Global Sticks is by no means the only North American manufacturer that has
recently come home from China. Not long ago, NCR decided to move production of
its automated teller machines to Georgia, while toy maker Wham-O Inc. shifted half of
its Frisbee and hula hoop production back to the United States. Caterpillar, which has
operations around the world, has chosen Texas as the site of its next major manufacturing plant.

pp. 175–176: A push-back against rampant consumerism is becoming more evident in corporate circles. Consider, for example, Patagonia's new marketing campaign. The outdoor

clothing company is asking everyone who wishes to sell second-hand Patagonia goods on its new eBay venture to sign a Common Threads agreement. The pledge includes an obligation to buy only what is necessary, to reuse items and to purchase used products whenever possible. Has Patagonia already seen the face of tomorrow's consumer?

pp. 175–176: Another sign of changing attitudes toward consumption and conservation in the developed world can be found in the design of Olympic Park, a sporting complex built for the 2012 Olympics in London. In a sharp departure from the massive edifices and monuments erected by past Olympic hosts, the motto of the London organizers is to "touch the ground lightly." Two-thirds of the structures built for the Olympics are temporary and will be taken down when the Games are over, including an 80,000-seat stadium in London's East End.

CHAPTER 9: ALL BETS ARE OFF

pp. 193–196: For the full story on the Yangs and the implications for China's resource consumption, see a November 2010 feature by Bloomberg reporter Fan Wenxin ("China's Rural Growth Spurs Copper Demand").

pp. 195–196: Politicians have called scrap metal theft in the United Kingdom a scourge and an epidemic. The government is changing laws to allow for unlimited fines for people caught trading in stolen scrap metal and to ban cash transactions in the industry. The public uproar over this low-tech criminal endeavor is fueled by high-profile thefts from churches and public monuments. Police say a memorial is stripped every week in London.

pp. 195–197: To put the acceleration of population growth in perspective, consider that the human population reached the 1 billion mark in 1804. It took 123 more years for it to reach 2 billion, in 1927. We hit 3 billion people thirty-two years later in 1959. From there population doubled to 6 billion by 1998. A little more than a decade after that, the 7 billionth person was born. According to the UN's latest projections, the global population is expected to reach 10 billion by 2083, provided, of course, the world can produce enough food to feed the additional people.

pp. 197–199: The total fertility rate, which measures the number of births per woman, shows the potential for population change in a given country. In OECD countries, a fertility rate of approximately 2.1 is considered the replacement rate for a population; in developing nations, the replacement rate is around 2.3 to account for higher mortality rates. Rates below these figures indicate a population that is declining and growing older, while higher rates point to the opposite. A fertility rate of 2.06 makes the United States the only G8 country with fertility levels close to the replacement rate. Canada's fertility rate reached a high of 3.93 in 1959 and has since dropped steadily, bottoming out at 1.49 in 2000. The figures for global fertility rates come from the CIA World Factbook (https://www.cia.gov/library/publications/the-world-factbook/rankorder/2127rank.html).

pp. 198–199: While fertility rates have fallen markedly in developed nations, they remain stubbornly high throughout much of the developing world. To get an idea of what fertility rates mean for population growth, consider projections for countries with the highest readings. With a fertility rate of seven children per woman, Niger's population is forecast to more than triple, from 16.5 million to more than 55 million, by 2050, according to the United Nations. Somalia's birthrate isn't far behind: a fertility rate of 6.4 means its population will nearly triple, from 10 million to close to 30 million, over the next four decades. With a fertility rate of 6.39, Mali's population will increase from 14 million to 42 million, while Uganda, with a rate of 6.38, will see its numbers swell from 34 million to almost 95 million by 2050.

pp. 199–200: The proverb "Women hold up half the sky" is the inspiration for the title of a best-selling book, *Half the Sky: Turning Oppression into Opportunity for Women Worldwide* (2009). Pulitzer Prize–winning authors Nicholas Kristof and Sheryl WuDunn argue that the key to economic progress is the unleashing of the untapped potential of women. The treatment of women in the developing world, they contend, is the most pervasive human rights violation of our time. The book argues that investing in the health and autonomy of women not only moves us toward improving morally reprehensible circumstances but also leads to economic benefits that shouldn't be overlooked.

CHAPTER 10: WILL TRIPLE-DIGIT OIL PRICES SAVE THE PLANET?

p. 201: James Lovelock recounts his early days at NASA and the development of Gaia theory in *The Ages of Gaia: A Biography of Our Living Earth* (1988). Now in his nineties, Lovelock still conducts occasional experiments from his home laboratory in southwest England.

p. 203: The IPCC released its first comprehensive assessment report about the state of scientific, technical and socioeconomic knowledge on climate change in 1990. Other major reports followed in 1995, 2001 and 2007. The fifth assessment report is slated for completion in late 2014.

pp. 207–208: Despite the Kyoto Protocol—which set an emissions reduction target of 6 percent below 1990 levels by 2012—emissions are on the rise. Global emissions have increased at an annual clip of 3 percent over the last decade, roughly three times the pace of the previous decade. The combustion of coal has accounted for more than half of the increase in global emissions during this time.

pp. 220–221: According to BP's *Statistical Review*, total energy consumption rebounded at a blistering pace of 5.6 percent in 2010, the strongest annual growth rate since 1973. Nevertheless, total energy consumption in OECD economies remains roughly in line with levels of a decade ago. Over the same period, energy consumption in the developing world has increased more than 60 percent.

CONCLUSION

pp. 224–225: The Green Revolution is not without its critics. Some environmental groups oppose high-yield agricultural techniques, believing the use of inorganic fertilizers, pesticides and controlled irrigation puts undue pressure on the environment. Other critics believe industrial farming techniques leave agriculture in the hands of corporate interests at the expense of small farms. For a broader discussion of the issues, see "Forgotten Benefactor of Humanity" in the January 1997 issue of *The Atlantic*. The story is by Gregg Easterbrook, a versatile journalist who, inter alia, also writes a column for ESPN.com under the moniker Tuesday Morning Quarterback (www.theatlantic.com/magazine/archive/1997/01/forgotten-benefactor-of-humanity/6101/).

p. 229: Norman Borlaug may be the person most responsible for helping the world avoid the Malthusian fate predicted by Paul Ehrlich in *The Population Bomb*. Ironically, the pair's thinking is more aligned than a quick glance at history would suggest. In his Nobel lecture, for instance, Borlaug notes "the ticktock of the [population] clock will continue to grow louder and more menacing each decade." The full text of his lecture is available at www.nobelprize.org/nobel_prizes/peace/laureates/1970/borlaug-lecture.html.

ACKNOWLEDGMENTS

I HAVE BEEN VERY fortunate to work on this book with a great editor, Paul Haavardsrud, who did an outstanding job both on the page and with the research. *The Big Flatline* evolved over the course of our many editing sessions at the Higher Ground Café in Calgary, where Paul lives, which is only fitting since oil plays such a pivotal role in the story.

I would also like to thank Nick Garrison, the equally great editor of my first book, *Why Your World Is About to Get a Whole Lot Smaller*, for telling me that it was time for me to write a sequel, a suggestion he delivered to me with much encouragement at one of our annual dates to see a Toronto Maple Leafs game.

Anne Collins, my publisher at Random House Canada, once again did a great job in quarterbacking the book through editorial rounds and a crash publication schedule. Likewise, Sharon Klein, my trusted publicist, has done another outstanding job on organizing the publicity and marketing of the book.

I'd like to thank Peter Victor of York University for the information he sent me on Germany's Kurzarbeit program, as well as David Foot of the University of Toronto for data on international birthrates. Also I would like to thank two of my former colleagues at CIBC World Markets: Benjamin Tal, Deputy Chief Economist, for information on potential growth rates in North America; and Karl Kainz, my old broker, for drawing my attention to the Anthropocene.

Lastly, I would like to thank my agent, Rick Broadhead, and once again my lawyer and friend, Aaron Milrad, for his wise counsel and guidance.

INDEX

NOTE ON AUTHOR

JEFF RUBIN WAS THE chief economist at CIBC World Markets for almost twenty years. During that period, he placed first ten times in Brendan Wood's institutional investor ranking of top Bay Street economists. He was among the first economists in the world to accurately predict the onset and timing of triple-digit oil prices.

In 2009, Mr. Rubin left CIBC World Markets to publish his first book, *Why Your World Is About to Get a Whole Lot Smaller*. The book won the National Business Book Award in Canada, was long-listed for the Financial Times and Goldman Sachs Business Book of the Year Award in the UK and has been published in French, Spanish, German, Italian, Portuguese and Chinese. Jeff Rubin's writing and commentary have been featured on CNBC, on CNN, on CBC radio and television and in *The Globe and Mail* and *The Huffington Post*. He lives in Toronto.